CHU·KIA WANG
CHARLES G. SALMON
University of Wisconsin—Madison

REINFORCED CONCRETE DESIGN
Third Edition

Thomas Y. Crowell
Harper & Row, Publishers
New York, Hagerstown, Philadelphia, San Francisco, London

Sponsoring Editor: Charlie Dresser
Project Editor: Penelope Schmukler
Designer: Emily Harste
Production Manager: Marion Palen
Compositor: Syntax International Pte., Ltd.
Printer and Binder: The Maple Press Company
Art Studio: Danmark & Michaels Inc.
Cover Photo: Emily Harste

REINFORCED CONCRETE DESIGN, Third Edition

Library of Congress Cataloging in Publication Data

Wang, Chu-kia, 1917–
   Reinforced concrete design.

   (Series in civil engineering)
   Includes bibliographical references and index.
   1. Reinforced concrete construction.
I. Salmon, Charles G., joint author.   II. Title.
TA683.2.W3 1978   624′.1834   78-16240
ISBN 0-7002-2514-5

Contents

Strength of Members under Combined Bending and Azial Load. Deep Beams. Brackets and Corbels. Shear Friction. Selected References. Problems.

Axial Load. Length Effects. Lateral Ties. Spiral Reinforcement and Longitudinal Bar Placement. Limits on Percentage of Reinforcement. Maximum Strength in Axial Compression—ACI Code. Balanced Condition—Rectangular Sections. Balanced Condition—Circular Sections with Round Core. Investigation of Strength in Compression Controls Region—Rectangular Sections. Investigation of Strength in Tension Controls Region—Circular Sections. Design for Ultimate Strength—Region I, Minimum Eccentricity. Design for Ultimate Strength—Region II, Compression Controls ($e_{min} < e < e_b$). Design for Ultimate Strength—Region III, Tension Controls ($e > e_b$). Axial Tension and Bending Moment. Working Stress Method. Biaxial Bending and Compression. Selected References. Problems.

Chapter 14 Deflections, 479

Deflections—General. Deflections for Elastic Sections. Modulus of Elasticity. Moment of Inertia. Instantaneous Deflections in Design. Creep Effect on Deflections under Sustained Load. Shrinkage Effect on Deflections under Sustained Load. Creep and Shrinkage Deflection—ACI Code Method. Creep and Shrinkage Deflection—Alternate Procedures. ACI Minimum Depth of Flexural Members. Span-to-Depth Ratio to Account for Cracking and Sustained Load Effects. ACI Code Deflection Provisions—Beam Examples. Selected References. Problems.

Chapter 15 Length Effects on Columns, 528

General. Buckling of Concentrically Loaded Columns. Equivalent Pin-End Lengths. Moment Magnification—Simplified Treatment for Members in Single Curvature without End Translation (i.e., No Sidesway). Moment Magnification—Members Subjected to End Moments Only; No Joint Translation. Moment Magnification—Members with Sidesway Possible. Beam-Columns in Rigid Frames. Alignment Charts for Effective Length Factor k. Interaction Diagrams—Effect of Slenderness. Strength Reduction Factors. ACI Code—Moment Magnifier Approximate Method. ACI Code—Slenderness Ratio Limitations. ACI Code—General Analysis. Restraining Effect of Beams. Examples. Selected References. Problems.

Chapter 16 Design of Two-Way Systems—Slabs Supported on Beams, 591

General Description. General Design Concept of ACI Code. Total Factored Static Moment. Longitudinal Variation in Moments and Shears—ACI Methods. Ratio of Flexural Stiffness of Longitudinal Beam to Slab. Minimum Slab Thickness for Deflection Control. Direct-Design Method—Longitudinal Distribution of Total Static Moment. Direct-Design Method—Effect of Pattern Loadings on Positive Moment. Direct-Design Method —Procedures for Computation of Longitudinal Moment. Transverse Distribution of Longitudinal Moment. Slab Thickness Requirement in Flexure and Shear. Beam Size Requirement in Flexure and Shear. Reinforcement in Slab. Equivalent-Frame Method. Selected References. Problems.

Chapter 17 Design of Two-Way Systems—Flat Slab and Flat-Plate Floors, 646

General Description. General Design Concept of ACI Code. Total Static Design Moment. Nominal Requirements for Slab Thickness and Size of Edge Beams, Column Capital, and Drop Panel. Direct-Design Method—Longitudinal Distribution of Total Static Moment. Transverse Distribution of Longitudinal Moment. Design of Slab Thickness and Reinforcement for Flexure. Shear Strength in Two-Way Slab Systems. Shear Reinforcement in Flat-Plate Floors. Direct-Design Method—Moments in Columns. Transfer of Moments to Columns. Openings and Corner Connections in Flat Slabs. The Equivalent-Frame Method. Selected References. Problems.

Preface

The publication of this third edition reflects the continuing change that is occurring in the design procedures relating to reinforced concrete structures. The transition from the working stress method as the major design philosophy to the strength design method has now largely been accomplished. Current reinforced concrete design focuses on the two basic requirements of providing adequate *strength* as well as satisfactory *serviceability*.

The specific occurrence dictating a third edition at this time is the publication of the 1977 American Concrete Institute (ACI) Building Code. The changes that have been approved in yearly supplements to the 1971 ACI Code have been combined; in addition, many editorial changes have been made in the Code that change its image (though not the substance) and thus require subtle (and sometimes not so subtle) changes in the explanatory approach.

These editorial changes include rearrangement of material and renumbering of sections, significant changes in terminology and symbols used, and the change from shear "stress" to shear "force" format.

Included in this third edition is a judicious introduction to metrication using SI units as an addition to the primary use of US customary units. While the 1977 ACI Code is not a metric code except for providing a metric equivalent table in the back, the authors believe that sufficient metrication should be included in a textbook so that some familiarity may be gained with SI units. The text provides data on metric reinforcing bars that are commonly used in many parts of the world, some design tables for material strengths in SI units, a few numerical examples in SI units, and many problems at the ends of the chapters with SI given numerical data in parenthesis at the end of the problem statement.

Regarding the choice between the Standard Metric unit of force (kilogram force, kgf) or the SI unit of force (Newton = kilogram meter per second per second), the authors have concluded that use of the Newton in accordance with ASTM (American Society for Testing and Materials) Standard E380 is likely to become the accepted approach in the US. Thus, in most parts of this book, the Newton (N) or kilonewton (kN) is used to measure force. Some use of kilogram force per centimeter squared (kgf/cm^2) has been included because of its long-time usage in the non-English-speaking parts of the world. For the convenience of the readers, some conversion factors for forces, stresses, uniform loading, and moments are provided on a separate page just after this preface.

This third edition follows the same philosophical approach that has gained the wide acceptance of users since the first edition was published in 1965. Herein, as previously, strength and behavior of concrete elements are treated with the primary objective of explaining and justifying the ACI Code rules and formulas.* Then numerous examples are presented illustrating the general approach to

---

*Since nearly continuous reference is made to the 1977 ACI Code, the reader will find it desirable to secure a copy of it and the Commentary from the American Concrete Institute, Box 19150, Detroit, Michigan 48219. (Current ACI policy precludes extensive quotation in a textbook appendix.)

design and analysis. Considering the limited scope of most examples, attempts to reach practical results are made insofar as possible.

Considerable emphasis is placed on presenting for the beginning, as well as the advanced, student the basic concepts deemed essential to properly understand and apply the ACI Code rules and formulas. The treatment is incorporated into the chapters in such a way that the reader may either study in detail the concepts in logical sequence, or merely accept a qualitative explanation and proceed directly to the design process using the ACI Code.

Depending on the proficiency required of the student, this textbook may provide material for two courses of three- or four-semester hours each. It is suggested that the beginning course in concrete structures for undergraduate students might contain the material of Chapters 1 through 9, 13, and the spread footing portion of Chapter 20, excepting Sections 5.13 through 5.16 and 13.21 through 13.23. In addition, the first portion of Chapter 21, "Introduction to Prestressed Concrete," is recommended for the first course. The second course may start with the continuous beam in Chapter 10, utilizing that to review many of the topics in Chapters 1 through 9. The remaining chapters—particularly Chapter 14 on deflections; Chapter 15 on length effects on columns; Chapter 16 and 17 on slabs subject to two-way action; the omitted portion of Chapter 5 relating to shear strength affected by axial force, deep beams, and brackets; Chapter 19 on torsion, and Chapter 21 on prestressed concrete—are suggested for inclusion.

Special features of the third edition are: (a) complete revision of the two chapters on two-way slab systems to reduce their length and improve teachability; (b) a new chapter on monolithic beam-to-column joints (Chapter 11); (c) a new chapter on composite construction (Chapter 22); (d) expanded introductory treatment of prestressed concrete design and behavior (Chapter 21); and (e) a completely revised chapter on combined bending and axial force effects on short length members, including new treatment of axial tension.

This complete revision has retained important special features of the second edition, including (a) comprehensive treatment of design for torsion; (b) detailed treatment of computation of beam deflections; (c) introductory treatment of yield line theory for slabs; (d) important extensive treatment of bar development length, cutoff, and anchorage requirements using the moment capacity diagram; and (e) treatment of shear requirements for effect of axial loads, deep beams, and brackets (corbels).

The authors continue to be indebted to students, colleagues, and other users of the first two editions who have suggested improvements of wording, identified errors, and recommended items for inclusion or omission. These suggestions have been duly considered and included in this complete revision wherever possible. Users of this third edition are urged to communicate with the authors regarding all aspects of this book; particularly on identification of errors and suggestions for improvement.

The authors again gratefully acknowledge the continued patience and encouragement of their wives, Vera Wang and Bette Salmon, and to them affectionately dedicate this book.

Chu-Kia Wang and Charles G. Salmon

Conversion Factors

Some Conversion Factors, between US Customary and SI Metric
Units, Useful in Reinforced Concrete Design

	To Convert	*To*	*Multiply by*
Forces	kip force	kg force	453.6
	kip force	kN	4.448
	kg force	lb	2.205
	N	lb	0.2248
Stresses	psi	kgf/cm^2	0.07031
	ksi	N/mm^2	6.895
	kgf/cm^2	psi	14.22
	N/mm^2	ksi	0.1450
Uniform Loading	kip/ft	kg/m	1488
	kip/ft	kN/m	14.59
	kg/m	lb/ft	0.6720
	kN/m	lb/ft	68.52
Moments	ft-kip	kgf-m	138.2
	ft-kip	kN-m	1.356
	kgf-m	ft-lb	7.233
	kN-m	ft-kip	0.7376

Basis (ASTM E380): 1 in. = 25.4 mm; 1 lb force = 4.448 221 615 260 5
Newtons; 1 kg force = 9.80665 Newtons.

Series in Civil Engineering

1

Introduction, Materials, and Properties

1.1 Reinforced Concrete Structures

The three most common materials from which most structures are built are timber, steel, and reinforced (including prestressed) concrete. Lightweight materials such as aluminum and plastics are also becoming more common in use. Reinforced concrete is unique in that two materials, reinforcing steel and concrete, are used together; thus the principles governing the structural design in reinforced concrete differ in many ways from those involving design in one material.

Many structures are built of reinforced concrete: bridges, viaducts, buildings, retaining walls, tunnels, tanks, conduits, and others. This text deals primarily with fundamental principles in the design and investigation of reinforced concrete members subjected to axial force, bending moment, shear, torsion, or combinations of these. Thus these principles are basically applicable to the design of any type of structure, so long as information is known about the variation of axial force, shear, moment, etc., along the length of each member. Although *analysis* and *design* may be treated separately, they are inseparable in practice, especially in the case of reinforced concrete structures, which are usually statically indeterminate. In such cases relative sizes of members are needed in the preliminary analysis that must precede the final design; so the final conciliation between analysis and design is largely a matter of trial, judgment, and experience.

Reinforced concrete is a logical union of two materials: plain concrete, which possesses high compressive strength but little tensile strength, and reinforcing steel rods embedded in the concrete which can provide the needed strength in tension. For instance, the capacity of the beam shown

Water Tower Place, 74 stories, 859 ft high, hotel-condominium-shopping complex, Chicago, Ill. (Courtesy of Portland Cement Association.)

in Fig. 1.1.1 is greatly increased by placing steel bars in the tension zone. However, since reinforcement steel is capable of resisting compression as well as tension, it is also used to provide part of the carrying capacity in reinforced concrete columns, and frequently in the compression zone of beams.

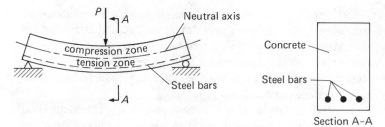

Fig. 1.1.1
Position of bars in a reinforced concrete beam.

Steel and concrete work readily in combination for several reasons: (1) bond (interaction between bars and surrounding hardened concrete) prevents slip of the bars relative to the concrete; (2) proper concrete mixes provide adequate impermeability of the concrete against bar corrosion; and (3) sufficiently similar rates of thermal expansion—that is, 0.0000055 to 0.0000075 for concrete and 0.0000065 for steel per degree Fahrenheit (°F), or 0.000010 to 0.000013 for concrete and 0.000012 for steel per degree Celsius (°C)—introduce negligible stresses between steel and concrete under atmospheric changes of temperature.

Transverse cracks of small width may appear near the reinforcing bars placed in the tension regions of ordinary reinforced concrete (unless pre-stressed); such cracks are expected and do not interfere with the performance of the member.

1.2 Historical Background

Joseph Monier, the owner of an important nursery in Paris, generally deserves the credit for making the first practical use of reinforced concrete in 1867. He recognized many of its potential uses, and successfully undertook to expand the application of the new method [1].† Prior to Monier's work, however, the method of reinforcing concrete with iron was known and in some cases even protected by patents. Ancient Grecian structures have been found which show that builders knew something about the reinforcing of stonework for added strength [2].

In the mid-1800s, Lambot in France constructed a small boat which he exhibited at the Paris Exposition of 1854 and on which he received a patent in 1855. In Lambot's patent was shown a reinforced concrete beam and a column reinforced with four round iron bars. Another Frenchman, Francois Coignet, published a book in 1861 describing many applications and uses of reinforced concrete. In 1854 W. B. Wilkinson of England took out a patent for a reinforced concrete floor.

Monier acquired his first French patent in 1867 for iron reinforced concrete tubs. This was followed by his many other patents, such as for pipes and tanks in 1868, flat plates in 1869, bridges in 1873, and stairways

† Numbers in brackets refer to the Selected References at the end of the chapter.

in 1875. In 1880–1881, Monier received German patents for railroad ties, water feeding troughs, circular flower pots, flat plates, and irrigation channels, among others. Monier's iron reinforcement was mainly made to conform to the contour of the structural element and generally strengthen it. He apparently had no quantitative knowledge regarding its behavior or any method of making design calculations [1].

In the United States the pioneering efforts were made by Thaddeus Hyatt, originally a lawyer, who conducted experiments on reinforced concrete beams in the 1850s. In a perfectly correct manner the iron bars in Hyatt's beams were located in the tension zone, bent up near the supports, and anchored in the compression zone. Additionally, transverse reinforcement (known as vertical stirrups) was used near the supports. However, Hyatt's experiments were unknown until 1877 when he published his work privately. As head of the Concrete-Steel Company of San Francisco, E. L. Ransome apparently used some form of reinforced concrete in the early 1870s. He continued to increase the application of wire rope and hoop iron to many structures and was the first to use and have patented in 1884 the deformed (twisted) bar.

The Monier German patents were sold to G. A. Wayss and Company of Germany in 1880. Tests of structural strength were conducted by German engineers during the 1880s. Theories and computational methods were published by Koenen and Wayss in 1886. Test results of Wayss and J. Bauschinger were published in 1887.

In 1890, Ransome built the Leland Stanford Jr. Museum in San Francisco, a reinforced concrete building two stories high and 312 ft (95 m) long. Since that time, development of reinforced concrete in the United States has been rapid. During the period 1891–1894, various investigators in Europe published theories and test results; among them were Moeller (Germany), Wunsch (Hungary), Melan (Austria), Hennebique (France), and Emperger (Hungary), but practical use was less extensive than in the United States.

Throughout the entire period 1850–1900, relatively little was published, as the engineers working in the reinforced concrete field considered construction and computational methods as trade secrets. One of the first publications that might be classified as a textbook was that of Considère in 1899. By the turn of the century there was a multiplicity of systems and methods with little uniformity in design procedures, allowable stresses, and systems of reinforcing. In 1903, with the formation in the United States of a joint committee of representatives of all organizations interested in reinforced concrete, uniform application of knowledge to design was initiated. The development of standard specifications is discussed in Chap. 2.

In the first decade of the twentieth century, progress in reinforced concrete was rapid. Extensive testing to determine beam behavior, compressive strength of concrete, and modulus of elasticity was conducted by A. N. Talbot at the University of Illinois, by F. E. Turneaure and M. O. Withey at the University of Wisconsin, and by Bach in Germany, among others. From about 1916 to the mid-1930s, research centered on axially loaded column behavior. In the late 1930s and 1940s, eccentrically loaded columns, footings, and the ultimate strength of beams received special attention.

During the 1950s, emphasis was given to the study of prestressed concrete, and in the 1960s, to strength as a design criterion, particularly with regard to shear-related failures in concrete beams. Parameters affecting shear strength have been studied, with considerable attention focused on torsional strength, including its interaction with bending moment and shear. Behavior of various types of slab floor systems has been experimentally studied, particularly with regard to strength and cracking. Earthquake resistance of structures, including behavior of shear walls, has received and is continuing to attract wide attention. More knowledge about the structural behavior of reinforced concrete has probably been obtained since 1950 than in all previous years combined.

Understanding of reinforced concrete behavior is still far from complete; building codes and specifications that give design procedures are continually changing to reflect latest knowledge.

1.3 Concrete

Plain concrete is made by mixing cement, fine aggregate, coarse aggregate, water, and frequently admixtures. When reinforcing steel is placed in the forms and wet concrete mix is placed around it, the final solidified mass becomes reinforced concrete (see Fig. 1.3.1). The strength of concrete depends on many factors: notably the proportion of the ingredients and the conditions of temperature and moisture under which it is placed and cured.

Contained in subsequent sections are brief discussions of the materials in and the properties of plain concrete. The treatment is intended to be only introductory; an interested reader should consult standard references devoted entirely to the subject of plain concrete [3,4].

1.4 Cement

Cement is a material that has adhesive and cohesive properties enabling it to bond mineral fragments into a solid mass. Although this definition can apply to many materials, the cements of interest for reinforced concrete construction are those that can set and harden in the presence of water—the so-called *hydraulic cements*. These consist primarily of silicates and aluminates of lime made from limestone and clay (or shale) which is ground, blended, fused in a kiln, and crushed to a powder. Such cements chemically combine with water (hydration) to form a hardened mass. The usual hydraulic cement used for reinforced concrete is known as *portland cement*, because of its resemblance when hardened to Portland stone found near Dorset, England. The name was originated in a patent obtained by Joseph Aspdin of Leeds, England, in 1824.

Concrete made with portland cement ordinarily requires about 14 days to attain adequate strength so that forms can be removed and construction and dead loads carried. The design strength of such concrete is reached at about 28 days. This ordinary portland cement is identified by ASTM

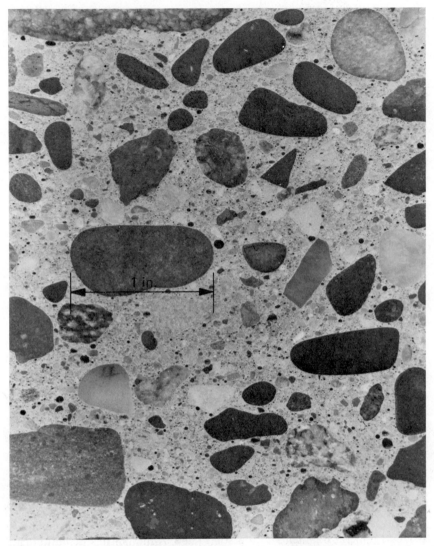

Fig. 1.3.1
Cross section of concrete. Cement and water paste completely coats each aggregate particle and fills all of the space between particles. (Courtesy of Portland Cement Association.)

(American Society for Testing and Materials) C150 [5] as Type I. Other types of portland cement and their intended uses are given in Table 1.4.1.

Two other categories of portland cement are in wide usage: *air-entraining portland cement* (ASTM C175) and *portland blast-furnace-slag cement* or *portland-pozzolan cement* (ASTM C595). Air-entraining portland cement may be referred to by the types given in Table 1.4.1 followed by the letter A, as IA, IIA, etc.

Air-entraining portland cement contains a chemical admixture finely ground with the cement to produce intentionally air bubbles on the order

Table 1.4.1

Types of Portland Cement[a]

Type	Usage
I	Ordinary construction where special properties are not required
II	Ordinary construction exposed to moderate sulfate action, or where moderate heat of hydration is desired
III	When high early strength is desired
IV	When low heat of hydration is desired
V	When high sulfate resistance is desired

[a] According to ASTM C150[5].

of 0.02 in. (0.5 mm) diameter uniformly distributed throughout the concrete. Such air entrainment will give the concrete improved durability against frost action, as well as better workability. Air-entraining agents may also be added to the regular types of cement in ASTM C150 at the time the concrete is mixed.

Portland blast-furnace-slag cement has lower heat of hydration than ordinary Type I cement and is useful for mass concrete structures such as dams; and because of its high sulfate resistance, it is used in seawater construction. Portland-pozzolan cement is a blended mixture of ordinary Type I cement with pozzolana. Pozzolana is a finely divided material containing silica in a reactive form so that it can combine with lime in the presence of water to form stable calcium silicates. The silicates have cementitious properties, thus permitting some reduction in the amount of cement required. In general, these cements gain strength slowly and produce less heat during hydration; thus they are widely used in mass concrete construction.

1.5 Aggregates

Since aggregate usually occupies about 75% of the total volume of concrete, its properties have a definite influence on the behavior of hardened concrete. Not only does the strength of the aggregate affect the strength of the concrete, its properties also greatly affect durability (resistance to deterioration under freeze-thaw cycles). Since aggregate is less expensive than cement, it is logical to try to use the largest percentage feasible. In general, for maximum strength, durability, and best economy, the aggregate should be packed and cemented as densely as possible. Hence aggregates are usually graded by size and a proper mix has specified percentages of both *fine* and *coarse* aggregates.

Fine aggregate (sand) is any material passing through a No. 4 sieve[†] [i.e., less than about $\frac{3}{16}$ in. (5 mm) diameter]. Coarse aggregate (gravel) is any material of larger size. The maximum size of coarse aggregate permitted (ACI-3.3.3)[‡] is governed by the clearances between sides of forms and

[†] According to ASTM Standard E11.
[‡] Numbers refer to sections in ACI Standard 318-77, *Building Code Requirements for Reinforced Concrete* [6].

between adjacent bars and may not exceed "one-fifth of the narrowest dimension between sides of forms, one-third of the depth of slabs, nor three-fourths of the minimum clear spacing between individual reinforcing bars . . . ." Additional information concerning aggregate selection and use is to be found in a report of ACI Committee 621 [7].

Natural stone aggregates conforming to ASTM C33 [8] are used in the majority of concrete construction, giving a unit weight for such concrete of about 145 pcf (pounds per cubic foot) or 2320 kg/m³ (kilograms per cubic meter). When steel reinforcement is added, the weight of *normal weight* reinforced concrete is taken for calculation purposes as 150 pcf, or 2400 kg/m³. Actual weights for concrete and steel are rarely, if ever, computed separately. For special purposes, lightweight or extra heavy aggregates are used.

Structural lightweight concretes [10] are usually made from aggregates conforming to ASTM C330 [9] which are produced artificially in a kiln, such as expanded clays and shales. The unit weight of such concrete typically ranges from 70 to 115 pcf (see Fig. 1.5.1). Lightweight concretes ranging down to 30 pcf (often known as cellular concretes) are also used for insulating purposes and for masonry units. When lightweight materials are used for both coarse and fine aggregates in structural concrete, it is termed *all-lightweight* concrete. When only the coarse aggregate is of lightweight material but normal weight sand is used for the fine aggregate, it is said to be *sand-lightweight* concrete. Often the term "sand replacement" is used in connection with lightweight concrete. This refers to replacing all or part of the lightweight aggregate fines with natural sand [12]. Additional information relating to structural lightweight concrete is to be found in guides [11,13,14] prepared by ACI Committees 213 and 523.

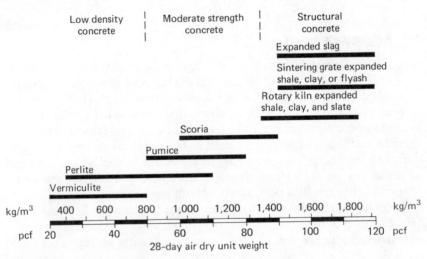

Fig. 1.5.1

Approximate unit weight and use classification of lightweight aggregate concretes (from Ref. 11).

Heavyweight, high-density concrete is used for shielding against gamma and x radiation in nuclear reactor containers and other structures [15]. Naturally occurring iron ores, titaniferous iron ores, "hydrous iron ores" (i.e., containing bound and adsorbed water), and barites [16] are crushed to suitable size for use as aggregates. Heavyweight concretes weigh typically from 200 to 250 pcf (3200 to 4000 kg/m^3).

1.6 Admixtures

In addition to cement, coarse and fine aggregates, and water, other materials known as *admixtures* may be added to the concrete mix immediately before or during the mixing. Admixtures may be used to modify the properties of the concrete to make it better serve its intended use or for better economy.

Some of the important purposes of admixtures are as follows:

1. To increase resistance to deterioration resulting from freeze-thaw cycles and the use of ice-removal salts (air-entraining admixtures).
2. To increase workability without increasing water content, or to decrease the water content at the same workability (finely divided minerals including pozzolans, such as fly ash, are generally used for this purpose).
3. To accelerate the rate of strength development at early ages (calcium chloride is the best known and most widely used accelerator).
4. To retard the setting and thereby reduce heat evolution (ASTM C494 admixtures).
5. To increase the strength (water-reducing and set-controlling admixtures, ASTM C494, Chemical Admixtures for Concrete).

Air-entraining admixtures are probably the most widely used type. Air entrainment provides a high degree of resistance to the disruptive action of freezing and thawing and of deicing chemicals. Plasticity and workability are also improved, permitting a reduction in water content. Uniformity of placement with little segregation can be achieved. In addition, air-entrained concrete is more water tight and has greater resistance to sulfate action. For exposed concrete, the resulting reduced strength (less than 15%) is far less important than the improved resistance to frost action [17].

The ACI Committee 212 Guide [17] provides extended discussion about the effects of numerous admixtures and contains 130 references.

1.7 Compressive Strength

The strength of concrete is controlled by the proportioning of cement, coarse and fine aggregates, water, and various admixtures. The ratio of water to cement is the chief factor for determining concrete strength, as shown in Fig. 1.7.1. The lower the water–cement ratio, the higher the compressive strength. A certain minimum amount of water is necessary for the proper chemical action in the hardening of concrete; extra water increases

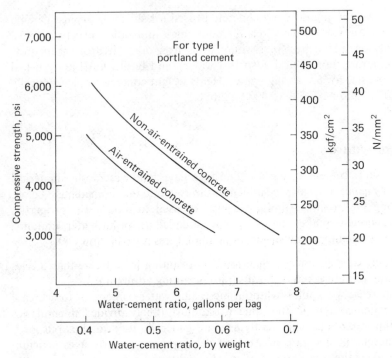

Fig. 1.7.1

Effect of water-cement ratio on 28-day compressive strength. Average values for concrete containing 1.5 to 2% trapped air for non-air-entrained concrete, and no more than 5 to 6% air for air-entrained concrete (from Ref. 18).

the workability (how easily the concrete will flow) but reduces strength. A measure of the workability is obtained by a *slump test*. A truncated cone-shaped metal mold 12 in. (30 cm) high is filled with fresh concrete, the mold is then lifted off, and a measurement is made of the distance the top of the wet mass "slumps" from its original position before the mold was removed. The smaller the slump, the stiffer and less workable is the mix. In building construction, a 3 to 4 in. (75 to 100 mm) slump is common. Vibration of the concrete mix will greatly improve workability and even very stiff no-slump concrete can be placed [20].

Information regarding proportioning of concrete mixes is available in ACI Standard 211.1 for normal weight concrete, ACI Standard 211.2 for structural lightweight concrete, and ACI Standard 211.3 for no-slump concrete [18,19,20]. Actual strength of concrete in place in the structure is also greatly affected by quality control procedures for placement and inspection. Details regarding good practice may be found in Refs. 21 and 22.

The strength of concrete is denoted in the United States by f'_c, which is the compressive strength in psi of test cylinders 6 in. in diameter by 12 in. high measured on the 28th day after they are made. In many other parts of the world, the standard test unit is the cube, frequently of 20 cm to a side.

Since nearly all the behavior of reinforced concrete is related to the 28-day compressive strength, it is important to realize that such strength differs depending on the size and shape of the standard test specimen. Since the cylinder strength test does not exhibit exactly the same properties as the cube strength test, it has been difficult to define a constant relationship between them. Factors such as tensile strength of concrete and size of the contact area of the testing machine have more effect on the cube strength than on the cylinder strength. As an average, one may assume that for ordinary weight concrete, the 6 × 12 in. (15 × 30 cm) cylinder strength is 80% of the 20-cm cube strength and 83% of the 15-cm cube strength [23]. For lightweight concrete, cylinder strength and cube strength are nearly equal.

Even in the United States tests of concrete in existing structures are often made using other than the standard 6 × 12 in. cylinder. For such tests, cores of other than 6 in. diameter are usually cut from the concrete. Tests of these are usually on cylinders having a height-to-diameter ratio of 2 to 1 but smaller than the standard cylinder. To draw proper conclusions, it is necessary to know the effect of test specimen size.

The stress-strain behavior of concrete is dependent on its strength, age at loading, rate of loading, aggregates and cement properties, and type and size of specimens [24,25]. Typical curves for specimens loaded at 28 days using normal testing speeds are shown in Fig. 1.7.2. One may note that lower-strength concrete has greater deformability (ductility) than higher-strength concrete, and the maximum stress is reached at a compressive strain between 0.0015 and 0.002. Ultimate strain at crushing of concrete varies from 0.003 to as high as 0.008; however, the maximum strain for practical cases is 0.003–0.004. The ACI Building Code [6] states that (ACI-10.2.3) "The maximum usable strain at the extreme concrete compression fiber shall be assumed equal to 0.003."

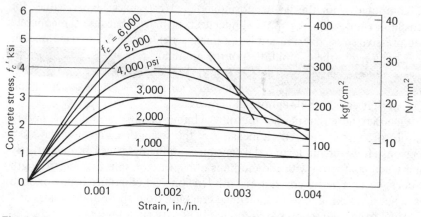

Fig. 1.7.2
Typical stress-strain curves for concrete under short-time loading.

In usual reinforced concrete design, specified concrete strengths of 3000 to 4000 psi (roughly 20 to 30 N/mm^2) are used for nonprestressed structures, and 5000 to 6000 psi (roughly 35 to 42 N/mm^2) for prestressed concrete. For special situations, concrete ranging from 6000 to 11,000 psi (42 to 75 N/mm^2) has been used [26]. Ready-mix concrete is being used with strengths to 9000 psi (62 N/mm^2) for columns on lower stories of high-rise buildings.

1.8 Tensile Strength

The strength of concrete in tension is also an important property that greatly affects the extent and size of cracking in structures. Tensile strength is usually determined by using the *split-cylinder* test in which the same size cylinder used for the compression test is placed in the testing machine lying on its side so that the compression load P is applied uniformly along the length of the cylinder in the direction of the diameter. The cylinder will split in half when the tensile strength is reached. The stress is computed by $2P/[\pi(\text{diameter})(\text{length})]$ based on theory of elasticity for a homogeneous material in a biaxial state of stress.[†] Tensile strength is a more variable property than compressive strength, and is about 10 to 15% of it. The split-cylinder tensile strength f_{ct} has been found to be proportional to $\sqrt{f'_c}$,[‡] such that

$$f_{ct} = 6\sqrt{f'_c} \text{ to } 7\sqrt{f'_c} \text{ psi} \qquad \text{for normal-weight concrete}$$
$$f_{ct} = 5\sqrt{f'_c} \text{ to } 6\sqrt{f'_c} \text{ psi} \qquad \text{for lightweight concrete}$$

The ACI Code has indirectly used $f_{ct} = 6.7\sqrt{f'_c}$ psi for normal-weight concrete, $f_{ct} = 5.7\sqrt{f'_c}$ for sand-lightweight concrete, and $f_{ct} = 5\sqrt{f'_c}$ for all-lightweight concrete (ACI-11.2).

Tensile strength in flexure, known as *modulus of rupture*, is also important when considering cracking and deflection of beams. The modulus of rupture f_r, computed from the flexure formula $f = Mc/I$, gives higher values for tensile strength than the split-cylinder test, primarily because the concrete compressive stress distribution is not linear when tensile failure is imminent as is assumed in the computation of the nominal Mc/I stress. It is generally accepted (ACI-9.5.2.3) that an average value for the modulus of rupture f_r may be taken as $7.5\sqrt{f'_c}$ ($0.62\sqrt{f'_c}$ N/mm^2) for normal-weight concrete and 75% of that value for all-lightweight concrete.

One may note that neither the split-cylinder nor the modulus of rupture tensile strength is correctly a measure of the strength under uniform axial tension. However, uniform axial tension is difficult to measure accurately and when compared with the modulus of rupture or split-cylinder strength it does *not* give better correlation with tension-related failure behavior such as flexural cracking in beams, inclined cracking from shear and torsion, and splitting from interaction of reinforcing bars with surrounding concrete.

[†] See, for example, S. Timoshenko and J. N. Goodier, *Theory of Elasticity*, 2nd ed., McGraw-Hill, 1951, pp. 85, 107.

[‡] $\sqrt{f'_c}$ is in psi-units; thus $f'_c = 3000$ psi, $\sqrt{f'_c} = 54.8$ psi. When f'_c is in kilogram-force per square centimeter (kgf/cm^2), the constant in front of $\sqrt{f'_c}$ is to be multiplied by 0.265; when f'_c is in newtons per square millimeter (N/mm^2), the constant in front of $\sqrt{f'_c}$ is to be multiplied by 0.083.

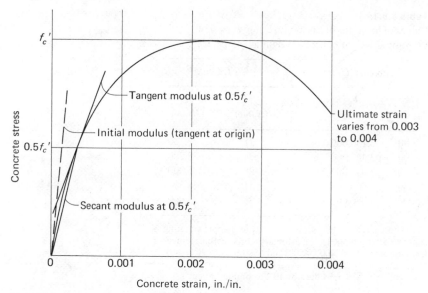

Fig. 1.9.1
Stress-strain curve for concrete.

1.9 Modulus of Elasticity

The modulus of elasticity of concrete varies, unlike that of steel, with strength. It also depends, though to a much lesser extent, on the age of concrete, properties of the aggregates and cement, rate of loading, and the type and size of specimen. Furthermore, since concrete exhibits some permanent set even under small loads, there are various definitions of the modulus of elasticity.

Referring to Fig. 1.9.1, representing a typical stress-strain curve for concrete [25], the initial modulus, the tangent modulus, and the secant modulus are noted. Usually the secant modulus at from 25 to 50% of the compressive strength f'_c is considered to be the modulus of elasticity. For many years the modulus was approximated adequately as 1000 f'_c by the ACI Code; but with the rapidly increasing use of lightweight concrete, the variable of density needed to be included. As the result of a statistical analysis of available data, the empirical formula

$$E_c = 33w^{1.5}\sqrt{f'_c} \tag{1.9.1}$$

was developed [27] for values of w between 90 and 155 lb/cu ft. Equation (1.9.1) may be considered as the secant modulus for a compressive stress at service-load level. For normal-weight concrete weighing 145 pcf, the formula gives $E_c = 57,600\sqrt{f'_c}$. For normal-weight concrete ACI-8.5.1 suggests

$$E_c = 57,000\sqrt{f'_c} \tag{1.9.2}†$$

---

† $E_c = 4730\sqrt{f'_c}$ when f'_c is in N/mm²

$E_c = 15,100\sqrt{f'_c}$ when f'_c is in kgf/cm²

Table 1.9.1
Values of Modulus of Elasticity (Using $E_c = 33w^{1.5}\sqrt{f'_c}$
for normal-weight concrete weighing 145 pcf)

U.S. Customary Units		S.I. Units[b]	
f'_c (psi)	E_c (psi)	f'_c (N/mm²)	E_c (N/mm²)
3000	3,150,000	21[a]	21,700
3500	3,400,000	24	23,200
4000	3,640,000	28	25,000
4500	3,860,000	31	26,300
5000	4,070,000	35	28,000

[a] These metric values are rounded values approximating concrete strengths in U.S. Customary units; actual equivalents for 3000, 3500, 4000, 4500, and 5000 psi are 20.7, 24.1, 27.6, 31.0, and 34.5 N/mm², respectively.
[b] Multiply N/mm² values by 10.2 to obtain kgf/cm².

Values of modulus of elasticity for various concrete strengths appear in Table 1.9.1.

1.10 Creep and Shrinkage

Creep and shrinkage are time-dependent deformations, that along with cracking provide the greatest concern for the designer because of the inaccuracies and unknowns that surround them. Concrete is elastic only under loads of short duration, and because of additional deformation with time, the effective behavior is that of an inelastic material. Deflection after a long period of time is therefore difficult to predict, but its control is needed to assure serviceability during the life of the structure.

Creep. Creep is the property of concrete (and other material) by which it continues to deform with time under sustained loads at unit stresses within the accepted elastic range (say, below 0.5 f'_c). This inelastic deformation increases at a decreasing rate during the time of loading, and its total magnitude may be several times as large as the short-time elastic deformation. Frequently creep is associated with shrinkage, since both are occurring simultaneously and often provide the same net effect: increased deformation with time. As may be noted by the general relationship of deformation versus time in Fig. 1.10.1, the "true elastic strain" decreases since the modulus of elasticity E_c is a function of concrete strength f'_c which increases with time.

Although creep is separate from shrinkage, it is related to it. Many expressions are available for predicting creep [28,29]. The internal mechanism of creep, or "plastic flow" as it is sometimes called, may be due to

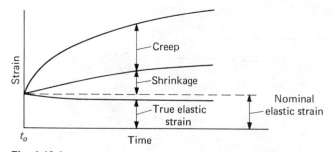

Fig. 1.10.1
Change in strain of a loaded and drying specimen; t_0 is the time of application of load (from Ref. 28).

any one or a combination of the following: (1) crystalline flow in the aggregate and hardened cement paste; (2) plastic flow of the cement paste surrounding the aggregate; (3) closing of internal voids; and (4) the flow of water out of the cement gel due to external load and drying. None of these alone seems to entirely account for creep. The gel theory seems to predominate at low-stress levels, whereas the crystalline theory predominates at high-stress levels [30].

Factors affecting the magnitude of creep are (1) the constituents—such as the composition and fineness of the cement, the admixtures, and the size, grading, and mineral content of the aggregates; (2) proportions such as water content and water–cement ratio; (3) curing temperature and humidity; (4) relative humidity during period of use; (5) age at loading; (6) duration of loading; (7) magnitude of stress; (8) surface–volume ratio of the member; and (9) slump.

Accurate prediction of creep is complicated because of the variables involved; however, a general prediction method [29] gives a standard creep coefficient equation (4 in. or less slump, 40% relative humidity, moist cured, and loading age of 7 days)

$$C_t = \frac{\text{creep strain}}{\text{initial elastic strain}}$$

$$= \frac{t^{0.60}}{10 + t^{0.60}} C_u \qquad (1.10.1)$$

shown in Fig. 1.10.2, where t is duration of loading (days) and C_u is ultimate creep strain (Ref. 29 suggests using 2.35 for average conditions). Correction factors are given for relative humidity, loading age, minimum thickness of member, slump, percent fines, and air content. For practical purposes, the only factors significant enough to require correction are humidity and age at loading.

The effect of unloading may be seen from Fig. 1.10.3 where at a certain time t_1 the load is removed. There is an immediate elastic recovery and a long-time creep recovery, but a residual deformation remains.

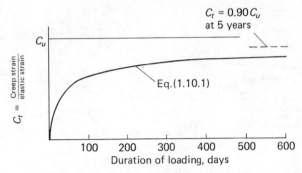

Fig. 1.10.2
Standard creep coefficient variation with duration of loading
(for 4 in. or less slump, 40% relative humidity, moist cured,
and loading age of 7 days).

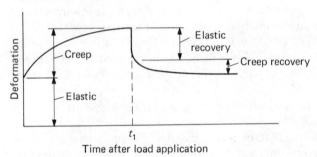

Fig. 1.10.3
Typical creep and recovery relationship (from Ref. 28).

Shrinkage. Shrinkage, broadly defined, is volume change that is unrelated
to load application. It is possible for concrete cured continuously under
water to increase in volume; however, the usual concern is with a decrease
in volume. A discussion of the mechanisms of shrinkage may be found in
Ref. 4 (pp. 283–299). In general the same factors have been found to influence
shrinkage strain as those that influence creep—primarily those factors
related to moisture loss.

The general prediction method [29] gives a standard shrinkage strain
equation (for 4 in. or less slump, 40% ambient relative humidity and minimum
thickness of member 6 in. or less, after 7 days moist cured)

$$\epsilon_{sh} = \left(\frac{t}{35 + t} \right) (\epsilon_{sh})_u \qquad (1.10.2)$$

shown in Fig. 1.10.4, where t is time (days) after moist curing, and $(\epsilon_{sh})_u$ is
ultimate shrinkage strain (Ref. 29 suggests using $800(10^{-6})$ in./in. for average
conditions). Correction factors are given with the primary one relating to
humidity H,

$$\text{correction factor} = 1.40 - 0.01H \qquad \text{for } 40\% \leq H \leq 80\%$$
$$\text{correction factor} = 3.00 - 0.03H \qquad \text{for } 80\% \leq H \leq 100\%$$

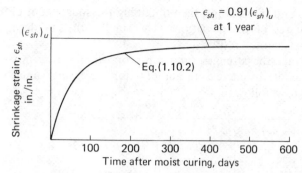

Fig. 1.10.4
Standard shrinkage strain variation with time after moist
during (for 4 in. or less slump, 40% ambient relative humidity
and minimum thickness of member 6 in. or less, after 7 days
moist cured).

Shrinkage, particularly when restrained unsymmetrically by reinforcement, causes deformations generally additive to those of creep. For proper
serviceability, it is desirable to predict or compensate for shrinkage in the
structure.

1.11 Concrete Quality Control

In reinforced concrete design the concrete sections are proportioned and
reinforced using a *specified compressive strength* f'_c (28-day compressive
strength). The strength f'_c for which each part of a structure has been designed
should be clearly indicated on the design drawings. In the United States,
as indicated in Sec. 1.7, f'_c is based on cylinder strength (6 × 12 in. cylinders),
evaluated in accordance with ACI standard 214 [31].

Concrete is a material whose strength and other properties are not
precisely predictable, so that test cylinders from a mix designed to provide,
say, 3000 psi (roughly 20 N/mm²) concrete will show considerable variability.
Because of this, mixes must be designed to provide an average compressive
strength greater than the specified value f'_c.

ACI-4.7 indicates that adequate control of strength occurs when the
probable frequency of tests[†] more than 500 psi (3.4 N/mm²) below the
specified value f'_c will not exceed 1 in 100 and the probable frequency of an
average of three consecutive tests below f'_c will not exceed 1 in 100.

When the ready-mix plant or other concrete production facility has a
record based on at least 30 consecutive strength tests for materials and
conditions similar to those expected, the *standard deviation* σ can be computed based on those tests to establish how variable is the concrete strength.

Standard deviation is calculated by first computing the simple average
of the tests results, taking the absolute value of the difference (deviation)

[†] According to ACI-4.8.1.4, a strength test is the "average of two cylinders from the same
sample, tested at 28 days or the specified earlier age."

between each test value and the average, then obtaining the square root of the average of the squares of the deviations. The smaller the standard deviation, the more consistent the results.

ACI-4.3.1 indicates that the strength used for proportioning the mix must exceed the specified f'_c by increasing amounts for increasing values of the standard deviation, as follows:

Increase above Specified Strength f'_c for Concrete Mix Design		Standard Deviation, σ	
(psi)	(N/mm²)	(psi)	(N/mm²)
400	2.8	0–300	0–2.1
550	3.8	300–400	2.1–2.8
700	4.8	400–500	2.8–3.4
900	6.2	500–600	3.4–4.1
1200	8.3	above 600	above 4.1

Thus if the designer has used a specified strength f'_c of 4000 psi, and the concrete producer has shown a standard deviation of 450 psi, the mix should be designed for an average strength of 4700 psi. Further, when suitable tests are not available, the mix must be designed to produce an average strength 1200 psi above the specified strength.

With regard to evaluation and acceptance of concrete, ACI-4.8 provides requirements for the numbers of samples that must be taken. ACI-4.8.2.3 indicates that the strength level of an individual class of concrete shall be considered satisfactory if the averages of all sets of three consecutive strength test results equal or exceed the required f'_c and no individual strength test falls below the required f'_c by more than 500 psi.

It should be noted that the term "quality control" entails much more than designing the concrete mix and evaluating the cylinder strength tests. The foregoing discussion of concrete strength variation should merely give an awareness of the fact that concrete having a specified compressive strength f'_c cannot be expected to provide precisely known actual strength and other properties.

Quality control in the broader sense for reinforced concrete construction is a subject of great importance, but generally lies outside the scope of this text. Reference 32 provides an excellent overall discussion of this subject.

1.12 Steel Reinforcement

Steel reinforcement may consist of bars, welded wire fabric, or wires. For usual construction, bars (called *deformed bars*) having lugs or protrusions (*deformations*) are used (see Fig. 1.12.1). Such deformations inhibit longitudinal movement of the bar relative to the concrete that surrounds it. These deformed bars are available in the United States in sizes $\frac{3}{8}$ to $2\frac{1}{4}$ in. (9.5 to 57 mm) nominal diameter.

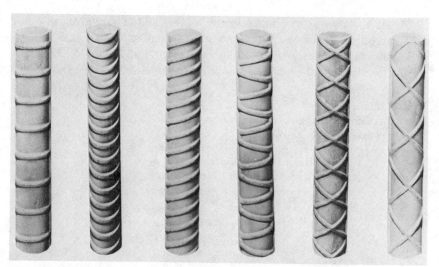

Fig. 1.12.1
Deformed reinforcing bars. (Courtesy of Concrete Reinforcing Steel Institute.)

Sizes of ASTM bars are indicated by numbers (see Table 1.12.1). For sizes #3 through #8, they are based on the number of eighths of an inch included in the nominal diameter of the bars. Bars of designation #9 through #11 (though round) correspond to the former 1 in. square, $1\frac{1}{8}$ in. square, and $1\frac{1}{4}$ in. square sizes, whereas bars designated as #14 and #18 have cross-sectional areas equal to those of $1\frac{1}{2}$ and 2 in. square sizes, respectively. The nominal diameter of a deformed bar is equivalent to the diameter of a plain bar having the same weight per foot as the deformed bar.

Table 1.12.1
Reinforcing Bar Dimensions and Weights (Standard ASTM bars used in U.S.A.)

Bar Number	Nominal Dimensions					
	Diameter		Area		Weight	
	(in.)	(mm)	(sq. in.)	(cm²)	(lb/ft)	(kg/m)
3	0.375	9.5	0.11	0.71	0.376	0.559
4	0.500	12.7	0.20	1.29	0.668	0.994
5	0.625	15.9	0.31	2.00	1.043	1.552
6	0.750	19.1	0.44	2.84	1.502	2.235
7	0.875	22.2	0.60	3.87	2.044	3.041
8	1.000	25.4	0.79	5.10	2.670	3.973
9	1.128	28.7	1.00	6.45	3.400	5.059
10	1.270	32.3	1.27	8.19	4.303	6.403
11	1.410	35.8	1.56	10.06	5.313	7.906
14	1.693	43.0	2.25	14.52	7.65	11.38
18	2.257	57.3	4.00	25.81	13.60	20.24

Metric bar sizes as recommended by UNESCO [23] are given in Table 1.12.2 and those of the new Canadian Standard are in Table 1.12.3.

Reinforcing bar steel may be of several types: (1) ASTM A615 [33], billet steel of Grades 40 and 60 having minimum specified yield stresses[†] of 40,000

Table 1.12.2
Metric Bar Dimensions and Weights (Sizes as recommended by UNESCO [23])

Diameter (mm)	Area (cm^2)	Weight (kg/m)	Comparison to U.S. Bars Bar Number (Area)
6	0.28	0.211	
8	0.50	0.377	— 3 (0.71 cm^2)
10	0.79	0.596	
12	1.13	0.852	— 4 (1.29 cm^2)
14	1.54	1.16	
16	2.01	1.52	— 5 (2.00 cm^2)
18	2.54	1.92	— 6 (2.84 cm^2)
20	3.14	2.37	
22	3.80	2.87	— 7 (3.87 cm^2)
25	4.91	3.70	— 8 (5.10 cm^2)
28	6.16	4.65	— 9 (6.45 cm^2)
30	7.07	5.33	
32	8.04	6.07	—10 (8.19 cm^2)
			—11 (10.06 cm^2)
40	12.56	9.47	—14 (14.52 cm^2)
50	19.63	14.8	
60	28.27	21.3	—18 (25.81 cm^2)

Table 1.12.3
Canadian Standard Metric Bar Dimensions and Weights

Bar Number	Diameter (mm)	Area (cm^2)	Weight (kg/m)	Comparison to U.S. Bars Bar Number (Area)
10	11.3	1.0	0.784	— 3 (0.71 cm^2)
				— 4 (1.29 cm^2)
15	16.0	2.0	1.568	— 5 (2.00 cm^2)
				— 6 (2.84 cm^2)
20	19.5	3.0	2.352	— 7 (3.87 cm^2)
25	25.2	5.0	3.920	— 8 (5.10 cm^2)
30	29.9	7.0	5.488	— 9 (6.45 cm^2)
				—10 (8.19 cm^2)
35	35.7	10.0	7.840	—11 (10.06 cm^2)
45	43.7	15.0	11.760	—14 (14.52 cm^2)
55	56.4	25.0	19.600	—18 (25.81 cm^2)

[†] The term "yield stress" refers to either *yield point*, the well-defined deviation from perfect elasticity, or *yield strength*, the value obtained by a specified offset strain for material having no well-defined yield point.

and 60,000 psi, respectively (276 and 414 N/mm^2); (2) ASTM A616 [34], rail steel of Grades 50 and 60; (3) ASTM A617 [35], axle steel of Grades 40 and 60; and (4) ASTM A706 [36], low-alloy steel of Grade 60 intended for applications where welding or bending, or both, are important.

The billet steel is newly made steel with its chemical content sufficiently controlled to provide necessary ductility. Axle and rail steel bars are made from steel that is rerolled from old axles and rails and are in general less ductile than those of billet steel. Because of relatively little extra cost, the Grade 60 steel has rapidly replaced the formerly predominately used Grade 40 steel. All of the bar sizes in Table 1.12.1 are available in Grade 60 billet steel and low-allow steel; however, only #3 through #11 bars are available in Grade 40 billet steel and in rail or axle steel.

Welded wire fabric is used in thin slabs, thin shells, and other locations where available space would not permit the placement of deformed bars with proper cover and clearance. Welded wire fabric (WWF), consists of cold drawn wire in orthogonal patterns, square or rectangular, resistance welded at all intersections. The wires may be smooth (ASTM A82 [37]) or deformed (ASTM A496 [38]). The wire is specified by the symbol W (for smooth wires) or D (for deformed wires) followed by a number representing the cross-sectional area in hundredths of a square inch, varying from 1.5 to 31. On design drawings it is usually indicated by the symbol WWF followed by spacings of the wires in the two 90° directions. Thus WWF6 × 8 − W7 × W7 indicates welded wire fabric with 6-in. longitudinal spacing, 8-in. transverse spacing, and both sets of wires smooth and having a cross-sectional area of 0.07 sq in. The steel used for the wire is that having a minimum specified yield stress of 70,000 psi. Additional information about welded wire fabric may be obtained from the *Building Design Handbook* [39].

Wires in the form of individual wires or groups of wires forming *strands* are used for prestressed concrete. There is a great variety of wire and strands of different strengths and properties, the most prevalent being the 7-wire stress relieved strand conforming to ASTM A416 [40]. These strands have a center wire enclosed by six helically wound outside wires. Usual nominal diameters for 7-wire strands are $\frac{1}{4}, \frac{3}{8}$, and $\frac{1}{2}$ in. The minimum ultimate tensile strength for Grade 250 strands is 250,000 psi (1720 N/mm^2), and for Grade 270 is 270,000 psi (1860 N/mm^2); there is no well-defined yield point. Typically under service conditions these prestressed strands have a stress of 150,000 to 160,000 psi (1030 to 1100 N/mm^2).

The modulus of elasticity for all nonprestressed steel may be taken (ACI-8.5.2) as 29,000,000 psi (200,000 N/mm^2). For prestressing steel it is lower and somewhat variable, therefore it must be obtained from the manufacturer. A value of 27,000,000 psi (186,000 N/mm^2) is often used for 7-wire strands conforming to ASTM A416.

SELECTED REFERENCES

1. Hans Straub. *A History of Civil Engineering*. London: Leonard Hill, 1952 (pp. 208–211).
2. R. S. Kirby, Sidney Withington, A. B. Darling, and F. G. Kilgour. *Engineering in History*. New York: McGraw-Hill, 1956.

3. George E. Troxell, Harmer E. Davis, and Joe W. Kelly *Composition and Properties of Concrete* (2nd ed.). New York: McGraw-Hill, 1968.
4. A. M. Neville. *Properties of Concrete* (2nd ed.). New York: Halstead Press, 1973.
5. *Standard Specifications for Portland Cement* (ASTM C150–76a). Philadelphia: American Society for Testing and Materials, 1976.
6. *Building Code Requirements for Reinforced Concrete* (ACI Std. 318–77). Detroit: American Concrete Institute, 1977.
7. ACI Committee 621. "Selection and Use of Aggregates for Concrete," *ACI Journal, Proceedings*, **58,** November 1961, 513–542.
8. *Standard Specifications for Concrete Aggregates* (ASTM C33–74a). Philadelphia: American Society for Testing and Materials, 1974.
9. *Standard Specifications for Lightweight Aggregates for Structural Concrete* (ASTM C330–76). Philadelphia: American Society for Testing and Materials, 1976.
10. *Lightweight Concrete* (SP–29). Detroit: American Concrete Institute, 1971. (Symposium papers)
11. ACI Committee 213. "Guide for Structural Lightweight Aggregate Concrete," *ACI Journal, Proceedings*, **64,** August 1967, 433–469.
12. J. A. Hanson. "Replacement of Lightweight Aggregate Fines with Natural Sand in Structural Concrete," *ACI Journal, Proceedings*, **61,** July 1964, 779–793.
13. ACI Committee 523, "Guide for Cast-in-Place Low-Density Concrete," *ACI Journal, Proceedings*, **64,** September 1967, 529–535.
14. ACI Committee 523. "Guide for Cellular Concretes Above 50 pcf, and for Aggregate Concretes Above 50 pcf with Compressive Strengths Less Than 2500 psi," *ACI Journal, Proceedings*, **72,** February 1975, 50–66.
15. *Concrete for Radiation Shielding* (Compilation No. 1, 2d ed.). Detroit: American Concrete Institute, 1962.
16. Katharine Mather. "High Strength, High Density Concrete," *ACI Journal, Proceedings*, **62,** August 1965, 951–962.
17. ACI Committee 212. "Guide for Use of Admixtures in Concrete," *ACI Journal, Proceedings*, **68,** September 1971, 646–676.
18. *Recommended Practice for Selecting Proportions for Normal Weight Concrete* (ACI Std. 211.1–74). Detroit: American Concrete Institute, 1974.
19. *Recommended Practice for Selecting Proportions for Structural Lightweight Concrete* (ACI Std. 211.2–69). Detroit: American Concrete Institute, 1969.
20. *Recommended Practice for Selecting Proportions for No-Slump Concrete*, (ACI Std. 211.3–75). Detroit: American Concrete Institute, 1975.
21. *Recommended Practice for Measuring, Mixing, Transporting, and Placing Concrete* (ACI Std. 304–73). Detroit: American Concrete Institute, 1973.
22. *ACI Manual of Concrete Inspection* (Spec. Publ. No. 2. 5th ed.). Detroit: American Concrete Institute, 1967.
23. UNESCO. *Reinforced Concrete: An International Manual*, London: Butterworth, 1971 (pp. 19–22).
24. Hjalmar Granholm. *A General Flexural Theory of Reinforced Concrete*. New York: Wiley, 1965 (pp. 23–36).
25. E. Hognestad, N. W. Hanson, and D. McHenry. "Concrete Stress Distribution in Ultimate Strength Design," *ACI Journal, Proceedings*, **52,** December 1955, 455.
26. Cameron MacInnis and Donald V. Thomson. "Special Techniques for Producing High Strength Concrete," *ACI Journal, Proceedings*, **67,** December 1970, 996–1002.
27. Adrian Pauw. "Static Modulus of Elasticity of Concrete as Affected by Density," *ACI Journal, Proceedings*, **57,** December, 1960, 679–687.
28. Adam M. Neville and Bernard L. Meyers, "Creep of Concrete: Influencing Factors and Prediction," *Symposium on Creep of Concrete* (SP–9). Detroit: American Concrete Institute, 1964 (pp. 1–33).

29. Dan E. Branson and M. L. Christiason. "Time-Dependent Concrete Properties Related to Design—Strength and Elastic Properties, Creep, and Shrinkage," *Designing for Effects of Creep, Shrinkage, Temperature in Concrete Structures* (SP–27). Detroit: American Concrete Institute, 1971 (pp. 257–277).
30. Iqbal Ali and Clyde E. Kesler. "Mechanisms of Creep in Concrete," *Symposium on Creep of Concrete* (SP–9). Detroit: American Concrete Institute, 1964 (pp. 35–63).
31. *Recommended Practice for Evaluation of Compression Test Results of Field Concrete* (ACI Std. 214–65). Detroit: American Concrete Institute, 1965.
32. "Inspection and Quality Control of Concrete," Symposium series of papers, *ACI Journal, Proceedings*, **65,** August 1968, 639–658. Discussion, **66,** February 1969, 154–157 (includes other references).
33. *Standard Specification for Deformed and Plain Billet-Steel Bars for Concrete Reinforcement* (ASTM A615–76a). Philadelphia: American Society for Testing and Materials, 1976.
34. *Standard Specification for Rail-Steel Deformed and Plain Bars for Concrete Reinforcement* (ASTM A616–76). Philadelphia: American Society for Testing and Materials, 1976.
35. *Standard Specification for Axle Steel Deformed and Plain Bars for Concrete Reinforcement* (ASTM A617–76). Philadelphia: American Society for Testing and Materials, 1976.
36. *Standard Specification for Low-Alloy Steel Deformed Bars for Concrete Reinforcement* (ASTM A706–76). Philadelphia: American Society for Testing and Materials, 1976.
37. *Standard Specifications for Cold-Drawn Steel Wire for Concrete Reinforcement* (ASTM A82–76). Philadelphia: American Society for Testing and Materials, 1976.
38. *Standard Specification for Deformed Steel Wire for Concrete Reinforcement* (ASTM A496–72). Philadelphia: American Society for Testing and Materials, 1972.
39. *Building Design Handbook*. Washington, D.C.: Wire Reinforcement Institute, 1960.
40. *Standard Specifications for Uncoated Seven-Wire Stress-Relieved Strand for Prestressed Concrete* (ASTM A416–74). Philadelphia: American Society for Testing and Materials, 1974.

2

Design
Methods
and Requirements

2.1 ACI Building Code

When two different materials, such as steel and concrete, act together, it is understandable that the analysis for strength of a reinforced concrete member has to be partly empirical, although mostly rational. These semi-rational principles and methods are being constantly revised and improved as results of theoretical and experimental research accumulate. The American Concrete Institute, serving as a clearinghouse for these changes, issues building code requirements, the most recent of which is the *Building Code Requirements for Reinforced Concrete* (ACI 318–77), hereafter referred to as the ACI Code [Ref. 6, Chap. 1].[†]

Thus the ACI Code is a Standard of the American Concrete Institute. In order to achieve legal status, it must be adopted by a governing body as a part of its general building code. The ACI Code is partly a specification-type code, which gives acceptable design and construction methods in detail, and partly a performance code, which states desired results rather than details of how such results are to be obtained. A building code, legally adopted, is intended to prevent people from being harmed; therefore it specifies minimum requirements consistent with good safety. It is important to realize that a building code is not a recommended practice, nor is it a design handbook, nor is it intended to replace engineering knowledge, judgment, or experience. It does *not* relieve the designer of the responsibility for having a safe economical structure.

[†] The reader is advised to have the ACI Code as a ready reference while using this text.

Lake Point Tower, Chicago, apartment building, 70 stories high. (Courtesy of Portland Cement Association.)

2.2 Ultimate Strength and Working Stress Design Methods

Two philosophies of design have long been prevalent. The working stress method was the principal one used from the early 1900s until the early 1960s. Since 1963 there has been a rapid transition to the ultimate strength method because of its more rational approach. This latter method, referred to by the present ACI Code as "proportioning for adequate strength," is deemed conceptually more realistic to establish structural safety.

2.3 Working Stress Method

In the working stress method (referred to by the present ACI Code as the "alternate design method"), a structural element is so designed that the stresses resulting from the action of *service loads* and computed by the mechanics of elastic members do not exceed some predesignated allowable values. Service load is the load, such as dead, live, snow, wind, and earth-quake, which is assumed actually to occur when the structure is in service.

The allowable stresses are prescribed by a building code (see Sec. 2.1) to provide a factor of safety against attainment of some upper limiting stress, such as the specified compressive strength f'_c for concrete and the minimum specified yield stress f_y for nonprestressed reinforcement steel. As an example the allowable stress in compression for concrete is $0.45f'_c$ (ACI-Appen. B.3), and the allowable stress in tension on reinforcing bars is 20,000 psi for Grades 40 and 50 steel, and 24,000 psi for Grade 60 and above. Thus for properly designed structural elements, the stresses computed under the action of service loads will be well within the elastic range, so that the straight-line variation between stress and strain is used.

Some of the obstacles to the working stress method are as follows.

1. Since the limitation is on the total stress under service load, there is no simple way to account for different degrees of uncertainty of various kinds of load. Generally the dead load (gravity load due to weight of structural elements and permanent attachments) is known more accurately than the live load, which is code prescribed and may have unknown and variable distribution.
2. Creep and shrinkage, which contribute major time-dependent effects on a structure, are not easily accounted for by elastic calculation of stresses.
3. Concrete stress is not proportional to strain up to its crushing strength, so that the inherent safety provided is unknown when a percentage of f'_c is used as the allowable stress.

2.4 Ultimate Strength Method

In the ultimate strength method ("strength method" in the ACI Code), the service loads are increased sufficiently by factors (often referred to as load factors) to obtain the ultimate design load. The structure or structural element is then proportioned to provide the desired ultimate strength. The computation of this strength takes into account the nonlinear stress-strain behavior of concrete.

The term "ultimate strength" has been in common usage by practitioners and building codes at least since about 1956. However, the theoretical strength computed under the provisions of the Code is only a code-defined value; it is not necessarily the actual "ultimate" value. Hence, the ACI Code makes no reference to "ultimate strength," instead it uses the expressions "strength design method" and "proportioning for adequate strength." Throughout this text, any reference to "ultimate strength" will mean the ACI Code-defined "strength."

2.5 Comments on Design Methods

Historically, ultimate strength was the earliest approach to design since the failure load could be measured by test without a knowledge of the magnitude or distribution of internal stresses. With the interest in and understanding of the elastic methods of analysis in the early 1900s, the elastic working stress method was adopted almost universally by specifications as the best for design. As more detailed understanding of the actual behavior of reinforced concrete structures subjected to loads in excess of the service loads developed, adjustments in the theory and in the design procedures were made.

The first modification of the elastic working stress method resulted from the study of axially loaded columns in the early 1930s. The 1940 Joint Committee Report and the 1941 ACI Code included axially loaded column design procedures with a basis in ultimate strength behavior. Next, working stress methods were modified to account for creep of concrete in beams with compression steel and in eccentrically loaded columns. The early history of the ACI Code has been summarized by Kerekes and Reid [1].

The 1956 ACI Code was the first that officially recognized and permitted the ultimate strength method of design, the result of work by ACI–ASCE Committee 327 [2]. The 1963 ACI Code treated the working stress method and the ultimate strength method on an equal basis; but actually the major portion of the working stress method was modified to reflect ultimate strength behavior. With the relegation of the working stress method to a small section referred to as the "alternate method," the 1971 ACI Code entirely accepted the ultimate strength method. The 1977 ACI Code has put the "alternate design method" in Appendix B. Because the ACI Code has eliminated most of the confusion arising from the use of two parallel methods, the term "strength" instead of the term "ultimate strength" has been adopted.

No matter which of the above philosophies is employed in a design, *serviceability* must also be considered. Serviceability factors that may be of more importance than strength are excessive deflection, detrimental cracking, excessive amplitude or frequency of vibration, and excessive noise transmission. The designer must consider both *strength* and *serviceability*. Any one, or a combination, of the strength and serviceability factors may provide a criterion for the limit of structural usefulness.

It is likely that in the near future the "alternate design method" will disappear and the only use for the elastic concepts of the working stress method will be in the computation of deflections, which are of interest under service loads rather than at ultimate strength.

2.6 Safety Provisions

Structures and structural members must always be designed to carry some reserve load beyond what is expected under normal use. Such reserve capacity is provided to account for a variety of factors, which may be grouped in two general categories; factors relating to overload and factors relating to undercapacity. Overloads may arise from changing the use for which the structure was designed, from underestimation of the effect of loads by oversimplification in calculation procedures, and from effects of construction sequence and methods. Undercapacity may result from adverse variations in material strengths, workmanship, dimensions, control, and degree of supervision, even though individually these items may be within required tolerances.

Conventionally, the term "safety factor" has been used in working stress design to designate nominally the ratio between the yield point stress (real, as for steel; nominally defined, as for concrete) and the allowable working stress. Such use has resulted in structures and structural elements with the same "safety factor" but considerably variant in their ultimate capacity to service load ratio. Thus the term "safety factor" as conventionally applied has little meaning so far as the prediction of ultimate capacity is concerned.

The variability in the ratio of the ultimate capacity to service load under the working stress method has been a major factor in the transition to the use of the ultimate strength method. To distinguish clearly between the conventional term "safety factor" and the ultimate capacity to service-load ratio, the term "load factor" has traditionally been adopted for the latter.

The ACI Code has separated the safety provision into factors for overload U and factors for undercapacity ϕ. The basic overload equation (ACI-9.2.1) for structures in such locations and of such proportions that the effects of wind and earthquake may be neglected is

$$U = 1.4D + 1.7L \tag{2.6.1}$$

where

   U = required strength (based on possible overload)
   D = dead load under service conditions
   L = live load under service conditions

The undercapacity factor ϕ, the other part of the safety provision, is prescribed (ACI-9.3) to be as follows:

	ϕ Factors
(a) Bending, with or without axial tension	0.90
(b) Axial tension	0.90
(c) Shear and torsion	0.85
(d) Compression members, spirally reinforced	0.75[†]
(e) Compression members, tied	0.70[†]
(f) Bearing on concrete	0.70
(g) Bending in plain concrete	0.65

Even though the overload factors U and the undercapacity factors ϕ are itemized separately in the ACI Code, they are in fact complementary parts of the provision to insure adequate safety. The total theoretical strength (satisfying equilibrium and compatibility of stress and strain) to be designed for is U/ϕ. Because the ϕ factors vary for different types of member action, the designer generally will use them at various stages in the calculations. The overload provision is best accounted for at the beginning of the design, where the service loads are multiplied by their respective factors in U giving what are called *factored loads*. For consistency throughout this text, terms

---

[†] For combined compression and bending, ϕ value may be variable and increase to 0.90 as the axial compression decreases to zero.

will be used according to definitions (ACI-2.1) of the ACI Code. For that purpose *design loads* are *factored loads*—that is, the loads after the overload provision has been applied.

The purpose of a safety provision is to limit the probability of failure and yet to permit economical structures. Obviously if cost is no object, it is easy to design a structure whose probability of failure is nil. To arrive properly at suitable factors for safety, the relative importance of various items must be established. Some of those items are

(a) Seriousness of a failure, either to humans or goods
(b) Reliability of workmanship and inspection
(c) Expectation of overload and to what magnitude
(d) Importance of the member in the structure
(e) Chance of warning prior to a failure

By assigning percentages to the above items and evaluating the circumstances for any given situation, proper factors for safety may be determined for each case. The ACI Code committee has combined experience with historical precedent to arrive at the given overload and undercapacity factors. The normal range of the factor for safety U/ϕ is from 1.55 to 2.4 for reinforced concrete structural elements. The subject of safety provisions for reinforced concrete has been summarized by Ferguson [3]. Randall has presented an interesting historical perspective of present safety provisions [4].

In recent years considerable attention has been focused on using theory of probability as a basis for a design code, thus providing a more rational basis for the various components comprising the U and ϕ factors. A series of ACI Committee 348 (structural safety) papers [5,6,7,8] gives an excellent overview of this approach. It is pointed out [7] that the following five safety conditions have formed the basis for the current practice in structural analysis and design.

1. The probability of a real loading in excess of the nominal service load $D + L$ must be satisfactorily small.
2. The probability of a real loading in excess of the ultimate loading, say $U = 1.4D + 1.7L$, must be very small or near to zero during the life of the structure.
3. The probability of unsatisfactory performance at the ultimate load U must be satisfactorily small.
4. The probability of unsatisfactory performance under a load test, say $0.85U$ as given in ACI-20.4.3, must be very small or near to zero.
5. The probability of unsatisfactory performance at the working load $D + L$ must be practically zero.

It is noted that conditions 1 and 2 relate to the overload provision U along with analysis methods, whereas conditions 3, 4, and 5 relate to the capacity reduction factor ϕ as well as the methods for computing strength.

Future code revisions are expected to incorporate more of the probability concepts in establishing design factors for safety. The current status is reflected in a collection of discussion and opinion [9].

2.7 Overload Provisions for Various Load Combinations

In addition to the basic provision for load factors on dead load plus live load given by Eq. (2.6.1), other service loads may also act.

For wind load W acting in combination with other loads, ACI-9.2.2 provides

$$U = 0.75(1.4D + 1.7L + 1.7W) \tag{2.7.1}$$

Because wind is of a transient nature and acts with its maximum magnitude for a short duration, it has been traditional to allow an overstress of $33\frac{1}{3}\%$ under the working stress method. The same effect is accomplished by using three-quarters of the factored load when wind effect is included.

Frequently a more severe situation arises with wind loading if live load is absent; this possibility must be considered. When live load is absent, Eq. (2.7.1) becomes

$$U = 1.05D + 1.275W \tag{2.7.2}$$

Furthermore for situations in which dead load is a gravity stabilizing effect in combination with wind (such as a tower or wall), the possibility of a reduced dead load must be considered rather than overload; thus ACI-9.2.2 also gives

$$U = 0.9D + 1.3W \tag{2.7.3}$$

When lateral earth pressure H is involved, it is treated as live load; thus

$$U = 1.4D + 1.7L + 1.7H \tag{2.7.4}$$

but when dead or live load (or both) reduces the effect of earth pressure, then

$$U = 0.9D + 1.7H \tag{2.7.5}$$

For liquid pressure F, Eqs. (2.7.4) and (2.7.5) are used except $1.7H$ is replaced with $1.4F$. Since liquid density is generally accurately known, its pressure is treated as dead load using the 1.4 factor. On the other hand soil properties are more variable, thus earth pressure is treated as live load using the 1.7 factor.

Where the structural effects T of differential settlement, creep, shrinkage, or temperature change may be significant, they are to be included with dead load (ACI-9.2.7),

$$U = 0.75(1.4D + 1.4T + 1.7L) \tag{2.7.6}$$

The 0.75 factor is to recognize the low probability of having these effects occur simultaneously with full dead and live load.

Any structure or structural element *must be designed for the most severe of any of the load combinations* given by Eq. (2.6.1) and Eqs. (2.7.1) to (2.7.6).

2.8 Handbooks

It may be pointed out that this textbook does not appreciably consider office practices or the use of design aids. Once concepts and principles are thoroughly understood, the use of curves and tables can greatly speed up design. There are several handbooks in common use, the *Design Handbook*, Vols. 1 and 2 [10,11], published by ACI; and the *CRSI Handbook* [12,13], published by the Concrete Reinforcing Steel Institute. These publications contain many useful tables and charts that can speed up design for the experienced designer.

The importance of correct and clear detailing work cannot be over-emphasized. For this the reader is referred to the *Manual of Standard Practice for Detailing Reinforced Concrete Structures* (ACI 315-74) [14], which is essentially a drafting manual but which does aid the designer by bringing details of the various structures into focus.

2.9 Dimensions and Tolerances

Although the designer may tend to think of dimensions, clearances, and bar locations as exact, practical considerations require that there be accepted tolerances. These tolerances are the permissible variations from dimensions given on drawings.

Overall dimensions of reinforced concrete members are usually specified by the engineer in whole inches for beams, columns, and walls; sometimes half inches for thin slabs; and often 3-in. increments for more massive elements such as plan dimensions for footings. Formwork for the placing of these members must be built carefully so that it does not deform excessively under the action of workmen, construction machinery loads, and wet concrete. Accepted tolerances for variation in cross-sectional dimensions of columns and beams and in the thickness of slabs and walls are $+\frac{1}{2}$ in. and $-\frac{1}{4}$ in. [15]. For concrete footings accepted variations in plan dimensions are $+2$ in. and $-\frac{1}{2}$ in. [15], whereas the thickness has an accepted tolerance of -5% of specified thickness [15]. The capacity reduction factor ϕ is intended to account for the situation in which several acceptable tolerances may combine to measurably reduce the strength.

Reinforcing bars are normally specified in 3-in. length increments and the placement tolerances are given in the ACI Code (ACI-7.5.2). For minimum clear concrete protection and for the effective depth d (distance from compression of face of concrete to center of tension steel) in flexural members, walls, and compression members, the specified tolerances are as follows:

Effective Depth, d		Tolerances			
		On Effective Depth		On Minimum Clear Cover	
(in.)	(mm)	(in.)	(mm)	(in.)	(mm)
$d \leq 8$	200^a	$+\frac{3}{8}$	± 10	$-\frac{3}{8}$	-10
$d > 8$	200	$\pm\frac{1}{2}$	± 12	$-\frac{1}{2}$	-12

^{a} 1977 ACI Code does not include metric values; conversions are approximate.

Notwithstanding the stated tolerances on cover, the resulting cover shall not be less than two-thirds of the minimum cover specified on structural drawings or on specifications. Since the effective depth and the clear concrete cover are both components of total depth, the tolerances on those dimensions are directly related. When the tolerances on bar placement and cover accumulate, the overall dimension tolerance may be exceeded; thus field adjustment may have to be made. This may be particularly important on very thin sections such as in precast and shell structures.

For location of bars along the longitudinal dimension, and of bar bends, the tolerance is ± 2 in. except at discontinuous ends where tolerance shall be $\pm \frac{1}{2}$ in. (ACI-7.5.2).

2.10 Accuracy of Computations

When one understands that variations exist in material strength for both steel and concrete and that variations in dimensions are inevitable (and acceptable), it becomes clear that design of reinforced concrete structures does not require a high degree of precision.

The designer should place highest priority on determining proper location and length of steel reinforcement to carry the tension forces, thus making up for that capacity which is deficient in the concrete. Failures, when they occur, generally result from gross underestimating of tensile forces or lack of identification of how the structure or element will behave under loads. They are rarely the result of carrying too few significant figures in the design computations. However, significant figures may be lost in arithmetic operations, and gross errors may sometimes result from sloppiness. *It is recommended, therefore, more for systematic control of calculations and for ease in checking than for any improved effect on the final structure, that computations in all steps be carried to three significant figures.*

SELECTED REFERENCES

1. Frank Kerekes and Harold B. Reid, Jr. "Fifty Years of Development in Building Code Requirements for Reinforced Concrete," *ACI Journal, Proceedings*, **50,** February 1954, 441.
2. ACI-ASCE Committee 327. "Ultimate Strength Design," *ACI Journal, Proceedings*, **52,** January 1956, 505–524.
3. P. M. Ferguson. "Recent Trends in Ultimate Strength Design," *Transactions ASCE*, **127,** Part II, 1962, 324.
4. Frank A. Randall, Jr. "Historical Notes on Structural Safety," *ACI Journal, Proceedings*, **70,** October 1973, 669–679.
5. H. C. Shah. "The Rational Probabilistic Code Format," *ACI Journal, Proceedings*, **66,** September 1969, 690–697.
6. Robert G. Sexsmith and Mark F. Nelson. "Limitations in Application of Probabilistic Concepts," *ACI Journal, Proceedings*, **66,** October 1969, 823–828.
7. Jack R. Benjamin and N. C. Lind. "A Probabilistic Basis for a Deterministic Code," *ACI Journal, Proceedings*, **66,** November 1969, 857–865.
8. C. Allin Cornell. "A Probability-Based Structural Code," *ACI Journal, Proceedings*, **66,** December 1969, 974–985.

9. R. C. Reese, D. E. Allen, C. A. Cornell, Luis Esteva, R. N. White, R. G. Sexsmith, and George Winter. "Probabilistic Approaches to Structural Safety," *ACI Journal, Proceedings*, **73,** January 1976, 37–49.

10. *Design Handbook—In Accordance with the Strength Design Method of ACI 318–71* (2nd ed.), Vol. 1 (SP–17). Detroit: American Concrete Institute, 1973.

11. *Design Handbook—In Accordance with the Strength Design Method of ACI 318–77* (2nd ed.), Vol. 2 (Columns) (SP–17A). Detroit: American Concrete Institute, 1978.

12. *CRSI Handbook* (2nd ed.). Chicago: Concrete Reinforcing Steel Institute, 1975 (816 pp.).

13. *CRSI Handbook—Structural Lightweight Concrete Design Supplement.* Chicago: Concrete Reinforcing Steel Institute, 1974 (220 pp.).

14. ACI Committee 315. *Manual of Standard Practice for Detailing Reinforced Concrete Structures* (ACI 315–74). Detroit: American Concrete Institute, 1974.

15. *Recommended Practice for Concrete Formwork* (ACI Std. 347–68). Detroit: American Concrete Institute, 1968.

3

Strength
of Rectangular
Sections
in Bending

3.1 General Introduction

Until 1956 the strength computation for reinforced concrete members was made solely on the basis of allowable working stresses, service (or working) loads, and the straight-line theory of flexure. Since the adoption of the 1971 ACI Code, the concepts involved in the working stress method are used relatively little for designing members to have adequate strength, but are important for establishing serviceability at working stresses. The working stress method and serviceability considerations are therefore dealt with in Chap. 4.

The ultimate strength method of design, in which ultimate loads and ultimate strength of sections are used, was first permitted as an alternate method of design in the 1956 ACI Code and later became a substantial part of the 1963 Code. The 1971 ACI Code relegated the working stress method to a small section of the Code and was devoted primarily to the "ultimate strength method," as it has been commonly called for more than 30 years. Since only one method predominates, there is less chance of confusion over whether the term "strength" might refer to the safe service load (working stress method) or to the failure condition under overload (ultimate strength method). Thus ACI has dropped the term "ultimate" and the structure or structural element is required to be designed for "strength." The 1977 ACI Code removes the alternate design (working stress) method from the body of the Code and places it in Appendix B.

"Strength" may now be used in the more general sense to include various modes of failure other than that of the concrete reaching its expected crushing strain (as is used for the criterion of bending strength). A second reason for

Rectangular tapered beams; cantilevers and rigid frame, University of Wisconsin Stadium, Madison, Wis. (Photo by C. G. Salmon.)

deletion of the term "ultimate" is that the strength considered for design is a code-defined strength, and may in fact not be "ultimate" in its literal sense.

In the strength method the *factored loads* (including moments, shears, axial forces, etc.) are obtained by multiplying the service loads by factors to cover possible overloads and variations in design assumptions. The *design strength* of a section is obtained by multiplying the *nominal strength* (based on statical equilibrium and compatibility of stress and strain) by an under-capacity factor to account for adverse variations in material strengths, workmanship, dimensions, control, and degree of supervision.

In discussing the ACI strength method of design for reinforced concrete structures, attention must be called to the difference between loads on the structure as a whole and loads on the cross sections of individual members. The elastic methods of structural analysis are used first to compute the service loads in the individual members due to the action of service loads on the entire structure. Only then are the overload factors applied to the service loads acting on the individual cross sections.

Research is continuing on the feasibility of using the inelastic, or limit, method of structural analysis in which design loads in the individual members are determined directly from the ultimate loads acting on the whole structure. This is called "limit design" and is introduced briefly in Sec. 10.12.

3.2 Basis of Ultimate Flexural Strength

The modern analytical approach to reinforced concrete beam strength was originated by F. Stüssi in 1932 [1]. The general stress-strain behavior for concrete as presented in Sec. 1.7 shows the nonlinearity of stress and strain at stress levels above about $0.5f_c'$. Since the compression zone of a beam should be expected to have the same general variation of stress and strain as the test specimen (standard cylinder or cube), the compressive stress distribution for a beam that has achieved its theoretical (nominal) strength [2,3,4] should be as shown in Fig. 3.2.1.

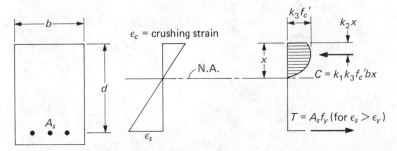

d = effective depth; distance from compression face to centroid of tension steel

(a) Singly reinforced beam

(b) Ultimate strain condition

(c) Stress condition at ultimate strain condition

Fig. 3.2.1
Conditions at theoretical strength in flexure (ultimate strength).

Maximum strength is assumed to be reached when the strain in the extreme compression fiber is equal to the crushing strain ϵ_c of concrete. When crushing occurs (usually a somewhat sudden occurrence), the strain in the tension steel A_s *could* be either larger or smaller than the strain f_y/E_s at first yield, depending on the relative proportion of steel to concrete. If the steel amount were low enough, it would yield prior to crushing of the concrete, resulting in a ductile failure mode in which there is large deformation. On the other hand a large quantity of steel would allow the steel to remain elastic at the time of crushing of the concrete, causing a brittle or sudden mode of failure. The ACI Code has provisions which, by limiting the amount of tension steel, are intended to insure the ductile mode of failure at the specified ultimate strength.

Although the compressive stress distribution in a beam has the same general shape as for a test cylinder, the maximum stress is less than f_c', say $k_3 f_c'$ (see Fig. 3.2.1c). The average stress over a beam of constant width is $k_1 k_3 f_c'$; and the centroid location of the roughly parabolic distribution is $k_2 x$, where x is the neutral-axis location. Thus the compressive force C is the volume of the stress solid

$$C = k_1 k_3 f_c' x b \tag{3.2.1}$$

and for the ductile failure condition, the tensile force T is

$$T = A_s f_y \tag{3.2.2}$$

Equilibrium requires $C = T$, from which

$$x = \frac{A_s f_y}{k_1 k_3 f'_c b} \tag{3.2.3}$$

The nominal flexural strength then may be expressed as

$$M_n = T(\text{arm}) = T(d - k_2 x)$$
$$= A_s f_y (d - k_2 x) \tag{3.2.4}$$

Substituting Eq. (3.2.3) for x into Eq. (3.2.4) gives

$$M_n = A_s f_y \left(d - \frac{k_2}{k_1 k_3} \frac{A_s f_y}{f'_c b} \right) \tag{3.2.5}$$

One may note that if strength is the quantity that is of interest, it is readily obtainable from Eq. (3.2.5) *if the quantity $k_2/(k_1 k_3)$ is known.* It is not necessary to have values for k_1, k_2, or k_3 individually if the value for the combined term is known. Experimental results [2,3] have established values for the combined term, as well as the individual k values, with some of the results shown in Fig. 3.2.2. From that figure, $k_2/(k_1 k_3)$ ranges from about 0.55 to 0.63.

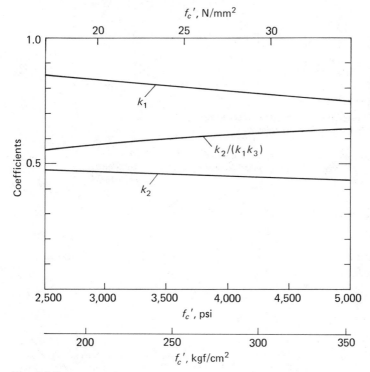

Fig. 3.2.2
Stress-solid parameters (adapted from Ref. 2).

The values experimentally determined at ultimate strength (i.e., crushing of the concrete) necessarily involved variation in the ultimate compressive strain ϵ_c for the various tests. The ACI Code (ACI-10.2.3) considers the maximum usable strain to be 0.003. Some countries use a value of 0.0035, which makes little difference in the computed flexural strength.

3.3 Whitney Rectangular Stress Distribution

The computation of flexural strength based on the approximately parabolic stress distribution of Fig. 3.2.1c may be done using Eq. (3.2.5) with given values of $k_2/(k_1 k_3)$. However, it is desirable for the designer to have a simple method in which basic static equilibrium is used.

In the 1930s Whitney [5,6] proposed the use of a rectangular compressive stress distribution to replace that of Fig. 3.2.1c. As shown in Fig. 3.3.1c, an average stress of $0.85 f'_c$ is used with a rectangle of depth $a = \beta_1 x$, determined so that $a/2 = k_2 x$. Whitney determined that β_1 should be 0.85 for concrete with $f'_c \leq 4000$ psi, and 0.05 less for each 1000 psi of f'_c in excess of 4000 psi.[†]

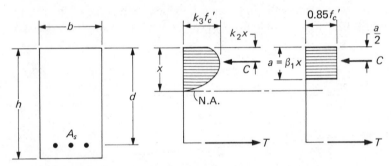

d = effective depth; distance from compression face of concrete to centroid of tension steel

(a) Beam

(b) Actual stress distribution

(c) Whitney rectangular stress block

Fig. 3.3.1
Definition of Whitney rectangular stress distribution.

The flexural strength, using the equivalent rectangle, is obtained from Fig. 3.3.1 as follows:

$$C = 0.85 f'_c ba \qquad (3.3.1)$$

$$T = A_s f_y \qquad (3.3.2)$$

[†] $\beta_1 = 0.85$ for $f'_c \leq 280$ kgf/cm² (or 28 N/mm²) and reduces by 0.05 for each 70 kgf/cm² (or 7 N/mm²) of f'_c in excess of 280 kgf/cm² (28 N/mm²). Also, the ACI Code limits β_1 to not less than 0.65 (ACI-10.2.7).

where the use of f_y assumes that the steel yields prior to crushing of the concrete. Equating $C = T$ gives

$$a = \frac{A_s f_y}{0.85 f'_c b} \tag{3.3.3}$$

$$M_n = A_s f_y (d - a/2) \tag{3.3.4}$$

which on substituting Eq. (3.3.3) into Eq. (3.3.4) gives

$$M_n = A_s f_y \left(d - 0.59 \frac{A_s f_y}{f'_c b} \right) \tag{3.3.5}$$

Note that 0.59 corresponds to $k_2/(k_1 k_3)$ of Eq. (3.2.5). The ACI Code explicitly accepts the Whitney rectangle (ACI-10.2.7). One may also note that β_1 is only needed to establish the neutral-axis location for determining the steel strain. So long as the steel strain is above yield, the flexural strength M_n is not affected by the value of β_1.

3.4 Investigation of Rectangular Sections in Bending with Tension Reinforcement Only

The quantities defining a rectangular section with tension reinforcement only are b, d, and A_s (Fig. 3.3.1a). Such a section is said to be *singly reinforced*. The steel area A_s is, of course, furnished by the combined area of an integral number of reinforcing bars. Protective covering is necessary around the bars in order to make the steel and concrete act together and, also very importantly, to provide fire protection. At high temperatures (say above 600°F) the yield strength and modulus of elasticity begin to reduce markedly, so that concrete cover is needed for insulation. Minimum cover requirements are generally prescribed by code (see ACI-7.7).

Since the tensile strength of concrete is normally neglected, the shape of the beam on the tension side of the neutral axis and the amount of concrete cover do not affect the flexural strength. Thus the critical depth dimension for strength is the *effective depth d* rather than the overall depth h. The effective depth is defined as the distance from the extreme fiber in compression to the centroid of the tension steel area. When the tension steel is comprised of bars in several layers satisfying the minimum spacing requirement between layers, the centroid of the combined area is usually used, with all bars assumed to behave in the same manner.

Investigation of a rectangular section in bending is made to establish whether or not the section has adequate *strength* for given applied service loads (or service-load moments). The system must also be serviceable; that is, it must perform satisfactorily under service loads without detrimental effects, such as excessive deflection, cracking, or vibration. *Serviceability* generally is treated in Chap. 4, and the detailed discussion of deflection appears in Chap. 14.

ACI Code Strength Method. According to the ACI Code, the required strength U for a section in bending is obtained by applying load factors (i.e., overload provision) to the moment due to dead load D, live load L, wind load W, earthquake load E, lateral earth pressure H, fluid pressure F, and structural effects T, as discussed in Sec. 2.6 (ACI-9.2). The design flexural strength ϕM_n is the product of the capacity reduction factor ϕ and the nominal flexural strength M_n (i.e., the so-called ultimate strength).

The basic load factors U in the overload provision are 1.4 and 1.7, used as follows:

$$U = 1.4D + 1.7L$$

and the ϕ factor for flexure is 0.90. The terms U, D, and L of the overload provision may also represent quantities that are functions of load, such as moment, shear, and axial force. If M_u is defined as the moment under factored load and M_D and M_L are the service dead-load and live-load moments, respectively, the basic overload provision for flexure may be expressed as

$$M_u = 1.4M_D + 1.7M_L \tag{3.4.1}$$

The *strength requirement* for flexure may then be expressed as

$$M_n \geq \frac{M_u}{\phi} \tag{3.4.2}$$

or

$$M_n \geq \frac{1.4M_D + 1.7M_L}{0.90} \tag{3.4.3}$$

when both parts of the safety provision are put on the same side of the equation.

For computation of the nominal flexural strength M_n, the following assumptions (ACI-10.2) are made:

1. The strength of members shall be based on satisfying the applicable conditions of equilibrium and compatibility of strains.
2. Strain in the reinforcing steel and concrete shall be assumed directly proportional to the distance from the neutral axis.
3. The maximum usable strain at the extreme concrete compression fiber shall be assumed equal to 0.003.
4. The tensile strength of the concrete is to be neglected (except for certain prestressed concrete conditions).
5. The modulus of elasticity of nonprestressed steel reinforcement may be taken as 29,000,000 psi (2,040,000 kgf/cm^2 or 200,000 N/mm^2).
6. For practical purposes the relationship between the concrete compressive stress distribution and the concrete strain when theoretical strength is reached may be taken as (ACI-10.2.7) an equivalent rectangular stress distribution, wherein a concrete stress intensity of $0.85f'_c$ is assumed to be uniformly distributed over an equivalent compressive zone bounded by the edges of the cross section and a straight line located parallel to the neutral axis at a distance $a = \beta_1 x$ from the fiber of maximum compressive strain. The distance x from the fiber of maximum strain to the

neutral axis is measured in a direction perpendicular to that axis. The value of β_1 is given by the following equation:

For f'_c less than 4000 psi,

$$\beta_1 = 0.85 \tag{3.4.4}$$

For f'_c greater than 4000 psi,

$$\beta_1 = 0.85 - 0.05\left(\frac{f'_c - 4000}{1000}\right) \tag{3.4.5}$$

It should be noted that assumption (6) describes the Whitney rectangular compressive stress distribution (see Sec. 3.3), but other shapes of stress solids, such as the trapezoid and the parabola, have been used [7] and are acceptable for use according to ACI-10.2.6.

EXAMPLE 3.4.1   Determine the nominal flexural strength M_n of the rectangular section shown in Fig. 3.4.1, given $f'_c = 5000$ psi, $f_y = 50,000$ psi, $b = 14$ in., $d = 21.5$ in., and $A_s = 4$-#10 bars.

Solution: Assume the steel yields when the strength is reached. From Fig. 3.4.1 the internal forces are

$$C = 0.85f'_c ba = 0.85(5)(14)a = 59.5a$$
$$T = A_s f_y = 5.08(50) = 254 \text{ kips}$$

For equilibrium, $C = T$; therefore

$$a = \frac{254}{59.5} = 4.27 \text{ in.}$$

$$\beta_1 = 0.80 \qquad \text{for } f'_c = 5000 \text{ psi}$$

The neutral-axis position is

$$x = \frac{a}{\beta_1} = \frac{4.27}{0.80} = 5.34 \text{ in.}$$

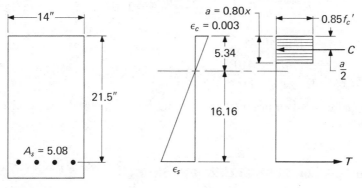

(a) Cross section   (b) Actual condition

Fig. 3.4.1
Singly reinforced beam of Example 3.4.1.

The strain in the tension steel when the strain 0.003 is reached in the concrete is, by straight-line proportion,

$$\epsilon_s = \frac{d - x}{x}(0.003) = \frac{16.16}{5.34}(0.003) = 0.0091$$

$$\epsilon_y = \frac{f_y}{E_s} = \frac{50}{29,000} = 0.00172$$

When the flexural strength (ultimate strength) is reached, ϵ_s is 5.3 times ϵ_y, which means that large and gradual deflection is presumed to occur before the crushing of concrete. The assumption that the steel yields has been shown valid.

The nominal flexural strength is

$$M_n = C\left(d - \frac{a}{2}\right) \quad \text{or} \quad T\left(d - \frac{a}{2}\right)$$

$$= 254(21.5 - 2.13)\tfrac{1}{12} = 410 \text{ ft-kips (556 kN-m)}$$

EXAMPLE 3.4.2 For the beam of Example 3.4.1, determine the safe service moment M_w that may be applied according to the ACI Code, if 60% of the total moment is dead load and 40% is live load.

Solution: From Example 3.4.1,

$$M_n = \text{nominal strength} = 410 \text{ ft-kips}$$
$$M_u = \text{required strength} = 1.4M_D + 1.7M_L$$
$$\phi = 0.90 \text{ for flexure}$$

For safety, Eq. (3.4.3) requires that

$$M_n \geq \frac{M_u}{\phi} = \frac{1.4M_D + 1.7M_L}{0.90}$$

which if $M_D = 0.60M_w$ and $M_L = 0.40M_w$,

$$\frac{M_u}{\phi} = \frac{1.4(0.60)M_w + 1.7(0.40)M_w}{0.90} = 1.69M_w$$

Thus the safe service moment is

$$M_w = \frac{M_n}{1.69} = \frac{410}{1.69} = 243 \text{ ft-kips (329 kN-m)}$$

The safety factor between nominal strength (ultimate strength) and service load is 1.69 for this case.

3.5 Balanced Condition at Ultimate Strength

The *balanced* condition is a strain condition (Fig. 3.5.1a) at which the maximum strain at the extreme concrete compression fiber just reaches 0.003 simultaneously with the tension steel reaching a strain $\epsilon_y = f_y/E_s$. An

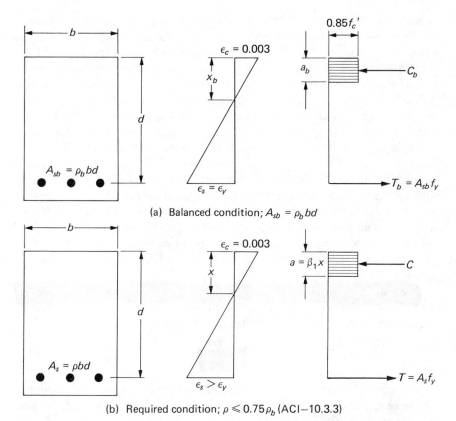

(a) Balanced condition; $A_{sb} = \rho_b bd$

(b) Required condition; $\rho \leqslant 0.75\rho_b$ (ACI–10.3.3)

Fig. 3.5.1
Balanced condition and ACI Code limitation.

amount of tension steel A_{sb} would provide the neutral-axis distance x_b for this balanced condition. If the actual A_s were greater than A_{sb} (known as an *overreinforced* beam), equilibrium of internal forces ($C = T$) would mean an increase in the depth a of the compression stress block (and thereby also make x exceed x_b), so that the strain ϵ_s would be less than ϵ_y when $\epsilon_c = 0.003$. The failure of an overreinforced beam will be sudden when the concrete reaches the strain 0.003 although the beam will exhibit little deformation (steel does not yield) to warn of impending failure.

On the other hand when actual A_s is less than A_{sb} (known as the *underreinforced* beam), the tensile force reduces so that internal force equilibrium reduces the depth a of the compression stress block (and thereby makes x less than x_b) giving a strain ϵ_s greater than ϵ_y. In this case, with the steel having yielded, the beam will have noticeable deflection prior to the concrete reaching the crushing strain of 0.003.

Thus the relative amount of tension steel compared to that in the balanced condition will affect significantly the mode of failure.

The ACI Code provides for the ductile failure mode by limiting the amount of tension steel to not more than 75% of the amount in the balanced condition. This is a somewhat indirect way of controlling the strain diagram at the point of imminent failure. A more direct way of controlling ductility would be to prescribe a maximum value for the neutral-axis distance x when strength is reached. By the straight-line strain diagram (Fig. 3.5.1b), putting a limit of $0.75x_b$ on x insures a value of ϵ_s sufficiently greater than ϵ_y to give a large deformation at failure. The limit on tension steel given by ACI-10.3.3 is identical to requiring that x be less than $0.75x_b$ for *singly reinforced* beams. However, limiting x to a maximum of $0.75x_b$ is not the same as limiting A_s to a maximum of $0.75A_{sb}$ when the compression zone of the beam contains steel or is other than rectangular in shape. This will be shown later in Sec. 3.8 on compression steel and in Chap. 9 for T sections.

In actual structures the provided design strength ϕM_n, being equal to or slightly greater than the required strength M_u, is always much larger than the actual service moment acting on the beam. Thus the attainment of M_n in the beam is an imaginary situation or, put in another way, a philosophy of design. In this philosophy it is considered more conservative to restrict the ultimate condition to that of Fig. 3.5.1b, wherein the ductile failure mode can be expected.

The symbol ρ, commonly called the *reinforcement ratio* or *percentage*, may be conveniently used to represent the relative amount of tension reinforcement in a beam. Thus using the dimensions of Fig. 3.5.1,

$$\rho = \frac{A_s}{bd} \tag{3.5.1}$$

The reinforcement ratio ρ_b in the balanced condition may be obtained by applying the equilibrium and compatibility conditions. From the linear strain condition, Fig. 3.5.1a,

$$\frac{x_b}{d} = \frac{\epsilon_c}{\epsilon_c + \epsilon_y} = \frac{0.003}{0.003 + f_y/29,000,000} = \frac{87,000}{87,000 + f_y} \tag{3.5.2}$$

The compressive force C_b is

$$C_b = 0.85f'_c b \beta_1 x_b$$

The tensile force T_b is

$$T_b = f_y A_{sb} = \rho_b bd f_y$$

Equating C_b to T_b gives

$$0.85f'_c b \beta_1 x_b = \rho_b bd f_y$$

$$\rho_b = \frac{0.85f'_c}{f_y} \beta_1 \left(\frac{x_b}{d}\right) \tag{3.5.3}$$

which on substitution of Eq. (3.5.2) gives

$$\rho_b = \frac{0.85f'_c}{f_y} \beta_1 \left(\frac{87,000}{87,000 + f_y}\right) \tag{3.5.4}$$

where the stresses f_y and f'_c are in psi.

Representative values of $0.75\rho_b$ for several values of f'_c and f_y are shown in Table 3.5.1.

Table 3.5.1

Maximum Reinforcement Ratio ρ for Singly Reinforced Beams (Corresponding to $0.75\rho_b$)

f_y	$f'_c = 3000$ psi $\beta_1 = 0.85$	$f'_c = 3500$ psi $\beta_1 = 0.85$	$f'_c = 4000$ psi $\beta_1 = 0.85$	$f'_c = 5000$ psi $\beta_1 = 0.80$	$f'_c = 6000$ psi $\beta_1 = 0.75$
40,000 psi	0.0278	0.0325	0.0371	0.0437	0.0491
50,000 psi	0.0206	0.0241	0.0275	0.0324	0.0364
60,000 psi	0.0160	0.0187	0.0214	0.0252	0.0283

f_y	$f'_c = 21$ N/mm^2 $\beta_1 = 0.85$	$f'_c = 24$ N/mm^2 $\beta_1 = 0.85$	$f'_c = 28$ N/mm^2 $\beta_1 = 0.85$	$f'_c = 35$ N/mm^2 $\beta_1 = 0.80$	$f'_c = 42$ N/mm^2 $\beta_1 = 0.75$
280 N/mm²	0.0277	0.0317	0.0369	0.0435	0.0489
350 N/mm²	0.0205	0.0235	0.0274	0.0322	0.0362
420 N/mm²	0.0159	0.0182	0.0213	0.0250	0.0281

f_y	$f'_c = 200$ kgf/cm^2 $\beta_1 = 0.85$	$f'_c = 240$ kgf/cm^2 $\beta_1 = 0.85$	$f'_c = 280$ kgf/cm^2 $\beta_1 = 0.85$	$f'_c = 320$ kgf/cm^2 $\beta_1 = 0.82$	$f'_c = 360$ kgf/cm^2 $\beta_1 = 0.79$
2800 kgf/cm²	0.0266	0.0319	0.0372	0.0410	0.0444
3500 kgf/cm²	0.0197	0.0236	0.0276	0.0304	0.0330
4200 kgf/cm²	0.0153	0.0184	0.0214	0.0236	0.0256

EXAMPLE 3.5.1. Determine whether or not the amount of steel used in the beam ($b = 14$; $d = 21.5$; $A_s = 5.08$; $f'_c = 5000$; $f_y = 50,000$) of Example 3.4.1 (Fig. 3.4.1) is acceptable according to the ACI Code.

Solution: (a) Determine the balanced amount of steel using basic principles, according to the ACI Code. From Fig. 3.5.2,

$$x_b = \frac{0.003(21.5)}{0.003 + 50/29,000} = 13.65 \text{ in.}$$

$$\beta_1 = 0.80 \text{ for } f'_c = 5000 \text{ psi}$$
$$a_b = 0.80(13.65) = 10.92 \text{ in.}$$
$$C_b = 0.85(5)(14)(10.92) = 650 \text{ kips}$$

$$A_{sb} = \frac{650}{50} = 13.0 \text{ sq in.}$$

(b) Compare actual steel used with the maximum permitted by the ACI Code.

$$\text{max } A_s = 0.75A_{sb} = 0.75(13.0) = 9.75 \text{ sq in.}$$
$$\text{actual } A_s = 5.08 \text{ sq in.} < 9.75 \text{ sq in.} \qquad \text{OK}$$

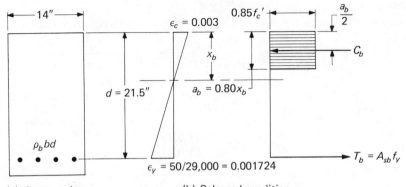

(a) Cross section   (b) Balanced condition

Fig. 3.5.2
Balanced condition for Example 3.5.1 (actual condition shown in Fig. 3.4.1).

ACI-10.3.3 is satisfied. Ordinarily this check should be made *before* an investigation of strength is made in cases where the ACI Code is to be satisfied.

If the maximum steel permitted is expressed in terms of the reinforcement ratio ρ,

$$\max \rho = 0.75\rho_b = \frac{9.75}{14(21.5)} = 0.0324$$

which agrees with Table 3.5.1.

3.6 Design of Rectangular Sections in Bending with Tension Reinforcement Only

In the design of rectangular sections in bending with tension reinforcement only, the problem is to determine b, d, and A_s from the required value of $M_n = M_u/\phi$, and the given material properties f'_c and f_y.

The two conditions of equilibrium are

$$C = T \tag{3.6.1a}$$

and

$$M_n = (C \text{ or } T)\left(d - \frac{a}{2}\right) \tag{3.6.1b}$$

Since there are three unknowns but only two conditions, there should be many possible solutions. If the reinforcement ratio ρ is preset, then from Eq. (3.6.1a)

$$0.85f'_c ba = \rho bd f_y$$

$$a = \rho\left(\frac{f_y}{0.85f'_c}\right)d \tag{3.6.2}$$

Substituting Eq. (3.6.2) into Eq. (3.6.1b),

$$M_n = \rho b d f_y \left[d - \frac{\rho}{2} \left(\frac{f_y}{0.85 f_c'} \right) d \right] \qquad (3.6.3)$$

A strength *coefficient of resistance* R_u may be obtained by dividing Eq. (3.6.3) by bd^2 and letting

$$m = \frac{f_y}{0.85 f_c'} \qquad (3.6.4a)$$

Thus

$$R_u = \frac{M_n}{bd^2} = \rho f_y (1 - \tfrac{1}{2}\rho m) \qquad (3.6.4b)$$

The relationship between ρ and R_u for various values of f_c' and f_y is shown in Fig. 3.6.1.

In some situations the values of b and d may be preset, which is equivalent to having R_u preset; then ρ may be determined by solving the quadratic equation (3.6.4). Thus

$$R_u = \rho f_y (1 - \tfrac{1}{2}\rho m)$$

from which

$$\rho = \frac{1}{m} \left(1 - \sqrt{1 - \frac{2mR_u}{f_y}} \right) \qquad (3.6.5)$$

The procedure (without being concerned with certain practical decisions) to be used in the strength design of rectangular sections with tension reinforcement only involves the following steps:

1. Assume a value of ρ equal to or less than $0.75\rho_b$, but greater than the minimum ρ of $200/f_y$ (ACI-10.5). The balanced value ρ_b may be obtained from basic principles or from Eq. (3.5.4),

$$\rho_b = \frac{0.85\beta_1 f_c'}{f_y} \left(\frac{87,000}{87,000 + f_y} \right)$$

and

$$\text{for } f_c' \le 4000 \text{ psi} \qquad \beta_1 = 0.85$$

$$\text{for } f_c' > 4000 \text{ psi} \qquad \beta_1 = 0.85 - 0.05 \left(\frac{f_c' - 4000}{1000} \right) \ge 0.65$$

2. Determine the required bd^2 from

$$\text{required } bd^2 = \frac{M_n}{R_u}$$

in which

$$R_u = \rho f_y (1 - \tfrac{1}{2}\rho m)$$

with

$$m = \frac{f_y}{0.85 f_c'}$$

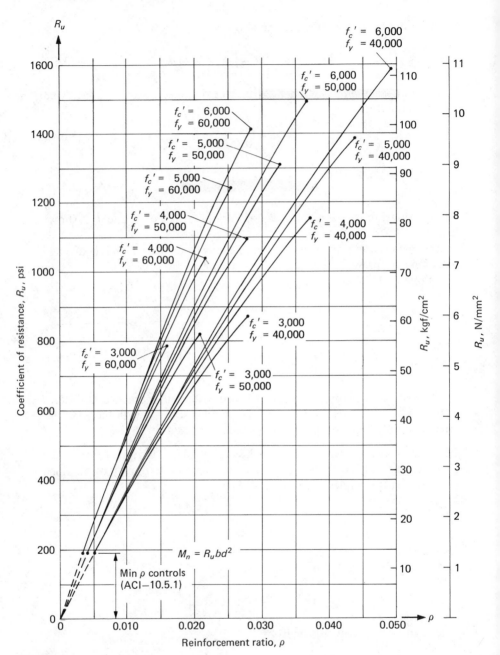

Fig. 3.6.1
Strength curves (R_u vs ρ) for singly reinforced rectangular sections. Upper limit of curves is at $0.75\,\rho_b$.

3. Choose a suitable set of values of b and d so that the provided bd^2 is approximately equal to the required bd^2. (Note: Actually d is not chosen, rather the overall depth h is chosen and d is computed from h while maintaining the desired minimum protective cover.)

4. Determine the revised value of ρ after computing $R_u = M_n/bd^2$ for the selected section using one of the following methods:
   (a) By formula (most exact),

$$\rho = \frac{1}{m}\left(1 - \sqrt{1 - \frac{2mR_u}{f_y}}\right)$$

   (b) By curves (Fig. 3.6.1)
   (c) By approximate proportion (on the safe side if revised R_u is smaller than original R_u), the revised ρ is

$$\rho \approx (\text{original } \rho)\,\frac{(\text{revised } R_u)}{(\text{original } R_u)}$$

   It may be noted from Fig. 3.6.1 that the relationship between R_u and ρ is approximately linear over short distances, even though the actual equation is a quadratic one.
5. Compute A_s from

$$A_s = (\text{revised } \rho)(\text{actual } bd)$$

6. Select reinforcement and check the strength of the section to be certain that

$$M_n \geq \frac{M_u}{\phi} \qquad \text{or} \qquad M_u \leq \phi M_n$$

EXAMPLE 3.6.1   Determine a set of values of b, d, and A_s that will carry a bending moment M_u of 400 ft-kips (factors for overload have been applied). Use $f'_c = 4000$ psi and $f_y = 40,000$ psi.

Solution:

$$\rho_b = \frac{0.85\beta_1 f'_c}{f_y}\left(\frac{87,000}{87,000 + f_y}\right) = \frac{0.85(0.85)(4)}{40}\left(\frac{87}{87 + 40}\right) = 0.0495$$

$$0.75\rho_b = 0.0371$$

Arbitrarily assume that $\rho = 0.03$,

$$m = \frac{f_y}{0.85f'_c} = \frac{40}{0.85(4)} = 11.76$$

$$R_u = \rho f_y(1 - \tfrac{1}{2}\rho m) = 0.03(40,000)[1 - (\tfrac{1}{2})(0.03)(11.76)] = 988$$

$$M_n = \frac{M_u}{\phi} = \frac{400}{0.90} = 444 \text{ ft-kips}$$

$$\text{required } bd^2 = \frac{M_n}{R_u} = \frac{444(12,000)}{988} = 5400 \text{ in.}^3$$

Try $b = 14$ in. and $d = \sqrt{5400/14} = 19.64$ in. Use $b = 14$ in. and compute d to be 21.5 in. after selecting overall depth (d is usually $2\frac{3}{8}$ to $2\frac{5}{8}$ in. less than overall depth if one layer of steel can be used; this is illustrated in

Example 3.7.2). The effective depth d is now greater than required for $\rho = 0.03$ in order to get a convenient depth, or perhaps to reduce deflection.

$$\text{required } R_u = \frac{M_n}{\text{provided } bd^2} = \frac{444(12{,}000)}{14(21.5)^2} = 824 \text{ psi}$$

$$\rho = \frac{1}{m}\left(1 - \sqrt{1 - \frac{2mR_u}{f_y}}\right) = \frac{1}{11.76}\left[1 - \sqrt{1 - \frac{2(11.76)(824)}{40{,}000}}\right]$$

$$= 0.0240$$

$$A_s = \rho bd = 0.0240(14)(21.5) = 7.22 \text{ sq in.}$$

Two layers of reinforcement will be required. Use 3-#11 and 2-#10, $A_s = 7.22$ sq in.

Check: A review of the correctness of the above computations in which formulas are used may be had by considering the simple statics shown in Fig. 3.6.2.

$$T = A_s f_y = 7.22(40) = 289 \text{ kips}$$

$$a = \frac{C \text{ or } T}{0.85 f'_c b} = \frac{289}{0.85(4)(14)} = 6.07 \text{ in.}$$

$$M_n = (C \text{ or } T)\left(d - \frac{a}{2}\right) = 289[21.5 - 0.5(6.07)]\tfrac{1}{12}$$

$$= 444 \text{ ft-kips (602 kN-m)} \qquad\qquad \text{OK}$$

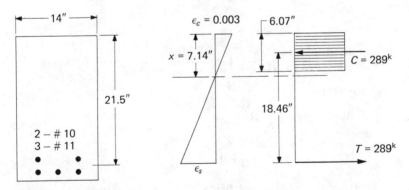

Fig. 3.6.2
Section for Example 3.6.1.

It should be observed that the beam of Example 3.6.1 with 2.4% reinforcement, which requires placement in two layers, is significantly smaller in concrete cross-sectional area than traditional designs under the working stress method would have made it. Deflection thus becomes an essential consideration in designing beams by the strength method. The subject of deflection is treated in Chap. 14.

3.7 Practical Selection for Beam Sizes, Bar Sizes, and Bar Placement

In the previous section the procedure and example for the design of rectangular sections in bending with tension reinforcement only have been treated on the assumption that the design moment $M_n = M_u/\phi$ is already known. This is rarely the case, however, because the design moment must include the effect of the weight of the beam itself which has not yet been designed. In reality, then, the dead weight of the beam has to be assumed at the outset; a trial beam size is then obtained and may be readjusted if its effect on the design moment is significantly different from the assumed value.

The choice of the steel percentage ρ is very much dependent on the limitation of the deflection of the beam. Years of experience with the working stress method showed that deflection problems were rarely encountered with beams having a steel reinforcement ratio ρ not more than one-half the maximum permissible value. The use of this amount (one-half of $0.75\rho_b = 0.375\rho_b$) may provide a suitable *guide* for the preliminary choice of the reinforcement ratio.

For the selection of an integral number of bars to meet a total steel area requirement, it is desirable to tabulate the combined area of several bars at a time. Table 3.7.1 gives bar areas for up to 10 bars of the different sizes.

Table 3.7.1

Total Areas for Various Numbers of Reinforcing Bars

Bar Size	Nominal Diameter (in.)	Weight (lb/ft)	Number of Bars									
			1	*2*	*3*	*4*	*5*	*6*	*7*	*8*	*9*	*10*
#3	0.375	0.376	0.11	0.22	0.33	0.44	0.55	0.66	0.77	0.88	0.99	1.10
#4	0.500	0.668	0.20	0.40	0.60	0.80	1.00	1.20	1.40	1.60	1.80	2.00
#5	0.625	1.043	0.31	0.62	0.93	1.24	1.55	1.86	2.17	2.48	2.79	3.10
#6	0.750	1.502	0.44	0.88	1.32	1.76	2.20	2.64	3.08	3.52	3.96	4.40
#7	0.875	2.044	0.60	1.20	1.80	2.40	3.00	3.60	4.20	4.80	5.40	6.00
#8	1.000	2.670	0.79	1.58	2.37	3.16	3.95	4.74	5.53	6.32	7.11	7.90
#9	1.128	3.400	1.00	2.00	3.00	4.00	5.00	6.00	7.00	8.00	9.00	10.00
#10	1.270	4.303	1.27	2.54	3.81	5.08	6.35	7.62	8.89	10.16	11.43	12.70
#11	1.410	5.313	1.56	3.12	4.68	6.24	7.80	9.36	10.92	12.48	14.04	15.60
#14[a]	1.693	7.65	2.25	4.50	6.75	9.00	11.25	13.50	15.75	18.00	20.25	22.50
#18[a]	2.257	13.60	4.00	8.00	12.00	16.00	20.00	24.00	28.00	32.00	36.00	40.00

[a] #14 and #18 bars are used primarily as column reinforcement and are rarely used in beams.

For the placement of bars within the beam width, ACI-7.6.1 specifies the clearance needed between bars to permit proper concrete placement around them. This clearance is 1 in. or the nominal diameter of the bar, whichever is greater. When two or more layers of bars are required, the minimum clearance between layers is 1 in. (ACI-7.6.2). Table 3.7.2 gives minimum beam widths for various numbers of equal-sized bars, computed in the manner described above.

Table 3.7.2

Minimum Beam Width (Inches) According to the ACI Code[a]

Size of Bars	Number of Bars in Single Layer of Reinforcement							Add for Each Added Bar
	2	3	4	5	6	7	8	
#4	6.1	7.6	9.1	10.6	12.1	13.6	15.1	1.50
#5	6.3	7.9	9.6	11.2	12.8	14.4	16.1	1.63
#6	6.5	8.3	10.0	11.8	13.5	15.3	17.0	1.75
#7	6.7	8.6	10.5	12.4	14.2	16.1	18.0	1.88
#8	6.9	8.9	10.9	12.9	14.9	16.9	18.9	2.00
#9	7.3	9.5	11.8	14.0	16.3	18.6	20.8	2.26
#10	7.7	10.2	12.8	15.3	17.8	20.4	22.9	2.54
#11	8.0	10.8	13.7	16.5	19.3	22.1	24.9	2.82
#14	8.9	12.3	15.6	19.0	22.4	25.8	29.2	3.39
#18	10.5	15.0	19.5	24.0	28.6	33.1	37.6	4.51

Table shows minimum beam widths when stirrups are used.

For additional bars, add dimension in last column for each added bar.

For bars of different size, determine from table the beam width for smaller size bars and then add last column figure for each larger bar used.

[a] Assumes maximum aggregate size does not exceed three-fourths of the clear space between bars (ACI-3.3.3).

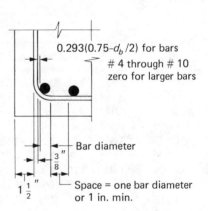

0.293(0.75−d_b/2) for bars #4 through #10 zero for larger bars

Bar diameter

$\frac{3}{8}$"

$1\frac{1}{2}$"

Space = one bar diameter or 1 in. min.

Note: For bars #4 through #10, the bar diameter d_b is less than the minimum bend diameter of $1\frac{1}{2}$ in. for #3 stirrups (ACI–7.2.2); thus, assuming the longitudinal bar makes contact at the middle of the stirrup bend, an amount 0.293(0.75 − 0.5d_b) is included at both sides in determining minimum width.

In order to assist the designer further in making choices for beam sizes, bar sizes, and bar placement, the following guidelines are being suggested. These may be regarded as accepted practice, and are *not* ACI Code requirements. Undoubtedly situations will arise in which the experienced designer will, for good and proper reasons, make a selection not conforming to the guidelines.

For Beam Sizes

1. Use whole inches for overall dimensions; except slabs may be in $\frac{1}{2}$-in. increments.

2. Beam stem widths are most often in multiples of 2 or 3 in.; such as 9, 10, 12, 14, 15, 16, and 18.
3. Minimum specified clear cover is measured from outside the stirrup or tie to the face of the concrete. (Thus beam effective depth d has rarely, if ever, a dimension to the whole inch.)
4. An economical rectangular beam proportion is one in which the overall depth-to-width ratio is between about 1.5 to 2.0.
5. For tee-shaped beams, typically the flange thickness represents about 20% of overall depth (see Chap. 9 for treatment of T-shaped sections).

For Reinforcing Bars
6. Maintain bar symmetry about the centroidal axis which lies at right angles to the bending axis (i.e., symmetry about the vertical axis in usual situations).
7. Use at least two bars wherever flexural reinforcement is required.
8. Use bars #11 and smaller for usual sized beams.
9. Use no more than two bar sizes and no more than two standard sizes apart for steel in one face at a given location in the span (i.e., #7 and #9 bars may be acceptable, but #9 and #4 bars would not).
10. Place bars in one layer if practicable. Try to select bar size so that no less than two and no more than five or six bars are put in one layer.
11. Follow requirements of ACI-7.6.1 and 7.6.2 for clear distance between bars and between layers.
12. When different sizes of bars are used in several layers at a location, place the largest bars in the layer nearest the face of beam.

EXAMPLE 3.7.1　Select an economical rectangular beam size and select bars using the ACI strength method. The beam is a simply supported span of 40 ft and it is to carry a live load of 1.4 kips/ft and a dead load of 0.8 kip/ft (not including beam weight). Without actually checking deflection, use a steel percentage ρ such that excessive deflection is unlikely. Use $f'_c = 4000$ psi, and $f_y = 60,000$ psi.

Solution:　(a) Decide on a percentage of reinforcement to use. Arbitrarily choose $\rho = 0.012$ (note that $0.375\rho_b = 0.0107$) as a guideline for this problem.
　(b) Determine the desired R_u using Eq. (3.6.4).

$$m = \frac{f_y}{0.85f'_c} = \frac{60}{0.85(4)} = 17.65$$

$$R_u = \rho f_y(1 - \tfrac{1}{2}\rho m)$$
$$= 0.012(60,000)[1 - 0.5(0.012)(17.65)] = 644 \text{ psi}$$

(c) Determine factored moments.

$$M_u = 1.4M_D + 1.7M_L$$

$$M_L = \frac{1.4(40)^2}{8} = 280 \text{ ft-kips}$$

$$M_D = \frac{(0.8 + 0.4)(40)^2}{8} = 240 \text{ ft-kips}$$

using a beam weight estimated at 0.4 kip/ft, based on unit weight of reinforced concrete at 150 pcf.

$$M_u = 1.4(240) + 1.7(280) = 336 + 477 = 813 \text{ ft-kips}$$

$$\text{required } M_n = \frac{M_u}{\phi} = \frac{813}{0.90} = 904 \text{ ft-kips}$$

(d) Determine required bd^2 from R_u.

$$\text{required } bd^2 = \frac{M_n}{R_u} = \frac{904(12,000)}{644} = 16,850 \text{ in.}^3$$

(e) Establish beam size. Select width b and determine the corresponding required value for effective depth d. Make a table of possibilities.

Chosen b	Required d
12	37.5
15	33.5
18	30.6 ← Try
20	29.1

Selecting the 18-in. width will give a beam whose overall depth is between $1\frac{1}{2}$ and 2 times its width (suggested guideline).

Determine overall depth in order to verify the assumed weight. Assuming that the bars to be selected will fit in one layer, the minimum overall depth may be computed (see Fig. 3.7.1)

$$h = d + 1\frac{1}{2} \text{ in. cover} + \frac{3}{8} \text{ diam stirrup} + \text{bar radius, say } \frac{1}{2} \text{ in.}$$
$$= d + (2\frac{3}{8} \text{ to } 2\frac{1}{2} \text{ in.})$$
$$= 30.6 + 2.5 = 33.1 \text{ in.}$$

The overall depth would be in whole inches; so try 34 in. Since the guideline value of $R_u = 644$ psi is not a rigorous requirement, the overall depth selected could be somewhat less or somewhat more than the computed requirement

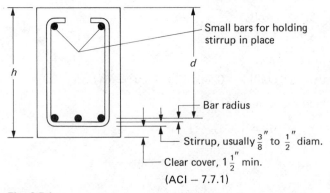

Fig. 3.7.1
Quantities added to effective depth d to get overall depth h for beams with one layer of tension steel.

in order to obtain a desired dimension. The stirrup is reinforcement to provide shear strength for the beam and should always be allowed for at this stage of the design. The actual size and spacing of stirrups is determined after the cross section and tension bars have been selected, and the subject is treated in Chap. 5.

Check weight,

$$w = \frac{18(34)}{144}(0.15) = 0.638 \text{ kip/ft}$$

$$\text{revised } M_D = \frac{(0.8 + 0.638)}{8}(40)^2 = 288 \text{ ft-kips}$$

$$\text{revised } M_u = 1.4(288) + 477 = 404 + 477 = 881 \text{ ft-kips}$$

$$\text{revised required } M_n = \frac{881}{0.9} = 980 \text{ ft-kips}$$

$$\text{revised required } bd^2 = \frac{980(12,000)}{644} = 18,250 \text{ in.}^3$$

For $b = 18$ in., the new required $d = 31.9$ in.

$$\text{required } h = 31.9 + 2.5 = 34.4 \text{ in.}$$

The depth could be increased to 35 in. but the even number 34 in. is preferred. Use $h = 34$ in. If the depth is changed, the weight is to be recomputed and the value of M_n corrected.

(f) Select the reinforcement. Compute the value of d from the overall dimension h,

$$\text{actual } d = h - (\approx 2.5 \text{ in.}) \quad \text{for one layer of bars}$$
$$= 34 - 2.5 = 31.5 \text{ in.}$$

When the overall depth is increased or decreased, the clear cover distance (ACI-7.7.1) is the one that is held constant; thus the effective depth will shift;

$$\text{actual } R_u = \frac{M_n}{bd^2} = \frac{980(12,000)}{18(31.5)^2} = 658 \text{ psi}$$

The steel requirement may be determined from Eq. (3.6.5), from the curves of Fig. 3.6.1, or estimated by straight-line proportion. Using the latter and knowing that

$$R_u = 644 \text{ psi} \quad \text{for } \rho = 0.012$$

find approximate ρ for $R_u = 658$ psi,

$$\text{approx } \rho = 0.012\left(\frac{658}{644}\right) = 0.0123$$

[using Eq. (3.6.5) would have given the same value]

$$\text{approx } A_s = \rho bd = 0.0123(18)(31.5) = 6.95 \text{ sq in.}$$

Select 4-#10 and 2-#9 bars, $A_s = 7.08$ sq in. (Table 3.7.1). Check whether 4-#10 and 2-#9 will fit into an 18-in. width in one layer.

$$\frac{\text{clear spacing}}{\text{between bars}} = \frac{18 - 2(1.5) - 2(0.375) - 4(1.27) - 2(1.128)}{5}$$

$$= \frac{18 - 3.0 - 0.75 - 5.08 - 2.26}{5}$$

$$= 1.38 \text{ in.} > 1.27 \text{ in.} \qquad\qquad \text{OK}$$

Subtracted from the overall width are the combined values of the minimum clear cover on both sides (3.0), one stirrup diameter on both sides (0.75), 4-#10 bar diameters (5.08), and 2-#9 bar diameters (2.26). The result is divided by the number of spaces between bars, and this is the clearance that must exceed the diameter of the larger bar (ACI-7.6.1). Table 3.7.2 gives the minimum beam width for 6-#10 bars as 17.8 in.

(g) Check capacity.

$$C = 0.85f_c'ba = 0.85(4)18a = 61.2a$$

$$T = A_s f_y = 7.08(60) = 425 \text{ kips}$$

$$a = \frac{425}{61.2} = 6.95 \text{ in.}$$

$$M_n = A_s f_y\left(d - \frac{a}{2}\right) = \frac{425(31.5 - 3.47)}{12} = 994 \text{ ft-kips}$$

$$M_u = 881 \text{ ft-kips} < \phi M_n = 0.9(994) = 895 \text{ ft-kips} \qquad \text{OK}$$

Use 18 × 34 beam with 4-#10 and 2-#9 bars, as shown in Fig. 3.7.2.

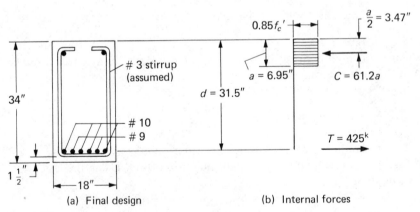

(a) Final design (b) Internal forces

Fig. 3.7.2
Design for Example 3.7.1.

EXAMPLE 3.7.2   Design a floor slab to carry a uniform live load of 350 psf (pounds per square foot) on a simple span of 23 ft, given $f_c' = 3000$ psi and $f_y = 60,000$ psi. Use the ACI Code. Keep the percentage of reinforcement at about 30% of the balanced amount so that deflection is unlikely to be excessive.

Solution: The design of a slab is usually made by taking a 1-ft wide typical strip for calculation purposes rather than the entire slab width. This is known as a one-way slab that acts as a wide beam. The common situation of the one-way slab continuous across several beams is treated in detail in Chap. 8.

(a) Determine factored moment.

$$U = 1.4D + 1.7L = 1.4(0.15 \text{ kip/ft estimated}) + 1.7(0.350)$$
$$= 0.210 + 0.595 = 0.805 \text{ kip/ft/ft of width}$$

$$M_u = \frac{0.805(23)^2}{8} = 53.2 \text{ ft-kips/ft of width}$$

$$\text{required } M_n = \frac{M_u}{\phi} = \frac{53.2}{0.90} = 59.2 \text{ ft-kips/ft}$$

(b) Since $\rho = 0.3\rho_b$ is desired, using $\rho = 0.0160(0.3/0.75) = 0.0064$ based on Table 3.5.1,

$$R_u = \rho f_y (1 - \tfrac{1}{2}\rho m)$$

where

$$m = \frac{f_y}{0.85 f'_c} = \frac{60}{0.85(3)} = 23.5$$

$$R_u = 0.0064(60,000)[1 - 0.5(0.0064)(23.5)]$$
$$= 355 \text{ psi}$$

(c) Determine bd^2 required for R_u and select trial slab thickness.

$$\text{required } bd^2 = \frac{M_n}{R_u} = \frac{59.2(12,000)}{355} = 2000 \text{ in.}^3$$

Since a slab is designed by using a 1-ft strip, b is 12 in. Then required $d = 12.9$ in. The required total thickness is obtained by adding on the clear cover required ($\frac{3}{4}$-in. minimum as per ACI-7.7.1) and the bar radius. Stirrups are rarely used in slabs so the $\frac{3}{8}$-in. allowance used for beams (Example 3.7.1) is not included here.

$$\text{total thickness, } h = 12.9 + 0.75 + 0.50$$
$$= 14.15 \text{ in.} \qquad\qquad \text{Try } 14\tfrac{1}{2} \text{ in.}$$

(d) Check weight.

$$w = \frac{14.5}{12}(0.15) = 0.181 \text{ kip/ft}$$

This value exceeds the amount estimated, but a repeat of the preceding steps will show that the theoretical total thickness is still about 14.5 in.

Correct the moment for use in selecting steel.

$$\text{corrected } U = 1.4(0.181) + 1.7(0.350) = 0.849 \text{ kip/ft}$$

$$\text{corrected } M_n = 59.2\left(\frac{0.849}{0.805}\right) = 62.3 \text{ ft-kips/ft}$$

(e) Determine the steel to be used.

$$\text{actual } d = h - 0.75 - 0.5(\text{est}) = 14.5 - 1.25 = 13.25 \text{ in.}$$

$$\text{actual } R_u = \frac{M_n}{bd^2} = \frac{62.3(12,000)}{12(13.25)^2} = 354 \text{ psi}$$

The actual percentage ρ may be determined from Eq. (3.6.5), from the curves of Fig. 3.6.1, or estimated by straight-line proportion (see Example 3.7.1). Since the R_u provided is nearly exactly that desired, the ρ value will not change from the starting value,

$$\text{required } A_s = 0.0064(12)(13.25) = 1.02 \text{ sq in./ft}$$

Try #7 @ 7 in. spacing, $A_s = 1.03$ sq in./ft

For slabs, bars are not selected by picking a total number; instead they are selected on the basis of an average area provided per foot of width. One #7 gives 0.60 sq in., or 0.60 sq in./ft if a bar is spaced every 12 in. For #7 bars spaced at 7 in., the average area provided is 0.60 (12/7) = 1.03 sq in./ft. Table 3.7.3 gives average areas per foot of width provided by various bar spacings.

Table 3.7.3
Average Area per Foot of Width Provided by Various Bar Spacings

Bar Size Number	Nominal Diameter (in.)	Spacing of Bars in Inches													
		2	$2\frac{1}{2}$	3	$3\frac{1}{2}$	4	$4\frac{1}{2}$	5	$5\frac{1}{2}$	6	7	8	9	10	12
3	0.375	0.66	0.53	0.44	0.38	0.33	0.29	0.26	0.24	0.22	0.19	0.17	0.15	0.13	0.11
4	0.500	1.18	0.94	0.78	0.67	0.59	0.52	0.47	0.43	0.39	0.34	0.29	0.26	0.24	0.20
5	0.625	1.84	1.47	1.23	1.05	0.92	0.82	0.74	0.67	0.61	0.53	0.46	0.41	0.37	0.31
6	0.750	2.65	2.12	1.77	1.51	1.32	1.18	1.06	0.96	0.88	0.76	0.66	0.59	0.53	0.44
7	0.875	3.61	2.88	2.40	2.06	1.80	1.60	1.44	1.31	1.20	1.03	0.90	0.80	0.72	0.60
8	1.000		3.77	3.14	2.69	2.36	2.09	1.88	1.71	1.57	1.35	1.18	1.05	0.94	0.78
9	1.128		4.80	4.00	3.43	3.00	2.67	2.40	2.18	2.00	1.71	1.50	1.33	1.20	1.00
10	1.270			5.06	4.34	3.80	3.37	3.04	2.76	2.53	2.17	1.89	1.69	1.52	1.27
11	1.410			6.25	5.36	4.69	4.17	3.75	3.41	3.12	2.68	2.34	2.08	1.87	1.56

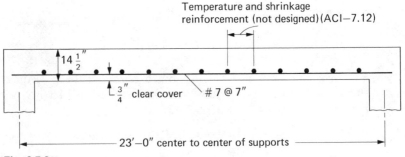

Fig. 3.7.3
Slab design of Example 3.7.2.

(f) Capacity check and design sketch. Make a check of capacity by using statics (not illustrated here; see Example 3.7.1); select steel transverse to the main steel for temperature, shrinkage, and distribution of loading (not illustrated here, but treated in Chap. 8); and draw design sketch (see Fig. 3.7.3). *Use* $14\frac{1}{2}$-in. thick slab, with #7 @ 7 as main reinforcement.

EXAMPLE 3.7.3 Compute the strength of the beam of Fig. 3.7.4, 500 mm wide and 760 mm deep overall, containing 3–40-mm diameter (40∅) bars in the outer layer and 2–32-mm diameter (32∅) bars in the inner layer. The stirrup is 10∅, and minimum clear cover is 40 mm with 25 mm between layers. Use $f'_c = 25$ N/mm^2, $f_y = 400$ N/mm^2, and $E_s = 200{,}000$ N/mm^2.

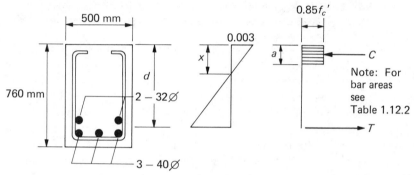

Fig. 3.7.4
Beam analysis with metric dimensions, Example 3.7.3.

Solution: (a) Determine that the steel is within the permissible limits of the ACI Code. Examine the balanced condition (see Sec. 3.5).

$$\epsilon_y = \frac{f_y}{E_s} = \frac{400}{200{,}000} = 0.0020$$

$$x_b = \frac{0.003}{0.003 + 0.002}d = 0.600d$$

$$d = 760 - 40 - 10 - \frac{3(12.57)20 + 2(8.04)81}{3(12.57) + 2(8.04)} = 760 - 40 - 10 - 38$$

$$= 672 \text{ mm}$$

$f'_c = 25$ N/mm$^2 < f'_c = 4000$ psi; $\quad \beta_1 = 0.85 \quad$ (see Table 3.5.1)

$a_b = \beta_1 x_b = 0.85(0.600)672 = 343$ mm

$C_b = 0.85 f'_c b a_b = 0.85(0.025)(500)(343) = 3640$ kN

$T_b = A_{sb} f_y$

$C_b = T_b$

$$A_{sb} = \frac{3640(1000)}{400} = 9100 \text{ mm}^2 \ (91.0 \text{ cm}^2)$$

max $A_s = 0.75(91.0) = 68.3$ cm^2

Since the actual $A_s = 53.8$ cm^2 is less than the maximum permitted, the beam is acceptable (deflection might be a problem, so it should be checked).

(b) Determine the nominal flexural strength, M_n.

$$C = 0.85f_c'ba = 0.85(0.025)(500)a = 10.6a$$
$$T = A_sf_y = 5380(0.400) = 2150 \text{ kN}$$

$$a = \frac{2150}{10.6} = 203 \text{ mm}$$

$$M_n = T(d - 0.5a) = 2150[672 - 0.5(203)]\tfrac{1}{1000} = 1230 \text{ kN-m}$$

3.8 Investigation of Rectangular Sections in Bending with Both Tension and Compression Reinforcement

Rectangular sections with both tension and compression reinforcement are also called "doubly reinforced" sections. Because the compressive strength of concrete is high, the need for compression reinforcement *to obtain adequate strength* is not great. In beams where compression reinforcement might be used in order to reduce the size of the cross section, deflection may be excessive, and there may be difficulty in placing all of the tension reinforcement within the width of the beam, even if two or more layers of bars are used. In addition, shear stress will become high so that a large amount of shear reinforcement might be required.

The use of compression reinforcement for deflection control (to reduce the creep and shrinkage deflection) is the usual reason for its use when the strength method is used.

The investigation of a doubly reinforced section such as that shown in Fig. 3.8.1 involves the determination of the nominal flexural strength M_n with b, d, d', A_s, A_s', f_c', and f_y as the given data. The investigation is similar to that for the singly reinforced beam except the compressive force C is

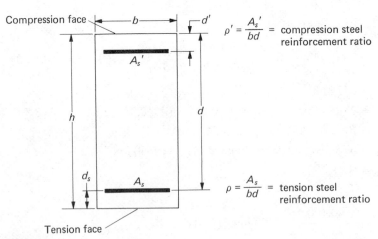

Fig. 3.8.1
Doubly reinforced beam cross section.

composed of two parts, one in the concrete and the other in the steel. The actual stress in the compression steel at ultimate strength may be the yield stress, or it may be something less, depending on the position of the neutral axis. The stress used in the compression steel must be compatible with the strain in the compression steel at ultimate strength.

In the case of the beam with compression steel, the ACI Code states that ρ shall not exceed $0.75\rho_b$ (just as for the singly reinforced beam), but in addition states (ACI-10.3.3) that "the portion of ρ_b balanced by compression reinforcement need not be reduced by the 0.75 factor." This alternate wording actually means that the maximum $x = 0.75x_b$, thus giving the same ductility requirement in terms of the strain diagram as that for a beam without compression reinforcement. When compression steel is used, $0.75\rho_b$ does not indicate the same ductility as when compression steel is not used.

EXAMPLE 3.8.1   Determine the nominal ultimate moment capacity M_n of the rectangular section shown in Fig. 3.8.2a, given $f'_c = 5000$ psi, $f_y = 60,000$ psi, $b = 14$ in., $d = 26$ in., $d' = 3$ in., $A'_s = 2$-#8 bars and $A_s = 8$-# 10 bars.

Solution: (a) Determine A_{sy} in the compression steel yield condition. Refer to Fig. 3.8.2c where the strain diagram is defined by points A and B. Point B is obtained by letting the strain in the compression steel exactly equal ϵ_y.

$$x_y = \frac{0.003(3)}{0.003 + 0.00207} = 9.67 \text{ in.}$$

$$a_y = \beta_1 x_y = 0.80(9.67) = 7.74 \text{ in.}$$
$$C_{cy} = 0.85f'_c b a_y = 4.25(14)(7.74) = 460 \text{ kips}$$
$$C_{sy} = (f_y - 0.85f'_c)A'_s = (60 - 4.25)(1.58) = 88 \text{ kips}^\dagger$$
$$T_y = C_{cy} + C_{sy} = 460 + 88 = 548 \text{ kips}$$

$$A_{sy} = \frac{548}{60} = 9.13 \text{ sq in.}$$

Since the actual A_s is greater than A_{sy}, actual x is larger than x_y, $\epsilon'_s > \epsilon_y$, and compression steel yields. An alternative would be to assume compression steel yields and check it afterwards, as shown in part (c).

(b) Determine the maximum permissible A_s. From Fig. 3.8.2b, using the balanced condition defined by points A and C on the strain diagram,

$$x_b = \frac{0.003(26)}{0.003 + 0.00207} = 15.39 \text{ in.}$$

$$\text{max } x = 0.75x_b = 0.75(15.39) = 11.54 \text{ in.}$$

which defines the strain line through points A and D in Fig. 3.8.2b.

---

† It is noted that the components of the compressive force nominally are the portions carried by the steel and by the concrete, respectively. For the convenience of knowing the point of action, however, the compressive force in the concrete is taken larger than the real amount by stressing $0.85f'_c$ over the steel area, whereas the compressive force in the steel is taken less by the same amount. The total compressive force is correct. The components C_c and C_s will hereinafter be computed as shown in this example.

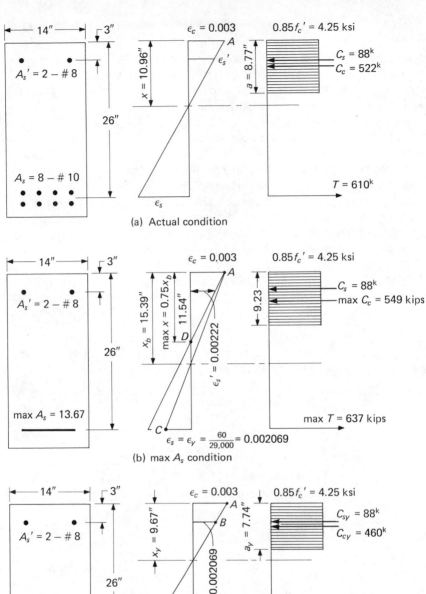

(a) Actual condition

(b) max A_s condition

(c) Compression steel yield condition

Fig. 3.8.2
Section for Example 3.8.1.

$$\text{max } a = \beta_1 x = 0.80(11.54) = 9.23 \text{ in.}$$
$$\text{max } C_c = 0.85 f'_c ba = 4.25(14)(9.23) = 549 \text{ kips}$$

$$\epsilon'_s = \frac{11.54 - 3.00}{11.54}(0.003)$$

$$= 0.00222 > \epsilon_y \quad \text{(compression steel yields)}$$
$$C_s = (f_y - 0.85f'_c)A'_s = (60 - 4.25)1.58 = 88 \text{ kips}$$
$$\text{max } T = 549 + 88 = 637 \text{ kips}$$

One may note that in determining the maximum T the portion 88 kips "balanced by compression reinforcement" (ACI-10.3.3) is *not* reduced by the 0.75 factor. It is believed that the thought process illustrated here provides better understanding of the concept than does the wording in ACI-10.2.2.

$$\text{max permissible } A_s = \frac{637}{60} = 10.62 \text{ sq in.} > (\text{actual } A_s = 10.16 \text{ sq in.}) \quad \text{OK}$$

One may note that the tension steel in this case is 78% of the full balanced amount (i.e., if A_{sb} were computed using $x = x_b$), greater than the 75% acceptable for a beam without compression steel. This is acceptable since compression steel provides ductility; so that the greater the proportion of the compression force is carried by compression steel, the closer the maximum tension steel can approach the balanced amount.

(c) Determine M_n in the actual condition. From Fig. 3.8.2a, using a strain condition defined by point A and the requirement of equilibrium ($C = T$),

$$T = 60(10.16) = 610 \text{ kips}$$
$$C_s = (60 - 4.25)(1.58) = 88 \text{ kips}$$
$$C_c = 0.85f'_c ba = 4.25(14)a$$

$$a = \frac{C_c}{4.25(14)} = \frac{610 - 88}{4.25(14)} = 8.77 \text{ in.}$$

$$x = \frac{8.77}{\beta_1} = \frac{8.77}{0.80} = 10.96 \text{ in.}$$

Instead of doing the work in part (b), this value of $x = 10.96$ in. may be checked against $0.75x_b = 11.54$ in.

$$\epsilon'_s = \frac{10.96 - 3.00}{10.96}(0.003) = 0.00218 > \epsilon_y \qquad \text{OK}$$

The check on ϵ'_s verifies the conclusion in part (a).

$$M_n = C_c\left(d - \frac{a}{2}\right) + C_s(d - d')$$

$$= 522[26 - 0.5(8.77)]\tfrac{1}{12} + 88(26 - 3)\tfrac{1}{12} = 941 + 169$$
$$= 1110 \text{ ft-kips } (1500 \text{ kN-m})$$

Note that the work shown in parts (a) and (c) is to explain why the checks on (1) if actual $x < 0.75x_b$ and (2) if actual $\epsilon'_s < \epsilon_y$ are needed in part (c). In a usual problem the work shown in part (c) is all that is necessary (if both checks can be verified).

EXAMPLE 3.8.2   Repeat the solution for Example 3.8.1, except that A_s is 4-#11 bars instead of 8-#10 bars. Also determine the percentage increase in the capacity of the beam over the same beam without compression steel.

Solution: (a) Determine A_{sy} in the compression steel yield condition. From Example 3.8.1, $A_{sy} = 9.13$ sq in. Since actual A_s is less than A_{sy}, the compression steel does not yield.

   (b) Determine M_n in the actual condition. Let the location of the neutral axis in Fig. 3.8.3 be the unknown. Equating $(C_c + C_s)$ to T,

$$4.25(14)(0.80x) + \left[29\left(\frac{3}{x}\right)(x-3) - 4.25 \right](1.58) = 60(6.24)$$

Solving the quadratic equation for x,

$$x = 6.46 \text{ in.}$$
$$a = \beta_1 x = 0.80(6.46) = 5.17 \text{ in.}$$

Then

$$C_c = 4.25(14)(5.17) = 307.6 \text{ kips}$$
$$\epsilon'_s = \frac{6.46 - 3.00}{6.46}\, 0.003 = 0.00161 < \epsilon_y$$
$$C_s = [29(1.61) - 4.25](1.58) = 66.9 \text{ kips}$$
$$C_c + C_s = 307.6 + 66.9 = 374.5 \text{ kips}$$
$$T = A_s f_y = 6.24(60) = 374.4 \text{ kips} \qquad \text{(Check)}$$
$$M_n = 307.6[26 - 0.5(5.17)]\tfrac{1}{12} + 66.9(26-3)\tfrac{1}{12} = 600 + 128$$
$$= 728 \text{ ft-kips } (988 \text{ kN-m})$$

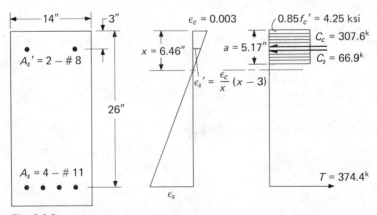

Fig. 3.8.3
Section for Example 3.8.2.

(c) Determine M_n if the compression steel had not existed. From Fig. 3.8.2b in Example 3.8.1a, using maximum C_c

$$\max A_s = \frac{549}{60} = 9.15 \text{ sq in.} > (\text{actual } A_s = 6.24 \text{ sq in.}) \qquad \text{OK}$$

$$T = 6.24(60) = 374.4 \text{ kips}$$

$$a = \frac{374.4}{4.25(14)} = 6.29 \text{ in.}$$

$$M_n = 374.4[26 - 0.5(6.29)]\tfrac{1}{12} = 713 \text{ ft-kips (966 kN-m)}$$

Thus even though in part (b) the 128 ft-kips representing the contribution of compression steel was 17.5% of the total, the addition of the compression steel to the singly reinforced beam actually added only 2.1% $[(728-713)/713]$ to the original capacity. This is a common situation; the compression steel was not used because the compression zone without it was inadequate for strength, but instead it was used for deflection control.

3.9 Criterion for the Compression Steel Yield Condition

It may be shown that the criterion to insure that the compression steel in a doubly reinforced section yields at ultimate strength is

$$\rho - \rho'\left(1 - \frac{0.85f'_c}{f_y}\right) \geq 0.85\beta_1\left(\frac{f'_c d'}{f_y d}\right)\left(\frac{87,000}{87,000 - f_y}\right) \qquad (3.9.1)$$

Referring to Fig. 3.9.1, the criterion for yielding of the compression steel is

$$\epsilon'_s \geq \epsilon_y \qquad (3.9.2)$$

The internal forces in Fig. 3.9.1 are

$$T = \rho bdf_y$$
$$C_c = 0.85f'_c\beta_1 xb$$
$$C_s = (f_y - 0.85f'_c)\rho' bd$$

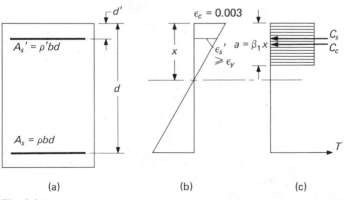

(a)   (b)   (c)

Fig. 3.9.1
Compression steel yield condition.

Equating T to $C_c + C_s$ and solving for x,

$$x = \frac{f_y d}{0.85 \beta_1 f'_c} \left[\rho - \rho' \left(1 - \frac{0.85 f'_c}{f_y} \right) \right] \qquad (3.9.3)$$

From Fig. 3.9.1b

$$\epsilon'_s = \frac{\epsilon_c}{x} (x - d') \qquad (3.9.4)$$

Substituting Eq. (3.9.4) in Eq. (3.9.2) gives

$$\frac{\epsilon_c}{x} (x - d') \geq \epsilon_y \qquad \text{or} \qquad \frac{87,000}{x} (x - d') \geq f_y$$

or

$$x \geq \frac{87,000 d'}{87,000 - f_y} \qquad (3.9.5)$$

Equation (3.9.1) may be obtained by substituting Eq. (3.9.3) in Eq. (3.9.5).

3.10 Design of Rectangular Sections in Bending with Both Tension and Compression Reinforcement

When a rectangular section of given dimensions is required to have a strength greater than that which may be supported when it is reinforced with the maximum permissible amount of tension reinforcement, compression reinforcement becomes necessary. However, such necessary use of compression steel for strength is rare. The principal reason for using compression reinforcement is to reduce long-time deflection due to creep and shrinkage.

The longical procedure for designing a doubly reinforced section is to determine first whether compression steel is needed for strength. This may be done by comparing the required moment capacity with the moment capacity of a singly reinforced section in which the maximum permissible amount of tension steel has been used.

Having decided that compression steel is to be used, be it required for strength or desirable for deflection control, the designer now needs to determine the amount of tension steel A_s and compression steel A'_s. In doing so he can draw upon the two equilibrium equations; namely,

$$C_c + C_s = T \qquad (3.10.1)$$

and

$$M_n = C_c \left(d - \frac{\beta_1 x}{2} \right) + C_s (d - d') \qquad (3.10.2)$$

wherein the symbols are those defined in Fig. 3.8.1. Further, in verifying the solution he must check to see that the tension steel as finally used does not make the neutral-axis distance x exceed 75% of the balanced condition value and that the compression steel does in fact yield (Eq. 3.9.1) when it has been so assumed in the equilibrium equations (Eqs. 3.10.1 and 3.10.2). If the compression steel does not yield, the equilibrium conditions must be reformulated using a stress f'_s in the compression steel proportional to the strain in that steel.

A unique solution is obtainable once the actual x is preset. This actual x has a maximum limit of $0.75x_b$. If deflection control is an important consideration, the actual x may be preset at a much smaller value than $0.75x_b$, perhaps $0.375x_b$ or smaller.

EXAMPLE 3.10.1 Determine the A_s and A'_s required to carry a service live-load moment of 390 ft-kips and a service dead-load moment of 200 ft-kips, using $b = 14$ in., $d = 26$ in., $d' = 3$ in., $f'_c = 5000$ psi, $f_y = 60,000$ psi, and the ACI Code, as shown in Fig. 3.10.1a.

Solution: (a) Determine the required strength.

$$M_u = 1.4(200) + 1.7(390) = 280 + 664 = 944 \text{ ft-kips}$$

$$\text{required } M_n = \frac{M_u}{\phi} = \frac{944}{0.90} = 1047 \text{ ft-kips}$$

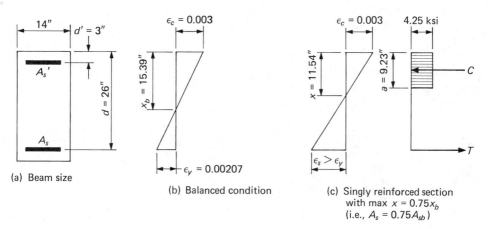

(a) Beam size

(b) Balanced condition

(c) Singly reinforced section with max $x = 0.75x_b$ (i.e., $A_s = 0.75A_{sb}$)

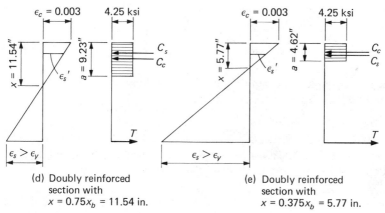

(d) Doubly reinforced section with $x = 0.75x_b = 11.54$ in.

(e) Doubly reinforced section with $x = 0.375x_b = 5.77$ in.

Fig. 3.10.1
Section for Examples 3.10.1 and 3.10.2.

(b) Determine the maximum capacity and reinforcement allowed by ACI Code for a singly reinforced section. The location of the neutral axis at the balanced condition (Fig. 3.10.1b) may be obtained as

$$x_b = \frac{\epsilon_c}{\epsilon_c + \epsilon_y} d = \frac{3}{3 + 60/29} 26 = 15.39 \text{ in.}$$

$$\max x = 0.75(15.39) = 11.54 \text{ in.} \qquad \text{(Fig. 3.10.1c)}$$

$$\max C = 0.85 f'_c b \beta_1 x = 4.25(14)(0.80)(11.54) = 549 \text{ kips}$$

$$\max A_s \text{ in singly reinforced section} = 549/60 = 9.15 \text{ sq in.}$$

$$\max M_n \text{ of singly reinforced section} = (549)(26 - 4.62)/(12)$$
$$= 977 \text{ ft-kips} \qquad (1330 \text{ kN-m})$$

The required M_n exceeds the maximum capacity obtainable without compression steel; therefore compression steel is needed for strength.

(c) Determine the minimum compression reinforcement required. Maintain max $x = 0.75x_b = 11.54$ in. (Fig. 3.10.1d). Let

$$M_{nc} = 977 \text{ ft-kips} \qquad \text{(from part (b))}$$

$$M_{ns} = M_n - M_{nc} = 1047 - 977 = 70 \text{ ft-kips}$$

$$\text{required } C_s = \frac{70(12)}{26 - 3} = 36.5 \text{ kips}$$

Will compression steel yield when $x = 11.54$ in.?

$$\epsilon'_s = \frac{11.54 - 3.00}{11.54}(0.003) = 0.0022 > \epsilon_y$$

$$C_s = A'_s(f_y - 0.85f'_c) = 36.5 \text{ kips}$$

$$\text{required } A'_s = \frac{36.5}{60 - 4.25} = 0.65 \text{ sq in.}$$

$$T = \max C_c + C_s = 549 + 36.5 = 585.5 \text{ kips}$$

$$\text{required } A_s = \frac{585.5}{60} = 9.76 \text{ sq in.}$$

This amount of tension steel is exactly the maximum permitted by the ACI Code.

In this example the remaining steps of selecting actual bars and making a final check of capacity are not shown.

EXAMPLE 3.10.2 Redesign the section of Example 3.10.1 so that the actual neutral axis location is at 0.375 of that in the balanced condition. Assume that the purpose is for deflection control.

Solution: (a) Determine M_{nc} corresponding to locating the actual neutral axis at 0.375 of the balanced condition value. This is one of an unlimited number of arbitrary choices of how to divide M_n into M_{nc} and M_{ns}. Use of this assumption seems a rational choice consistent with the guideline value for deflection control on a singly reinforced beam, as discussed in Sec. 3.7. Thus, referring to Fig. 3.10.1e,

$$\text{actual } x = 0.375x_b = 0.375(15.39) = 5.77 \text{ in.}$$
$$\text{actual } a = 0.80x = 0.80(5.77) = 4.62 \text{ in.}$$
$$C_c = 0.85f'_c ba = 0.85(5)(14)(4.62) = 275 \text{ kips}$$
$$T_1 = C_c = 275 \text{ kips}$$
$$M_{nc} = 275[26 - 0.5(4.62)]\tfrac{1}{12} = 542 \text{ ft-kips}$$

Let A_{sc} be the part of tension steel to match the concrete in compression; then

$$A_{sc} = \frac{T_1}{f_y} = \frac{275}{60} = 4.58 \text{ sq in.}$$

(b) Determine steel requirements for both faces of the beam.

$$M_{ns} = 1047 - 542 = 505 \text{ ft-kips}$$

$$C_s = T_2 = \frac{505(12)}{26 - 3} = 264 \text{ kips}$$

$$\epsilon'_s = \frac{5.77 - 3.0}{5.77}(0.003) = 0.00144 < \epsilon_y$$

Compression steel does not yield. Assuming the proportions for M_{nc} and M_{ns} are desired to be as initially assumed, then compression steel A'_s and additional tension steel to carry T_2 will be added in such a way to *maintain* $x = 5.77$ in. Thus

$$f'_s = 0.00144(29{,}000 \text{ ksi}) = 41.8 \text{ ksi}$$

so that the stress used is in agreement with the strain on the compression steel.

$$A'_s = \frac{264}{41.8 - 4.25} = 7.02 \text{ sq in.}$$

$$A_{ss} = \frac{264}{60} = 4.40 \text{ sq in.}$$

$$A_s = A_{sc} + A_{ss} = 4.58 + 4.40 = 8.98 \text{ sq in.}$$

Select 9-#9 in two layers for tension steel, and 4-#11 as compression reinforcement. The 4-#11 ($A'_s = 6.24$ sq in.) is the maximum steel that will fit into one layer.

(c) Check the strength of the section. Since the compression steel selected was less than 7.02 sq in., the proportions in M_{nc} and M_{ns} will change. This may be acceptable since the division was arbitrary. An analysis approach is presented which may be used as the alternative to that used in Example 3.8.2 wherein a quadratic equation was solved for the neutral-axis location x.

Since a smaller amount of compression steel is used than that required to locate the neutral axis at $0.375x_b$, the actual neutral axis will be lower if the section is to carry the same bending moment. Estimate the compression steel stress to be 45 ksi based on the original design situation (41.8 ksi).

$$C_c = 0.85f'_c ba = 0.85(5)(14)a = 59.5a$$
$$C_s = A'_s(f'_s - 0.85f'_c) = 6.24(45 - 4.25) = 254 \text{ kips}$$
$$T = A_s f_y = 9.00(60) = 540 \text{ kips}$$
$$C_c + C_s = T$$

$$a = \frac{540 - 254}{59.5} = 4.81 \text{ in.}; \qquad x = \frac{4.81}{0.80} = 6.00 \text{ in.}$$

$$\epsilon'_s = \frac{6.00 - 3.00}{6.00}(0.003) = 0.0015$$

$$f'_s = 0.0015(29,000) = 43.5 \text{ ksi}$$

Since this does not agree with the 45 ksi assumed, make a new assumption, say try $f'_s = 44$ ksi:

$$\text{revised } C_s = 6.24(44 - 4.25) = 248 \text{ kips}$$

$$a = \frac{540 - 248}{59.5} = 4.19 \text{ in.}; \qquad x = \frac{4.91}{0.80} = 6.14 \text{ in.}$$

$$\epsilon'_s = \frac{6.14 - 3.00}{6.14}(0.003) = 0.001535$$

$$f'_s = 0.001535(29,000) = 44.5 \text{ ksi}$$

Repeated trials may be made until computed f'_s agrees with the assumed value. In this case assume present agreement is close enough.

$$C_c = 59.5a = 59.5(4.91) = 292 \text{ kips}$$
$$C_s = 248 \text{ kips}$$
$$M_n = 292[26 - 0.5(4.91)]\tfrac{1}{12} + 248(26 - 3)\tfrac{1}{12}$$
$$= 573 + 475 = 1048 \text{ ft-kips} (1420 \text{ kN-m})$$
$$\approx 1047 \text{ ft-kips required} \qquad\qquad \text{OK}$$

A comparison of three possible designs for this doubly reinforced section as worked out in detail in Examples 3.10.1 and 3.10.2 is tabulated below:

Example 3.10.1, part c, $\quad x = 11.54$ in. $\quad A_s = 9.76$ sq in. $\quad A'_s = 0.65$ sq in.
Example 3.10.2, part b, $\quad x = 5.77$ in. $\quad A_s = 8.98$ sq in. $\quad A'_s = 7.02$ sq in.
Example 3.10.2, part c, $\quad x = 6.14$ in. $\quad A_s = 9.00$ sq in. $\quad A'_s = 6.24$ sq in.

It may be observed that when there is a large amount of compression steel that does not yield due to the linear strain variation across the depth of the section, varying the amount of compression steel has essentially the effect of changing only the proportions in M_{nc} and M_{ns}. It has a negligible effect (say typically 3 to 4%) on total capacity. The choice of 9-#9 (tension steel) and 4-#10 (compression steel) is acceptable. Deflection may still need checking but it will probably be within acceptable limits.

SELECTED REFERENCES

1. Jack R. Janney, Eivind Hognestad, and Douglas McHenry. "Ultimate Flexural Strength of Prestressed and Conventionally Reinforced Concrete Beams," *ACI Journal, Proceedings*, **52**, February 1956, 601–620.
2. Eivind Hognestad, N. W. Hanson, and Douglas McHenry. "Concrete Stress Distribution in Ultimate Strength Design," *ACI Journal, Proceedings*, **52**, December 1955, 455–479.
3. Hjalmar Granholm. *A General Flexural Theory of Reinforced Concrete*. New York; Wiley, 1965.
4. Eivind Hognestad. "Confirmation of Inelastic Stress Distribution in Concrete," *Journal of Structural Division*, ASCE, **83**, Paper No. 1189, No. ST2, March 1957.
5. C. S. Whitney. "Plastic Theory in Reinforced Concrete Design," *Transactions ASCE*, **107**, 1942, 251–326.
6. C. S. Whitney and Edward Cohen. "Guide for Ultimate Strength Design of Reinforced Concrete," *ACI Journal, Proceedings*, **53**, November 1956, 455–475.
7. ACI-ASCE Joint Committee: "Report on ASCE-ACI Joint Committee on Ultimate-Strength Design," *ASCE, Proceedings*, **81**, Paper No. 809, October 1955. See also *ACI Journal, Proceedings*, **52**, January 1956, 505–524.

PROBLEMS

All problems[†] are to be done in accordance with the strength method of the ACI Code (except Probs. 3.1 and 3.2), and all loads given are *service* loads, unless otherwise indicated. Wherever possible basic principles are to be used for solutions, avoiding the direct use of formulas.

REVIEW PROBLEMS IN MECHANICS OF MATERIALS

3.1 An elastic homogeneous beam of material capable of carrying both tension and compression is simply supported over a span of 20 ft (6 m) center to center of

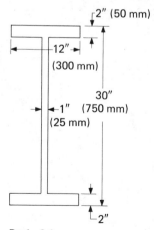

Prob. 3.1

[†] Most problems may be solved as problems stated in U.S. Customary units, or as problems in metric units using quantities in parenthesis at the end of the statement. The metric conversions are approximate to avoid implying higher precision for the given information in metric units than that for the U.S. Customary units.

supports. It is carrying a uniformly distributed load of 2 klf (kips per linear ft) (30 kN/m) in addition to a concentrated load of 10 kips (44 kN) located 5 ft (1.5 m) from the right end of the span. **(a)** Compute the maximum flexural stress on the section shown in the accompanying figure, using only basic statics and the internal-couple method, $M = (C$ or $T)$ (internal-couple moment arm). **(b)** Check by using the flexure formula, $f = Mc/I$.

3.2 The elastic homogeneous beam of the accompanying figure is simply supported on a span of 25 ft (7.5 m), and carries a uniform loading of 1 kip/ft (15 kN/m) plus a concentrated load of 9 kips (40 kN) at 8 ft (2.4 m) from the left end of the span. Compute maximum tensile and compressive stresses using **(a)** basic statics of the internal-couple method, $M = (C$ or $T)$ (internal-couple moment arm); and **(b)** the flexure formula, $f = Mc/I$.

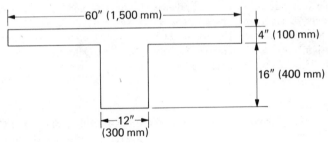

Prob. 3.2

REINFORCED CONCRETE PROBLEMS

3.3 For each of the beams in the accompanying figure using $f'_c = 3500$ psi, $f_y = 60,000$ psi, and the internal-couple method with the Whitney rectangular stress block, determine the nominal flexural capacity M_n. If the loading is 60% live load and the basic overload provision for dead-load plus live-load controls, what is the service moment capacity? ($f'_c = 24$ N/mm² and $f_y = 420$ N/mm².)

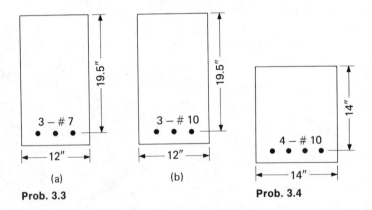

Prob. 3.3   **Prob. 3.4**

3.4 Using basic principles, prove whether or not the beam of the accompanying figure is underreinforced, balanced, or overreinforced according to its behavior at ultimate strength. Does the beam violate the ACI Code? If so, in what respect? Use $f'_c = 4000$ psi and $f_y = 58,000$ psi. ($f'_c = 28$ N/mm² and $f_y = 400$ N/mm².)

3.5 Determine the required effective size (dimensions b and d) and steel area A_s for a rectangular beam cross section (using a d/b ratio of about 1.75) to carry 1.0 kip/ft live load and 1.3 kips/ft dead load (including beam weight) on a simply supported span of 24 ft. Without making the practical decision of choosing an overall beam size and selecting actual bars, determine (see ACI-10.3.3 and 10.5.1). **(a)** the largest effective size; and **(b)** the smallest effective size that would be permitted. Use $f'_c = 3000$ psi and $f_y = 60,000$ psi. (Live load = 15 kN/m; dead load = 19 kN/m; span = 7.3 m; $f'_c = 21$ N/mm²; $f_y = 420$ N/mm².)

3.6 Repeat Prob. 3.5, except use $f'_c = 4000$ psi and use a d/b ratio of 2.0. ($f'_c = 28$ N/mm².)

3.7 Repeat Prob. 3.5, except use $f'_c = 4000$ psi and use a d/b ratio of 1.25. ($f'_c = 28$ N/mm².)

3.8 Select the economical reinforcement for a beam 12 in. wide by 22 in. deep overall to carry dead-load and live-load moments of 15 ft-kips and 60 ft-kips, respectively. Use $f'_c = 3000$ psi, $f_y = 40,000$ psi. (Width = 300 mm; depth = 560 mm; dead-load moment = 20 kN-m; live-load moment = 80 kN-m; $f'_c = 21$ N/mm²; $f_y = 280$ N/mm².)

3.9 Select economical reinforcement for a beam 20 in. wide by 40 in. overall depth to carry a live-load moment of 500 ft-kips and a dead-load moment (including beam weight) of 300 ft-kips. Use reinforcement in only one face. Though a check of deflection cannot be made with the given information, would you expect such a check to show that deflection is excessive? Explain your answer. Use $f'_c = 4000$ psi and $f_y = 60,000$ psi. (Beam size = 500 mm × 1000 mm; live-load moment = 70 t-m; dead-load moment = 40 t-m; $f'_c = 280$ kgf/cm²; $f_y = 4200$ kgf/cm².)

3.10 Design a rectangular beam for a 30-ft simply supported span to carry a live load of 2 kips/ft and a dead load of 1 kip/ft, in addition to the weight of the beam. Use $f'_c = 3500$ psi, $f_y = 40,000$ psi. (Span = 9 m; live load = 30 kN/m; dead load = 15 kN/m; $f'_c = 24$ N/mm²; $f_y = 280$ N/mm².) **(a)** Assuming no deflection limitation, design the smallest singly reinforced size of beam permitted. **(b)** Design a singly reinforced beam of such size that deflections would not be expected to be excessive under normal design circumstances. (Hint: Use $\rho =$ approximately one-half of the maximum permitted by the ACI Code.)

3.11 Design a rectangular beam to carry a live load of 1.5 kips/ft and a dead load of 1.5 kips/ft, in addition to the beam weight, for a simple span of 32 ft. Use an approximate steel ratio ρ of about 0.375 of the balanced amount (one-half of the maximum permitted), and also satisfy ACI-Table 9.5a. Use $f'_c = 4000$ psi and $f_y = 60,000$ psi. (Live load = 2000 kg/m; dead load = 2000 kg/m; span = 9.8 m; $f'_c = 300$ kgf/cm²; $f_y = 4200$ kgf/cm².)

3.12 Assuming no deflection limitation, and without using compression reinforcement, select the smallest rectangular section permitted by the ACI Code using the same size for the entire 28-ft beam of the accompanying figure. The live load is 1.5 kips/ft and the dead load is 1 kip/ft in addition to the weight of the beam. Select steel for both maximum positive and negative moment locations. Use $f'_c = 3500$ psi and $f_y = 40,000$ psi. (Note: Live load is always to be applied in the manner to cause the most severe effect; spans may be fully loaded, partially loaded, or unloaded, as is necessary for maximum stress.) (Live load = 20 kN/m; dead load = 15 kN/m; main span = 6 m; cantilever = 2.5 m; $f'_c = 24$ N/mm²; $f_y = 280$ N/mm².)

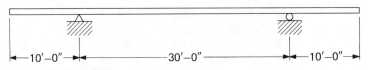

Probs. 3.12 and 3.13

3.13 Repeat Prob. 3.12, except use 2.0 kips/ft live load, and 1.25 kips/ft dead load, in addition to the beam weight, and increase the main span from 20 to 24 ft. (Live load = 30 kN/m; dead load = 17 kN/m; main span = 7.3 m; cantilever = 2.4 m.)

3.14 For the double overhanging cantilever beam shown, design the smallest practical rectangular cross section (without compression steel) to be used for entire 50 ft of beam. Select steel for both positive- and negative-moment regions. The live load is 1.5 kips/ft and the dead load is 1.0 kip/ft, in addition to the beam weight. Assume there is no deflection limit. Use f'_c = 3500 psi and f_y = 60,000 psi. (Refer to note at end of Prob. 3.12) (Live load = 2000 kg/m; dead load = 1500 kg/m; main span = 9.2 m; cantilevers = 3 m; f'_c = 250 kgf/cm²; f_y = 4200 kgf/cm².)

Probs. 3.14 and 3.15

3.15 Repeat Prob. 3.14, except assume the beam is part of a floor system supporting nonstructural elements likely to be damaged by large deflections. (Hint: Refer to ACI-Table 9.5a and Prob. 3.10.) Does $\rho = 0.5\rho_{max}$ seem a reasonable approach? Comment.

3.16 For the beam with compression reinforcement given in the accompanying figure and using f'_c = 4000 psi, f_y = 40,000 psi, compute the nominal flexural capacity M_n using the principles of statics with the internal couple. As a part of the procedure, verify whether or not the compression steel reaches yield under ultimate

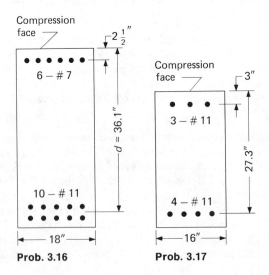

Prob. 3.16   **Prob. 3.17**

load by using basic principles and if it does not yield, use a compression steel stress at ultimate condition proportional to the ultimate strain in compression steel. Verify that the tension steel does not exceed the maximum permitted by the ACI Code. ($f'_c = 28$ N/mm^2; $f_y = 280$ N/mm^2.)

3.17 For the beam with compression reinforcement given in the accompanying figure, and using $f'_c = 4000$ psi and $f_y = 60,000$ psi, compute the nominal flexural capacity M_n using the principles of statics with the internal couple. Make sure to verify whether or not the compression steel reaches yield under ultimate load. With the given compression steel, determine the maximum tension steel the ACI Code would permit for this section. ($f'_c = 300$ kgf/cm^2; $f_y = 4200$ kgf/cm^2.)

3.18 If a rectangular beam with $b = 12$ in. and $d = 19.5$ in. has 3-#10 for tension reinforcement and 2-#10 (centered $2\frac{1}{2}$ in. from face of beam) for compression reinforcement, what percent increase in the nominal flexural capacity M_n is provided by the 2-#10 over that provided without any compression steel? Use $f'_c = 3500$ psi and $f_y = 60,000$ psi.

3.19 A rectangular section with $b = 14$ in. and effective depth $d = 21.5$ in. has 4-#10 as tension reinforcement and 2-#10 as compression reinforcement centered 2.5 in. from the face of the beam. Determine the strength M_n for this section. How much can the strength be increased by adding tension steel only? At the point where compression steel is needed to further increase capacity, what ratio of A'_s to A_s would be required to be added? Use $f'_c = 5000$ psi and $f_y = 60,000$ psi. ($b = 350$ mm; $d = 546$ mm; tension steel, 4–32 mm diam.; compression steel, 2–32 mm diam. centered 63.5 mm from face; $f'_c = 35$ N/mm^2; $f_y = 420$ N/mm^2.)

3.20 Redesign the steel for the beam size selected for Prob. 3.13, using compression steel so that the net reinforcement ratio ($\rho - \rho'$) will be about one-half the maximum permitted for a singly reinforced beam.

3.21 Redesign the beam of Prob. 3.12 with compression steel using the same small cross section selected for that problem. Provide for M_{nc} to be carried by the singly reinforced beam using $\rho = 0.375\rho_b$. If Prob. 3.12 has not been worked, use the smallest size rectangular beam permitted for one singly reinforced.

3.22 For the conditions of Prob. 3.14, using a rectangular section of 14 × 22 in. overall, design for compression steel so that A'_s is about $0.5A_s$, in order to control creep and shrinkage deflection (section 350 mm × 560 mm).

4

Rectangular Sections in Bending under Service Load Conditions

4.1 General Introduction

As discussed in Chap. 2, there have been two generally accepted philosophies of design and investigation—working stress and ultimate strength. In Chap. 3 the strength method (i.e., ultimate strength) was treated using overload factors, undercapacity factors, and the flexural strength of sections where stress is no longer proportional to strain. This chapter considers the working stress method in which service loads, allowable working stresses, and the linear relationship between stress and strain are used.

The working stress method is referred to by the present ACI Code as the *alternate design method*. With increasing emphasis on clear distinction between the design criteria of *strength* and *serviceability*, the term "strength" has come to mean capacity when failure is imminent under severe overload, whereas "serviceability" means satisfactory performance under service-load (i.e., working stress) conditions. Satisfactory performance may be defined in terms of (1) deflection within acceptable limits so that supported non-structural elements such as walls, partitions, and ceilings are not damaged; (2) cracking controlled to prevent large crack widths that are either unsightly or may permit water to enter causing corrosion of steel and perhaps deterioration of concrete. Other serviceability requirements such as vibration and noise control may also be important but lie outside the scope of this book. Though not encouraged, the ACI "alternate design method" does make use of the working stress approach to satisfy strength requirements. The assumptions and concepts relating to that method are discussed in the following sections.

City Hall, Toronto, Ontario, Canada. (Courtesy of Portland Cement Association.)

4.2 Fundamental Assumptions

Four basic assumptions are used in the working stress method for flexural members:

1. Plane sections remain plane after bending; that is, the variation in strain is linear across the depth of the member.
2. Stress is proportional to strain.
3. Concrete does not take tension (concrete cracks under tension).
4. Perfect bond exists between steel and concrete such that no slip occurs.

The first assumption is quite accurate; the second is reasonably accurate for stresses below about one-half f'_c, the 28-day compressive strength.

Regarding the third assumption, it is true that some of the concrete close to the neutral axis on the tension side may not be cracked; however, the magnitude of tensile stress transmitted is generally so small that, for reason of simplicity, the steel is assumed to take all of the tensile stress. The fourth assumption regarding bond is a good one. The subject of bond, or the longitudinal interaction between reinforcing bars and the surrounding concrete, is treated in Chap. 6.

4.3 Equilibrium Conditions

Two equilibrium conditions apply to a section subjected to bending only: (1) the resultant internal compressive force must be equal to the resultant internal tensile force; and (2) the moment of the internal couple, composed of the resultant compressive and tensile forces, must be equal to the applied bending moment. In fact, these two equilibrium conditions must hold true regardless of whether the service load is acting or failure is imminent under overload, the only difference being that the stress distribution across the depth is linear in one but not in the other.

The resultant compressive force may be entirely from concrete stresses or it may be from a combination of the stresses in concrete and those in the compression reinforcement. The resultant tensile force, of course, comes entirely from the tension reinforcement.

EXAMPLE 4.3.1   Using the equilibrium conditions, determine the working stresses in the steel and on the extreme fiber of concrete in the section of Fig. 4.3.1a due to an applied service-load moment M_w of 2000 in.-kips. The modulus of elasticity for the concrete is 3×10^6 psi and for the steel is 30×10^6 psi.

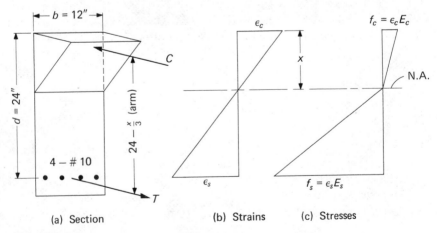

(a) Section   (b) Strains   (c) Stresses

Fig. 4.3.1
Section for Example 4.3.1.

Solution: The assumptions of linear strain and stress proportional to strain are shown in Fig. 4.3.1b and c. The first step in the solution is to locate the neutral axis (NA). The internal forces are obtained by computing the volume of the stress solids. Thus the internal compressive force in the concrete is

$$C = \tfrac{1}{2} f_c bx = 6.0 f_c x$$

The internal tensile force is

$$T = f_s A_s = f_s (4)(1.27) = 5.08 f_s$$

Equating C to T gives

$$\frac{f_s}{f_c} = \frac{6.0x}{5.08}$$

The ratio of f_s to f_c may also be obtained using the linear strain relationship and Hooke's law, as shown in Fig. 4.3.1,

$$\frac{\epsilon_s}{\epsilon_c} = \frac{24 - x}{x}$$

$$\frac{f_s}{f_c} = \frac{E_s \epsilon_s}{E_c \epsilon_c} = n \frac{\epsilon_s}{\epsilon_c} = 10 \frac{(24 - x)}{x}$$

in which n is the modular ratio E_s/E_c. Equating the two expressions for f_s/f_c,

$$\frac{6.0x}{5.08} = \frac{10(24 - x)}{x}$$

$$6x^2 = 50.8(24 - x)$$

$$x^2 + 8.47x = 203.2$$

Solving by completing the square gives

$$(x + 4.23)^2 = 203.2 + (4.23)^2$$

$$x = \sqrt{221.1} - 4.23 = 10.63 \text{ in.}$$

Note that, other than the *ratio* of the moduli of elasticity, only the properties of the section (depth, width, and steel area) affect the position of the neutral axis.

Using the second equilibrium condition,

$$M_w = 2000 \text{ in.-kips} = (C \text{ or } T) \times \text{arm}$$

The moment *arm* of the internal couple, or the distance from centroid of compressive solid to centroid of tension steel, equals for the case of the triangular wedge compressive solid,

$$\text{arm} = 24 - \frac{x}{3} = 24 - \frac{10.63}{3} = 20.46 \text{ in. (520 mm)}$$

Then for the given applied bending moment,

$$C = T = \frac{M_w}{\text{arm}} = \frac{2000}{20.46} = 97.8 \text{ kips (435 kN)}$$

The stresses are determined from the expressions for the stress solid volumes,

$$f_c = \frac{C}{6x} = \frac{97,800}{6(10.63)} = 1530 \text{ psi } (10.5 \text{ N/mm}^2)$$

$$f_s = \frac{T}{5.08} = \frac{97,800}{5.08} = 19,300 \text{ psi } (133 \text{ N/mm}^2)$$

4.4 Stress-Strain Relations

As discussed in Chap. 1, the stress-strain curve for steel is linear below the proportional limit, but that of concrete is only approximately linear, even at or below the allowable working stress. The modulus of elasticity of steel varies little with its strength, whereas that of concrete varies with its density and strength. In the ACI Code, E_s is assumed to be 29,000,000 psi (200,000 N/mm^2), and E_c is expressed as $w^{1.5}33\sqrt{f'_c}$, in which w is the density of concrete. Table 1.9.1 gives values for the modulus of elasticity of concrete, E_c.

Since the radio of the moduli of elasticity is one of the quantities that determine the location of the neutral axis, it is of greater interest for computing stresses than are the actual values of E_c or E_s.

The modular ratio $n = E_s/E_c$ may be taken (ACI–Appendix B.5.4) as the nearest whole number, but not less than 6. Except in deflection calculations, the value of n for lightweight concrete shall be assumed to be the same as for normal weight concrete of the same strength. It is suggested that the values in Table 4.4.1 be used for normal weight concrete.

Table 4.4.1
Practical Values for Modular
Ratio, n

f'_c (psi)	n	f'_c (N/mm^2)^a
3000	9	21
3500	8.5	24
4000	8	28
4500	7.5	31
5000	7	35
6000	6.5	41

^{a} For practical use, multiply
N/mm^2 by 10 to obtain value in
kgf/cm^2.

4.5 Method of Transformed Section

In the method of transformed section, the section of steel and concrete is transformed into a homogeneous section of only concrete by replacing the actual steel area with an equivalent area (i.e., imaginary area) in concrete.

In this transformation, two conditions must be satisfied. Let A_s and A_t be the areas of and f_s and f_t be the tensile stresses in the actual steel and the equivalent concrete, respectively. First, the equilibrium condition requires that the total tensile force be the same, or

$$A_s f_s = A_t f_t \tag{4.5.1}$$

Second, the compatibility of deformation condition requires that the unit elongation be the same; or

$$\frac{f_s}{E_s} = \frac{f_t}{E_c} \tag{4.5.2}$$

Defining the modular ratio $n = E_s/E_c$ and solving Eqs. (4.5.1) and (4.5.2),

$$A_t = nA_s \tag{4.5.3}$$

$$f_t = \frac{f_s}{n} \tag{4.5.4}$$

Thus the equivalent concrete area A_t is n times the actual steel area, and the equivalent tensile stress f_t (i.e., imaginary stress) is $1/n$ times the actual tensile stress.

Equations (4.5.3) and (4.5.4) are very useful in working stress design computations because a reinforced concrete section may then be treated as a section of one material, with the equivalent concrete on the tension side taking tension.

It may be noted that the use of transformed section is particularly convenient in that the common flexure formula Mc/I then applies so long as there is linear variation of stress with strain.

4.6 Investigation for Safety of Rectangular Sections in Bending with Tension Reinforcement Only

In problems of investigation for safety the properties of the section, the modular ratio, and the allowable working stresses are given. The problem may be (1) to compare the actual working stresses with the allowable working stresses for a given service-load bending moment, or (2) to determine the allowable service-load bending moment that the section may carry.

Two general approaches to investigation for safety may be used. In the "internal-force" method, as used in Example 4.3.1, the external bending moment is equated to the internal resisting couple. This couple is composed of an internal compressive force C above the neutral axis and an internal tensile force T below the neutral axis, at a distance apart equal to the moment arm. In the transformed section method, the well-known flexure formula Mc/I is used, in which I is the moment of inertia I_{cr} of the transformed cracked section about its centroidal axis. Note that the neutral axis coincides with the centroidal axis only in a section under pure bending (without axial load).

The detailed procedure for investigating a rectangular section in bending with tension reinforcement only is illustrated in the following example.

EXAMPLE 4.6.1   Given $f'_c = 3000$ psi, allowable $f_s = 20,000$ psi, and the ACI Code, determine the allowable service-load bending moment M_w that the rectangular section as shown in Fig. 4.6.1a may carry. Find the neutral axis by the transformed section method; then find M_w using both the internal-force and the transformed section methods.

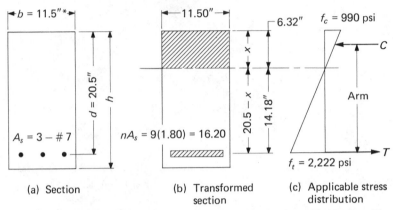

(a) Section	(b) Transformed section	(c) Applicable stress distribution

*The $11\frac{1}{2}$-in. beam width is an uncommon dimension, but is used here to provide a number conveniently followed in calculations. For typical beam widths refer to Sec. 3.7.

Fig. 4.6.1
Section for Example 4.6.1.

Solution: (a) Locate the neutral axis using transformed area (Fig. 4.6.1b). For $f'_c = 3000$ psi, the modular ratio n may be taken as 9 (see Table 4.4.1). The area $11.50x$ above the neutral axis is in compression, whereas the equivalent tension area $nA_s = 16.20$ sq in. is assumed to be concentrated at a distance $20.50 - x$ below the neutral axis.

Equating the first moments of the compression and tension areas about the neutral or centroidal axis,

$$\tfrac{1}{2}(11.50)x^2 = 16.20(20.50 - x)$$
$$x = 6.32 \text{ in.}$$

(b) Determine applicable stress distribution. If the allowable compressive stress (see ACI-Appendix B.3.1) in concrete of $f_c = 0.45f'_c = 1350$ psi is realized at the extreme compressive face, the corresponding actual tensile stress f_t in the equivalent concrete would be

$$\text{actual } f_t = (1350)\frac{14.18}{6.32} = 3029 \text{ psi}$$

which cannot be since it exceeds the allowable f_t of $20,000/9 = 2222$ psi. The applicable stress variation is shown in Fig. 4.6.1c, in which the actual f_t is made equal to the allowable f_t of 2222 psi. The actual f_c is, by proportion,

$$\text{actual } f_c = 2222(6.32/14.18) = 990 \text{ psi}$$

(c) Use the stress-solid internal-couple method to find allowable M_w.

$$\text{actual } C = \tfrac{1}{2}(0.990)(11.50)(6.32) = 36.0 \text{ kips}$$
$$\text{actual } T = 2.222(16.20) \quad \text{or} \quad 20(1.80) = 36.0 \text{ kips}$$

Note that the two internal forces are equal. This is always a good check on the correctness of x.

$$\text{actual arm} = 20.50 - \frac{6.32}{3} = 18.39 \text{ in.}$$

$$\text{allowable } M_w = 36.0(18.39)\tfrac{1}{12} = 55.2 \text{ ft-kips}$$

(d) Use the transformed section method to find M_w. The transformed cracked section moment of inertia is

$$I_{cr} = \tfrac{1}{3}(11.5)(6.32)^3 + 16.20(14.18)^2$$
$$= 968 + 3260 = 4230 \text{ in.}^4$$

By the flexure formula,

$$\text{allowable } M_w = \frac{0.990(4230)}{6.32(12)} \quad \text{or} \quad \frac{2.222(4230)}{14.18(12)} = 55.2 \text{ ft-kips (74.9 kN-m)}$$

4.7 Underreinforced, Ideally Reinforced, and Overreinforced Sections

Attention will now be called to the distinction between underreinforced, ideally reinforced, and overreinforced sections. These distinctions in the working stress method relate to *allowable stresses* and should not be confused with underreinforced, balanced, and overreinforced sections as used in Chap. 3 regarding mode of potential failure when the flexural strength is reached. An *ideally reinforced* section in the working stress method is one in which the neutral axis is so situated that the allowable stresses for both steel and concrete may be reached simultaneously. It is the case in which both steel and concrete are used most efficiently in accordance with the working stress method.

The underreinforced section contains less steel than the ideally reinforced section; thus its neutral (or centroidal) axis is nearer to the compressive face and only the allowable steel stress, not the allowable concrete stress, can be reached under maximum loading. In a similar manner the overreinforced section contains more steel than if it were ideally reinforced, and only the allowable concrete stress can be reached. Many sections overreinforced from the viewpoint of the working stress method have less tension steel than 75% of the balanced reinforcement in the strength method.

For the purpose of illustration, the three sections in Fig. 4.7.1 having the same size but different amounts of reinforcing steel may be compared.

The first section is the one just investigated in Example 4.6.1; similar work is performed on the other two sections, and the results are compiled in Fig. 4.7.1. The section of Fig. 4.7.1b is called "ideally reinforced" because

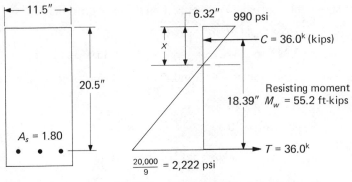

(a) Underreinforced section

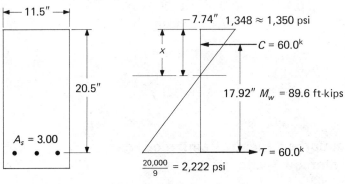

(b) Ideally reinforced section

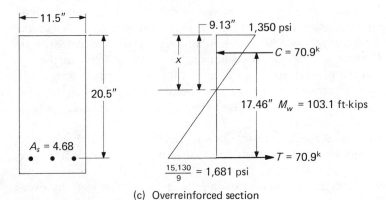

(c) Overreinforced section

Fig. 4.7.1
Under, ideally, and overreinforced sections.

at capacity load the allowable working stresses of $f_c = 1350$ psi and $f_s = 20,000$ psi are attained simultaneously. The section of Fig. 4.7.1a is called "underreinforced" because it contains less steel than the ideally reinforced section. Similarly, the section of Fig. 4.7.1c is said to be "overreinforced" because it contains more steel than the ideally reinforced section. Note additionally that the moment arm for the underreinforced section is slightly greater, and the moment arm for the overreinforced section is slightly less, than on the ideally reinforced section.

4.8 Design of Rectangular Sections in Bending with Tension Reinforcement Only

In problems of design, the bending moment, the modular ratio, and the allowable working stresses are given. The task is to determine the values of b, d, and A_s. The attainment of an ideally reinforced section can rarely be accomplished with exactness, because b and h (d is derived from h) are usually adjusted to a desirable whole inch (occasionally $\frac{1}{2}$ in.) and A_s must be provided by an integral number of bars. In building construction it is common to use the same b and h for a group of beams having approximately equal loadings and span lengths.

The procedure for determining the theoretical values of b, d, and A_s of an ideally reinforced section will be described, without reference for the time being to the adjustment to convenient values of b and h or to the choice of bars. Consider the ideally reinforced section of Fig. 4.8.1. From similar triangles obc and dbf, $bc/bf = oc/df$ or

$$k = \frac{\text{ideal } x}{d} = \frac{\text{allowable } f_c}{\text{allowable } f_s/n + \text{allowable } f_c} \tag{4.8.1}$$

The term k is defined as the ratio of the ideal x to the effective depth d. Then

$$\text{ideal moment arm } jd = d - \frac{x}{3} = d - \frac{kd}{3}$$

or

$$j = 1 - \frac{k}{3} \tag{4.8.2}$$

The term j is defined as the ratio of the ideal moment arm jd to the effective depth d. Equating the internal forces C and T and calling $A_s = \rho bd$,

$$\tfrac{1}{2}(\text{allowable } f_c)(bkd) = (\text{allowable } f_s)(\rho bd)$$

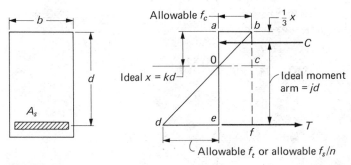

Fig. 4.8.1
An ideally reinforced section.

from which

$$\rho = \frac{k \text{ (allowable } f_c)}{2 \text{ (allowable } f_s)} \tag{4.8.3}$$

This ρ is the reinforcement ratio for an ideally reinforced beam. Equating the bending moment M_w to Cjd,

$$M_w = \tfrac{1}{2}(\text{allowable } f_c)(bkd)(jd) = \tfrac{1}{2}(\text{allowable } f_c)jkbd^2 = Rbd^2$$

in which

$$R = \tfrac{1}{2}(\text{allowable } f_c)jk \tag{4.8.4}$$

Equating the bending moment M_w to Tjd, $M_w = A_s$ (allowable f_s)jd, from which

$$A_s = \frac{M_w}{(\text{allowable } f_s)jd} \tag{4.8.5}$$

The constants k, j, ρ, and R as expressed in Eqs. (4.8.1) to (4.8.4) will be called the four *design constants* of an ideally reinforced section. Their values depend on the allowable working stresses f_c and f_s and on the value of n. It is to be noted that k, j, and ρ are dimensionless constants, but R is usually in psi.

The procedure for determining the theoretical values of b, d, and A_s of an ideally reinforced section may be summarized as follows:

1. Find the required value of bd^2 from M_w/R.
2. Assume a value of b and determine d (select b and h and check weight). See Sec. 3.7 for practical selection of beam sizes.
3. Determine A_s from ρbd and check its value from $M_w/[(\text{allowable } f_s)(jd)]$.

It is to be noted that there may be many usable solutions in accordance with the above procedure.

EXAMPLE 4.8.1   Design the cross section for a rectangular beam to carry a uniform live load of 1.9 kips/ft and a uniform dead load of 1.0 kip/ft (not including beam weight) on a simply supported span of 32 ft. Use the ACI Code with $f'_c = 4000$ psi and $f_y = 60,000$ psi (Grade 60 steel).

Solution: (a) Determine design constants for an ideally reinforced section. The allowable stresses (ACI-Appendix B.3) are $f_c = 0.45f'_c = 1800$ psi, $f_s = 24,000$ psi for Grade 60 steel, and $n = 8$. Referring to Fig. 4.8.2b and using similar triangles,

$$k = \frac{1800}{1800 + 24,000/8} = 0.375$$

$$j = 1 - \frac{k}{3} = 0.875$$

$$R = \tfrac{1}{2}f_ckj = \tfrac{1}{2}(1800)(0.375)(0.875) = 295 \text{ psi}$$

$$\rho = \frac{1}{2}\frac{kf_c}{f_s} = \frac{1}{2}(0.375)\frac{1800}{24,000} = 0.01405$$

(b) Determine preliminary size. Estimating beam weight per foot at 0.5 kip/ft,

$$M_w \text{ (live load)} = \tfrac{1}{8}(1.9)(32)^2 = 243 \text{ ft-kips}$$
$$M_w \text{ (dead load)} = \tfrac{1}{8}(1.0 + 0.5)(32)^2 = 192 \text{ ft-kips}$$
$$M_w = 243 + 192 = 435 \text{ ft-kips}$$

Since there is no size limitation, it is desired to make the beam approximately ideally reinforced. Thus

$$\text{required } bd^2 = \frac{M_w}{R} = \frac{435(12,000)}{295} = 17,700 \text{ in.}^3$$

Trial b	Required d	
12	38.4	
15	34.4	
18	31.4	← Try

Overall depth required (assuming two layers of equal sized bars) = 31.4 + clear cover + stirrup diam. + bar diameter + 0.5 of clear between layers, where clear cover is 1.5 in. (ACI-7.7.1) and stirrup diameter is $\tfrac{3}{8}$ or $\tfrac{1}{2}$ in. usually [Note: Stirrups enclosing the main steel, as shown in Fig. 4.8.2, provide shear capacity. Since nearly all beams contain stirrups, whose size is generally not definitely established until later in the design process (see Chap. 5), provision for them should be made.] Bar diameter is say 1 in. One-half clear between layers is 0.5 in. (ACI-7.6.2). Thus for two layers of bars the overall depth is about $3\tfrac{1}{2}$ to 4 in. greater than the required d.

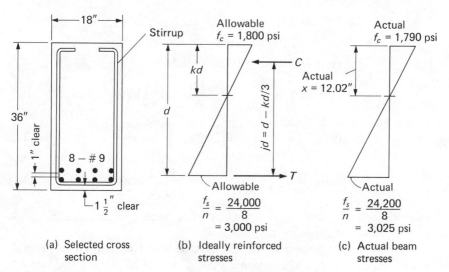

(a) Selected cross section

(b) Ideally reinforced stresses

(c) Actual beam stresses

Fig. 4.8.2
Section for Example 4.8.1.

Overall depth $h = 31.4 + 4.0 = 35.4$ in. Try a beam 18×36.

(c) Check weight, and revise step (b) if necessary.

$$\text{weight} = \frac{18(36)}{144}(0.15) = 0.675 \text{ kip/ft}$$

$$\text{corrected } M_w = 243 + \tfrac{1}{8}(1.675)(32)^2$$
$$= 243 + 214 = 457 \text{ ft-kips}$$

For $b = 18$ in,

$$\text{revised required } d = 32.1 \text{ in.}$$

$$\text{required } h = 32.1 + \approx 4 = 36.1 \approx 36 \text{ in.} \qquad \text{OK}$$

A beam 18×36 appears acceptable.

(d) Determine steel area required. If #8 bars may possibly be used, 3.5 in. instead of 4.0 might be subtracted from h to obtain d.

$$\text{actual } d \approx 36 - 3.5 = 32.5 \text{ in.}$$

$$\text{required } A_s = \frac{M_w}{f_s jd} = \frac{457(12)}{24(0.875)(32.5)} = 8.03 \text{ sq in.}$$

Try 8-#9 in two layers; $A_s = 8.00$ sq in.

(e) Check the section:

$$d = 36 - 1.5 - 0.5 - 1.128 - 0.5 = 32.37 \text{ in.}$$
$$\underset{\displaystyle \llcorner\!\!-\text{(stirrup diameter estimate)}}{}$$

Locate neutral axis:

$$18x\left(\frac{x}{2}\right) = 8.0(8)(32.37 - x)$$

$$x^2 + 7.12x = 230$$
$$x = 12.02 \text{ in.}$$
$$\text{arm} = 32.37 - 12.02/3 = 28.36 \text{ in.}$$

$$C = T = \frac{M_w}{\text{arm}} = \frac{457(12)}{28.36} = 193.5 \text{ kips}$$

$$\text{actual } f_s = \frac{T}{A_s} = \frac{193.5}{8.0} = 24.2 \text{ ksi} \approx 24 \text{ ksi} \qquad \text{OK}$$

$$\text{actual } f_c = \frac{C}{(\frac{1}{2})bx} = \frac{193.5}{0.5(18)12.02} = 1.79 \text{ ksi} < 1.80 \text{ ksi} \qquad \text{OK}$$

Even though the steel stress is slightly high, usual practice would accept an overstress not exceeding about 3 to 4%.

Selection of beam size and of bars has been done according to the general guidelines of Sec. 3.7. The designer must also be certain that the bars fit into the beam width (see Table 3.7.2) without violating code clearance requirements (ACI-7.6.1). The same cover requirements apply for the side of a beam as for the top or bottom. The selected cross section is shown in Fig. 4.8.2.

If in the preceding example a section 18×34 ($d \approx 30$ in.) instead of 18×36 ($d = 32.37$) is used, it is obvious that the A_s required must be larger than 8.00 in order to resist the same bending moment. The 18×34 section, containing more than its ideal reinforcement, must be an overreinforced section. On the other hand if a section 18×40 ($d \approx 36$ in.) is used, the A_s required will be smaller than 8.00. The 18×40 section, containing less than its ideal reinforcement, must be an underreinforced section. In the following two examples the exact amounts of steel required in the overreinforced and underreinforced sections, respectively, are determined.

Design of an Overreinforced Section

EXAMPLE 4.8.2   For the service-load moment $M_w = 457$ ft-kips (final M_w for Example 4.8.1), determine the required A_s if a section 18×34 in. were to be used. Use $f'_c = 4000$ psi, $f_y = 60,000$ psi, and the ACI Code.

Solution: (a) Allowable stresses and design constants. From ACI-Appendix B.3, allowable $f_c = 1800$ psi, allowable $f_s = 24,000$ psi, $n = 8$. Design constants are $k = 0.375$, $j = 0.875$, and $R = 295$ psi (see Example 4.8.1 for computation).

(b) Determine whether design is to be underreinforced, overreinforced, or, by chance, ideally reinforced. (In this case, having solved Example 4.8.1, we know this will be overreinforced.) Estimating two layers of steel, $d \approx 30$ in.

$$\text{required } R = \frac{M_w}{bd^2} = \frac{457(12,000)}{18(30)^2} = 339 \text{ psi}$$

Since this exceeds the ideal R, the section would not carry 457 ft-kips if it were ideally reinforced.

As shown in Fig. 4.8.3, the compressive force C must be increased from that of an ideally reinforced section. One way this can be accomplished is

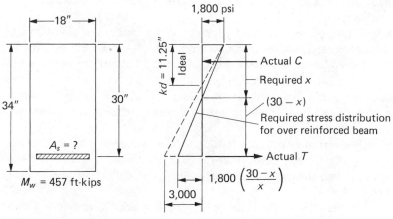

Fig. 4.8.3
Section for Example 4.8.2.

by adding extra tension steel for the sole purpose of lowering the neutral axis. Thus the extra steel is there to give the necessary neutral-axis location and will be acting under very low actual stress.

(c) Determine the required stress distribution.

$$M_w = (\text{required } C)(d - x/3)$$
$$457(12) = \tfrac{1}{2}(1.80)(18x)(30 - x/3)$$

Solving the quadratic equation for the required neutral-axis distance x,

$$\text{required } x = 13.23 \text{ in.}$$
$$C = \tfrac{1}{2}(1.80)(18)(13.23) = 214 \text{ kips}$$
$$\text{arm} = d - x/3 = 25.59 \text{ in.}$$
$$M_w = C \text{ times (arm)} = 214(25.59)\tfrac{1}{12} = 457 \text{ ft-kips} \quad \text{(Check)}$$

In order for the neutral axis to be at $x = 13.23$ in., the stress used to compute the required steel area must be the value defined by the straight-line stress relationship; a much smaller value than the code-specified allowable f_s of 24 ksi. Thus the reduced allowable value is

$$\text{allowable } f_s = nf_c \left(\frac{d - x}{x} \right)$$

$$= 8(1.80) \left(\frac{30 - 13.23}{13.23} \right) = 18.3 \text{ ksi}$$

(d) Determine required steel area.

$$\text{required } A_s = \frac{T}{\text{allowable } f_s} = \frac{214}{18.3} = 11.7 \text{ sq in.}$$

The selection of bars, recomputation of d, and a final check of stresses are steps omitted here.

As a section becomes more overreinforced, the reduced allowable stress may get so small as to make an overreinforced beam impractical or impossible. The alternative is to use compression steel to increase the compressive force.

Computation by the ACI strength method shows that the use of a maximum reinforcement ratio of $0.75\rho_b$ (a steel area of 11.6 sq in.) would yield a nominal strength M_n of 1410 ft-kips, which is 3.1 times the working moment M_w of 457 ft-kips. Even if almost all of the working moment is from live load, the U/ϕ value can only be as large as $1.7/0.90 = 1.89$. However, the overreinforced beam concept in the working stress method has been useful because it indirectly aids in deflection control. If a beam is to be significantly overreinforced, the tension steel is uneconomically used at a low stress; this generally means that the designer will use compression steel as an alternative, thus greatly reducing long-time deflection due to creep and shrinkage.

The ACI strength method, as dealt with in Chap. 3, provides a clear separation between the strength of a beam and its serviceability requirements for deflection control.

Design of an Underreinforced Section

EXAMPLE 4.8.3   For the service-load moment $M_w = 457$ ft-kips (final M_w for Example 4.8.1), determine the required A_s if a section 18×40 in. were to be used. Use $f_c' = 4000$ psi, $f_y = 60,000$ psi, and the ACI Code.

Solution: (a) Allowable stresses and design constants. From ACI-Appendix B.3, allowable $f_c = 1800$ psi, allowable $f_s = 24,000$ psi, $n = 8$. Design constants are $k = 0.375$, $j = 0.875$, and $R = 295$ psi (see Example 4.8.1 for computation).

(b) Determine whether design is to be underreinforced, overreinforced, or, by chance, ideally reinforced. Estimating two layers of steel, $d \approx 36$ in.,

$$\text{required } R = \frac{M_w}{bd^2} = \frac{457(12,000)}{18(36)^2} = 235 \text{ psi}$$

Since this is less than the ideal R, the section, if ideally reinforced, would carry more bending moment than necessary. Thus less steel will be needed than the ideal amount, and the section should be designed as underreinforced.

Shown in Fig. 4.8.4, the required compressive force C is less than that of an ideally reinforced section. The neutral-axis distance x will be smaller than kd and the actual concrete stress will be less than the allowable.

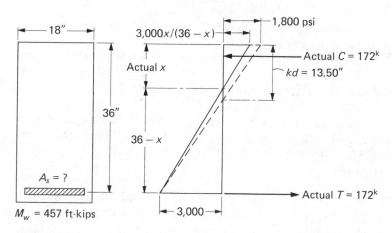

Fig. 4.8.4
Section for Example 4.8.3.

(c) Determine the required stress distribution.

$$M_w = (\text{actual } C)(d - x/3)$$

$$457(12) = \frac{1}{2}\left(\frac{3.00x}{36 - x}\right)(18x)\left(36 - \frac{x}{3}\right)$$

$$x^3 - 108x^2 - 609x + 22,000 = 0$$

Solving the cubic equation for the required neutral-axis position,

required $x = 12.29$ in.

$$f_c = \frac{3000x}{36 - x} = \frac{3000(12.29)}{36 - 12.29} = 1560 \text{ psi}$$

$$C = \tfrac{1}{2} f_c bx = \tfrac{1}{2}(1.56)(18)(12.29) = 172 \text{ kips}$$

available arm $= 36 - 12.29/3 = 31.9$ in.

$$M_w = 172(31.9)\tfrac{1}{12} = 457 \text{ ft-kips} \qquad \text{(Check)}$$

$$\text{required } A_s = \frac{T \text{ or } C}{\text{allowable } f_s} = \frac{172}{24} = 7.16 \text{ sq in.}$$

Since the steel controls for the underreinforced beam, the effort of solving the cubic equation only provides the slightly larger moment arm (31.9 in.) compared with the ideal jd (31.5 in.); thus an approximate value of the A_s required may be determined from the following formula:

$$A_s \begin{pmatrix} \text{in } underreinforced \\ \text{sections only} \end{pmatrix} = \frac{M_w}{(\text{allowable } f_s)(\text{design constant } j)(\text{actual } d)}$$

$$\text{(4.8.6)}$$

For the present problem,

$$A_s = \frac{457(12)}{24(0.875)(36)} = 7.25 \text{ sq in.}$$

This value of A_s is very close to its correct value using the cubic equation, and the error is on the safe side.

The A_s required in an *underreinforced* section with tension reinforcement only is usually determined from Eq. (4.8.6). In practical design the only time the cubic solution value for the moment arm is used is when it is readily available from design aids.

For *overreinforced* sections, however, Eq. (4.8.6) should *never* be used. For instance, had it been used in Example 4.8.2, the A_s required would have been $(457)(12)/[24(0.875)(30)] = 8.7$ sq in., which is far from the correct value of 11.7 sq in.

EXAMPLE 4.8.4   For $f'_c = 4000$ psi and $f_y = 60,000$ psi, compare the reinforcement ratio ρ for an ideally reinforced beam (working stress) with the maximum ρ permitted in strength design (Chap. 3).

Solution: (a) For the ideally reinforced beam, $f_c = 0.45 f'_c$ and $f_s = 24,000$ psi. Using Eq. (4.8.3), with $k = 0.375$ (see Ex. 4.8.1)

$$\text{ideal } \rho = \frac{k \text{ (allowable } f_c)}{2 \text{ (allowable } f_s)}$$

$$= \frac{0.375(0.45)(4000)}{2(24,000)} = 0.0141$$

(b) For strength design, maximum ρ for a singly reinforced beam is obtained from Table 3.5.1,

$$\text{max } \rho = 0.0283$$

In general, the ideally reinforced value of ρ is approximately one-half of the maximum permitted by the strength method. Other values for the ideal reinforcement ratio are given in Table 4.8.1.

Table 4.8.1

Ratio ρ for Ideally Reinforced Rectangular Beams According to Working Stress Method[a]

f_y		$f'_c = 3000\ psi$ $(21\ N/mm^2)$ $n = 9$	$f'_c = 3500\ psi$ $(24\ N/mm^2)$ $n = 8.5$	$f'_c = 4000\ psi$ $(28\ N/mm^2)$ $n = 8$	$f'_c = 5000\ psi$ $(35\ N/mm^2)$ $n = 7$
(psi)	(N/mm^2)				
40,000	280	0.0128	0.0158	0.0188	0.0248
50,000	350	0.0128	0.0158	0.0188	0.0248
60,000	410	0.0095	0.0117	0.0141	0.0186

[a] Note: S.I. equivalents are approximate, given to two significant figures.

4.9 Design of Rectangular Sections in Bending with Both Tension and Compression Reinforcement

When the size of a rectangular section is limited to given values and the bending moment is decidedly larger than the resisting moment of the section if ideally reinforced, the working stress method indicates the use of both tension and compression reinforcement. This would, in effect, restrict the amount of tension steel to about 0.40 to 0.60 of the maximum permitted in the strength method. The only unknowns in such a case are the values of the tension steel A_s and the compression steel A'_s. In practice there may be complications as to whether all the required A_s can be placed in one layer within the width of the section, because the effective depth d will have to be further reduced from the available h if two layers of steel become necessary. In this discussion it is assumed that the effective depth d is given, and this will be measured from the extreme compressive face to the centroid of the tension steel, regardless of the number of layers used.

The "two-couple" method is commonly used to determine the required values of A_s and A'_s in a doubly reinforced section. In this method the bending moment is considered equal to the sum of two resisting couples, one of which is provided by an ideally reinforced section with tension steel only, and the other by the compression steel and the remainder of the tension steel. Thus the section with compression steel is designed as an ideally reinforced section in that the compression steel and the extra tension steel for the second resisting couple are so proportioned that the neutral axis is maintained in the ideally reinforced position. By referring to Fig. 4.9.1, the procedure for determining A_s and A'_s is as follows:

1. Compute $M_{w1} = Rbd^2$.
2. Compute $A_{s1} = \rho bd$ and check with $A_{s1} = M_{w1}/[(\text{allowable } f_s)(jd)]$.
3. Compute $M_{w2} = M_w - M_{w1}$.
4. Compute $C_2 = T_2 = M_{w2}/(d - d')$.
5. Compute $A_{s2} = T_2/\text{allowable } f_s$.

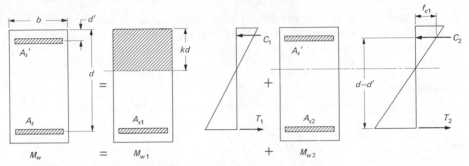

Fig. 4.9.1
Two-couple method for doubly reinforced sections.

6. Compute $A_s = A_{s1} + A_{s2}$.
7. Compute $f_{c1} = $ (allowable f_c)$(kd - d')/kd$.
8. Compare $2nf_{c1}$ with allowable f_s.
9. Compute $A'_s = C_2/[(2n - 1)f_{c1}]$ if $2nf_{c1} < $ allowable f_s;
   compute $A'_s = C_2/$(allowable $f_s - f_{c1}$) if $2nf_{c1} > $ allowable f_s.

Steps 1 to 6 are self-explanatory. Steps 7 to 9 will now be explained.

In a rectangular section with tension reinforcement only, concrete alone takes the compression. In a doubly reinforced section, concrete and steel act together to take the compression. If concrete and steel were both elastic, that is, if all deformation occurred at the instant when load was applied and disappeared when the load was removed, the method of transformed section should still apply; that is, the compression steel would be replaced by an equivalent concrete area equal to n times its actual area. However, as discussed in Sec. 1.10 concrete under stress deforms (creeps) with time and it also is subject to shrinkage over a period of time. These time-dependent effects do not occur in the steel. Hence as concrete continues to deform, even at or below its allowable working stress, there is a continuous transfer of load from concrete to steel. In order that the straight-line variation of stress across the depth of the section may be applied to doubly reinforced sections, one way of approximating the effect of this transfer of load is to increase the equivalent concrete area of compression steel to more than n times the actual steel area.

An effective modular ratio of $2n$ is permitted by ACI-Appendix B.5.5 when transforming the compression reinforcement into equivalent concrete area for *stress computations*. The ACI provision means actually that the stress in the compression reinforcement in an elastic analysis is $2nf_{c1}$ (see Fig. 4.9.1), but it may not exceed the allowable f_s. This accounts approximately for the transfer of load to the compression steel, but also prevents one from assuming a compression capacity of steel that exceeds its tensile capacity. Thus steps 7 and 8 are explained.

The compression steel actually displaces some concrete area which has already been counted on in taking the internal force C_1 in the first resisting couple. Thus the internal force C_2 represents the excess from the compression reinforcement over that required to replenish the little force $f_{c1}A'_s$ already included in the internal force C_1; or $C_2 = (2nf_{c1}$ or allowable f_s, whichever is smaller) $A'_s - f_{c1}A'_s$. The expressions in step 9 are obtained by solving the above equation for A'_s.

EXAMPLE 4.9.1 Given $M_w = 105$ ft-kips, $f'_c = 3000$ psi, Grade 40 steel, and the ACI Code, determine A_s and A'_s (if any) required if $b = 13$ in., $d = 16$ in., and $d' = 2.5$ in.

Solution: According to ACI-Appendix B.3, $n = 8$, allowable $f_s = 20,000$ psi, and allowable $f_c = 1350$ psi. Design constants are $k = 0.378$, $j = 0.874$, $\rho = 0.0128$, $R = 223$ psi.

$$M_{w1} = Rbd^2 = 223(13)\frac{(16)^2}{12,000} = 61.8 \text{ ft-kips}$$

$$A_{s1} = 0.0128(13)(16) = 2.66 \text{ sq in.}$$

$$A_{s1} = \frac{M_{w1}}{f_s jd} = \frac{61.8(12)}{(20)(0.874)(16)} = 2.65 \text{ sq in.}$$

$$M_{w2} = M_w - M_{w1} = 105.0 - 61.8 = 43.2 \text{ ft-kips}$$

$$C_2 = T_2 = \frac{M_{w2}}{d - d'} = \frac{43.2(12)}{16 - 2.5} = 38.4 \text{ kips}$$

$$A_{s2} = \frac{T_2}{f_s} = \frac{38.4}{20} = 1.92 \text{ sq in.}$$

$$A_s = A_{s1} + A_{s2} = 2.65 + 1.92 = 4.57 \text{ sq in.} \qquad \text{(tension steel)}$$
$$kd = 0.378(16) = 6.05 \text{ in.}$$

$$f_{c1} = 1350\frac{6.05 - 2.50}{6.05} = 792 \text{ psi}$$

$$2nf_{c1} = 2(9)(792) = 14,260 \text{ psi} < 20,000 \text{ psi} \qquad \text{(max allowable)}$$

which means that the use of $2n$ is acceptable.

$$A'_s = \frac{C_2}{(2n - 1)f_{c1}} = \frac{38.4}{(17)(0.792)} = 2.85 \text{ sq in.} \qquad \text{(compression steel)}$$

4.10 Investigation for Safety of Rectangular Sections in Bending with Both Tension and Compression Reinforcement

The investigation for safety of a rectangular section in bending with both tension and compression reinforcement is complicated by the provision that the stress in the latter must be either $2nf_{c1}$ or allowable f_s, whichever is smaller. On the other hand when calculating deflections, $2n$ should not be used in the computation of moment of inertia of the transformed area because creep and shrinkage (time-dependent effects) are accounted for in a different way (see Chap. 14 on deflections).

In making the investigation, a trial transformed section is first assumed by amplifying the compression steel area $2n$ times and the tension steel area n times in order to arrive at their respective equivalent areas in concrete. Part of the equivalent concrete area of the compression steel is to substitute for the concrete area displaced by the compression steel; thus the additional equivalent concrete area of the compression steel A'_s is only $(2n - 1)A'_s$. After the centroidal axis of this trial transformed section is located, it is then possible to determine the applicable stress diagram, on which either the allowable f_c or the allowable f_s/n is attained. If the value of $2nf_{c1}$, in which f_{c1} is the concrete stress at the level of the compression steel, is smaller than the allowable f_s, the trial transformed section is confirmed, and subsequent calculations may follow.

If, however, the value of $2nf_{c1}$ on the basis of the trial transformed section exceeds the allowable f_s, then the equivalent concrete area of the compression steel should be taken less than $2nA'_s$. Thus the trial transformed section is no longer valid. At this point it is best to determine the correct location of the neutral axis (which will be very close to that of the trial transformed section) by equating the total compressive force to the total tensile force. The additional compressive force owing to the presence of the compression steel, in this instance, is (allowable $f_s - f_{c1})A'_s$.

EXAMPLE 4.10.1   Given $f'_c = 4000$ psi, Grade 40 steel, and the ACI Code, determine the allowable bending moment that the doubly reinforced section as shown in Fig. 4.10.1a may carry.

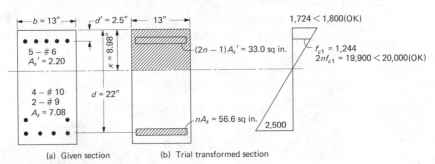

(a) Given section   (b) Trial transformed section

Fig. 4.10.1
Section for Example 4.10.1.

Solution: According to ACI-Appendix B.3, $n = 8$, allowable $f_s = 20,000$ psi, and allowable $f_c = 1800$ psi.

(a) Determine the centroidal axis of the trial transformed section.

$$\frac{13x^2}{2} + 33.0(x - 2.5) = 8(7.08)(22 - x)$$

Solving for x,

$$x = 8.98 \text{ in.}$$

(b) Compare $2nf_{c1}$ with the allowable f_s:

$$2nf_{c1} = 2(8)(1724)\left(\frac{8.98 - 2.50}{8.98}\right) = 19,900 \text{ psi} < 20,000 \text{ psi}$$

The trial transformed section is confirmed.

(c) Determine the allowable bending moment by the internal-couple method.

$$C_1 = \tfrac{1}{2}(1.724)(13)(8.98) = 100.6 \text{ kips}$$
$$C_2 = 33(1.244) = 41.0 \text{ kips}$$
$$T = 20(7.08) = 141.6 \text{ kips}$$
$$\text{allowable } M_w = 100.6(22 - 8.98/3)\tfrac{1}{12} + 41.0(19.5)\tfrac{1}{12} = 226 \text{ ft-kips}$$

(d) Check the allowable bending moment using the transformed section method:

$$I_{cr} = \tfrac{1}{3}(13)(8.98)^3 + 33.0(8.98 - 2.5)^2 + 56.6(22.0 - 8.98)^2$$
$$= 3140 + 1390 + 9600 = 14,100 \text{ in.}^4$$

$$M_w = \frac{f_c I_{cr}}{x} = \frac{1.724(14,100)}{8.98(12)} = 226 \text{ ft-kips}$$

or

$$M_w = \frac{f_s I_{cr}}{n(d - x)} = \frac{2.50(14,100)}{(22.0 - 8.98)12} = 226 \text{ ft-kips} \qquad \text{(Check)}$$

It requires mentioning that unit stresses used in the working stress method in sections with compression steel are *nominal stresses*, because the actual stresses depend on the entire loading history of the beam; for example, how much of the load is permanent, how long it has been on, and how many times it has been loaded and unloaded. Under any given load, the portion of the compressive force actually carried by the concrete and the portion carried by the steel are nearly impossible to determine, although the total calculated compressive force is relatively correct.

4.11 Serviceability—Deflections

Whether safety of a beam or floor system is established by the working stress method (ACI "alternate design method") or by the ultimate strength method (ACI "strength method"), excessive deflection may make the system unserviceable. When flexural members support or are attached to partitions and other construction likely to be damaged by large deflection, deflection computations *under service-load conditions* will usually be necessary. Even in situations in which excessive deflection may not crack or damage anything, large noticeable deflection is psychologically disturbing to humans.

For the many ordinary situations of "members not supporting or attached to partitions or other construction likely to be damaged by large deflections," ACI-Table 9.5(a) provides minimum thickness for beams and one-way slabs unless deflections are computed. When the minimum thickness of ACI-Table 9.5(a) is exceeded, deflection must be computed and must satisfy the limits of ACI-Table 9.5(b).

Since the deflection that concerns the designer is a service-load phenomenon, the elastic beam properties are a necessary part of the computations. Properties such as neutral-axis location and moment of inertia involve the basic assumptions of the working stress method, and hence are dealt with in this chapter.

Since the applied service-load moment usually far exceeds the moment that causes the tension concrete to crack, the so-called properties of the "cracked section" are needed. In earlier sections of this chapter the neutral axis of the cracked section has been located by either (a) the stress-solid internal-couple method, or (b) the transformed section method (see Secs. 4.3 and 4.6).

Deflection calculations involve using a formula of the type,

$$\Delta = K \frac{M_w L^2}{E_c I_e} \tag{4.11.1}$$

where

K = constant that depends on the loading and support conditions

L = span length

M_w = maximum service-load moment

E_c = concrete modulus of elasticity

I_e = effective moment of inertia

The effective moment of inertia I_e used by the ACI Code (ACI-9.5) involves both the gross section moment of inertia I_g (commonly without steel) and the transformed cracked section moment of inertia I_{cr}. The following example shows the computation of the moment of inertia of the transformed cracked section for a section having both tension and compression steel.

EXAMPLE 4.11.1. Determine the moment of inertia of the transformed cracked section to be used in deflection calculation for the doubly reinforced section shown in Fig. 4.11.1, using $f'_c = 4000$ psi.

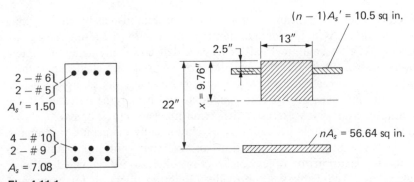

Fig. 4.11.1
Doubly reinforced section of Example 4.11.1.

Solution: According to ACI-Appendix B.5.4, $n = 8$. The implication of the ACI Code is that for deflection computation the modular ratio n should be used for obtaining the equivalent concrete area of both tension and compression steel. The time-dependent effects are accounted for by putting a multiplier on the elastic deflection, rather than by changing the modular ratio to $2n$ for compression steel, as was done in Secs. 4.9 and 4.10.

(a) Locate neutral axis.

$$\frac{13x^2}{2} + 10.5(x - 2.5) = 56.64(22 - x)$$

Solving for x,

$$x = 9.76 \text{ in.}$$

(b) Determine transformed cracked section moment of inertia.

$$I_{cr} = \tfrac{1}{3}(13)(9.76)^3 + 10.5(9.76 - 2.5)^2 + 56.64(22 - 9.76)^2$$
$$= 4030 + 550 + 8480 = 13,100 \text{ in.}^4$$

The methods and underlying concepts relating to the calculation of deflection are treated in Chap. 14, which is devoted entirely to that subject.

4.12 Serviceability—Flexural Crack Control for Beams and One-Way Slabs

Cracking in concrete is generally the result of the following actions [1,2]: (1) volumetric change, including that due to drying shrinkage, creep under sustained load, thermal stresses, and chemical incompatibility of concrete components; (2) internal or external direct stress due to continuity, reversible load, long-time deflection, camber in prestressed concrete, or differential movement in structures; and (3) flexural stress due to bending.

Visible cracking is generally initiated by either internal microcracking (volumetric change would usually induce this type) or flexural microcracks. Flexural microcracks are surface cracks that are not visible except by careful close investigation and are generally initiated by flexural stress. Once flexural microcracks have formed, a slight increase in flexural load causes these cracks to open up suddenly to measurable widths. An excellent bibliography on cracking is contained in an ACI Committee 224 report [1].

The increasing use of high-strength steels and the accelerated trend toward using the strength method for design have brought concern for control of cracking. Using the strength method with Grade 60 steel, the service-load stress may be as high as 60% of the yield stress. This may be shown by taking the nominal safety factor as the average overload factor (say 1.55) divided by $\phi(0.90)$. Thus

$$f_s \text{ (service conditions)} = \frac{f_y}{1.55/0.90} = 0.58 f_y$$

This means that under some service-load conditions, the stress in steel (say, $0.60 f_y = 36,000$ psi) may be 50% or more greater than service-load stresses (say $f_s = 20,000$ psi) that exist in many older structures designed by the working stress method.

Because of the compatibility in strain between concrete and steel, the 50% or more increase in steel strain would seem to indicate the same percentage increase in crack width. Furthermore, even at low steel stress levels, say 9000 psi (63 N/mm^2), flexural microcracking has been found to occur [2]. As larger cracks form, the effects of a corrosive environment may be detrimental to the steel. Such factors as humidity, salt air, alternate wetting and drying, or freezing and thawing may accelerate corrosion and contribute to concrete deterioration in the vicinity of large width cracks. Wide cracks may also be unsightly and contribute to doubt about structural safety. Although cracking cannot be expected to be eliminated, it is generally more desirable to have many fine hair cracks than a few wide cracks. Thus crack control is a mather of controlling the distribution and size of cracks rather than eliminating them.

To control cracking it is better to use several smaller bars at moderate spacing than larger bars of equivalent area. The objective is therefore one of distributing the reinforcement in the concrete tension zone; hence the words of the title of ACI-10.6, "Distribution of flexural reinforcement," which contains the crack control provisions for beams and one-way slabs. Control of cracking is particularly important when reinforcement with a yield stress in excess of 40,000 psi (280 N/mm^2) is used; or when reinforcement percentages exceed the amount of reinforcement traditionally used in the working stress method. For the strength method the comparable percentage is about $0.375\rho_b$ (one-half the maximum permitted amount).

Good bar arrangement in the cross section will usually lead to adequate crack control even when Grade 60 bars are used. Entirely satisfactory structures have been built, particularly in Europe, using design yield stresses exceeding 80,000 psi (560 N/mm^2), which is the current specified limit in ACI-9.4.

Extensive laboratory studies [1,3–13] have verified the generally accepted belief that crack width is proportional to steel stress. Two other significant variables have been found to be the thickness of concrete cover and the area of concrete surrounding each individual reinforcing bar in the zone of maximum tension.

The ACI Code provisions (ACI-10.6.4) are based on the Gergely-Lutz [6] expression for crack width, as follows:

$$w = C\beta_h f_s \sqrt[3]{d_c A} \tag{4.12.1}$$

where, referring to Fig. 4.12.1,

w = crack width at the tension face of the beam (in. or mm)

$\beta_h = h_2/h_1$, the ratio of the distances to the working stress neutral axis from the extreme tension fiber and from the centroid of the main tension reinforcement

f_s = service-load stress in the steel (ksi or N/mm^2)

d_c = thickness of concrete cover measured from the extreme tension fiber to the center of the bar located closest thereto (in. or mm)

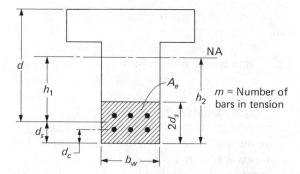

Fig. 4.12.1
Dimensional notation for Gergely-Lutz equation (4.12.1).

$A = A_e/m$, effective tension area of concrete surrounding the main tension reinforcing bars and having the same centroid as that reinforcement, divided by the number of bars (sq in. or mm²)

$m =$ number of bars; for different sizes use $m = A_s/(d_b$ for largest bar)

$C =$ an experimental constant (76×10^{-6} sq in./kip for U.S. Customary units or 11.0×10^{-6} mm²/N for S.I. units)

Equation (4.12.1) represents the most probable maximum crack width on the bottom face of a beam. Because of considerable scatter expected, even under carefully controlled laboratory conditions, crack width calculations should serve only as a guide to good detailing of bars and not as values to use for comparison with measured cracks in a building that is in service. Consequently Eq. (4.12.1) has been converted into a form in which a simple calculation could be made to arrive at reasonable reinforcing details as indicated by experience and laboratory tests, without actually emphasizing crack width. Thus dividing Eq. (4.12.1) by $C\beta_h$, the quantity z is defined,

$$z = f_s\sqrt[3]{d_c A} = \frac{w}{C\beta_h} \qquad (4.12.2)$$

For simplification β_h may be taken at an approximate value of 1.2. In order to have numerical values for the quantity $w/(C\beta_h)$ in the ACI Code, crack widths have been limited to 0.016 and 0.013 in. (0.41 and 0.33 mm) for interior and exterior exposure, respectively. Substitution of these values in Eq. (4.12.2) gives

$$z_{\text{limit}} = \frac{16}{0.076(1.2)} = 175 \text{ kips/in. (interior) (30.6 kN/mm)}$$

$$z_{\text{limit}} = \frac{13}{0.076(1.2)} = 142.5 \approx 145 \text{ kips/in. (exterior) (25.4 kN/mm)}$$

which are limits specified in ACI-10.6.4 when the design yield stress f_y for tension reinforcement exceeds 40,000 psi (280 N/mm²).

The Gergely-Lutz expression has been found [14,15] to apply also to one-way slabs (wide beams). However, the average value for $\beta_h = h_2/h_1$ (see Fig. 4.12.1) is about 1.35 for floor slabs, rather than 1.2 which applies to beams. Accordingly for the same crack control on one-way slabs as for beams the limits of z should be reduced by the factor $1.20/1.35$ [i.e., z should be limited to 155 kips/in. (27.1 kN/mm) for interior exposure and about 130 kips/in. (22.9 kN/mm) for exterior exposure].

For two-way slabs, the above crack control procedure and limiting z values do not apply; other recommendations are given in the ACI Committee 224 Report [1]. Chapter 16 on two-way slabs also contains brief treatment.

When structures are "subject to very aggressive exposure or designed to be watertight," the requirements for z are not sufficient (ACI-10.6.5). For guidance ACI Committee 224 gives reduced permissible crack widths for various exposure conditions. Their values would reduce the z limitation to as little as 45 kips/in. (7.9 kN/mm) for water-retaining structures.

In recognition of the undesirability of having to make an additional analysis using working stress method to determine f_s for use in Eq. (4.12.2) when the strength method is otherwise being used, ACI-10.6.4 permits taking f_s as 60% of the specified yield stress f_y in lieu of using the working stress computation. This will be a conservative approach because it will frequently overestimate the stress f_s. When a steel percentage approximately equal to that in an ideally reinforced section in the working stress method is used (corresponds in strength method to $\rho \approx 0.375\rho_b$, the value of f_s for Grade 60 steel would be about 24,000 psi which is only 40% of the yield stress.

EXAMPLE 4.12.1   Check the crack control provisions of the ACI Code against the cross section selected in Example 4.8.1 (Fig. 4.8.2a). The selected beam has $b = 18$ in., $h = 36$ in., 8-#9 bars in two layers, #3 stirrups, 1.5 in. clear cover at bottom, and 1 in. clear between layers; $f'_c = 4000$ psi and Grade 60 steel are used.

Solution: The crack control provision of the ACI Code is given under the heading "Distribution of flexural reinforcement in beams and one-way slabs." Compute z of ACI-10.6.4:

$$z = f_s \sqrt[3]{d_c A}$$

$f_s = 24.2$ ksi (computed in Example 4.8.1) (167 N/mm^2)

d_c = distance to centroid of bottom layer

$\quad = 1.5$ (cover) $+ 0.375$ (stirrup) $+ 0.564$ (bar radius)

$\quad = 2.44$ in. (62 mm)

$A = A_e/m$

$A_e = 2d_s b$

d_s = distance to centroid of tension bar group

$\quad = 1.5$ (cover) $+ 0.375$ (stirrup) $+ 1.128$ (bar diam.) $+ 0.5$

$\quad = 3.50$ in. (89 mm)

$$A_e = 2(3.50)18 = 126 \text{ sq in. } (81,300 \text{ mm}^2)$$

$$m = \text{number of tension bars} = 8$$

$$A = 126/8 = 15.75 \text{ sq in./bar } (10,160 \text{ mm}^2/\text{bar})$$

$$z = 24.2\sqrt[3]{2.44(15.73)} = 81.5 \text{ kips/in.}$$

or in metric units

$$z = 167\sqrt[3]{62(10,160)}\tfrac{1}{1000} = 14.3 \text{ kN/mm}$$

Since this does not exceed the 175 and 145 kips/in. (30.6 and 25.4 kN/mm) allowed (ACI-10.6.4) for interior and exterior exposure, respectively, the selected cross section is acceptable.

EXAMPLE 4.12.2 Examine the crack control situation of Example 4.12.1 if 2-#18 bars had been used instead of 8-#9.

Solution: Referring to Fig. 4.12.2 for this cross section

$$d_c = d_s = 1.5 + 0.375 + \frac{2.257}{2} = 3.00 \text{ in.}$$

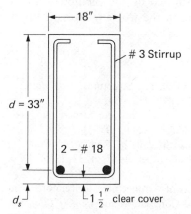

Fig. 4.12.2
Cross section for Example 4.12.2
(an unsatisfactory bar selection).

The steel stress f_s should be computed using elastic properties of the cross section, as follows:

$$18x\left(\frac{x}{2}\right) = 8.0(8)(33.0 - x)$$

$$x = 12.17 \text{ in.}$$

$$f_s = \frac{M_w}{A_s(\text{arm})} = \frac{457(12)}{8.0(33 - 12.17/3)} = 23.7 \text{ ksi}$$

If the elastic analysis is not made, f_s is to be taken at $0.60f_y$ which is 36.0 ksi (ACI-10.6.4).

$$A_e = 2(3.0)18 = 108 \text{ sq in.}$$

$$m = 2$$

$$A = \frac{A_e}{m} = \frac{108}{2} = 54 \text{ sq in./bar}$$

$$z = f_s\sqrt[3]{d_c A} = 23.7\sqrt[3]{3.0(54)}$$
$$= 129 \text{ kips/in.} < 145 \text{ kips/in.} \qquad \text{OK}$$

Even this generally undesirable bar arrangement (see guidelines of Sec. 3.7) seems to satisfy the crack control provision. If $0.60f_y$ had been used instead of the computed value for f_s,

$$z = 36.0\sqrt[3]{3.0(54)} = 196 \text{ kips/in.} > 175 \text{ kips/in.} \qquad \text{NG}$$

Because of the low allowable stresses in the working stress method, it does not seem likely that crack control will be a problem when that method is used. When the ACI "strength design method" is used, the computed flexural stress at service load may be significantly higher, because the maximum percentage of reinforcement permitted in that method is nearly twice that for the ideally reinforced section in the working stress method.

SELECTED REFERENCES

1. ACI Committee 224. "Control of Cracking in Concrete Structures, "*ACI Journal, Proceedings*, **69,** December 1972, 717–752. Disc. **70,** 430–434.
2. Edward G. Nawy. "Crack Control in Reinforced Concrete Structures," *ACI Journal, Proceedings*, **65,** October 1968, 825–836. Disc. **66,** 308–311.
3. Bengt B. Broms. "Crack Width and Crack Spacing in Reinforced Concrete Members," *ACI Journal, Proceedings*, **62,** October 1965, 1237–1256. Disc. 1749–1755.
4. Bengt B. Broms and LeRoy A. Lutz, "Effects of Arrangement of Reinforcement on Crack Width and Spacing of Reinforced Concrete Members," *ACI Journal, Proceedings*, **62,** November 1965, 1395–1410. Disc 1807–1812.
5. J. Ferry-Borges. *Cracking and Deformability of Reinforced Concrete Beams*, Report. Lisbon: Laboratorio Nacional de Engeharia Civil, December 1965 (44 pp.).
6. Peter Gergely and LeRoy A. Lutz. "Maximum Crack Width in Reinforced Concrete Flexural Members," *Causes, Mechanism, and Control of Cracking in Concrete*, SP-20. Detroit: American Concrete Institute, 1968 (pp. 87–117).
7. P. H. Kaar and Eivind Hognestad. "High Strength Bars as Concrete Reinforcement, Part 7; Control of Cracking in T-Beams Flanges," *Journal PCA Research and Development Laboratories*, **7**(1), January 1965, 42–53. Also PCA Development Department Bulletin D84.
8. Paul H. Kaar. "High Strength Bars as Concrete Reinforcement, Part 8: Similitude in Flexural Cracking of T-Beams Flanges," *Journal PCA Research and Development Laboratories*, **8**(2), May 1966, 2–12.
9. G. D. Base, J. B. Reed, A. W. Beeby, and H. P. J. Taylor. *An Investigation of the Crack Control Characteristics of Various Types of Bar in Reinforced Concrete*

Beams. Research Report No. 18. London: Cement and Concrete Association, December 1966, (44 pp.).

10. LeRoy A. Lutz, Nand K. Sharma, and Peter Gergely, "Increase in Crack Width in Reinforced Concrete Beams Under Sustained Loading," *ACI Journal, Proceedings*, **64**, September 1967, 538–546.

11. Paul H. Kaar. "An Approach to the Control of Cracking in Reinforced Concrete," *Causes, Mechanism, and Control of Cracking in Concrete*, SP-20. Detroit: American Concrete Institute, 1968, (pp. 141–157).

12. Mete A. Sozen and William L. Gamble. "Strength and Cracking Characteristics of Beams with #14 and #18 Bars Spliced with Mechanical Splices," *ACI Journal, Proceedings*, **66**, December 1969, 949–956.

13. A. W. Beeby. "The Prediction and Control of Flexural Cracking in Reinforced Concrete Members," *Cracking, Deflection, and Ultimate Load of Concrete Slab Systems*, SP–30. Detroit: American Concrete Institute, 1971, (pp. 55–75).

14. John P. Lloyd, Hassen M. Rejali, and Clyde E. Kesler. "Crack Control in One-Way Slabs Reinforced With Deformed Wire Fabric," *ACI Journal, Proceedings*, **66**, May 1969, 366–376.

15. A. W. Beeby. "An Investigation of Cracking in Slabs Spanning One Way," Technical Report No. TRA 433, Cement and Concrete Association, London, April 1970, (32 pp).

PROBLEMS

All problems are to be done in accordance with the ACI Code "alternate design method" (i.e., working stress method) unless otherwise indicated. When selecting bars be certain that they fit into the beam width (see Table 3.7.2) and allow for #3 stirrups (for metric use 10 mm diameter) around longitudinal bars #10 (32 mm) and smaller, and #4 stirrups (12 mm) around longitudinal bars larger than #10.

The metric units in parenthesis provide a problem approximately the same as that in U.S. Customary units; the conversions have been adjusted so that given information indicates comparable precision to that of the original given data. For all metric unit problems, consider the ACI allowable stresses for steel to be $f_s = 140$ N/mm^2 for $f_y = 280$ N/mm^2 and for $f_y = 350$ N/mm^2; and $f_s = 165$ N/mm^2 for $f_y = 420$ N/mm^2.

4.1 A reinforced concrete beam is 12 in. wide and 22 in. in overall depth, with 3-#9 bars centered $2\frac{1}{2}$ in. from the bottom of the beam. The moduli of elasticity are $E_c = 2.9 \times 10^6$ psi and $E_s = 29 \times 10^6$ psi. Determine the maximum stresses in the steel and the concrete (f_s and f_c max) if the applied bending moment is 85 ft-kips. **(a)** Use the stress-solid internal-couple method. **(b)** Use the flexure-formula method with transformed section. (Beam: width = 300 mm, depth = 560 mm, 3–28-mm bars centered 60 mm from bottom. $E_c = 20,000$ N/mm^2; $E_s = 200,000$ N/mm^2; $M_w = 115$ kN-m.)

4.2 What is the maximum allowable bending moment for the beam of Prob. 4.1 if the maximum allowable stresses are $f_s = 22,000$ psi and $f_c = 1200$ psi? ($f_s = 150$ N/mm^2; $f_c = 8.3$ N/mm^2.)

4.3 What is the maximum allowable bending moment for the beam of Prob. 4.1 if the maximum allowable stresses are $f_s = 19,000$ psi and $f_c = 1350$ psi? ($f_s = 130$ N/mm^2; $f_c = 9.5$ N/mm^2.)

4.4 Consider a beam with a 12-in. width and an effective depth of 19.5 in. which has 3-#7 bars in the tension face. The concrete has $f'_c = 3000$ psi, and the steel has a minimum specified yield strength of 40,000 psi.

(a) Determine the allowable bending moment.
(b) Is the beam underreinforced, ideally reinforced, or overreinforced?
(Beam: $b = 300$ mm; $d = 500$ mm; 3–20-mm diameter bars. $f'_c = 21$ N/mm^2; $f_y = 280$ N/mm^2.)

4.5 For the beam of Prob. 4.4, use 3-#10 bars instead of 3-#7.
(a) Determine the allowable bending moment.
(b) Is the beam underreinforced, ideally reinforced, or overreinforced?
(Use 3–32-mm diameter bars.)

4.6 What are the theoretically required effective depth and area of tension reinforcement for a rectangular beam 16 in. wide that is to resist a service-load moment of 400 ft-kips? Use $f'_c = 4000$ psi and $f_y = 60,000$ psi. ($b = 400$ mm; $M_w = 540$ kN-m; $f'_c = 28$ N/mm^2; and $f_y = 420$ N/mm^2.)

4.7 What are the required width and the required area of tension steel for a rectangular beam with a 28-in. effective depth that is to resist a service-load moment of 400 ft-kips? Use $f'_c = 4000$ psi and $f_y = 60,000$ psi. ($d = 710$ mm; $M_w = 55$ t.m; $f'_c = 280$ kgf/cm^2; and $f_y = 4200$ kgf/cm^2.)

4.8 A beam having a 12-in. width is to carry service-load moments of 70 ft-kips live load and 40 ft-kips dead load. Using $f'_c = 4000$ psi and Grade 50 steel, select the overall cross-section dimensions and select bars. Show sketch of final cross section, and check stresses. ($b = 300$ mm; $M_L = 95$ kN-m; $M_D = 54$ kN-m; $f'_c = 28$ N/mm^2; $f_y = 350$ N/mm^2.)

4.9 Design a reinforced concrete beam to carry a live load moment of 225 ft-kips on a simply supported span of 20 ft. Use $f'_c = 4000$ psi and $f'_y = 60,000$ psi. Use a beam width of 14 in. Show a sketch of the cross section with selected bars. Check stresses. ($M_L = 305$ kN-m; span $= 6.1$ m; $f'_c = 28$ N/mm^2; $f_y = 420$ N/mm^2; $b = 350$ mm.)

4.10 In order to reuse forms and eliminate multiple framing details, a reinforced concrete cross section 15 in. wide × 30 in. deep overall is to be used in a location where the maximum live-load moment is 100 ft-kips. The simply supported span is 24 ft. Use $f'_c = 3000$ psi and Grade 40 steel. Assume distance from the center of the bars to the bottom of the beam is 2.5 in. (a) Determine steel requirement using "exact" method. (b) Determine steel requirement using "approximate" method. Select bars, show placement in cross section, and check stresses. ($b = 380$ mm; $h = 760$ mm; $M_L = 136$ kN-m; span $= 7.3$ m; $f'_c = 21$ N/mm^2; $f_y = 280$ N/mm^2; cover $= 60$ mm.)

4.11 Suppose the cross section of Prob. 4.10 is to be used where the live-load moment is 200 ft-kips and the simply supported span is 26 ft. Select bars and show placement in the cross section for reinforcement in the tension face only. Check the stresses on the chosen section. ($M_L = 270$ kN-m; span $= 8$ m.)

4.12 Design the cross section for a beam to carry a live load of 5 kips/ft on a span of 28 ft. Use $f'_c = 3000$ psi and Grade 60 steel. (See Sec. 3.7 for practical proportions.) Show sketch of chosen cross section with bar placement and check stresses. ($w_L = 7500$ kg/m; span $= 8.5$ m; $f'_c = 210$ kgf/cm^2; $f_y = 4200$ kgf/cm^2.)

4.13 Design a reinforced concrete simply supported one-way floor slab to carry a uniformly distributed live load of 175 psf on a span of 18 ft center to center of supports. Use $f'_c = 3000$ psi, and Grade 40 steel. Make design sketch and check stresses. (Note: ACI-7.12). ($w_L = 850$ kg/m^2; span $= 5.5$ m; $f'_c = 21$ N/mm^2; $f_y = 280$ N/mm^2.)

4.14 Determine the areas of tension and compression reinforcement (also select bars) required in a beam 20 in. wide with an effective depth of 29 in. to the centroid of the tension steel, if the beam is to carry a bending moment of 475 ft-kips. Assume that $d' = 2.5$ in. Use $f'_c = 4000$ psi and Grade 60 steel. ($b = 500$ mm; $d = 740$ mm; $M_w = 645$ kN-m; $d' = 60$ mm; $f'_c = 28$ N/mm^2; $f_y = 420$ N/mm^2.)

4.15 Redesign the beam of Prob. 4.11 using compression reinforcement that may be assumed to be centered at $2\frac{1}{2}$ in. (60 mm) from the compression face of the beam.

4.16 For the beam of the accompanying figure:
(a) Determine the allowable moment capacity M_w.
(b) Compute the transformed cracked section moment of inertia that would be needed for a deflection calculation.
Use concrete with $f'_c = 4000$ psi and Grade 60 steel. ($f'_c = 28$ N/mm^2; $f_y = 420$ N/mm^2.)

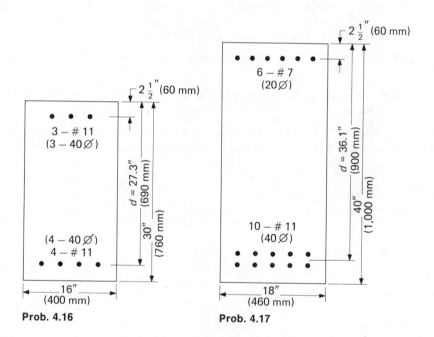

Prob. 4.16   **Prob. 4.17**

4.17 For the given beam of the accompanying figure compute the transformed cracked section moment of inertia I_{cr} that would be needed for a deflection calculation; that is, use modular ratio n (instead of $2n$) when transforming the compression steel. Use $f'_c = 4000$ psi and $f_y = 60,000$ psi. ($f'_c = 28$ N/mm^2; $f_y = 420$ N/mm^2.)

4.18 Design an irregular-shaped beam for a building whose floor system is composed of precast slabs. The 3-in. ledges are required for the support of the precast sections. The total moment to be carried is 50 ft-kips, and the cross section to be used is given in the accompanying figure. Because of forming costs, a large number of beams are being made with the same cross section. Use $f'_c = 3000$ psi and $f_y = 40,000$ psi.

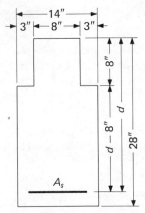

Prob. 4.18

4.19 Derive an equation for actual k (i.e., x/d) in terms of ρ and n for investigating rectangular sections with tension reinforcement only. Plot k versus ρ for $n = 9$ from $\rho = 0.005$ to 0.035 in increments of 0.005.

4.20 Check the ACI crack control provisions for the tension steel detail of Prob. 4.16.

4.21 Check the ACI crack control provisions for the tension steel detail of Prob. 4.17. Assume 1.5 in. (38 mm) clear cover and that a #3 stirrup is used.

4.22 Check the ACI crack control provisions for the tension steel details of the beams designed for whichever of Probs. 4.8 through 4.13 have already been worked.

5

Shear Strength, Inclined Cracking, and Shear Reinforcement

5.1 Introduction

In this chapter the shear strength of nonprestressed flexural members is treated. Effects of axial compression and tension are included in Sec. 5.13. Consideration is also given to the special requirements for deep beams (Sec. 5.14), brackets and corbels (Sec. 5.15), and the shear-friction concept (Sec. 5.16). Shear strength of prestressed concrete members is treated in Chap. 21. Shear effects arising from torsion and from its combination with bending or shear, or both, are treated in Chap. 19.

Considering the simple beam shown in Fig. 5.1.1, the bending moment M at section A-A causes compressive stresses in the concrete above the neutral axis, and tensile stresses in the reinforcement and in the concrete below the neutral axis had it not yet been cracked. To satisfy the vertical resolution equation of equilibrium, the summation of the vertical shear stresses across the section must be equal to the shear force V. Below the neutral axis there is nearly a state of pure shear as shown in Fig. 5.1.2 which gives rise to a

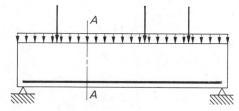
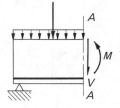

Fig. 5.1.1
Shear force and bending moment in a simple beam.

Inclined shear crack; test by D. R. Buettner at the University of Wisconsin, Madison.

tensile stress of equal magnitude on a 45° plane. This diagonal tension constitutes the main cause of inclined cracking. Thus the failures in beams commonly referred to as "shear failures" are actually tension failures at the inclined cracks. One of the earliest to recognize this was E. Morsch in Germany in the early 1900s [1].

The factors influencing shear strength and formation of inclined cracks are so numerous and complex that a definitive conclusion regarding the correct mechanism of inclined cracking that results from high shear is not yet agreed upon. Bresler and MacGregor [2] have introduced an excellent systematic correlation of the basic concepts, and this work has been expanded and updated by ACI–ASCE Committee 426 [3]. In this chapter the concepts

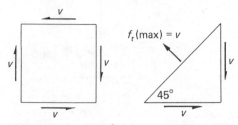

Fig. 5.1.2
Pure shear and principal tensile stress.

of horizontal and vertical shear, with the resulting principal tensile stress, are presented first so that the reader may gain a feeling for the potential direction of inclined cracks. Then follows a presentation of recent knowledge in regard to the variables affecting shear strength, leading up to the ACI Code provisions.

5.2 Shear Stress

A uniformly loaded simple beam is shown in Fig. 5.2.1. Consider the free body of the elemental block $abcd$, as shown in Fig. 5.2.1b, where kd is the general neutral-axis distance (not necessarily the ideal value used in Chap. 4). Horizontal force equilibrium requires

$$v_y b\, dz = C_2 - C_1 \tag{5.2.1}$$

in which v_y is the unit horizontal shear stress on a plane at a distance y from the neutral axis. In the working stress range,

$$C_1 = \tfrac{1}{2}(f_{c1} + f_{c1y})b(kd - y)$$

$$f_{c1y} = \frac{y}{kd}f_{c1}$$

$$C_1 = \frac{1}{2}f_{c1}\left(1 + \frac{y}{kd}\right)(kd - y)b = \frac{1}{2}f_{c1}bkd\left[1 - \left(\frac{y}{kd}\right)^2\right] \tag{5.2.2}$$

Dividing the bending moment M_1 on section 1-1 by the arm of the internal couple gives the full compressive force on section 1-1; or

$$\frac{M_1}{\text{arm}} = \frac{1}{2}f_{c1}b(kd)$$

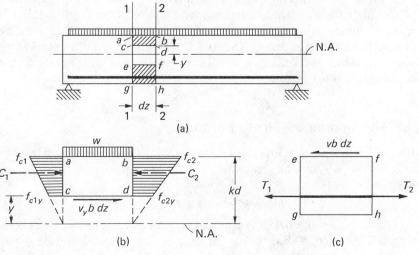

(a)

(b)

(c)

Fig. 5.2.1
Horizontal shear stress in a beam.

Substitution of f_{c1} from the above expression into Eq. (5.2.2) gives

$$C_1 = \frac{M_1}{\text{arm}}\left[1 - \frac{y^2}{(kd)^2}\right] \qquad (5.2.3)$$

Similarly,

$$C_2 = \frac{M_2}{\text{arm}}\left[1 - \frac{y^2}{(kd)^2}\right] \qquad (5.2.4)$$

Substituting Eqs. (5.2.3) and (5.2.4) into Eq. (5.2.1) gives

$$v_y = \left(\frac{M_2 - M_1}{dz}\right)\frac{1}{b(\text{arm})}\left[1 - \frac{y^2}{(kd)^2}\right] \qquad (5.2.5)$$

$$= \frac{V}{b(\text{arm})}\left[1 - \frac{y^2}{(kd)^2}\right]$$

Equation (5.2.5) is valid from $y = 0$ at the neutral axis to the extreme concrete compression fiber where $y = kd$. Proceeding from the extreme compression fiber to the neutral axis, the differential horizontal force $C_2 - C_1$ increases to a maximum. Thus at the neutral axis $y = 0$, Eq. (5.2.5) gives the maximum shear stress

$$v = \frac{V}{b(\text{arm})} \qquad (5.2.6)$$

During the years since the early 1900s until 1963, the rational philosophy was to reason that in regions where bending stress was low or where flexural cracks existed, a state of pure shear was assumed to exist. In such a case the maximum principal stress (see Fig. 5.1.2), a tensile stress acting at 45°, equals the shear stress. It was from this reasoning that the shear stress, as calculated from Eq. (5.2.6), was considered to represent the diagonal tensile stress. It should be mentioned that authoritative sources have always stated that the computed shear stress represented only a *measure of* diagonal tension rather than the actual tensile stress. The present attitude is that since the inclined cracking effects are complex, the "arm" in Eq. (5.2.6) may be considered as constant and represented by the effective depth d. Hence a nominal shear stress obtained by dividing the shear force by the effective area bd can be used in design. The ACI Code uses the term "nominal shear strength," which is taken as the product of the nominal shear stress and the beam web area $b_w d$.

5.3 The Combined-Stress Formula

If at a certain point below the neutral axis in a homogeneous beam the tensile stress is f_t and the shear stress is v, the principal tensile stress $f_t(\text{max})$ is given by

$$f_t(\text{max}) = \tfrac{1}{2}f_t + \sqrt{(\tfrac{1}{2}f_t)^2 + v^2} \qquad (5.3.1)$$

The derivation of Eq. (5.3.1) is available in most textbooks on elementary strength of materials. But because of its importance here, it will be shown again.

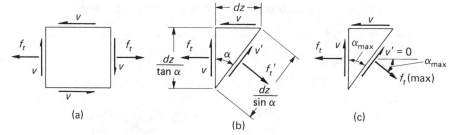

Fig. 5.3.1
Stress condition of an elemental block.

Using equilibrium of the forces acting on the free body in the directions of f'_t and v' shown in Fig. 5.3.1b and calling the width of the beam b,

$$f'_t\left(\frac{b\,dz}{\sin\alpha}\right) = f_t\left(\frac{b\,dz}{\tan\alpha}\right)\cos\alpha + v(b\,dz)\cos\alpha + v\left(\frac{b\,dz}{\tan\alpha}\right)\sin\alpha$$

$$v'\left(\frac{b\,dz}{\sin\alpha}\right) = f_t\left(\frac{b\,dz}{\tan\alpha}\right)\sin\alpha + v(b\,dz)\sin\alpha - v\left(\frac{b\,dz}{\tan\alpha}\right)\cos\alpha$$

from which

$$f'_t = \tfrac{1}{2}f_t(1 + \cos 2\alpha) + v\sin 2\alpha$$
$$v' = \tfrac{1}{2}f_t\sin 2\alpha - v\cos 2\alpha$$

The value of α_{max}; that is, α which makes f'_t maximum and at the same time makes v' zero, may be found by differentiating the expression for f'_t with respect to α. Equation (5.3.1) may be obtained by substituting

$$\tan 2\alpha_{max} = \frac{v}{\tfrac{1}{2}f_t} \tag{5.3.2}$$

into the expression for f'_t.

The principal tensile stress $f_t(max)$ in the diagonal direction, which is at an angle α_{max} with the beam axis, is at least as large as either f_t or v. It is nearly equal to the longitudinal tensile stress f_t if the shear stress v is small and its direction is nearly horizontal. It is nearly equal to the shear stress v if the longitudinal tensile stress f_t is small and its direction is nearly at 45° with the beam axis. Since concrete is weak in tension, these principal tensile stresses are undoubtedly correlated to inclined cracking as shown in Fig. 5.3.2.

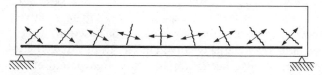

Fig. 5.3.2
Directions of potential cracks in a simple beam.

5.4 Behavior of Beams without Shear Reinforcement

As shown in Sec. 5.3, high shear stress on a beam results in the formation of inclined cracks. This is particularly true for beams having only longitudinal reinforcement; that is, reinforcement designed to carry the tensile and compressive normal forces arising from bending moment. In order to prevent the formation of inclined cracks, transverse reinforcement (known as "shear reinforcement") in the form of closed or U-shaped stirrups is used in the vertical or inclined directions to enclose the main longitudinal reinforcement along the faces of the beam (see Fig. 5.6.1 in Sec. 5.6).

The following discussion considers the behavior of beams without shear reinforcement and includes the concepts summarized by ACI–ASCE Committee 426 [3].

Inclined cracking in the webs of reinforced or prestressed concrete beams may develop either in the absence of flexural cracks in the vicinity or as an extension of a previously developed flexural crack. An inclined crack occurring in a beam that was previously uncracked due to flexure is known as a *web-shear crack* as shown in Fig. 5.4.1a. An inclined crack originating at the top of and becoming an extension to a previously existing flexural crack is known as a *flexure-shear crack*, as shown in Fig. 5.4.1b. The critical flexural crack is referred to as the "initiating crack."

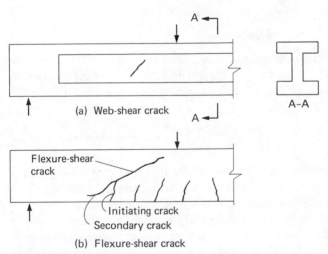

Fig. 5.4.1
Types of inclined cracks (from Ref. 2).

Web-shear cracks are relatively rare, particularly in nonprestressed beams. These cracks occur in thin-webbed I-shaped beams having relatively large flanges, common only in prestressed concrete construction. This is discussed further in Chap. 21 which is devoted entirely to prestressed concrete. Web-shear cracks may also occur near the inflection points or bar cutoff points on continuous reinforced concrete beams subjected to axial tension [4].

Flexure-shear cracks are the usual type found in both reinforced and prestressed concrete. In nonprestressed reinforced concrete beams, flexural cracking is expected under service load. The flexural cracks, usually extending approximately vertically into the beam, cause no distress to the beam until a critical combination of flexural and shear stresses develops near the interior extremity of one of the cracks. The inclined crack then forms. The rate of transformation of the initiating flexural crack into the flexure-shear crack depends on the rate of growth and height of flexural cracks, as well as the magnitude of shear stresses acting near the tops of flexural cracks.

The transfer of shear in reinforced concrete members occurs by a combination of the following mechanisms [3], as shown in Fig. 5.4.2:

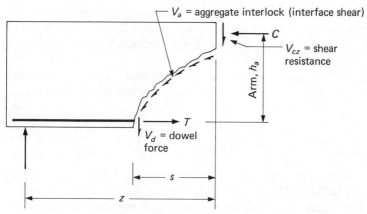

Fig. 5.4.2
Redistribution of shear resistance after formation of inclined crack.

(a) Shear resistance of the uncracked concrete, V_{cz}.
(b) Aggregate interlock (or interface shear transfer) force V_a, tangentially along a crack [5,6], and similar to a frictional force due to irregular interlocking of the aggregates along the rough concrete surfaces on each side of the crack.
(c) Dowel action, V_d, the resistance of the longitudinal reinforcement to a transverse force [7].
(d) Arch action (see Fig. 5.4.5a) on relatively deep beams.
(e) Shear reinforcement resistance, V_s, from vertical or inclined stirrups (not available in beams without shear reinforcement).

The ability of a beam to achieve a higher capacity after an inclined crack has formed depends on whether or not the portion of shear formerly carried by uncracked concrete can be redistributed across the inclined crack. The mechanisms (a) through (d) mentioned above all participate in the redistribution, the success of which determines the shear capacity and the degree of seriousness of the crack formation.

For rectangular beams without shear reinforcement, it is reported [3,8] that after an inclined crack has formed, the proportion of the shear transferred by the various mechanisms is as follows: 15 to 25% by dowel action; 20 to 40% by the uncracked concrete compression zone; and 33 to 50% by aggregate interlock or interface shear transfer.

Inclined cracks begin and grow depending on the relative magnitudes of shear stress v and flexural stress f_t, as used in Sec. 5.3. These controlling stresses may be expressed

$$v = k_1 \frac{V}{bd} \tag{5.4.1a}$$

$$f_t = k_2 \frac{M}{bd^2} \tag{5.4.1b}$$

where k_1 and k_2 are proportionality constants. The discussion of Sec. 5.2 may serve to justify the shear stress as proportional to V/bd; and in the presentation of Chaps. 3 and 4 the flexural capacity M has been related to bd^2 through the use of a dimensional coefficient R which has the same units as the flexural stress.

From Sec. 5.3 one may note that the principal tensile stress is a function of the ratio f_t/v. Another expression for f_t/v may be obtained from Eqs. (5.4.1); thus

$$\frac{f_t}{v} = \frac{k_2}{k_1} \frac{M}{Vd} = k_3 \frac{M}{Vd} \tag{5.4.2}$$

For a simple beam symmetrically loaded with two equal concentrated loads (see Fig. 5.4.3), the ratio M/V may be thought of as the distance a over which the shear is constant. This distance a is known as the *shear span*. For the general case where the shear is continually varying, the "shear span" may be expressed as

$$a = \frac{M}{V} \tag{5.4.3}$$

which has a value at every point along a beam.

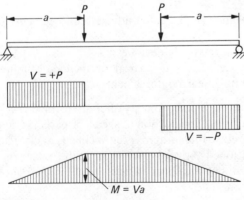

Fig. 5.4.3
Basic definition of shear span a.

Using Eq. (5.4.3) in Eq. (5.4.2), the ratio f_t/v becomes

$$\frac{f_t}{v} = k_3\left(\frac{a}{d}\right) \tag{5.4.4}$$

The shear span to depth ratio a/d has also been shown experimentally to be a highly influencial factor in establishing shear strength [1,2,3,9–11]. When factors other than a/d are kept constant, the variation in shear capacity may be illustrated by Fig. 5.4.4 using the results for rectangular beams.

From Fig. 5.4.4 four general categories of failure may be established: (1) deep beams with $a/d < 1$; (2) short beams with a/d ratios from 1 to about $2\frac{1}{2}$, in which the shear strength exceeds the inclined cracking capacity; (3) usual beams of intermediate length having a/d ratios from about $2\frac{1}{2}$ to 6, in which the shear strength equals the inclined cracking strength; and (4) long beams with a/d greater than 6, whose flexural capacity is less than their shear strength.

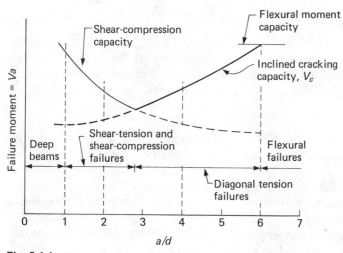

Fig. 5.4.4
Variation in shear capacity with a/d for rectangular beams (adapted from Ref. 2).

Deep Beams: $a/d \leq 1$. For a deep beam, shear stress has the predominant effect. After inclined cracking occurs, this beam tends to behave like a tied-arch wherein the load is carried by direct compression extending around the shaded area of Fig. 5.4.5a and by the tension in the longitudinal steel. Once the inclined crack develops, the beam transforms quickly into a tied-arch which exhibits considerable reserve capacity. Several modes of failure are possible [12,13,14] for the tied-arch system, as shown in Fig. 5.4.5b.

Possible modes of failure are indicated in Fig. 5.4.5b; they are (1) an anchorage failure; that is, pullout of the tension reinforcement at the support; (2) a crushing failure at the reactions; (3) a "flexural failure" arising from either a crushing of concrete near the top of the arch or a yielding of

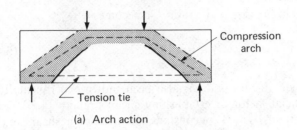

(a) Arch action

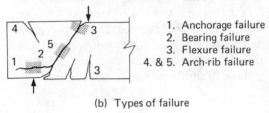

1. Anchorage failure
2. Bearing failure
3. Flexure failure
4. & 5. Arch-rib failure

(b) Types of failure

Fig. 5.4.5
Modes of failure in deep beams, $a/d \leq 1.0$ (adapted from Ref. 2).

the tension reinforcement; (4) failure of the arch rib due to an eccentricity of the arch thrust, resulting in either a tension crack over the support at point 4 of Fig. 5.4.5b or a crushing of concrete on the underside of the rib at point 5.

Short Beams: $1 < a/d \leq 2\frac{1}{2}$. Just as for deep beams, for short beams the ultimate shear capacity also exceeds the inclined cracking capacity. Failure occurs at some load higher than that which caused the inclined crack to form. After the flexure-shear crack develops, the crack extends further into the compression zone as the load increases. It also propagates as a secondary crack toward the tension reinforcement and then progresses horizontally along that reinforcement. Failure eventually results, either (1) by an anchorage failure at the tension reinforcement, called a "shear-tension" failure (Fig. 5.4.6a); or (2) by a crushing failure in the concrete near the compression face, called a "shear-compression" failure (Fig. 5.4.6b).

Usual Beams of Intermediate Length: $2\frac{1}{2} < a/d \leq 6$. For intermediate length beams, vertical flexural cracks are the first to form, followed by the inclined flexure-shear cracks. At the beginning several flexural cracks tend to bend over creating beam segments between cracks, the "teeth" shown in Fig. 5.4.7. When the root of the "tooth," as a result of the increasing number of flexural cracks, is so reduced [15] in size that it becomes unable to carry the moment arising from ΔT, it breaks to form the inclined flexure-shear crack. At the sudden occurrence of the inclined crack, the beam is not able to redistribute the load, as in the situation of smaller a/d ratio. In other words the formation of the inclined crack represents the ultimate shear capacity of beams in this category, for which the term "diagonal tension failure" has been given [2]. This is the usual category for beam design.

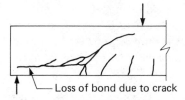

Loss of bond due to crack

(a) Shear-tension failure

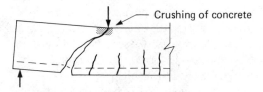

Crushing of concrete

(b) Shear-compression failure

Fig. 5.4.6
Typical shear failures in short beams, $a/d = 1$ to $2\frac{1}{2}$
(adapted from Ref. 2).

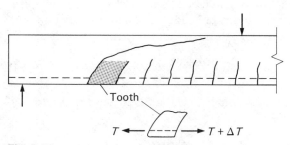

Tooth

$T \longleftarrow \quad \longrightarrow T + \Delta T$

Fig. 5.4.7
"Diagonal tension failure" or "tooth cracking failure" on
intermediate length beams; a/d about $2\frac{1}{2}$ to 6.

Long Beams: $a/d > 6$. The failure of long beams starts with yielding of
the tension reinforcement and ends by crushing of the concrete at the
section of maximum bending moment. In addition to the nearly vertical
flexural cracks at the section of maximum bending moment, slightly inclined (from the vertical) cracks may be present before failure between the
support and the section of maximum bending moment. Nevertheless, the
ultimate strength of the beam is entirely dependent on the magnitude of
the maximum bending moment and is not affected by the size of the shear
force.

In summary, shear tends to cause inclined cracks. When no such cracks
form before the theoretical flexural strength is reached, the effect of shear
is negligible. Beams may fail upon formation of an inclined crack, as for
the so-called "diagonal tension" failures when a/d is between about $2\frac{1}{2}$ and
6, or there may be considerable reserve capacity. In order for the beams

with reserve capacity to maintain a state of equilibrium, stresses must be redistributed after the formation of the inclined crack. Present knowledge of how the redistribution actually takes place is limited; thus for the design of all but deep beams the shear strength is assumed to be reached when the inclined crack forms.

5.5 Shear Strength of Beams without Shear Reinforcement

The strength at which an inclined crack (usually a flexure-shear crack as in Fig. 5.4.1b) forms is taken to be the shear strength of a beam without shear reinforcement, according to the intent of the ACI Code. After establishing on a rational basis those variables that are involved, the relationship between them was statistically determined from test results [1].

It is assumed that the load-carrying capacity is reached when the principal tensile stress in Eq. (5.3.1) reaches the tensile strength of concrete, which is proportional to $\sqrt{f_c'}$. Although the exact distributions of the flexural and shear stresses in a cross section are not known, it may be assumed that flexural tensile stress f_t varies as E_c/E_s times the tensile stress in the reinforcement and that v varies as the average shear stress. Assume also that E_c is proportional to $\sqrt{f_c'}$ and let V_n and M_n be the nominal ultimate shear force and nominal ultimate bending moment at a section.

As already shown by Eq. (5.4.1a), the shear stress may be written

$$v = k_1 \frac{V_n}{bd} \tag{5.5.1}$$

The stress in the steel is proportional to $M_n/A_s d$, and the tensile stress f_t in the concrete then becomes

$$f_t \propto \frac{E_c f_s}{E_s} \propto \frac{E_c M_n}{E_s d A_s} \propto \frac{M_n \sqrt{f_c'}}{E_s d A_s} \propto \frac{M_n}{bd^2} \left(\frac{\sqrt{f_c'}}{\rho E_s} \right)$$

The above expression for f_t may be written as

$$f_t = \frac{k_4}{E_s} \left(\frac{\sqrt{f_c'}}{\rho} \right) \frac{M_n}{bd^2} \tag{5.5.2}$$

in which k_4 is a dimensionless constant and E_s has a definitely known value. Also, the tensile strength of concrete may be represented by

$$f_t(\max) = k_5 \sqrt{f_c'} \tag{5.5.3}$$

Substituting Eqs. (5.5.1) to (5.5.3) in the principal stress equation, Eq. (5.3.1),

$$k_5 \sqrt{f_c'} = \frac{V_n}{bd} \left[\frac{1}{2} \frac{k_4}{E_s} \frac{M_n \sqrt{f_c'}}{V_n d} \frac{1}{\rho} + \sqrt{\left(\frac{1}{2} \frac{k_4}{E_s} \frac{M_n \sqrt{f_c'}}{V_n d} \frac{1}{\rho} \right)^2 + k_1^2} \right]$$

or

$$\frac{V_n}{bd \sqrt{f_c'}} = k_5 / \left[\frac{1}{2} \frac{k_4}{E_s} \frac{M_n \sqrt{f_c'}}{V_n d} \frac{1}{\rho} + \sqrt{\left(\frac{1}{2} \frac{k_4}{E_s} \frac{M_n \sqrt{f_c'}}{V_n d} \frac{1}{\rho} \right)^2 + k_1^2} \right] \tag{5.5.4}$$

In Eq. (5.5.4) the variables are observed to be $V_n/(bd\sqrt{f'_c})$ and $M_n\sqrt{f'_c}/(E_s\rho V_n d)$. It may be noted that these two variables are nondimensional quantities, because $\sqrt{f'_c}$ is considered to be in force per unit area. In the statistical study the nominal ultimate shear force V_n was defined as that causing the critical inclined crack and M_n as the corresponding moment at the top of the initiating crack (Fig. 5.4.1). On the basis of 440 tests [1], as shown in Fig. 5.5.1, the relationship between these two variables, on using the correct value of E_s, was obtained as follows:

$$\frac{V_n}{bd\sqrt{f'_c}} = 1.9 + 2500\,\frac{\rho V_n d}{M_n\sqrt{f'_c}} \le 3.5 \qquad (5.5.5)$$

Equation (5.5.5) is generally considered [3,10,15–22] to be acceptable for predicting the flexure-shear cracking load, particularly for $M_n/(V_n d)$ (i.e., shear span/depth) ratios of about $2\frac{1}{2}$ to 6, with considerable conservatism for lower $M_n/(V_n d)$ values. Thus the favorable factors for the shear strength of beams without shear reinforcement are a high percentage ρ of longitudinal reinforcement and a high ratio of $V_n d$ to M_n, that is, a low a/d ratio.

Since 1963, the ACI Code has accepted the relationship of Eq. (5.5.5) as the shear (inclined cracking) strength of beams without shear reinforcement. Thus defining V_c as the nominal strength of such beams, Eq. (5.5.5) using the web width b_w for b becomes

$$V_c = \left[1.9\sqrt{f'_c} + 2500\,\frac{\rho V_n d}{M_n}\right]b_w d \le 3.5 b_w d\sqrt{f'_c} \qquad (5.5.6)$$

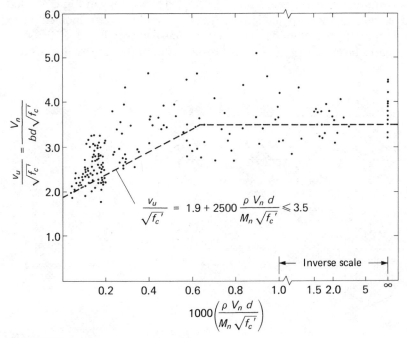

Fig. 5.5.1
Derivation of design shear equation, Eq. (5.5.5) (adapted from Ref. 1).

Eq. (5.5.6) may also be expressed in terms of nominal unit stress $v_c = V_c/b_w d$; or

$$v_c = 1.9\sqrt{f_c'} + 2500\frac{\rho V_n d}{M_n} \le 3.5\sqrt{f_c'} \tag{5.5.7}$$

Equations (5.5.6) and (5.5.7) are in fact identical to the ACI Code Formula (11-6), which states

$$V_c = \left(1.9\sqrt{f_c'} + 2500\rho_w \frac{V_u d}{M_u}\right)b_w d \le 3.5\sqrt{f_c'}b_w d \tag{5.5.8}$$

with the exception that the factored shear force V_u and the factored moment M_u are used instead of the nominal capacities $V_n = V_u/\phi$ and $M_n = M_u/\phi$. The effect of this deviation is small because the ratio V_u/M_u remains approximately equal to the ratio V_n/M_n in spite of some difference in the under-capacity factors ϕ for shear and for moment or combined axial compression with bending. Note also that the reinforcement ratio $\rho_w = A_s/(b_w d)$ is used in the ACI Code formula, where b_w is the web width for a T-section rather than the flange width. It is recommended [23] that for tapered webs, such as for joists, b_w should be the smaller of the web thickness at the neutral axis or the average web thickness. For a rectangular section, $b_w = b$. The value of $V_u d/M_u$ shall not be taken greater than 1.0 except when axial compression is present, which has the effect of limiting V_c at and near the points of inflection.

Continuous Beams. The application of Eq. (5.5.8) for continuous beams has recently been subject to question [3,23]. The compression-strut action on a continuous beam is shown in Fig. 5.5.2. The analogy in Fig. 5.4.3 that M/V equals the shear span a implies that at the point of zero moment there is a support to accommodate a compression-strut (see Fig. 5.4.5a). For a continuous beam as in Fig. 5.5.2, the distances a_1 and a_2 are analogous to a

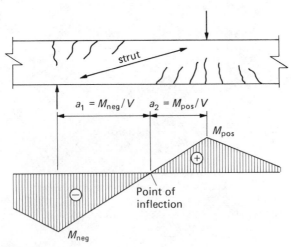

Fig. 5.5.2
Crack pattern, compression strut, and bending moment diagram near support on continuous beam.

in Fig. 5.4.3; however, there is no support to take a compression-strut reaction at the inflection point. The actual strut would relate to a longer length $a_1 + a_2$. Thus Ferguson [23] recommends using $d/(a_1 + a_2)$ for concentrated loads and 0.25 for uniform load, respectively, as the *effective* depth to shear-span ratio in place of $V_n d/M_n$ (or $V_u d/M_u$) in Eqs. (5.5.6) through (5.5.8). Alternatively, he recommends using $v_c = 2\sqrt{f_c'}$ for continuous beams.

Lightweight Concrete. It has been shown [24–26] that the same general relationships as those used for normal-weight concrete are valid for lightweight concrete, with a slight modification. In lightweight concrete, the tensile strength f_{ct} based on the split cylinder (see Sec. 1.8) provides a better correlation with inclined cracking strength than does the compressive strength f_c'. Since for normal-weight concrete the splitting tensile strength f_{ct} is approximately $6.7\sqrt{f_c'}$, this value may be substituted into Eq. (5.5.8); thus for lightweight concrete

$$V_c = \left[1.9 \left(\frac{f_{ct}}{6.7} \right) + 2500 \frac{\rho_w V_u d}{M_u} \right] b_w d \le 3.5 \left(\frac{f_{ct}}{6.7} \right) b_w d \qquad \textbf{(5.5.9)}$$

as prescribed in accordance with ACI-11.2.1.1. In order that shear strength for lightweight concrete beams not exceed that for normal-weight concrete, $f_{ct}/6.7$ may not be taken to exceed $\sqrt{f_c'}$.

Tests have shown [24] that inclined cracking strength for lightweight concrete varies from about 60 to 100% of the values for normal-weight concrete of the same nominal compressive strength, depending on the particular aggregates used. More recent studies [26] have shown that using 0.75 to 0.85 of the tensile strength related term $\sqrt{f_c'}$ for normal-weight concrete in shear-strength equations is a reasonable and generally conservative approach.

Thus ACI-11.2.1.2 permits multiplying all values of $\sqrt{f_c'}$ appearing in shear (or torsion) equations by 0.75 for "all-lightweight" concrete and by 0.85 for "sand-lightweight" concrete when the split cylinder strength f_{ct} is not specified. For "all-lightweight" concrete,

$$V_c = \left[0.75(1.9\sqrt{f_c'}) + 2500 \frac{\rho_w V_u d}{M_u} \right] b_w d \le 0.75(3.5)\sqrt{f_c'} b_w d \quad \textbf{(5.5.10)}$$

for "sand-lightweight" concrete,

$$V_c = \left[0.85(1.9\sqrt{f_c'}) + 2500 \frac{\rho_w V_u d}{M_u} \right] b_w d \le 0.85(3.5)\sqrt{f_c'} b_w d \quad \textbf{(5.5.11)}$$

Linear interpolation is permitted when partial sand replacement is used.

5.6 Function of Shear Reinforcement

The common types of shear reinforcement, as shown in Fig. 5.6.1, are (1) stirrups perpendicular to the longitudinal reinforcement; (2) stirrups making an angle of 45° or more with longitudinal reinforcement; (3) longitudinal bars bent so that the axis of the bent portion makes an angle of 30°

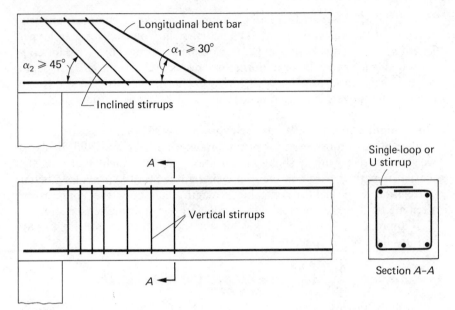

Fig. 5.6.1
Typical stirrup bent-bar arrangements.

or more with the axis of the longitudinal portion of the bar; and (4) combinations of (1) or (2) with (3). Spirals, including rectangular helices, are also permitted by the ACI Code.

In a simple steel truss as shown in Fig. 5.6.2a, the upper and lower chords are in compression and tension, respectively, and the diagonal members, usually called web members, are alternately in compression and tension. The shear strength of a reinforced concrete beam may be increased by the use of shear reinforcement, similar in its action to the tensile web members in a truss. The shear reinforcement must be anchored in the compression zone of the concrete and is usually hooped around the longitudinal tension reinforcement. The action of inclined and vertical shear reinforcement, as shown in Fig. 5.6.2c and e, may be described by the analogous truss action in Fig. 5.6.2b and d.

Although the truss analogy has formed a simple explanation for stirrup behavior in beams for many years, it does not include several significant components of shear force transmission. Although shear reinforcement increases the ultimate shear strength of a member, such reinforcement contributes little to the shear resistance prior to the formation of inclined cracks.

The shear reinforcement has three primary functions [3] to provide shear strength by allowing a redistribution of internal forces across any inclined crack that may form; these are (see Fig. 5.6.3) (1) to carry part of the shear, V_s; (2) to restrict the growth of the inclined crack and thus help maintain aggregate interlock (or interface shear transfer) V_a; and (3) to tie the longitudinal bars in place and thereby increase their dowel capacity, V_d. In addition to these primary functions, dowel action on the stirrups may

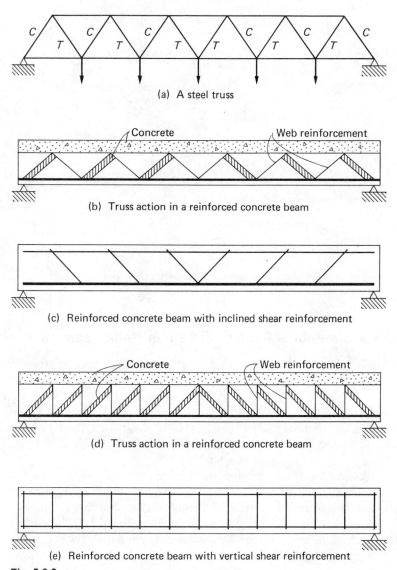

(a) A steel truss

(b) Truss action in a reinforced concrete beam

(c) Reinforced concrete beam with inclined shear reinforcement

(d) Truss action in a reinforced concrete beam

(e) Reinforced concrete beam with vertical shear reinforcement

Fig. 5.6.2
Truss analogies.

transfer a small force across a crack, and the confining action of the stirrups on the compression concrete may slightly increase its strength.

If the amount of shear reinforcement is too little, it will yield immediately at the formation of the inclined crack, and the beam then fails. If the amount of shear reinforcement is too high, there will be a shear-compression failure before yielding of the web steel. The optimum amount of shear reinforcement should be such that both the shear reinforcement and the compression zone continue to carry increasing shear after the formation of the inclined crack until yielding of the steel in the web, thus ensuring a gradual failure.

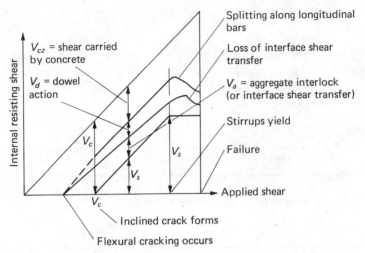

Fig. 5.6.3
Distribution of internal shears in beams with shear reinforcement (adapted from Ref. 3).

5.7 Shear Strength of Beams with Shear Reinforcement

The traditional approach to design for shear strength has been to consider the total nominal ultimate shear strength V_n as the sum of two parts,

$$V_n = V_c + V_s \qquad (5.7.1)$$

in which V_n is the nominal shear strength; V_c is the shear strength of the beam attributable to the concrete (see Fig. 5.6.3); and V_s is the shear strength contributed by the shear reinforcement.

An expression for V_s may be developed from the truss analogy. Assume that an inclined crack in the 45° direction extends all the way from the longitudinal reinforcement to the compression surface and that it intersects an average of N shear reinforcing bars, as shown in Fig. 5.7.1. The portion V_s carried across the crack by the shear reinforcement equals the sum of the vertical components of the tensile forces developed in the shear reinforcement.

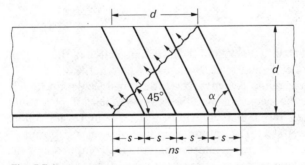

Fig. 5.7.1
Spacing of shear reinforcement.

Thus

$$V_s = NA_v f_y \sin \alpha \tag{5.7.2}$$

in which A_v is the area of shear reinforcement within a distance s, and f_y is the tensile yield stress in the shear reinforcement. From the trigonometry,

$$Ns = d(\cot 45° + \cot \alpha) = d(1 + \cot \alpha)$$

Thus

$$V_s = \frac{d(1 + \cot \alpha)}{s} A_v f_y \sin \alpha = \frac{A_v f_y (\sin \alpha + \cos \alpha) d}{s} \tag{5.7.3}$$

or if $\alpha = 90°$,

$$V_s = \frac{A_v f_y d}{s} \tag{5.7.4}$$

As reported by the ACI–ASCE Joint Committee, a comparison of calculations based on Eqs. (5.7.1) to (5.7.4) with results of 166 tests shows that the calculated values are conservative [1]. There have been a number of more recent studies [5,22,23,27–31,52] attempting to develop a more accurate relationship to account for the behavior of shear reinforcement.

The reader may note that bent bars or inclined stirrups are rarely used as shear reinforcement in the United States because of the high fabrication and labor costs involved.

5.8 Lower and Upper Limits for Amount of Shear Reinforcement

It has been noted in Sec. 5.6 that the amount of shear reinforcement should be neither too low nor too high in order to insure the yielding of steel when the failure strength in shear is reached. The ACI Code (ACI Formula 11-14) requires a minimum shear reinforcement area A_v equal to

$$\min A_v = 50 \frac{b_w s}{f_y} \tag{5.8.1}$$

in which b_w is the beam web width.

From Eq. (5.7.4) this minimum amount corresponds to

$$V_s = \frac{A_v f_y d}{s} = \frac{f_y d}{s} \left(50 \frac{b_w s}{f_y} \right) = 50 b_w d \tag{5.8.2}$$

or in terms of nominal unit stress on area $b_w d$,

$$v_s = \frac{V_s}{b_w d} = \frac{50 b_w d}{b_w d} = 50 \text{ psi} \tag{5.8.3}$$

To insure that the amount of shear reinforcement is not too high, a maximum value of

$$v_s \le 6\sqrt{f'_c} \text{ to } 8\sqrt{f'_c}$$

is usually specified; ACI–11.5.6.8 gives the upper limit for v_s as $8\sqrt{f'_c}$.

5.9 Critical Section for Nominal Shear Strength Calculation

In experimental work the critical section for computing the nominal shear strength was the location of the first inclined crack. Since most testing was made on simply supported beams under simple loading arrangements, it was difficult to extend such results to generalized loadings on continuous structures.

In order to plot the test points for the development of Eq. (5.5.6) two assumptions based on observations were used: (1) For shear span to depth ratio (a/d) greater than 2, the critical inclined crack is expected at d from the section of maximum moment; and (2) for shear span to depth ratio (a/d) less than 2, an inclined crack is expected at the center of the shear span.

Thus for gradually varying shear (such as under uniform loading), ACI-11.1.3.1 permits taking the critical section at a distance d from the face of support, in recognition of the fact that the first inclined crack is likely to form further out in the span. Shear reinforcement is also to be provided between the face of support and the distance d therefrom, using the same requirements as at the critical section.

When a situation such as in Fig. 5.9.1 exists, inclined cracking may occur at or even inside the face of support; in which case the critical section is to be taken at the face of support. Also when concentrated loads occur within the distance d from the face of support, calculations should be made starting at the face of support.

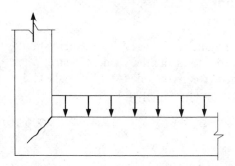

Fig. 5.9.1
Inclined crack when the reaction induces tension in the member. Critical crack is at the face of support.

5.10 ACI Code Provisions for Shear Strength of Beams

Some parts of the ACI Code that relate directly to the shear strength of beams are quoted in Table 5.10.1 for convenience.

In the ACI strength method of designing shear reinforcement, the required shear strength V_n is obtained by applying the overload factors U to the service-load shears, and then dividing by the undercapacity factor ϕ; thus

$$\text{required } V_n = \frac{V_u}{\phi} \tag{5.10.1}$$

Using the undercapacity factor of 0.85 and the basic load factors 1.4 and 1.7 (see Sec. 2.6), Eq. (5.10.1) becomes

$$\text{required } V_n = \frac{1.4V_D + 1.7V_L}{0.85} \tag{5.10.2}$$

The nominal shear stress may then be computed,

$$v_n = \frac{V_n}{b_w d} = \frac{V_u}{\phi b_w d} \tag{5.10.3}$$

When the beam is uniformly loaded, the maximum value of V_u is to be taken at a distance d from the face of support.

In order to clarify further the intent of the critical section provision, the ACI Code states, "When the reaction, in direction of applied shear, introdues compression into the end regions of a member ... sections located less than a distance d from face of support may be designed for the same shear V_u as that computed at a distance d." The situation of Fig. 5.9.1 shows the reaction introducing tension into the end region and thus would *not* satisfy the requirement for taking the critical section at the distance d from the face of support.

The minimum amount of shear reinforcement (ACI-11.5.5.1) is required wherever

$$\text{required } V_n > \frac{V_c}{2} \quad \text{or} \quad V_u > \frac{\phi V_c}{2} \tag{5.10.4}$$

except for thin slablike members which experience has shown may perform satisfactorily without shear reinforcement. The thin slablike member exceptions include (a) slabs, (b) footings, (c) floor joist construction, and (d) beams where the total depth does not exceed 10 in., $2\frac{1}{2}$ times the flange thickness for T-shaped sections, or one half of the web width. The requirement of minimum shear reinforcement may be waived if tests are conducted which show that the required ultimate flexural and shear capacities can be developed.

Shear reinforcement is designed to provide the excess capacity beyond that which the concrete is capable of carrying. Thus

$$\text{required } V_s = V_n - V_c \tag{5.10.5}$$

where the strength V_s is computed from Eqs. (5.7.3) or (5.7.4). Alternatively, the shear reinforcement contribution to strength may be expressed in terms of nominal unit stress v_s by dividing Eqs. (5.7.3) and (5.7.4) by $b_w d$. Thus in terms of shear force,

$$V_s = \frac{A_v f_y d}{s}(\sin \alpha + \cos \alpha) \tag{5.10.6a}$$

or in terms of shear stress,

$$v_s = \frac{A_v f_y}{b_w s}(\sin \alpha + \cos \alpha) \qquad (5.10.6b)$$

When vertical stirrups ($\alpha = 90°$) are used, Eqs. (5.10.6) become

$$V_s = \frac{A_v f_y d}{s} \qquad \text{or} \qquad v_s = \frac{A_v f_y}{b_w s} \qquad (5.10.7)$$

Equations (5.10.6) and (5.10.7) are the same as ACI Formulas (11-18) and (11-17), respectively. Note that A_v is the total stirrup area at a given section along a beam; for vertical U stirrups, A_v is twice the cross-sectional area of the stirrup bar.

For the nominal strength V_c [or nominal stress $v_c = V_c/(b_w d)$] attributable to the concrete, ACI-11.3.1.1 and 11.3.2.1 permit

Table 5.10.1
Shear Strength of Members under Bending Only—ACI Code

Item	Strength Design ($\phi = 0.85$)	Code
1	$V_u \le \phi V_n$	Formula (11-1), 11.1.1
	$V_n = V_c + V_s$	Formula (11-2), 11.1.1
	$v_n = v_c + v_s$ (alternate using unit stresses)	
	where	
	$v_n = \dfrac{V_n}{b_w d}$	
	Maximum V_u at a distance d from face of support in usual situations	11.1.3.1
2	Simplified method:	
	$V_c = 2\sqrt{f'_c} b_w d$	Formula (11-3), 11.3.1.1
	More detailed method:	
	$V_c = \left(1.9\sqrt{f'_c} + 2500 \rho_w \dfrac{V_u d}{M_u}\right) b_w d \le 3.5\sqrt{f'_c} b_w d$	Formula (11-6), 11.3.2.1
	$V_u d/M_u$ not to exceed unity	
	Allow 10% increase for joists	8.11.8
	Lightweight concrete when f_{ct} is specified:	
	Use smaller of $f_{ct}/6.7$ or $\sqrt{f'_c}$ for $\sqrt{f'_c}$	11.2.1.1
	Lightweight concrete when f_{ct} is not specified:	
	Use $0.75\sqrt{f'_c}$ to $0.85\sqrt{f'_c}$ in cases of all lightweight to sand lightweight concrete	11.2.1.2

Table 5.10.1 (*cont.*)
Shear Strength of Members under Bending Only—ACI Code

Item	Strength Design ($\phi = 0.85$)	Code
3	$V_s = \dfrac{A_v f_y d}{s}(\sin\alpha + \cos\alpha)$	Formula (11-18), 11.5.6.3
	$V_s = A_v f_y \sin\alpha \le 3\sqrt{f'_c} b_w d$ (single bar)	Formula (11-19), 11.5.6.4
	$\min A_v = \dfrac{50 b_w s}{f_y}$	Formula (11-14), 11.5.5.3
	f_y not to exceed 60,000 psi	11.5.2
	V_s not to exceed $8\sqrt{f'_c} b_w d$	11.5.6.8
4	Shear reinforcement shall be provided wherever	11.5.5.1
	$V_u > \phi V_c/2$ (or $v_n > v_c/2$)	
	except for slabs, footings, joists, and small beams shallower than 10 in., $2\frac{1}{2}$ times flange thickness, or $b_w/2$	
5	For vertical stirrups:	
	$\max s = \dfrac{d}{2} \le 24$ in. if $V_s \le 4\sqrt{f'_c} b_w d$	11.5.4.1
	$\max s = \dfrac{d}{4} \le 12$ in. if $V_s > 4\sqrt{f'_c} b_w d$	11.5.4.3

(a) For the *simplified method*,

$$V_c = 2\sqrt{f'_c} b_w d \qquad (\text{or } v_c = 2\sqrt{f'_c}) \qquad (5.10.8)$$

From Fig. 5.5.1 this value appears to be conservative; however, recent studies [3,19] have shown otherwise when ρ_w is below about 0.012. For values of ρ_w lower than 0.012, the following is suggested [19,32],

$$V_c = (0.8 + 100\rho_w)\sqrt{f'_c} b_w d \qquad (5.10.9)$$

(b) For the *more detailed method*,

$$V_c = \left(1.9\sqrt{f'_c} + 2500\rho_w \frac{V_u d}{M_u}\right) b_w d \le 3.5\sqrt{f'_c} b_w d \qquad (5.10.10)$$

Equation (5.10.10) is identical to Eq. (5.5.8). Note the discussion under Eq. (5.5.8) in regard to the limitation of the value of $V_u d/M_u$ to 1.0, and the recommendations for substitute $V_u d/M_u$ values for shear strength on continuous beams.

The usual maximum spacing for vertical stirrups is $d/2$ when $v_s \le 4\sqrt{f'_c}$. For the occasional situation where v_s exceeds $4\sqrt{f'_c}$ in a portion of the span, the maximum spacing is $d/4$ (but not more than 12 in.) for that portion, but for the remainder of the span where $v_s \leq 4\sqrt{f'_c}$, the $d/2$ maximum (but not more than 24 in.) still applies.

5.11 Working Stress Method—ACI Code, Appendix B

The nominal shear stress in the "alternate design method", as prescribed in Appendix B.7 of the ACI Code is to be based on the service-load shears without applying the overload factors U or the undercapacity factors ϕ; thus

$$v = \frac{V_D + V_L}{b_w d} \tag{5.11.1}$$

The allowable concrete stresses and the limiting maximum stresses for shear are taken as approximately 55% for beams, joists, walls, and one-way slabs, and 50% for two-way slabs and footings, respectively, of the stresses used for ultimate strength.

Thus for beams the allowable stresses for concrete, using approximately 55% of Eqs. (5.10.8) and (5.10.10) are (ACI-Appendix B.3.1)

$$v_c = 1.1\sqrt{f'_c} \tag{5.11.2}$$

or (ACI-Appendix B.7.4.4)

$$v_c = \sqrt{f'_c} + 1300\rho_w \frac{Vd}{M} \leq 1.9\sqrt{f'_c} \tag{5.11.3}$$

Note that reducing the allowable stresses to 55% is equivalent to using a U/ϕ value of $1/0.55 = 1.82$. Assuming equal dead and live loads gives an average overload factor of $\frac{1}{2}(1.4 + 1.7) = 1.55$, which with $\phi = 0.85$ results in a U/ϕ value of 1.82.

The procedure for the working stress method is identical to that for the strength method. The minimum area of web reinforcement is the same as for the strength method, as given by Eq. (5.8.1). The limiting maximum stresses, as discussed in Sec. 5.8 and as related to maximum web reinforcement spacing (ACI-Appendix B.7.5.4), are also reduced to 55 or 50% of their corresponding values in the strength method.

Since the procedures are the same as for the strength method, the use of the alternate method for designing web reinforcement offers little advantage, except the results could be more or less conservative depending on whether the dead load is larger or smaller than the live load.

5.12 Shear Strength of Beams—Design Examples

Three examples are presented to illustrate the basic procedure of designing vertical stirrups. In the first example, the complete design procedure for flexure and shear is shown for a simple beam, emphasizing both the simplified and the more detailed methods of spacing the stirrups. Some of the more practical aspects are discussed in the second example. Use of metric units is shown for the third example. Design of shear reinforcement in the continuous spans of a slab-beam-girder floor system is treated in Chap. 10.

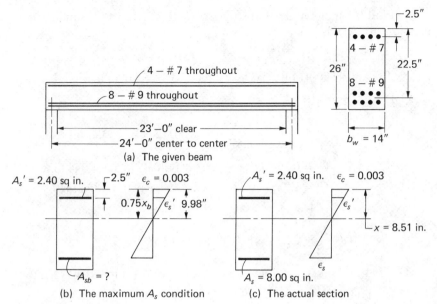

Fig. 5.12.1
Beam for Example 5.12.1.

EXAMPLE 5.12.1   For the given beam shown in Fig. 5.12.1a, first determine the maximum uniform dead and live loads under service condition permitted by the ACI strength method. Then using those maximum service loads design the shear reinforcement using vertical stirrups and the strength method. Assume that service live-load to dead-load ratio is 1.5, $f'_c = 4000$ psi, and $f_y = 60,000$ psi ($f'_c = 28$ N/mm^2; $f_y = 420$ N/mm^2).

Solution: (a) Check whether tension steel exceeds the maximum amount permitted (Fig. 5.12.1b).

$$x_b = \frac{0.003(22.5)}{0.003 + 0.00207} = 13.31 \text{ in.}$$

$$\text{max } x = 0.75x_b = 0.75(13.31) = 9.98 \text{ in.}$$

For $x = 9.98$ in.,

$$\epsilon'_s = \frac{9.98 - 2.5}{9.98}(0.003) = 0.00225 > \epsilon_y; \qquad f'_s = f_y$$

$$\text{max } C_c = 0.85f'_c b\beta_1(\text{max } x)$$
$$= 0.85(4)(14)(0.85)(9.98) = 404 \text{ kips (1800 kN)}$$
$$C_s = A'_s(f_y - 0.85f'_c)$$
$$= 2.40(60 - 3.4) = 136 \text{ kips (605 kN)}$$
$$\text{max } T = \text{max } C = 404 + 136 = 540 \text{ kips}$$
$$\text{max } A_s = \frac{\text{max } T}{f_y} = \frac{540}{60} = 9.00 \text{ sq in.} > (8\text{-}\#9 = 8.00) \qquad \text{OK}$$

(b) Find the nominal flexural strength M_n (Fig. 5.12.1c). Assuming compression steel yields,

$$0.85f'_c b\beta_1 x + A'_s(f_y - 0.85f'_c) = A_s f_y$$
$$0.85(4)(14)(0.85x) + 2.40(60 - 3.4) = 8.00(60)$$
$$x = 8.51 \text{ in.}$$

$$\epsilon'_s = 0.003\frac{8.51 - 2.5}{8.51} = 0.00212 > \epsilon_y \quad \text{OK}$$

$$C_c = 0.85f'_c b\beta_1 x = 0.85(4)(14)(0.85)(8.51) = 344 \text{ kips}$$
$$C_s = A'_s(f_y - 0.85f'_c) = 2.40(60 - 3.4) = 136 \text{ kips}$$
$$T = A_s f_y = 8.00(60) = 480 \text{ kips}$$

$$d - \frac{a}{2} = 22.5 - \tfrac{1}{2}(0.85)(8.51) = 18.88 \text{ in.}$$

$$M_n = 344(18.88)\tfrac{1}{12} + 136(20)\tfrac{1}{12} = 541 + 227 = 768 \text{ ft-kips (1040 kN-m)}$$
$$\tfrac{1}{8}(w_u)(24)^2 = \phi M_n = 0.90(768) = 691 \text{ ft-kips}$$
$$w_u = 9.60 \text{ kips/ft (140 kN/m)}$$
$$w_L = 1.5w_D$$
$$w_u = 1.4w_D + 1.7(1.5w_D)$$

service dead load $w_D = \dfrac{9.60}{1.4 + 2.55} = 2.43 \text{ kips/ft (35.5 kN/m)}$

service live load $w_L = 3.64 \text{ kips/ft (53.2 kN/m)}$

(c) Design of shear reinforcement, using the simplified method with a constant value for V_c.

The shear to be designed for must be the maximum that may possibly act at each point along the span; that is, an envelope of maximum shear is needed. Note that for bending moment on a simply supported span the maximum value occurs at every point along the span when the full span is loaded; however, for shear the maximum shear occurs with partial span loading for every point along the span except at the supports. Unless the designer can justify other treatment, the live load should always be treated as variable position loading acting wherever it may cause the greatest effect, whereas the dead load would be fixed position loading. For most ordinary situations an approximate shear envelope may be acceptable, using a straight-line relationship between the maximum shear at the support and the maximum shear at midspan. Such a procedure will always be conservative.

For this beam (see Fig. 5.12.2a), the maximum shear at the centerline of support is

$$V_u = \frac{w_u L}{2} = \frac{9.60(24)}{2} = 115.2 \text{ kips}$$

The maximum shear possible at midspan occurs with live load on half

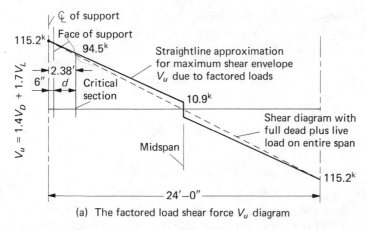

(a) The factored load shear force V_u diagram

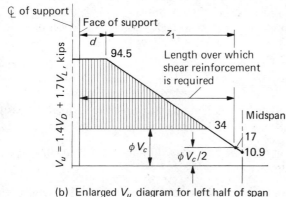

(b) Enlarged V_u diagram for left half of span

Fig. 5.12.2
Design of shear reinforcement in Example 5.12.1 by the simplified
method.

the span,

$$V_u = \frac{w_L L}{8} = \frac{3.64(24)}{8} = 10.9 \text{ kips}$$

The dead load shear (with full span loaded) is zero at midspan.

The critical section for determining the closest stirrup spacing may be taken according to ACI-11.1.3.1 at a distance d from *face* of support; in this case $d = 22.5$ in. and the support width is 12 in., making the critical section $(22.5 + 6 = 28.5 \text{ in.})$ 2.38 ft from the center of the support. By linear interpolation, V_u at d from the face is

$$V_u = 115.2 - \left(\frac{115.2 - 10.9}{12}\right)2.38 = 94.5 \text{ kips}$$

The design requirement between the face of support and the critical section is considered to be constant (in this case 94.5 kips).

The factored shear V_u diagram for the left half of this symmetrical structure is shown enlarged in Fig. 5.12.2b. The design may be made using factored load shear V_u or required nominal strength $V_n = V_u/\phi$. Since the design of elements for moment, shear, and axial force may involve different ϕ factors, it is good practice to include the overload factors in the design diagrams but not to divide by ϕ. Thus using a V_u diagram there is also a direct focus on the basic requirement of ACI-11.1.1, that is,

$$V_u \le \phi V_n = \phi V_c + \phi V_s$$

The design shear strength attributable to the concrete is

$$\phi V_c = \phi(2\sqrt{f_c'}b_w d)$$
$$= 0.85(2\sqrt{4000})(14)(22.5)\tfrac{1}{1000} = 34 \text{ kips}$$

The difference between V_n and V_c (or V_u and ϕV_c) must be provided for by shear reinforcement; the portion crosshatched in Fig. 5.12.2b. For most beams (ACI-11.5.5.1) shear reinforcement may *not* be terminated when V_n equals V_c, but rather must be continued until $V_n = V_c/2$ (or $V_u = \phi V_c/2$) (Fig. 5.12.2b). The distance over which shear reinforcement is required *from the face of support* is

$$d + z_1 = 22.5 + \left(\frac{94.5 - 17}{94.5 - 10.9}\right)(12 - 2.38)(12) = 130 \text{ in.}$$

Over this distance of 130 in., the maximum spacing of the vertical U stirrups to be used in this example may be governed by any one of three requirements.

1. Strength requirement (ACI-11.5.6.2) based on factored load shear. Using #3 vertical U stirrups,

$$\max \phi V_s = \max V_u - \phi V_c = 94.5 - 34 = 60.5 \text{ kips}$$

$$\max s = \frac{\phi A_v f_y d}{\phi V_s} = \frac{(0.85)(2)(0.11)(60)22.5}{60.5} = 4.2 \text{ in.}$$

that applies from face of support out to the critical section. Maximum spacing permitted based on required strength increases as V_s decreases toward midspan.

2. Requirement for minimum area of shear reinforcement (ACI-11.5.5.3).

$$\max s = \frac{A_v f_y}{50 b_w} = \frac{2(0.11)60,000}{50(14)} = 18.9 \text{ in.}$$

that applies wherever $V_n > V_c/2$.

3. Requirement based on every potential 45° inclined crack being intersected by shear reinforcement (ACI-11.5.4.1 and 11.5.4.2). Since $V_s = 60.5/\phi = 71$ kips is less than $4\sqrt{f_c'}b_w d = 80$ kips everywhere along the beam,

$$\max s = \frac{d}{2} = 11.25 \text{ in.}$$

Note that for this problem, requirement 2 does not govern at all.

In general, the decision regarding stirrup size is controlled by the closest spacing required. If stirrups must be closer together than 3 in., the next larger bar size should be used. In this case, #3 stirrups will be used since they may be placed 4 in. (4.2 computed maximum) apart in the region where V_s is largest.

To determine the set of spacings to be used, the designer may prefer to scale from the shear force or shear stress diagram (as is done for the next example; see Fig. 5.12.4c), or compute the location as is done for this example (see Table 5.12.1). Whether location z is computed or scaled, a table of V_s (or ϕV_s) versus s should be used. The limiting spacings of 4.2 and 11.25 have already been explained. The intermediate spacings of 5, 6, 8, and 10 in. are those chosen by the designer as practical possibilities.

Table 5.12.1

Spacing of Vertical Stirrups (Example 5.12.1)

s	$\phi V_s = \dfrac{\phi A_v f_y d}{s(1000)} = \dfrac{252}{s}$	$z = $ distance from face of support $= 22.5 + \dfrac{60.5 - \phi V_s}{94.5 - 10.9}(144 - 28.5)$
4.2 in.	60.5 kips (max)	0 to 22.5 in.
5	50.4	$22.5 + \dfrac{115.5}{83.6}(10.1) = 22.5 + 14.0 = 37$ in.
6	42.0	$(18.5) = 22.5 + 25.6 = 48$
8	31.5	$(29.0) = 22.5 + 40.1 = 63$
10	25.2	$(35.3) = 22.5 + 48.8 = 71$
11.25 max	22.4	$(38.1) = 22.5 + 52.6 = 75$

Since spacings of stirrups cannot be varied continuously, they must change by "jumps." One conservative policy is to use a spacing, say of 6 in., only beyond the theoretical point at which a 6-in. spacing may be used (in this case, 48 in. or more from the face of support). In a less conservative manner, the next larger spacing may be used somewhat before the point at which this spacing may be used. With this in mind, the set of spacings to be used is

$$2 \text{ in.} | 9 @ 4 \text{ in.} \mid 2 @ 5 \text{ in.} \mid 4 @ 6 \text{ in.} \mid 6 @ 10 \text{ in.} \mid \approx 130 \text{ in.}$$
$$\text{required}$$
$$2 \qquad 38 \qquad 48 \qquad 72 \qquad 132$$

The first stirrup is placed a half space from the support, a common procedure. Many designers prefer to place the first stirrup a full space from the face of support for closely spaced stirrups. Note that in the adopted set of spacings, 5-in. spacing is used after $z = 38$ in. ($z = 37$ in. theoretically required); 6-in. spacing is used after $z = 48$ in. ($z = 48$ in. theoretically required); and 10-in. spacing is used after $z = 72$ in. ($z = 71$ in. theoretically required).

(d) Examine the effect of using the more detailed procedure involving $\rho_w V_u d / M_u$ (ACI-11.3.2.1). For practical purposes, this method is commonly used only near the critical section to justify a larger spacing for stirrups than might otherwise be indicated.

At the critical section,

$$V_u = 94.5 \text{ kips} \qquad \text{(Fig. 5.12.2a)}$$

$$V_c = \left(1.9\sqrt{f'_c} + 2500\rho_w \frac{V_u d}{M_u}\right) b_w d$$

$$\rho_w = \frac{A_s}{b_w d} = \frac{8(1.0)}{14(22.5)} = 0.0254$$

The loading causing $V_u = 94.5$ kips at the critical section is dead load over the entire span plus live load between the critical section and the right end of the beam; however, it is always conservative to use the value of M_u at the critical section when full dead and live loads are acting over the entire beam. Thus using the maximum M_u at the critical section,

$$M_u = \frac{w_u}{2}(2.38)(24 - 2.38) = \frac{9.60}{2}(2.38)(21.62) = 247 \text{ ft-kips}$$

$$\frac{V_u d}{M_u} = \frac{94.5(22.5)}{247(12)} = 0.717 < 1.0 \text{ max} \qquad\qquad \text{OK}$$

$$v_c = 1.9\sqrt{4000} + 2500(0.0254)(0.717)$$
$$= 166 \text{ psi} < (3.5\sqrt{f'_c} = 221 \text{ psi}) \qquad\qquad \text{OK}$$
$$\phi V_c = \phi v_c b_w d = 0.85(0.166)(14)(22.5) = 44.4 \text{ kips}$$
$$\phi V_s = V_u - \phi V_c = 94.5 - 44.4 = 50.1 \text{ kips}$$

The stirrup spacing based on the strength requirement (ACI-11.5.6.2) at the critical section is

$$\max s = \frac{\phi A_v f_y d}{\phi V_s} = \frac{0.85(2)(0.11)(60)22.5}{50.1} = 5.0 \text{ in.}$$

In this case the spacings arrived at by the simplified method could be revised to 2 in., 9 at 5 in., 4 at 6 in., and 6 at 10 in., resulting in a saving of two stirrups on each side of the beam. Thus the gain from using the more detailed procedure is small for this example.

The reader may note qualitatively the effect of using the more detailed procedure by examining Fig. 5.12.3.

EXAMPLE 5.12.2   Design the locations of #3 vertical U stirrups to be used in the beam of Fig. 5.12.4. The beam is to carry service dead and live loads of 5.2 and 6.0 kips/ft, respectively. Use $f'_c = 3500$ psi and $f_y = 60,000$ psi.

Solution: (a) The factored shear sorce V_u and nominal shear stress v_n diagrams for design (envelopes of maximum values for different loading conditions) are as shown in Fig. 5.12.4. The effect of partial live load on shear is approximated by passing a straight line through the maximum shear values at the support and at midspan.

$$1.4w_D = 1.4(5.2) = 7.28 \text{ kips/ft}$$
$$1.7w_L = 1.7(6.0) = 10.20 \text{ kips/ft}$$

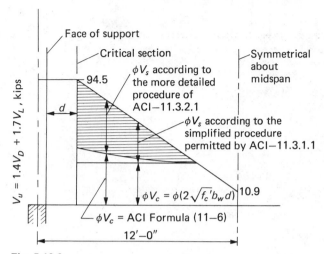

Fig. 5.12.3
Shear strength to be carried by shear reinforcement. Comparison of simplified method with more detailed method of Example 5.12.1.

At the support,

$$V_u = \tfrac{1}{2}(7.28 + 10.20)(12) = 105 \text{ kips}$$

$$v_n = \frac{V_u}{\phi bd} = \frac{105,000}{0.85(12)21.5} = 478 \text{ psi}$$

At midspan,

$$V_u = \tfrac{1}{8}(10.20)(12) = 15.3 \text{ kips}$$

$$v_n = \frac{V_u}{\phi bd} = \frac{15,300}{0.85(12)(21.5)} = 69.8 \text{ psi}$$

Note that the shear at midspan due to dead load is zero; but positive live-load shear at midspan is largest when only the right half of the span is loaded. The use of the nominal unit stress format is illustrated in this example.

(b) Simplified method.

$$v_c = 2\sqrt{f'_c} = 2\sqrt{3500} = 118 \text{ psi}$$

The shear stress at the distance d from the face of the support is

$$v_n (\text{at } z = d) = 478 - \frac{(6 + 21.5)}{72}(478 - 69.8) = 323 \text{ psi}$$

$$v_s = v_n - v_c = 323 - 118 = 205 \text{ psi}$$
$$4\sqrt{f'_c} = 237 \text{ psi} \quad (\text{ACI-11.5.4.3})$$

Where $v_s > 4\sqrt{f'_c}$, the maximum spacing of vertical stirrups should not exceed $d/4$, otherwise $d/2$. In this case the spacing limitation $d/2$ applies wherever stirrups are needed.

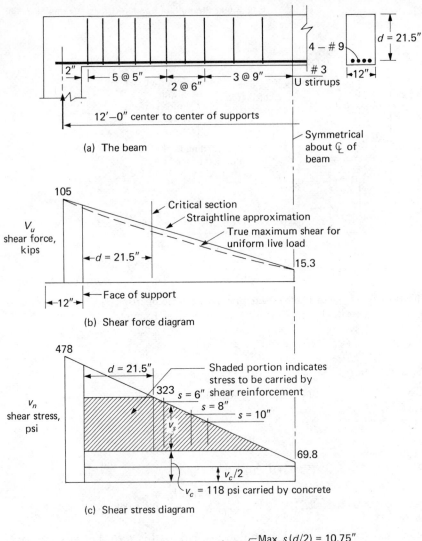

4 – #9

$d = 21.5''$

#3
U stirrups

|←12"→|

2"|←— 5 @ 5" —→|←— 3 @ 9" —→|

2 @ 6"

12'–0" center to center of supports

(a) The beam

Symmetrical
about ₵ of
beam

105

Critical section
Straightline approximation
True maximum shear for
uniform live load

V_u
shear force,
kips

|←$d = 21.5''$→|

15.3

|←12"→|←Face of support

(b) Shear force diagram

478

$d = 21.5''$

Shaded portion indicates
stress to be carried by
$s = 6''$ shear reinforcement

323

$s = 8''$

$s = 10''$

v_n
shear stress,
psi

V_s

69.8

$v_c/2$

$v_c = 118$ psi carried by concrete

(c) Shear stress diagram

Max. $s\,(d/2) = 10.75''$

6" 8" 10"

12

Face of support

s
stirrup
spacing,
inches

8

Permitted

Provided

4

Provided

2"

5 @ 5 = 2'–1"

2 @ 6"

3 @ 9"

#3 stirrups

(d) Stirrup requirement diagram

Fig. 5.12.4
Stirrup placement for Example 5.12.2.

Try #3 vertical U stirrups.

$$A_v f_y = 2(0.11)(60,000) = v_s bs$$

$$v_s s = \frac{13,200}{12} = 1100$$

which for the maximum v_s of 205 psi permits

$$\max s = \frac{1100}{205} = 5.4 \text{ in.}$$

The maximum spacing for the minimum percentage of web reinforcement (minimum v_s of 50 psi) is

$$\max s = \frac{1100}{50} = 22 \text{ in.} > \frac{d}{2} = 10.75 \text{ in.}$$

Thus the spacing cannot be more than 10.75 in. when v_s gets small.

The placement of stirrups will be done by scaling from the diagram of Fig. 5.12.4c. To facilitate this, Table 5.12.3 is computed using spacings considered desirable by the designer. The shear stress v_s values are plotted as horizontal lines marked $s = 6$, 8, and 10 in. on Fig. 5.12.4c; then their intersections with the maximum shear stress line are projected downward to the base line. Stirrups are then laid out with a scale beginning a distance $s/2$ from the face of support. (Some designers place the first stirrup a full space from the face of support for small spacings.) The same spacing necessary at the critical section is specified by ACI-11.1.3.1 to be used between the face of support and the critical section. Thus one may start at $s/2$ from support with a 5-in. spacing until within $s/2$ of the capacity line for the next desired spacing, which in this case is slightly beyond the vertical line projected from $s = 6$ in. The ACI Code requires shear reinforcement until the stress $v_n \leq v_c/2$. In this case the entire beam must be provided with stirrups, because the smallest v_n (69.8 psi) is larger than $v_c/2$ (59 psi).

Table 5.12.3
Spacing of Vertical Stirrups (Example 5.12.2)

s	$v_s = \dfrac{1100}{s}$	$v_n = v_c + v_s$
5.4	205	323
6	183	301
8	138	256
10	110	228
max 10.75	102	220

To illustrate clearly what has been done, a diagram showing permitted and provided stirrup spacings is given in Fig. 5.12.4d. In this case some shifting of spacing has been made to avoid leaving a small fragmental space at midspan. One more space at 5 in. was used than necessary and the three

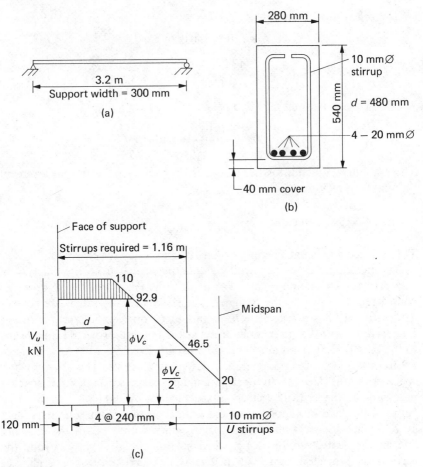

Fig. 5.12.5
Beam and stirrup design for Example 5.12.3.

spaces adjacent to midspan were reduced to 9 in. from the permitted 10 in. in order to eliminate a small space near midspan.

The final design details are shown in Fig. 5.12.4a.

EXAMPLE 5.12.3 Determine the vertical stirrup requirement for the beam of Fig. 5.12.5. Use 10-mm diameter ($10\varnothing$) bars for U stirrups, $f'_c = 24$ N/mm², and $f_y = 280$ N/mm². The service live load is 3000 kg/m and the service dead load is 4400 kg/m (including beam weight).

Solution: (a) Determine maximum design shear force V_u envelope. Convert from kg to kN by multiplying by 0.00981.

$$1.4w_D = 1.4(4400) = 6160 \text{ kg/m } (60.4 \text{ kN/m})$$
$$1.7w_L = 1.7(3000) = 5100 \text{ kg/m } (50.0 \text{ kN/m})$$
$$w_u = 11,260 \text{ kg/m } (110 \text{ kN/m})$$

For maximum shear at d (480 mm) from face of support, place live load on remainder ($3.2 - 0.15 - 0.48 = 2.57$ m) of the span.

$$V_u \text{ at critical section} = 60.4(1.6 - 0.15 - 0.48) + 50.0\frac{(3.2 - 0.15 - 0.48)^2}{2(3.2)}$$

$$= 58.6 + 51.6 = 110 \text{ kN}$$

$$V_u \text{ at midspan} = \tfrac{1}{8}(50.0)(3.2) = 20.0 \text{ kN}$$

The straight-line approximation maximum shear envelope is given as Fig. 5.12.5c. (Note that in the two previous examples, the straight-line approximation is made between centerline of support and midspan. The present approximation is closer to the "exact" maximum shear curve.)

(b) Determine stirrup spacing. If the factored load shear force V_u diagram is used,

$$v_c = 2\sqrt{f_c'} \quad \text{(U.S. Customary units)}$$
$$= 0.166\sqrt{f_c'} \quad \text{with } f_c' \text{ in N/mm}^2$$
$$= 0.166\sqrt{24} = 0.813 \text{ N/mm}^2$$
$$\phi V_c = \phi v_c b_w d = 0.85(0.813)(280)(480)\tfrac{1}{1000} = 92.9 \text{ kN}$$

At the critical section,

$$\max \phi V_s = V_u - \phi V_c = 110 - 92.9 = 17.1 \text{ kN}$$

Since the limiting $v_s = 4\sqrt{f_c'}$ for $d/2$ spacing limitation, and $v_c = 2\sqrt{f_c'}$ in U.S. Customary units, limiting V_s should be $2V_c$ in all systems; or

$$\text{limiting } \phi V_s = 2\phi V_c = 186 \text{ kN} > \max \phi V_s = 17.1 \text{ kN}$$

Thus maximum spacing cannot exceed $d/2$.

For 10-mm diameter U stirrups, $A_v = 2(78.5) = 157 \text{ mm}^2$. The spacing requirement for strength is

$$s = \frac{\phi A_v f_y d}{\phi V_s} = \frac{(0.85)(157)(0.280)480}{\phi V_s} = \frac{17,900}{\phi V_s \text{ (in kN)}}$$

The stirrup spacing requirements are as follows:

1. Strength requirement at the critical section,

$$\max s = \frac{17,900}{17.1} = 1050 \text{ mm}$$

2. Maximum spacing $d/2$,

$$\max s = \frac{d}{2} = \frac{480}{2} = 240 \text{ mm} \qquad \text{(Controls)}$$

3. Maximum spacing for minimum shear reinforcement (ACI-11.5.5.3),

$$\min \phi V_s = \phi(50 \text{ psi})b_w d$$
$$= \phi(0.345 \text{ N/mm}^2)b_w d$$
$$= 0.85(0.345)(280)(480)\tfrac{1}{1000} = 39.4 \text{ kN}$$

$$\max s = \frac{17{,}900}{39.4} = 454 \text{ mm} > \frac{d}{2}$$

Use 240-mm spacing for the portion where stirrups are required. The final stirrup arrangement is shown in Fig. 5.12.5c.

(c) Examine the stirrup requirement if Eq. (5.10.9) with $v_c = (0.8 + 100\rho_w)\sqrt{f'_c}$ (U.S. Customary units) is used for $\rho_w < 0.012$.

$$v_c = (0.8 + 100\rho)\sqrt{f'_c} \qquad (f'_c \text{ in psi})$$
$$= 0.083(0.8 + 100\rho)\sqrt{f'_c} \qquad (f'_c \text{ in N/mm}^2)$$

$$\rho_w = \frac{4(314)}{280(480)} = 0.00935$$

$$v_c = 0.083(0.8 + 0.935)\sqrt{24} = 0.705 \text{ N/mm}^2$$
$$\phi V_c = \phi v_c b_w d = 0.85(0.705)(280)(480)\tfrac{1}{1000} = 80.5 \text{ kN}$$
$$\max \phi V_s = V_u - \phi V_c = 110 - 80.5 = 29.5 \text{ kN}$$

For the strength requirement at the critical section,

$$\max s = \frac{17{,}900}{\phi V_s} = \frac{17{,}900}{29.5} = 607 \text{ mm}$$

For this problem, $d/2$ would still control with stirrups spaced at 240 mm maximum. Even though the ACI Code does not require the use of Eq. (5.10.9) at present, the designer should be conservative about the use of stirrups when ρ_w is less than about 0.012.

5.13 Shear Strength of Members under Combined Bending and Axial Load

The presence of an axial compressive load on a reinforced concrete flexural member decreases the longitudinal tensile stress and the resulting tendency for inclined cracking. Conversely the addition of an axial tensile load increases the longitudinal tensile stress and the tendency for inclined cracking. Thus, for the same bending moment, the shear strength of a member is increased by the addition of an axial compressive load and decreased by an axial tensile load. Relatively little experimental work is available on shear strength in the presence of axial load [3,33,34].

Axial Compression. Since inclined cracking is dependent on the combination of normal stress due to flexure and shear stress as discussed in Secs. 5.3 through 5.5, the addition of axial compression tends to delay the

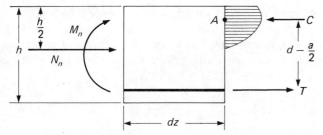

Fig. 5.13.1
Member under combined axial compression and bending moment.

opening of the shear crack and prevent its extending as far into the beam. Consider the free body of a short length of beam dz as shown in Fig. 5.13.1. Taking moments about point A, the line of action of the internal compressive force C,

$$T\left(d - \frac{a}{2}\right) = M_n - N_n\left[\frac{h}{2} - d + \left(d - \frac{a}{2}\right)\right] \tag{5.13.1}$$

As assumed in the development of the basic formula for the flexure-shear inclined cracking capacity,

$$f_t \text{ (tensile stress in concrete)} \propto \frac{f_s \text{ (tensile stress in steel)}}{n}$$

Thus

$$f_t \propto \frac{T}{nA_s} = \frac{M_n - N_n[(h/2) - d + (d - a/2)]}{nA_s(d - a/2)} \tag{5.13.2}$$

Letting $n = E_s/E_c$, $A_s = \rho bd$, $(d - a/2)$ be approximated by $7d/8$, E_c be proportional to $\sqrt{f'_c}$, and k be a proportionality constant, Eq. (5.13.2) may be written

$$f_t = \frac{k}{E_s} \frac{\sqrt{f'_c}}{\rho} \frac{M_n - N_n[(h/2) - d + 7d/8]}{bd^2} \tag{5.13.3}$$

which is analogous to Eq. (5.5.2) if a moment equivalent to M_n of Eq. (5.5.2) is defined as

$$\text{equivalent } M_n = M_n - N_n\left(\frac{4h - d}{8}\right) \tag{5.13.4}$$

Since Eq. (5.13.4) is to be used in the more detailed expression for V_c, Eq. (5.5.8), where the ratio V_u/M_u (rather that the ratio V_n/M_n) is used. The ϕ factors would divide out and thus need not be included. ACI-11.3.2.2 states that M_m shall replace M_u in the expression for V_c, where

$$M_m = M_u - N_u\left(\frac{4h - d}{8}\right) \tag{5.13.5}$$

which is ACI Formula (11-7). Note that N_u is positive for compression and that M_m should never be used as a negative value. Also $V_u d/M_m$ is permitted to have values greater than unity. This equivalent M procedure is to be used in the more detailed method for *combined axial compression and bending only*. Experience [4] has shown the method to be unsafe for axial tension.

When the simplified method is used with axial compression, an alternate equation is given by ACI-11.3.1.2:

$$V_c = 2\left(1 + \frac{N_u}{2000A_g}\right)\sqrt{f'_c}b_wd \tag{5.13.6}$$

which is ACI Formula (11-4).

The upper limit for the nominal ultimate shear strength of unreinforced webs under bending only has been prescribed to be $3.5\sqrt{f'_c}b_wd$. This upper limit should be adjusted upward in the presence of an axial compression. As explained below, this adjustment factor may be rationally put into the form

$$\text{adjustment factor} = \sqrt{1 + \frac{N_u}{500A_g}} \tag{5.13.7}$$

In Eqs. (5.13.6) and (5.13.7) N_u is the design (factored) axial compressive load, and A_g is the gross area of the concrete section.

The formula for the principal tensile stress f_t (max) in terms of the tensile stress f_t and the shear stress v has been derived in Sec. 5.3 to be

$$f_t (\text{max}) = \tfrac{1}{2}f_t + \sqrt{(\tfrac{1}{2}f_t)^2 + v^2}$$

Solving this equation for v,

$$v = f_t (\text{max})\sqrt{1 - \frac{f_t}{f_t (\text{max})}} \tag{5.13.8}$$

It may be seen from Eq. (5.13.8) that the shear strength of a member under bending only becomes a constant if f_t is zero or if the bending moment approaches zero. Empirically this constant is the upper limit $3.5\sqrt{f'_c}$. For a member under an axial compressive load N_u without bending moment, f_t is a constant that is equal to $-N_u/A_g$. Substituting this value of f_t in Eq. (5.13.8) and using an average value of 500 psi for f_t (max), the upper limit of ultimate strength in members under combined bending and axial load becomes

$$V_c (\text{max}) = vb_wd = 3.5\sqrt{f'_c}\sqrt{1 + \frac{N_u}{500A_g}}b_wd \tag{5.13.9}$$

Axial Tension. Since the equivalent M_u method using M_m in place of M_u is unsafe for axial tension, a simple linear reduction for V_c has been specified in ACI-11.3.2.3 of the ACI Code. Thus

$$V_c = 2\left(1 + \frac{N_u}{500A_g}\right)\sqrt{f'_c}b_wd \tag{5.13.10}$$

which is ACI Formula (11-9). Note that N_u is negative for tension.

In order to show the relationship between ACI formulas and experimental results, Fig. 5.13.2 is presented. The crosshatched portion on the compression side represents the reasonable range when using the $\rho Vd/M$ procedure.

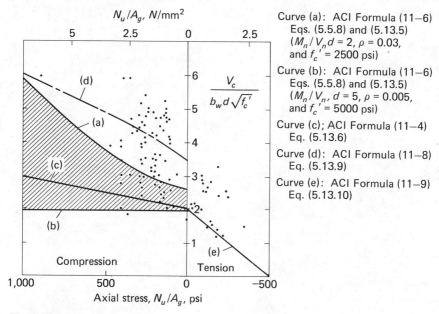

Curve (a): ACI Formula (11–6)
Eqs. (5.5.8) and (5.13.5)
($M_n / V_n d = 2$, $\rho = 0.03$,
and $f_c' = 2500$ psi)

Curve (b): ACI Formula (11–6)
Eqs. (5.5.8) and (5.13.5)
(M_n / V_n, $d = 5$, $\rho = 0.005$,
and $f_c' = 5000$ psi)

Curve (c); ACI Formula (11–4)
Eq. (5.13.6)

Curve (d): ACI Formula (11–8)
Eq. (5.13.9)

Curve (e): ACI Formula (11–9)
Eq. (5.13.10)

Fig. 5.13.2
Effect of axial load on inclined cracking shear stress (dots indicate test results) (adapted from Ref. 4).

Some parts of the ACI Code are quoted in Table 5.13.1 so that the shear strength of members under bending only may be compared with that of members under combined bending and axial load.

EXAMPLE 5.13.1   Show the effect of axial load on the ACI shear strength V_c of an unreinforced web for the beam of Example 5.12.1. Compute V_c for the critical section at d from the face of support, where $V_u = 94.5$ kips and $M_u = 247$ ft-kips. As in Example 5.12.1 use $f_c' = 4000$ psi, $b = 14$ in., $d = 22.5$ in., $h = 26$ in., and 8-#9 bars for the tension steel.

Solution: (a) Axial compression.

$$\rho_w = \frac{A_s}{bd} = \frac{8(1.00)}{14(22.5)} = 0.0254$$

Using Eq. (5.5.8) or ACI Formula (11-6),

$$V_c = \left(1.9\sqrt{f_c'} + 2500\rho_w \frac{V_u d}{M_u}\right) b_w d$$

$$\frac{V_c}{\sqrt{f_c'}b_w d} = 1.9 + \frac{2500(0.0254)(1.88)}{\sqrt{4000}}\left(\frac{V_u}{M_u}\right)$$

$$= 1.9 + 1.89\frac{V_u}{M_u}$$

Table 5.13.1

Effect of Axial Load on the Shear Strength of Unreinforced Webs—ACI Code

	Simplified Method	More Detailed Method
Bending only	Formula (11-3), 11.3.1.1 $$V_c = 2\sqrt{f'_c}b_w d$$	Formula (11-6), 11.3.2.1 $$V_c = \left(1.9\sqrt{f'_c} + 2500\rho_w \frac{V_u d}{M_u}\right)b_w d \leq 3.5\sqrt{f'_c}b_w d$$ $V_u d/M_u$ not to exceed unity
Bending and axial compression	Formula (11-4), 11.3.1.2 $$V_c = 2\left(1 + \frac{N_u}{2000A_g}\right)\sqrt{f'_c}b_w d$$ Formula (11-8), 11.3.2.2 $$V_c \leq 3.5\sqrt{f'_c}b_w d\sqrt{1 + \frac{N_u}{500A_g}}$$ N_u is positive for compression and N_u/A_g is in psi	Formula (11-7), 11.3.2.2 $$M_m = M_u - N_u\left(\frac{4h - d}{8}\right)$$ Use M_m for M_u in Formula (11-6) $V_u d/M_u$ has no limitation Formula (11-8), 11.3.2.2 $$V_c \leq 3.5\sqrt{f'_c}b_w d\sqrt{1 + \frac{N_u}{500A_g}}$$ N_u is positive for compression and N_u/A_g is in psi
Bending and axial tension	11.3.1.3 $$V_c = 0$$ Design shear reinforcement for total shear	Formula (11-9), 11.3.2.3 $$V_c = 2\left(1 + \frac{N_u}{500A_g}\right)\sqrt{f'_c}b_w d$$ N_u is negative for tension and N_u/A_g is in psi

Eq. (5.13.5) or ACI Formula (11-7) gives M_m to replace M_u in the above equation;

$$M_m = M_u - N_u\left(\frac{4h - d}{8}\right)$$

$$= M_u - N_u\left[\frac{4(26) - 22.5}{8(12)}\right] = M_u - 0.849N_u$$

where M_u is in ft-kips.

At the critical section, $M_u = 247$ ft-kips and $V_u = 94.5$ kips,

$$M_m = 247 - 0.849N_u = 247 - \frac{N_u}{A_g}(0.849)(14)(26)$$

$$= 247 - 309\frac{N_u}{A_g}$$

Values for the $\rho_w V_u d/M_u$ formula as well as the upper limit equation, Eq. (5.13.9) or ACI Formula (11-8), are tabulated in Table 5.13.2. The results are shown in Fig. 5.13.3.

Table 5.13.2
Shear Strength with Axial Compression—Example 5.13.1

N_u/A_g (psi)	M_m (ft-kips)	$1.89\,V_u/M_m$	$V_c/(\sqrt{f'_c}b_w d)$	$3.5\sqrt{1+0.002N_u/A_g}$
50	232	0.77	2.67	$3.5(1.05) = 3.67$
100	216	0.83	2.73	$3.5(1.095) = 3.83$
200	185	0.96	2.86	$3.5(1.183) = 4.14$
400	123	1.44	3.35	$3.5(1.342) = 4.70$
600	62	2.88	4.78	$3.5(1.484) = 5.19$
800	0	—	—	$3.5(1.612) = 5.64$

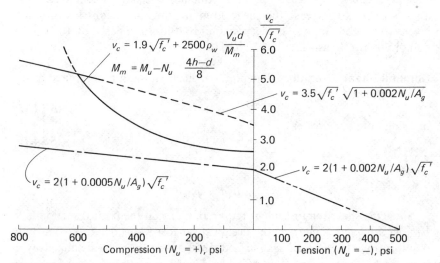

Fig. 5.13.3
Shear-strength variation with axial load: Example 5.13.1, with $f'_c = 4000$ psi, $\rho_w = 0.0254$, $M_u = 247$ ft-kips, $V_u = 94.5$ kips, $d = 22.5$ in., $h = 26$ in., and $A_g = 364$ sq in.

(b) Axial tension. The simple linear expression, Eq. (5.13.10) (ACI Formula 11-9), is plotted in Fig. 5.13.3.

5.14 Deep Beams

When the shear span ($a = M/V$) to depth ratio of beams is as low as about 1 or less, the actual total shear strength far exceeds that at inclined cracking, as shown in Fig. 5.4.4. After inclined cracking occurs, the beam can still carry a considerably larger load until the occurrence of one of the failure modes shown in Fig. 5.4.5. For this type of beam, the inclined crack usually forms at an angle with the vertical much less than 45°; often it is nearly vertical. Because of this, shear reinforcement, when required, must consist of both horizontal and vertical bars.

If in the design of deep beams the shear strength which exceeds that at the formation of the inclined crack is to be utilized, shear reinforcement will have to be relatively more closely spaced than for ordinary beams in order to control and restrain the crack from opening a wide amount. Finally, because actual failure (Fig. 5.4.5) frequently relates to an anchorage failure of the main tension bars, proper embedment is of great importance.

The ACI Code gives shear-related provisions for deep beams in ACI-11.8. The provisions apply to beams whose clear span to effective depth ratio (L_n/d) is less than 5 and which are *loaded at the top or compression face* and supported at the bottom. This is referred to as being *directly loaded*. The higher strength indicated by ACI Formula (11-29) does not exist when the member is primarily loaded by beams framing from the side (said to be *indirectly loaded*). For indirectly loaded beams having a/d less than about 2.5, the vertical compressive stress component between the load and reaction does not exist to increase the shear strength; thus provisions for ordinary beams (ACI-11.3) apply. The deep beam provisions are based on the results of more than 250 tests [3,12,21,32,35–38].

Nominal Shear Strength. The nominal shear strength is computed as for ordinary beams,

$$V_n = V_c + V_s \qquad (5.14.1a)$$

or using nominal stresses

$$v_n = v_c + v_s \qquad (5.14.1b)$$

where

$$v_n = \frac{V_n}{b_w d} = \frac{V_u}{\phi b_w d}$$

Since the shear reinforcement required, if any, at the critical section *is to be used throughout the span*, the design shear force V_u is determined at only one location. The *critical section* is defined as located at a distance (say z) from the face of support; thus ACI-11.8.4 states

    (a) $z = 0.15L_n$ for uniform loading

    (b) $z = 0.50a$ for concentrated loading

where a is the distance from the face of support to the concentrated load (i.e., shear span).

    (c) $z \leq d$

Strength Attributable to the Concrete. ACI-11.8.5 permits using the *simplified method* with the same concrete contribution V_c to shear strength as for ordinary beams, or

$$V_c = 2\sqrt{f_c'} b_w d \qquad (5.14.2)$$

but in the *more detailed procedure* ACI Formula (11-29) allows a multiplier on the concrete shear strength of ordinary beams, or

$$V_c = \left(3.5 - 2.5\frac{M_u}{V_u d}\right)\left(1.9\sqrt{f_c'} + 2500\rho_w\frac{V_u d}{M_u}\right)b_w d \qquad (5.14.3)$$

$$V_c \leq 6\sqrt{f_c'} b_w d \qquad (5.14.4)$$

The multiplier has an upper limit,

$$\left(3.5 - 2.5 \frac{M_u}{V_u d}\right) \le 2.5 \qquad (5.14.5)$$

which is reached at $M_u/(V_u d) = 0.4$.

The values of M_u and V_u are the factored bending moment and factored shear occurring simultaneously at the critical section.

Strength from Shear Reinforcement. The basic equation requiring both horizontal and vertical reinforcement is given as ACI Formula (11-30),

$$V_s = \left[\frac{A_v}{s}\left(\frac{1 + L_n/d}{12}\right) + \frac{A_{vh}}{s_2}\left(\frac{11 - L_n/d}{12}\right)\right] f_y d \qquad (5.14.6)$$

where

A_v = vertical stirrup area
A_{vh} = longitudinal shear reinforcement area
s = spacing of vertical stirrups
s_2 = vertical spacing of longitudinal shear reinforcement

ACI-11.8.8 and 11.8.9 provides for minimum amounts of shear reinforcement, A_v and A_{vh}.

$$\min A_v = 0.0015bs \qquad (5.14.7)$$

$$s \le \frac{d}{5} \le 18 \text{ in.}$$

$$\min A_{vh} = 0.0025bs_2 \qquad (5.14.8)$$

$$s_2 \le \frac{d}{3} \le 18 \text{ in.}$$

where b is the width of beam at compression face. The minimum amount of horizontal and vertical shear reinforcement is required throughout the span (ACI-11.8.10) whenever $V_n > V_c/2$ (ACI-11.5.5.1).

Limitations on Nominal Shear Strength. The limitations on strength are best itemized in terms of the nominal stress $v_n = V_n/(b_w d)$ since they will then be independent of $b_w d$.

The maximum shear stress v_n allowed by ACI-11.8.3 is

$$\max v_n \le 8\sqrt{f_c'} \qquad \text{for } \frac{L_n}{d} \le 2 \qquad (5.14.9)$$

$$\max v_n = \frac{2}{3}\left(10 + \frac{L_n}{d}\right)\sqrt{f_c'} \qquad \text{for } \frac{L_n}{d} > 2 \qquad (5.14.10)$$

This gives a maximum value of v_n varying from $8\sqrt{f_c'}$ to $10\sqrt{f_c'}$. The upper value $10\sqrt{f_c'}$ that is permitted when $L_n/d = 5$ is approximately the same as the limit of $8\sqrt{f_c'}$ on v_s for longer beams (ACI-11.5.6.8).

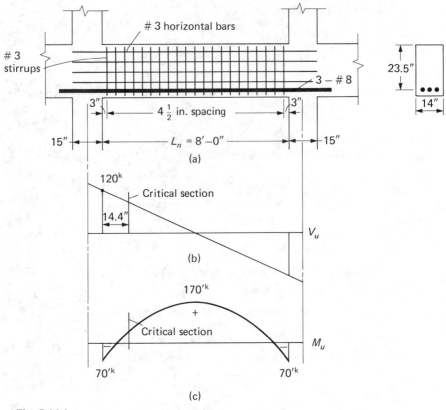

Fig. 5.14.1
Design of shear reinforcement in a deep beam, Example 5.14.1.

EXAMPLE 5.14.1 Design the shear reinforcement required for the beam of Fig. 5.14.1, which is to support heavy machinery. The service loading consists of 3 kips/ft dead load and 15.2 kips/ft live load (including impact effect). The moment and shear diagrams (including provision for overload factors U) are given in Fig. 5.14.1. Use $f'_c = 3500$ psi and $f_y = 60,000$ psi.

Solution: Since this is a beam of short span with heavy direct loading at the compression face, it is quite likely a deep beam according to ACI-11.8.
(a) Determine if deep beam provisions apply.

$$\frac{L_n}{d} = \frac{8(12)}{23.5} = 4.08 < 5 \quad \text{(ACI-11.8 applies)}$$

(b) Critical section (ACI-11.8.4). For uniform loading,

$$0.15L_n = 0.15(8)(12) = 14.4 \text{ in.} < d = 23.5 \text{ in.}$$

Critical section is taken at 14.4 in. from face of support.
(c) Shear strength of unreinforced web at critical section (ACI-11.8.5), in terms of $v_c = V_c/(b_w d)$. Simplified method:

$$v_c = 2\sqrt{f'_c} = 2\sqrt{3500} = 118 \text{ psi}$$

More detailed procedure:

$$v_c = \left(3.5 - 2.5\frac{M_u}{V_u d}\right)\left(1.9\sqrt{f'_c} + 2500\rho_w \frac{V_u d}{M_u}\right)$$

$$w_u = 3(1.4) + 15.2(1.7) = 4.2 + 25.8 = 30 \text{ kips/ft}$$

$$V_u = 120 - 30\left(\frac{14.4}{12}\right) = 84 \text{ kips}$$

$$M_u = -70 + \frac{1}{2}(120 + 84)\left(\frac{14.4}{12}\right) = 52 \text{ ft-kips}$$

$$\frac{M_u}{V_u d} = \frac{52(12)}{84(23.5)} = 0.316 < 0.4$$

Maximum value for $\left(3.5 - 2.5\dfrac{M_u}{V_u d}\right) = 2.5$ applies:

$$v_c = 2.5\left[1.9\sqrt{f'_c} + 2500\rho_w \frac{1}{0.316}\right]$$

$$= 2.5\left[1.9\sqrt{3500} + \frac{2500}{0.316}\left(\frac{3(0.79)}{14(23.5)}\right)\right]$$

$$= 2.5[112 + 57] = 423 \text{ psi}$$

$$\max v_c = 6\sqrt{f'_c} = 6(59.2) = 355 \text{ psi (controls)}$$

(d) Nominal shear stress. At critical section,

$$v_n = \frac{V_u}{\phi bd} = \frac{84,000}{0.85(14)(23.5)} = 300 \text{ psi}$$

$$v_n \text{ (max allowed)} = \frac{2}{3}\left(10 + \frac{L_n}{d}\right)\sqrt{f'_c}$$

$$= \frac{2}{3}(10 + 4.08)\sqrt{f'_c}$$

$$= 9.4\sqrt{f'_c} = 557 \text{ psi} > 300 \text{ psi} \qquad\qquad \text{OK}$$

Since $v_n > \frac{1}{2}v_c$, that is, 300 psi > 355/2 psi, the minimum amount of shear reinforcement is required.

(e) Shear reinforcement (ACI-11.8.8, 11.8.9, and 11.8.10). For vertical reinforcement,

$$\min A_v = 0.0015bs$$

which when #3 bars are used becomes

$$\max s = \frac{2(0.11)}{0.0015(14)} = 10.5 \text{ in.}$$

but the spacing s shall not exceed

$$\max s = \frac{d}{5} = \frac{23.5}{5} = 4.7 \text{ in. (controls)} \qquad \text{or 18 in.}$$

For horizontal reinforcement,

$$\min A_{vh} = 0.0025bs_2$$

which for #3 bars in pairs on each face of beam gives

$$\max s_2 = \frac{2(0.11)}{0.0025(14)} = 6.3 \text{ in. (controls)}$$

but the spacing shall not exceed

$$\max s_2 = \frac{d}{3} = \frac{23.5}{3} = 7.8 \text{ in.} \qquad \text{or 18 in.}$$

Use #3 vertical U stirrups spaced at $4\frac{1}{2}$ in. throughout the beam, and #3 bars horizontally in each face spaced at about 5 in. to give proper cover (4-#3 bars horizontally in each face). The results are shown in Fig. 5.14.1a.

EXAMPLE 5.14.2   Design the shear reinforcement for a simple beam that carries two concentrated service live loads of 126 kips each on a clear span of 12 ft, as shown in Fig. 5.14.2. The beam has a width of 14 in. and an effective depth d of 36 in. Use $f'_c = 3500$ psi and $f_y = 60,000$ psi.

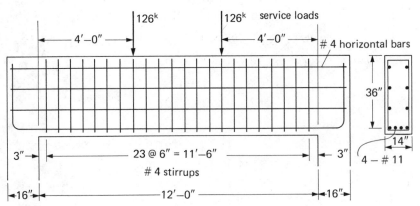

Fig. 5.14.2
Beam for Example 5.14.2.

Solution: For this beam, $L_n/d = 144/36 = 4$; thus it is a deep beam according to ACI-11.8.

(a) Critical section (ACI-11.8.4). For concentrated loads, using the shear span of $a = 4$ ft,

$$0.50a = 0.50(4.0) = 2.0 \text{ ft} < d = 3 \text{ ft}$$

Critical section is taken at 2.0 ft from face of support.

(b) Shear strength of unreinforced web at critical section (ACI-11.8.5). The factored concentrated load is

$$126(1.7) = 214 \text{ kips}$$

Neglect the uniform dead load which is small compared to the concentrated load.

Using the more detailed procedure, at the critical section,

$$\frac{M_u}{V_u d} = \frac{214(2)}{214(3)} = 0.67$$

The multiplier for deep beam action is then

$$3.5 - 2.5\frac{M_u}{V_u d} = 3.5 - 2.5(0.67) = 1.83 < 2.5 \qquad \text{OK}$$

$$v_c = 1.83\left[1.9\sqrt{f'_c} + 2500\rho_w\frac{V_u d}{M_u}\right]$$

$$\rho_w = \frac{4(1.56)}{14(36)} = 0.0124$$

$$v_c = 1.83\left[1.9\sqrt{3500} + \frac{2500(0.0124)}{0.67}\right]$$

$$= 1.83[112 + 46.3] = 290 \text{ psi}$$

$$\max v_c = 6\sqrt{f'_c} = 6(59.2) = 355 \text{ psi}$$

$$V_c = v_c b_w d = 290(14)(36)\tfrac{1}{1000} = 146 \text{ kips}$$

(c) Nominal shear strength. At critical section,

$$\text{required } V_n = \frac{V_u}{\phi} = \frac{214}{0.85} = 252 \text{ kips}$$

$$v_n \text{ (max allowed)} = \frac{2}{3}\left(10 + \frac{L_n}{d}\right)\sqrt{f'_c}$$

$$= \frac{2}{3}(10 + 4)\sqrt{f'_c} = 9.33\sqrt{f'_c} = 552 \text{ psi}$$

$$\max V_n = (0.552)(14)(36) = 278 \text{ kips} > 252 \text{ kips} \qquad \text{OK}$$

Since required $V_n > V_c$ (252 > 146), vertical and horizontal reinforcement is required for strength.

(d) Shear reinforcement. According to ACI-11.8.7,

$$\frac{A_v}{s}\left(\frac{1 + L_n/d}{12}\right) + \frac{A_{vh}}{s_2}\left(\frac{11 - L_n/d}{12}\right) = \frac{V_s}{f_y d}$$

or for $L_n/d = 4$, $V_s = 252 - 146 = 106$ kips, $b = 14$ in., and $f_y = 60,000$ psi,

$$\frac{A_v}{s}\left(\frac{5}{12}\right) + \frac{A_{vh}}{s_2}\left(\frac{7}{12}\right) = \frac{106}{60(36)} = 0.049$$

$$\min A_v = 0.0015bs, \qquad \max s = \frac{d}{5} = 7.2 \text{ in.}$$

$$\min A_{vh} = 0.0025bs_2, \qquad \max s_2 = \frac{d}{3} = 12 \text{ in.}$$

Try using #4 bars horizontally in each face at about 11 in.

$$\text{min required } A_{vh} = 0.0025(14)11 = 0.38 \text{ sq in.}$$
$$\text{provided } A_{vh} = (0.20)2 = 0.40 \text{ sq in.} > 0.38 \text{ sq in.} \qquad \text{OK}$$

$$\frac{A_v}{s}\left(\frac{5}{12}\right) + \frac{0.40}{11}\left(\frac{7}{12}\right) = 0.049$$

$$\frac{A_v}{s} = [0.049 - 0.021]\frac{12}{5} = 0.067$$

For the #4 U stirrups, $A_v = 2(0.20) = 0.40$,

$$\text{required } s = \frac{0.40}{0.067} = 6.0 \text{ in.} < \frac{d}{5} \qquad \text{OK}$$

Use #4 vertical stirrups @ 6 in. *throughout span.* Note that the main flexural steel is extended into the supports as far as practical and bent upward to obtain maximum embedment. Anchorage of bars is the subject of Chap. 6.

5.15 Brackets and Corbels

Brackets and corbels projecting from the faces of columns are widely used in precast concrete construction to support beams and girders, as shown in Fig. 5.15.1. Until recent years, brackets and corbels have been designed under the assumption that they are cantilever beams, with the usual beam provisions for shear being applied. However, as discussed in Sec. 5.4 and shown in Fig. 5.4.4, when a/d is less than about 1.0, deep beam theory, rather than simple flexural theory, should apply. Brackets and corbels, furthermore, differ from the deep beams discussed in Sec. 5.14 in that design calculations for horizontal forces must also be made. The beams supported on the corbels change in length, and because they are attached to the bracket, restrained creep, shrinkage, and temperature deformations of the beam give rise to horizontal forces (N_{uc} in Fig. 5.15.1).

Typically, reinforcement for brackets or corbels has in the past consisted of several bars across the width of the bracket bent as shown in Fig. 5.15.2a. When minimum bend radii are considered, the actual arrangement is as

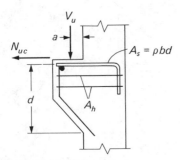

Fig. 5.15.1
Bracket or corbel.

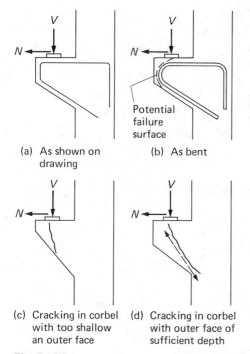

(a) As shown on drawing

(b) As bent

Potential failure surface

(c) Cracking in corbel with too shallow an outer face

(d) Cracking in corbel with outer face of sufficient depth

Fig. 5.12.2
Corbel details and possible failure modes (from Ref. 39).

in Fig. 5.15.2b, in which case a potential failure surface is indicated by the dashed line. When the outer face is too shallow, the critical inclined crack will form in the location shown in Fig. 5.15.2c. When the bracket is deep enough, the crack will tend to extend back into the column (Fig. 5.15.2d) with the portion between the crack and the sloping face acting as a compression element. If the compression strut can be developed, the bracket wil have reserve capacity after the crack forms; if the strut cannot develop (as in Fig. 5.15.2c), failure will be instantaneous upon formation of the crack.

ACI Code Provisions. The design provisions of the ACI Code are based on the results of more than 200 tests, and the formulas prescribed are simplified approximations of exponential expressions given by Kriz and Raths [39].

ACI-11.9 gives requirements that apply to brackets and corbels having shear span to depth ratios (a/d) equal to unity or less.

(a) Horizontal force N_u acting. The computed nominal shear stress v_n may not exceed the value from ACI Formula (11-31),

$$v_n = \left[6.5 - 5.1 \sqrt{\frac{N_{uc}}{V_u}} \right]\left[1 - 0.5\frac{a}{d} \right]\left\{ 1 + \left[64 + 160 \sqrt{\left(\frac{N_{uc}}{V_u}\right)^3} \right]\rho \right\} \sqrt{f'_c}$$

$$(5.15.1)$$

where d is the effective depth at face of support, but shall not be taken greater than twice the depth of the corbel or bracket at the outside edge of the bearing area (see Fig. 5.15.3). The other quantities are defined as shown in Fig. 5.15.3.

Limitations when designing for V_u and N_{uc} are as follows:

1. $0.04 f'_c / f_y < \rho \leq 0.13 f'_c / f_y$ (ACI-11.9.4, 11.9.7).
2. N_{uc} / V_u shall not be taken less than 0.20 (ACI-11.9.4).
3. N_{uc} shall be regarded as live load even when it results from creep, shrinkage, or temperature change (ACI-11.9.4).
4. Area A_h of closed stirrups or ties shall not be less than $0.50 A_s$ (ACI-11.9.6).

(b) Horizontal force $N_{uc} = 0$. The computed nominal shear stress v_n may not exceed the value from ACI Formula (11-32), which is Eq. (5.15.1) with $N_{uc} = 0$,

$$v_n = 6.5 \left(1 - 0.5 \frac{a}{d} \right)(1 + 64 \rho_v) \sqrt{f'_c} \qquad (5.15.2)$$

where

$$\rho_v = \frac{A_s + A_h}{bd}$$

A_h = shear reinforcement, as in Fig. 5.15.1.

Limitations when designing for V_u only are as follows:

1. $\rho_v \leq 0.20 f'_c / f_y$ (ACI-11.9.5).
2. $0.5 A_s \leq A_h \leq A_s$ (ACI-11.9.5, 11.9.6).
3. $\rho \geq 0.04 f'_c / f_y$ (ACI-11.9.7).

The reason for using ρ in Eq. (5.15.1) while using ρ_v in Eq. (5.15.2) is that Kriz and Raths [39] have noted, "Whereas stirrups make a considerable and consistent contribution to the strength of a corbel subject to vertical load only, their contribution to the strength of a corbel subject to combined vertical and horizontal loads is smaller and more variable." Thus A_s only is used in Eq. (5.15.1) when the horizontal tension is present, whereas both

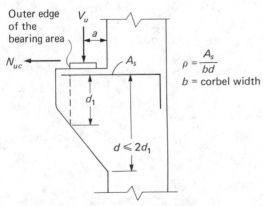

Fig. 5.15.3
Effective depth of bracket or corbel.

A_s and A_h are used in Eq. (5.15.2) when only vertical loading is involved. Stirrups (A_h) are used in both cases, but they are added extra—not considered in Eq. (5.15.1)—when horizontal tension may act.

For all cases the minimum amount A_h of closed ties or stirrups parallel to the main tension reinforcement shall be uniformly distributed within two thirds of the effective depth adjacent to the main tension reinforcement.

When brackets and corbels are so short that a/d is one-half or less, ACI-11.9.2 allows them to be designed using the shear-friction provisions, as discussed in Sec. 5.16 (ACI-11.7), because for such cases the shear crack will form nearly parallel to the shear force along the critical section. However, all limitations on quantity and spacing of reinforcement of ACI-11.9 still apply.

Recommendation for Good Practice in Detailing. Reference 39 provides several recommendations for good detailing, as follows:

1. The tension reinforcement should be anchored as close to the outer face of the corbel as cover requirements permit. A recommended way of accomplishing this is by welding a crossbar to the ends of the tension reinforcing bars, with the size of such crossbar at least equal to the maximum size of the main tension bars (see Fig. 5.15.4, Detail A).

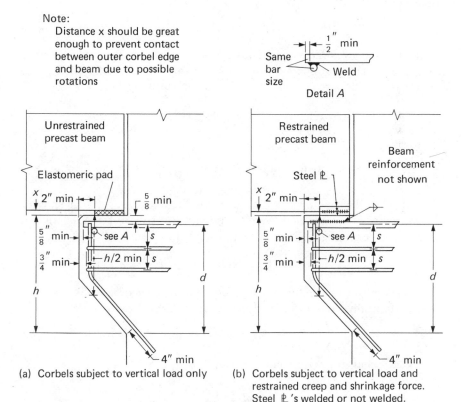

(a) Corbels subject to vertical load only

(b) Corbels subject to vertical load and restrained creep and shrinkage force. Steel ℓ's welded or not welded.

Fig 5.15.4
Recommended corbel details (from Ref. 39).

2. The total depth of a corbel under the outer edge of a bearing plate resting on the corbel should be not less than half the total depth of the corbel at the face of the column.
3. The outer edge of a bearing plate resting on a corbel should be placed not closer than 2 in. from the outer edge of the corbel.
4. When corbels are designed to resist horizontal forces, steel bearing plates welded to the tension reinforcement should be used to transfer the horizontal forces directly to the tension reinforcement.

Details and design aids for brackets and corbels are given in the *PCI Design Handbook* [40].

EXAMPLE 5.15.1   Design a typical interior corbel that projects from a 14-in. square tied column. It must support a dead-load reaction of 30 kips and a live-load reaction of 50 kips, resulting from gravity loads. Assume that suitable bearings are provided for the supported prestressed concrete girder so that horizontal restraint forces are eliminated. The tolerance gap between the beam end and column face is 1 in. Use $f'_c = 5000$ psi, $f_y = 60,000$ psi, and the ACI Code.

Solution: (a) Design loads:

$$V_u = 1.4V_D + 1.7V_L = 1.4(30) + 1.7(50) = 127 \text{ kips}$$

(b) Preliminary bracket size. The shear span a is dependent on the bearing length required to support the reaction on the concrete. ACI-10.16 gives nominal bearing strength as $0.85f'_c A_b$, so that using $\phi = 0.70$ (ACI-9.3.2),

$$V_u = \phi(0.85f'_c)A_b$$

$$\text{bearing plate width} = \frac{127,000}{0.70(0.85)(5000)14} = 3.1 \text{ in.}$$

Use $3\frac{1}{2}$ in. for bearing plate width. Allowing the tolerance gap of 1 in. clear between face of column and beam for possible overrun in beam length and in case the beam might also be 1 in. too short, the shear span is

$$a = 2 + \tfrac{1}{2}\text{(bearing plate width)} = 2 + 1.75 = 3.75 \text{ in.}$$

The depth of the section may be determined considering the a/d ratio to vary typically from 0.15 to 0.4[39]. If $a/d = 0.3$,

$$d = 3.75/0.3 = 12.5 \text{ in.}$$

(c) Nominal shear stress under load.

$$v_n = \frac{V_n}{b_w d} = \frac{V_u}{\phi b d} = \frac{127,000}{0.85(12)12.5} = 854 \text{ psi}$$

(d) Shear strength (ACI-11.9.5) and shear reinforcement required. Using Eq. (5.15.2),

$$v_n = 6.5\left(1 - 0.5\frac{a}{d}\right)(1 + 64\rho_v)\sqrt{f_c'}$$

$$v_n = 6.5[1 - 0.50(0.3)](1 + 64\rho_v)\sqrt{5000}$$
$$= 6.5(0.85)(1 + 64\rho_v)70.7 = 390(1 + 64\rho_v)$$

The required steel reinforcement ratio is

$$\text{required } \rho_v = \left(\frac{854}{390} - 1\right)\frac{1}{64} = 0.0186$$

Check maximum value of ρ_v permitted (ACI-11.9.5):

$$\text{max } \rho_v = \frac{0.20f_c'}{f_y} = \frac{0.20(5)}{60} = 0.0167 < 0.0186 \qquad \text{NG}$$

The effective depth must be increased. Try $d = 13.5$ in.:

$$\frac{a}{d} = \frac{3.75}{13.5} = 0.278$$

$$v_n = \frac{V_u}{\phi bd} = \frac{127,000}{0.85(14)(13.5)} = 790 \text{ psi}$$

$$v_n = 6.5(0.86)(1 + 64\rho_v)70.7 = 395(1 + 64\rho_v)$$

$$\text{required } \rho_v = \left(\frac{790}{395} - 1\right)\frac{1}{64} = 0.0156 < 0.0167 \qquad \text{OK}$$

If $A_h = 0.50A_s$ minimum,

$$\rho_v = \frac{A_s + A_h}{bd} = \frac{1.5A_s}{bd}$$

$$A_s = 0.0156(14)(13.5)/1.5 = 1.97 \text{ sq in.}$$

For min $\rho = 0.04f_c'/f_y = 0.04(5)/60 = 0.0033$, then

$$\text{min } A_s = 0.0033(14)13.5 = 0.63 \text{ sq in.} < 1.97 \qquad \text{OK}$$

Use 5–#6 as main tension steel, $A_s = 2.20$ sq in.,

$$A_h = \frac{1.97}{2} = 0.98 \text{ sq in.}$$

Use 3-#4 closed stirrups, $A_h = 1.20$ sq in.
Spacing of stirrups should be within the upper two-thirds of the depth, $(\frac{2}{3})135 = 9$ in. Use 3 in. spacing for the 3-#4 stirrups.

(e) Overall corbel dimensions:

$$\text{overall depth, } h = 13.5 + 1 + 0.375 = 14.88 \text{ in.}$$

Use $h = 15$ in. Note that 1-in. cover is chosen; this is acceptable for precast columns (ACI-7.7.2) where the cover may be as little as the $\frac{3}{4}$-in. bar diameter, but would have to be $1\frac{1}{2}$ in. for cast-in-place members.

length of corbel projection = 2 in. + $\frac{1}{2}$ bearing width + shear span, a

= 2 in. + 1.75 + 3.75 = 7.5 in.

Use $7\frac{1}{2}$ in. for length of corbel projection.

depth of outer face of corbel = approx half of overall depth at face

$$= \frac{15}{2} = 7.5 \text{ in.}$$

Use 8 in. for depth at outer face of corbel.
Final design is shown in Fig. 5.15.5.

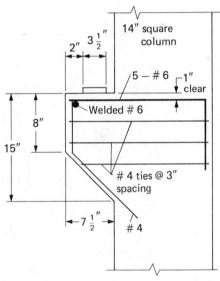

Fig. 5.15.5
Final design for Example 5.15.1.

EXAMPLE 5.15.2   Design a bracket that is to support gravity dead and live loads of 15 and 25 kips, respectively. The vertical reaction is 10 in. from the face of a 14-in. square column. Provide a horizontal reaction of 10 kips due to creep and shrinkage of a restrained beam. Use $f'_c = 5000$ psi, $f_y = 40,000$ psi, and the ACI Code.

Solution: (a) Design loads:

$$V_u = 1.4(15) + 1.7(25) = 21 + 42.5 = 63.5 \text{ kips}$$
$$N_{uc} = 1.7(10) = 17 \text{ kips}$$

ACI-11.9.4 states that N_{uc} is to be regarded as live load when it results from creep, shrinkage, or temperature change.

$$\frac{N_{uc}}{V_u} = \frac{17}{63.5} = 0.268 > 0.20 \text{ min}$$ OK

$$\max \rho = \frac{0.13f'_c}{f_y} = \frac{0.13(5)}{40} = 0.0162$$

(b) Shear strength (ACI-11.9.4). Using Eq. (5.15.1),

$$v_n = [6.5 - 5.1\sqrt{0.268}]\left[1 - 0.5\left(\frac{a}{d}\right)\right]$$

$$\times \{1 + [64 + 160\sqrt{(0.268)^3}]\rho\}\sqrt{5000}$$

$$= 3.86\left(1 - \frac{0.5a}{d}\right)(1 + 86.2\rho)70.7$$

which, using $a/d = 0.5$ and $\rho = \max \rho$, gives

$$v_n = 3.86(0.75)(2.4)70.7 = 492 \text{ psi}$$

(c) Determine effective depth. Try $v_n = 450$ psi; then the effective depth required is

$$d = \frac{V_u}{\phi b(450)} = \frac{63,500}{0.85(14)450} = 11.9 \text{ in.}$$

which would mean a/d of close to one. Try $d = 13.5$ in. (overall about 15 in.); then

$$\frac{a}{d} = \frac{10}{13.5} = 0.74$$

(d) Determine steel reinforcement.

$$v_n = 3.86[1 - 0.5(0.74)](1 + 86.2\rho)70.7$$
$$= 172(1 + 86.2\rho)$$

$$v_n = \frac{V_u}{\phi bd} = \frac{63,500}{0.85(14)13.5} = 395 \text{ psi}$$

$$\text{required } \rho = \left[\frac{395}{172} - 1\right]\frac{1}{86.2} = 0.0151 < 0.0162$$ OK

$$\min \rho = \frac{0.04f'_c}{f_y} = \frac{0.04(5)}{40} = 0.005 < 0.0151$$ OK

$$\text{required } A_s = 0.0151(14)(13.5) = 2.85 \text{ sq in.}$$
$$A_h = 0.5A_s = 1.43 \text{ sq in.}$$

Use 5-#7 for main tension steel, $A_s = 3.00$ sq in.

Use 3-#5 closed stirrups, $A_h = 0.62(3) = 1.86$ sq in., the spacing of which should be $(\frac{2}{3})13.5/3 = 3.0$ in. Use 3-in. spacing.

(e) Overall bracket dimensions. Assuming that a 1-in. thick bearing plate is to be welded to the main tension reinforcement, the overall depth is

$$h = \text{bearing plate} + \text{bar radius} + \text{effective depth}, d$$
$$= 1 + 0.44 + 13.5 = 14.94 \text{ in., say } 15 \text{ in.}$$

$$\text{bearing plate length} = \frac{V_u}{\phi 0.85 f'_c (\text{column width})}$$

$$= \frac{63,500}{0.70(0.85)5000(14)} = 1.53 \text{ in.}$$

Use a 3-in. plate length as the practical minimum.

$$\text{length of bracket projection} = 2 \text{ in.} + \tfrac{1}{2} \text{ bearing plate} + \text{shear span}, a$$
$$= 2 + 1.5 + 10 = 13.5 \text{ in.}$$

$$\text{depth of outer face of bracket} = \tfrac{1}{2} \text{ overall depth} = 7\tfrac{1}{2} \text{ in.}$$

Final design is shown in Fig. 5.15.6.

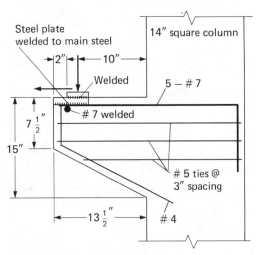

Fig. 5.15.6
Final design for Example 5.15.2.

5.16 Shear-Friction

For situations in which a shear crack may form in the direction of applied shear as a slippage along a plane (not as an inclined tension crack), a different approach to design is necessary. Such situations arise when the shear span to depth ratio (a/d) is less than about 0.5. These cases are frequently found in precast construction around the shear interface such as at the junction of a corbel (bracket) with a column (Fig. 5.16.1a), between a precast beam and a cast-in-place floor slab, at a precast beam bearing (Fig. 5.16.1b), or at a steel bracket attachment to a concrete column (Fig. 5.16.1c). This shear-

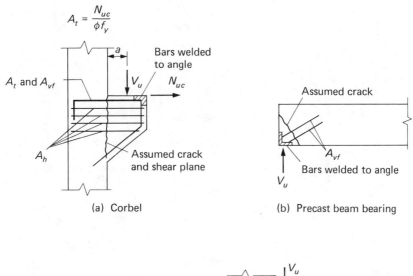

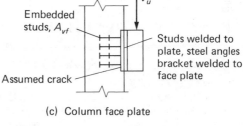

Fig. 5.16.1
Uses for the shear-friction concept (adapted from Ref. 35).

friction behavior is essentially a pure shear along a plane rather than a diagonal tension.

Consider a block of concrete as in Fig. 5.16.2a acted on by collinear shear forces V such that a failure plane would form along plane a-a. Since the crack along a-a will tend to be rough, the sliding motion will produce a separation, as in Fig. 5.16.2b. One might imagine slippage along a sawtooth that forces the crack to open; as it opens the reinforcement is put in tension, with a resulting compression or clamping force on the concrete. A frictional force is then developed equal to the compression in the concrete (or the tension in the bars) times the coefficient of friction. If one may assume that the separation is sufficient to load the steel reinforcement to its yield stress, the shearing resistance then equals the frictional force; thus (ACI-11.7.3)

$$V_n = A_{vf} f_y \mu \qquad (5.16.1)$$

where A_{vf} is the area of reinforcement extending across the potential crack at 90° to it, and μ is the coefficient of friction between materials along the potential crack. This concept of shear-friction has been verified experimentally [41–48].

ACI-11.7.1 states that shear-friction provisions apply where, "it is appropriate to consider shear transfer across a given plane such as an existing

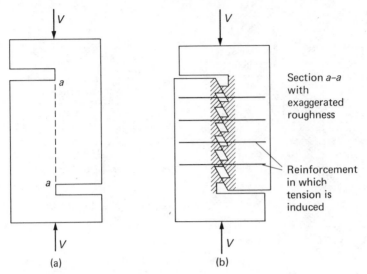

Fig. 5.16.2
Idealization of the shear-friction concept.

or potential crack, an interface between dissimilar materials, or an interface between two concretes cast at different times."

The required nominal shear-friction strength is $V_n = V_u/\phi$, in which case displacement in the direction of the shear force is considered to be resisted by friction, which is maintained at a constant value by the shear-friction reinforcement located approximately perpendicular to the assumed crack (ACI-11.7.2).

The required nominal shear-friction strength is $V_n = V_u/\phi$, in which case Eq. (5.16.1) becomes

$$A_{vf} = \frac{V_u}{\phi f_y \mu} \tag{5.16.2}$$

where

μ = coefficient of friction

= 1.4 for concrete cost monolithically

= 1.0 for concrete placed against hardened concrete

= 0.7 for concrete placed against as-rolled structural steel.

Just as for regular stirrups, f_y may not be taken greater than 60,000 psi.

The maximum nominal shear stress may not exceed $0.2f_c$ nor 800 psi, which means according to ACI-11.7.4 that

$$\max V_n = v_n A_c = 0.2f'_c A_c \le 800 A_c \tag{5.16.3}$$

where A_c is the area of concrete section resisting shear transfer (sq in.).

Since the steel A_{vf} across the potential crack as determined by Eq. (5.16.2) is only that necessary to provide the clamping action that produces friction, any *external* direct tension on the assumed crack must be provided for by additional reinforcement (ACI-11.7.7).

To insure attainment of a uniform frictional force along the assumed crack, the "shear-friction reinforcement shall be well distributed across the assumed crack and shall be adequately anchored on both sides by embedment, hooks, or welding to special devices" (ACI-11.7.8).

To obtain the maximum frictional force in situations other than monolithically cast concrete, special precautions are necessary (ACI-11.7.9 and 11.7.10). For shear transferred at the junction where new concrete is placed against previously hardened concrete, the interface is to be rough with approximately $\frac{1}{4}$-in. height between the high and low points along the rough surface and should be clean (free of laitance). For shear transferred between as-rolled steel and concrete, the steel is to be clean and without paint.

In the use of the shear-friction approach to corbels and brackets, additional clarification is required in order to apply ACI-11.7. Experimentally [42] the shear-friction theory gives a good lower bound expression for the shear strength V_n in the presence of tension N_{nc},

$$V_n = (A_{st} f_y - N_{nc})\mu \qquad (5.16.4)$$

where $A_{st} = A_s + A_h$, including all steel extending across the potential crack; that is, including that closest to the top of the corbel as well as that in closed hoops distributed in the upper portion of the corbel.

Noting that required $V_n = V_u/\phi$ and required $N_{nc} = N_{uc}/\phi$, and dividing Eq. (5.16.4) by μf_y, gives

$$\frac{V_u}{\phi \mu f_y} = A_{st} - \frac{N_{uc}}{\phi f_y} \qquad (5.16.5)$$

Substituting Eq. (5.16.2) into Eq. (5.16.5) gives

$$A_{st} = A_{vf} + \frac{N_{uc}}{\phi f_y} \qquad (5.16.6)$$

If the same philosophy is adopted as used for developing Eq. (5.15.1) (ACI Formula 11-31)—namely, when a tension N_{uc} is acting, neglect any contribution from hoop reinforcement, A_h—then A_{st} of Eq. (5.16.6) corresponds to A_s of ACI-11.9. When N_{uc} is not acting, the contribution of A_h should be included.

Thus ACI-11.7 as applied to corbels may be interpreted as follows:

(a) When N_{uc} acts with V_u,

$$A_s = A_{vf} + \frac{N_{uc}}{\phi f_y} \qquad (5.16.7)$$

where $\phi = 0.90$ for axial tension.

(b) When V_u acts alone,

$$A_s + A_h = A_{vf} \qquad (5.16.8)$$

Equations (5.16.7) and (5.16.8) gives definitions for A_s and A_h to which limits on quantity and spacing may be applied as required by ACI-11.9.2.

Recent work by Mattock et al. [48,49] has provided better understanding of bracket and corbel behavior. As a simplification for design, Mattock has recommended that the shear-friction provisions of ACI-11.7 may also apply when a/d exceeds 0.5, if the flexural strength is satisfactory computed according to ACI-10.2. This could eliminate the elaborate equations of ACI-11.9. The shear-friction approach may also be used for lightweight concrete [51], if the coefficient of friction μ is multiplied by 0.75 for all-lightweight concrete having a unit weight not less than 92 pcf (1480 kg/m³), and multiplied by 0.85 for sand-lightweight concrete having a unit weight not less than 105 pcf (1690 kg/m³). Some additional modification [50] is also to be made in the limiting v_n stresses of $0.2f'_c$ and 800 psi (ACI-11.7.4) when lightweight concrete is involved. The model code (not ACI) clauses proposed for this procedure appear in Ref. 50.

EXAMPLE 5.16.1 Redesign the bracket of Example 5.15.1, using the shear-friction provisions.

Solution: (a) Given the following data (from Example 5.15.1) for a 14-in. square column, $f'_c = 5000$ psi, and $f_y = 60,000$ psi,

$$V_u = 127 \text{ kips}$$
$$N_{uc} = 0$$
$$a = \text{shear span} = 3.75 \text{ in.}$$

(b) Nominal strength (ACI-11.7.4), using unit stress $v_n = V_n/A_c$, where $A_c = bd$,

$$v_n = \frac{V_u}{\phi A_c} \leq 0.2f'_c \quad \text{or } 800 \text{ psi}$$

$$\max v_n = 800 \text{ psi} < 0.2f'_c = 1000 \text{ psi}$$

$$\min d = \frac{V_u}{\phi b(\max v_n)} = \frac{127,000}{0.85(14)800} = 13.3 \text{ in.}$$

If overall $h = 15$ in., $d \approx 13.5$ in. (allowing 1 in. cover), check

$$\frac{a}{d} = \frac{3.75}{13.5} = 0.28 < 0.5$$

Thus shear-friction provisions are applicable for this corbel, since $a/d \leq 0.5$ (ACI-11.9.2).

(c) Shear-friction reinforcement.

$$A_{vf} = \frac{V_u}{\phi f_y \mu} = \frac{127}{0.85(60)1.4} = 1.78 \text{ sq in.}$$

using $\mu = 1.4$ for monolithically cast concrete.

(d) Main tension reinforcement. The quantity and spacing limitations of ACI-11.9 for brackets and corbels still apply according to Eq. (5.16.8),

$$A_{vf} = A_s + A_h$$

$$\min A_s = \left(\frac{0.04f'_c}{f_y}\right) bd$$

$$= \frac{0.04(5)}{60}(14)(13.5) = 0.63 \text{ sq in.}$$

Also

$$0.50A_s \leq A_h \leq A_s$$

Using

$$\min A_h = 0.5A_s$$

$$\text{required } A_s = \frac{A_{vf}}{1.5} = \frac{1.78}{1.5} = 1.19 \text{ sq in.} > 0.63 \text{ sq in.} \qquad \text{OK}$$

Also

$$\max \rho_v = \frac{A_s + A_h}{bd} \leq 0.20 \frac{f'_c}{f_y}$$

or

$$\max (A_s + A_h) = \left(\frac{0.20f'_c}{f_y}\right) bd = 5(0.63) = 3.15 \text{ sq in.}$$

which exceeds the required amount, $A_{vf} = 1.78$ sq in. and is acceptable.

Use overall depth, $h = 15$ in. For steel, select 3-#6 for A_s and 3-#4 ties for A_h, providing $A_s + A_h = 2.52$ sq in. The arrangement used in Example 5.15.1 provides $A_s + A_h = 2.20 + 1.20 = 3.40$ sq in. versus the required value of 2.96 sq in. Thus for this problem the shear-friction provisions combined with the bracket and corbel quantity limitations of ACI-11.9 require less steel than did the bracket (corbel) designed entirely under the provisions of ACI-11.9.

Use 3-#6 for A_s and 3-#4 closed ties for A_h.

(e) Overall dimensions. The overall depth is 15 in. as determined above. The depth at the outer face of corbel should then be $15/2 = 7.5$ in., say 8 in. The length of corbel projection is $7\frac{1}{2}$ in. as determined in Example 5.15.1. The final design is shown in Fig. 5.16.3.

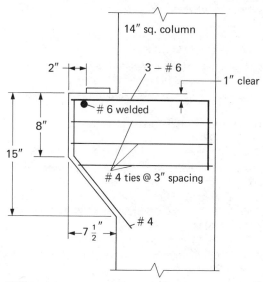

Fig. 5.16.3
Corbel designed for Example 5.16.1.

SELECTED REFERENCES

1. ACI-ASCE Committee 326. "Shear and Diagonal Tension," *ACI Journal, Proceedings*, **59**, January, February, and March 1962, 1–30, 277–344, and 352–396.
2. Boris Bresler and James G. MacGregor. "Review of Concrete Beams Failing in Shear," *Journal of Structural Division*, ASCE, **93**, February 1967 (ST1), 343–372.
3. ACI-ASCE Committee 426. "The Shear Strength of Reinforced Concrete Members—Chapters 1 to 4," *Journal of Structural Division*, ASCE, **99**, June 1973, 1091–1187.
4. James G. MacGregor and John M. Hanson. "Proposed Changes in Shear Provisions for Reinforced and Prestressed Concrete Beams," *ACI Journal, Proceedings*, **66**, April 1969, 276–288. Disc. 849–851.
5. R. C. Fenwick and Thomas Paulay. "Mechanisms of Shear Resistance of Concrete Beams," *Journal of Structural Division*, ASCE, **94**, (ST10), October 1968, 2325–2350.
6. T. Paulay and P. J. Loeber. "Shear Transfer by Aggregate Interlock," *Shear in Reinforced Concrete*, Vol. 1 (SP–42). Detroit: American Concrete Institute, 1974 (pp. 503–537).
7. David W. Johnson and Paul Zia. "Analysis of Dowel Action," *Journal of Structural Division*, ASCE, **97**, May 1971 (ST5), 1611–1630.
8. H. P. J. Taylor. "The Fundamental Behavior of Reinforced Concrete Beams in Bending and Shear," *Shear in Reinforced Concrete*, Vol. 1 (SP–42). Detroit: American Concrete Institute, 1974 (pp 43–77).
9. JoDean Morrow and I. M. Viest. "Shear Strength of Reinforced Concrete Frame Members Without Web Reinforcement," *ACI Journal, Proceedings*, **53**, March 1957, 833–869.
10. G. N. J. Kani. "Basic Facts Concerning Shear Failure," *ACI Journal, Proceedings*, **63**, June 1966, 675–692. Disc. pp. 1511–1528.
11. R. Diaz de Cossio and S. Loera. Discussion of "Basic Facts Concerning Shear Failure," by G. N. J. Kani, *ACI Journal, Proceedings*, **63**, December 1966, 1511–1514.
12. H. A. Rawdon de Paiva and Chester P. Siess. "Strength and Behavior of Deep Beams in Shear," *Journal of Structural Division*, ASCE, **91**, October 1965 (ST5), 19–42.
13. Howard P. J. Taylor. "Shear Strength of Large Beams," *Journal of Structural Division*, ASCE, **98**, November 1972 (ST11), 2473–2490.
14. R. F. Manual. "Failure of Deep Beams," *Shear in Reinforced Concrete*, Vol. 2 (SP–42). Detroit: American Concrete Institute, 1974 (pp. 425–440).
15. G. N. J. Kani. "The Riddle of Shear Failure and Its Solution," *ACI Journal, Proceedings*, **61**, April 1964, 441–467.
16. G. N. J. Kani. "How Safe Are Our Large Reinforced Concrete Beams," *ACI Journal, Proceedings*, **64**, March 1967, 128–141.
17. James G. MacGregor. Discussion of "How Safe Are Our Large Reinforced Concrete Beams," G. N. J. Kani, *ACI Journal, Proceedings*, **64**, September 1967, 603–604.
18. William J. Krefeld and Charles W. Thurston. "Studies of the Shear and Diagonal Tension Strength of Simply Supported Reinforced Concrete Beams," *ACI Journal, Proceedings*, **63**, April 1966, pp. 451–476. Disc. 1469–1476.
19. K. S. Rajagopalan and P. M. Ferguson. "Exploratory Shear Tests Emphasizing Percentage of Longitudinal Steel," *ACI Journal, Proceedings*, **65**, August 1968, 634–638. Disc. **66**, 150–154.
20. Theodore C. Zsutty. "Beam Shear Strength Prediction by Analysis of Existing Data," *ACI Journal Proceedings*, **65**, November 1968, 943–951.

21. Theodore C. Zsutty. "Shear Strength Prediction for Separate Categories of Simple Beam Tests," *ACI Journal, Proceedings*, **68,** February 1971, 138–143.

22. Gerhard T. Suter and Robert F. Manuel. "Diagonal Crack Width Control in Short Beams," *ACI Journal, Proceedings*, **68,** June 1971, 451–455.

23. Phil M. Ferguson. *Reinforced Concrete Fundamentals* (3rd ed.). New York: Wiley, 1973 (pp. 104–107).

24. J. A. Hanson. "Tensile Strength and Diagonal Tension Resistance of Structural Lightweight Concrete," *ACI Journal, Proceedings*, **58,** July 1961, 1–40.

25. E. Hognestad, R. C. Elstner, and J. A. Hanson, "Shear Strength of Reinforced Structural Lightweight Aggregate Concrete Slabs," *ACI Journal, Proceedings*, **61,** June 1964, 643–656.

26. Don L. Ivey and Eugene Buth. "Shear Capacity of Lightweight Concrete Beams," *ACI Journal, Proceedings*, **64,** October 1967, 634–643.

27. G. N. J. Kani. "A Rational Theory for the Function of Web Reinforcement," *ACI Journal, Proceedings*, **66,** March 1969, 185–197. Disc. 769–774.

28. Fung-Keu Kong, Peter J. Robins, and David F. Cole. "Web Reinforcement Effects in Deep Beams," *ACI Journal, Proceedings*, **67,** December 1970, 1010–1017.

29. Fung-Keu Kong and Peter J. Robins. "Web Reinforcement in Lightweight Concrete Deep Beams," *ACI Journal, Proceedings*, **68,** July 1971, 514–520.

30. P. E. Regan and M. H. Khan. "Bent-Up Bars as Shear Reinforcement," *Shear in Reinforced Concrete*, Vol. 1 (SP–42). Detroit: American Concrete Institute, 1974 (pp. 249–266).

31. H. C. Sorensen. "Efficiency of Bent-Up Bars as Shear Reinforcement," *Shear in Reinforced Concrete*, Vol. 1 (SP–42). Detroit: American Concrete Institute, 1974 (pp. 267–283).

32. J. G. MacGregor. "The Design of Reinforced Concrete Beams for Shear," *Shear in Reinforced Concrete*, Vol. 2 (SP–42). Detroit: American Concrete Institute, 1974 (pp. 503–537).

33. Alan H. Mattock. "Diagonal Tension Cracking in Concrete Beams With Axial Forces," *Journal of Structural Division*. ASCE, **95,** September 1969 (ST9), 1887–1900.

34. Munther J. Haddadin, Sheu-Tien Hong, and Alan M. Mattock. "Stirrup Effectiveness in Reinforced Concrete Beams With Axial Force," *Journal of Structural Division*, ASCE, **97,** September 1971 (ST9), 2277–2297.

35. ACI Committee 318. *Commentary on Building Code Requirements for Reinforced Concrete (ACI 318–77)*. Detroit: American Concrete Institute, 1977.

36. Edward Cohen, Robert A. Crist, H. A. R. dePaiva, Robert G. Mathey, K. O. O'Donnell, and J. A. Sbarounis. "Shear Design for Brackets and Deep Beams." Presented at 20th Fall Convention at DesMoines, Iowa. Detroit: American Concrete Institute, November, 1967.

37. K. N. Smith and S. M. Fereig. "Effect of Loading and Supporting Conditions on the Shear Strength of Deep Beams," *Shear in Reinforced Concrete*, Vol. 2 (SP–42). Detroit: American Concrete Institute, 1974 (pp. 441–460).

38. G. Somerville. "The Behavior and Design of Reinforced Concrete Corbels," *Shear in Reinforced Concrete*, Vol. 2 (SP–42). Detroit: American Concrete Institute, 1974 (pp. 477–502).

39. L. B. Kriz and C. H. Raths. "Connections in Precast Concrete Structures— Strength of Corbels," *PCI Journal*, **10** (1), February 1965, 16–47.

40. *PCI Design Handbook*. Chicago: Prestressed Concrete Institute, 1971 (pp. 6–13 to 6–17).

41. Philip W. Birkeland and Halvard W. Birkeland. "Connections in Precast Concrete Construction," *ACI Journal, Proceedings*, **63,** March 1966, 345–368.

42. R. F. Mast. "Auxiliary Reinforcement in Precast Concrete Connections," *Journal of Structural Division*, ASCE, **94,** June 1968 (ST6), 1485–1504.
43. J. A. Hofbeck, I. O. Ibrahim, and Alan H. Mattock. "Shear Transfer in Reinforced Concrete," *ACI Journal, Proceedings,* **66,** February 1969, 119–128. Disc. 678–680.
44. A. H. Mattock and N. M. Hawkins. "Research on Shear Transfer in Reinforced Concrete," *PCI Journal,* **17,** March–April 1972, 55–75.
45. Bjorn R. Hermansen and John Cowan. "Modified Shear-Friction Theory for Bracket Design," *ACI Journal, Proceedings,* **71,** February 1974, 55–60.
46. A. H. Mattock. Disc. of "Modified Shear-Friction Theory for Bracket Design," by B. R. Hermansen and J. Cowan, *ACI Journal, Proceedings,* **71,** August 1974, 421–423.
47. A. H. Mattock. "Shear Transfer in Concrete Having Reinforcement at an Angle to the Shear Plane," *Shear in Reinforced Concrete,* Vol. 1 (SP–42). Detroit: American Concrete Institute, 1974 (pp. 17–42).
48. Alan H. Mattock, L. Johal, and H. C. Chow. "Shear Transfer in Reinforced Concrete with Moment or Tension Acting Across the Shear Plane," *PCI Journal,* **20,** July–August 1975, 76–93.
49. Alan H. Mattock, K. C. Chen, and K. Soongswang. "The Behavior of Reinforced Concrete Corbels," *PCI Journal,* **21,** March–April 1976, 52–77.
50. Alan H. Mattock. "Design Proposals for Reinforced Concrete Corbels," *PCI Journal,* **21,** May–June 1976, 18–42.
51. Alan H. Mattock, W. K. Li, and T. C. Wang. "Shear Transfer in Lightweight Reinforced Concrete," *PCI Journal,* **21,** January–February 1976, 20–39.
52. Kitcha Leksukhum and R. B. L. Smith. "Comparative Study of Bent-Up Bars with Other Forms of Secondary Reinforcement in Beams," *ACI Journal, Proceedings,* **68,** January 1971, 32–35.

PROBLEMS

All problems[†] are to be worked in accordance with the strength method of the ACI Code unless otherwise indicated, and all stated loads are service loads.

5.1   The simply supported beam of 16-ft. span is to carry a uniform dead load of 1.5 kips/ft (including beam weight) and a uniform live load of 2.4 kips/ft.
   (a) Determine the adequacy of the #3 U stirrups that are spaced at 8 in. Use the simplified method with constant V_c.

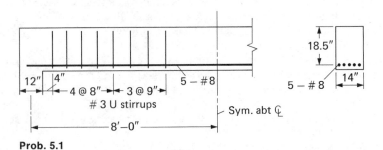

Prob. 5.1

---

† Most problems may be solved as problems stated in U.S. Customary units, or as problems in metric units using quantities in parenthesis at the end of the statement. The metric conversions are approximate to avoid implying higher precision for the given information in metric units than that given for the U.S. Customary units.

(b) Draw the curve of shear capacity ϕV_n provided versus the capacity V_u required for the entire beam. Use $f'_c = 3500$ psi and $f_y = 40,000$ psi.

5.2 The beam of the accompanying figure carries a uniform live load of 3.0 kips/ft in addition to its own weight. Assume a support width of 12 in., and use $f'_c = 3000$ psi and $f_y = 40,000$ psi,

(a) Draw the maximum factored shear V_u envelope.

(b) Draw the curve of required stirrup spacing using the simplified procedure permitted by ACI-11.3.1.1; show also the spacing provided.

(c) Determine if the spacings used in the figure satisfy the ACI Code requirement according to the simplified method.

(d) Repeat (b) using the more detailed procedure of ACI-11.3.2.1; show also the spacings provided.

(e) Determine if the spacings used in the figure are satisfactory according to the analysis of (d).

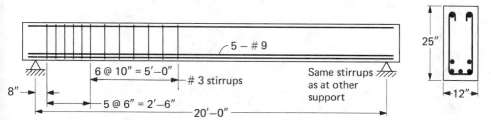

Prob. 5.2

5.3 For the portion of the continuous beam shown, with the given maximum shear envelope V_u, determine the spacings to be used for #3 U stirrups. Dimension and show the stirrups on the given portion of beam. Use the simplified method of constant V_c, with $f'_c = 3500$ psi and $f_y = 60,000$ psi. (Beam: $b = 300$ mm; $d = 530$ mm; support width = 300 mm; half span = 2.7 m; V_u at support = 260 kN; V_u at midspan = 80 kN; use 10-mm diameter stirrups; $f'_c = 24$ N/mm²; $f_y = 420$ N/mm².)

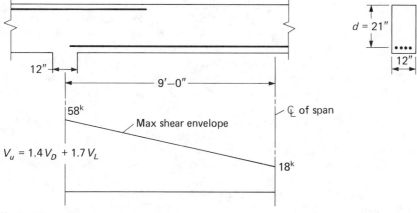

Prob. 5.3

5.4 The given 20-ft simply supported beam must carry a dead load of 6 kips/ft (including beam weight) and a live load of 10 kips/ft. Use $f'_c = 4000$ psi and $f_y = 40,000$ psi.
(a) Using the simplified method of ACI-11.3.1.1, design the stirrups and detail their location. Use an economical bar size for the U stirrups. Explicitly show the length over which stirrups are required.
(b) Repeat (a) but use the more detailed procedure of ACI-11.3.2.1.

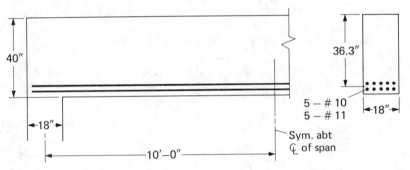

Prob. 5.4

5.5 For a simply supported span of 32 ft, with uniform dead load of 2.3 kips/ft (including beam weight) and live load of 3.7 kips/ft, determine and detail the #4 vertical U-stirrup spacing using 1-in. multiples. Use $f'_c = 3750$ psi and $f_y = 50,000$ psi, and the simplified method with constant V_c. The support width is 12 in., and the beam section is shown in the accompanying figure.

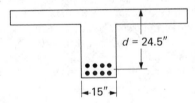

Prob. 5.5

5.6 A reinforced concrete simple beam ($b = 250$ mm, $d = 410$ mm) must carry on a span of 5.5 m the single concentrated moving load of 45 kN plus a uniform dead load of 30 kN/m (including beam weight). Calculate and detail the stirrup spacing for 12 mm diameter vertical U stirrups; support width is 300 mm, $f'_c = 24$ N/mm²; $f_y = 420$ N/mm². Apply the simplified method using a constant value for V_c. ($V_c = 0.166\sqrt{f'_c}b_w d$ for f'_c in N/mm², ACI-11.3.1.1.)

5.7 The beam in the accompanying figure is to carry dead load of 1.4 kips/ft (including beam weight) and live load of 1.6 kips/ft. Use $f'_c = 3500$ psi, $f_y = 40,000$ psi, and neglect any compression steel effect.
(a) Using the simplified procedure, calculate and detail the #3 single U-stirrup spacing for the beam.
(b) Repeat (a) using the more detailed procedure involving $\rho V d/M$. How many stirrups could be eliminated as compared to the simplified method?

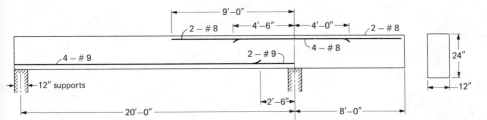

Prob. 5.7

5.8 The beam in the accompanying figure is to carry dead load of 55 kN/m (including beam weight) and live load of 72 kN/m. Use $f'_c = 24$ N/mm², $f_y = 420$ N/mm².
(a) Using the simplified procedure, calculate and detail the single U-stirrup spacing for the beam. Use most economical size stirrups.
(b) Repeat (a) using the more detailed procedure involving $\rho Vd/M$.

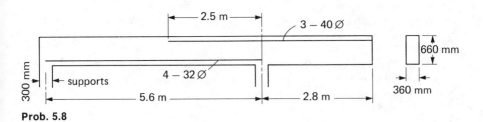

Prob. 5.8

5.9 The beam of the accompanying figure is to carry 1.6 kips/ft live load and 0.90 kips/ft dead load (including beam weight). Using $f'_c = 3000$ psi and $f_y = 40{,}000$ psi, investigate the beam for stirrup adequacy according to the simplified method using constant V_c. If design is not adequate, indicate what revision is necessary.

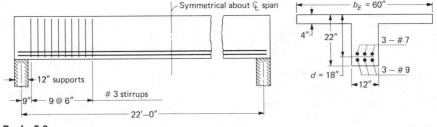

Prob. 5.9

5.10 Completely design and detail the stirrups for the beam of Prob. 5.9 (ignore the spacings given), using the more detailed $\rho Vd/M$ method of ACI-11.3.2.1.

5.11 The beam of the accompanying figure carries a live load of 2.7 kips/ft in addition to the weight of the slab and beam. Calculate and detail the vertical U-stirrup spacing for #3 stirrups. Use $f'_c = 3000$ psi and $f_y = 40{,}000$ psi.
(a) Use simplified procedure of ACI-11.3.1.1.
(b) Use more detailed procedure of ACI-11.3.2.1.

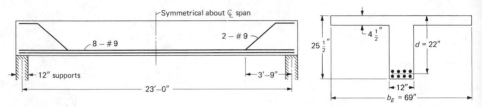

Prob. 5.11

5.12 A reinforced concrete simply supported beam of span 5.5 m carries a concentrated dead load of 2300 kg at 1.8 m from the left support, and a uniform dead load of 8900 kg/m. The width of support is 300 mm. The rectangular beam has a 300-mm width and a 650 mm effective depth d. Use $f'_c = 28$ N/mm² and $f_y = 420$ N/mm². Calculate and specify by dimensioning, the spacings to be used for 10-mm diameter U stirrups. Use the simplified procedure of ACI-11.3.1.1.

5.13 For a rectangular beam of 14 in. width and effective depth 22.5 in. with $f'_c = 4000$ psi and $f_y = 60,000$ psi, determine the maximum V_u for this beam for the following conditions:
(a) When no stirrups are to be used.
(b) When minimum percentage of web reinforcement (#3 U stirrups) is used according to ACI-11.5.5.3; specify the spacing to be used.
(c) When maximum percentage of stirrups are used (#4 U stirrups); specify the spacing to be used.

5.14 The beam of the accompanying figure is to carry a uniform live load of 0.6 kips/ft in addition to the concentrated load shown and the beam weight. Use $f'_c = 4000$ psi and $f_y = 50,000$ psi.
(a) If the bent-up longitudinal bars are counted on to resist diagonal tension, is the beam adequate as shown?
(b) If the beam is not adequate, prescribe the number and location of #3 U stirrups required to act along with the bent-up bars?

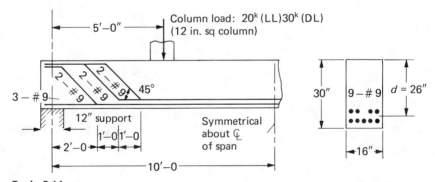

Prob. 5.14

5.15 If an axial compression N_{uc} of 140 kips (includes overload factors) is acting additionally on the beam of Example 5.12.1, determine the number of stirrups that may be eliminated by taking the compression into account when computing V_c by the more detailed procedure involving $\rho V d/M$. (Note: This compressive force is approximately $0.1 f'_c A_g$ and might reasonably be neglected when designing the section for flexure.)

5.16 Reinvestigate the shear reinforcement for the beam of Prob. 5.1 if an axial tensile force of 35 kips live load is acting. Redesign stirrups for the beam using the more detailed procedure of ACI-11.3.2.1.

5.17 Redesign the stirrups for the beam of Prob. 5.4 if an axial compressive force of 70 kips dead load and 120 kips live load is acting.
(a) Use simplified method using ACI Formula (11-4).
(b) Use more detailed $\rho V d/M$ method.

5.18 The deep beam of the accompanying figure has been designed by using $f_y = 50,000$ psi and $f'_c = 3750$ psi.
(a) Determine if shear reinforcement is required.
(b) If so, determine the required spacing for #3 vertical U stirrups.

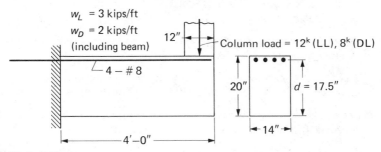

Prob. 5.18

5.19 Design the shear reinforcement for the beam shown. The rectangular beam is to support heavy machinery, and the service loading is 12 kips/ft dead load and

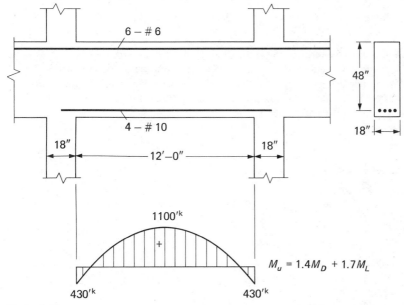

Prob. 5.19

40 kips/ft live load (including impact). The design moment diagram (including overload factors U) is given in the accompanying figure. Use $f'_c = 4000$ psi and $f_y = 60,000$ psi.

5.20 Design the flexural and shear reinforcement for a beam 16 in. wide × 52 in. deep overall to carry two concentrated live loads of 200 kips each symmetrically placed at 4 ft from the ends of a 20-ft span having support widths of 2 ft. Assume simple support similar to Fig. 5.14.2. Use $f'_c = 4000$ psi and $f_y = 60,000$ psi. (Beam: $b = 400$ mm; $h = 1.3$ m; concentrated loads = 890 kN; Distance from ends = 1.2 m; span = 6 m; support width = 0.6 m; $f'_c = 28$ N/mm^2; $f_y = 420$ N/mm^2.)

5.21 Design a bracket (corbel) that projects from one side of a 16 × 16 column to support a vertical load of 35 kips dead load and 65 kips live load. Assume that suitable bearings are provided so that horizontal restraint is eliminated. The reaction is located 5 in. from the column face. Use $f'_c = 5000$ psi and $f_y = 60,000$ psi. (Column size = 400 × 400 mm; dead load = 160 kN; live load = 290 kN; reaction 130 mm from column face; $f'_c = 35$ N/mm^2; $f_y = 420$ N/mm^2.)

5.22 Design for the conditions of Prob. 5.21 except take the reaction location 9 in. (230 mm) from the column face.

5.23 Repeat Prob. 5.21 if the reaction is from a restrained beam that induces a horizontal tension equal to 50% of the total gravity reaction.

5.24 Repeat Prob. 5.22 if the reaction is from a restrained beam that induces a horizontal tension equal to 40% of the total gravity reaction.

5.25 Redesign the bracket (corbel) or Example 5.15.1 considering that the supported prestressed girder is welded to the bracket. Creep, shrinkage, and temperature effects on the restrained girder induce a horizontal force of 50 kips on the bracket.

5.26 Redesign the bracket (corbel) of Prob. 5.21 if the reaction is 3.5 in. (90 mm) from the column face. Apply the shear-friction provisions of the ACI Code.

5.27 Redesign the bracket (corbel) of Prob. 5.23 if the reaction is 3.5 in. (90 mm) from the column face. Apply the shear-friction provisions of the ACI Code.

5.28 Design the details of the bearing shoe on a prestressed girder of 12 in. width. Assume an angle will be used across the width for bearing as in Fig. 5.16 lb. The reaction is 35 kips dead load and 40 kips live load. The girder concrete has $f'_c = 6000$ psi. Assume no horizontal restraint is developed.

6

Bond
Stress
and Development
of Reinforcement

6.1 General

Bond stress is the force per unit of nominal surface area of a reinforcing bar acting parallel to the bar on the interface between the bar and the surrounding concrete. It has been customary to compute bond stress by dividing the change in the tensile force within the bar at two adjacent sections by the cylindrical surface area of the bar between these two sections based on the nominal diameter, thus ignoring the extra bearing area provided by the ribbed deformations.

Bond stress may also be thought of as the rate of transfer of load between concrete and steel. In other words if there is bond stress there is a change in steel stress, or conversely if there is a change in steel stress, there must be bond stress.

A basic requirement in reinforced concrete construction is that the steel and surrounding concrete act together, and that under service load there is no slip of the bar relative to its surrounding concrete. From an ultimate strength point of view, slippage of bars relative to surrounding concrete may or may not result in overall failure of the beam. Even though there may be complete separation of bars and concrete over much of the length, a beam may continue to carry load as long as the bars cannot pull out at the ends. Mechanical end anchorages may be used to accomplish integrity of the system, or wherever possible, bars should be anchored by embedment beyond the point where the loading causes maximum flexure a distance adequate to develop the full tensile capacity of the bar.

The concepts of bond stress and anchorage (either by development of reinforcement or mechanical anchorage) are presented in the next several

Brunswick Building, Chicago. (Courtesy of Portland Cement Association.)

sections. An excellent summary also appears in ACI Committee 408 reports [1,2], and more recently the mechanics of bond and slip has been explained by Lutz and Gergely [14].

6.2 Anchorage Bond

Design of longitudinal and shear reinforcement to accommodate the moment and shear at sections along a beam has been treated in Chaps. 3, 4, and 5. For resisting the bending moment, an area of longitudinal steel is provided to carry a tensile force. It must also be realized that no matter what area is provided, if the bars are not anchored in the concrete sufficiently so that bond between steel and concrete can develop the applied tensile force, the bars will pull out. The moment capacity of a beam is, therefore, a three-dimensional relationship involving not only the cross-sectional properties at a location along the span, but also the embedment lengths in both directions therefrom.

Consider a uniformly loaded cantilever beam as shown in Fig. 6.2.1a, which has been properly proportioned for flexural strength. To illustrate the principle, assume that the tension reinforcement consists of one single bar of diameter d_b. When the bar segment AB is considered as a free body as shown in Fig. 6.2.1b, the tensile force at B, which is $f_s(\pi d_b^2/4)$, must be transmitted to the concrete by bond stress in the embedment length $L_1 = AB$. If u is the average unit bond stress over the nominal surface area $\pi d_b L_1$, then

$$u\pi d_b L_1 = f_s \pi \frac{d_b^2}{4}$$

or

$$u = \frac{f_s d_b}{4L_1} \tag{6.2.1}$$

Thus when the anchorage bond stress that is capable of being developed is u, the development length required for a given f_s becomes

$$\text{development length } L_1 = \frac{f_s}{4u} d_b \tag{6.2.2}$$

The same situation exists in free body BC, as shown in Fig. 6.2.1c. Thus the maximum tensile force at B has to be developed by embedment through

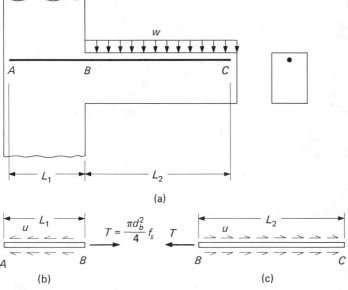

Fig. 6.2.1
Anchorage bond in tension bars.

the distances BA or BC. Where space limitations prevent anchoring the bars the proper amount, such bars may be terminated by a standard hook. A tension bar terminated by a standard hook may be considered to develop by mechanical action a tensile stress f_h that is proportional to the tensile strength of concrete (ACI-12.5), thus reducing the embedment length required.

When the strength method is used for design, the objective is to develop the yield stress f_y in the steel; therefore f_s of Eq. (6.2.2) becomes f_y. Also the bond stress u is the nominal unit stress when a pullout failure is imminent; that is, the ultimate bond stress capacity u_u. Thus the development length L_d required for the anchoring of bars acting at yield stress is

$$\text{development length } L_d = \frac{f_y d_b}{4u_u} \tag{6.2.3}$$

Adequate development lengths must be provided for reinforcing bars in compression as well as in tension.

6.3 Flexural Bond

As moment varies along a span, the tensile force in the steel also varies; this induces a longitudinal interaction between the bars and the surrounding concrete, known as *flexural bond stress*. High flexural bond stress exists at locations along the span where the rate of change of tensile stress in the bars is high, such as at points of inflection within continuous spans and at simply supported ends of beams, even though the tensile force to be developed at such locations is zero.

Consider a segment DD' of the reinforcing bar in the same cantilever beam used in Sec. 6.2. As shown by the free body of DD' in Fig. 6.3.1b, T_D

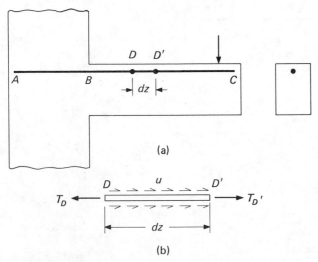

(a)

(b)

Fig. 6.3.1
Flexural bond in a tension bar.

is slightly greater than $T_{D'}$. Let jd be the moment arm between the internal forces C and T,

$$T_D = \frac{M_D}{jd} \quad \text{and} \quad T_{D'} = \frac{M_{D'}}{jd} \tag{6.3.1}$$

Also

$$u\pi d_b\, dz = T_D - T_{D'} \tag{6.3.2}$$

in which d_b is the diameter of the single bar. Substituting Eq. (6.3.1) in Eq. (6.3.2),

$$u = \frac{M_D - M_{D'}}{dz}\left(\frac{1}{\pi d_b\, jd}\right) = \frac{dM}{dz}\left(\frac{1}{\pi d_b\, jd}\right) = \frac{V}{\pi d_b\, jd} \tag{6.3.3}$$

Equation (6.3.3) gives the flexural bond stress in the tension bar at any cross section of the beam.

6.4 Flexural Bond Stress in a Group of Tension Bars

Consider a single bar of diameter d_b in a group of which the total area is ΣA_s. In applying the flexural bond formula, Eq. (6.3.3), the numerator should then be multiplied by the factor $(\pi d_b^2/4)/\Sigma A_s$ on the assumption that each bar carries a part of the total tensile force in the same proportion as its area is to the total area, ΣA_s. Equation (6.3.3) then becomes

$$u = \frac{V}{(4/d_b)(\Sigma A_s)jd} \tag{6.4.1}$$

It may be seen from Eq. (6.4.1) that in a group of bars of mixed sizes the largest flexural bond stress occurs around the bar with the largest diameter. If the group consists of N bars of uniform size, Eq. (6.4.1) becomes

$$u = \frac{V}{(4/d_b)(N\pi d_b^2/4)jd} = \frac{V}{(N\pi d_b)jd} = \frac{V}{\Sigma o\, jd} \tag{6.4.2}$$

where Σo is the total perimeter $N\pi d_b$ of all tension bars at the section.

Since in ordinary practice there would be several bars taking the total tension, Eqs. (6.4.1) and (6.4.2) are the formulas for computing the flexural bond stress in a group of bars of different and equal size, respectively.

6.5 Flexural Bond Stress in Compression Reinforcement

Consider the compression bar in the cantilever beam shown in Fig. 6.5.1a which has been designed as a doubly reinforced beam. Equating the horizontal forces acting on the free body DD' in Fig. 6.5.1b,

$$u\pi d_b\, dz = C_D - C_{D'} \tag{6.5.1}$$

Let k be the fraction of the bending moment at section D taken by the compression reinforcement and its counterpart in the tension reinforcement.

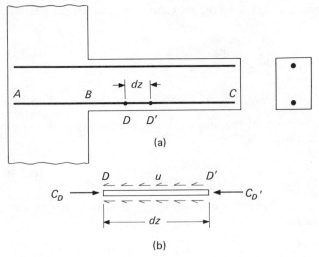

Fig. 6.5.1
Flexural bond in a compression bar.

Then

$$C_D - C_{D'} = \frac{k(M_D - M_{D'})}{jd} \qquad (6.5.2)$$

Substituting Eq. (6.5.2) in Eq. (6.5.1),

$$u = \frac{k(M_D - M_{D'})}{dz}\left(\frac{1}{\pi d_b jd}\right) = k\frac{dM}{dz}\left(\frac{1}{\pi d_b jd}\right) = \frac{kV}{\pi d_b jd} \qquad (6.5.3)$$

The fraction k is usually one half or less. Consequently flexural bond stress is rarely high on compression reinforcement.

6.6 The Nature of Bond Failure

Formerly when steel reinforcement consisted of plain bars (relatively smooth bars without lug deformations), bond was thought of as an adhesion between concrete paste and the surface of the bar. Even with low tensile stress in reinforcement, there would be sufficient slippage to break the adhesion immediately adjacent to a crack in the concrete, leaving only friction as a means of resisting any bar movement relative to the surrounding concrete over the slip length. Shrinkage can also cause frictional drag against the bars. Typically, a hot rolled *plain* bar may either pull loose by longitudinal splitting if the adhesion and friction resistances are high enough, or just pull out leaving a round hole when adhesion and friction resistances are low.

Deformed bars were designed to change the behavior pattern so that there would be less reliance on friction and adhesion (though they still exist) and more reliance on the bearing of the lugs against the concrete. A so-called "bond failure" with deformed bars in ordinary weight concrete

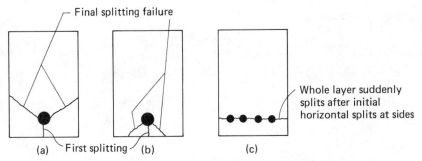

Fig. 6.6.1
Splitting cracks and ultimate splitting failure modes (from Ref. 1).

is nearly always a splitting failure [1]. In a splitting failure the concrete splits into two or three segments due to the wedging action of the lugs against the concrete, as shown by the several typical splitting crack patterns in Fig. 6.6.1. The interacting forces between the deformed bar and the surrounding concrete may be seen from Fig. 6.6.2.

When small size bars are used with large cover, or when there may tend to be air pockets at the underside of bars cast in the top of beams, the lugs bearing against the concrete may crush it and result in a pullout failure without splitting the concrete. This nonsplitting failure has also been reported for larger bars on lightweight concrete [1]. Although splitting is the usual bond failure mode, it is noted that an initial splitting crack on one face of a beam does *not* constitute failure. Progressive splitting is the first sign of bond distress and may be considered the usual cause of bond collapse. Confinement of tension steel by stirrups, ties, or spirals may significantly delay bond collapse until several splitting cracks have formed.

Early studies on bond strength (combining splitting and friction) of deformed bars were a carry-over from studies on plain bars, and primarily consisted of pullout tests [4,5,9,11,12,15]. In pullout tests the concrete is confined so that the results may provide data concerning anchorage but probably little about the factors that relate to splitting. The focus on splitting as the important bond failure mode was given impetus by the work of Ferguson, Turpin, and Thompson [6].

Because of the incomplete knowledge about bond strength and of the interrelationship between bond, shear, and moment, present design practice makes use of a large number of experimental studies. In general, bond

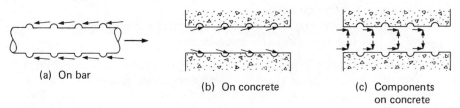

Fig. 6.6.2
Forces between bar and concrete (from Ref. 6).

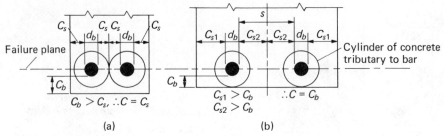

Fig. 6.6.3
Concrete cylinder hypothesis for splitting failure (18).

strength is directly proportional to $\sqrt{f'_c}$ (i.e., proportional to the tensile strength of the concrete) and inversely proportional to the bar diameter.

Recent studies [18] have hypothesized that the action of splitting arises from a stress condition analogous to a concrete cylinder surrounding a reinforcing bar and acted upon by the outward radial components (Fig. 6.6.2c) of the bearing forces from the bar. The cylinder would have an inner diameter equal to the bar diameter d_b and a thickness C equal to the smaller of C_b, the clear bottom cover, or C_s, half of the clear spacing to the next adjacent bar (see Fig. 6.6.3). The tensile strength of this concrete cylinder determines the strength against splitting. If $C_s < C_b$, a side-split type of failure occurs (Fig. 6.6.1c). When $C_s > C_b$, longitudinal cracks through the bottom cover form first (first splitting cracks in Fig. 6.6.1a,b). If C_s is only nominally greater than C_b, the secondary splitting will be side splitting along the plane of the bars. If C_s is significantly greater than C_b, the secondary splitting will also be through the bottom cover to create a V-notch failure (Fig. 6.6.1b).

6.7 Reasons for not Using Flexural Bond Stress in Strength Design

When evaluating the strength of a beam, flexural bond stress does not provide an adequate measure of the margin of safety against a splitting (or bond) failure. The reasons may be divided into two general categories: (1) inability of the flexural bond stress equations (Eqs. 6.4.1 and 6.4.2) to measure accurately bond stress along tension reinforcement in a beam; and (2) lack of correlation between *localized* slippage from high flexural bond stress and the strength of a beam as represented by splitting and subsequent loss of anchorage of the tension bars.

Several situations may be identified where flexural bond stress as computed by Eqs. (6.4.1) and (6.4.2) is inaccurate:

1. The tension concrete is uncracked in a region of low bending moment; thus the flexural bond stress is overestimated as concrete still carries part of the tensile force.
2. At a point where high bending moment exists, according to Eqs. (6.4.1) and (6.4.2) the low shear would indicate low flexural bond stress; however,

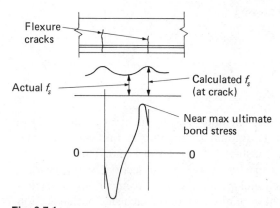

Fig. 6.7.1
Probable bond stress between cracks when beam shear
is zero (from Ref. 5).

at a flexural crack (see Fig. 6.7.1) in such a region the steel carries all
of the tensile force; but adjacent to such a crack, bond stress is likely
to be high since the concrete shares in carrying the tension [5,12].
3. In the vicinity of a shear-related inclined crack, such as that of Fig. 5.4.2,
not only does high bond stress exist adjacent to the crack but in addition
the tensile force T computed at z from the support actually acts at a
much closer distance from the support; that is, at the shear crack intersection with the longitudinal steel.
4. At locations where some bars are terminated in a tension zone, there
is an abrupt change in the distribution of the total tensile force among
the bars, causing stress concentrations [8,20] and bond stresses greatly
in excess of formula predictions.

Thus the computed flexural bond stress represents only a nominal stress
and does not correctly reflect true behavior. If the bars remain adequately
anchored so as to continue to carry their required tensile force, no reduction
in strength should result from a so-called "local failure." The design approach
of the ACI Code is to utilize the ultimate strength concept of requiring
adequate anchorage, that is, development length, and eliminate computation
of nominal flexural bond stress which had been a major design consideration
since the early 1900s.

6.8 Moment Capacity Diagram—Bar Bends and Cutoffs

As stated in Sec. 6.2, the moment capacity of a beam at any section along
its length is a function of its cross section and the embedment length of its
reinforcement. The concept of a diagram showing this three-dimensional
relationship can be a valuable aid in determining cutoff or bend points of
longitudinal reinforcement. It may be recalled from Chaps. 3 and 4 that in
terms of the cross section, the moment capacity for a singly reinforced

rectangular beam may be expressed

$$M_n = A_s f_y (d - a/2)$$

in the strength method, or

$$M_w = A_s f_s (d - x/3)$$

in the alternate working stress method. The moment arms $(d - a/2)$ or $(d - x/3)$ change somewhat as amount of reinforcement varies, but may be assumed to be relatively constant for any given beam. Thus it may be assumed that the moment capacity at any given section of the beam is proportional to the cross-sectional area of the reinforcement at that section, assuming proper development of reinforcement on each side of that section. At locations where embedment is less than that necessary to develop full tensile capacity, the moment capacity is reduced proportionally.

EXAMPLE 6.8.1   Compute and draw the moment capacity diagram qualitatively for the beam of Fig. 6.8.1.

Solution: The procedure is basically the same whether ultimate strength moment capacity or working stress moment capacity is desired.

The maximum capacity in each region is represented by the horizontal portions of the diagram in Fig. 6.8.1. In this example there are five bars of one size in section C-C; thus the maximum moment capacity represented by each bar is in this case approximately one-fifth of the total capacity. Actually, the sections with four and two bars will have more than four-fifths and two-fifths, respectively, of the total capacity of the section containing five bars, due to the slight increase in moment arm when the number of bars in the section decreases.

At point *a*, the location where the fifth bar terminates, this bar has zero embedment length to the left and thus has zero capacity. Proceeding to the right from point *a*, the bar may be counted on to carry a tensile force proportional to its embedment from point *a* up to a maximum development length L_d where, according to Eq. (6.2.3),

$$L_d = \frac{f_y d_b}{4 u_u}$$

For instance, if the yield stress $f_y = 40,000$ psi is to be developed and #8 bars are used with an ultimate bond stress capacity of 520 psi, the development length necessary would be

$$L_d = \frac{40,000(1)}{4(520)} = 19.2 \text{ in.}$$

In Fig. 6.8.1, point *b* represents the point where the fifth bar is anchored a distance L_d and can therefore carry its full tensile capacity. The other cutoff points are treated in the same way.

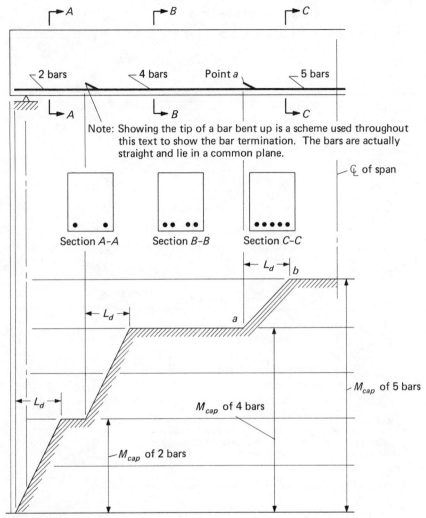

Fig. 6.8.1
Moment capacity diagram.

EXAMPLE 6.8.2   Demonstrate qualitatively the use of the moment capacity diagram for verification of the locations of cutoff or bend points in a design. Assume that the main cross section with five equal-sized bars provides exactly the required capacity at midspan for this simply supported beam with uniform load, as shown in Fig. 6.8.2.

Solution: The factored moment diagram and the moment capacity diagram for the chosen arrangement are shown in Fig. 6.8.2.

(a) Proportion into each bar according its area the maximum moment capacity M_{cap} of the beam with five bars. In this case, each bar may be assumed to carry one-fifth of the total. Alternatively, especially in the strength method of design since the calculation is simple, compute actual M_{cap} for

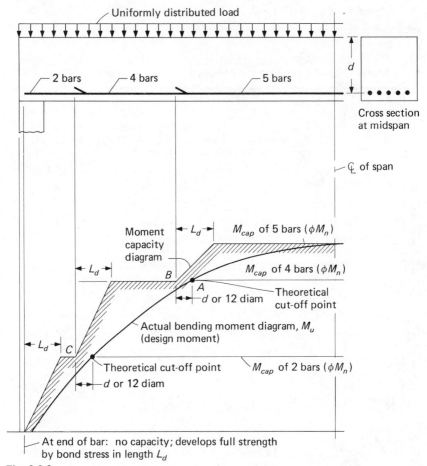

Fig. 6.8.2
Verification of bar cutoffs with the moment capacity diagram.

each potential bar grouping that may be used; in the present case, for five bars, four bars, and two bars.

(b) Decide what bars must extend entirely across the span and into the support; ACI-12.12.1 states that "At least one-third of the positive moment reinforcement in simple members ... shall extend along the same face of the member into the support." In beams the reinforcement must extend into the support at least 6 in. In this case two bars would have to extend into the support.

(c) Decide on the order of cutting or bending the remaining bars. The least amount of longitudinal reinforcement will be obtained when the resulting moment capacity diagram is closest to the design moment diagram. With that thought in mind, and proceeding from maximum moment region to the support, cut off one bar as soon as permissible.

(d) Cutoff restrictions. Point A of Fig. 6.8.2 is the theoretical location to the left of which the capacity represented by the remaining four bars is adequate. To provide for a safety factor against shifting of the moment diagram (especially in continuous spans) and to provide partially for the difficulty arising from a potential diagonal crack, the ACI Code provides that there should be an extension beyond the point where a bar theoretically may be terminated or bent into the compression face. In ACI-12.11.3 is the statement, "Reinforcement shall extend beyond the point at which it is no longer required to resist flexure for a distance equal to the effective depth of the member or 12 bar diameters, whichever is greater, except at supports of simple spans and at the free end of cantilevers."

(e) Once cutoff or bend points are located, a check is made by drawing the moment capacity diagram to insure no encroachment on the design moment diagram.

(f) Other restrictions. Since points B and C of Fig. 6.8.2 are bar terminations in a tension zone, the stress concentrations described in Sec. 6.7 are present, effectively reducing the shear strength of the beam [20]. Thus at least one of the three special conditions of ACI-12.11.5 must be satisfied for cutoffs to be acceptable. However, if these bars were bent up and anchored in the compression zone, no further investigation would be necessary.

6.9 Basic Development Length for Tension Reinforcement

The term "development length" has been defined in Sec. 6.2 as the length of embedment needed to develop the yield stress in the reinforcement. Equation (6.2.3) gives an expression for the development length L_d in terms of the yield stress f_y, the bar diameter d_b, and the ultimate bond stress capacity u_u as follows:

$$L_d = \frac{f_y d_b}{4u_u} \qquad [6.2.3]$$

The four formulas for the basic development length of tension reinforcement as stated in ACI-12.2.2 and shown below may be derived by using Eq. (6.2.3) and a set of values of ultimate bond stress capacity u_u for different bar sizes; thus

1. For #11 or smaller bars, the larger of

$$L_d = 0.04\frac{A_b f_y}{\sqrt{f'_c}} \qquad \text{or} \quad 0.0004d_b f_y \qquad (6.9.1)^\dagger$$

2. For #14 bars,

$$L_d = 0.085\frac{f_y}{\sqrt{f'_c}} \qquad (6.9.2)$$

---

† In S.I. units, Eq. (6.9.1) becomes:
For 32-mm diameter bars or smaller,

$$L_d = 0.019\frac{A_b f_y}{\sqrt{f'_c}} \qquad \text{or} \quad 0.058\,d_b f_y$$

with L_d and d_b in mm, A_b in mm^2, and f_y and f'_c in N/mm^2.

3. For #18 bars,

$$L_d = 0.11 \frac{f_y}{\sqrt{f'_c}} \qquad (6.9.3)$$

4. For deformed wire (but not deformed wire fabric),

$$L_d = 0.03 \frac{d_b f_y}{\sqrt{f'_c}} \qquad (6.9.4)$$

In Eqs. (6.9.1) to (6.9.4), the dimensional units of L_d and d_b are inches; of A_b, square inches; and of f_y and $\sqrt{f'_c}$, pounds per square inch. Basic development lengths for tension reinforcement in some of the common situations are given in Table 6.9.1.

Modifications of these basic formulas for special situations are discussed in Sec. 6.10. Except for lap splices (Sec. 6.19) and anchorage of stirrups (Sec. 6.18), the minimum L_d to be used after all modifications are applied is 12 in.

The ACI basic expressions for L_d involve reducing the average ultimate unit bond stress capacities u_u given in the 1963 ACI Code (see Table 6.9.2) by a factor 5/6 so as to give an increased development length. The original bond stress capacities were developed for use in both flexural bond and anchorage bond stress calculations, and for many years the ACI Code had both requirements. When there is adequate length of embedment in both directions from a section, however, even though the flexural bond stress may be locally high at this section, the structural integrity is maintained as long as the bars cannot pull out. This strength concept recognizes that the bond stress may become redistributed so that it is nearly uniform along the embedment length when pullout failure is imminent. The present ACI Code requires longer embedment lengths than were used in the 1963 Code to decrease the possibility of a splitting failure until the resistance developed between the bar and its surrounding concrete can become nearly uniform along the length L_d measured from the end of the bar.

Using, then, 5/6 of the bond stress capacities itemized in Table 6.9.2 for u_u in the development length formula, Eq. (6.9.1) for #11 and smaller bars may be substantiated as follows:

$$L_d = \frac{f_y d_b}{4u_u} = \frac{f_y d_b}{4[(5/6)(9.5\sqrt{f'_c}/d_b)]} = 0.0402 \frac{A_b f_y}{\sqrt{f'_c}}$$

$$L_d \geq \frac{f_y d_b}{4u_u} = \frac{f_y d_b}{4[(5/6)800]} = 0.000375 d_b f_y$$

Likewise, for #14 bars (Eq. 6.9.2),

$$L_d = \frac{f_y d_b}{4u_u} = \frac{f_y(1.693)}{4[(5/6)6\sqrt{f'_c}]} = 0.0847 \frac{f_y}{\sqrt{f'_c}}$$

and for #18 bars (Eq. 6.9.3),

$$L_d = \frac{f_y d_b}{4u_u} = \frac{f_y(2.257)}{4[(5/6)6\sqrt{f'_c}]} = 0.113 \frac{f_y}{\sqrt{f'_c}}$$

Table 6.9.1
Basic Development Length L_d for Tension Reinforcement

	ASTM Bars with L_d in Inches					
	$f_y = 40,000\ psi$			$f_y = 60,000\ psi$		
	$f'_c\ (psi)$			$f'_c\ (psi)$		
Bar Size	3000	4000	5000	3000	4000	5000
#3	12[a]	12[a]	12[a]	9[b]	9[b]	9[b]
#4	12[a]	12[a]	12[a]	12	12	12
#5	10[b]	10[b]	10[b]	15	15	15
#6	12.8	12	12	19.2	18	18
#7	17.5	15.2	14	26.2	22.8	21
#8	23.1	20.0	17.9	34.6	30.0	26.8
#9	29.2	25.3	22.6	43.8	38.0	33.9
#10	37.1	32.2	28.8	55.6	48.2	43.1
#11	45.5	39.5	35.4	68.4	59.2	53.0
#14	62.1	53.8	48.1	93.1	80.6	72.1
#18	80.3	69.6	62.2	121	104	93.3

	Metric Bars with L_d in Centimeters					
	$f_y = 280\ N/mm^2$			$f_y = 420\ N/mm^2$		
Bar Diameter (mm)	$f'_c\ (N/mm^2)$			$f'_c\ (N/mm^2)$		
	21	28	35	21	28	35
10	30[a]	30[a]	30[a]	24.4[b]	24.4[b]	24.4[b]
12	30[a]	30[a]	30[a]	29.2[b]	29.2[b]	29.2[b]
16	26.0[b]	26.0[b]	26.0[b]	39.0	39.0	39.0
20	36.5	32.5	32.5	54.7	48.7	48.7
22	44.1	38.2	35.7	66.2	57.3	53.6
25	57.0	49.4	44.2	85.5	74.0	66.2
28	71.5	61.9	55.4	107	92.9	83.1
32	93.3	80.8	72.3	140	121	108
40[c]	140	121	109	210	182	163
50[c]	180	155	139	269	233	209
60[c]	216	187	167	324	280	251

[a] Development length is governed by 12 in. (30 cm) minimum even with top bar modification (see Sec. 6.10).

[b] If no modification factors greater than 1.0 are to be used, value is 12 in. (30 cm) minimum.

[c] On basis of bar area, coefficients in Eqs. (6.9.2) and (6.9.3) are changed to 0.075 for 40-mm bar, 0.096 for 50-mm bar, and 0.1154 for 60-mm bar.

For *deformed* wire, using 5/6 of a basic bond stress capacity of $10\sqrt{f'_c}$ (see Ref. 16),

$$L_d = \frac{f_y d_b}{4u_u} = \frac{f_y d_b}{4[(5/6)10\sqrt{f'_c}]} = 0.03\frac{d_b f_y}{\sqrt{f'_c}}$$

Table 6.9.2
Average Ultimate Bond Stress Capacities as Given by 1963 ACI Code

Deformed Bars	Basic Bond Stress u_u	Top Bars, u_u
Tension: #11 and smaller	$\dfrac{9.5\sqrt{f'_c}}{d_b} \le 800$ psi	$\dfrac{6.7\sqrt{f'_c}}{d_b} \le 560$ psi
Tension: #14 and #18	$6\sqrt{f'_c}$	$4.2\sqrt{f'_c}$
Compression: All sizes	$13\sqrt{f'_c} \le 800$ psi	$13\sqrt{f'_c} \le 800$ psi

Some of the numerical constants as obtained above have been rounded off to obtain those adopted in the ACI Code.

6.10 Factors to Modify Basic Development Length

Modifications to the basic development lengths for tension reinforcement are prescribed by ACI-12.2.3 and 12.2.4 to account for conditions that may either decrease or increase the tendency for splitting.

Unfavorable conditions indicating a weaker situation so as to require an increased development length over the basic one are (1) when horizontal bars are placed so that more than 12 in. of concrete is cast in the member below the bars, known as *top bars;* (2) when the reinforcement yield stress f_y exceeds 60,000 psi; and (3) when lightweight aggregate concrete is used.

Favorable conditions that permit a reduction in the required development length from the basic value are (1) when reinforcement is laterally spaced at least 6 in. on center with at least 3 in. from the edge bar to the face of the member measured in the direction of the spacing (i.e., typically slabs); (2) when more reinforcement than required for strength has been used in the flexural member; and (3) when bars are confined by enclosure within a spiral (such as in a beam-column member; see Chap. 13).

A summary of the modification factors given by ACI-12.2.3 and 12.2.4 appears in Table 6.10.1. These multipliers are to be applied cumulatively, as illustrated in Example 6.10.1.

The requirement of extra development length for top bars has long been a provision of the ACI Code in recognition of the fact that top cast bars exhibit reduced strength apparently due to the settling away of concrete from the bar on its underside [1,11]. The exact variation of bond strength with depth of concrete below the bars has not been established. Limited tests with concrete depths of 12 to 18 in. and with high-strength steel bars have indicated the ultimate splitting resistance to be lowered about 10 to 20% [1].

For lightweight concrete, the increased development lengths are necessary because bars may pull out without splitting the concrete [2].

The reductions in development length permitted for wide lateral spacing and for confinement in a spiral are in recognition of the favorable influence of these factors in restricting the propagation of splitting; however, the

Table 6.10.1

Modification Factors for Basic Development Length (ACI-12.2.3 and 12.2.4)

Condition	Multiplier
1. Top bars; horizontal reinforcement with more than 12 in. of concrete cast beneath the bars	1.4
2. Reinforcement with f_y greater than 60,000 psi	$2 - \dfrac{60,000}{f_y}$

3. Lightweight concrete:
  (a) "All-lightweight" concrete
    "Sand-lightweight" concrete
    (Linear interpolation may be used when partial sand replacement is used)
 	
  or
 	
  (b) When average splitting tensile strength f_{ct} is specified, and concrete is proportioned according to ACI-4.2
	1.33
	1.18
	
	$\dfrac{6.7\sqrt{f'_c}}{f_{ct}} \geq 1.0$

4. Wide lateral spacing of bars; at least 6 in. on center and at least 3 in. from the edge bar to the face of member	0.8
5. Excess reinforcement is used for a flexural member	$\dfrac{\text{required } A_s}{\text{provided } A_s} \leq 1.0$
6. Bars enclosed within a spiral not less than $\frac{1}{4}$ in. diameter and not more than 4 in. pitch	0.75

specific multipliers are somewhat arbitrary. Bars within stirrups and ties also show improved resistance to splitting but no quantitative relationship has been established.

EXAMPLE 6.10.1 Determine the development length L_d required for the #9 bars A on the top of a 15-in. slab, as shown in Fig. 6.10.1. Use $f_y = 70,000$ psi, and $f'_c = 4000$ psi.

Solution: The basic development length for a #9 bar is

$$L_d = 0.04 \frac{A_b f_y}{\sqrt{f'_c}} = 0.04 \frac{1.0(70,000)}{\sqrt{4000}} = 44.3 \text{ in.} \qquad \text{(Controls)}$$

or

$$L_d = 0.0004 d_b f_y = 0.0004(1.128)(70,000) = 31.6 \text{ in.}$$

Since the concrete thickness below the top bars exceeds 12 in., the 1.4 multiplier must be used.

The correction factor for high yield stress is

$$2 - \frac{60,000}{70,000} = 2 - 0.84 = 1.16$$

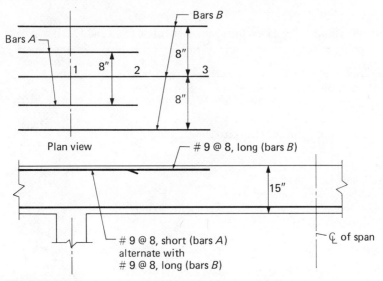

Fig. 6.10.1
Top bars for Example 6.10.1.

Referring to Fig. 6.10.1 the bars A are developed over the distance 1–2, while the bars B are developed over the distance 2–3. The spacing to be used for the comparison of the wide spacing requirement in Case 4, Table 6.10.1, is the spacing of the *closest bars that terminate at the same point*. In other words, the spacing for both bars A and B is 8 in. Thus the 0.8 multiplier may be used.

The development length for this situation is

$$L_d = 44.3(1.4)(1.16)(0.8) = 57.5 \text{ in.}$$

6.11 Development Length for Compression Reinforcement

Relatively little is known about bond on compression bars, except that the weakening effect of flexural tension cracks is not present and there is the beneficial effect of the end bearing of the bars on the concrete. The ultimate bond stress capacity of compression bars in all sizes has been taken as $13\sqrt{f'_c}$ but not to exceed 800 psi in the 1963 ACI Code, as listed in Table 6.9.2. Without the necessity of reducing the bond stress capacity to 5/6 of its value, the development length expression for compression reinforcement may be obtained from Eq. (6.2.3) as

$$L_d = \frac{f_y d_b}{4u_u} = \frac{f_y d_b}{4(13)\sqrt{f'_c}} = 0.0192\left(\frac{f_y d_b}{\sqrt{f'_c}}\right)$$

which ACI-12.3 gives as

$$L_d = 0.02\left(\frac{f_y d_b}{\sqrt{f'_c}}\right) \qquad (6.11.1)$$

Using the upper limit of 800 psi for u_u,

$$L_d = \frac{f_y d_b}{4u_u} = \frac{f_y d_b}{4(800)} = 0.000312 f_y d_b$$

which ACI-12.3 gives as

$$L_d = 0.0003 f_y d_b \qquad \textbf{(6.11.2)}$$

The required development length is the larger of Eqs. (6.11.1) and (6.11.2), and *shall not be less than 8 in.*

When excess bar area is provided so that the A_s provided exceeds the A_s required, Eqs. (6.11.1) or (6.11.2), whichever controls, may be reduced by applying the multiplier (required A_s/provided A_s).

When reinforcement is enclosed by spirals (typically in columns; see Chap. 13) which are not less than $\frac{1}{4}$ in. in diameter and not more than 4-in. pitch, Eqs. (6.11.1) or (6.11.2) may be reduced by 25%. Confinement by spirals has been shown to increase the strength of all types of concrete members; hence the somewhat arbitrary 25% reduction in the required development length. Thus, in general, the development length for compression reinforcement is

$$L_d = \left[\begin{array}{c}\text{Eqs. (6.11.1)}\\ \text{or (6.11.2)}\end{array}\right]\left[\frac{\text{required } A_s}{\text{provided } A_s}\right]\left[\begin{array}{c}0.75 \text{ for enclosure}\\ \text{by spirals}\end{array}\right] \geq 8 \text{ in.} \qquad \textbf{(6.11.3)}$$

6.12 Development Length for Bundled Bars

When space for proper clearance is restricted and large steel areas are required, groups of parallel bars are sometimes bundled. Not more than four bars bundled in contact (ACI-7.6.6), enclosed by stirrups or ties, may be arranged with no more than two bars in the same plane into typical bundle shapes, such as triangular, square, or L shaped for three- and four-bar bundles (see Fig. 6.12.1). Bars larger than #11 shall not be bundled in beams or girders, primarily to insure proper control of cracking (see ACI Commentary-7.6.6). In flexural members, termination of individual bars within a bundle at points along the span must be at different points offset by at least 40 bar diameters. Where spacing requirements and minimum clear cover are based on bar size, one bundle of bars shall be treated as a single bar of an equivalent diameter derived from the total area of the bars in the bundle. In applying the crack control provisions of ACI-10.6.4 (see Chap. 4, Sec. 4.12) to bundled bars, this assumption of treating a bundle of bars as a single large bar may be overly conservative. An alternative is suggested by Lutz [17].

Fig. 6.12.1
Bundled bar arrangements (bars are in contact with each other).

When considering bond strength for a bundle of bars, the three-bar triangular pattern and the four-bar arrangement will have $16\frac{2}{3}$ and 25% reduction, respectively, in the total surface contact of bars with surrounding concrete. In order to allow further for the difficulty of getting good bond at the reentrant corner where the bars in the bundle touch each other, additional reduction appears logical.

The requirements of ACI-12.4 specify that the development length of the bundle shall be based on that for the individual bar in the bundle, increased by 20% for a three-bar bundle and 33% for a four-bar bundle.

Experimental results for beams and columns with bundled reinforcement are reported in Ref. 7, and some practical applications are presented in Ref. 13.

6.13 Equivalent Development Length of Standard Hooks

For tensile stress situations in which either straight embedment is inadequate to provide for the necessary development length or it is desired to have the full capacity of a bar available in the shortest distance of embedment, a standard hook as defined in ACI-7.1 and 7.2 and shown in Fig. 6.13.1 may be used. Hooks are not considered effective in adding to the compressive resistance of reinforcement.

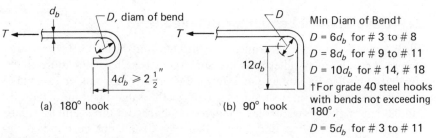

Fig. 6.13.1
Standard hooks for development of main tension reinforcement.

In general the anchorage capacity of a hook *in mass concrete* is about the same as that of a straight bar with the same total length of embedment [16,19]. Quite commonly hooks in *structural members* are located close to a free surface where splitting forces proportional to the tensile capacity of the bar will govern the hook capacity. Because of the tendency for splitting failures, hooks may have less capacity than provided by an equal length of straight embedment.

In the past it was customary to consider the actual length around the bend of a hook to the end of the bar as an alternative to the mechanical anchorage provided by the hook. With 90° hooks particularly, designers have often assumed that satisfactory anchorage is obtained by adding length to the end of the bar in excess of the 12 bar diameters (Fig. 6.13.1b) required as part of the hook. This is an unsatisfactory practice.

Table 6.13.1

Coefficient ξ for Tensile Stress Developed by a
Standard Hook (ACI-Table 12.5.1).

Bar Sizes	$f_y = 40,000\ psi$ All Bars	$f_y = 60,000\ psi$ Top Bars	Other Bars
#3 to #5	360	540	540
#6	360	450	540
#7 to #9	360	360	540
#10	360	360	480
#11	360	360	420
#14	330	330	330
#18	220	220	220

The tensile stress in a bar that may be considered to be developed by a hook is given in ACI-12.5 as

$$f_h = \xi\sqrt{f_c'} \qquad (6.13.1)$$

where ξ is the coefficient given by Table 6.13.1 and f_h is in psi. The value of ξ may be increased 30% where enclosure (such as by closed ties, stirrups, or spirals) is provided perpendicular to the plane of the hook.

The coefficients in Table 6.13.1 were obtained by updating the hook provisions of the 1963 ACI Code. The coefficients were established such that for $f_c' = 3000$ psi (1) the maximum tensile *stress* developed is $0.5f_y$; (2) the maximum tensile *force* developed is 50 kips; and (3) the average bond stress over the equivalent embedment length L_e does not exceed the bond stress capacity given in the 1963 ACI Code (see Table 6.9.2).

For design purposes, it is frequently desirable to convert the effect of a hook into an equivalent length L_e of embedment. This is accomplished by substitution of the tensile stress f_h that is considered to be developed by a hook into the development length expressions, Eqs. (6.9.1) through (6.9.4), replacing f_y by f_h. The results are presented in Table 6.13.2.

EXAMPLE 6.13.1 Illustrate the establishment of the values of the coefficient ξ and of the equivalent embedment length L_e of #4, #8, and #18 bar 180° standard hooks, for the case of top bars, with $f_c' = 4000$ psi, and $f_y = 60,000$ psi. The ultimate bond stress capacity given in the 1963 ACI Code for top bars (see Table 6.9.2 also) is $6.7\sqrt{f_c'}/d_b \le 560$ psi for #11 and smaller bars, and $4.2\sqrt{f_c'}$ for #14 and #18 bars. Check the computed values with those shown in Tables 6.13.1 and 6.13.2.

Solution: The values of the coefficient ξ are controlled by the three requirements as described in this section. For the first requirement,

$$f_h = \xi\sqrt{3000} = 0.5f_y = 0.5(60,000)$$
$$\xi = 548 \qquad \text{for all bar sizes}$$

Table 6.13.2

Equivalent Embedment Length L_e (in.) Provided by
Standard Hooks in Top Bars[a]

Bar Size	$f_y = 40,000$ psi f'_c (psi)			$f_y = 60,000$ psi f'_c (psi)		
	3000	4000	5000	3000	4000	5000
#3	3.0	3.4	3.8	4.4	5.1	5.7
#4	3.9	4.5	5.1	5.9	6.8	7.6
#5	4.9	5.7	6.3	7.4	8.5	9.5
#6	6.3	6.8	7.6	7.9[c]	8.5[c]	9.5[c]
#7	8.6	8.6	8.9	8.6[e]	8.6[e]	8.9[e]
#8	11.4	11.4	11.4	11.4[e]	11.4[e]	11.4[e]
#9	14.4	14.4	14.4	14.4[e]	14.4[e]	14.4[e]
#10	18.3	18.3	18.3	18.3[d]	18.3[d]	18.3[d]
#11	22.5	22.5	22.5	22.5[b]	22.5[b]	22.5[b]
#14	28.0	28.0	28.0	28.0	28.0	28.0
#18	24.2	24.2	24.2	24.2	24.2	24.2

[a] Values also valid for other than top bars, except as footnoted.
[b] Use 116.5% of this for other than top bars.
[c] Use 120% of this for other than top bars.
[d] Use 133% of this for other than top bars.
[e] Use 150% of this for other than top bars.

For the second requirement,

$$T = 50,000 = f_h A_b = \xi\sqrt{3000}A_b$$

$$\xi = \frac{912}{A_b} = 4560\ (\#4),\qquad 1153\ (\#8),\qquad 228\ (\#18)$$

For the third requirement (see Fig. 6.13.1a for bend diameter D),

$$\xi\sqrt{3000}A_b = u_u\pi d_b\left[\frac{\pi D}{2} + (\text{smaller of } 4d_b \text{ and } 2.5 \text{ in.})\right]$$

from which

$$\xi\ (\#4) = \frac{(\text{smaller of 735 and 560})\pi(0.5)[\pi(3)(0.5) + 2.5]}{54.8(0.20)} = 578$$

$$\xi\ (\#8) = \frac{(\text{smaller of 367 and 560})\pi(1.0)[\pi(3)(1.0) + 4]}{54.8(0.79)} = 357$$

$$\xi\ (\#18) = \frac{4.2\sqrt{3000}\pi(2.257)[\pi(5)(2.257) + 4(2.257)]}{54.8(4.00)} = 330$$

To satisfy all three requirements, the values of the coefficient ξ are 548 for #4, 357 for #8, and 228 for #18, all being top bars of 60,000 psi yield strength. These values compare well with 540, 360, and 220 shown in Table 6.13.1 (ACI-Table 12.5.1).

The values of the equivalent embedment length L_e are computed from replacing f_y in Eqs. (6.9.1) to (6.9.4) by $f_h = \xi\sqrt{f'_c}$; thus for $f'_c = 4000$ psi

$$L_e \,(\#4) = 0.04 A_b \xi \qquad \text{but not less than } 0.0004 d_b \xi \sqrt{f'_c}$$
$$= 0.04(0.20)(540) \qquad \text{or } 0.0004(0.5)(540)\sqrt{4000}$$
$$= 4.3 \text{ in. or } 6.8 \text{ in.,} \qquad L_e = 6.8 \text{ in.}$$
$$L_e \,(\#8) = 0.04 A_b \xi \qquad \text{but not less than } 0.0004 d_b \xi \sqrt{f'_c}$$
$$= 0.04(0.79)(360) \qquad \text{or } 0.0004(1.0)(360)\sqrt{4000}$$
$$= 11.4 \text{ in.} \qquad \text{or } 9.1 \text{ in.;} \qquad L_e = 11.4 \text{ in.}$$
$$L_e \,(\#18) = 0.11 \xi = 0.11(220) = 24.2 \text{ in.}$$

These values of the equivalent embedment length of 6.8 in., 11.4 in., and 24.2 in. are shown in Table 6.13.2 for top bars at $f_y = 60,000$ psi and $f'_c = 4000$ psi.

6.14 Bar Cutoffs in Negative-Moment Region of Continuous Beams

The general concept of drawing the moment capacity diagram to investigate the adequacy of a given beam has been presented in Sec. 6.8. In this and the next two sections, several situations are discussed in which the ACI Code provisions are applied to establish cutoff points, aided by the drawing of the moment capacity diagram. Three factors are involved: (1) adequate horizontal offset from theoretical cutoff points to provide safety against the possible shifting of the moment diagram due to unusual loading arrangements; (2) adequate embedment lengths so that full bar capacity is available where needed; and (3) sufficient relief from stress concentrations when bars are terminated in a tension zone.

Cutoffs in the negative-moment region of continuous beams can best be explained by means of a specified case. Referring to Fig. 6.14.1, assume that it is desired to cut two out of four bars as close as possible (point C) to the support, and then terminate the remaining two as soon as feasible (point E). In accordance with ACI-12.13.3, the area provided by bars $R2$ must exceed one-third the total reinforcement area provided for negative moment. In a general situation the horizontal distance between points C and E is greater than the development length L_d for bars $R2$; the special case wherein this is not so will be discussed later.

Point A represents the maximum moment at the face of support; the full moment capacity provided by bars $R1$ and $R2$ is somewhat greater than required. The theoretical cutoff for the two $R1$ bars is at point B. Point C is then located (ACI-12.11.3) horizontally to the right from point B a distance equal to the effective depth of the member or 12 diameters of bars $R1$. Point D is located horizontally to the left of point C a distance equal to the development length L_d for bars $R1$. Since points A and D will generally

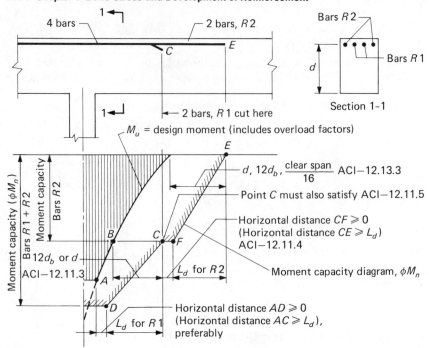

Fig. 6.14.1
Bar cutoff in negative moment region of continuous beams.

be approximately horizontal with one another, point D must lie at or to the right of point A in order to provide adequate capacity at the face of support. When extra capacity is provided, the safety may be considered adequate when the line CD intersects the face of support line at or below point A (satisfying ACI-12.13.2).

Point E is next established by extension, according to ACI-12.13.3, beyond the point of inflection (point of zero moment) "not less than the effective depth of the member, $12d_b$, or one-sixteenth of the clear span, whichever is greater." Point F, where the bars $R2$ will become capable of carrying their full capacity, is located L_d horizontally to the left of point E. In order that the moment capacity diagram does not encroach closer than $12d_b$ or d to point B, point F must lie to the right of point C.

The special case wherein the horizontal distance between points C and E is smaller than the development length L_d for bars $R2$ is shown in Fig. 6.14.2. The moment capacity diagram is indicated by $EC'F'D$, because the variation between the moment capacities at C' and F' has to be linear since development of capacity is assumed to be proportional to the amount of embedment up to a maximum length of L_d. The requirement to allow for the shifting of the design moment curve is to be satisfied by making sure that the distance BM is larger than the effective depth d or 12 diameters of bars $R1$.

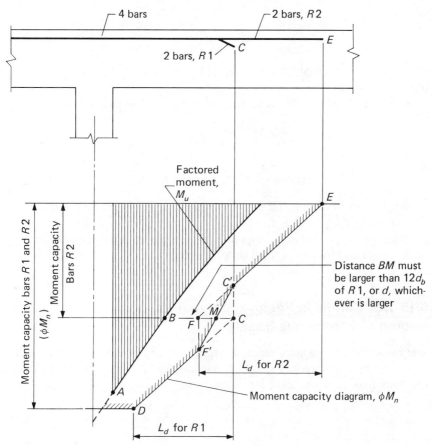

Fig. 6.14.2
Special case of Fig. 6.14.1 wherein the distance CE is less than L_d for bars $R2$.

Cutting Bars in the Tension Zone. Since point C is still in the tension zone (though only slightly), the provisions of ACI-12.11.5 to minimize stress concentrations must be checked. *One* of the following three conditions must be satisfied *at point C:*

1. The shear at the cutoff point does not exceed two-thirds of that permitted, or

$$V_u \leq \tfrac{2}{3}\phi V_n = \tfrac{2}{3}\phi(V_c + V_s) \tag{6.14.1a}$$

or using stresses, $V_n/(b_w d)$,

$$v_n \leq \tfrac{2}{3}(v_c + v_s) \tag{6.14.1b}$$

2. Excess stirrup area is provided to give a capacity of v_s at 60 psi above that required for shear and torsion. The excess stirrups are to be used along the terminated bar over a distance from the termination point equal to three-fourths of the effective depth of the member. The spacing of such

stirrups must not exceed

$$\max s = \frac{d}{8\beta_b} \tag{6.14.2}$$

where β_b is the ratio of area of longitudinal bars cut off to the total area of bars at the section.

3. For #11 and smaller bars, the following may be satisfied at the cutoff point:

$$V_u \le \tfrac{3}{4}\phi V_n = \tfrac{3}{4}\phi(V_c + V_s) \tag{6.14.3}$$

and

$$\text{provided } M_u \ge 2 \text{ (required } M_u) \tag{6.14.4}$$

When it may be impractical or undesirable to satisfy the above described provisions of ACI-12.11.5, the cutoff point may be extended until it is in the compression zone, or the bars may be bent across into the opposite face of the beam and then continued or terminated.

6.15 Bar Cutoffs in Positive-Moment Region of Continuous Beams

Bar cutoffs in the positive-moment region of continuous beams are to be explained by reference to Fig. 6.15.1. Assume that it is desired to cut two of the four bars that are used for resisting the maximum positive moment.

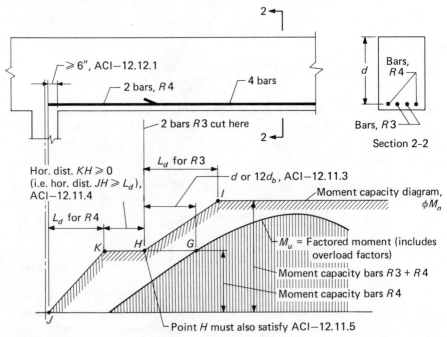

Fig. 6.15.1
Bar cutoff in positive moment region of continuous beams.

The area provided by bars $R4$ must exceed one-fourth (one-third for simple spans) of the total reinforcement area provided for positive moment, in accordance with ACI-12.12.1. In a general situation the horizontal distance between points J and H is greater than the development length L_d for bars $R4$; the special case wherein this is not so will be discussed later in the section.

Point G is first located by computing the moment capacity of the continuing bars $R4$. The cutoff point H must lie to the left of point G at least 12 diameters of bars $R3$ or the effective depth d, whichever is larger. Point I is then located horizontally to the right from point H a distance equal to the development length L_d for the bars $R3$. Point J is located at the end of the bars $R4$, and point K is located horizontally to the right of point J, a distance equal to the development length L_d for the bars $R4$. The cutoff at point H must satisfy ACI-12.11.3 by giving a moment capacity diagram that is offset horizontally from the factored moment diagram at every point (except at the support) by 12 bar diameters or the effective depth d, whichever is greater.

It is to be noted that whereas ACI-12.12.1 requires the $R4$ bars to extend into the support a distance of 6 in. minimum, ACI-12.12.2 requires full development of the tensile yield strength of such bars at the face of support when the flexural member is part of the primary lateral load resisting system. Such would be the case if significant moments are developed in the member as a result of wind or earthquake loading.

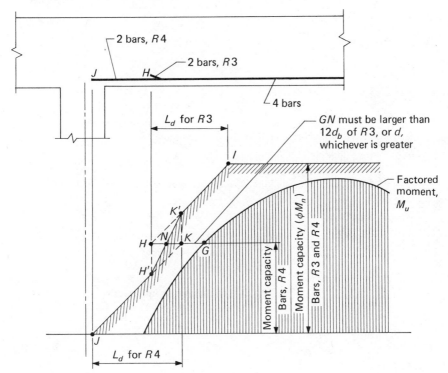

Fig. 6.15.2
Special case of Fig. 6.15.1 wherein the distance JH is less than L_d for bars $R4$.

The special case wherein the horizontal distance between points J and H is smaller than the development length L_d for bars $R4$ is shown in Fig. 6.15.2. The moment capacity diagram is indicated by $JH'K'I$. The requirement to allow for the shifting of the factored moment curve is satisfied by making sure that the distance GN is larger than the effective depth d or 12 diameters of bars $R3$.

In addition, since the cutoff at point H lies in the tension zone, one of the conditions of ACI-12.11.5 must be satisfied [see Eqs. (6.14.1) through (6.14.4)].

6.16 Bar Cutoffs in Uniformly Loaded Cantilever Beams

Bar cutoffs in uniformly loaded cantilever beams can best be discussed by examining Fig. 6.16.1. Assume that of the six bars provided for the maximum

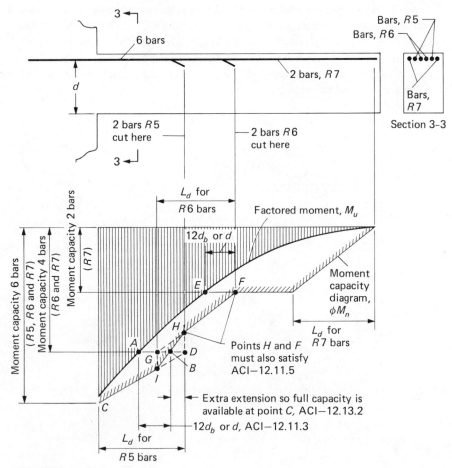

Fig. 6.16.1
Bar cutoff in a uniformly loaded cantilever beam.

moment, it is desired to cut two bars $R5$ as soon as possible, then cut two more bars $R6$, and run the remaining two bars $R7$ out to the end of the cantilever.

The following steps illustrate the cutoff determination and check:

1. Locate the theoretical cutoff point A where the moment capacity of four bars (bars $R6$ and $R7$) is adequate; extend 12 diameters of bars $R5$ or the effective depth of the member, whichever is greater, to arrive at point B.
2. Determine the development length L_d for the bars $R5$ that are intended to be cut. Full capacity from the $R5$ bars is available at the distance L_d to the left of the cutoff point.
3. Since the horizontal distance CB is less than L_d, less than full capacity of the $R5$ bars will be available at the support had they been cut at point B; therefore extend cutoff location to point D so that the horizontal distance CD equals L_d. (ACI-12.11.5 must also be satisfied since the proposed cut location lies in a tension zone.)
4. Locate point E, the theoretical location where only the two $R7$ bars are required for moment; extend 12 diameters of bars $R6$ or the effective depth of the member, whichever is greater, to arrive at point F. (ACI-12.11.5 must also be satisfied for point F since it lies in a tension zone.)
5. Determine the development length L_d required for the $R6$ bars being cut; these two bars will have their full capacity available at point G, a distance L_d to the left of point F.
6. In the region from G to D the moment capacity consists of partial contributions from the bars $R5$ and $R6$ plus the full contribution of bars $R7$. The combined moment capacity (represented by line IH) is the sum of the linear contributions. The intent of ACI-12.11.3 is satisfied if the moment capacity diagram encloses the factored moment diagram by an adequate amount of horizontal offset equal to the effective depth of the member or 12 bar diameters (of the cutoff bars), whichever is greater. At a support or the end of a cantilever, this horizontal offset need not be as large because there is little likelihood of shifting of the factored moment curve near such locations. In this case, the line IH passes by chance through point B, satisfying the offset requirement. Point H should also have the necessary horizontal offset.
7. When any part of the line IH encroaches closer than $12d_b$ of the $R5$ bars or d, whichever is greater, then either or both of the proposed cut locations (points D and F) must be extended toward the end of the cantilever. A convenient and practical procedure is to extend point F to the right until point G coincides with point D.

EXAMPLE 6.16.1   For the cantilever beam shown in Fig. 6.16.2 determine the distance L_1 from the support to the point where 2-#8 bars may be cut off. Draw the resulting moment capacity diagram for the entire beam. Use $f'_c = 3000$ psi and $f_y = 60{,}000$ psi.

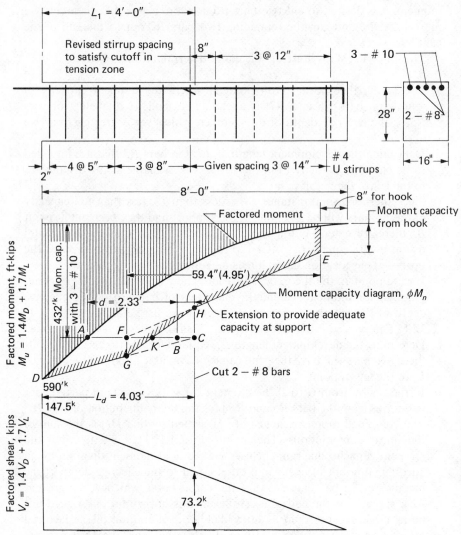

Fig. 6.16.2
Beam of Example 6.16.1.

Solution: (a) Check the maximum moment capacity of the section.

$$0.75\rho_b \text{ (Table 3.5.1)} = 0.0160$$

$$\rho = \frac{3(1.27) + 2(0.79)}{16(28)} = 0.0120 < 0.75\rho_b \qquad \text{OK}$$

$$C = 0.85(3)16a = 40.8a$$

$$T = [3(1.27) + 2(0.79)]60 = (3.81 + 1.58)60 = 323 \text{ kips}$$

$$a = \frac{323}{40.8} = 7.92 \text{ in.}$$

$$M_n = 323[28 - 0.5(7.92)]\tfrac{1}{12} = 648 \text{ ft-kips}$$

$$\phi M_n = 0.90(648) = 584 \text{ ft-kips} \approx M_u = 590 \text{ ft-kips} \qquad \text{OK}$$

(b) Determine the theoretical cutoff point for 2-#8 bars. The moment capacity remaining with 3-#10 bars is

$$C = 40.8a$$

$$T = 3.81(60) = 229 \text{ kips}$$

$$a = \frac{229}{40.8} = 5.60 \text{ in.}$$

$$\phi M_n = 0.90(229)[28 - 0.5(5.60)]\tfrac{1}{12} = 432 \text{ ft-kips}$$

Plot on the factored moment diagram and locate the theoretical cutoff point A. Extend to the right 12 bar diameters or the effective depth of the member, whichever is greater, to arrive at point B.

$$d = 28 \text{ in. } (2.33 \text{ ft}) > 12d_b = 12(1.0) = 12 \text{ in.}$$

(c) Determine development length for #8 bars. The basic development length is obtained by using Eqs. (6.9.1) or (6.9.2); thus

$$L_d = 0.04\frac{f_y A_b}{\sqrt{f'_c}} = 0.04\left(\frac{60,000(0.79)}{\sqrt{3000}}\right) = 34.6 \text{ in.}$$

or

$$L_d = 0.0004 f_y d_b = 0.0004(60,000)1.0 = 24 \text{ in.}$$

The larger value governs and agrees with the value given by Table 6.9.1. For top bars the development length must be increased by 40% (as per Table 6.10.1).

$$L_d \text{ (for } \#8) = 34.6(1.4) = 48.4 \text{ in. } (4.03 \text{ ft})$$

Since point B, the proposed cutoff point, lies only about 3.5 ft from the support, the #8 bars would not have full capacity at the support. Thus extend the proposed cutoff to point C which is located at L_d (for #8) from the support (satisfying ACI-12.1 and 12.13.2).

(d) Check ACI-12.11.5 for cutting bars at point C in the tension zone. The shear strength, including contribution of stirrups, is first computed. Using the simplified method of constant V_c,

$$V_c = 2\sqrt{f'_c}b_w d = 2\sqrt{3000}(16)(28)\tfrac{1}{1000} = 49.1 \text{ kips}$$

$$V_s = \frac{A_v f_y d}{s} = \frac{2(0.20)(60)28}{14} = 48.0 \text{ kips}$$

The nominal strength at point C is

$$V_n = V_c + V_s = 49.1 + 48.0 = 97.1 \text{ kips}$$

$$\text{percent stressed in shear} = \frac{V_u}{\phi V_n} = \frac{73.2}{0.85(97.1)} = 89\% > 75\% \qquad \text{NG}$$

Try using one more 8-in. stirrup spacing, followed by 3 @ 12 in., instead of 3 @ 14 in. (See dotted stirrups in Fig. 6.16.2.)

$$V_s = 48.0\left(\frac{14}{8}\right) = 84.0 \text{ kips}$$

$$\text{percent stressed in shear} = \frac{73.2}{0.85(49.1 + 84)} = 65\%$$

This is acceptable since the two-thirds limit of ACI-12.11.5.1 is now satisfied.

(e) Check whether the continuing #10 bars have adequate embedment to the right of point C.

$$L_d \text{ (for } \#10) = L_d \text{ (for } \#8)\frac{A_b\,(\#10)}{A_b\,(\#8)}$$

$$= 48.4\left(\frac{1.27}{0.79}\right) = 77.7 \text{ in. (6.47 ft)}$$

Straight embedment will give a moment capacity diagram encroaching closer to the factored moment diagram than 12 bar diameters or the effective depth of the member. The #10 bars would satisfy literally the statement of ACI-12.11.4, which requires "continuing reinforcement shall have an embedment length L_d beyond the point where bent or terminated reinforcement is no longer required to resist flexure." In other words, the distance from point A to the end of the cantilever must be at least L_d (for #10). The authors believe in a somewhat more conservative approach, requiring the moment capacity diagram to have an offset from the factored moment diagram, except at or near a simple support or the free end of a cantilever, equal to 12 bar diameters or the effective depth d, whichever is greater.

In this case try standard 90° hooks (see Fig. 6.13.1) on the ends of the #10 bars. From Table 6.13.2, the hook will provide an equivalent embedment length of 18.3 in. The remainder (77.7 − 18.3 = 59.4 in.) must be obtained by straight embedment.

(f) Moment capacity diagram.

$$\text{moment capacity from hook} = \frac{18.3}{77.7}(432) = 102 \text{ ft-kips}$$

Thus point E may be plotted. The hook capacity may be considered to begin at the tangent to the radius (see Fig. 6.13.1b) which is nearly 8 in. (1.5 in. cover + 1.27 bar diameter + $4d_b$ = 7.85 in.) from the free end of the cantilever. Locate point F at 59.4 in. to the left of point E. The horizontal distance FE plus the hook comprise the full development length required for the #10 bars.

Between points C and F there is partial contribution from all bars. The linear sum of contributions from the #8 and #10 bars is represented by the line GH. Thus the complete moment capacity diagram is given by the line DGHE. Note is made that the distance AK (20 in.) is more than $12d_b$ (12 in.) but is short of the effective depth d (28 in.). Perhaps this is acceptable in view of the low possibility of a horizontal shift of the moment diagram for a cantilever beam.

(g) Final decision. Cut 2-#8 bars at 4'–0'' from the support; revise the stirrup spacing as shown by the dotted stirrups in Fig. 6.16.2, and use 90° standard hooks on the ends of the #10 bars.

6.17 Development of Reinforcement at Simple Supports and at Points of Inflection

The concept of requiring the development of reinforcement on both sides of a section where the bars are to be fully stressed may also be applied to the continuation of positive reinforcement beyond either the center line of a simple support or a point of inflection.

Simple Supports. Referring to Fig. 6.17.1, consider the point A on the factored moment curve near a simple support, where the moment value is equal to the moment capacity of the bars continuing into the support. The distance from point A to the end of the bars must be at least equal to the required development length L_d as computed from ACI-12.2 [Eqs. (6.9.1) to (6.9.4) with modifications of Sec. 6.10]. This requirement given in ACI-12.12.3 is that the available embedment length must equal or exceed L_d, or

$$\text{available embedment length} = L_a + 1.3\frac{M_n}{V_u} \geq L_d \qquad (6.17.1)$$

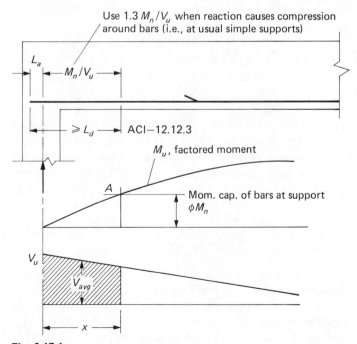

Fig. 6.17.1
Development of reinforcement at a simple support.

where

M_n = nominal flexural strength of the remaining bars

$$= A_s f_y \left(d - \frac{a}{2} \right), \text{ or}$$

= moment capacity in the working stress method (ACI-Appendix B.4 and B.5),

V_u = factored load shear at the support, or

= the service-load shear in the working stress method (ACI-Appendix B.4),

L_a = sum of the embedment length beyond the centerline of support and the equivalent embedment length of any furnished hook or mechanical anchorage.

The distance x between the point A and the centerline of support in Fig. 6.17.1 is approximately equal to

$$x = \frac{M_n}{V_u} \qquad (6.17.2)$$

because the area of the shaded portion of the shear diagram equals the *change* in moment between the center of support and point A; thus the ordinate on the factored moment diagram at A is

$$V_{avg} \text{ (say, } 0.9 V_u) x = \phi M_n$$

Comparing Eq. (6.17.1) and Eq. (6.17.2), it is seen that Eq. (6.17.1) is identical to

$$L_a + 1.30x \geq L_d$$

wherein the 1.30 factor is in recognition of the fact that the bars extending into a simple support have less tendency to cause splitting when confined by a compressive reaction [10].

Inflection Points. Since an inflection point is a point of zero moment located away from a support (refer to Fig. 6.17.2), bars in that region are not confined by a compressive reaction; therefore the 1.30 factor is interpreted as not to apply. In this case the embedment length that must exceed the required development length L_d (ACI-12.12.3) may be stated as

$$\text{available embedment length} = \begin{bmatrix} \text{actual } L_a, \text{ but} \\ \text{not exceeding the} \\ \text{larger of } 12d_b \text{ or } d \end{bmatrix} + \frac{M_n}{V_u} \geq L_d \qquad (6.17.3)$$

wherein M_n and V_u refer to the nominal flexural strength and the factored load shear at the point of inflection. The limitation of the usable L_a to 12 bar diameters or the effective depth has been applied because there is no experimental evidence to show that long anchorage length will be fully effective in developing a bar in a short length between the point of inflection and a point of maximum stress [3].

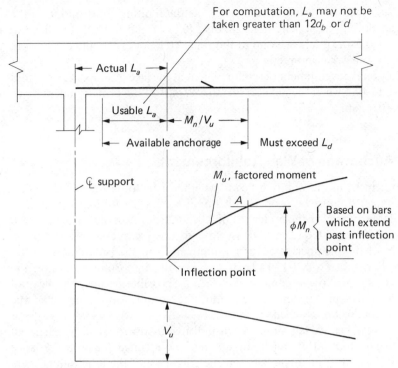

Fig. 6.17.2
Development of reinforcement at an inflection point.

As another means of justification for Eq. (6.17.2), it may be shown that this equation does in fact involve the investigation of the flexural bond stress at the simple support or the point of inflection. Note that the distance x is a measure of the partial contribution to the total required development length L_d.

The flexural bond stress on the largest bar at the simple support or the point of inflection is, by Eq. (6.4.1),

$$u_u = \frac{V_n d_b}{4(\Sigma A_s)(\text{moment arm})} = \frac{(V_u/0.85)d_b}{4(\Sigma A_s)(\text{moment arm})} \qquad \textbf{(6.17.4)}$$

But for the equivalent development length x, at an anchorage bond stress of $(5/6)u_u$, [in the same manner as for the development of Eq. (6.2.1)],

$$\frac{5}{6}u_u = \frac{f_y \pi d_b^2/4}{\pi d_b x} \qquad \textbf{(6.17.5)}$$

Equating the u_u between Eqs. (6.17.4) and (6.17.5),

$$x = \frac{20.4}{20}\left[\frac{f_y(\Sigma A_s)(\text{moment arm})}{V_u}\right] \approx \frac{M_n}{V_u}$$

which is Eq. (6.17.2).

Thus by incorporating the distance x as the limiting contribution to the required development length L_d in Eqs. (6.17.1) and (6.17.3), the flexural bond stress is (as it has been up to the 1963 ACI Code) actually considered, although somewhat indirectly.

Additional development of reinforcement at the face of support is required by ACI-12.12.2 when the flexural member is part of the primary lateral load resisting system.

6.18 Anchorage of Web Reinforcement

Reinforcement in the web of a beam, whether it be for shear or for torsion (see Chap. 19), must be properly anchored so that its full tensile capacity is available at or near the middepth of a beam. For proper function, the web reinforcement must be "carried as close to the compression and tension surfaces of the member as cover requirements and the proximity of other steel will permit." (ACI-12.14.1). It is especially important to extend the stirrups as close to the compression face as possible because the flexural tension cracks may extend deeply into the compression zone when the ultimate load is approached.

The ends of single leg, simple U, or multiple U stirrups shall be anchored as shown in Fig. 6.18.1. Such stirrups may be inclined but in accordance with ACI-11.5.1.2 the angle between the stirrups and the longitudinal bars must be at least 45°. It may be noted that the standard hook referred to in Fig. 6.18.1a includes not only those permitted for main reinforcement alone (already shown before in Fig. 6.13.1), but also those permitted for stirrup and tie anchorage only—that is, either a 90° or 135° turn plus an extension of at least six bar diameters but not less than $2\frac{1}{2}$ in. at the free end of the bar (ACI-7.1). A summary of standard hooks for stirrups and ties appears in Fig. 6.18.2.

For U stirrups of welded smooth wire fabric, anchorage may be accomplished (ACI-12.14.2.4) using either "(a) two longitudinal wires running at

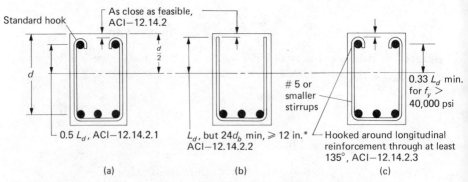

† The 12-in. minimum does not apply to welded deformed wire fabric satisfying ACI- 12.8.2.

Fig. 6.18.1

Anchorage of deformed bar or deformed wire stirrups.

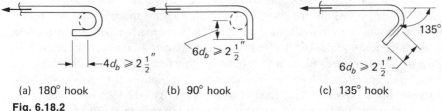

(a) 180° hook   (b) 90° hook   (c) 135° hook

Fig. 6.18.2
Standard hooks for stirrups and ties (ACI-7.1).

a 2-in. spacing along the beam at the top of the U," or "(b) one longitudinal wire not more than $d/4$ from the compression face and a second wire closer to the compression face and spaced at least 2 in. from the first. The second wire may be beyond a bend or on a bend which has an inside diameter of at least 8 wire diameters." These provisions are illustrated in Fig. 6.18.3.

When *closed* stirrups are desired, one practical procedure is to use a pair of U stirrups without hooks (Fig. 6.18.1b) placed to form a closed unit. If this is done, ACI-12.14.5 requires laps of $1.7L_d$ for proper splicing. When members are at least 18 in. deep and the tensile capacity $A_b f_y$ of the stirrup does not exceed 9 kips, splices are adequate if the legs extend the full available depth of the member.

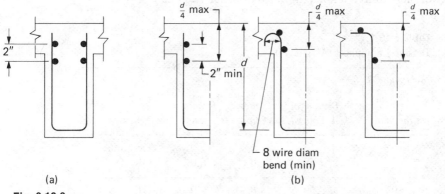

(a)   (b)

Fig. 6.18.3
Anchorage for welded smooth wire fabric stirrups (ACI-12.14.2.4).

6.19 Tension Lap Splices

Whenever bar lengths required in a structure exceed the length available or the length that may be economically shipped, splices are necessary. Splicing may be accomplished by simple lapping of bars either in contact or separated. As an alternative, butt connections may be made by welding.

In general, splices should be located away from points of maximum tensile stress, and splicing should be staggered along the length of the bars. In other words all of the bars should not be spliced at one location [1].

The beam with splices should be as ductile as one without splices. The ACI Code provisions are intended to assure that no splice failure will occur when the full nominal ultimate strength in flexure is reached at the spliced location. Requirements for minimum clear spacing of *contact* splices (ACI-7.6.4) are to insure adequate amount of concrete for the development of full anchorage capacity; but in *noncontact* lap splices the individual bars should *not* be spaced transversely too far apart (ACI-12.15.2.3).

The overlap distance required in tension lap splices should be equal to or larger than the development length L_d of the bar because stress concentrations near the splice ends tend to produce splitting at early stages of loading unless special precautions are taken [18,21,22]. Classes *A*, *B*, and *C* tension lap splices are defined by ACI-12.16.1 to have overlap distances of $1.0L_d$, $1.3L_d$, and $1.7L_d$, respectively, but a total lap of not less than 12 in. The class of tension lap splice to be used depends on (1) the percentage of bars being spliced of the total number within the required lap distance, and (2) the stress level in the unspliced bars at the splice location.

A summary of the requirements for the three classes of tension lap splices appears in Table 6.19.1. The provisions apply equally to deformed bar or deformed wire splices. Lap splices may not be used for bars larger than #11 (ACI-12.15.2.1). As stated previously in Sec. 6.12, the lap lengths prescribed in Table 6.19.1 shall be increased 20% for a three-bar bundle and 33% for a four-bar bundle (ACI-12.15.2.2). Bars spliced by noncontact lap splices in flexural members shall not be spaced transversely farther apart than one-fifth of the required lap length nor 6 in. (ACI-12.15.2.3).

Table 6.19.1
Tension Lap Splices (ACI-12.16)

$\left(\dfrac{A_s\ Required}{A_s\ Provided}\right)$ at the Splice	Percent of A_s Spliced	Splice Class	Required Lap	Notes
≤ 0.5	≤ 75	A	L_d	Desirable
	> 75	B	$1.3L_d$	OK
> 0.5	≤ 50	B	$1.3L_d$	OK
	> 50	C	$1.7L_d$	Avoid if possible

The required overlap distances shown in Table 6.19.1 are determined by the basic development length requirements of ACI-12.2.2 multiplied by the modification factors (ACI-12.2.3 and 12.2.4) shown previously in Table 6.10.1, but the resulting lap requirement may not be less than 12 in.

The ratio (A_s required/A_s provided) column in Table 6.19.1 refers to the percentage of available capacity that is utilized. The ratio may also be considered as the percent of f_y to which the bars are stressed. When the factored moment M_u is only 50% of the moment capacity (ϕM_n), the ratio would be considered 0.5. In general, temperature, shrinkage, and load distribution reinforcement should be considered as fully stressed for the purpose of designing splices.

Members under Compression and Bending. For compression members there are two categories of special splice provisions (ACI-12.18):

1. Design in the upper part of the "compression controls" region such that (Fig. 13.6.2) the reinforcement at the face of the member *opposite* the face subject to maximum compression has (when strength is reached) a tensile stress of $0.5f_y$ or less (it may be compressive): (a) Any type of splice may be used appropriate to the stress acting when strength is reached. (b) A minimum tensile strength from the splices in combination with any continuing un-spliced bars must be provided in each face of the member; this minimum strength must be twice the calculated tension in the face of the member but not less than one-quarter of the maximum tensile strength $A_s f_y$ of all bars in that face of the member.

2. Design in the lower part of "compression controls" region or in "tension controls" region (Fig. 13.6.2) where the reinforcement at the face of the member *opposite* the face subject to maximum compression has (when strength is reached) a tensile stress greater than $0.5f_y$: (a) Lap splices (Class B or C) may be used and must develop the full yield stress f_y. (b) Full welded splices or full positive connections may be used (see Sec. 6.20).

The analysis of compression members is treated in Chap. 13. For use with compression member analysis the ratio (A_s required)/(A_s provided) may also be considered as a percentage of f_y acting on the bars when strength of the section is reached. The stress in the tension bars is that obtained from a strength analysis, satisfying compatibility of stress and strain at each bar or layer of bars.

6.20 Welded Tension Splices and Mechanical Connections

A welded tension butt splice or mechanical connection is used in situations where large tensile forces are to be transmitted across the splice or large bars need to be spliced and the lap splice may be impractical or prohibited. Bars larger than #11 may not be lap spliced (ACI-12.15.2.1). Tension tie members also may not be lap spliced (ACI-12.16.5). A tension tie is a member (a) carrying a tensile force large enough to cause tension over the entire section; (b) having a stress level in the reinforcement high enough to require every bar to be fully effective; and (c) having limited concrete cover on its sides [3].

These tension splices, referred to as *full welded splices* or *full mechanical connections* (ACI-12.15.3), are required to develop in tension at least 125% of the specified yield strength of the bar when used in regions of high stress.

The full welded splice is intended primarily for relatively large bars (#6 and larger) in main members [3]. The tensile capacity required is intended to ensure sound full penetration welds—that is, to produce splices capable of developing the ultimate strength of the bars spliced. According to the

ACI Commentary [3], "the 25% increase beyond the specified yield strength was selected as both an adequate minimum for safety and a practical maximum for economy."

In regions of low stress (i.e., where less than 50% of available capacity is being used) welded splices or mechanical connections of less capacity than 125% are permitted (ACI-12.15.3.5 and 12.16.4). In these situations welded lap joints of reinforcing bars, either with or without backup material, or other welded bar arrangements, may be allowed. However, such splices must be "staggered at least 24 in. and in such manner as to develop at every section at least twice the calculated tensile force at that section but not less than 20,000 psi for the total area of reinforcement provided."

In computing the capacity, spliced bars may be rated at the specified splice strength (assuming it is less than the strength of the bars), whereas any unspliced bars are to be rated in proportion to their length of bar development to the splice point (but not to exceed the maximum bar capacity at embedment L_d). For example, a welded splice may be specified to provide 90% of the full capacity of the bars being spliced, in which case that bar area is taken as 90% of its actual area for computing capacity; for unspliced bars that have been embedded, say only $0.5L_d$, the bar area used for strength calculation should be taken as one-half the actual area.

6.21 Compression Lap Splices

The minimum overlap in compression lap splices when f'_c is not less than 3000 psi must be at least equal to the following (ACI-12.17.1):

For $f_y \leq 60{,}000$ psi,

$$\text{lap} = 0.0005 f_y d_b \quad \text{or } L_d \quad \text{or 12 in.} \quad \text{(whichever is largest)}$$

For $f_y > 60{,}000$ psi,

$$\text{lap} = (0.0009 f_y - 24) d_b \quad \text{or } L_d \quad \text{or 12 in.} \quad \text{(whichever is largest)}$$

where

$$L_d = \frac{0.02 f_y d_b}{\sqrt{f'_c}} \qquad \text{(Will not control)}$$

less 25% for spiral enclosure satisfying ACI-12.3.3b. When f'_c is less than 3000 psi, the lap length is to be increased by one-third.

For compression members whose main steel is surrounded by closed ties throughout the lap length, the required lap may be taken at 0.83 of that otherwise required, but not less than 12 in. A minimum percentage of column tie area is also required by ACI-12.17.2. Column ties are discussed in Chap. 13 (Sec. 13.8).

For members whose main steel is surrounded by a closely wound spiral, the required lap may be taken at 0.75 of that otherwise required, but not less than 12 in. Spiral reinforcement is discussed in Chap. 13 (Sec. 13.9).

Table 6.21.1
Bar Diameters Required for
Compression Lap Splices for
$f'_c \geq 3000$ psi (ACI-12.17.1)

Yield Stress f_y ksi	Bar Diameters[a]		
	Spiral Column	Tied Column	Others
40	15	16.6	20
50	18.75	20.75	25
60	22.5	24.9	30
75	32.6	36.2	43.5
80	36.0	39.9	48.0

[a] When computing splice length, the minimum to be used is 12 in.

The number of bar diameters required for the overlap in compression lap splices is summarized in Table 6.21.1.

6.22 Compression End Bearing Connections, Welded Splices, and Mechanical Connections

End bearing connections are allowed for compression only, wherein the load in the bars is transmitted by bearing of square cut ends held in concentric contact by a suitable device. According to ACI-12.17.5.2 bar ends must terminate in flat surfaces within $1\frac{1}{2}°$ of right angles to the axis of the bars and be fitted within $3°$ of full bearing after assembly. End bearing splices are only permitted when the member contains closed ties, closed stirrups, or spirals.

When welded splices or mechanical connections are used in compression, the requirements are the same as for tension splices—that is, the development of 125% of the yield strength of the bars, except where less than 50% of the full unspliced bar capacity is required by the design load (ACI-12.15.3 and 12.16.4).

6.23 Design Examples

Two complete examples in the design of reinforced concrete flexural members are presented here for the purpose of showing the design for flexure, shear, and development of reinforcement, all in the same beam.

EXAMPLE 6.23.1 Design the simply supported beam shown in Fig. 6.23.1a. The dead load is 0.9 kip/ft, not including the weight of the beam.

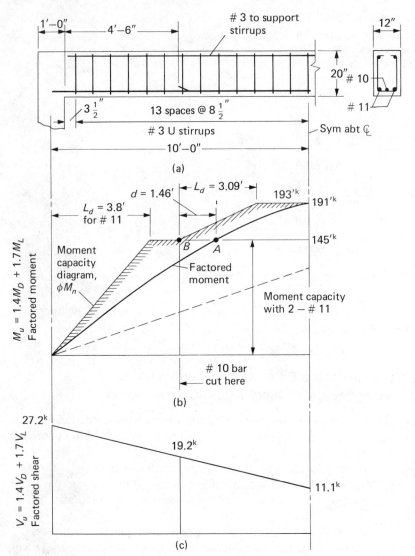

Fig. 6.23.1
Simple span beam of Example 6.23.1.

The live load consists of a concentrated load of 13 kips at midspan. Use $f'_c = 3000$ psi, $f_y = 40,000$ psi, and the ACI strength method.

Solution: (a) Design for flexure. Assume that a rectangular section with tension reinforcement only will be used at a reinforcement ratio somewhat lower than the maximum permissible value. Using basic principles as illustrated in Sec. 3.5, or the value from Table 3.5.1,

$$\text{max permissible } \rho = 0.75\rho_b = 0.0278$$

Arbitrarily selecting an approximate $\rho = 0.025$ and using Eq. (3.6.4) or the direct statics as illustrated in Sec. 3.6,

$$m = \frac{f_y}{0.85f_c'} = 15.7$$

$$R_u = \rho f_y(1 - \tfrac{1}{2}\rho m) = 804 \text{ psi}$$

Assume weight of beam is 0.2 kip/ft,

$$w_u = 1.4(0.9 + 0.2) = 1.54 \text{ kips/ft (dead load)}$$
$$W_u = 1.7(13) = 22.1 \text{ kips (live load)}$$
$$M_u = \tfrac{1}{8}(1.54)(20)^2 + \tfrac{1}{4}(22.1)(20) = 77 + 110.5 = 188 \text{ ft-kips}$$

$$\text{required } M_n = \frac{M_u}{\phi} = \frac{188}{0.90} = 209 \text{ ft-kips}$$

$$\text{required } bd^2 = \frac{M_n}{R_u} = \frac{209(12,000)}{804} = 3120 \text{ in.}^3$$

If $b = 12$ in.

$$d = \sqrt{\frac{3120}{12}} = 16.1 \text{ in.}$$

$$\text{required } h = d + \text{approx } 2\tfrac{1}{2} \text{ in. for one layer of bars}$$
$$= 16.1 + 2.5 = 18.6 \text{ in.}$$

The minimum thickness for deflection control is (ACI-Table 9.5a),

$$\min h = \frac{L}{16} = \frac{20(12)}{16} = 15 \text{ in.}$$

if the member is *not* supporting or attached to partitions or other construction likely to be damaged by large deflections. Use $h = 20$ in., thus $d = \text{approx } 17.5$ in.

$$\text{weight of beam} = \frac{12(20)}{144}(0.15) = 0.25 \text{ kip/ft}$$

$$\text{revised } w_u = 1.4(0.9 + 0.25) = 1.61 \text{ kips/ft (dead load)}$$
$$\text{revised } M_u = \tfrac{1}{8}(1.61)(20)^2 + 110.5 = 80.5 + 110.5 = 191 \text{ ft-kips}$$

$$\text{revised } M_n = \frac{191}{0.90} = 212 \text{ ft-kips}$$

$$\text{required } R_u = \frac{M_n}{bd^2} = \frac{212(12,000)}{12(17.5)^2} = 692 \text{ psi}$$

The steel percentage may then be found from Eq. (3.6.5), Fig. 3.6.1, or approximately by straight-line proportion,

$$A_s \approx 0.025(12)(17.5)\left(\frac{692}{804}\right) = 4.52 \text{ sq in.}$$

Try 2-#11 and 1-#10 bars ($A_s = 4.39$ sq in.). Assuming #3 U stirrups, the minimum width of beam to accommodate these bars is 10.54 in. (see Table 3.7.2) which is less than the width of beam being used.
Check capacity.

$$C = 0.85f'_c ba = 0.85(3)12a = 30.6a$$
$$T = A_s f_y = 4.39(40) = 176 \text{ kips}$$

$$a = \frac{176}{30.6} = 5.75 \text{ in.}$$

$$M_n = T\left(d - \frac{a}{2}\right) = 176[17.5 - 0.5(5.75)]\tfrac{1}{12}$$

$$= 214 \text{ ft-kips} > 212 \text{ ft-kips required} \qquad \text{OK}$$

(b) Make the preliminary selection of the cutoff point for 1-#10. The remaining moment capacity with 2-#11 bars is

$$C = 30.6a$$
$$T = 2(1.56)40 = 125 \text{ kips}$$

$$a = \frac{125}{30.6} = 4.08 \text{ in.}$$

$$\phi M_n = 0.90(125)[17.5 - 0.5(4.08)]\tfrac{1}{12} = 145 \text{ ft-kips}$$

The value of 145 ft-kips is plotted on the factored M_u diagram to locate the theoretical cutoff point A. The actual potential cutoff location (point B) is found by extending from point A toward the support a distance of 12 bar diameters or the effective depth of the member, whichever is greater (ACI-12.11.3).

$$12d_b = 12\left(\frac{1.27}{12}\right) = 1.27 \text{ ft}$$

$$d = \frac{17.5}{12} = 1.46 \text{ ft} \qquad \text{(Controls)}$$

The cutoff at point B will be acceptable only if the shear does not exceed two-thirds of the shear strength at point B (ACI-12.11.5.1). An alternative is to provide extra stirrups in accordance with ACI-12.11.5.2.

(c) Determine development lengths. Using Eq. (6.9.1) or ACI-12.2 gives

$$L_d (\#10) = 0.04\frac{A_b f_y}{\sqrt{f'_c}} = 0.04(1.27)\frac{40,000}{\sqrt{3000}} = 37.1 \text{ in. (3.09 ft)} \qquad \text{(Controls)}$$

but not less than

$$L_d (\#10) = 0.0004d_b f_y = 0.0004(1.27)(40,000) = 20.3 \text{ in.}$$

$$L_d (\#11) = 37.1\left(\frac{1.56}{1.27}\right) = 45.5 \text{ in. (3.80 ft)}$$

(d) Design of shear reinforcement; simplified method with constant V_c.

$$V_u \text{ (at centerline of support)} = 1.61(10) + 11.1 = 27.2 \text{ kips}$$
$$V_u \text{ (at } d \text{ from face of support)} = 27.2 - 1.96(1.61) = 24.0 \text{ kips}$$
$$V_c = 2\sqrt{f'_c}b_w d = 2\sqrt{3000}(12)(17.5)\tfrac{1}{1000} = 23.0 \text{ kips}$$
$$\text{required } V_s = \text{required } V_n - V_c = V_u/\phi - V_c$$
$$= 24.0/0.85 - 23.0 = 28.2 - 23.0 = 5.2 \text{ kips}$$
$$\min V_s = 50b_w d = 50(12)(17.5)\tfrac{1}{1000} = 10.5 \text{ kips}$$

Since $V_s = 5.2$ kips is less than $V_s = 10.5$ kips to satisfy the minimum shear reinforcement requirement of ACI-11.5.5.3 based on $v_s = 50$ psi, use $V_s = 10.5$ kips to determine the stirrup spacing at the critical section. For #3 U stirrups, using Eq. (5.10.7),

$$V_s = \frac{A_v f_y d}{s}$$

$$\max s = \frac{A_v f_y d}{V_s} = \frac{0.22(40)(17.5)}{10.5} = 14.7 \text{ in.}$$

However, the stirrup spacing may not exceed $d/2 = 8.75$ in.

Try #3 stirrups @ $8\frac{1}{2}$ in. spacing. Stirrups at this spacing must be used until $V_n \leq V_c/2$, which for this beam means the entire span, because required V_n at midspan is $11.1/0.85 = 13.1$ kips and exceeds $V_c/2 = 11.5$ kips.

(e) Check cutoff point for satisfying the shear requirement of ACI-12.11.5 for cutting bars in the tension zone. The shear strength provided by #3 stirrups at $8\frac{1}{2}$ in. spacing is

$$V_n = V_c + V_s = 23.0 + \frac{0.22(40)(17.5)}{8.5} = 41.1 \text{ kips}$$

$$V_u \text{ at cutoff} = 19.2 \text{ kips}$$

$$\text{percent stressed in shear} = \frac{V_u}{\phi V_n} = \frac{19.2}{0.85(41.1)} = 55\% < 66\tfrac{2}{3}\% \qquad \text{OK}$$

Use 1-#10, 10′–0″ long placed symmetrically about midspan.

(f) Check development length requirement (indirectly flexural bond stress) at the support. According to ACI-12.12.3, it is required that

$$1.30\frac{M_n}{V_u} + L_a \geq L_d$$

$$M_n \text{ for 2-#11 bars} = \frac{145}{0.9} = 161 \text{ ft-kips}$$

V_u = factored load shear at centerline of support = 27.2 kips

L_a = embedment length beyond the center of support; assume zero here

$$1.30\frac{161(12)}{27.2} = 92.5 \text{ in.} > L_d = 45.5 \text{ in.} \qquad \text{OK}$$

Actually the moment capacity diagram provides this same check but more conservatively (i.e., without the 1.30 factor) since the horizontal distance from the center of support to point A exceeds L_d.

(g) Design sketch. The final conclusions are presented in Fig. 6.23.1a. Since $f_y = 40,000$ psi, the crack control provisions of ACI-10.6.4 need not be checked. If deflection control is important to prevent damage to partitions or other construction, the deflection must be checked according to ACI-9.5. Computation for deflections is treated in Chap. 14.

EXAMPLE 6.23.2   Design the overhanging beam shown in Fig. 6.23.2. The superimposed service uniform dead load is 4 kips/ft. Use $f'_c = 4000$ psi, $f_y = 60,000$ psi, and the ACI strength method.

Solution: (a) Design for flexure. Since tension reinforcement will be required in the top of the overhang, it may be desirable to run some bars straight across the top of the entire beam. This would also help reduce creep and shrinkage deflection under sustained load.

For deflection control, a guideline value of ρ equal to one-half the maximum permissible value may serve to establish the beam size.

$$\max \rho = 0.75 \, \rho_b = 0.0214 \qquad \text{(Table 3.5.1)}$$

Arbitrarily choose $\rho = 0.011$. $m = f_y/0.85f'_c) = 17.6$

$$R_u = \frac{M_u}{\phi bd^2} = \rho f_y(1 - \tfrac{1}{2}\rho m)$$

$$= 0.011(60,000)[1 - \tfrac{1}{2}(0.011)(17.6)] = 596 \text{ psi}$$

Estimating the beam weight at 0.3 kip/ft, the factored uniform loading is

$$w_u = 1.4(4.3) = 6.02 \text{ kips/ft}$$

The shear at the left support is

$$V_u = \frac{6.02(18)}{2} - \frac{0.5(6.02)(6.5)^2}{18} = 47.1 \text{ kips}$$

$$\max(+)M_u = \frac{(47.1)^2}{2(6.02)} = 184 \text{ ft-kips}$$

$$\max(-)M_u = \tfrac{1}{2}(6.02)(6.5)^2 = 127 \text{ ft-kips}$$

$$\text{required } bd^2 = \frac{M_u}{\phi R_u} = \frac{184(12,000)}{0.90(596)} = 4120 \text{ in.}^3$$

b	d	h
12	18.5	21
14	17.2	20

In selecting a size, the designer need not adhere rigidly to the value of $R_u = 596$ psi but may go either higher or lower, since the value of ρ is about

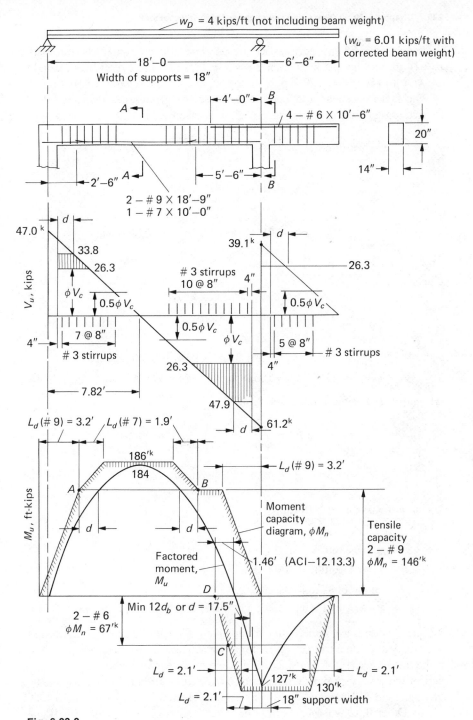

Fig. 6.23.2
Overhanging beam for Example 6.23.2.

in the middle of the permissible range. Use a rectangular section with $b = 14$ in. and $h = 20$ in., which gives $d \approx 17.5$ in. The revised beam weight is $14(20)(0.15)/144 = 0.29$ kip/ft, giving $w_u = 1.4(0.29 + 4.00) = 6.01$ kips/ft.

The factored shear and bending moment diagrams (i.e., using factored service loads) are shown in Fig. 6.23.2. At section A-A,

$$\text{required } R_u = \frac{M_u}{\phi b d^2} = \frac{184(12,000)}{0.90(14)(17.5)^2} = 572 \text{ psi}$$

$$A_s \approx 0.011 b d \left(\frac{\text{required } R_u}{596} \right)$$

$$A_s = 0.011(14)(17.5)\left(\frac{572}{596}\right) = 2.59 \text{ sq in.}$$

Use 2-#9 and 1-#7 $(A_s = 2.60$ sq in.)
Check:

$$C = 0.85 f'_c b a = 0.85(4)(14)a = 47.6a$$
$$T = A_s f_y = 2.60(60) = 156 \text{ kips}$$
$$a = 156/47.6 = 3.28 \text{ in.}$$
$$M_n = T(d - a/2) = 156(17.5 - 1.64)\tfrac{1}{12} = 206 \text{ ft-kips}$$
$$\phi M_n = 0.90(206) = 186 \text{ ft-kips} > M_u = 184 \text{ ft-kips} \qquad \text{OK}$$

At section B-B, obtain by proportion

$$\text{required } R_u = \frac{M_u}{\phi b d^2} = 572\left(\frac{127}{184}\right) = 395 \text{ psi}$$

$$A_s \approx 2.59\left(\frac{395}{572}\right) = 1.79 \text{ sq in.}$$

Use 4-#6 bars $(A_s = 1.76$ sq in.)
Check:

$$C = 47.6a$$
$$T = 1.76(60) = 106 \text{ kips}$$
$$a = 106/47.6 = 2.22 \text{ in.}$$
$$\phi M_n = 0.90(106)(17.5 - 1.11)\tfrac{1}{12} = 130 \text{ ft-kips} > 127 \text{ ft-kips} \qquad \text{OK}$$

The reader is reminded that for a given R_u, the required ρ expression is a quadratic function; however, for practical use it may be approximated to be linear (see Fig. 3.6.1). A check is then made for verification.

For simplicity in bar arrangement, no bending of bars is proposed. The arrangement of main reinforcement finally selected is shown in Fig. 6.23.2.

(b) Determine whether or not the crack control criterion of ACI-10.6.4 is satisfied at maximum positive moment region. Using ACI Formula 10-4 (see also Sec. 4.12),

$$z = f_s \sqrt[3]{d_c A}$$

where A is equal to the effective tension area of concrete surrounding the main tension reinforcing bars divided by the number of bars. Using 1.5 in.

of clear cover,

$$d_c = 1.5 \text{ (cover)} + 0.375 \text{ (stirrup)} + 0.52 \text{ (avg radius)} = 2.40 \text{ in.}$$

$$\text{number of bars} = \frac{A_s}{\text{area of largest bar}} = \frac{2.60}{1.0} = 2.6$$

$$A = \frac{2(2.40)(14)}{2.6} = 25.8 \text{ sq in./bar}$$

$$f_s = 0.60 f_y = 0.60(60) = 36 \text{ ksi}$$

$$z = 36 \sqrt[3]{2.40(25.8)} = 36(3.96) = 143 \text{ kips/in.}$$

which is less than the limit of 145 allowed by ACI-10.6.4 for exterior exposure. If 2-in. cover is used (ACI-7.7.1), computed z is 162 kips/in., which would be unacceptable for exterior exposure. The actual service-load stress is usually less than $0.60 f_y$ and the lesser value could be computed if needed to satisfy the crack control limitation (although little can be gained in this case because of the use of a load factor equal to 1.4 for all the loads).

(c) Development of reinforcement and bar cutoff. According to Eq. (6.9.1), the basic development lengths (ACI-12.2) are

$$L_d = 0.04 \frac{A_b f_y}{\sqrt{f'_c}} = 0.04 A_b \left(\frac{60,000}{\sqrt{4000}}\right) = 38 A_b$$

but not less than

$$0.0004 d_b f_y = 24 d_b$$
$$L_d (\#6) = 38(0.44) = 16.7 \text{ in.} < 24 d_b = \underline{18 \text{ in.}}$$
$$L_d (\#7) = 38(0.60) = \underline{22.8 \text{ in.}} \ (1.9 \text{ ft})$$
$$L_d (\#9) = 38(1.0) = \underline{38.0 \text{ in.}} \ (3.2 \text{ ft})$$

For top bars, according to ACI-12.2.3(a),

$$L_d (\#6) = 18.0(1.4) = \underline{25.2 \text{ in.}} \ (2.1 \text{ ft})$$

Examine the feasibility of cutting the 1-#7 in the positive-moment zone. The remaining 2-#9 would provide the following capacity,

$$C = 47.6a; \qquad T = 2(1.0)60 = 120 \text{ kips}$$
$$a = 2.52 \text{ in.}$$
$$\phi M_n = 0.90(120)(17.5 - 1.26)\tfrac{1}{12} = 146 \text{ ft-kips}$$

Based on moment capacity alone, the #7 bar could be cut at points A and B on the moment diagram of Fig. 6.23.2; however, ACI-12.11.5 must also be satisfied to cut bars in the tension zone. This is examined in combination with designing stirrups [see item (e) below].

In trying to cut the 2-#6 bars from the negative-moment region near section B-B, the bars are extended into the span farther than 12 bar diameters or the effective depth d in order to have full development of the provided steel at the face of support. Since this potential cut at point C is not in a tension zone, no further investigation of this cutoff location is required. On determining that the remaining 2-#6 bars can be cut off only a short distance farther into the span at point D, the decision is made to cut all 4-#6 bars at point D. If for some reason, such as the desire for compression steel for deflection control, two of the #6 bars were extended across the 18-ft span, then the other 2-#6 bars would be cut at point C.

At the simple support at the left end, and at the point of inflection near the right end, ACI-12.12.3 must be checked for positive-moment reinforcement. For the inflection point it is required that

$$\frac{M_n}{V_u} + L_a \geq L_d$$

Assuming that 1-#7 will be terminated (a conservative assumption for this computation), only the 2-#9 bars contribute to M_n. The actual L_a from the inflection point to the end of the bars exceeds d (17.5 in.); thus use $L_a = 17.5$ in.

$$\frac{146(12)}{0.90(47.0)} + 17.5 = 58.9 \text{ in.} > L_d = 38 \text{ in.} \qquad \text{OK}$$

For the simple support, ACI-12.12.3 requires

$$\frac{1.30M_n}{V_u} + L_a \geq L_d$$

In this case, $L_a = 7.5$ in. since the bars extend this amount beyond the center of the support. Assuming the #7 bar does not extend into the support,

$$\frac{1.30(146)12}{0.90(47.0)} + 7.5 = 61.3 \text{ in.} > L_d = 38 \text{ in.} \qquad \text{OK}$$

(d) Shear reinforcement. At d from the face of right support,

$$\max V_u = 61.2 - 6.01 \left(\frac{17.5 + 9}{12} \right) = 47.9 \text{ kips}$$

$$\max v_n = \frac{V_u}{\phi b_w d} = \frac{47,900}{0.85(14)(17.5)} = 230 \text{ psi}$$

$$v_c = 2\sqrt{f_c'} = 126 \text{ psi}$$

$$\max (v_n - v_c) = 230 - 126 = 104 \text{ psi} < 4\sqrt{f_c'}$$

$$\max s = d/2 = 8.75 \text{ in.}$$

Work with factored load shear V_u diagram to design stirrups.

$$\phi V_c = \phi v_c b_w d = 0.85(126)(14)(17.5)\frac{1}{1000} = 26.3 \text{ kips}$$

$$\max \phi V_s = \max V_u - \phi V_c = 47.9 - 26.3 = 21.6 \text{ kips}$$

For minimum percentage of stirrups (ACI-11.5.5.3),

$$\min \phi V_s = \phi 50 b_w d = 0.85(50)(14)(17.5)\frac{1}{1000} = 10.4 \text{ kips}$$

For strength, using #3 U stirrups,

$$\phi V_s = \frac{\phi A_v f_y d}{s} = \frac{0.85(0.22)(60)(17.5)}{s} = \frac{196}{s}$$

s	ϕV_s
9.1 in.	21.6 kips max

Since the strength requirement permits stirrups at 9.1 in. and is less restrictive than the $d/2$ limit, the maximum spacing at $d/2 = 8.75$ in. controls wherever stirrups are required.

Use #3 U stirrups at 8 in. spacing, as shown in Fig. 6.23.2.

(e) Check ACI-12.11.5 for cutting #7 bar at points A and B in the tension zone. Since the continuing #9 bars *do not* provide double the required moment capacity at the cutoff point, ACI-12.11.5.3 cannot be satisfied.

Check ACI-12.11.5.1, for #3 U stirrups at 8 in. as provided,

$$\phi V_s = \frac{196}{s} = \frac{196}{8} = 24.5 \text{ kips}$$

V_u at points A and $B = 30$ kips (scaled)

$$\text{percent stressed} = \frac{V_u}{\phi V_n} = \frac{V_u}{\phi(V_c + V_s)}$$

$$= \frac{30}{26.3 + 24.5} = 59\% < 67\% \qquad\qquad \text{OK}$$

Cut 1-#7 bar at points A and B (length $= 10$ ft).

(f) Moment capacity diagram. Figure 6.23.2 shows the comparison between the factored moment diagram M_u and the moment capacity diagram provided by the selected reinforcing bars. In computing the moment capacity, any effect of steel in the compression side of the beam has been neglected because it would have negligible effect since it was not required for strength. At the left end of the beam, the 2-#9 have been extended as far as feasible into the support in order to have the bars develop their full capacity at point A. The available embedment to the left of point A was nearly exactly the 3.2 ft required.

(g) Deflection. Even though the reinforcement ratio ρ being used was expected to control the deflection; nevertheless the deflection must be investigated if excessive deflection may cause damage to partitions or other construction.

(h) Design sketch. The final arrangement of longitudinal steel and stirrups is shown in Fig. 6.23.2. The stirrup locations are dimensioned on the V_u diagram. Omitted from the elevation view of the beam are the nominal sized (say #4 or #5) longitudinal bars arbitrarily added for the stirrups to wrap around wherever the stirrups would otherwise have no support to hold them in vertical position. These pairs of bars would be located in this beam at both top and bottom faces of the beam where no longitudinal bars are shown in the figure. Cross-section views showing bars have been omitted here.

SELECTED REFERENCES

1. ACI Committee 408. "Bond Stress—The State of the Art," *ACI Journal, Proceedings*, **63,** November 1966, 1161–1190. Disc. 1569–1570.
2. ACI Committee 408. "Opportunities in Bond Research," *ACI Journal, Proceedings*, **67,** November 1970, 857–869 (contains 67 references.)
3. ACI Committee 318. *Commentary on Building Code Requirements for Reinforced Concrete* (ACI 318–71). Detroit, Michigan: American Concrete Institute, 1971 (96 pp.).
4. Herbert J. Gilkey, Stephen J. Chamberlain, and Robert W. Beal. "Bond Between Concrete and Steel," *Iowa Engineering Experiment Station Bulletin*, No. 147, Iowa State College, 1940.
5. T. D. Mylrea. "Bond and Anchorage," *ACI Journal, Proceedings*, **44,** March 1948, 521–552.
6. Phil M. Ferguson, Robert D. Turpin, and J. Neils Thompson. "Minimum Bar Spacing as a Function of Bond and Shear Strength," *ACI Journal, Proccedings*, **50,** June 1954, 869–887.
7. N. W. Hanson and Hans Reiffenstuhl. "Concrete Beams and Columns with Bundled Reinforcement," *Journal of the Structural Division*, ASCE, **84,** October 1958, (ST6), 1–23.
8. Phil M. Ferguson and Farid N. Matloob. "Effect of Bar Cutoff on Bond and Shear Strength of Reinforced Concrete Beams," *ACI Journal, Proceedings*, **56,** July 1959, 5–23.
9. Phil M. Ferguson and J. Neils Thompson. "Development Length for Large High Strength Reinforcing Bars," *ACI Journal, Proceedings*, **62,** January 1965, 71–93. Disc. 1153–1156.
10. Raymond E. Untrauer and Robert L. Henry. "Influence of Normal Pressure on Bond Strength," *ACI Journal, Proceedings*, **62,** May 1965, 577–586.
11. Phil M. Ferguson, John E. Breen, and J. Neils Thompson. "Pullout Tests on High Strength Reinforcing Bars," *ACI Journal, Proceedings*, **62,** August 1965, 933–950.
12. Ervin S. Perry and J. Neils Thompson. "Bond Stress Distribution on Reinforcing Steel in Beams and Pullout Specimens," *ACI Journal, Proceedings*, **63,** August 1966, 865–875.
13. Frank D. Steiner. "Suggested Applications for Bundled Bars," *ACI Journal, Proceedings*, **64,** April 1967, 213–214.
14. LeRoy A. Lutz and Peter Gergely. "Mechanics of Bond and Slip of Deformed Bars in Concrete," *ACI Journal, Proceedings*, **64,** November 1967, 711–721. Disc., **65,** 412–414.
15. E. L. Kemp, F. S. Brezny, and J. A. Unterspan. "Effect of Rust and Scale on the Bond Characteristics of Deformed Reinforcing Bars," *ACI Journal, Proceedings*, **65,** September 1968, 743–756. Disc., **66,** 224–226.
16. John A. Hribar and Raymond C. Vasko. "End Anchorage of High Strength Steel Reinforcing Bars," *ACI Journal, Proceedings*, **66,** November 1969, 875–883. Disc, **67,** 423–424.
17. LeRoy A. Lutz. "Crack Control Factor for Bundled Bars and for Bars of Different Sizes," *ACI Journal, Proceedings*, **71,** January 1974, 9–10.
18. C. O. Orangun, J. O. Jirsa, and J. E. Breen. "A Reevaluation of Test Data on Development Length and Splices," *ACI Journal, Proceedings*, **74,** March 1977, 114–122.
19. John Minor and James O. Jirsa. "Behavior of Bent Bar Anchorages," *ACI Journal, Proceedings*, **72,** April 1975, 141–149.
20. Anthony M. Kao and Raymond E. Untrauer. "Shear Strength of Reinforced Concrete Beams with Bars Terminated in Tension Zones," *ACI Journal, Proceedings*, **72,** December 1975, 720–722.

21. Phil M. Ferguson and John E. Breen. "Lapped Splices for High Strength Re-
    inforcing Bars," *ACI Journal, Proceedings,* **62,** September 1965, 1063–1078.
22. John P. Lloyd and Clyde E. Kessler. "Splices and Anchorages in One-Way Slabs
    Reinforced with Deformed Wire Fabric," *ACI Journal, Proceedings,* **67,** August
    1970, 636–642.

PROBLEMS

All problems are to be done in accordance with the strength method of the ACI Code,
and all loads given are *service* loads, unless otherwise indicated. All moment capacity
diagrams used in these problems must be drawn to scale directly below a side view of
the beam drawn to the same longitudinal scale.

6.1 Draw the free-body diagram for the 3-in. slice shown crosshatched on the beam
given in the accompanying figure. Using working stress assumptions, compute
and show on the diagram values for the internal forces on each side of the slice.
(a) Compute the average flexural bond stress on the bars over the 3-in. slice.
(b) Compute the average flexural bond stress on the bars over the distance from
section *A* to the left end of the beam.
(c) What is the average anchorage bond stress resisting the tensile force at
section *A*?
(d) Explain what happens if the flexural bond stress in part (a) is so high that
slippage occurs over the 3-in. slice. What determines the adequacy of the beam?
Assume loading is within the usual service range.

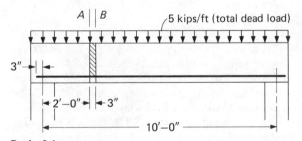
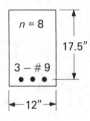

Prob. 6.1

6.2 For the simply supported beam shown, draw to scale directly below the beam
the moment capacity (ϕM_n) diagram. Dimension all critical moment values and
horizontal distances to critical points. Assume that the cutoff location 3 ft from

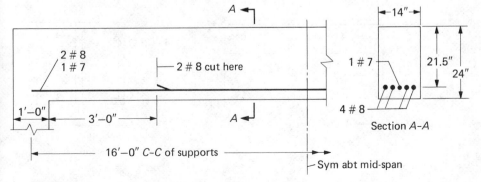

Prob. 6.2

the support satisfies the requirements of ACI-12.11.5, and that ACI-12.12.3 is satisfied. What is the maximum uniformly distributed service load that the beam may be permitted to carry (assume 50% live load and 50% dead load)? Use $f'_c = 3500$ psi and $f_y = 40,000$ psi.

6.3 For the cantilever beam of the accompanying figure having $f'_c = 3000$ psi and $f_y = 40,000$ psi:
(a) Draw to scale directly below a figure of the beam the moment capacity (ϕM_n) diagram. Be sure to include the 2 ft embedment into the support, and assume that the full cross-section capacity in that region is based on that at the support.
(b) Investigate the adequacy for development of reinforcement if the beam is subjected to uniform dead and live loads of 1.8 kips/ft (including weight of beam) and 2.1 kips/ft, respectively. Neglect any concern about cutting bars in the tension zone (ACI-12.11.5).

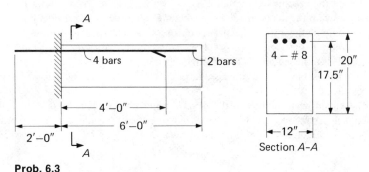

Prob. 6.3

6.4 For the beam of Prob. 6.3, but with #9 bars instead of #8 and $f_y = 60,000$ psi and $f'_c = 4000$ psi, investigate the adequacy for development of reinforcement if the beam is subjected to a uniform live load of 2.4 kips/ft and uniform dead load of 2.1 kips/ft (including beam weight). Compare factored moment M_u with the moment capacity (ϕM_n) diagram. Consider all factors involved, including ACI-12.11.5 for cutting bars in the tension zone. Assume #3 U stirrups at 8 in. spacing are used in the vicinity of the cutoff point.

6.5 For the beam of the accompanying figure, investigate the adequacy for development of reinforcement if the beam must carry uniform dead and live loads of

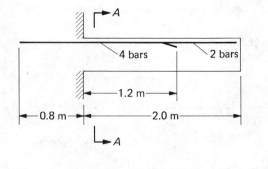

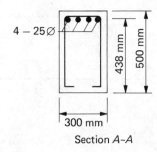

Prob. 6.5

3100 kg/m (including weight of beam) and 3500 kg/m, respectively. Compare factored moment M_u with the moment capacity (ϕM_n) diagram. Consider all factors involved, including ACI-12.11.5 for cutting bars in the tension zone. Assume that 10 mm diameter U stirrups at 200-mm spacings are used in the vicinity of the cutoff point. Use $f'_c = 28$ N/mm^2 and $f_y = 420$ N/mm^2.

6.6   For the cantilever beam of the accompanying figure, determine the safe uniformly distributed load w (dead load, DL, plus live load, LL) that the beam may be permitted to carry, if the dead load to live load ratio is 0.8. Use $f'_c = 4000$ psi and $f_y = 40,000$ psi. Show the comparison of factored moment M_u with the moment capacity diagram (ϕM_n). (For S.I. problem use bars: 3–25 mm diameter; 10 mm diameter stirrups; $f'_c = 28$ N/mm^2; $f_y = 280$ N/mm^2.)

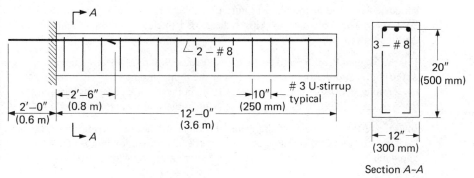

Prob. 6.6

6.7   If the beam of the accompanying figure is to carry uniformly distributed loads of 4.0 kips/ft live load and 1.9 kips/ft dead load (including beam weight), determine the adequacy of the bar cutoffs and the development of reinforcement. Stirrups are #3 at 6 in. spacing where bars A are cut, and #3 at 8 in. spacing where bars B are cut. As part of the solution, draw the moment capacity (ϕM_n) diagram to scale directly below the beam. Use $f'_c = 5000$ psi and $f_y = 60,000$ psi.

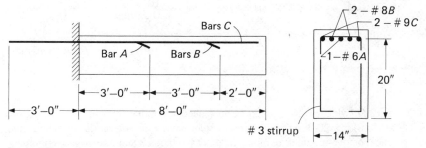

Prob. 6.7

6.8   Neglecting any compression reinforcement effect, plot the moment capacity (ϕM_n) diagram (positive moment over the 20-ft span and negative moment for the steel over the support) for the beam of the accompanying figure. Use $f'_c = 3000$ psi and $f_y = 40,000$ psi.

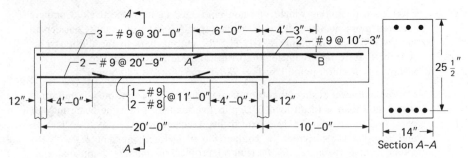

Prob. 6.8

6.9 For the beam of Prob. 6.8, check the development of reinforcement at the simply supported end and at the point of inflection closest to the right support on the 20-ft span. The loads are 1.4 kips/ft dead load (including beam weight) and 2.8 kips/ft live load.

6.10 For the beam of Prob. 6.8 and the loading of Prob. 6.9, determine the acceptability of the cut locations at points A and B near the right support.
(a) Assume #3 U stirrups are spaced at 10 in. in the vicinity of the cut locations.
(b) Assume #3 U stirrups are spaced at 12 in. in the vicinity of the cut locations.

6.11 Investigate the adequacy of the beam shown in the accompanying figure for **(a)** bar cutoffs and **(b)** stirrups. The uniform dead and live loading is 950 kg/m and 4400 kg/m, respectively. Use $f'_c = 28$ N/mm^2 and $f_y = 420$ N/mm^2.

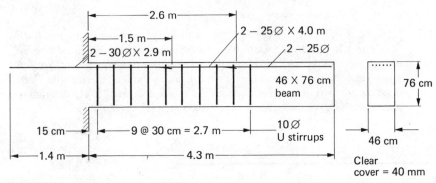

Prob. 6.11

6.12 A 12-in. wide by 24-in. deep beam (effective depth = 21.5 in.) is used as the section for a 20-ft simply supported span having an 8-ft cantilever at one end. The positive-moment reinforcement is 4-#9 bars and the negative-moment reinforcement is 4-#8 bars. The loading to be carried is a live load of 1.6 kips/ft and a dead load of 1.4 kips/ft (including beam weight). Determine the lengths of bars (3-in. increments) if two of the four bars in both the positive- and the negative-moment regions are to be terminated as soon as practicable. The remaining bars are to be extended as required by the ACI Code. Width of supports is 12 in. and #3 U stirrups spaced at 10 in. are used in any potential cutoff region. Verify your design by showing for one set of axes the required moment (M_u)

envelope and the provided moment capacity (ϕM_n) diagram. Use $f'_c = 3500$ psi and $f_y = 40{,}000$ psi.

6.13 Repeat Prob. 6.12, except consider the negative-moment reinforcement is 2-#8 and 1-#9 and the positive-moment reinforcement is 2-#9 and 2-#8. The factored moment and shear envelopes for uniform loading are as shown in the accompanying figure. Determine the lengths of bars if one #9 is to be cut off in the negative-moment zone and two #8 are to be cut in the positive-moment zone. Assume #3 U stirrups are spaced at 10 in. in any potential cutoff region. Use a moment capacity (ϕM_n) diagram to verify your answer.

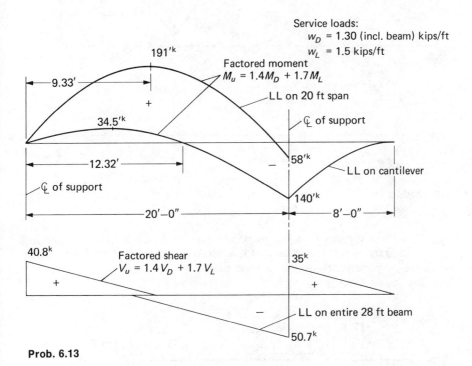

Prob. 6.13

6.14 A 12-in. wide by 24-in. (overall size) beam is used as the section for a 20-ft simply supported span having an 8-ft cantilever at one end. Support widths are 12 in. The positive-moment reinforcement is 2-#8 and 2-#7 and the negative-moment reinforcement is 4-#7. The factored moment and shear envelopes for uniform loading are as shown in the accompanying figure. Assume that two #7 bars are to be bent up near the right support in the 20-ft span and are to be cut as soon as feasible on the cantilever. Locate the bend-up and bend-down points as well as the cut point on the cantilever. Assume #3 stirrups are spaced at 10 in. in the entire negative-moment region. Verify your design by showing the moment capacity (ϕM_n) diagram. Use $f'_c = 3500$ psi and $f_y = 60{,}000$ psi.

6.15 In the accompanying figure, a cantilever slab (for example, for a retaining wall) varies in thickness from 24 in. at its supported end to 12 in. at its free end, with $2\frac{1}{2}$ in. clear cover over the reinforcement. Assuming that #7 bars at 6 in. spacing are effective at the supported end, at what distance from the supported end may every other #7 bar be cut off? Verify your result by showing the provided

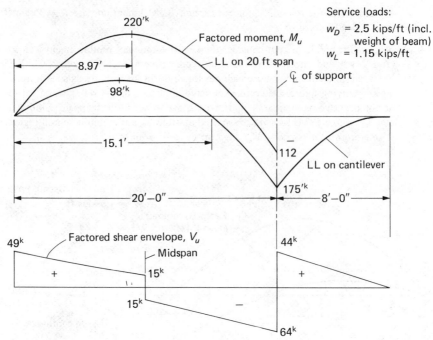

Service loads:

w_D = 2.5 kips/ft (incl. weight of beam)

w_L = 1.15 kips/ft

Prob. 6.14

moment capacity (ϕM_n) diagram superimposed on the bending moment (M_u) diagram. Use $f'_c = 3000$ psi and $f_y = 40,000$ psi. Assume the loading is entirely earth pressure and neglect the beam weight.

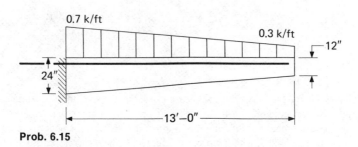

Prob. 6.15

PROBLEMS UTILIZING CONCEPTS OF CHAPTERS 1 THROUGH 6

6.16 Design, including design sketch, a reinforced concrete cantilever beam 14 ft long to carry a live load of 2.5 kips/ft. The beam size may not exceed 15 in. wide and 24 in. deep. Use $f'_c = 4000$ psi and $f_y = 60,000$ psi. (For S.I. problem use length = 4.3 m; live load = 3700 kg/m; $f'_c = 28$ N/mm²; $f_y = 420$ N/mm².)

6.17 Design, including design sketch, a cantilever beam 14 ft long to carry a live load of 3.0 kips/ft. Without actually satisfying a deflection limit, design a beam of such size that no serious problem with excessive deflection is to be expected. Use $f'_c = 4000$ psi and $f_y = 60,000$ psi. (For S.I. problem use live load = 4400 kg/m; length = 4.3 m; $f'_c = 28$ N/mm²; $f_y = 420$ N/mm².)

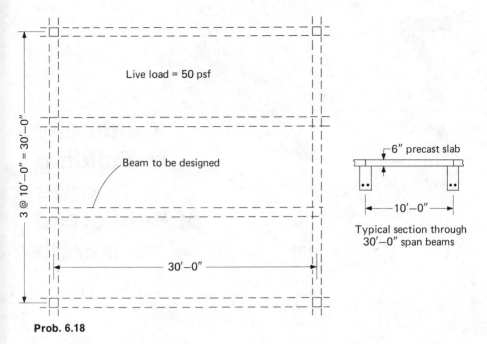

Live load = 50 psf

Beam to be designed

3 @ 10′–0″ = 30′–0″

30′–0″

6″ precast slab

10′–0″

Typical section through 30′–0″ span beams

Prob. 6.18

6.18 The floor system shown in the accompanying figure is given. The floor consists of 6-in. precast slab sections of 10 ft span. The live load is 50 psf, and the maximum depth available is 30 in. from the top of the floor slab. Completely design the beam indicated as a simply supported one. Use 1-in. multiples for beam depth and width. Use $f'_c = 4000$ psi and $f_y = 60,000$ psi.

7

Continuity in Building Frames of Reinforced Concrete

7.1 Common Building Frames

Reinforced concrete building construction commonly has floor slabs, beams, girders, and columns continuously placed to form a monolithic system. Consider the plan of typical slab–beam–girder floor construction shown in Fig. 7.1.1. Section *A-A* through the slab shows that the slab is supported on 10 beams. Intermediate beams such as *B*1, *B*2, and *B*3 are supported on the girders, whereas beams on the column lines such as *B*4, *B*5, and *B*6 are supported directly by the columns. Girders such as *G*1, *G*2, and *G*3 also go directly into the columns.

Beams such as *B*4, *B*5, and *B*6 are not only continuous beams, they are also built integrally with the upper and lower columns. For correct analysis, then, the complete frame in this plane, which may consist of, say, 10 or 15 stories or more should be analyzed as a rigid frame. In the analysis for gravity load on common and regular building frames, the beams and the adjacent columns may be isolated and treated as a unit (Fig. 7.1.2), with the far ends of the columns assumed as fixed. This assumption should not be used for wind loading, however. For wind analysis, except for very tall structures, a simplified approximate method may be used [1].

Girders *G*1, *G*2, and *G*3 may be treated in the same manner as the beams. Relative stiffness for columns, beams, and girders must be first assumed or established by preliminary design and later reviewed, as would be done in the analysis and design of any statically indeterminate rigid frame.

The continuous slab is supported at the beams, and the beams *B*1, *B*2, and *B*3 are supported at the girders. The supporting beams or girders possess torsional rigidity which may be approximated by using equivalent

Rigid frame bridge piers, I-75 near Detroit. (Photo by C. G. Salmon.)

supporting columns with fixed far ends. The stiffness factors to be used for such equivalent columns are discussed in Sec. 19.16 of Chap. 19 on torsion.

7.2 Positions of Live Load for Moment Envelope

The live-load positions that cause the largest bending moments in slabs, beams, and girders are discussed in this section. Bending moments to be used in the design of columns are treated separately later.

Consider the continuous beam *ABCDEFGH* with its adjacent columns as shown in Fig. 7.2.1a. The influence lines for bending moment at any point in the central portion of span *CD* and at a section just to the left of support *D* are shown in Fig. 7.2.1b and c, respectively. From these influence lines the following cases for uniform live load are indicated:

1. For maximum positive moment within a span, load that span and all other alternate spans.
2. For maximum negative moment within a span, load the two spans adjacent to that span and all other alternate spans.
3. For maximum negative moment at a support, load the two spans adjacent to that support and all other alternate spans.
4. For maximum positive moment at a support, load the two spans beyond each of the two spans adjacent to that support and all other alternate spans.

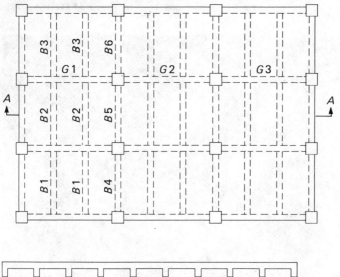

Section A-A

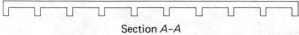

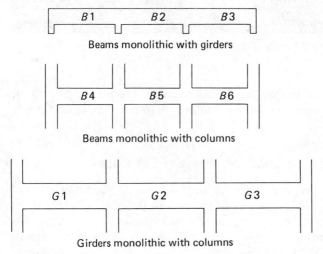

Beams monolithic with girders

Beams monolithic with columns

Girders monolithic with columns

Fig. 7.1.1
Slab–beam–girder floor.

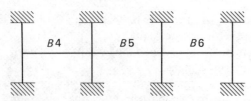

Fig. 7.1.2
Beams and adjacent columns.

240

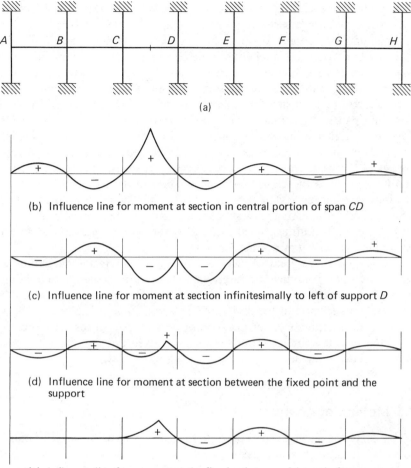

(a)

(b) Influence line for moment at section in central portion of span *CD*

(c) Influence line for moment at section infinitesimally to left of support *D*

(d) Influence line for moment at section between the fixed point and the support

(e) Influence line for moment at the fixed point near right end of span

Fig. 7.2.1
Influence lines for continuous spans.

It may be noted that loading cases 1 and 2 in the preceding paragraph are complementary; that is, their combination results in *all* spans being loaded. Loading cases 3 and 4 are also complementary. It may be noted further that loading cases 1 and 3 are primary; that is, they result in moments of the same sign as dead load. Loading cases 2 and 4, on the other hand, are secondary; they result in moments opposite in sign to those due to dead load. When the secondary live-load moment is numerically larger than the dead-load moment, there is moment reversal.

The loading cases thus far mentioned involve loading entire spans, that is, no partially loading of a span. These full span loading cases correctly give maximum and minimum bending moment in the midspan region (roughly the middle 40 to 50%) of a span as well as *at* the support. The correct maximum (or minimum) values are not obtained, however, for approximately 25 to 30% of the span nearest the supports.

A qualitative examination of Fig. 7.2.1b and c shows that if an influence line were drawn for a series of specific points along span *CD* between the midspan and the support, the peak ordinate in the positive portion of such influence line would get smaller and smaller. Also, the *slope* of the influence line at point *C* goes upward to the right for the midspan influence line but it is downward to the right for the support *D* influence line.

As successive influence lines are drawn for the points along the span from midspan to the support, there must be some location for which the slope of the influence line at *C* is horizontal. Such point is called a *fixed point*, giving an influence line illustrated by Fig. 7.2.1e. Any loading on spans to the left of the span under study will cause no moment at this fixed point. The fixed point is the closest location to the support for which full span loadings give the correct maximum or minimum bending moments. The influence line for a section between a fixed point and the support is as shown by Fig. 7.2.1d, indicating partial loading for the span in question to obtain maximum or minimum bending moment.

From a practical point of view, partial span loading for maximum or minimum bending moments is rarely actually done in the design of building frames because the effect of doing so on the design is small enough as to not justify the effort. For the design of long spans, such as highway bridges, the full consideration of the proper loading (loading partial span as indicated by influence lines) for locations between the fixed point and the support would usually be made.

7.3 Method of Analysis

When using the strength method of design, the analysis of the continuous concrete structure is made using *factored loads*; that is, the service loads multiplied by the overload factors *U*. Thus the structural analysis is to be made assuming an elastic system even though the factored load may cause inelastic effects. After obtaining the moments and shears assuming an elastic structure under the factored load condition, each section is proportioned to provide adequate strength. Although the procedure may seem somewhat inconsistent, it has been found to provide safe and adequate designs. The other possible approach would be to utilize the true ultimate or collapse condition, using the so-called limit design (discussed in Sec. 10.12) for continuous beams or frames, and yield-line theory (Chap. 18) for slabs. These two methods are not incorporated in the ACI Code, although the Code does contain provisions for adjustments to the results of elastic analysis to reflect present knowledge of collapse behavior.

There are numerous methods of statically indeterminate structural analysis that may be used. Selection of a method for a particular structure is not within the scope of this book. When the digital computer is used, matrix methods will usually be preferred [2]. For computation using non-programmable or small programmable calculators the moment-distribution method is probably the most convenient method for analyzing the rigid frame involving several continuous spans with the far ends of upper and lower columns fixed. The moment-distribution method is described in most textbooks on statically indeterminate structures, so it will not be developed here. The application to a six-span continuous beam with upper and lower columns is illustrated in the following example.

EXAMPLE 7.3.1   Determine the maximum and minimum moments at the middle and the ends of each span in a rigid frame with six equal spans as shown in Fig. 7.3.1. Assume that the uniform live load w_L is twice the uniform dead load w_D, and that the stiffness factor K_c (representing $4EI/L$) of the column is twice the stiffness factor K_b of the beam span. Express all moments in terms of wL^2 in which $w = w_D + w_L$ and L is the span length.

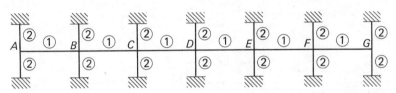

Fig. 7.3.1
A six-span continuous frame showing relative stiffnesses.

Solution: All moments will be expressed numerically in terms of $wL^2(10^{-4})$. The FEM (fixed-end moment) due to w_D and $w_L = \pm\frac{1}{12}wL^2 = \pm 833wL^2(10^{-4})$, whereas the FEM due to w_D only $= \pm\frac{1}{12}w_DL^2 = \pm\frac{1}{36}wL^2 = \pm 278wL^2(10^{-4})$.

Seven loading conditions as shown in Fig. 7.3.2 need to be investigated. The moment distribution is shown in Tables 7.3.1 to 7.3.7. For moment distribution, clockwise rotational moments acting on the member ends are taken as positive. The last section of Table 7.3.1 below "Final M" is a relative slope check. For prismatic members the final moment at end A of a member AB expressed in slope-deflection terminology is

$$M_{ab} = \text{FEM}_{ab} + \left(\frac{4EI}{L}\right)\theta_a + \left(\frac{2EI}{L}\right)\theta_b$$

where FEM_{ab} is the original fixed-end moment at end A, and θ_a and θ_b are the slopes of the elastic curve at ends A and B, respectively. The quantity $4EI/L$ is the stiffness K at one end of a prismatic member with its far end fixed. The change from fixed-end moment to final moment, ΔM_{ab}, is

$$\Delta M_{ab} = M_{ab} - \text{FEM}_{ab} = \left(\frac{4EI}{L}\right)\theta_a + \left(\frac{2EI}{L}\right)\theta_b$$

Also

$$\Delta M_{ba} = M_{ba} - \text{FEM}_{ba} = \left(\frac{4EI}{L}\right)\theta_b + \left(\frac{2EI}{L}\right)\theta_a$$

Solving for θ_a and θ_b gives

$$\theta_a = \frac{\Delta M_{ab} - \frac{1}{2}\Delta M_{ba}}{3EI/L} \quad \text{and} \quad \theta_b = \frac{\Delta M_{ba} - \frac{1}{2}\Delta M_{ab}}{3EI/L}$$

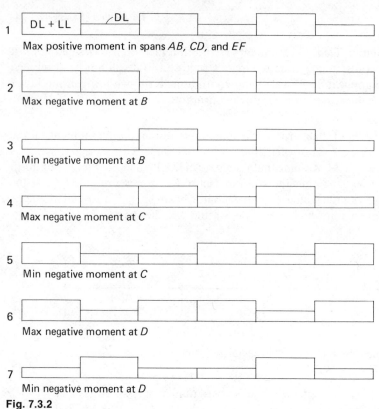

1. Max positive moment in spans *AB, CD,* and *EF*

2. Max negative moment at *B*

3. Min negative moment at *B*

4. Max negative moment at *C*

5. Min negative moment at *C*

6. Max negative moment at *D*

7. Min negative moment at *D*

Fig. 7.3.2
Loading conditions.

Table 7.3.1
Loading Condition No. 1 (Fig. 7.3.2)

Joint	A	B		C		D		E		F		G
Member	AB	BA	BC	CB	CD	DC	DE	ED	EF	FE	FG	GF
Distribution factor	$\frac{1}{5}$	$\frac{1}{6}$	$\frac{1}{6}$	$\frac{1}{6}$	$\frac{1}{6}$	$\frac{1}{6}$	$\frac{1}{6}$	$\frac{1}{6}$	$\frac{1}{6}$	$\frac{1}{6}$	$\frac{1}{6}$	$\frac{1}{5}$
FEM	−833	+833	−278	+278	−833	+833	−278	+278	−833	+833	−278	+278
Balance	+167	−92	−92	+92	+92	−92	−92	+92	+92	−92	−92	−56
Carry-over	−46	+83	+46	−46	−46	+46	+46	−46	−46	+46	−28	−46
Balance	+9	−22	−22	+15	+15	−15	−15	+15	+15	−3	−3	+9
Carry-over	−11	+4	+8	−11	−8	+8	+8	−8	−1	+8	+4	−1
Balance	+2	−2	−2	+3	+3	−3	−3	+1	+1	−2	−2	0
Final *M*	−712	+804	−340	+331	−777	+777	−334	+332	−772	+790	−399	+184
Change	+121	−29	−62	+53	+56	−56	−56	+54	+61	−43	−121	−94
$-\frac{1}{2}$ change	+14	−60	−26	+31	+28	−28	−27	+28	+22	−30	+47	+60
sum	+135	−89	−88	+84	+84	−84	−83	+82	+83	−73	−74	−34
$\theta_{rel} = \text{sum}/K$	+135	−89	−88	+84	+84	−84	−83	+82	+83	−73	−74	−34

Table 7.3.2

Loading Condition No. 2 (Fig. 7.3.2)

Member	AB	BA	BC	CB	CD	DC	DE	ED	EF	FE	FG	GF
FEM	−833	+833	−833	+833	−278	+278	−833	+833	−278	+278	−833	+833
Balance	+167	0	0	−92	−92	+92	+92	−92	−92	+92	+92	−167
Carry-over	0	+83	−46	0	+46	−46	−46	+46	+46	−46	−83	+46
Balance	0	−6	−6	−8	−8	+15	+15	−15	−15	+22	+22	−9
Carry-over	−3	0	−4	−3	+8	−4	−8	+8	+11	−8	−4	+11
Balance	+1	+1	+1	−1	−1	+2	+2	−3	−3	+2	+2	−2
Final M	−668	+911	−888	+729	−325	+337	−778	+777	−331	+340	−804	+712

Table 7.3.3

Loading Condition No. 3 (Fig. 7.3.2)

Member	AB	BA	BC	CB	CD	DC	DE	ED	EF	FE	FG	GF
FEM	−278	+278	−278	+278	−833	+833	−278	+278	−833	+833	−278	+278
Balance	+56	0	0	+92	+92	−92	−92	+92	+92	−92	−92	−56
Carry-over	0	+28	+46	0	−46	+46	+46	−46	−46	+46	−28	−46
Balance	0	−12	−12	+8	+8	−15	−15	+15	+15	−3	−3	+9
Carry-over	−6	0	+4	−6	−8	+4	+8	−8	−1	+8	+4	−1
Balance	+1	−1	−1	+2	+2	−2	−2	+1	+1	−2	−2	0
Final M	−227	+293	−241	+374	−785	+774	−333	+332	−772	+790	−399	+184

Table 7.3.4

Loading Condition No. 4 (Fig. 7.3.2)

Member	AB	BA	BC	CB	CD	DC	DE	ED	EF	FE	FG	GF
FEM	−278	+278	−833	+833	−833	+833	−278	+278	−833	+833	−278	+278
Balance	+56	+92	+92	0	0	−92	−92	+92	+92	−92	−92	−56
Carry-over	+46	+28	0	+46	−46	0	+46	−46	−46	+46	−28	−46
Balance	−9	−5	−5	0	0	−8	−8	+15	+15	−3	−3	+9
Carry-over	−2	−4	0	−2	−4	0	+8	−4	−1	+8	+4	−1
Balance	0	+1	+1	+1	+1	−1	−1	+1	+1	−2	−2	0
Final M	−187	+390	−745	+878	−882	+732	−325	+336	−772	+790	−399	+184

Table 7.3.5
Loading Condition No. 5 (Fig. 7.3.2)

Member	AB	BA	BC	CB	CD	DC	DE	ED	EF	FE	FG	GF
FEM	−833	+833	−278	+278	−278	+278	−833	+833	−278	+278	−833	+833
Balance	+167	−92	−92	0	0	+92	+92	−92	−92	+92	+92	−167
Carry-over	−46	+83	0	−46	+46	0	−46	+46	+46	−46	−83	+46
Balance	+9	−14	−14	0	0	+8	+8	−15	−15	+22	+22	−9
Carry-over	−7	+4	0	−7	+4	0	−8	+4	+11	−8	−4	+11
Balance	+1	−1	−1	0	0	+1	+1	−2	−2	+2	+2	−2
Final M	−709	+813	−385	+225	−228	+379	−786	+774	−330	+340	−804	+712

Table 7.3.6
Loading Condition No. 6 (Fig. 7.3.2)

Member	AB	BA	BC	CB	CD	DC	DE	ED	EF	FE	FG	GF
FEM	−833	+833	−278	+278	−833	+833	−833	+833	−278	+278	−833	+833
Balance	+167	−92	−92	+92	+92	0	0	−92	−92	+92	+92	−167
Carry-over	−46	+83	+46	−46	0	+46	−46	0	+46	−46	−83	+46
Balance	+9	−22	−22	+8	+8	0	0	−8	−8	+22	+22	−9
Carry-over	−11	+4	+4	−11	0	+4	−4	0	+11	−4	−4	+11
Balance	+2	−1	−1	+2	+2	0	0	−2	−2	+1	+1	−2
Final M	−712	+805	−343	+323	−731	+883	−883	+731	−323	+343	−805	+712

Table 7.3.7
Loading Condition No. 7 (Fig. 7.3.2)

Member	AB	BA	BC	CB	CD	DC	DE	ED	EF	FE	FG	GF
FEM	−278	+278	−833	+833	−278	+278	−278	+278	−833	+833	−278	+278
Balance	+56	+92	+92	−92	−92	0	0	+92	+92	−92	−92	−56
Carry-over	+46	+28	−46	+46	0	−46	+46	0	−46	+46	−28	−46
Balance	−9	+3	+3	−8	−8	0	0	+8	+8	−3	−3	+9
Carry-over	+1	−4	−4	+1	0	−4	+4	0	−1	+4	+4	−1
Balance	0	+1	+1	0	0	0	0	0	0	−1	−1	0
Final M	−184	+398	−787	+780	−378	+228	−228	+378	−780	+787	−398	+184

Thus

$$\theta_a \text{ (relative)} = \left(\frac{\Delta M_{ab} - \frac{1}{2}\Delta M_{ba}}{K}\right)$$

$$\theta_b \text{ (relative)} = \left(\frac{\Delta M_{ba} - \frac{1}{2}\Delta M_{ab}}{K}\right)$$

Although not shown, the relative slope check as shown in Table 7.3.1 has been performed for the moment distribution in Tables 7.3.2 to 7.3.7.

The controlling values of final moments at the left and right ends of each span, M_L and M_R, for the various critical conditions are taken from Tables 7.3.1 through 7.3.7 and entered in Table 7.3.8. Note that the designer's sign convention for bending moment, in which a positive moment causes compression on the top side of the beam, is used in Table 7.3.8.

Table 7.3.8
Summary of Results of Moment Distribution Analysis

Line Number		Span	M_L	M_R	Values of M_L and M_R from Table No.	$M_s = M_0 - \frac{1}{2}(M_L + M_R)$
1	For maximum positive moment at midspan	AB	−712	−804	7.3.1	+492
2		BC	−790	−772	7.3.1	+469 ($M_0 = +1250$)
3		CD	−777	−777	7.3.1	+473
4	For minimum positive or maximum negative moment at midspan	AB	−184	−399	7.3.1	+125
5		BC	−340	−331	7.3.1	+ 81 ($M_0 = +417$)
6		CD	−332	−334	7.3.1	+ 84
7	For maximum negative moment at	A of AB	−712		7.3.1	
8		B of AB		−911	7.3.2	
9		B of BC	−888		7.3.2	
10		C of BC		−878	7.3.4	
11		C of CD	−882		7.3.4	
12		D of CD		−883	7.3.6	
13	For minimum negative or maximum positive moment at	A of AB	−184		7.3.1	
14		B of AB		−293	7.3.3	
15		B of BC	−241		7.3.3	
16		C of BC		−225	7.3.5	
17		C of CD	−228		7.3.5	
18		D of CD		−228	7.3.7	

NOTE: Values of moments in $wL^2(10^{-4})$.

The moment at the midspan M_s may be determined by superposition of the effect of end moments with that of the simple beam moment due to transverse loading,

$$M_s = M_0 - \tfrac{1}{2}(M_L + M_R)$$

in which M_0 is the moment at the midspan for a simple beam. When the end moments are not equal, the maximum moment in the span does not occur at midspan, but its value is close to that at midspan.

For the purpose of illustration, the moment diagram for the maximum and minimum positive moments at midspan, using results of the first loading condition in Fig. 7.3.2, is shown in Fig. 7.3.3. First the simple beam moment diagrams for the total load and for dead load only are drawn to scale in Fig. 7.3.3a. Next the end moments for each span are taken from Table 7.3.8 and plotted in Fig. 7.3.3b. Note that because of symmetry, only the moment diagrams for the first three spans are shown. The final moment diagrams in Fig. 7.3.3b are drawn by rotating the base lines for zero end moments in Fig. 7.3.3a to those connecting the end moments in Fig. 7.3.3b.

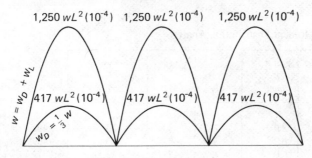

(a) Simple beam moment diagrams

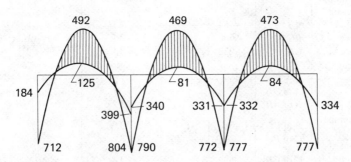

(b) Moment diagrams for maximum and minimum positive midspan moments

Fig. 7.3.3

Moment diagrams for Example 7.3.1.

In this example the dead load has been applied over the entire span in each of the seven loading conditions of Fig. 7.3.2. This has been done because an important purpose of the example is to justify the use of approximate moment coefficients as discussed in the next section. An alternative approach would be to use eight loading conditions; one condition for dead load only plus the same seven live-load conditions but without the dead load applied simultaneously. Another alternative for the live-load cases would be to load one span at a time and carry out the moment distribution. Because of symmetry only three distributions would be required; live load in spans 1, 2, and 3 separately. Moments and shears due to load on spans 4, 5, or 6 can be deduced from load on spans 3, 2, or 1, respectively. The procedure of loading one span at a time with live load will require less moment distribution operations but more effort in combining the appropriate cases to obtain the maximum and minimum moments at the various locations. Separation of dead- and live-load reactions to columns is frequently desirable, because if a loading combination that includes wind or earthquake must be considered, different live-load factors U must be used according to ACI-9.2.

7.4 ACI Moment Coefficients

It is specified in ACI-8.3 that (1) the theory of elastic analysis is to be used in analyzing frames or continuous construction; (2) except for prestressed concrete, approximate methods of frame analysis may be used for buildings of usual types of construction, spans, and story heights; and (3) except for prestressed concrete, design for the moments and shears as listed in ACI-8.3.3 is satisfactory in the case of two or more approximately equal spans (the larger of two adjacent spans not exceeding the shorter by more than 20%) with loads uniformly distributed, where the unit live load does not exceed 3 times the unit dead load. The approximate method mentioned in (2) is usually taken as the method of isolating one floor at a time (with its upper and lower columns) as outlined in Sec. 7.3.

It seems desirable to examine the moment coefficients in ACI-8.3.3. Observation of Table 7.3.8 in the preceding section shows that for a six-span frame in which the ratio of ΣK_{col} to K_{bm} is 4 and the ratio of w_L to w_D is 2, critical values of moments may vary within the following limits:

Exterior span:
  Exterior end $-0.0184wL^2$ and $-0.0712wL^2$
  Midspan $+0.0125wL^2$ and $+0.0492wL^2$
  Interior end $-0.0293wL^2$ and $-0.0911wL^2$

First interior span:
  Exterior end $-0.0241wL^2$ and $-0.0888wL^2$
  Midspan $+0.0081wL^2$ and $+0.0469wL^2$
  Interior end $-0.0225wL^2$ and $-0.0878wL^2$

Second interior span:
  Exterior end $-0.0228wL^2$ and $-0.0882wL^2$
  Midspan $+0.0084wL^2$ and $+0.0473wL^2$
  Interior end $-0.0228wL^2$ and $-0.0883wL^2$

Similar values may be worked out for other values of $(\Sigma K_{col})/K_{bm}$ and of w_L/w_D. It may be observed that the maximum positive moments in the first and second interior spans are about equal, that the maximum positive moment in the exterior span is higher than that in the interior spans, that the maximum negative moment at the interior end of the exterior span has the largest numerical value, and that the maximum negative moments at both ends of all interior spans are about equal. The moment coefficients in ACI-8.3.3 are in agreement with these observations.

As a matter of further justification of the ACI moment coefficients, a comparison of these values with the largest possible theoretical values [3] is shown in Table 7.4.1. Certainly the largest possible theoretical values will be for the case of $w_L/w_D = 3$, which is the limit set forth in ACI-8.3.3. In this instance, secondary live-load moments with signs opposite to that of dead load occur infrequently; or, if they do occur, their values are small. Thus as long as the ratio of live load to dead load is well within 3 and span lengths do not differ considerably, there will be no moment reversal so that the ACI moment coefficients are reasonably close and, in general, on the safe side. It may be noted, however, that the ACI moment coefficients are

Table 7.4.1

Comparison of ACI Moment Coefficients with Theoretical Values

Location of Section	ACI	Theoretical Coefficients			
		Value	Number of Spans	$(\Sigma K_{col})/K_{bm}$	w_L/w_D
Positive moment					
End Spans					
If discontinuous end is unrestrained	$+\frac{1}{11}$	$+0.094$	3	0	3
If discontinuous end is integral with the support	$+\frac{1}{14}$	$+0.073$	3	0.5	3
Interior spans	$+\frac{1}{16}$	$+0.063$	4 or more	0.5	3
Negative moment at exterior face of first interior support					
Two spans	$-\frac{1}{9}$	-0.111	2	0.5	3
More than two spans	$-\frac{1}{10}$	-0.107	4 or more	0.5	3
Negative moment at other faces of interior supports	$-\frac{1}{11}$	-0.092	4 or more	2	3
Negative moment at face of all supports for (a) slabs with spans not exceeding 10 ft and (b) beams and girders where $(\Sigma K_{col})/K_{bm}$ exceeds 8 at each end of the span	$-\frac{1}{12}$	-0.083	any number	∞	any ratio
Negative moment at interior faces of exterior supports for members built integrally with their supports					
Where the support is a spandrel beam or girder	$-\frac{1}{24}$	-0.036	4 or more	0.5	3
		-0.050	4 or more	1	3
Where the support is a column	$-\frac{1}{16}$	-0.064	4 or more	2	3

in terms of (wL_n^2), in which L_n is the clear span for positive moment and the average of the two adjacent clear spans for negative moment, negative moments being those at the face of supports and not at the centerline of support. On the other hand, the theoretical coefficients are in terms of wL^2, in which L is the distance between centerlines of supports, and coefficients for negative moments refer to those at the centerlines of support.

7.5 ACI Moment Diagrams

In designing any span in a multispan continuous rigid frame subjected to live load where moment coefficients are used, two primary sets of shear and moment diagrams are inherently being assumed. In the general case, one will result from the loading position that causes maximum positive moment within the span, and the other will result from assuming that the maximum negative moments occur simultaneously at both ends. Actually the loading

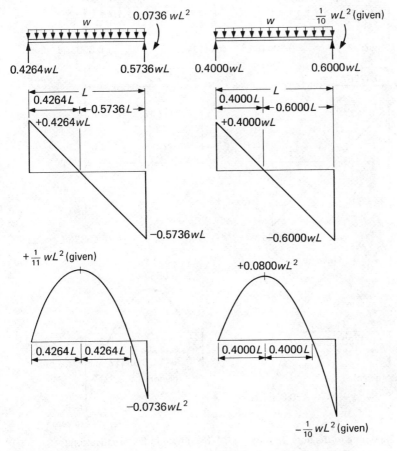

(a) Maximum in the positive zone   (b) Maximum in the negative zone

Fig. 7.5.1

Exterior span with discontinuous end unrestrained.

position that causes maximum moment at one end is different from that which causes maximum negative moment at the other end; however, by assuming that both maximum negative end moments occur simultaneously, a critical curve having greater magnitude than either of the two actual curves is obtained.

The ACI moment coefficients (ACI-8.3.3) as shown in Table 7.4.1 are the common values from the two primary conditions as described in the preceding paragraph. No secondary moment coefficients are suggested by the Code, the reason being that so long as the design live- to dead-load ratio is limited to 3, no moment reversal would occur; that is, there can be only positive moment in the midspan region and only negative moment in the support region.

In Fig. 7.5.1 to 7.5.4, inclusive, are shown the two primary sets of shear and moment diagrams, for the various conditions, to be used in the design of continuous spans in accordance with the ACI moment coefficients.

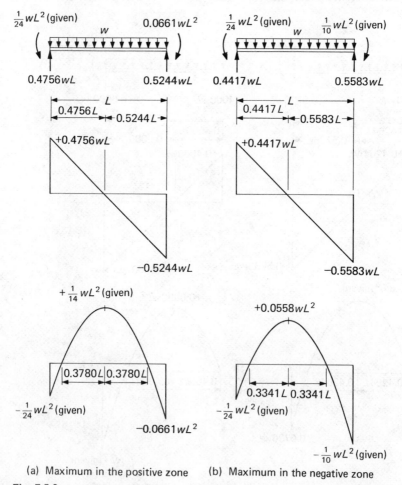

(a) Maximum in the positive zone   (b) Maximum in the negative zone

Fig. 7.5.2

Exterior span with exterior support built integrally with spandrel beam or girder.

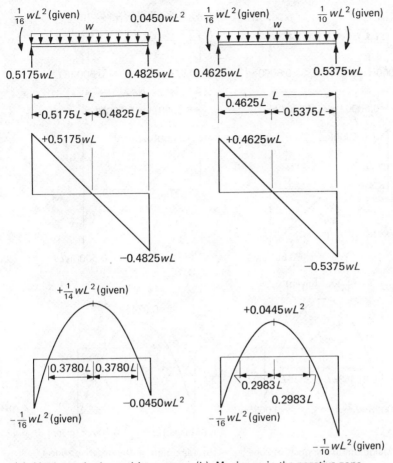

(a) Maximum in the positive zone   (b) Maximum in the negative zone

Fig. 7.5.3

Exterior span with exterior support built integrally with column.

The reader should utilize the fundamentals of shear and moment diagrams to verify the numerical ordinates on these diagrams. For instance, in the case of maximum positive moment in Fig. 7.5.2a the distance x from the left support to the point of zero shear may be determined from the relationship that the change of moment between any two sections is equal to the area of the shear diagram between these two sections. Thus

$$\frac{wx^2}{2} = \left(\frac{1}{24} + \frac{1}{14}\right)wL^2$$

from which

$$x = 0.4756L$$

Also, the distance x between the section of maximum positive moment to the point of zero moment is

$$\frac{wx^2}{2} = \frac{1}{14}wL^2$$

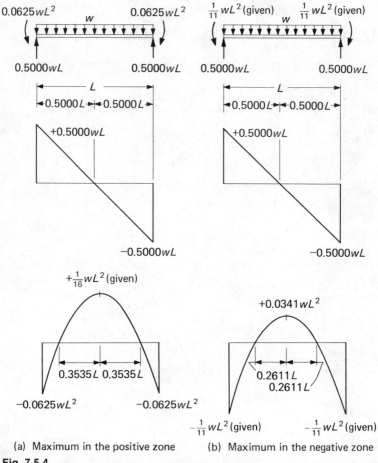

(a) Maximum in the positive zone   (b) Maximum in the negative zone

Fig. 7.5.4
Interior span.

from which

$$x = 0.3780L$$

Any time a designer uses moment coefficients for determining the final design moments, as permitted by the approximate method of ACI-8.3.3, the moment diagrams that correspond to such coefficients should be used when establishing bar bend or cutoff locations. The use of a given moment coefficient implies a statically compatible moment diagram.

7.6 Design Shears

Inasmuch as the design of shear reinforcement is dependent on the variation of shear forces along the span, the maximum shear force at any section due to the combination of dead and live loads should be determined. When

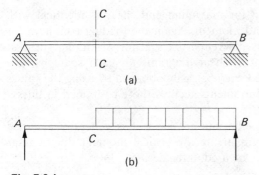

Fig. 7.6.1
Maximum live-load shear at section C-C.

the live load consists of important concentrated loads such as in the design of highway bridge spans, accurate calculations of such maximum shears at all sections must be performed. Even in a simple beam subjected to uniform live load, the maximum shear at a section such as C-C in Fig. 7.6.1a is caused by load on portion CB of the span (Fig. 7.6.1b) and not by load on the entire beam. The same situation will occur at any intermediate section in a continuous span.

In buildings of usual types of construction, spans, and story heights, wherein the idealized rigid frame such as shown in Fig. 7.6.2a is taken into consideration, the use of partial span loading of uniform live load is commonly ignored, although theoretically it is necessary for the computation of maximum shear at any section within the span. When partial span loading is not considered necessary, the maximum shears at only the ends can be used to establish an approximate shear envelope.

The influence line for end shear at C of span CD in the rigid frame of Fig. 7.6.2a is shown in Fig. 7.6.2b. It can be seen that in the case of uniform

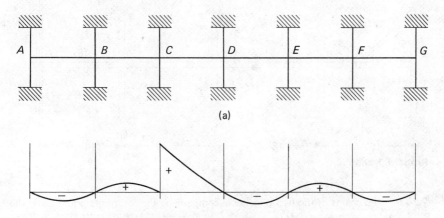

(b) Influence line for maximum end shear at C of span CD

Fig. 7.6.2
Shear in rigid frames.

live load the loading position for maximum end shear is identical with that for maximum negative end moment. Again the loading condition for maximum shear at one end is different from that for maximum shear at the other end. These two critical shear diagrams for each span, when a continuity analysis is performed, may be easily obtained by using the values of the maximum negative end moments such as those contained in lines 7 through 12 of Table 7.3.8.

When the ACI moment coefficients are used, it is generally assumed that the shear diagrams accompanying the critical moment diagrams as shown in Fig. 7.5.1 to 7.5.4 may be used in the design.

SELECTED REFERENCES

1. *Continuity in Concrete Building Frames* (4th ed.). Chicago: Portland Cement Association, 1959.
2. C. K. Wang. *Matrix Methods of Structural Analysis* (2nd ed.). Madison, Wisconsin American Publishing Company, 1970.
3. A. J. Boase and J. T. Howell. "Design Coefficients for Building Frames," *ACI Journal*, *Proceedings*, **36,** September 1939, 21–36. (See also *Reinforced Concrete Design Handbook*, Publication SP-3, American Concrete Institute, 1965, pp. 267–270.)

PROBLEMS

7.1 Compute and draw the envelope of bending moments (diagram showing range over which bending moment may vary) due to factored loads for the beams of the frame of the accompanying figure, using a continuity analysis method such as moment distribution. The uniform factored dead load is 1 kip/ft and the uniform factored live load is 2 kips/ft.

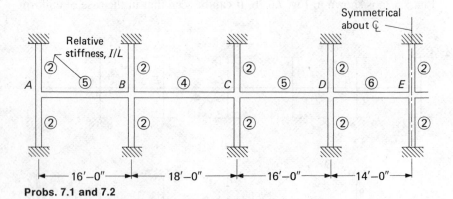

Probs. 7.1 and 7.2

7.2 For the beams of the frame in the accompanying figure, compute and draw the bending moment envelope using the coefficients of ACI-8.3.3. (If Prob. 7.1 has also been solved, compare the moments by giving the percentage difference in the maximum values obtained by coefficients as compared with the more exact values of a continuity analysis.)

7.3 Consider an equal-span, uniform-section continuous beam over many supports. Compute and show diagrams for dead-load coefficients of wL^2 for moments at critical locations in the exterior and first interior spans. Could the coefficients for the first interior span be applied appropriately to the other interior spans? Recommend dead-load coefficients for equal spans.

7.4 Repeat Problem 7.3 for the case where alternate spans are 20% longer than the others (1.2L), taking the exterior span as a short one (L).

7.5 For an equal-span, uniform-section continuous beam over many supports, compute and show diagrams for live-load coefficients in terms of wL^2 for maximum negative moments at **(a)** the first interior support; **(b)** the second interior support; and **(c)** the typical interior support. Recommend live-load coefficients.

7.6 For an equal-span, uniform-section continuous beam over many supports, compute and show diagrams for live-load coefficients in terms of wL^2 for the maximum positive moment in **(a)** the exterior span; **(b)** the first interior span; and **(c)** the typical interior span. Recommend live-load coefficients.

8

Design
of One-Way
Slabs

8.1 Definition

One of the most common types of floor construction is the slab-beam-girder system, as has been briefly described in Sec. 7.1. The slab panel, bounded on its two long sides by the beams and on its two short sides by the girders, is usually at least twice as long as it is wide. In such a condition the dead and live load acting on the slab area may be considered as being entirely supported in the short or transverse direction by the beams, hence the term "one-way slab." Two-way slabs on beams are treated in Chap. 16, ribbed-joist floor construction in Chap. 10 (Secs. 10.10 and 10.11) and flat slabs in Chap. 17.

The determination of an optimum floor framing plan—that is, the spacing of columns, beams, and girders—depends on both the functional and the structural requirements. In most cases preliminary calculations are necessary for several different layouts, and after comparison the most suitable and economical plan is chosen.

8.2 Design Methods

Since the loading on a one-way slab is nearly all transferred in the short direction, such a slab continuous over several supports may be treated as a beam. Because sufficiently accurate results are obtained, ACI-8.3.3 permits the use of moment and shear coefficients in the case of two or more approximately equal spans (the larger of two adjacent spans not exceeding the shorter by more than 20%) with loads uniformly distributed, where the unit

Lennox Square Buildings, Atlanta. (Courtesy of Portland Cement Association.)

live load does not exceed three times the unit dead load. These coefficients are in terms of clear span L_n and the values given are for critical locations, that is, faces of support for shears and negative moments and midspan regions for positive moments.

When the conditions of ACI-8.3.3 are not satisfied, an elastic analysis is required. Approximate methods are permitted in "buildings of usual types of construction, spans, and story heights."

One such approximate procedure applicable to equal spans, where dead load and live load are to be treated separately (say, when $w_L/w_D > 3$), is to use the coefficients given in Appendix 3 of the 1940 Joint Committee Report [1]. Other approximate methods are available for determining critical moments and shears, short of a formal elastic analysis according to a procedure such as that described in Chap. 7, which does not seem justified on a slab. The *Reinforced Concrete Design Handbook* [2] provides an Appendix with moment coefficients that are nearly as exact as those which would be obtained by a formal method such as moment distribution.

Generally, span lengths between centers of supports are used in elastic analysis, notably in the computation for fixed-end moments and stiffness factors. Similarly, the results of an elastic analysis show only the negative bending moments at centers of supports. It will be shown that the negative bending moment at the face of support, the value of which should be used in the design of the member itself, may be obtained by reducing from the maximum value at the center of support by a quantity equal to $Vb/3$, where V is the shear force at either the center or at the face of support, and b is the width of support.

Consider an ideal situation where a member AB is fixed at points A and B and subjected to a uniform load, as shown in Fig. 8.2.1. The elastic curve is shown as $AA'B'B$ in Fig. 8.2.1a, where there are rotation and deflection at A' and B'. The bending moment at A' (Fig. 8.2.1) is

$$M = -\frac{wL^2}{12} + \frac{wL}{2}\left(\frac{b}{2}\right) - \frac{w(b/2)^2}{2} = -\left(\frac{wL^2}{12} - \frac{wLb}{4} + \frac{wb^2}{8}\right) \quad \text{(8.2.1)}$$

Now if the same member is considered to be fixed at A' and B' as shown in Fig. 8.2.2, the bending moment at A' (Fig. 8.2.2) is

$$M = -\frac{w(L-b)^2}{12} = -\left(\frac{wL^2}{12} - \frac{wLb}{6} + \frac{wb^2}{12}\right) \quad \text{(8.2.2)}$$

The quantity shown in Eq. (8.2.2) is numerically larger than in Eq. (8.2.1)

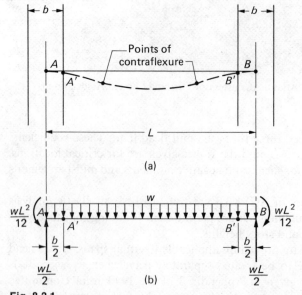

Fig. 8.2.1
Single span fixed at points A and B.

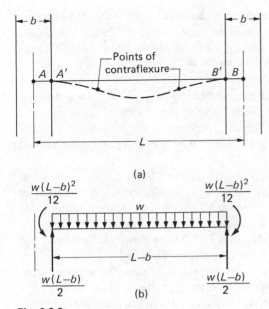

Fig. 8.2.2
Single span fixed at points A' and B'.

by an amount $wLb/12$, provided the terms involving b^2 are neglected. However, the condition in Fig. 8.2.2 is believed to be more correct because at a relatively stiff support, such as a column or girder, there can be very little change in rotation or deflection between the points A and A'. Thus the moment at the face of support is less than that at the center of support by a quantity equal to $Vb/3$ [Eq. (8.2.2)] rather than $Vb/2$ [Eq. (8.2.1)] if V is taken as $wL/2$ and, again, if the term involving b^2 is neglected (see also Ref. 3).

On the other hand, the moment at the center of span in Fig. 8.2.2 is less than that in Fig. 8.2.1. Inasmuch as the elastic analysis results are associated with the concept of Fig. 8.2.1, midspan moments so obtained are on the safe side, and, in general, no attempt is necessary to correct them to the concept of Fig. 8.2.2.

8.3 Thickness of Slab

In designing a one-way slab, a typical imaginary strip 12 in. wide is usually considered. The continuous slab may be designed as a continuous beam except that the width of this beam is known to be 12 in. Thus as far as concrete dimensions are concerned, the slab thickness is the only unknown.

The thickness of the slab depends on the deflection, bending, and shear requirements. Deflection requirements are imposed to prevent excessive deformations that might adversely affect the strength or serviceability of the structure. According to ACI-Table 9.5a, one-way slabs must have at least a minimum slab thickness (for Grade 60 steel) of $L/20$, $L/24$, $L/28$, or $L/10$ depending on whether L is the length of a simply supported, a one end continuous, a both ends continuous, or a cantilever span. If the slab supports or is attached to construction likely to be damaged by large deflections, deflections must be computed and shown to satisfy the limits of ACI-Table 9.5b. An extensive treatment of deflections will be found in Chap. 14.

To satisfy the bending requirement, the effective depth provided should be greater than that required as computed from $M_n = R_u b d^2$ using strength design, where R_u is a function of the desired percentage of reinforcement. In equal continuous spans the negative moment at the exterior face of the first interior support is the largest; therefore this negative moment should be used to establish the slab thickness.

The shear requirement does not usually control, but it should be checked. Because of practical space limitations, shear reinforcement is not used in a slab; thus the governing factored shear V_u, which in equal continuous spans occurs at the exterior face (the distance d therefrom) of the first interior support, must be kept below ϕV_c of ACI-11.2 for lightweight concrete and ACI-11.3 for nonprestressed ordinary weight concrete.

According to ACI-7.7.1c, the concrete protective covering for reinforcement (#11 and smaller) in slabs shall be not less than $\frac{3}{4}$ in. at surfaces not exposed directly to the ground or the weather. Also, when the top of a monolithic slab is the wearing surface and when unusual wear is expected as in buildings of the warehouse or industrial class, it has been customary to use an additional depth of $\frac{1}{2}$ in. of concrete protective covering over that required by the design of the member. The ACI Code no longer specifies such extra slab thickness for wearing surface and in ACI-8.12 *permits*, on the discretion of the designer, a monolithic floor finish to be considered as part of the structural member. For nonstructural purposes, any concrete floor finish may be considered as part of the required cover or total thickness requirement.

EXAMPLE 8.3.1   Establish the thickness of the floor slab as shown in the second-floor framing plan of Fig. 8.3.1 for a service live load of 100 psf. Use $f'_c = 3000$ psi, $f_y = 40,000$ psi, and the strength method of the ACI Code. Assume an exterior staircase so that no openings are to be made in the slabs.

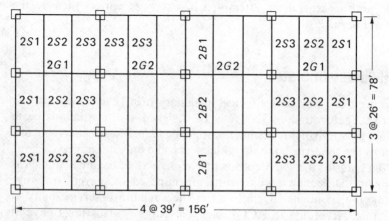

Fig. 8.3.1
Second-floor framing plan.

Solution: Since live load does not appear to exceed 3 times the dead load, the design will be done in accordance with ACI moment coefficients and their corresponding shear and moment diagrams (see Sec. 7.5).

(a) Minimum thickness. For spans with one end and both ends continuous, the respective minimum thicknesses, h, from ACI-Table 9.5a are $L/24$ and $L/28$. Since the table values are for $f_y = 60,000$ psi, they must be corrected for $f_y = 40,000$ psi by multiplying by 0.8.

$$\min h = \frac{L}{24}(0.8) = \frac{L}{30} = \frac{13(12)}{30} = 5.2 \text{ in. (for 2S1)}$$

$$\min h = \frac{L}{28}(0.8) = \frac{L}{35} = \frac{13(12)}{35} = 4.5 \text{ in. (for 2S2 and 2S3)}$$

Assume a $4\frac{1}{2}$-in. slab. The weight of the slab is $(4.5/12)(0.15) = 0.056$ kips/sq-ft. If deflection is of concern in the end span, that span could be made 5 in. thick or compression reinforcement could be used (see Example 14.12.2 for deflection calculation for a similar end span.)

(b) Bending moment requirement. Assume width of supporting beams to be 13 in. Note that 13 in., an uncommon dimension for width, is used rather than 12 in. to permit easier following of the numerical calculations.

$$w_D = 0.056(1.4) = 0.079 \text{ kip/ft/ft of width}$$
$$w_L = 0.100(1.7) = 0.170 \text{ kip/ft/ft of width}$$
$$\text{clear span} = 13 - \tfrac{13}{12} = 11.92 \text{ ft}$$
$$M_u = \tfrac{1}{10}(0.079 + 0.170)(11.92)^2 = 3.54 \text{ ft-kips/ft of width}$$

Choose a reinforcement percentage ρ equal to about $0.375\rho_b$, or one-half the maximum permitted by the ACI Code, in order to have reasonable deflection control. From Table 3.5.1,

$$0.375\rho_b = 0.5(0.0278) = 0.0139$$

Then using Eq. (3.6.4) or Fig. 3.6.1, find R_u,

$$m = \frac{f_y}{0.85f'_c} = \frac{40,000}{0.85(3000)} = 15.7$$

$$R_u = \rho f_y(1 - \tfrac{1}{2}\rho m)$$
$$= 0.0139(40,000)[1 - 0.5(0.0139)(15.7)] = 495 \text{ psi}$$

$$\text{required } d = \sqrt{\frac{M_u}{\phi R_u b}} = \sqrt{\frac{3.54(12,000)}{0.90(495)12}} = 2.82 \text{ in.}$$

Assume #5 bars.

$$\text{required } h = 2.82 + 0.31 + 0.75 = 3.88 \text{ in.}$$

Use $h = 4\frac{1}{2}$ in.

$$\text{provided } d = 4.50 - 0.31 - 0.75 = 3.44 \text{ in.}$$

(c) Shear requirement.

$$\max V_u = 1.15\frac{w_u L_n}{2} = 1.15\frac{0.249(11.92)}{2} = 1.71 \text{ kips/ft of width}$$

The design shear strength, ϕV_c, for a member without shear reinforcement is

$$\phi V_c = \phi[2\sqrt{f'_c}bd]$$
$$= 0.85(2\sqrt{3000})(12)(3.44)\tfrac{1}{1000} = 3.84 \text{ kips/ft} > 1.71 \text{ kips/ft}$$

The slab is acceptable for a member without stirrups. Note that to be strictly correct the shear force at a distance d from the face of support should have been used, in which case the factored shear would have been even less than 1.71 kips/ft.

8.4 Choice of Reinforcement

The choice of reinforcement depends primarily on the steel area and secondarily on development length requirements. The steel areas required at the principal sections, namely those at the middle and at the ends of each span, are first computed. Then a *tentative* choice of reinforcement may be made. A common arrangement of reinforcement in floor slabs is as shown in Fig. 8.4.1, in which the straight and bent (trussed) bars are placed alternately. The straight bars across the bottom are ordinarily one size smaller than the bent bars. Frequently, in thin slabs of under 5 in. of thickness, straight bars are used in both the top and bottom in all spans. Some designers prefer straight bars in all cases.

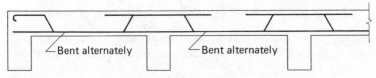

Bent alternately   Bent alternately

Fig. 8.4.1
A common arrangement of slab reinforcement.

Development length requirements should next be examined. The positive-moment bars that are bent up into the negative-moment region have ample embedment. The bars that continue along the bottom of the slab and extend into the support at least 6 in. (ACI-12.12.1) must be checked for adequate development at points of inflection (ACI-12.12.3). In addition, the bars extending straight across the top beyond the bend-down points must be checked for satisfactory embedment (ACI-12.13.3).

Some other limitations affecting the choice of reinforcement in slabs are (1) that in structural slabs of uniform thickness the minimum amount of reinforcement in the direction of the span shall not be less than that required for shrinkage and temperature reinforcement (ACI-7.12), and (2) that the principal reinforcement shall be centered not farther apart than three times the slab thickness nor more than 18 in. (ACI-7.6.5).

EXAMPLE 8.4.1 Choose the arrangement of reinforcement in the $4\tfrac{1}{2}$-in. floor slab 2S1, 2S2, and 2S3, as designed in Example 8.3.1.

Solution: (a) Area requirements. The ACI moment coefficient, the bending moment, the steel area required, and the tentative choice of reinforcement at the critical section are shown in lines 1 to 6 of Table 8.4.1. The arrangement of reinforcement is shown in Fig. 8.4.2. Choice of this steel should begin at the typical interior support. In this case, #4 bars at 6 in. are chosen. At the middle of the first and typical interior spans, the required area would be furnished by #3 straight (st) bars at 12 in. in addition to the #4 bent (bt) bars at 12 in. which were already there. As a matter of practical judgment, however, some designers would not use bars smaller than #4 for main reinforcement. Since the decision has now been made on the 6 in. and 12 in. spacings, the bent-bar size in the exterior span follows automatically. These spacings satisfy the limitations of ACI-7.6.5.

(b) Development length requirements at inflection points. In order to confirm the choice of longitudinal reinforcement made on the basis of the required areas only, it is necessary to review the development length requirements. The requirements of ACI-12.12.3 must be checked at the exterior supported end (point 1) and at the inflection points 2 to 6. In addition, embedment equal to the requirement development length must be provided in both directions from the maximum moment points at the faces of supports (points 7 through 12). Finally, embedment of the straight portion of the bars at the top of the slab beyond extreme points of inflection (points 13 through 17) must satisfy ACI-12.13.3.

From the ACI shear and moment diagrams in Fig. 7.5.2 and 7.5.4, the shears at inflection points on the typical 1-ft width of slab are

$$V_1 = V_2 = 0.3780 w L_n = 0.3780(0.249)(11.92) = 1.13 \text{ kips}$$
$$V_3 = V_4 = V_5 = V_6 = 0.3535 w L_n = 0.3535(0.249)(11.92) = 1.05 \text{ kips}$$

For the bars (#3) that extend past the inflection points into the supports, the required development length (from Table 6.9.1) is

$$L_d (\#3) = 12 \text{ in. min}$$

The requirement of ACI-12.12.3 at inflection points (such as point 2) is

$$\frac{M_n}{V_u} + L_a \geq L_d$$

For #3 @ 12 in.,

$$C = 0.85(3)12a = 30.6a$$
$$T = 0.11(40) = 4.4 \text{ kips}$$
$$a = \frac{4.4}{30.6} = 0.14 \text{ in.}$$
$$M_n = 4.4(3.44 - 0.07)\tfrac{1}{12} = 1.24 \text{ ft-kips/ft}$$
$$V_u = 1.13 \text{ kips (computed above)}$$
$$L_a = 12 d_b \text{ max} = 4.5 \text{ in.}$$
$$\frac{1.24(12)}{1.13} + 4.5 = 13.1 + 4.5 = 17.6 \text{ in.} > L_d = 12 \text{ in.} \qquad \text{OK}$$

This calculation applies identically to other inflection points (3 through 6).

Table 8.4.1

Choice of Reinforcement

Line Number	2S1			2S2			S3		
	Support	Middle	Support	Support	Middle	Support	Support	Middle	Support
1. ACI moment coefficient	$-\frac{1}{24}$	$+\frac{1}{14}$	$-\frac{1}{10}$	$-\frac{1}{11}$	$+\frac{1}{16}$	$-\frac{1}{11}$	$-\frac{1}{11}$	$+\frac{1}{16}$	$-\frac{1}{11}$
2. M_u (ft-kips) = line (1) × 0.249 (11.92)² = 35.4	−1.48	+2.53	−3.54	−3.22	+2.21	−3.22	−3.22	+2.21	−3.22
3. Required $R_u = \dfrac{\text{line (2)} \times 12{,}000}{0.9(12)(3.44)^2}$ (psi) = line (2) × 94.0	139	238	333	303	208	303	303	208	303
4. Required $\rho \approx \dfrac{\text{line (3)} \times 0.0139}{495} = \dfrac{\text{line (3)}}{35{,}600}$	0.0039 (0.005 min.)	0.0067	0.0094	0.0085	0.0059	0.0085	0.0085	0.0059	0.0085
5. Required A_s = line (4) × 12(3.44) (sq in./ft) = line (4) × 41.3	0.21	0.28	0.39	0.35	0.25	0.35	0.35	0.25	0.35
6. Provided A_s	#4 @ 12 st (0.20)	#4 @ 12 bt #3 @ 12 st (0.31)	#4 @ 12 bt #4 @ 12 st (0.39)	#4 @ 12 bt #4 @ 12 bt (0.39)	#4 @ 12 bt #3 @ 12 st (0.31)	#4 @ 12 bt #4 @ 12 bt (0.39)	#4 @ 12 bt #4 @ 12 bt (0.39)	#4 @ 12 bt #3 @ 12 st (0.31)	

Table 8.5.1

Steel Areas in Continuity Analysis

Item	2S1			2S2			2S3		
	Support	Middle	Support	Support	Middle	Support	Support	Middle	Support
Theoretical coefficient from Table 1A, Reinforced Concrete Design Handbook (ACI-SP-3)	−0.035	+0.070	−0.106	−0.103	+0.057 −0.007	−0.095	−0.096	+0.061 −0.004	−0.098
M_u (ft-kips) = coefficient × 0.249(13)² = 42.1	−1.47	+2.95	−4.47	−4.34	+2.40 −0.30	−3.58	−4.04	+2.57	−4.21
M_u (ft-kips) at face of support (see Fig. 8.5.2)	−1.07		−3.90	−3.83		−3.12	−3.54		−3.70
Required $R_u = M_u × 94.0$ (see Table 8.4.1)	101	277	367	360	226	294	333	242	348
Required A_s (sq in./ft)	0.12	0.32	0.43	0.42	0.26	0.34	0.39	0.28	0.41

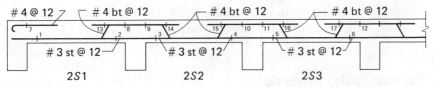

Fig. 8.4.2
Longitudinal reinforcement in Example 8.4.1.

At the exterior end, which might be considered a simple support, the requirement of ACI-12.12.3

$$1.30\frac{M_n}{V_u} + L_a \geq L_d$$

is satisfied by inspection.

(c) Cutoff points for negative-moment reinforcement. The distance from the face of support to the cutoff location (beyond point 13, for instance) must be (1) greater than L_d, and (2) adequate to satisfy ACI-12.13.3. For #4 bars, from Table 6.9.1

$$L_d = 12 \text{ in.}$$

To satisfy ACI-12.13.3, the moment diagram of Fig. 7.5.2b corresponding to the ACI coefficients may be used to locate the point of inflection. The required distance to the cut location is

$$(0.5583 - 0.3341)(11.92) + \frac{11.92}{16} = 3.42 \text{ ft}$$

which compares favorably with the commonly used value of 0.3 of the clear span, as suggested by the *CRSI Handbook* [4].

(d) Bend-up or bend-down location. Since the bend slope is usually about 45°, the bend can be defined by locating either the bend-up or the bend-down location. The moment diagram of Fig. 7.5.2a can be used to determine the bend-up location near the right end of slab 2S1.

The percent of moment capacity remaining after the bend-up is approximately proportional to the percent of total positive-moment steel area remaining in the bottom of the slab.

Moment corresponding to #3 @ 12 in.

$$= \frac{0.11}{0.31}\left(\frac{wL^2}{14}\right) = 0.0253wL^2$$

The theoretical location, measured from the face of support, where the moment is $0.0253wL^2$ is

$$0.5244L - 0.5L\sqrt{(\tfrac{1}{14} - 0.0253)8} = 0.22L$$

This compares reasonably close to the *CRSI Handbook* [4] suggested value of 0.25 of the clear span from the face of support to the bend-up location.

The theoretical bend-down location may be similarly determined by referring to the right end portion of the moment diagram shown in Fig. 7.5.2b.

8.5 Continuity Analysis

When the necessary conditions for using the ACI-8.3.3 moment and shear coefficients are not satisfied, an elastic analysis is required. As discussed in Sec. 8.2, several approaches to the elastic analysis requirement may be used. The adjustment of negative moments permitted (ACI-8.4) under certain conditions should not be applied with any of the moment coefficient methods used to design one-way slabs. The subject of redistribution of bending moment to conform partially with true ultimate load behavior is treated in Chap. 10.

In the interest of obtaining a comparison of answers, an elastic analysis will be made to determine the required steel area at all critical sections of the slab used in Examples 8.3.1 and 8.4.1. It is noted that the choice of reinforcement based on either the ACI coefficients or an elastic analysis will be practically identical, as should be expected for the conditions of this design.

EXAMPLE 8.5.1   Using the results of the slightly approximate elastic method as given in the *Reinforced Concrete Design Handbook* [2], determine the required steel areas at all critical sections of the continuous slab of Examples 8.3.1 and 8.4.1.

Solution: The 12-span continuous slab is supported on 13 beams. The restraining action of the beams on the slab may be accounted for by using equivalent upper and lower columns. It has been suggested [3] that equivalent stiffness factors may be used as shown in Fig. 8.5.1. Using this equivalent stiffness ratio and a ratio of w_L to w_D equal to 2, the theoretical moment coefficients could be determined by a formal elastic analysis as demonstrated in Chap. 7. However, the results of this analysis are available [2], as presented in Table 8.5.1. Note that these coefficients are in terms of wL^2, in which L is the distance between centers of supporting beams. Although the moments within the span may be thus computed, the moments at the face of support may be determined by deducting $Vb/3$ (see Fig. 8.5.2) as discussed in Sec. 8.2

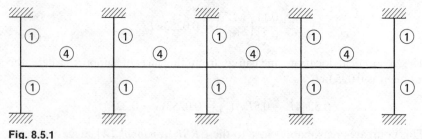

Fig. 8.5.1
Equivalent stiffness ratio for continuous slab.

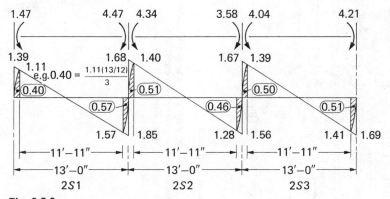

Fig. 8.5.2
Shear diagram for Example 8.5.1.

from the negative moment at the center of support. The required computations are shown in Table 8.5.1 (see page 266).

The results generally show higher moments than those obtained by the ACI coefficients; the choice of reinforcement may be revised by changing the 6- and 12-in. spacings used in Example 8.4.1 to $5\frac{1}{2}$ and 11 in., respectively.

The moment reversal of 0.30 ft-kips may cause a tensile stress at the extreme top of the midspan in 2S2 of

$$\text{tensile stress} = \frac{0.30(12,000)}{(12)(4.5)^2/6} = 89 \text{ psi}$$

which is well below $5\phi\sqrt{f'_c} = 5(0.65)\sqrt{3000} = 178$ psi for plain concrete.

8.6 Shrinkage and Temperature Reinforcement

Reinforcement for shrinkage and temperature stresses normal to the principal reinforcement is required in structural floor and roof slabs, where the principal reinforcement extends in one direction only (ACI-7.12.1). Further, such reinforcement shall provide (ACI-7.12.2) for the following minimum ratios of reinforcement area to gross concrete area, but in no case shall such reinforcing bars be placed farther apart than 5 times the slab thickness nor more than 18 in. (ACI-7.12.3):

1. Slabs where Grades 40 or 50 deformed bars are used   0.0020
2. Slabs where Grade 60 deformed bars or welded wire fabric (smooth or deformed) are used   0.0018
3. Slabs where reinforcement with yield strength exceeding 60,000 psi measured at a yield strain of 0.35% is used $\dfrac{0.0018(60,000)}{f_y}$

EXAMPLE 8.6.1   Design the shrinkage and temperature reinforcement in the floor slab of Examples 8.3.1 and 8.4.1.

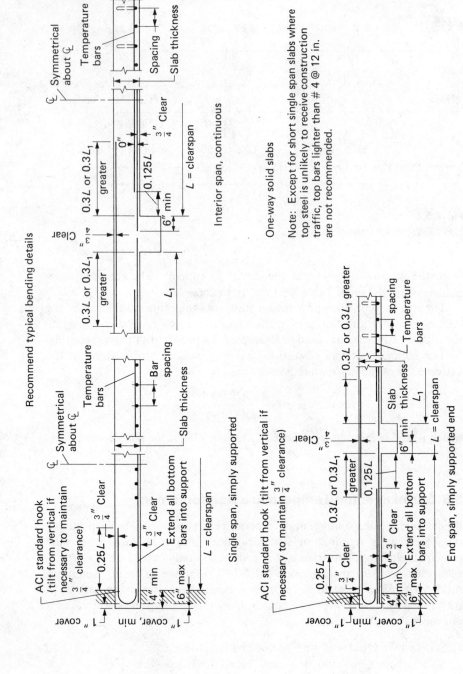

Fig. 8.7.1 One-way slab bar details (from *CRSI Handbook*, Ref. 4).

Solution: Area of shrinkage and temperature reinforcement is

$$A_s = \rho bh = (0.0020)(12)(4.5) = 0.11 \text{ sq in.}$$

Use #3 bars at 12 in. spacing.

8.7 Bar Details

Consistent with the shear and moment diagrams given in Chap. 7 for the ACI Code coefficients, acceptable standard bar bend distances, extensions, and anchorage lengths have been developed. For instance, typical bar details in end and interior spans of one-way slabs as presented in the *CRSI Handbook* [4] are reproduced in Fig. 8.7.1.

It must be noted that although typical bar details are of importance in office practice, they must be used with discretion and care so that they conform with the prevailing shear and moment diagrams.

SELECTED REFERENCES

1. Joint Committee. *Recommended Practice and Standard Specifications for Concrete and Reinforced Concrete*, submitted to constituent organizations, June 1940, American Concrete Institute, among others.
2. Committee 317. *Reinforced Concrete Design Handbook* (3d ed.) (SP-3). Detroit: American Concrete Institute, 1965.
3. *Continuity in Concrete Building Frames* (4th ed.). Chicago: Portland Cement Association, 1959.
4. *CRSI Handbook* (2nd ed.). Chicago: Concrete Reinforcing Steel Institute, 1975.

PROBLEMS

All problems are to be worked in accordance with the ACI Code and all stated loads are service loads, unless otherwise indicated.

8.1 Design for a warehouse a continuous one-way slab supported on beams 12 ft on centers as shown in the accompanying figure. Assume that beam stems are 12 in. wide. The dead load is 25 psf in addition to the slab weight, and the live load is 200 psf. Use $f'_c = 3000$ psi, $f_y = 40,000$ psi, and the strength method. Use ACI coefficients if permissible, and use only straight reinforcing bars. (For metric problem, use 3.7-m spans, 300-mm beam widths; superimposed dead load = 120 kg/m²; live load = 1000 kg/m²; $f'_c = 21$ N/mm²; $f_y = 280$ N/mm².)

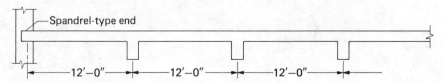

Probs. 8.1 through 8.4

8.2 Repeat Prob. 8.1 using a live load of 250 psf with $f'_c = 4000$ psi and $f_y = 60,000$ psi. (Metric: live load = 1200 kg/m²; $f'_c = 28$ N/mm²; $f_y = 420$ N/mm².)

8.3 Repeat Prob. 8.1 using a live load of 300 psf with $f'_c = 4000$ psi and $f_y = 60,000$ psi.

8.4 Repeat Prob. 8.1 using a live load of 350 psf with $f'_c = 4000$ psi and $f_y = 60,000$ psi.

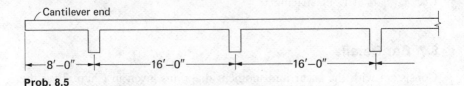

Prob. 8.5

8.5 Design a one-way slab for the conditions shown in the accompanying figure. Assume that beam stems are 12 in. wide. The live load is 175 psf and the slab will not be the final wearing surface. Use $f'_c = 4000$ psi, $f_y = 60,000$ psi, and the strength method. Use alternate bent and straight bar reinforcement if it seems practical.

9

T-Sections
in Bending

9.1 T-Sections

A comparison of the two sections shown in Fig. 9.1.1 indicates that the resisting moment of a rectangular section is identical with that of the T-section as long as they possess the same compression area above the neutral axis (NA) and the same steel area at the same effective depth. Thus, as far as bending is concerned, any T-section with a rectangular compression area, such as shown in Fig. 9.1.1b may be regarded as a rectangular section. It must be noted, however, that the maximum unit shear stresses in the two sections, due to the same shear force, are not equal because of the different width of the beam in the tension zone. When the neutral axis of a T-section

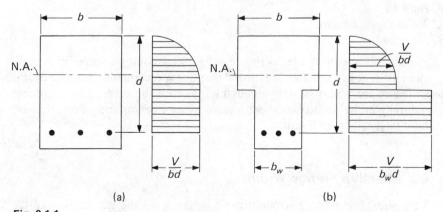

(a)   (b)

Fig. 9.1.1
Two equivalent sections in bending.

Exterior rigid frames; Water Tower Place, Chicago. (Courtesy of Portland Cement Association.)

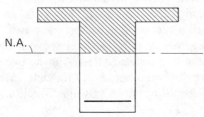

Fig. 9.1.2
A T-section in bending.

is located below the flange, as shown in Fig. 9.1.2, computation of its flexural strength requires different treatment than for a rectangular section. Beams with T-sections may be individually built as such; however, they also occur naturally in the positive-moment regions of floor beams and girders that are built integrally with a slab.

9.2 Effective Flange Width

Very wide beams do not conform in behavior to the assumption of the elementary theory of bending. In ordinary theory, bending stresses are

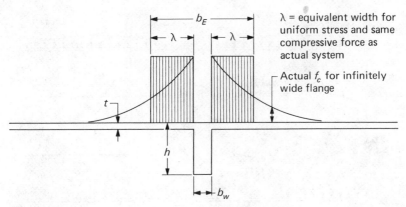

Fig. 9.2.1
Actual and equivalent compressive stress distribution over flange width.

assumed not to vary across the beam width. Simple theory, therefore, would dictate a constant stress at, say, the extreme fiber over the entire flange width of a T-section, no matter how great the overhang from the stem. More precisely, the bending stress based on the theory of elasticity decreases the more distant a point is from the stem of the beam. Thus, for a flange of infinite width the compressive stress in the flange varies as shown in Fig. 9.2.1.

Theoretical investigations for an infinitely long continuous beam on equidistant supports, with an infinitely large flange width and a small thickness compared to beam depth, have determined an effective flange width b_E over which the compressive stress may be considered constant. The total compression carried by the equivalent system is the same as that carried by the actual system. For such assumptions the equivalent width of overhang λ depends only on the type of loading and the span length of the beam. The theory, first developed by T. von Kármán, along with certain results is summarized by Timoshenko and Goodier [1] and Girkmann [2].

Whereas the aforementioned theory gives the equivalent width b_E for an infinite flange width as a function of the span length L, in practical situations other variables are important as well. These variables are the spacing of the beams, the width of the stem of the beam, and the relative thickness of the slab with respect to the total beam depth t/h. To illustrate the effect of loading, several cases (from Girkmann [2]) showing the variation of effective flange projection for a flange of zero stiffness between beams ($t/h = 0$) are given in Fig. 9.2.2.

In the case of a floor slab built integrally over floor beams, there is still transverse bending in the slab between beams, which also tends to reduce the effectiveness of the slab in carrying compression at points remote from the beam stem. Thus there is a valid reason for using a conservatively low effective flange width. The equivalent effective section in a T-beam floor system is shown crosshatched in Fig. 9.2.3.

The ACI Code (ACI-8.10.2) prescribes a limit on the effective flange width b_E of symmetrical T-beams to $\frac{1}{4}$ of the span length of the beam, or $b_w + 16t$, or the distance between the centerlines of beam sections, whichever

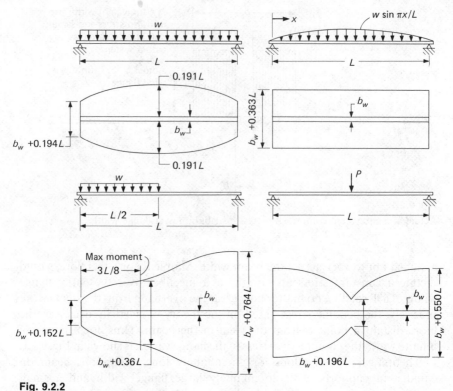

Fig. 9.2.2
Equivalent flange widths for infinite actual width beams with a rib cross-sectional area of 0.1 tL (adapted from Girkmann [2]).

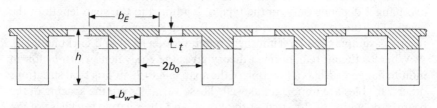

Fig. 9.2.3
Equivalent effective section in compression in a T-beam floor system.

is the smallest; ACI-8.10.3 states that for beams having a flange on one side only, the effective overhanging flange width shall not exceed $\frac{1}{12}$ of the span length of the beam, nor 6 times the thickness of the slab, nor $\frac{1}{2}$ the clear distance to the next beam. The flange thickness of isolated T-beams, as stipulated in ACI-8.10.4, shall not be less than $\frac{1}{2}$ the width of the web, and the total flange width not more than 4 times the width of the web.

Since the true effective width is very much dependent on the type of loading and on the relationships (Fig. 9.2.3) t/h, L/b_w, and L/b_0, the ACI criteria are very much simplified. They seem properly adequate for certain loading cases and are unduly conservative for others. The European Concrete Committee [3,4] has presented detail procedures for determining the values of effective flange width.

9.3 Investigation of T-Sections in Bending—Strength Method

In investigating the strength of a T-section in bending, the neutral-axis location determines whether the compression zone is T-shaped or rectangular.

The effective width b_E of the flange is an essential factor in the neutral-axis location. Available information indicates that as the strain at the extreme compression fiber increases toward its ultimate value, the width of the effective compression flange increases [4]. Therefore when applying the strength method using factored service loads, it is safe to use the smaller effective widths applicable under service-load conditions. The ACI Code therefore uses the same effective width for the strength design method as it has for many years used for the working stress method.

For the neutral axis to be at the base of the flange, as shown in Fig. 9.3.1a, the tension steel area A_s should be

$$A_s = \frac{0.85f_c'b\beta_1 t}{f_y} \qquad \text{for } x = t \qquad \text{(9.3.1a)}$$

In this case, the moment arm between the total compressive force C and the tensile force T is $d - a/2$, which is greater than $d - t/2$. When the amount of tension reinforcement is less than or equal to that of Eq. (9.3.1a), the T-section is to be investigated as a rectangular section, insofar as bending is concerned. Thus

$$M_n = A_s f_y \left(d - \frac{a}{2} \right) \qquad \text{(9.3.1b)}$$

in which

$$a = \frac{A_s f_y}{0.85f_c'b} \qquad \text{(9.3.1c)}$$

If the neutral axis occurs at a distance t/β_1 below the top surface of the flange as shown in Fig. 9.3.1b, the tension steel area A_s should be

$$A_s = \frac{0.85f_c'bt}{f_y} \qquad \text{for } x = \frac{t}{\beta_1} \qquad \text{(9.3.2a)}$$

on the basis of the assumption that a concrete stress intensity of $0.85f_c'$ should be assumed uniformly distributed over an equivalent compression zone bounded by the edges of the cross section and a straight line located parallel to the neutral axis at a distance $a = \beta_1 x$ from the extreme compressive

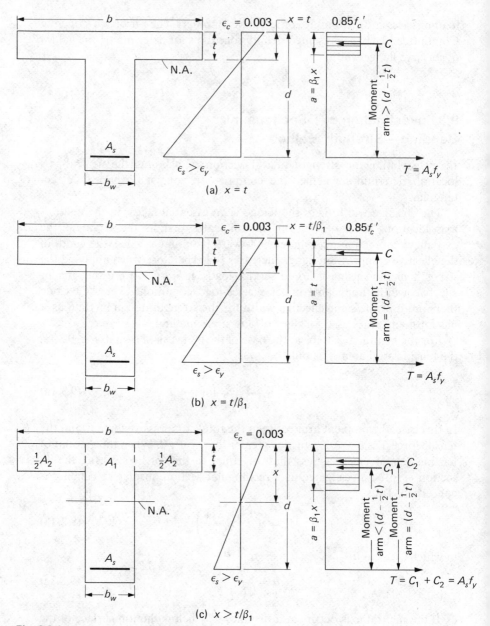

Fig. 9.3.1
Strength of T-sections in bending.

surface (ACI-10.2.7). Actually, using this assumption here is slightly less conservative than in a rectangular section. Following this assumption, the moment arm between the forces C and T is equal to $d - t/2$; thus

$$M_n = A_s f_y \left(d - \frac{t}{2} \right) \tag{9.3.2b}$$

In fact, Eq. (9.3.2b) may be used to compute the moment capacity of a T-section so long as the tension steel area is less than that of Eq. (9.3.2a), because the loss of economy in taking the moment arm between the forces C and T as $d - t/2$ is indeed very little when the value of A_s is between those of Eqs. (9.3.1a) and (9.3.2a).

When the tension steel area A_s is greater than that of Eq. (9.3.2a), the neutral-axis distance x is larger than t/β_1, which makes the depth of the equivalent compressive stress block larger than the flange thickness, as shown in Fig. 9.3.1c. In this case it is desirable to separate the total compressive force into forces C_1 and C_2; C_1 resulting from the stress on area A_1 and C_2 on area A_2. The moment arm for C_2 is equal to $d - t/2$ but that of C_1 is less than $d - t/2$. Thus

$$M_n = C_1\left(d - \frac{a}{2}\right) + C_2\left(d - \frac{t}{2}\right) \tag{9.3.3a}$$

in which

$$C_1 = 0.85f'_c b_w a \tag{9.3.3b}$$
$$C_2 = 0.85f'_c (b - b_w)t \tag{9.3.3c}$$

and

$$a = \frac{T - C_2}{0.85f'_c b_w} \tag{9.3.3d}$$

The tensile force T and the tension steel area A_s may also be separated into T_1 and T_2 and A_{s1} and A_{s2}, respectively.

Because the compressive strength of concrete is considered useful to a much greater extent in strength design than was the case for the working stress method, true T-sections seldom occur in reinforced concrete building floor beams. This is due to the large equivalent width of the compression area that is available.

EXAMPLE 9.3.1 Determine the nominal ultimate positive bending moment capacity M_n within the span of a floor beam whose projection below a $4\frac{1}{2}$-in. slab is 13×24 in. (effective depth is 25 in. for two layers of steel). Tensile reinforcement is 8-#8 bars. The span length of the beam is 26 ft and the beams are centered 13 ft apart. Use $f'_c = 3000$ psi, $f_y = 40,000$ psi, and the strength method of the ACI Code.

Solution: Following ACI-8.10.2, the effective flange width b_E is the smallest of $(26)(12)/4 = 78$ in.; $13 + 16(4.5) = 85$ in.; or $(13)(12) = 156$ in. Thus $b_E = 78$ in.

(a) Find A_s so that $x = 4\frac{1}{2}$ in. (Fig. 9.3.2).

$$C = 0.85f'_c b\beta_1 x = 0.85(3)(78)(0.85)(4.5) = 760 \text{ kips}$$

$$A_s = \frac{T \text{ or } C}{f_y} = \frac{760}{50} = 15.2 \text{ sq in.}$$

Thus the neutral axis for $A_s = 6.28$ sq in. occurs within the flange.

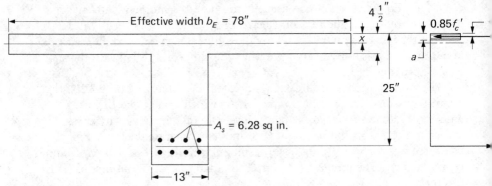

Fig. 9.3.2
T-section for Example 9.3.1.

(b) Treat as a rectangular section.

$$T = f_y A_s = 50(6.28) = 314 \text{ kips}$$

$$a = \frac{T \text{ or } C}{0.85 f'_c b} = \frac{314}{0.85(3)(78)} = 1.58 \text{ in.}$$

$$\text{moment arm} = d - \frac{a}{2} = 25 - 0.79 = 24.21 \text{ in.}$$

$$M_n = 314 \left(\frac{24.21}{12} \right) = 633 \text{ ft-kips}$$

EXAMPLE 9.3.2 Determine the nominal ultimate moment capacity M_n of the isolated T-section shown in Fig. 9.3.3 when $A_s = 12.48$ sq. in. (8-#11). Use $f'_c = 3000$ psi, $f_y = 50,000$ psi, and the strength method of the ACI Code.

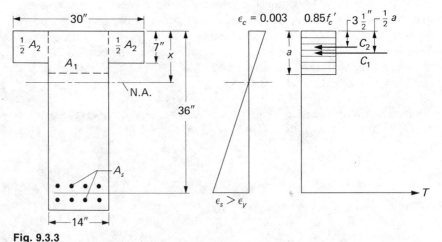

Fig. 9.3.3
T-section for Examples 9.3.2 and 9.4.1.

Solution: (a) Find A_s so that $x = t/\beta_1 = 7/0.85 = 8.32$ in.

$$C = 0.85f'_c b \beta_1 x = 0.85(3)(30)(7) = 535 \text{ kips}$$

$$A_s = \frac{T \text{ or } C}{f_y} = \frac{535}{50} = 10.70 \text{ sq. in.}$$

Thus not only does the neutral axis for $A_s = 12.48$ sq in. fall within the web, but the depth of the equivalent rectangular stress block is greater than the flange thickness.

(b) Treat by the two-couple method (Fig. 9.3.3).

$$T = A_s f_y = 12.48(50) = 624 \text{ kips}$$
$$C = C_1 + C_2 = 0.85f'_c A_1 + 0.85f'_c A_2$$
$$624 = 2.55(14a) + 2.55(16)(7)$$
$$a = 9.47 \text{ in.}$$

$$x = \frac{9.47}{0.85} = 11.13 \text{ in.}$$

$$C_1 = 2.55(14)(9.47) = 338 \text{ kips}$$
$$C_2 = 2.55(16)(7) = 286 \text{ kips}$$
$$M_n = C_1[36 - 0.5(9.47)]\tfrac{1}{12} + C_2(36 - 3.50)\tfrac{1}{12} = 880 + 774 = 1654 \text{ ft-kips}$$

9.4 Design of T-Sections in Bending—Strength Method

The design of T-shaped isolated beams involves the dimensions of the flange and web and the area of tension steel, or a total of five unknowns—one more if compression steel is used. Thus there are many possible solutions to the problem. Because of the large compression area in the flange, these T-sections, when used, are usually deep and wide enough so that the large quantity of tension steel may be placed within the width of the web in not more than two to four layers.

The more common T-sections are those in the region of positive bending in continuous monolithic slab-beam-girder systems. The size of the available flange is therefore definitely known and only the web size needs to be designed. The selection of web size for such beams is treated in Chap. 10.

Once the overall dimensions have been established, the design problem is to determine the amount of positive reinforcement. Thus it is important first to ascertain the location of the neutral axis associated with the positive moment. This may be done by first computing the moment capacity at which the depth of the rectangular compressive stress block is equal to the flange thickness.

EXAMPLE 9.4.1 Determine the amount of tension steel required in the T-section of Fig. 9.3.3 to take a dead-load moment of 370 ft-kips and a live-load moment of 520 ft-kips, using $f'_c = 3000$ psi, $f_y = 50,000$ psi, and the strength method of the ACI Code.

Solution: (a) Determine the maximum tension steel permitted by the ACI Code. For adequate ductility the ACI Code does not permit more tension steel than 75% of the amount for the balanced condition (see Sec. 3.5). For the balanced condition,

$$x_b = \left(\frac{0.003}{0.003 + f_y/E_s}\right)d = \left(\frac{0.003}{0.003 + 0.00172}\right)d$$

$$= 0.635d = 0.635(36) = 22.9 \text{ in.}$$

$$a_b = \beta_1 x_b = 0.85(22.9) = 19.4 \text{ in.}$$

Since $a_b > t$, the two-couple approach may be used, using C_1 and C_2 acting on areas A_1 and A_2, respectively, similar to what is shown in Fig. 9.3.3, except that $x = x_b$ and $a = a_b$.

$$C_1 = C_{1b} = 0.85f'_c b_w a_b = 0.85(3)(14)(19.4) = 693 \text{ kips}$$

$$A_{s1b} = \frac{693}{50} = 13.9 \text{ sq in.}$$

$$C_2 = 0.85f'_c(b - b_w)t = 0.85(3)(16)(7) = 286 \text{ kips}$$

$$A_{s2} = \frac{286}{50} = 5.72 \text{ sq in.}$$

Note that $C_2 = 286$ kips even if $x < x_b$, as long as $a \geq t$.
   The balanced amount of steel is

$$A_{sb} = A_{s1b} + A_{s2} = 13.9 + 5.72 = 19.6 \text{ sq in.}$$

The maximum A_s permitted by ACI-10.3.3 is then

$$\max A_s = 0.75(19.6) = 14.7 \text{ sq in.}$$

(b) For the given design moment, determine if the depth a of the rectangular stress distribution will be greater than $t = 7$ in. Compute nominal ultimate moment capacity for neutral-axis location, $x = t/\beta_1 = 7/0.85 = 8.23$ in.

$$C = 0.85f'_c bt = 0.85(3)(30)(7) = 535 \text{ kips}$$

$$M_n = C\left(d - \frac{t}{2}\right) = 535(36 - 3.50)\tfrac{1}{12} = 1450 \text{ ft-kips}$$

$$\text{required } M_n = \frac{1.4D + 1.7L}{\phi}$$

$$= [1.4(370) + 1.7(520)]/0.90$$

$$= \frac{1403}{0.90} = 1560 \text{ ft-kips} > 1450 \text{ ft-kips provided}$$

Thus a will be greater than 7 in.
   (c) Use the two-couple method (Fig. 9.3.3) to obtain A_s.

$$M_n = 0.85f'_c A_1\left(d - \frac{a}{2}\right) + 0.85f'_c A_2\left(d - \frac{t}{2}\right)$$

$$1560(12) = 2.55(14a)\left(36 - \frac{a}{2}\right) + 2.55(16)(7)(36 - 3.50)$$

$$a^2 - 72a = -527$$

$$a = 8.3 \text{ in.}$$

$$C_1 = 0.85f'_c b_w a = 0.85(3)(14)(8.3) = 296 \text{ kips}$$

$$A_{s1} = \frac{T_1}{f_y} = \frac{296}{50} = 5.92 \text{ sq in.}$$

$$C_2 = 0.85f'_c(b - b_w)t = 0.85(3)(16)(7) = 286 \text{ kips}$$

$$A_{s2} = \frac{T_2}{f_y} = \frac{286}{50} = 5.72 \text{ sq in.}$$

$$A_s = 5.92 + 5.72 = 11.64 \text{ sq in.}$$

Since the 11.64 sq in. required is less than the maximum permitted amount (14.7 sq in.), the design would be acceptable.

(d) Compare the ductility requirement for a T-section with that for a singly reinforced beam as discussed in Sec. 3.5. Locate the neutral axis when the beam contains the maximum steel permitted by the ACI Code. Assume $a > t$,

$$C_1 = 0.85f'_c b_w a = 0.85(3)(14)a = 35.7a$$
$$C_2 = 0.85f'_c(b - b_w)t = 0.85(3)(16)7 = 286 \text{ kips}$$
$$T = A_s f_y = 14.7(50) = 735 \text{ kips}$$
$$C = T$$

$$a = \frac{735 - 286}{35.7} = 12.6 \text{ in.} > t, \qquad \text{as assumed}$$

$$x = \frac{a}{\beta_1} = \frac{12.6}{0.85} = 14.8 \text{ in.}$$

$$\frac{x}{x_b} = \frac{14.8}{22.9} = 0.65$$

The neutral axis for this T-section actually is restricted to 0.65 of x_b, in effect requiring more ductility for the T-section than for singly or doubly reinforced rectangular beams.

9.5 Investigation of T-Sections in Bending—Working Stress Method

T-sections in bending must be investigated by the working stress method when service-load deflection calculations are needed. It is first necessary to determine whether or not the neutral or effective centroidal axis is below the flange. This may be done by comparing the first moment of the flange area about the base of the flange with that of the equivalent concrete area of steel. In the event that the neutral axis is within the flange, the T-section is to be treated as a rectangular section.

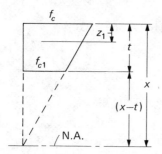

Fig. 9.5.1
Centroid of trapezoid.

When it is found that the neutral axis is definitely below the flange, the exact transformed section should include the small compression area between the base of flange and the neutral axis. It will be shown in the following example, however, that this area may be ignored in ordinary cases without appreciably affecting the results.

After the neutral axis is located, either the internal-force or the transformed section method may be used. The internal-force method affords a convenient check to assure that the total internal compressive force is equal to the internal tensile force; however, if the purpose of the analysis is a deflection calculation, then the transformed cracked section moment of inertia is the essential quantity required.

It may be noted that the centroid of a trapezoid such as shown in Fig. 9.5.1 is at distance z_1 from the extreme compressive face wherein z_1 may be found to be

$$z_1 = \frac{t}{3}\left(\frac{f_c + 2f_{c1}}{f_c + f_{c1}}\right) \tag{9.5.1}$$

EXAMPLE 9.5.1 Determine the transformed cracked section moment of inertia I_{cr} and the moment capacity M_w according to the working stress method for the floor beam described in Example 9.3.1. Use $f'_c = 3000$ psi, $f_y = 50,000$ psi, and the ACI Code. Solve the problem by first considering and then ignoring the compression area in the web.

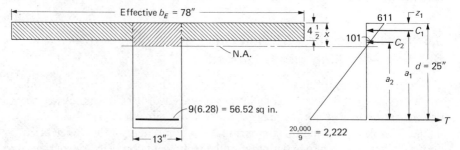

Fig. 9.5.2
T-section for Example 9.5.1, including web contribution.

Solution: The effective flange width is 78 in. as determined in Example 9.3.1. The equivalent concrete area of steel is $(9)(6.28) = 56.52$ sq in. Comparing the first moment of the flange area about its base with that of the equivalent concrete area of steel (Fig. 9.5.2),

$$(78)(4.5)(2.25) = 790, \quad (56.52)(20.5) = 1159, \quad 1159 > 790$$

Therefore the neutral axis is below the flange.

Case 1. Consider the compression area in the web. Taking moments about the unknown actual neutral axis (Fig. 9.5.2),

$$\frac{13x^2}{2} + (65)(4.5)(x - 2.25) = 56.52(25 - x)$$

$$x^2 + 53.70x = 318.63$$

$$x = 5.39 \text{ in.}$$

The transformed cracked section moment of inertia may then be computed about the neutral axis,

$$I_{cr} = \frac{78(4.5)^3}{12} + 78(4.5)(3.14)^2 + \frac{13(0.89)^3}{3} + 56.52(19.61)^2$$

$$= 25,800 \text{ in.}^4$$

The serviceability check of deflection will utilize I_{cr} as is illustrated in Chap. 14 on deflections.

The service-load moment capacity M_w according to the working stress method may be obtained by using either (a) the internal-force method or (b) the transformed-section method with the flexure formula.

Using the internal-force approach, the applicable stress distribution is determined when the allowable stress is reached at one of the extreme fibers. Usually in T-sections the steel controls (i.e., underreinforced according to the working stress method) because of the abundance of concrete compression area.

In this example, when the steel reaches the allowable f_s of 20,000 psi, the extreme fiber of concrete is at 611 psi; or

$$\text{actual } f_c = \left(\frac{20,000}{9}\right)\left(\frac{5.39}{19.61}\right) = 611 \text{ psi} < 1350 \text{ psi}$$

Referring to Fig. 9.5.2, where the applicable stress distribution is shown,

$$\text{actual } f_{c1} = (611)\left(\frac{0.89}{5.39}\right) = 101 \text{ psi}$$

$$C_1 = \frac{\frac{1}{2}(611 + 101)(78)(4.5)}{1000} = 124.9 \text{ kips}$$

$$C_2 = \frac{\frac{1}{2}(101)(13)(0.89)}{1000} = 0.6 \text{ kip}$$

$$T = (2.22)(56.52) \quad \text{or} \quad (20)(6.28) = 125.6 \text{ kips}$$

$$C_1 + C_2 \approx T \qquad \qquad \text{(Check)}$$

$$z_1 = \frac{4.5}{3}\left(\frac{611 + 202}{611 + 101}\right) = 1.71 \text{ in.}$$

$$a_1 = 25 - 1.71 = 23.29 \text{ in.}$$

$$a_2 = 20.50 - \tfrac{1}{3}(0.89) = 20.20 \text{ in.}$$

$$M_w = C_1 a_1 + C_2 a_2 = [124.9(23.29) + 0.6(20.20)]\tfrac{1}{12} = 243 \text{ ft-kips}$$

A check by the flexure-formula method may be made as follows:

$$M_w = \frac{611(25,800)}{(5.39)(12,000)} \quad \text{or} \quad \frac{2222(25,800)}{(19.61)(12,000)} = 243 \text{ ft-kips} \quad \text{(Check)}$$

Case 2. Ignore the compression area in the web. Taking moments about the unknown actual neutral axis (Fig. 9.5.3),

$$78(4.5)(x - 2.25) = 56.52(25 - x)$$

$$408x = 2203$$

$$x = 5.40 \text{ in.}$$

It is apparent that the neutral-axis location remains essentially the same as when the compression area in the web was included. Computing the moment of inertia I_{cr}, also neglecting the compression area in the web, gives

$$I_{cr} = \frac{78(4.5)^3}{12} + 78(4.5)(3.15)^2 + 56.52(19.60)^2 = 25,800 \text{ in.}^4$$

For deflection computation purposes, $I_{cr} = 25,800$ in.^{4} is all that can be justified (three significant figures at most).

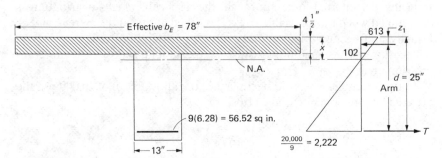

Fig. 9.5.3
T-section for Example 9.5.1, neglecting web contribution.

SELECTED REFERENCES

1. S. Timoshenko and J. N. Goodier. *Theory of Elasticity* (2d ed.). New York: McGraw-Hill, 1951 (pp. 171–177).
2. Karl Girkmann. *Flachentragwerke* (3d ed.). Vienna: Springer-Verlag, 1954 (pp. 116–123).
3. Franco Leve. "Work of the European Concrete Committee," *ACI Journal, Proceedings*, **57**, March 1961, 1049–1054.

4. Gottfried Brendel. "Strength of the Compression Slab of T-Beams Subject to Simple Bending," *ACI Journal, Proceedings*, **61**, January 1964, 57–76.

PROBLEMS

All problems[†] are to be done according to the ACI Code and all loads given are service loads unless otherwise indicated.

9.1 Determine the nominal ultimate moment capacity M_n for the beam cross section shown. The beam span is 30 ft. Use $f'_c = 4000$ psi and $f_y = 60,000$ psi. (Span = 9.1 m; $f'_c = 28$ N/mm²; $f_y = 420$ N/mm²; slab $t = 125$ mm; beam $h = 900$ mm; $b_w = 380$ mm.)

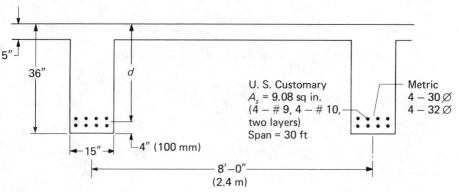

Prob. 9.1

9.2 Design the reinforcement for the beam shown, according to the strength method, if the dead-load moment is 65 ft-kips and the live-load moment is 100 ft-kips.

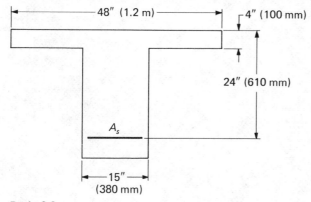

Prob. 9.2

[†] Problems may be solved as problems stated in U.S. Customary units, or as problems in metric units using the quantities in parenthesis at the end of the statement. The metric conversions are approximate to avoid implying higher precision for given information in metric units than for U.S. Customary units.

Use $f'_c = 3000$ psi and $f_y = 40.000$ psi. ($M_D = 88$ kN-m; $M_L = 135$ kN-m; $f'_c = 21$ N/mm²; $f_y = 280$ N/mm².)

9.3 Make a partial design of a simply supported T-beam floor system to meet the conditions shown in the accompanying figure. Use $f'_c = 3000$ psi, $f_y = 40,000$ psi, and the strength method. ($f'_c = 210$ kgf/cm²; $f_y = 2800$ kgf/cm².)

(a)Select the size of stem. Assume that a stem area consistent with a nominal shear stress $V_u/(\phi b_w d)$ equal to approximately $6\sqrt{f'_c}$ psi ($1.6\sqrt{f'_c}$ kgf/cm²) will result in an economical section.

(b)Determine the longitudinal reinforcement, and determine bar lengths and cutoff or bends, if any.

(c)Determine the minimum spacing and size of single-loop stirrups required, and comment on the suggested method of stem size selection given in part (a).

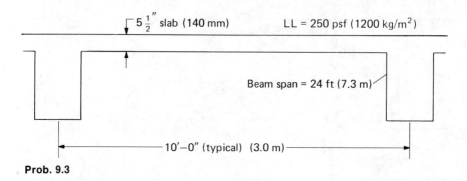

$5\frac{1}{2}''$ slab (140 mm)   LL = 250 psf (1200 kg/m²)

Beam span = 24 ft (7.3 m)

10'-0" (typical) (3.0 m)

Prob. 9.3

9.4 For the beam of Prob. 9.1, use the transformed section method to determine the transformed cracked section moment of inertia I_{cr} and the allowable moment capacity M_w (working stress method); (a) neglecting any compression in the web; and (b) including any compression in the web. Verify the result for M_w by using the internal-force method.

10

Continuous Slab-Beam-Girder and Concrete Joist Floor Systems

10.1 Introduction

The design of rectangular and T-sections has been treated in Chaps. 3, 4, and 9; shear strength and stirrup design in Chap. 5; development of reinforcement in Chap. 6; and continuity analysis in Chap. 7. The slab–beam–girder type of floor construction has generally been described and the design of one-way slabs illustrated in Chap. 8. In this chapter, complete designs of a typical floor beam and girder in a monolithic slab–beam–girder system will be shown. Primarily, what has been developed in the preceding chapters will be applied. Thus the reader may consider the material of this chapter as an integrated review of the subjects in the aforementioned chapters.

Also included in this chapter is the design of one-way concrete joist floors. On continuous spans, the concrete joists should be regarded as having rectangular sections near the supports and T-sections in the positive-moment region within the span.

It should be noted that in recent years a marked increase has occurred in the use of precast slabs, either conventionally reinforced or prestressed, placed on a monolithic beam and girder framing system. In such systems the slab rests on, but does not act with, the beams and girders; thus T-sections are not involved. The procedures discussed in this chapter are also generally applicable to this simpler system of rectangular beams.

Reinforced concrete building design may be a complicated venture, involving irregular floor plans and intricate structural framing. The simple floor framing plan used in the examples does not necessarily reflect a typical practical situation, but it does serve to illustrate the basic essentials of design.

Monolithic slab–beam–girder system; Liggett and Meyers Tobacco Company, Richmond, Va. (Courtesy of Portland Cement Association.)

10.2 Size of Beam Web

The size of the beam web for continuous T-shaped sections is usually controlled by the flexural and shear strength requirements at the exterior face of the first interior support. For typical conditions of equal spans and uniform dead and live loads, a negative moment of $\frac{1}{10}w(L_n)^2$ and a shear of $0.60wL_n$ (see Fig. 7.5.1) may be used in estimating the size of the beam. In the following discussion are given the detailed considerations involved in selecting the beam cross section based on the critical bending moment and shear.

Negative-Moment Requirement. The section of the beam resisting the negative bending moment at the face of the support is a rectangular section, even in T-section construction, because compression is at the lower part of the section. The tension reinforcement is provided (a) usually by straight bars extending across the top of the beam as required for negative moment; (b) sometimes by bent bars from both adjacent spans; or (c) sometimes by a combination of bent bars and additional straight bars across the top. The development of positive-moment reinforcement (ACI-12.12.1) requires some straight bars to continue along the bottom of the beam into the support; thus some portion of them could be utilized as compression reinforcement. Although compression reinforcement will rarely be required for strength, it is frequently desired for added ductility and for deflection control.

The guideline percentage ρ to be used for deflection control of singly reinforced rectangular beams has been suggested in Chap. 3 to be about $0.375\rho_b$ (one-half of the maximum permissible value). For the negative moment requirement on continuous T-sections, a higher value for ρ should be acceptable, because the gross moment of inertia of a typically proportioned T-section is roughly twice that of its rectangular portion. Thus it may be reasonable to design the negative-moment region of a T-shaped section using twice the percentage of reinforcement that would be used for reasonable deflection control on a completely rectangular beam, that is, the full $0.75\rho_b$ permitted by the ACI Code (or more if compression steel is utilized).

Positive-Moment Requirement.   In the positive-moment region the flange of the T-section is in compression. Since the effective flange width is large, it is rare that the depth a of the Whitney rectangular stress block will extend below the bottom of the flange. On the tension side, the amount of steel required will be inversely proportional to the depth of the section.

For sizing the beam web, the only consideration utilizing the positive moment is to establish the width required to maintain adequate clearances for a given number of bars. This should be examined because a somewhat deeper or shallower beam might still permit the required steel to fit into one or two layers, as the case may be.

Shear-Strength Requirement.   The designer may wish to establish the beam web size to achieve a certain maximum nominal shear stress. This may be desirable for economical stirrup size and spacings. The ranges of nominal shear stress for various reinforcement requirements in the beam web may be summarized as follows:

1. For $0 < v_n \leq v_c/2$, no shear reinforcement required (ACI-11.5.5.1).
2. For $v_c/2 < v_n \leq (v_c + 50)$, minimum shear reinforcement required according to ACI-11.5.5.3.
3. For $(v_c + 50) < v_n \leq (v_c + 4\sqrt{f'_c})$, computed shear reinforcement required for strength, with its maximum spacing limited to $(d/2)(1 + \cot \alpha)$ for either vertical or inclined stirrups where α is angle between stirrups and longitudinal axis of the member (ACI-11.5.4.2).
4. For $(v_c + 4\sqrt{f'_c}) < v_n \leq (v_c + 8\sqrt{f'_c})$, computed shear reinforcement required for strength, with its maximum spacing limited to $(d/4)(1 + \cot \alpha)$ for either vertical or inclined stirrups (ACI-11.5.4.3).

In the above summary, v_c may be taken as $2\sqrt{f'_c}$ for the simplified procedure for nonprestressed members under flexure only. The more detailed procedure involving $\rho V_u d/M_u$ has been treated in Chap. 5.

Except for unusual conditions involving short spans, heavy concentrated loads, heavily doubly reinforced sections, or combinations of these, the maximum nominal ultimate shear stress should be about $6\sqrt{f'_c}$ for reasonable stirrup size and spacing.

EXAMPLE 10.2.1.   Using the ACI strength method of design, establish the preliminary size for the floor beams 2B1-2B2-2B1 supported by girders as shown in the floor framing plan of Fig. 8.3.1. Use information previously described in Chap. 8.

Solution: For $f'_c = 3000$ psi and $f_y = 40,000$ psi, one may determine the maximum percentage $(0.75\rho_b)$ allowed by the ACI Code using basic principles, or from Table 3.5.1,

$$\max \rho = 0.75\rho_b = 0.0278$$

(a) Negative-moment requirement. Estimating the weight of the stem (portion of the web below the slab) at 0.3 kip/ft (2 sq ft of area), and applying the overload factors,

$$w_D = 1.4[0.056(13) + 0.3] = 1.44 \text{ kips/ft}$$
$$w_L = 1.7(0.100)(13) = 2.21 \text{ kips/ft}$$

Using basic principles with $\rho = 0.0278$, or Eq. (3.6.4) as follows,

$$m = \frac{f_y}{0.85f'_c} = 15.7$$

$$R_u = \rho f_y(1 - \tfrac{1}{2}\rho m) = 870 \text{ psi}$$

Assume width of supporting girders to be 18 in.

$$L_n = 26 - 1.5 = 24.5 \text{ ft}$$
$$\max M_u = \tfrac{1}{10}(1.44 + 2.21)(24.5)^2 = 219 \text{ ft-kips}$$
$$\text{required } bd^2 = \frac{M_u}{\phi R_u} = \frac{219(12,000)}{0.90(870)} = 3360 \text{ in.}^3$$

If $b = 13$ in.,

$$\text{required } d = \sqrt{\frac{3360}{13}} = 16.1 \text{ in.}$$

The minimum effective size permitted is 13×16.1, for which the steel area required would be

$$A_s = 0.0278(13)(16.1) = 5.82 \text{ sq in.}$$

In the negative-moment region the flange is available so that the steel does not have to fit within the web width.

Before making a decision, the shear stress and the steel requirement for positive moment should be considered.

(b) Shear requirement.

$$\max V_u = 1.15\left(\frac{wL_n}{2}\right)$$

$$= 1.15\left(\frac{3.65}{2}\right)(24.5) = 51.4 \text{ kips}$$

$$\max v_n = \frac{V_u}{\phi b_w d}$$

If it is desired that the nominal shear stress v_n does not exceed $6\sqrt{f'_c} = 329$ psi,

$$\text{required } b_w d = \frac{51,400}{0.85(329)} = 184 \text{ sq in.}$$

For $b = 13$ in., $d = 14.1$ in. (Actually the maximum shear may be taken at a distance d from the face of the support.)

(c) Positive-moment requirement. The effective flange width is

$$b_E = b_w + 16t = b_w + 16(4.5) = b_w + 72$$

or

$$\frac{L}{4} = 26\left(\frac{12}{4}\right) = 78 \text{ in.} \qquad \text{(Controls)}$$

or

$$c \text{ to } c \text{ spacing} = 13(12) = 156 \text{ in.}$$

Try $d = 20$ in.; estimate moment arm at 19 in.

$$M_u = \frac{1}{14} w L_n^2 = \frac{3.65}{14}(24.5)^2 = 156 \text{ ft-kips}$$

$$\text{required } A_s = \frac{M_u}{\phi f_y \text{ (arm)}} \approx \frac{156(12)}{0.90(40)(\approx 19)} = 2.74 \text{ sq in.}$$

This amount of steel should easily fit into a 13-in. wide beam in one layer.

(d) Minimum depth. According to ACI-Table 9.5a the minimum depth cannot be less than

$$\min h = \frac{L}{18.5}(0.8) = \frac{26(12)(0.8)}{18.5} = 13.5 \text{ in.}$$

The negative-moment region gives the most severe requirement. The designer must also keep in mind that if excessive deflection may cause damage, the deflection must be computed and satisfy ACI-Table 9.5b. The above check is only a minimum requirement where deflection is *not* likely to cause damage to nonstructural construction.

Frequently the size is chosen larger than the requirements would dictate. Sometimes this occurs because of the designer's desire that a large number of beams have the same external dimensions for economy of forming or perhaps because of ductwork or pipes that are to pass through the beams, necessitating larger sizes.

Use $b_w = 13$ in., $h = 22.5$ in. (which gives $d \approx 20$ in.). It is common to make the stem portion below the flange a whole inch increment, such as 18 in. for this case. The arbitrary size selected is larger than necessary; any size at least equal to that indicated by steps (a) through (d) would serve to illustrate the design procedure.

10.3 Continuous Frame Analysis for Beams

The shear and moment diagrams to be used in the design of the floor beams in the preceding example could have followed the ACI moment coefficients. However, since these coefficients are more suitable for use in frames involving, say, more than four continuous spans, and as a matter of illustration, the theory of elastic analysis will be used in the analysis of 2B1-2B2-2B1.

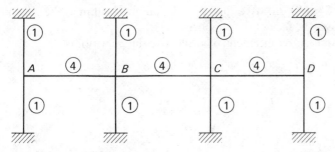

Fig. 10.3.1
Equivalent frame to approximate floor beams supported on girders.

Some designers would assume the girders to provide only vertical support to those floor beams supported on girders; thus a pure continuous beam analysis is made. The girders, however, have torsional stifiness that acts to restrain the rotation of the beam over these girder supports. Prior to 1971, neglect of torsional stiffness was permitted by the ACI Code where such stiffness did not exceed 20% of the flexural stiffness at the joint. Since 1971 the ACI Code requires that torsion be considered whenever the nominal torsion stress exceeds $1.5\sqrt{f'_c}$ psi ($0.12\sqrt{f'_c}$ for f'_c in N/mm^2). In the case with relatively large and stiff girders, the stiffness of the beam may reasonably be taken as twice the torsional stiffness provided by the girder, or if one thinks in terms of an equivalent beam and column frame system, it is as shown in Fig. 10.3.1. More details with regard to torsion are to be found in Chap. 19.

For the beams that frame into columns, however, the combination of the bending stiffness of the columns plus the torsional stiffness of the girders means that the relative end restraint is greater than in the aforementioned case. To design such beams properly, the sizes of the members must be estimated and the $(\Sigma K_{col})/K_{bm}$ ratio computed therefrom.

With regard to T-sections, there is considerable difference of opinion as to how its stiffness for continuous beams should be computed. A T-section certainly provides more stiffness in the positive-moment region where the flange is in compression than it does as a rectangular section in the negative-moment regions. The ACI Code prescribes no specific method but only that "Any reasonable assumptions may be adopted for computing the relative flexural and torsional stiffnesses of columns, walls, floors, and roof systems" (ACI-8.6.1). It has been common practice to use the gross moment of inertia, neglecting reinforcement, in computing the flexural stiffness of such elements. For T-sections usually the gross section of the effective flange width is included.

One of the commonly accepted methods [1] is to use a T-section moment of inertia equal to $2(\frac{1}{12}b_w h^3)$, which is equivalent to using an effective flange width of about 6 times the web width. Since the true stiffness is that of a span with variable moment of inertia along its length with the T-section stiffness over, say, the middle one-half of the span and the rectangular section stiffness over the end quarters, the equivalent system is approximately obtained by using the T-section with a flange width only twice the web width over the entire span. Examination of analyses using various stiffness ratios will show that a fairly wide variation in stiffness ratio may be accommodated with relatively small changes in bending moments.

In the following example, only the analysis of the floor beams supported on girders will be shown. Thus the equivalent rigid frame under consideration is the one shown in Fig. 10.3.1. An overestimate of the beam stiffness will give a conservative design for the beam; but such assumption should be reevaluated when designing the columns, if any.

EXAMPLE 10.3.1 By the theory of elastic analysis, determine the shear and moment diagrams to be used in the design of 2B1 and 2B2 in Example 10.2.1.

Solution:

$$\text{stem weight} = \frac{13(18)}{144}(0.15) = 0.244 \text{ kip/ft}$$

$$w_D = 1.4[0.056(13) + 0.244] = 1.36 \text{ kips/ft}$$
$$w_L = 1.7(0.100)(13) = 2.21 \text{ kips/ft}$$
$$\text{FEM due to } w_D = \tfrac{1}{12}(1.36)(26)^2 = 76.6 \text{ ft-kips}$$
$$\text{FEM due to } w_L = \tfrac{1}{12}(2.21)(26)^2 = 124.5 \text{ ft-kips}$$

The moment distribution (distribution factor *DF*) for loading conditions 1 through 5 as shown in Fig. 10.3.2 is given in Tables 10.3.1 to 10.3.5. Although

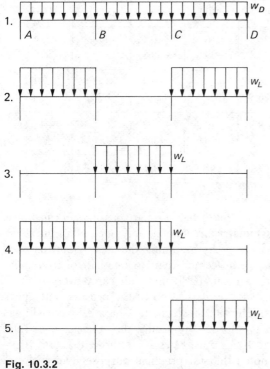

Fig. 10.3.2
Loading conditions.

Table 10.3.1
Loading Condition 1 (Dead Load Only)

Joint	A	B		C		D
Member	AB	BA	BC	CB	CD	DC
DF	0.667	0.400	0.400	0.400	0.400	0.667
FEM Balance	− 76.6 + 51.1	+ 76.6 0	− 76.6 0	+ 76.6 0	− 76.6 0	+ 76.6 − 51.1
Carry-over Balance	0 0	+ 25.6 − 10.2	0 − 10.2	0 + 10.2	− 25.6 + 10.2	0 0
Carry-over Balance	− 5.1 + 3.4	0 − 2.0	+ 5.1 − 2.0	− 5.1 + 2.0	0 + 2.0	+ 5.1 − 3.4
Total	− 27.2	+ 90.0	− 83.7	+ 83.7	− 90.0	+ 27.2

Table 10.3.2
Loading Condition 2 (Live Load Only on Spans 1 and 3)

Joint	A	B		C		D
Member	AB	BA	BC	CB	CD	DC
DF	0.667	0.400	0.400	0.400	0.400	0.667
FEM Balance	− 124.5 + 83.1	+ 124.5 − 49.8	0 − 49.8	0 + 49.8	− 124.5 + 49.8	+ 124.5 − 83.1
Carry-over Balance	− 24.9 + 16.6	+ 41.5 − 26.5	+ 24.9 − 26.5	− 24.9 + 26.5	− 41.5 + 26.5	+ 24.9 − 16.6
Carry-over Balance	− 13.2 + 8.8	+ 8.3 − 8.6	+ 13.2 − 8.6	− 13.2 + 8.6	− 8.3 + 8.6	+ 13.2 − 8.8
Total	− 54.1	+ 89.4	− 46.8	+ 46.8	− 89.4	+ 54.1

not shown here, short cuts in moment distribution are possible. For instance, for symmetrical structures symmetrically loaded, only one-half of the structure needs to be considered, either by assuming the center joint as fixed or by reducing the stiffness of the center span to one-half of its regular value. Another short cut may be in performing all carry-overs without balances, and doing a total balance at the end of the process. The check on moment distribution, as described in detail in Chap. 8, is not shown. One good check, however, is afforded by seeing that the sums of total moments in Tables 10.3.2 and 10.3.3 must be equal to those of Tables 10.3.4 and 10.3.5. It may also be noted that for practical purposes two cycles of

Table 10.3.3

Loading Condition 3 (Live Load Only on Span 2)

Joint	A	B		C		D
Member	AB	BA	BC	CB	CD	DC
DF	0.667	0.400	0.400	0.400	0.400	0.667
FEM	0	0	−124.5	+124.5	0	0
Balance	0	+49.8	+49.8	−49.8	−49.8	0
Carry-over	+24.9	0	−24.9	+24.9	0	−24.9
Balance	−16.6	+10.0	+10.0	−10.0	−10.0	+16.6
Carry-over	+5.0	−8.3	−5.0	+5.0	+8.3	−5.0
Balance	−3.3	+5.3	+5.3	−5.3	−5.3	+3.3
Total	+10.0	+56.8	−89.3	+89.3	−56.8	−10.0

Table 10.3.4

Loading Condition 4 (Live Load Only on Spans 1 and 2)

Joint	A	B		C		D
Member	AB	BA	BC	CB	CD	DC
DF	0.667	0.400	0.400	0.400	0.400	0.667
FEM	−124.5	+124.5	−124.5	+124.5	0	0
Balance	+83.1	0	0	−49.8	−49.8	0
Carry-over	0	+41.5	−24.9	0	0	−24.9
Balance	0	−6.7	−6.7	0	0	+16.6
Carry-over	−3.3	0	0	−3.3	+8.3	0
Balance	+2.2	0	0	−2.0	−2.0	0
Total	−42.5	+159.3	−156.1	+69.4	−43.5	−8.3

moment distribution are all that the basic relative stiffness assumptions can justify. Although three cycles are carried out in Tables 10.3.1 to 10.3.5, the two-cycle moments should be within a few percent of the values obtained by using three or more cycles.

The primary shear and moment diagrams for maximum positive and negative moments for beams 2B1 and 2B2 are given individually in Figs. 10.3.3 and 10.3.4. The secondary shear and moment diagrams are shown in Figs. 10.3.5 and 10.3.6. The primary and secondary moment diagrams are drawn separately for clarity in the example. Ordinarily they are super-imposed to become the moment envelope as shown in Fig. 10.6.1.

Table 10.3.5

Loading Conditions 5 (Live Load Only on Span 3)

Joint	A	B		C		D
Member	AB	BA	BC	CB	CD	DC
DF	0.667	0.400	0.400	0.400	0.400	0.667
FEM	0	0	0	0	− 124.5	+ 124.5
Balance	0	0	0	+ 49.8	+ 49.8	− 83.1
Carry-over	0	0	+ 24.9	0	− 41.5	+ 24.9
Balance	0	− 10.0	− 10.0	+ 16.6	+ 16.6	− 16.6
Carry-over	− 5.0	0	+ 8.3	− 5.0	− 8.3	+ 8.3
Balance	+ 3.3	− 3.3	− 3.3	+ 5.3	+ 5.3	− 5.5
Total	− 1.7	− 13.3	+ 19.9	+ 66.7	− 102.6	+ 52.5

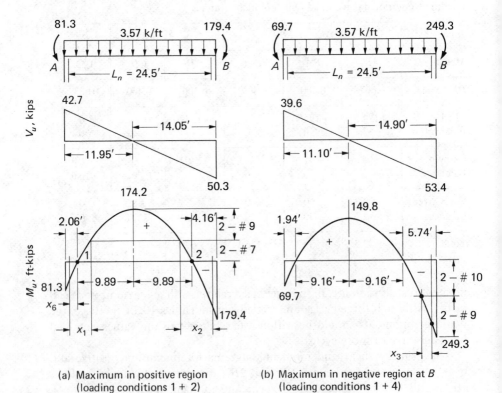

(a) Maximum in positive region
(loading conditions 1 + 2)

(b) Maximum in negative region at B
(loading conditions 1 + 4)

Fig. 10.3.3

Primary shear and moment diagrams for 2B1.

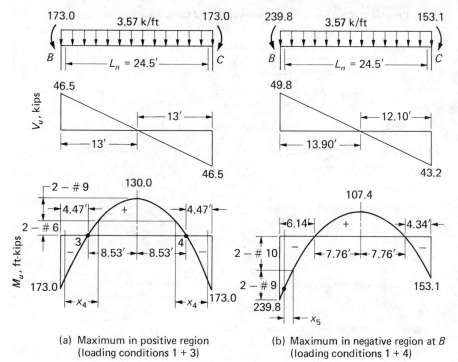

(a) Maximum in positive region (loading conditions 1 + 3)

(b) Maximum in negative region at B (loading conditions 1 + 4)

Fig. 10.3.4

Primary shear and moment diagrams for 2B2.

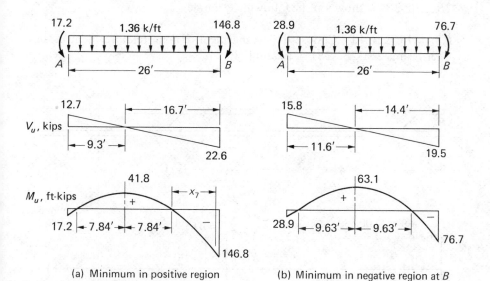

(a) Minimum in positive region (loading conditions 1 + 3)

(b) Minimum in negative region at B (loading conditions 1 + 5)

Fig. 10.3.5

Secondary shear and moment diagrams for 2B1.

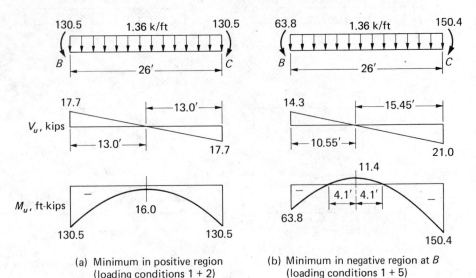

(a) Minimum in positive region
(loading conditions 1 + 2)

(b) Minimum in negative region at B
(loading conditions 1 + 5)

Fig. 10.3.6
Secondary shear and moment diagrams for 2B2.

10.4 Choice of Longitudinal Reinforcement in Beams

It will not be overemphasis to repeat here that the choice of longitudinal reinforcement depends on both the steel area and development length (or anchorage) requirements. The design of the main reinforcement in floor beams 2B1-2B2-2B1 is shown in the following example.

EXAMPLE 10.4.1   Choose the arrangement of main reinforcement in the floor beams 2B1-2B2-2B1 of Example 10.2.1.

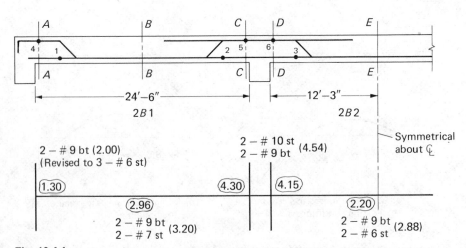

Fig. 10.4.1
Longitudinal reinforcement areas required and bars selected for beams 2B1 and 2B2.

Solution: (a) Flexural requirements. The critical moment is corrected to the face of support by subtracting $\Delta M = Vb/3$ from the moment at the center of support, as discussed in Sec. 8.2. The shear V for this condition is taken as that at the face of support. For sections (rectangular sections) A-A, C-C, and D-D (Fig. 10.4.1),

Section A-A:

$$M_u \text{ at face} = 81.3 - \frac{40.0(1.5)}{3} = 81.3 - 20.0 = 61.3 \text{ ft-kips}$$

$$\text{required } R_u = \frac{M_u}{\phi b d^2} = \frac{61.3(12,000)}{0.90(13)(20)^2} = 157 \text{ psi}$$

Using Eq. (3.6.5), or Fig. 3.6.1,

$$\text{required } \rho = \frac{1}{m}\left(1 - \sqrt{1 - \frac{2mR_u}{f_y}}\right)$$

$$m = \frac{f_y}{0.85f'_c} = \frac{40}{0.85(3)} = 15.7$$

$$\text{required } \rho = \frac{1}{15.7}\left(1 - \sqrt{1 - \frac{2(15.7)(157)}{40,000}}\right) = 0.004$$

$$\min \rho = \frac{200}{f_y} = \frac{200}{40,000} = 0.005 \qquad \text{(Controls)}$$

$$\text{required } A_s = 0.005(13)(20) = 1.30 \text{ sq in.}$$

Section C-C:

$$M_u \text{ at face} = 249.3 - \frac{50.7(1.5)}{3} = 249.3 - 25.3 = 224 \text{ ft-kips}$$

$$\text{required } R_u = \frac{224(12,000)}{0.90(13)(20)^2} = 574 \text{ psi}$$

From Fig. 3.6.1, or Eq. (3.6.5),

$$\text{required } \rho = 0.0165 > \min \rho \qquad\qquad \text{OK}$$
$$\text{required } A_s = 0.0165(13)(20) = 4.30 \text{ sq in.}$$

Section D-D:

$$M_u \text{ at face} = 239.8 - \frac{47.1(1.5)}{3} = 239.8 - 23.5 = 216 \text{ ft-kips}$$

$$\text{required } R_u = \frac{216(12,000)}{0.90(13)(20)^2} = 554 \text{ psi}$$

$$\text{required } A_s \approx 4.30\left(\frac{554}{574}\right) = 4.15 \text{ sq in.}$$

For sections (T-sections) B-B and E-E (Fig. 10.4.1),

$$\text{effective flange width } b_E = \frac{26(12)}{4} \qquad \text{or } 13 + 16(4.5) \qquad \text{or } 13(12)$$

$$b_E = 78 \text{ in.}$$

Section B-B:

$$\text{estimate moment arm} = 0.9d = 18 \text{ in.}$$

$$\text{required } A_s = \frac{M_u}{\phi f_y(\text{arm})} = \frac{174.2(12)}{0.90(40)(\approx 18)} = 3.23 \text{ sq in.}$$

Check:

$$C = 0.85 f'_c b_E a = 0.85(3)(78)a = 199a$$

$$T = 3.23(40) = 129 \text{ kips}$$

$$a = \frac{129}{199} = 0.65 \text{ in.}$$

$$\text{arm} = 20 - \frac{0.65}{2} = 19.7 \text{ in.}$$

$$\text{revised required } A_s = \frac{174.2(12)}{0.90(40)19.7} = 2.96 \text{ sq in.}$$

Section E-E:

$$\text{required } A_s = \frac{130.0(12)}{0.90(40)(\approx 19.7)} = 2.20 \text{ sq in.}$$

Check:

$$C = 199a$$

$$T = 2.20(40) = 88 \text{ kips}$$

$$a = \frac{88}{199} = 0.44 \text{ in.}$$

$$\text{arm} = 20 - \frac{0.44}{2} = 19.8 \text{ in.} \approx 19.7 \text{ in.} \qquad \text{OK}$$

On the basis of the areas required at sections A-A, B-B, C-C, D-D, and E-E, the arrangement of main reinforcement as shown in Fig. 10.4.1 is tentatively chosen. Note that the 2-#7 straight bars in 2B1 and the 2-#6 straight bars in 2B2 furnish the minimum one-fourth of the positive-moment reinforcement that must be extended into the support in each span.

In order to confirm the choice of main reinforcement, the development length requirements (ACI-12.12.3) must be checked, along with the crack control provisions of ACI-10.6. Also the bars at the face of the exterior support (location 4 in Fig. 10.4.1) should be fully developed.

(b) Development length requirements. (For checking ACI–12.12.3, the required development lengths are (using ACI-12.2 or from Table 6.9.1)

$$L_d \text{ (for } \#6) = 12.8 \text{ in.}$$
$$L_d \text{ (for } \#7) = 17.5 \text{ in.}$$
$$L_d \text{ (for } \#9) = 29.2(1.4) = 41 \text{ in.}$$

where the 1.4 factor is for top bars (see Table 6.10.1).

At location 1 (Fig. 10.4.1): For 2-#7, extending 6 in. beyond face of support,

$$C = 0.85f'_c ba = 0.85(3)(78)a = 199a$$
$$T = 2(0.60)40 = 48 \text{ kips}$$

$$a = \frac{48}{199} = 0.24 \text{ in.}$$

$$M_n = 48[20 - 0.5(0.24)]\tfrac{1}{12} = 79.5 \text{ ft-kips}$$
$$V_u = 42.7 - 3.57(2.06) = 35.4 \text{ kips}$$
$$L_a = d = 1.67 \text{ ft} < \text{actual length } 1.74 \text{ ft}$$

$$\frac{M_n}{V_u} + L_a = \frac{79.5}{35.4} + 1.67 = 3.91 \text{ ft} > L_d \, (\#7) \qquad \text{OK}$$

At location 2: For 2-#7, since M_n and V_u are identical to their values at location 1, this check is made by inspection.

At location 3: For 2-#6,

$$C = 199a; \qquad T = 2(0.44)40 = 35.2 \text{ kips}; \qquad a = 0.18 \text{ in.}$$
$$M_n = 35.2[20 - 0.5(0.18)]\tfrac{1}{12} = 58.5 \text{ ft-kips}$$
$$V_u = 46.5 - 3.57(4.47) = 30.5 \text{ kips}$$

$$\frac{M_n}{V_u} + L_a = \frac{58.5}{30.5} + 1.67 = 3.59 \text{ ft} > L_d \, (\#6) \qquad \text{OK}$$

In order to develop properly 2-#9 at location 4, either a straight embedment of 41 in. is required or a standard hook may be used. If a hook is used, according to Table 6.13.2, it will be equivalent to only 14.4 in. of straight embedment. A standard 90° hook will occupy 1.5 in. + $5d_b$ (see Fig. 6.13.1) from the exterior face. That would leave available for straight embedment,

$$\text{available embedment} = 18 - 1.5 - 5(1.128) = 10.85 \text{ in.}$$

The percent capacity that can be developed for the #9 top bars is

$$\text{percent capacity} = \frac{14.4 + 10.85}{41} = 61.5\%$$

If the #9 bars are 61.5% effective, the equivalent area of fully effective bars is $2.00(0.615) = 1.23$ sq in. which is only slightly less than the requirement of 1.30 sq in. In this case, it may be preferable to use straight bars of smaller diameter in the top of the beam at location 4.

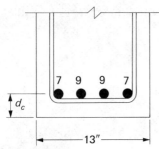

Fig. 10.4.2
Cross section for crack control investigation.

Try 3-#6 straight bars at location 4.

$$\text{required } L_d = 12.8(1.4) = 18 \text{ in.}$$

A standard hook will provide equivalent development length of 6.3 in.
(Table 6.13.2). The percent capacity available is

$$\text{percent capacity} = \frac{6.3 + [18 - 1.5 - 4(0.75)]}{18} = \frac{19.8}{18} > 100\%$$

The #6 bars will be fully developed if they are hooked at the exterior face.

(c) Crack control requirements. The most critical location to check is
where the largest bars are put into the smallest area, that is, at section *B-B*
(Fig. 10.4.1). Using Eq. (4.12.2) or ACI-10.6, and referring to Fig. 10.4.2,

$$z = f_s \sqrt[3]{d_c A} \le 175 \text{ kips/in.} \qquad \text{(interior exposure)}$$
$$d_c = 1.5 \text{ (cover)} + 0.375 \text{ (stirrup)} + 0.4375 \text{ (bar radius)} = 2.31 \text{ in.}$$

$$A = \frac{2d_c b_w}{\Sigma A_s/(A_b \text{ for } \#9)} = \frac{2(2.31)13}{(3.20/1.0)} = 14.4 \text{ sq in./bar}$$

$$z = 0.6(40)\sqrt[3]{2.31(14.4)} = 139 \text{ kips/in.} < 175 \qquad\qquad \text{OK}$$

Actually, because in this example f_y does not exceed 40,000 psi, the crack
control investigation is not required. However, the calculation is presented
to illustrate the procedure.

10.5 Shear Reinforcement in Beams

Although the portions of the bent bars in the body of the beam would
provide some shear strength in their vicinity, it will generally be a more
clean-cut procedure to depend on the vertical stirrups alone to provide the
entire shear-strength requirement and welcome the bent bars as giving
additional assistance. The design of shear reinforcement in 2B1-2B2-2B1 is
shown in the following example.

EXAMPLE 10.5.1   Design the shear reinforcement in the floor beams
2B1-2B2-2B1 of Example 10.2.1.

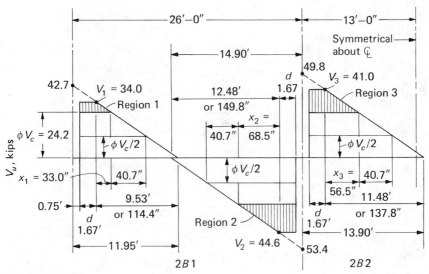

Fig. 10.5.1
Shear force diagram for 2B1 and 2B2.

Solution: The shear-force diagram for which shear reinforcement will be provided is taken from Figs. 10.3.3 and 10.3.4 and shown in Fig. 10.5.1. The maximum design shear should be taken at a distance equal to the effective depth from the face of support. Let V_1, V_2, and V_3 be the maximum design (factored) shear in regions 1, 2, and 3 as shown in Fig. 10.5.1; then using $w_u = 3.57$ kips/ft,

$$\phi V_c = \phi v_c b_w d = 0.85(2\sqrt{3000})(13)(20)\tfrac{1}{1000} = 24.2 \text{ kips}$$

$$V_1 = 3.57(9.53) = 34.0 \text{ kips}; \qquad x_1 = 114.4 \frac{34.0 - 24.2}{34.0} = 33.0 \text{ in.}$$

$$V_2 = 3.57(12.48) = 44.6 \text{ kips}; \qquad x_2 = 149.8 \frac{44.6 - 24.2}{44.6} = 68.5 \text{ in.}$$

$$V_3 = 3.57(11.48) = 41.0 \text{ kips}; \qquad x_3 = 137.8 \frac{41.0 - 24.2}{41.0} = 56.5 \text{ in.}$$

The shaded shear areas in Fig. 10.5.1 plus an additional distance of 40.7 in., equal to the distance to the location where $V_u = \phi V_c/2$, represent the portions of the beam where shear reinforcement is required. These portions are also designated as regions 1, 2, and 3 in Fig. 10.5.2.

Assume #3 vertical U stirrups. From Fig. 10.5.2 the maximum required ϕV_s anywhere on the beam is 20.4 kips. Since the largest required ϕV_s does not exceed that based on a nominal stress v_s of $4\sqrt{f'_c}$, the maximum permissible stirrup spacing may not exceed $d/2$.

$$\text{limit } \phi V_s = \phi(4\sqrt{f'_c}b_w d) = 2(\phi V_c) = 2(23.2) = 48.4 \text{ kips}$$

$$\text{max } \phi V_s = 20.4 \text{ kips} < \text{limit } \phi V_s \qquad \frac{d}{2} = 10 \text{ in. applies}$$

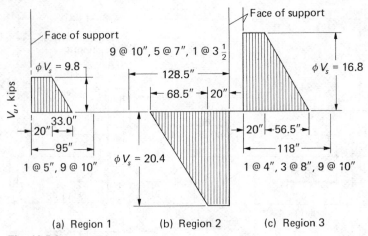

(a) Region 1   (b) Region 2   (c) Region 3

Fig. 10.5.2
Shear reinforcement in 2B1 and 2B2.

For a minimum percentage of shear reinforcement,

$$\min \phi V_s = \phi 50 b_w d = 0.85(50)(13)(20)\tfrac{1}{1000} = 11.1 \text{ kips}$$

The strength requirement to provide for the shear represented by the shaded areas of Fig. 10.5.2 is

$$V_s = \frac{A_v f_y d}{s}$$

$$s = \frac{\phi A_v f_y d}{\phi V_s} = \frac{0.85(0.22)(40)(20)}{\phi V_s} = \frac{149.6 \text{ kips in.}}{\phi V_s}$$

For region 1, a spacing of $d/2$ governs because the maximum $\phi V_s = 9.8$ kips is less than the 11.1 kips required for minimum stirrups and $\phi V_s = 11.1$ kips permits spacing of 13.5 in. which exceeds $d/2$.

Use 1 @ 5 in. and 9 @ 10 in. (95 in. from face of support).
For region 2 the strength requirement is shown in Table 10.5.1.

Table 10.5.1

s	ϕV_s	$\max \phi V_s - \phi V_s$	x (Distance from Face of Support) (in.)
7.4	20.4	$20.4 - 20.4 = 0$	
8	18.7	$20.4 - 18.7 = 1.7$	$20 + \dfrac{68.5}{20.4}(1.7) = 20 + 6 = 26$
9	16.6	$20.4 - 16.6 = 3.8$	$20 + \dfrac{68.5}{20.4}(3.8) = 20 + 13 = 33$
10	15.0	$20.4 - 15.0 = 5.4$	$20 + \dfrac{68.5}{20.4}(5.4) = 20 + 18 = 38$

Use 1 @ $3\frac{1}{2}$ in.; 5 @ 7 in.; and 9 @ 10 in. (128.5 in. from face of support).

For region 3 the strength requirement at the critical section is

$$\max s = \frac{149.6}{16.8} = 8.9 \text{ in.}$$

A spacing of 10 in. can be used at $20 + (16.8 - 15.0)(56.5)/16.8 = 26$ in. from the face of support.

Use 1 @ 4 in.; 3 @ 8 in.; and 9 @ 10 in. (118 in. from face of support).

As a practical matter, many designers would place stirrups by scaling from the maximum shear diagram (force or unit stress), rather than accurately compute distances as has been illustrated here. Further, the simplified procedure of ACI-11.3.1.1 for the value of V_c has been used in this example. The more detailed procedure involving $\rho V d/M$ does not seem appropriate unless an accurate shear envelope has been determined for the entire span. Such an envelope would include use of partial span loading for the maximum shear in the central portions of the beam spans, but it is not considered necessary for most ordinary beams in building frames.

10.6 Details of Bars in Beams

For typical conditions of equal spans and uniform load where moment and shear coefficients are used, standard bar details such as provided in the *ACI Detailing Manual* [2] may be used. When the moment and shear envelopes are available, bar bend or cutoff locations should be determined therefrom, as illustrated for this example.

EXAMPLE 10.6.1 Determine the bar dimensions of the main reinforcing bars in 2*B*1 and 2*B*2 of Example 10.2.1 (see Fig. 10.6.1).

Solution: (a) Maximum moment capacities. In determining bar cutoff or bend locations it is necessary first to locate the theoretical points where the bars are no longer required. Lines representing full capacity of the various bar combinations are computed. The effect of any compression steel will be small and is neglected. At section *A-A*, 3-#6

$$C = 0.85(3)(13)a; \qquad T = 3(0.44)40 = 52.8 \text{ kips}$$
$$\phi M_n = 0.90(52.8)(20 - 0.8)\tfrac{1}{12} = 76 \text{ ft-kips}$$

Note that ϕM_n is computed and plotted in Fig. 10.6.1 because the required moment envelope includes the overload factors *U* but has not been divided by ϕ to give the nominal ultimate requirement.
At section *B-B*, 2-#7

$$C = 0.85(3)(78)a = 199a; \qquad T = 2(0.60)40 = 48 \text{ kips}$$
$$\phi M_n = 0.90(48)(20 - 0.12)\tfrac{1}{12} = 71.5 \text{ ft-kips}$$

At section *B-B*, 2-#7 and 2-#9

$$C = 199a; \qquad T = 3.20(40) = 128 \text{ kips}$$
$$\phi M_n = 0.90(128)(20 - 0.32)\tfrac{1}{12} = 189 \text{ ft-kips}$$

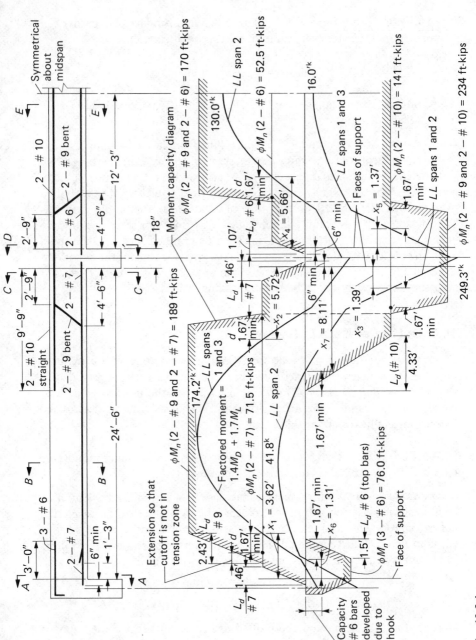

Fig. 10.6.1

At sections C-C and D-D, 2-#10

$$C = 33.1a; \qquad T = 2.54(40) = 101.5 \text{ kips}$$
$$\phi M_n = 0.90(101.5)(20 - 1.53)\tfrac{1}{12} = 141 \text{ ft-kips}$$

At sections C-C and D-D, 2-#9 and 2-#10

$$C = 33.1a; \qquad T = 4.54(40) = 181.5 \text{ kips}$$
$$\phi M_n = 0.90(181.5)(20 - 2.74)\tfrac{1}{12} = 234 \text{ ft-kips}$$

At section E-E, 2-#6

$$C = 199a; \qquad T = 2(0.44)40 = 35.2 \text{ kips}$$
$$\phi M_n = 0.90(35.2)(20 - 0.09)\tfrac{1}{12} = 52.5 \text{ ft-kips}$$

At section E-E, 2-#6 and 2-#9

$$C = 199a; \qquad T = 2.88(40) = 115.2 \text{ kips}$$
$$\phi M_n = 0.90(115.2)(20 - 0.29)\tfrac{1}{12} = 170 \text{ ft-kips}$$

(b) Extension of positive-moment reinforcement into supports. In order to satisfy ACI-12.12.1, the #7 straight bars in $2B1$ must extend at least 6 in. into both supports. Since there is no tensile requirement for these bars at the first interior support, the 6-in. minimum embedment is sufficient unless the bars are to be utilized as compression reinforcement, in which case the compression capacity of such bars must be developed at the face of support. In this case no compression capacity is required for strength or desired to increase ductility.

At the exterior support, the 6-in. embedment may not be adequate if the support is a column and the flexural member is part of the primary lateral-load resisting system; ACI-12.12.2 requires development of the full yield stress in tension at the face of support for such cases. In this example, the supporting member is a girder and is not a part of the primary lateral-load resisting system so that 6-in. embedment is sufficient. Similarly, the 2-#6 in beam $2B2$ are extended into the supports 6 in. The total length of the #6 and #7 straight bars is [24 ft 6 in. + 2(6 in.)] = 25 ft 6 in. (Bar lengths are usually specified in 3-in. increments.)

(c) Theoretical bend or cutoff locations. In detailing the bend-up and bend-down points for the #9 bars, and for establishing the cutoff for the #9 bars near section A-A, the distances x_1 through x_5 as marked in Fig. 10.6.1 (also shown as x_1, x_2 in Fig. 10.3.3a, x_3 in Fig. 10.3.3b, x_4 in Fig. 10.3.4a, and x_5 in Fig. 10.3.4b) are in practice determined more frequently by graphical means, although they are computed in this example. Thus referring to Fig. 10.3.3a,

$$\frac{3.57(11.20 - x_1)^2}{2} = \frac{3.57(13.30 - x_2)^2}{2} = 174.2 - 71.5 = 102.7 \text{ ft-kips}$$

which gives

$$x_1 = 3.62 \text{ ft}; \qquad x_2 = 5.72 \text{ ft}$$

In accordance with ACI-12.11.4, a distance of 12 bar diameters or the effective depth of the member, whichever is larger, must be subtracted from these distances. Thus the bend or cutoff locations could be

$$\text{bend-up or cutoff based on } x_1 = 3.62 - 1.67 = 1.95 \text{ ft}$$
$$\text{bend-up or cutoff based on } x_2 = 5.72 - 1.67 = 4.05 \text{ ft}$$

From Fig. 10.3.3b,

$$\frac{3.57(14.15 - x_3)^2}{2} = 149.8 + 141 = 290.8 \text{ ft-kips}$$

$$x_3 = 1.39 \text{ ft}$$
$$\text{bend-down or cutoff based on } x_3 = 1.39 + 1.67 = 3.06 \text{ ft}$$

From Fig. 10.3.4a,

$$\frac{3.57(12.25 - x_4)^2}{2} = 130.0 - 52.5 = 77.5 \text{ ft-kips}$$

$$x_4 = 5.66 \text{ ft}$$
$$\text{bend-up or cutoff based on } x_4 = 5.66 - 1.67 = 3.99 \text{ ft}$$

From Fig. 10.3.4b,

$$\frac{3.57(13.15 - x_5)^2}{2} = 107.4 + 141 = 248.4 \text{ ft-kips}$$

$$x_5 = 1.37 \text{ ft}$$
$$\text{bend-down or cutoff based on } x_5 = 1.37 + 1.67 = 3.04 \text{ ft}$$

The distances x_1 through x_5 with the effective depth $d = 1.67$ ft either added or subtracted locate correctly the theoretical *cutoff* points. For bending bars, the objective is to have the resulting moment capacity diagram maintain an offset from the factored moment diagram equal to, in this case, 1.67 ft (effective depth). Thus the actual bend-up or bend-down points will be offset from the theoretical cutoff points an amount equal to one-half the horizontal projection of the sloping portion of the bar. If the bend is at 45°, the offset would be $(d - d')/2$. Typically, the bend is at an approximately 45° angle but the locations of the bend-up and bend-down points are made 3-in. increment dimensions from the face of support.

For example, if the bend is at 45°, the horizontal projection will be

$$d - d' = 20 - 2.5 = 17.5 \text{ in. } (1.46 \text{ ft})$$

The bend-down position in beam 2B1 could be no closer than $x_3 + d - 1.46/2$, or 2.33 ft, from the face of support. The selected distance of 2.75 ft exceeds this and is acceptable. The bend-up position in beam 2B1 must be no farther from the face of support than $x_2 - d + 1.46/2$, or 4.78 ft. The selected distance of 4.5 ft is closer than 4.78 ft and is therefore acceptable. The situation in beam 2B2 is similar.

Use the bends shown in Fig. 10.6.1. The potential cutoff relating to x_1 requires further checking to satisfy ACI-12.11.5 for cutting bars in a tension zone.

(d) Inflection point extensions. ACI-12.13.3 requires an extension beyond the extreme point of inflection a distance equal to the largest of one-sixteenth of the clear span, the effective depth of the member, or 12 bar diameters. In this case the effective depth of the member, 1.67 ft, controls. The #6 and #10 bars in member 2B1 are terminated after the 1.67 ft extension. The cut bars develop their full capacity after an embedment equal to the development length L_d required for top bars (see Secs. 6.9 and 6.10).

(e) Check cutoff for 2-#9 bars in the tension zone. ACI-12.11.5 must be satisfied for the cutoff at $x_1 - d$ to be acceptable. Since the continuing bars (2-#7) provide more than double the area required for flexure at the potential cutoff point, it is necessary only to check whether or not the shear exceeds three-fourths of the shear strength (ACI-12.11.5.3).

$$V_u = 3.57(11.20 - 1.95) = 32.6 \text{ kips}$$

It is required that

$$V_u \leq 0.75\phi V_n = 0.75\phi(V_c + V_s)$$

The strength provided, including stirrups, is

$$\phi V_c + \phi V_s = 24.2 + \frac{149.6}{10} = 39.2 \text{ kips}$$

$$\text{percent strength utilized} = \frac{32.6}{39.2} = 83\% > 75\% \text{ permitted} \qquad \text{NG}$$

If the cutoff is to be made at the indicated location, the stirrup spacing must be reduced so that V_s increases. Alternatively, the 2-#9 bars may be extended to the inflection point where they will no longer be in the tension zone. Thus the #9 bars are cut off at 1 ft 3 in. from the face of support. In this case, there is little material saved by cutting so close to the support, but it serves to illustrate the procedure.

The summary of bar arrangement, lengths, dimensions, and moment capacity provided is shown in Fig. 10.6.1. The cross sections for the final choice at each designated section of Fig. 10.6.1 are shown in Fig. 10.6.2.

(f) Stirrup development. For stirrup supports, 2-#3 bars are provided in the central part of beam 2B1. The dimensions of the stirrups are shown in Fig. 10.6.3. The embedment required (ACI-12.14) beyond the middepth for development of the stirrups is

$$\text{required } L_d \, (\#3) = 12 \text{ in.} \qquad \text{(Table 6.9.1)}$$

for which a length of only $\frac{1}{2}(19.5) = 9.75$ in. is available. ACI-12.14.2.1 requires a straight embedment of $0.5L_d$, or 6 in. in this case, if a standard hook is used. Since 6 in. of straight embedment *is* available, a 90° hook is

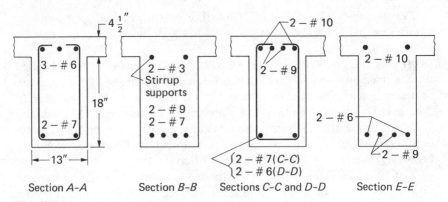

Fig. 10.6.2
Typical sections for 2B1 and 2B2 (refer to Fig. 10.6.1).

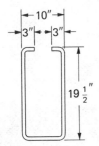

Fig. 10.6.3
Stirrup details in beams 2B1 and 2B2.

used. If $0.5L_d$ is not available in straight embedment, a 135° hook around the longitudinal reinforcement would have to be used (ACI-12.14.2.3) plus, if f_y exceeds 40,000 psi, a straight embedment of $0.33L_d$ measured from middepth to the point of tangency at the start of the hook.

10.7 Size of Girder Web

The maximum negative moment at the exterior face of the first interior support, for the purpose of determining the size of the girder web, may be taken as 0.8 of the maximum positive moment in a simple span with span length equal to the clear span of the girder and with loadings identical to those of the girder. The maximum shear at the same location may be taken as 1.20 times the reaction to the simple span described above. Note that the coefficients of ACI-8.3.3 cannot be used since concentrated loads are involved.

The concentrated loads on the girder may be taken as one-half of the total dead and live loads on the clear span of the beams on both sides of the girder. The dead and live uniform load on the girder will be the weight of the concrete and the live load on the floor, respectively, both within the width of the girder. This loading transfer is a sufficiently good approximation, although it is probable that the slab weight and floor load on a narrow strip parallel and close to either edge of the girder would act on the girder as uniform load instead of being carried by the one-way slab to the adjacent beams and thence to the girder as concentrated loads.

EXAMPLE 10.7.1   Design the floor girders 2G1-2G2-2G2-2G1 as shown in the floor framing plan of Fig. 8.2.1. Use information previously described in Chap. 8 and in the present chapter. Work through the choice of the size of the girder web in this example according to the strength method of the ACI Code.

Solution: The concentrated reactions from the beams are

$$\text{dead load} = 1.4(24.50)[(0.056)(13) + 0.244] = 33.4 \text{ kips}$$
$$\text{live load} = 1.7(24.50)(0.100)(13) = 54.2 \text{ kips}$$
$$\text{total load} = 33.4 + 54.2 = 87.6 \text{ kips}$$

Assuming 18×36 in. web, the uniform loads on the girder are

$$\text{uniform dead load} = 1.4 \left[\frac{18(40.5)(0.150)}{144} \right] = 1.06 \text{ kips/ft}$$

$$\text{uniform live load} = 1.7(0.100)(1.5) = 0.255 \text{ kip/ft}$$
$$\text{uniform total load} = 1.06 + 0.255 = 1.315 \text{ kips/ft}$$

maximum positive moment on a simple span (see Fig. 10.7.1)

$$= 87.6(12.25) + \tfrac{1}{8}(1.315)(37.5)^2$$
$$M_u = 1075 + 231 = 1306 \text{ ft-kips}$$

The estimated maximum negative moment in the girder at the exterior face of the first interior support is $0.8(1306) = 1045$ ft-kips, say 1050 ft-kips. From Fig. 10.7.1, estimate

$$d_{\text{neg}} = 40.50 - 4.75 = 35.75 \text{ in.}$$
$$d_{\text{pos}} = 40.50 - 3.50 = 37 \text{ in.}$$

The negative moment requirement is

$$\text{required } R_u = \frac{M_u}{\phi b d^2} = \frac{1050(12,000)}{0.90(18)(35.75)^2} = 609 \text{ psi}$$

which is less than the maximum $R_u = 870$ psi for $\rho = 0.75\rho_b$, and is an acceptable value. The girder system should be relatively stiff and will be so if this smaller R_u is used.

$$\text{required } A_s \text{ for } (-M) \approx 0.75\rho_b \left(\frac{609}{870} \right) bd = 0.0278 \left(\frac{609}{870} \right)(18)(35.75)$$

$$= 12.5 \text{ sq in.}$$

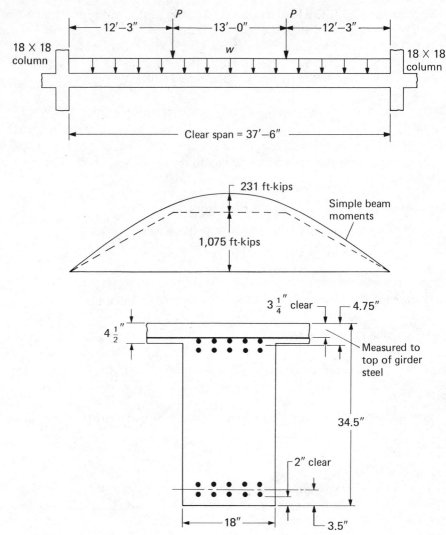

Fig. 10.7.1
Loading information for floor girders 2G1 and 2G2.

For the positive-moment requirement, using the coefficients of ACI-8.3.3 to obtain the approximate proportion between positive and negative moments,

$$\text{estimated } (+\,M) \approx \frac{10}{14}(-M) = \frac{10}{14}(1050) = 750 \text{ ft-kips}$$

$$\text{required } A_s \approx \frac{M_u}{\phi f_y \,(\text{arm})} = \frac{750(12)}{0.90(40)(\approx 33)} = 7.58 \text{ sq in.}$$

This may well fit into one layer (6-#10 requires a beam width of $17\frac{3}{4}$ in.).

For the shear requirement,

$$\max V_u = 1.20[87.6 + 1.315(18.75)] = 135 \text{ kips}$$

$$v_n = \frac{135,000}{0.85(18)(35.75)} = 247 \text{ psi} = 4.5\sqrt{f_c'}$$

The stem could be made smaller; with this large depth it is unlikely that deflection would be excessive. The 18 × 36 stem appears to be somewhat large though it could certainly be used. In this case because of the large depth, reduce the stem size to 18 × 30. Estimated effective depths become

$$d_{neg} = 29.75 \text{ in.}$$
$$d_{pos} = 31 \text{ in.}$$

$$\text{revised girder weight} = 1.4\left[\frac{18(34.5)}{144}(0.15)\right] = 0.91 \text{ kip/ft}$$

$$w_u = w_D + w_L = 0.91 + 0.255 = 1.165 \text{ kips/ft}$$
$$\text{revised } M_u \text{ (simple beam)} = 1075 + \tfrac{1}{8}(1.165)(37.5)^2 = 1280 \text{ ft-kips}$$

$$\text{required } R_u = \frac{0.8(1280)(12,000)}{0.90(18)(29.75)^2} = 860 \text{ psi} < 870 \text{ psi max} \quad \text{OK}$$

$$v_n \text{ at support} = \frac{131,500}{0.85(18)(29.75)} = 289 \text{ psi} = 5.3\sqrt{f_c'}$$

Use the 18 × 30 stem section.

10.8 Continuous Frame Analysis for Girders

Although floor girders subjected to large concentrated loads are structural members of common occurrence, the ACI Code makes no mention of moment coefficients for these cases. In the following example, the theory of elastic analysis is used in the analysis of 2G1-2G2-2G2-2G1.

EXAMPLE 10.8.1   By the theory of elastic analysis, determine the shear and moment diagrams to be used in the design of 2G1 and 2G2 in Example 10.7.1.

Solution: As discussed in Sec. 10.3, there are various ideas regarding what constitutes the correct stiffness for continuous T-sections. In accordance with the thought that the true stiffness is that of a span with a variable cross section, the effective flange width for an equivalent uniform moment of inertia section may be assumed to be twice the web width (Fig. 10.8.1). The principal effect of changing the stiffness of the girder (K_{gr}) occurs at the exterior support where the relative stiffness of the columns (K_{col}) compared to that of the girder is greatest. The centroid of the gross area of the T-section is at

$$\bar{y} = \frac{18(30)15 - 36(4.5)(2.25)}{18(30) + 36(4.5)} = \frac{7736}{702} = 11.0 \text{ in.}$$

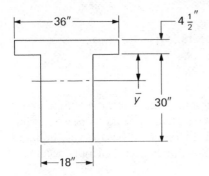

Fig. 10.8.1
T-section for stiffness computation.

The gross moment of inertia I_g is

$$I_g = \frac{36(4.5)^3}{3} + \frac{18(30)^3}{3} - 702(11.0)^2 = 78{,}100 \text{ in.}^4$$

$$K_{gr} = \frac{78{,}100}{39} = 2000 \text{ in.}^4/\text{ft}$$

If the size of the upper and lower columns were 18×18 in. and the column height were 15 ft,

$$K_{col} = \frac{18(18)^3/12}{15} = 583 \text{ in.}^4/\text{ft}$$

$$\frac{K_{gr}}{K_{col}} = \frac{2000}{583} = 3.43$$

In the rigid frame of Fig. 10.8.2 are shown the distribution factors

$$\frac{3.43}{3.43 + 1 + 1} = 0.632 \quad \text{and} \quad \frac{3.43}{3.43 + 3.43 + 1 + 1} = 0.387$$

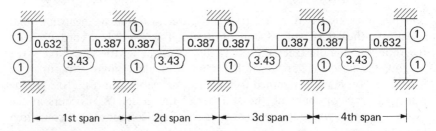

Fig. 10.8.2
Rigid frame system for 2G1-2G2-2G2-2G1.

The fixed-end moments are

$$\text{FEM due to dead load} = \frac{33.4(13)(26)}{39} + \frac{0.91(39)^2}{12} = 405 \text{ ft-kips}$$

$$\text{FEM due to live load} = \frac{54.2(13)(26)}{39} + \frac{0.255(39)^2}{12} = 502 \text{ ft-kips}$$

The results of moment distribution for the various loading conditions are given in Table 10.8.1.

Table 10.8.1
Summary of Moment Distribution Results Using Four Cycles

Joint	A	B		C		D		E
Member	AB	BA	BC	CB	CD	DC	DE	ED
DF	0.632	0.387	0.387	0.387	0.387	0.387	0.387	0.632
			Dead Load Only					
FEM	−405	+405	−405	+405	−405	+405	−405	+405
Total	−159	+487	−459	+380	−380	+459	−487	+159
			Live Load Only Spans 1 and 3					
FEM	−502	+502	0	0	−502	+502	0	0
Total	−244	+376	−182	+146	−326	+384	−229	−48
			Live Load Only Spans 1, 2, and 4					
FEM	−502	+502	−502	+502	0	0	−502	+502
Total	−188	+648	−641	+242	−96	+197	−385	+242
			Live Load Only Span 3					
FEM	0	0	0	0	−502	+502	0	0
Total	−8	−44	+73	+230	−375	+369	−220	−46
			Live Load Only Spans 2 and 3					
FEM	0	0	−502	+502	−502	+502	0	0
Total	+38	+176	−296	+605	−605	+296	−176	−38
			Load Live Only Spans 1 and 4					
FEM	−502	+502	0	0	0	0	−502	+502
Total	−234	+429	−270	−133	+133	+270	−429	+234

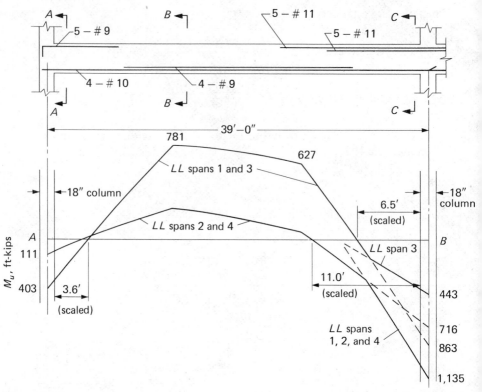

Fig. 10.8.3
Moment envelope and longitudinal bar arrangement for girder 2G1 (span 1).

The controlling moment envelopes for spans 2G1 and 2G2 are given in Figs. 10.8.3 and 10.8.4. In practice this composite diagram should be made instead of the individual moment and shear diagrams for each loading case. For investigating development length requirements at points of inflection, for checking cutoff acceptability in the tension zone, and for designing stirrups, an approximate shear envelope (only full span loadings) is used, as given in Fig. 10.8.5. Many designers would construct these envelopes directly from the end moments by scaling (plotting the simple span positive-moment diagram above a straight line joining the negative moments at the ends) and then use them directly for the remainder of the design.

10.9 Choice of Longitudinal Reinforcement in Girders

Again, the choice of longitudinal reinforcement depends on both the steel area and the development length requirements as dictated by the moment and shear envelopes such as shown in Figs. 10.8.3 through 10.8.5. Attention is called to ACI-8.10.5, applicable when the main reinforcement in the slab is parallel to the girder. For this situation transverse steel must be provided in the top of the slab to carry the load on the portion of the slab acting effec-

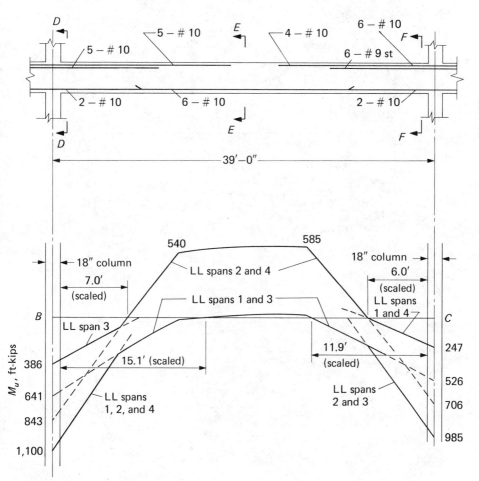

Fig. 10.8.4
Moment envelope and bar arrangement for girder 2G2 (span 2).

tively as the flange of the girder. The overhanging flange is assumed to act as a cantilever. The spacing of the transverse bars may not exceed 5 times the thickness of the flange or, in any case, 18 in.

EXAMPLE 10.9.1   Choose the arrangement of the main reinforcement in the floor girders 2G1-2G2-2G2-2G1 of Example 10.7.1.

Solution: Sections (rectangular sections) *A-A*, *C-C*, *D-D*, and *F-F* (Figs. 10.8.3, 10.8.4, and 10.9.1). Section *A-A*:

$$M_u \text{ at face} = 403 - \frac{97.5(1.5)}{3} = 403 - 49 = 354 \text{ ft-kips}$$

$$\text{required } R_u = \frac{M_u}{\phi b d^2} = \frac{354(12,000)}{0.90(18)(30.7)^2} = 278 \text{ psi}$$

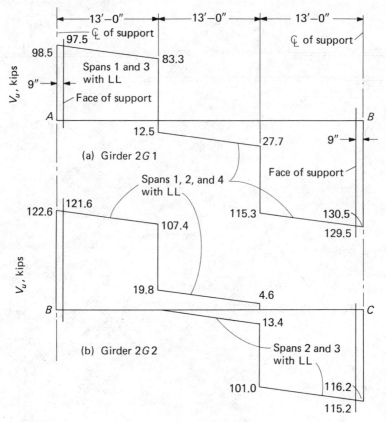

Fig. 10.8.5

Shear envelopes for girders 2G1 and 2G2 (full-span loadings only).

Either from Eq. (3.6.5), or from Fig. 3.6.1,

$$\text{required } \rho = 0.0075$$
$$\text{required } A_s = 0.0075(18)30.7 = 4.14 \text{ sq in.}$$

Sections C-C and D-D: The larger moment is at section C-C,

$$M_u \text{ at face} = 1135 - \frac{129.5(1.5)}{3} = 1070 \text{ ft-kips}$$

$$\text{required } R_u = \frac{1070(12,000)}{0.90(18)(29.3)^2} = 923 \text{ psi}$$

This value exceeds the maximum value of 870 psi allowed without using compression steel. In this case, only a small amount of compression steel is required; thus the positive-moment steel extended into the support at the bottom of the beam will be developed by proper embedment in order to utilize it as compression steel. Since the use of compression steel influences the tension steel requirement hardly at all, the tension requirement is computed just as if no compression steel were to be used. Estimating the required

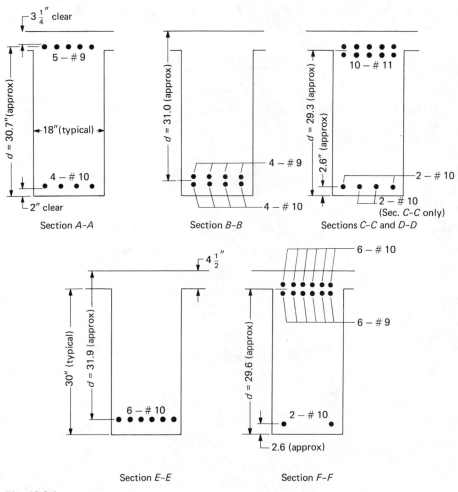

Fig. 10.9.1
Typical sections for 2G1 and 2G2 (refer to Figs. 10.8.3 and 10.8.4).

percentage from Fig. 3.6.1,

$$\text{required } A_s \approx 0.030(18)(29.3) = 15.8 \text{ sq in.}$$

Section F-F:

$$M_u \text{ at face} = 985 - \frac{115.2(1.5)}{3} = 985 - 58 = 927 \text{ ft-kips}$$

$$\text{required } R_u = \frac{927(12,000)}{0.90(18)(29.6)^2} = 785 \text{ psi}$$

Using straight-line approximation,

$$\text{required } A_s \approx 0.0278 \left(\frac{785}{870} \right)(18)29.6 = 13.4 \text{ sq in.}$$

Sections (T-sections) B-B and E-E (Figs. 10.8.3, 10.8.4, and 10.9.1):
Available flange width b_E,

$$\frac{39(12)}{4} = 117; \quad \text{or } \underline{18 + 16(4.5) = 90}; \quad \text{or } (26)(12) = 312.$$

It is likely that the depth a of the Whitney rectangular stress block will be less than the flange thickness t. Estimate $a = 2$ in. (about one-half flange thickness).
Section B-B: estimated $d = 31.0$ in.

$$\text{required } A_s = \frac{M_u}{\phi f_y \,(\text{arm})} = \frac{781(12)}{0.90(40)(31.0 - 1)} = 8.7 \text{ sq in.}$$

Check:

$$C = 0.85(3)(90)a = 229.5a$$
$$T = 8.7(40) = 348 \text{ kips}; \quad a = 1.52 \text{ in.}$$

$$\text{revised required } A_s = \frac{781(12)}{0.90(40)(31.0 - 0.76)} = 8.6 \text{ sq in.}$$

Section E-E:

$$\text{required } A_s = \frac{585(12)}{0.90(40)(31.9 - 1)} = 6.3 \text{ sq in.}$$

Check:

$$C = 229.5a; \quad T = 65(40) = 260 \text{ kips}$$
$$a = 1.14 \text{ in.}$$

$$\text{revised required } A_s = \frac{585(12)}{0.90(40)(31.9 - 0.57)} = 6.2 \text{ sq in.}$$

Confirmation of the tentative arrangement of main reinforcement as summarized in Fig. 10.9.2 awaits the check of development of reinforcement at the positive-moment inflection points (ACI-12.12.3), crack control when f_y exceeds 40,000 psi (does not apply for this problem), and deflection if excessive deflection will cause cracking of attached nonstructural elements.

Note in Fig. 10.9.2 that the requirements indicated in the compression zone at B and C are merely the minimums of one-fourth of the positive-

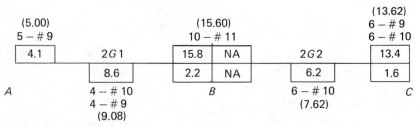

Fig. 10.9.2
Longitudinal reinforcement areas required and bars selected for girders 2G1 and 2G2.

moment steel required to satisfy ACI-12.12.1. It is likely that at B, which is the only place compression steel is required for strength, the minimum satisfying ACI-12.12.1 is sufficient.

The details of determining bar lengths are not shown; only the general arrangement is shown in Figs. 10.8.3 and 10.8.4.

Check maximum percentage reinforcement in negative-moment region at B (sections C-C and D-D), including effect of compression reinforcement. At balanced condition,

$$x_b = \left(\frac{0.003}{0.003 + f_y/E_s} \right) d = \left(\frac{87,000}{87,000 + 40,000} \right) d$$

$$= 0.685d = 0.685(29.3) = 20.1 \text{ in.}$$

$$\max x = 0.75x_b = 0.75(20.1) = 15.1 \text{ in.}$$

$$a = 0.85x = 0.85(15.1) = 12.8 \text{ in.}$$

At max A_s condition,

$$\epsilon_s' = \frac{15.1 - 2.6}{15.1}(0.003) = 0.0025 > \epsilon_y$$

Thus compression steel yields at max A_s condition.

$$\max C_c = 0.85f_c'ba = 0.85(3)(18)(12.8) = 586 \text{ kips}$$

Assume 2-#10 that extend through the support region at C-C and D-D are the only bars developed for compression reinforcement.

$$C_s = 2.54(40 - 2.55) = 95 \text{ kips}$$

$$\max T = \max C_c + C_s = 586 + 95 = 681 \text{ kips}$$

$$\max A_s = \frac{\max T}{f_y} = \frac{681}{40} = 17.0 \text{ sq in.}$$

Since the actual steel used (15.60) is less than max A_s, the design is acceptable.

Check the development length requirement at the positive-moment inflection points. From Fig. 10.8.5 (shear envelope), for span 1,

$$V_u \text{ (near left end)} = 97.5 - 3.6(1.165) = 93 \text{ kips}$$

$$V_u \text{ (near right end)} = 129.5 - 6.5(1.165) = 122 \text{ kips}$$

For span 2,

$$V_u \text{ (near left end)} = 121.6 - 7.0(1.165) = 113 \text{ kips}$$

$$V_u \text{ (near right end)} = 115.2 - 6.0(1.165) = 108 \text{ kips}$$

At the span 1 inflection points, 4-#10 bars continue along the bottom of the beam. The critical location is at the right inflection point where maximum V_u occurs.

$$V_u = 122 \text{ kips}$$

For 4-#10,

$$C = 0.85(3)(90)a = 229.5a$$
$$T = 5.08(40) = 203 \text{ kips}$$
$$a = 0.89 \text{ in.}$$
$$M_n = 203[31.9 - 0.5(0.89)]\tfrac{1}{12} = 532 \text{ ft-kips}$$
$$L_d \text{ for } \#10 \text{ bars} = 37.1 \text{ in. } (3.09 \text{ ft}) \qquad (\text{Table } 6.9.1)$$

$$\frac{M_n}{V_u} + L_a = \frac{532(12)}{122} + \frac{31.9}{12} = 7.02 \text{ ft} > 3.09 \text{ ft} \qquad\qquad \text{OK}$$

Note that L_a = effective depth, d, for this situation.

In span 2, only 2-#10 continue past the inflection point into the support. For 2-#10,

$$C = 229.5a; \qquad T = 2(1.27)(40) = 102 \text{ kips}$$
$$a = 0.44 \text{ in.}$$
$$M_n = 102[31.9 - 0.5(0.44)]\tfrac{1}{12} = 269 \text{ ft-kips}$$

$$\frac{M_n}{V_u} + L_a = \frac{269}{113} + \frac{31.9}{12} = 5.02 \text{ ft} > 3.09 \text{ ft} \qquad\qquad \text{OK}$$

The transverse steel required in the top of the flange of the girder may be computed as follows (Fig. 10.9.3):

$$M_u = \tfrac{1}{2}[0.100(1.7) + 0.056(1.4)](3)^2 = 1.12 \text{ ft-kips/ft}$$

$$\text{required } R_u = \frac{1.12(12,000)}{0.90(12)(2.94)^2} = 144 \text{ psi}$$

Since this is less than the value for min ρ, the minimum value controls.

$$A_s = \frac{200}{40,000}(12)(2.94) = 0.18 \text{ sq in.}$$

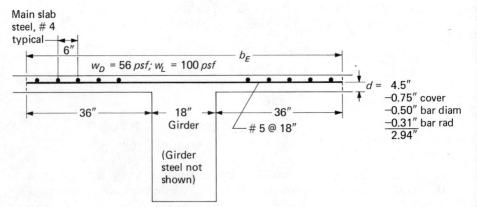

Fig. 10.9.3
Transverse steel across the top of girder.

Use #5 bars at 18 in. spacing. Generally the amount required for temperature and shrinkage in the slab according to ACI-7.12 is adequate for this purpose.

The bar arrangement is shown in Figs. 10.8.3 and 10.8.4 and cross sections are shown in Fig. 10.9.1. The shear reinforcement and dimensions of longitudinal reinforcement are not shown, because little new will be involved in their presentation.

10.10 One-Way Joist Floor Construction

One-way concrete joist construction (Fig. 10.10.1), sometimes called "ribbed-slab construction," consists of regularly spaced ribs monolithically built with a top floor slab and arranged to span in one direction. Such a system may also be designed as a two-way system (waffle slab) according to the procedures for two-way slab systems treated in Chaps. 16 and 17. The dimensions of the one-way joist system are usually such that only temperature and shrinkage reinforcement is required in the slab. The slab is usually in the range of 2 to 4 in. (50 to 100 mm) thick but may occasionally be as much as 6 in. (150 mm). The ribs (joists) of at least 4 in. (100 mm) width are usually tapered (Fig. 10.10.1b) and are spaced so that the clear spacing between adjacent ribs does not exceed 30 in. (760 mm). During construction removable and reusable form fillers are used in spaces between the joists. Such fillers may be standard-sized steel "pans" in 20 or 30 in. widths and 6, 8, 10, 12, 14, 16, and 20 in. depths. Sometimes form fillers are made from hardboard, fiberboard, glass-reinforced plastic, or corrugated cardboard. Occasionally, permanent fillers are used consisting of lightweight or normal-weight concrete blocks or clay tile blocks, as shown in Fig. 10.10.1c.

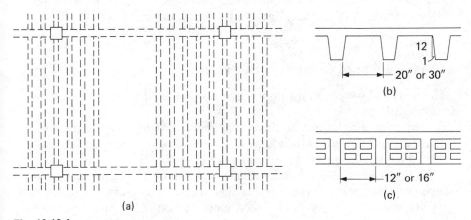

Fig. 10.10.1
Concrete joist floor construction.

The dead weight of typical concrete joist floors, either with hollow tile filler or with the use of removable forms, is shown in Table 10.10.1, which is taken from the *Reinforced Concrete Design Handbook* [3].

Table 10.10.1

Weight of Concrete Joist Floors, psf (for $2\frac{1}{2}$ in. slab)

Depth of Joist Only (in.)	20-in. Pans				30-in. Pans			12-in. Units			16-in. Units		
					Width of Joist (in.)								
	4	5	6	7	5	6	7	4	5	6	4	5	6
4								55	57	58	54	55	56
6	44	46	48		41	43		66	68	71	61	62	64
8	49	52	55		46	48		79	81	84	67	70	72
10	54	58	62		50	53		88	93	96	74	77	81
12	60	65	69	73	55	58	61	98	103	107	80	85	89
14		71	76	81	60	63	67						

Concrete joist floor construction is referred to in ACI-8.11. Some of the requirements are as follows:

1. The joists shall not be farther apart than 30 in. face to face. The ribs shall be not less than 4 in. wide and of a depth not more than $3\frac{1}{2}$ times the width.
2. The vertical shells of permanent fillers in contact with the joists may be included in strength calculations involving shear or negative bending moment provided the filler material has a unit compressive strength at least equal to that of the concrete in the joists. In this case the minimum slab thickness is $1\frac{1}{2}$ in. or $\frac{1}{12}$ of the clear distance between joists, whichever is smaller.
3. When removable forms or fillers having less compressive strength than required under (2) are used, the thickness of the concrete slab shall not be less than $\frac{1}{12}$ of the clear distance between joists, nor less than 2 in.

10.11 Design of Concrete Joist Floors

The design of concrete joist floors involves (1) the slab, (2) the joists, and (3) the girders.

Generally, shrinkage reinforcement is placed at right angles to the joists, and the concrete slab is treated as if it were of plain concrete. The short clear span between joists may be considered as being fixed at both ends.

The joist itself may be designed as a floor beam having a rectangular section in the region of negative bending and a T-section in the region of positive bending. The critical design moment curves for each span may either follow the ACI moment coefficients or be determined by a continuity analysis. Largely because of the interaction of slab with the closely spaced joists, ACI-8.11.8 permits the shear strength V_c provided by the concrete to be 10% higher than for regular beams.

The girder is designed as a floor girder, but the load from the joists may be considered as being uniformly distributed along the span.

In the case of joist floors over removable steel pans, tapered end forms are available that increase the effective joist width 2 in. on each side for 20-in. wide forms and $2\frac{1}{2}$ in. on each side for 30-in. wide forms in a distance of 3 ft from the end. This increased width may be necessary to take the large shear or negative bending moment near the end of the span.

In order to limit deflection on floor joist construction the minimum depth requirements of ACI-Table 9.5a for ribbed one-way slabs should be applied. Whenever excessive deflection may cause cracking or other adverse effects, deflections must be computed even if ACI-Table 9.5a has been satisfied.

EXAMPLE 10.11.1 Design the typical interior span of a concrete joist floor using fillers, in accordance with the ACI moment coefficients. Use center-to-center span = 26 ft, clear span = 24 ft 6 in., live load = 80 psf, $f'_c = 3000$ psi, $f_y = 40,000$ psi, and the strength method of the ACI Code.

Solution: (a) Slab design. Assume that a $2\frac{1}{2}$-in. slab will be used with 16-in. wide fillers. The flexural tensile stress capacity of plain concrete is given by ACI-15.11.2 as $5\sqrt{f'_c}$. Apply the overload factors U,

$$w_u = 1.4\left[\frac{(2.5)(150)}{12}\right] + 1.7(80) = 44 + 136 = 180 \text{ psf}$$

Assuming that the slab is fixed at its junction with the joist,

$$M_u = \frac{1}{12}(0.180)\left(\frac{16}{12}\right)^2 = 0.0266 \text{ ft-kip}$$

The strength of the plain concrete section is

$$\phi M_n = \phi f_t[\tfrac{1}{6}bh^2] = 0.65(5\sqrt{f'_c})[\tfrac{1}{6}bh^2]$$
$$= 0.65(274)[\tfrac{1}{6}(12)(2.5)^2]\tfrac{1}{12,000} = 0.186 \text{ ft-kip} > M_u \qquad \text{OK}$$

Actually the slab is underlaid by the fillers; thus there is very little chance of its being subjected to bending. Note that ACI-15.11.2 actually includes the ϕ factor as a multiplier on the tensile stress capacity rather than as a separate factor.

Shrinkage and temperature reinforcement (ACI-7.12) should be equal to $0.0018(12)(2.5) = 0.054$ sq in./ft. Use welded wire fabric WWF 4 × 12-W2/W1, selected from Table 10.11.1; A_s in direction perpendicular to joists = 0.060 sq in./ft, and A_s parallel to joists = 0.010 sq in./ft.

(b) Joist design. The overall depth of the joist floor must satisfy the minimum requirement of ACI-Table 9.5a unless deflections are computed.

$$\min h = \frac{L}{21}(0.8) = \frac{L}{26.2} = \frac{26(12)}{26.2} \approx 12 \text{ in.}$$

The *CRSI Handbook* [4] recommends using $L/24 = 26(12)/24 = 13$ in. Assume the use of joists 5 in. wide and 12 in. deep below the bottom of the slab, giving a total depth of 14.5 in. The dead weight (from Table 10.10.1) is 85 psf. Assume #5 bars.

Effective depth, $d = 14.5 - 0.75 - 0.31 = 13.4$ in.
$w_u = 1.4(85) + 1.7(80) = 119 + 136 = 254$ psf
Factored load per linear ft $= 0.254(21)/12 = 0.445$ kip/ft

The maximum negative bending moment is

$$M_u = \tfrac{1}{11}(0.445)(24.5)^2 = 24.2 \text{ ft-kips}$$

$$\text{required } R_u = \frac{M_u}{\phi b d^2} = \frac{24.2(12,000)}{0.90(5)(13.4)^2} = 359 \text{ psi}$$

Using Eq. (3.6.5) or Fig. 3.6.1,

$$\rho = \frac{1}{m}\left(1 - \sqrt{1 - \frac{2mR_u}{f_y}}\right)$$

$$m = \frac{f_y}{0.85f'_c} = \frac{40,000}{0.85(3000)} = 15.7$$

$$\rho = \frac{1}{15.7}\left(1 - \sqrt{1 - \frac{2(15.7)359}{40,000}}\right) = 0.0097$$

required A_s over support $= 0.0097(5)(13.4) = 0.65$ sq in.

With a reinforcement percentage so low, deflection should not be a problem even if excessive deflection may cause cracking of nonstructural elements.
  The shear at a distance d from the face of support is

$$V_u = 0.445(12.25 - 1.12) = 4.95 \text{ kips}$$

The shear strength of a joist without shear reinforcement is

$$\phi V_c = \phi(1.10)(2\sqrt{f'_c})b_w d$$
$$= 0.85(1.10)(2\sqrt{3000})(5)(13.4)\tfrac{1}{1000} = 6.86 \text{ kips} > 4.95 \text{ kips} \quad \text{OK}$$

The maximum positive bending moment is

$$M_u = \tfrac{1}{16}(0.445)(24.5)^2 = 16.7 \text{ ft-kips}$$

Table 10.11.1
Common Welded Wire Fabric for Temperature and Shrinkage Reinforcement

Spacing of Longitudinal and Transverse Wires	Designation Wire Size Designation Longitudinal/Transverse	A_s, Longitudinal Direction (sq in.)
WWF 4 × 12	W1.5/W1	0.045
WWF 4 × 12	W2/W1	0.060
WWF 4 × 12	W2.5/W1	0.075

Assume that the neutral axis falls within the flange and $a \approx 1$ in. Then, illustrating an alternative approach to the use of Eq. (3.6.5) for determining the required reinforcement,

$$\text{required } A_s \approx \frac{M_u}{\phi f_y \text{ (arm)}} = \frac{16.7(12)}{0.90(40)(13.4 - 0.5)} = 0.43 \text{ sq in.}$$

Determine moment arm more accurately using $b_E = 8(2) + 5 = 21$ in. (ACI-8.10.2),

$$C = 0.85f'_c ba = 0.85(3)(21)a = 53.6a$$
$$T = A_s f_y = 0.43(40) = 17.2 \text{ kips}$$
$$a = 17.2/53.6 = 0.32 \text{ in.}$$

$$\text{revised required } A_s = \frac{16.7(12)}{0.90(40)(13.4 - 0.16)} = 0.42 \text{ sq in.}$$

Since a is less than $t/2$, the effective section of the compression zone is rectangular. Use 1-#5 bottom bar, 1-#4 truss bar, and 1-#5 top bar (see Fig. 10.11.1).

$$\text{provided } A_s \text{ over support} = 0.71 \text{ sq in. } (2\text{-}\#4 + 1\text{-}\#5)$$
$$\text{provided } A_s \text{ at midspan} = 0.51 \text{ sq in. } (1\text{-}\#4 + 1\text{-}\#5)$$

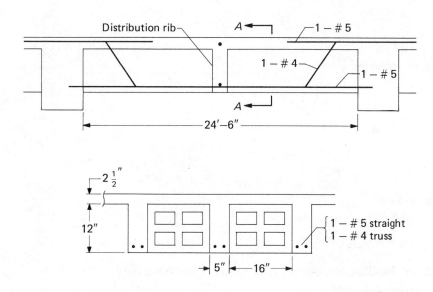

Section A-A

Fig. 10.11.1
Concrete joist floor using fillers, Example 10.11.1.

Consistent with a loading for the maximum positive moment in an interior span, the inflection point is at $0.354L$ from centerline of span (see Fig. 7.5.4a). Thus the development length requirement of ACI-12.12.3 must be checked. Only the #5 straight bar extends beyond the inflection point and into the support at least 6 in.

$$C = 0.85f'_c b_E a = 0.85(3)(21)a = 53.6a$$
$$T = 0.31(40) = 12.4 \text{ kips}$$
$$a = 0.23 \text{ in.}$$
$$M_n = 12.4[13.4 - 0.5(0.23)]\tfrac{1}{12} = 13.8 \text{ ft-kips}$$
$$V_u = 0.445(0.354)(24.5) = 3.9 \text{ kips}$$
$$L_a = 12d_b(\text{controls}) = 7.5 \text{ in.}$$
$$L_d(\#5) = 12 \text{ in.}$$

The equivalent embedment length provided is

$$\frac{M_n}{V_u} + L_a = \frac{13.8(12)}{3.9} + 7.5 = 42.5 + 7.5 = 50.0 \text{ in.} > L_d \qquad \text{OK}$$

Frequently a transverse distribution rib (Fig. 10.11.1) is used having a 4 in. minimum width and containing at least one #4 bar both top and bottom. Such a rib would be located at the third points of the span for spans greater than 30 ft.

If the support region requires extra joist width for negative moment or for shear, the ends of the joist may be tapered as shown in Fig. 10.11.2.

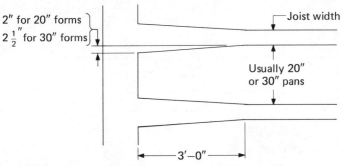

Fig. 10.11.2
Plan showing taper pan joists.

10.12 Redistribution of Moments—Introduction to Limit Analysis

Methods of proportioning beams for flexure, shear, and bar development requirements according to the strength method have been discussed in Chaps. 3, 5, and 6, and further illustrated in Secs. 10.1 through 10.11. When the inelastic behavior of concrete at a particular location has been accounted for in the design of that cross section based on its strength, it may seem somewhat illogical to have used an elastic analysis to determine the design moments and shears. However, because the evaluation of the true ultimate

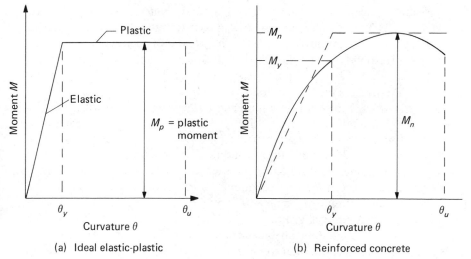

Fig. 10.12.1
Moment-curvature characteristics.

strength, or limit strength, of an entire structure requires difficult and elaborate analysis, the present safe conservative procedure is used.

The concept of redistribution of moments first introduced into the ACI Code in 1963 was the result of considerable research [5–19] into the limit behavior of the entire structure (primarily continuous beams, at present) beyond the elastic range to the point where the collapse load is reached. Concrete design, therefore, has moved toward limit design, or, as it is called in steel structures, "plastic" design.

The use of a plastic theory requires that the material involved actually behave plastically. Figure 10.12.1a shows the ideal relationship of moment M to curvature θ, where there is a perfectly elastic portion and an ideal plastic portion. Reinforced concrete exhibits an M/θ curve as shown in Fig. 10.12.1b which, although it differs markedly from the ideal, may be approximated by such an ideal system. It has been found that the lower the net reinforcement ratio $\rho - \rho'$, the closer is the actual moment-rotation behavior to the ideal.

Consider the simply supported beam of Fig. 10.12.2. The limit load on such a system is reached when the rotation angle under the load reaches

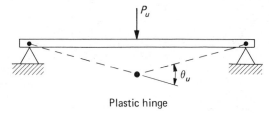

Plastic hinge

Fig. 10.12.2
Limit condition for simple beam.

the value θ_u which corresponds to an ultimate concrete strain (taken by ACI as 0.003). In limit analysis, the maximum moment achieved up to ultimate concrete strain is referred to as M_n (nominal ultimate moment), which corresponds to M_p, the plastic moment in the ideal system. For such simply supported beams the achieving of M_p or M_n at one location along the span represents the limit of the system, and the beam becomes a mechanism, deforming further without inducing further resistance. It will be shown that in a continuous structure (statically indeterminate system), the material at a section where M_p is first reached must undergo additional strain before that structure achieves its limit condition. This additional strain, with regard to bending of a section, is referred to as "rotation capacity." Reinforced concrete has a reasonable amount of rotation capacity when the net reinforcement percentage ρ or $\rho - \rho'$ is 50% or less of the balanced amount ρ_b for a singly reinforced beam.

Next, consider the statically indeterminate fixed-end beam of Fig. 10.12.3a, showing its moment diagram for stresses in the elastic range. As the load is increased, the moments at the fixed ends achieve M_p, while at all other points moments are still in the elastic range. Thus, at the point of reaching

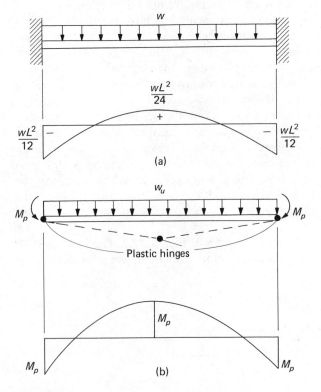

Fig. 10.12.3
Limit condition for a fixed-end beam.

M_p at the ends,

$$\frac{w_y L^2}{12} = M_p \qquad \text{and} \qquad w_y = \frac{12 M_p}{L^2}$$

where w_y is the load carried at an end curvature θ_y when M_p is just reached. In carrying this load, the beam is as stable as a simple beam and deflects less because of the end moments M_p. Figure 10.12.3b shows the limit condition of three plastic hinges (one more than the number of degrees of statical indeterminacy) and the associated moment diagram. The limit load may be computed using statics, such as the midspan equilibrium requirement

$$+ M_p = - M_p + \text{simple beam moment}$$

$$2 M_p = \frac{w_u L^2}{8}$$

$$w_u = \frac{16 M_p}{L^2}$$

Thus the capacity may be increased 33% after the plastic moment has been reached at the fixed ends, provided that sufficient additional deformation (rotation) can be accommodated at the fixed ends to permit development of the plastic moment at midspan. In other words, rotation capacity permitting, the positive and negative moments under any particular loading condition tend to equalize (assuming, of course, the strength of the section at the two regions is the same). For a thorough treatment of limit analysis the reader is referred to the work of Baker [5].

The aforementioned limit behavior has been thoroughly verified for structural steel, and its use under the term "plastic design" has become widespread. Steel being a very ductile material, rotation capacity in beams is available to a high degree. On the other hand, concrete, being a relatively brittle material, has traditionally been considered to have no appreciable plastic deformability. Reinforced concrete beams, when the net percentage of reinforcement $\rho - \rho'$ is low, will have their ultimate moment controlled by yielding of the steel while the concrete strain is still of low magnitude (see Fig. 10.12.4). Reserve rotation $\theta_u - \theta_y$ is then available for a redistribution of moments to occur before the ultimate concrete strain of about 0.003 is reached.

Research has shown that such a redistribution does occur in reinforced concrete beams when certain rotation capacity related conditions are met; therefore the ACI Code (ACI-8.4) allows the negative moments at the supports of continuous flexural members, calculated by elastic theory, to be increased or decreased by not more than

$$20 \left(1 - \frac{\rho - \rho'}{\rho_b} \right) \%$$

where ρ_b is the balanced percentage of reinforcement for a beam containing

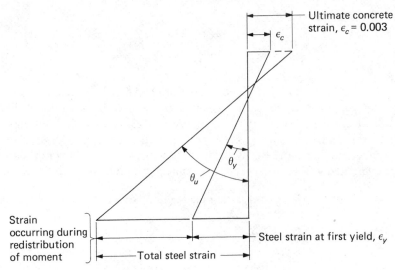

Fig. 10.12.4

Strain diagram for underreinforced concrete beams (steel governs ultimate capacity).

tension reinforcement only, given by Eq. (3.5.4) or ACI Formula 8-1,

$$\rho_b = \frac{0.85\beta_1 f'_c}{f_y}\left(\frac{87,000}{87,000 + f_y}\right)$$

The limits of applicability of this provision may be summarized as follows:

1. Application is limited to continuous flexural members.
2. No more than 20% of the negative moments for any given loading arrangement may be adjusted.
3. Bending moments used in such an adjustment must be obtained by an elastic analysis; moments from use of coefficients or other approximate methods may not be adjusted.
4. The *net* reinforcement ratio $\rho - \rho'$ at the cross section where the moment is *reduced* must not exceed one-half the balanced percentage ρ_b, as defined by ACI Formula 8-1.
5. Adjustment, when permitted, is made for each given loading condition. The envelope of the adjusted diagrams from all loading conditions is then used to proportion the members.

This method of partial redistribution of moments is generally conservative. Future codes will probably extend the method or go fully to a limit design approach once the plastic hinge behavior is more extensively understood, especially with regard to shear, development of reinforcement, and deflection.

In approaching a design, it may be advantageous to apply ACI-8.4 directly. It is likely, however, that more frequent use will occur when the design is in progress and the designer realizes that the conditions of the redistribution provision are met and savings appear possible. The following example illustrates an application of this provision.

EXAMPLE 10.12.1   Show the effects of redistribution on the moments obtained by elastic analysis for the floor beams 2B1 and 2B2 in Example 10.3.1.

Solution: The beams along with the critical moment diagrams are shown in Fig. 10.12.5. The elastic moments are those computed under factored loads (i.e., including overload factors U) in Tables 10.3.1 through 10.3.5, and these are shown in Figs. 10.3.3 through 10.3.6.

(a) Investigate negative moment region at B to determine the maximum percent moment adjustment. Referring to Fig. 10.4.1, and noting that $0.75\rho_b = 0.0278$ as used for design in Example 10.2.1,

$$\text{actual } \rho = \frac{4.54}{13(20)} = 0.0174$$

$$0.5\rho_b = 0.5\left(\frac{0.0278}{0.75}\right) = 0.0185 > 0.0174 \qquad\qquad \text{OK}$$

Moment redistribution is permissible at B.

$$\text{percent adjustment permitted} = 20\left(1 - \frac{\rho}{\rho_b}\right)$$

$$= 20\left(1 - \frac{0.0174}{2(0.0185)}\right) = 10.6\%$$

Since the steel in the compression zone was not fully developed at the faces of support (see Fig. 10.6.1), it may not be counted as compression steel. It might well be economical to develop the capacity of the steel in the compression zone at the support. This would increase the ductility in that region and allow a higher percentage of moment redistribution.

(b) Make adjustments to elastic moments. Examine first the loading for maximum positive moment in span AB, Fig. 10.12.5a. Increasing the negative moments by 10.6% reduces the maximum positive moment for this loading from 174 to 160 ft-kips. The increased negative moment for case (a) is still less than the negative moment occurring under other loadings. The 10.6% adjustment for case (b) is made by reducing the negative moment at B and increasing those at A and C, thus minimizing the effect on the positive moments. The increased positive moment in span 1 is still slightly less than the reduced controlling positive moment of 160 ft-kips from case (a). In case (c) the negative moments are increased 10.6%, thus reducing the positive moment in span 2 from 130 to 112 ft-kips.

The adjustment of the negative moments may be either an increase or decrease so long as the positive moments are also adjusted to satisfy static equilibrium. The envelope of adjusted moments would then be used to design the sections by the strength method. The net effect on the envelope is a reduction for both positive and negative moments. This is not actually a reduction in the safety factor below that used for a simply supported beam. It is a reduction in the excess strength that the system has by virtue

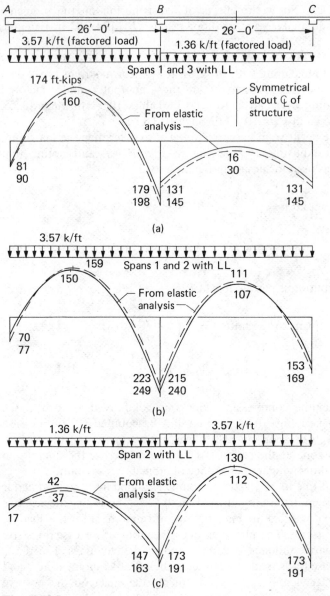

Fig. 10.12.5

Redistribution of elastically computed moments according to ACI-8.4.

of its continuity, one span with another. Since the redistribution does occur, partial utilization of it seems reasonable.

A simple application of limit design concepts to practical design has been presented by Furlong [20]. His method satisfies the ductility and strength requirements of limit design without the usual complexities that have impeded the acceptance of limit design into the ACI Code.

SELECTED REFERENCES

1. *Continuity in Concrete Building Frames* (4th ed.). Chicago: Portland Cement Association, 1959.
2. *Manual of Standard Practice for Detailing Reinforced Concrete Structures* (6th ed.), (ACI-315-74). Detroit: American Concrete Institute, 1974.
3. Committee 317, *Reinforced Concrete Design Handbook* (3rd ed.), (SP-3). Detroit, Michigan: American Concrete Institute, 1965.
4. *CRSI Handbook* (2nd ed.). Chicago: Concrete Reinforcing Steel Institute, 1975.
5. A. L. L. Baker. *The Ultimate Load Theory Applied to the Design of Reinforced and Prestressed Concrete Frames*. London: Concrete Publications, 1956.
6. A. H. Mattock. "Limit Design for Structural Concrete," *Journal of the Research and Development Laboratories*. Portland Cement Association, **1**, May 1959, 14–24.
7. G. C. Ernst and A. R. Riveland. "Ultimate Loads and Deflections from Limit Design of Continuous Structural Concrete," *ACI Journal, Proceedings*, **56,** October 1959, 274–286.
8. M. Z. Cohn. "Limit Design for Redundant Reinforced Concrete Structures," (Bibliography), *ACI Journal, Proceedings*, **58,** November 1961, 639–648, *Proceedings*, **59,** December 1962, 1873–1876.
9. ACI-ASCE Committee 428. "Limit Design of Reinforced Concrete Beams and Frames—Addendum" (Bibliography), *ACI Journal, Proceedings*, **60,** October 1963, 1471–1474.
10. Herbert A. Sawyer, Jr. "Design of Concrete Frames for Two Failure Stages," *Flexural Mechanics of Reinforced Concrete*, SP-12. Detroit, Michigan: American Concrete Institute/American Society of Civil Engineers, 1965, (pp. 405–437).
11. Alan H. Mattock. "Rotational Capacity of Hinging Regions in Reinforced Concrete Beams," *Flexural Mechanics of Reinforced Concrete* (SP-12). Detroit, Michigan: American Concrete Institute/American Society of Civil Engineers, 1965, (pp. 143–180). (Also PCA Development Department Bulletin D101.)
12. M. Z. Cohn. "Rotation Compatibility in the Limit Design of Reinforced Concrete Continuous Beams," *Flexural Mechanics of Reinforced Concrete* (SP-12). Detroit, Michigan: American Concrete Institute/American Society of Civil Engineers, 1965, (pp. 359–382).
13. W. G. Corley. "Rotational Capacity of Reinforced Concrete Beams," *Journal of Structural Division*, ASCE, **92** (ST5), October 1966, 121–146. (Also PCA Development Department Bulletin D108).
14. M. Z. Cohn. "Limit-Design Solutions for Concrete Structures," *Journal of Structural Division*, ASCE, **93** (ST1), February 1967, 37–57.
15. Richard M. Barker and Kenneth H. Murray. "Test Results on the Limit Analysis of a Fixed Ended T-Beam," *ACI Journal, Proceedings*, **64,** December 1967, 820–826.
16. ACI-ASCE Committee 428. "Progress Report on Code Clauses for 'Limit Design,'" *ACI Journal, Proceedings*, **65,** September 1968, 713–720. Disc. **66,** 221–223.
17. M. Z. Cohn. "Limit Design of Reinforced Concrete Frames," *Journal of Structural Division*, ASCE, **94** (ST10), October 1968, 2467–2483.
18. Edward G. Nawy, Rodolfo F. Danesi, and John J. Grosko. "Rectangular Spiral Binders Effect on Plastic Hinge Rotation Capacity in Reinforced Concrete Beams," *ACI Journal, Proceedings*, **65,** December 1968, 1001–1010. Disc. **66,** 497–498.
19. Harold W. Conner, Paul H. Kaar, and W. Gene Corley. "Moment Redistribution in Precast Concrete Frame," *Journal of Structural Division*, ASCE, **96,** (ST3), March 1970, 637–661.
20. Richard W. Furlong. "Design of Concrete Frames by Assigned Limit Moments," *ACI Journal, Proceedings*, **67,** April 1970, 341–353.

PROBLEMS

All problems[†] are to be worked in accordance with the strength method of the ACI Code, and all stated loads are service loads, unless otherwise indicated.

CONTINUOUS BEAM PROBLEMS

10.1 Design a rectangular beam continuous over three spans as shown in the accompanying figure. The live load is 2.75 kips/ft, and the dead load is 1.0 kip/ft in addition to the beam weight. The floor is to be a prefabricated system. Assume the supports to be 15 in. wide. Use $f'_c = 4000$ psi and $f_y = 60,000$ psi, and do not apply ACI–8.4 for moment redistribution. (Live load = 40 kN/m; dead load = 15 kN/m plus beam; supports 380 mm wide; $f'_c = 28$ N/mm²; $f_y = 420$ N/mm².)

(a) Determine the moment envelope using factored loads.

(b) Determine the bar bends or cutoff locations, or both, directly from the moment envelope.

(c) Use only full-span loadings for computing the shear envelope and use U stirrups of #3 size if possible.

(d) Design sketch is required.

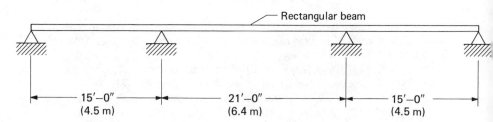

Rectangular beam

|← 15'–0" →|← 21'–0" →|← 15'–0" →|
| (4.5 m) | (6.4 m) | (4.5 m) |

Prob. 10.1

10.2 Redesign the beam of Prob. 10.1 as a monolithic T-section floor system. The beams are spaced 8 ft on centers and the slab is 6 in. thick. The 1.0 kip/ft dead load includes the slab but not the beam stem. (Beam spacing = 2.4 m; slab thickness = 150 mm.)

10.3 Design the beam ABC of the frame shown in the accompanying figure in which the relative stiffness EI/L are given. The beams are T-sections having a 6-in. slab. The dead load is 0.40 kip/ft (not including beam stem or slab) and the live load is 3.75 kips/ft. Assume the supports to be 15 in. wide. Use $f'_c = 4000$ psi and $f_y = 60,000$ psi. (150 mm slab; dead load = 6 kN/m; live load = 55 kN/m; supports 380 mm wide; $f'_c = 28$ N/mm²; $f_y = 420$ N/mm².)

10.4 Design the transverse beam indicated for the floor plan given in the accompanying figure. Assume that a warehouse live load of 375 psf is to be used. Assume a 5-in. slab placed monolithically with beams and girders, a width of support at longitudinal girders of 18 in., and that only a nominal minimum of

---

[†] Many problems may be solved as problems stated in U.S. Customary units or as problems in metric units using quantities in parenthesis at the end of the statement. The metric conversions are approximate to avoid implying higher precision for the given information in metric units than that for the U.S. Customary units.

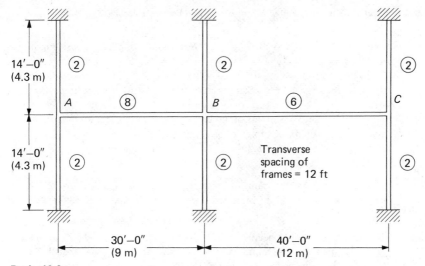

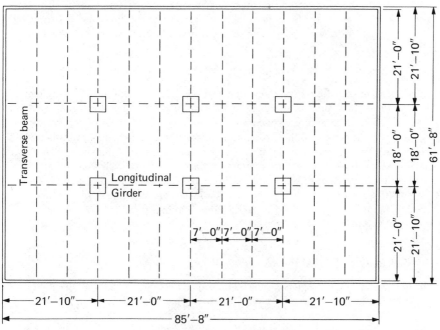

14'-0" (4.3 m)

14'-0" (4.3 m)

Transverse spacing of frames = 12 ft

30'-0" (9 m)

40'-0" (12 m)

Prob. 10.3

21'-0"

21'-10"

18'-0"

18'-0"

61'-8"

Transverse beam

Longitudinal Girder

21'-0"

21'-10"

7'-0" 7'-0" 7'-0"

21'-10"

21'-0"

21'-0"

21'-10"

85'-8"

Note: For metric problems use all lengths in meters = 0.305 times lengths in feet rounded to two significant figures.

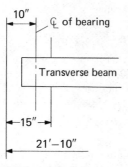

10"

€ of bearing

Transverse beam

15"

21'-10"

Section at wall

Prob. 10.4

moment restraint is provided by the exterior wall support (i.e., assume hinge for elastic analysis). Use $f'_c = 3500$ psi and $f_y = 60,000$ psi. For a comparison of the effect of considering torsional stiffness of longitudinal girders, divide the class into three parts, each using one of the following assumptions: **(a)** zero torsional stiffness of the two longitudinal girders; **(b)** torsional stiffness equal to 25% of the bending stiffness of the 21-ft span beam; and **(c)** torsional stiffness equal to 50% of the bending stiffness of the 21-ft span beam. (Live load = 18 kN/m^2; 130 mm slab thickness; support width = 460 mm; $f'_c = 24$ N/mm^2; $f_y = 420$ N/mm^2.)

10.5   Redesign the transverse beams of Prob. 10.4, except use spans 22-20-22 instead of the original spans 21-18-21, and use $f'_c = 4000$ psi and $f_y = 60,000$ psi. All other details are the same as in Prob. 10.4. ($f'_c = 28$ N/mm^2; $f_y = 420$ N/mm^2.)

10.6   Redesign the transverse beams of Prob. 10.4, except use spans 24-21-24 instead of original spans 21-18-21, and use $f'_c = 4000$ psi and $f_y = 60,000$ psi. All other details are the same as in Prob. 10.4. ($f'_c = 28$ N/mm^2; $f_y = 420$ N/mm^2.)

10.7   Using the moment and shear envelopes of Figs. 10.8.3 and 10.8.5, determine the actual lengths from the faces of support to the cutoff points for girder 2G1. Verify by drawing the moment capacity diagram superimposed on the moment envelope.

10.8   Same as Prob. 10.7 except use Fig. 10.8.4 for 2G2 instead of Fig. 10.8.3 for 2G1.

10.9   Design the four-span longitudinal girder indicated for the floor system of Prob. 10.4. In lieu of using the more accurate loadings from the results of Prob. 10.4., use concentrated dead and live loads of 15 and 60 kips, respectively, plus the weight of the girder. Assume that the columns are 18 in. square and 15 ft. high and that the beam receives equivalent restraint from monolithic attachment to the 15-in. reinforced concrete exterior wall. Assume also that the columns are fixed at the far ends. Use $f'_c = 3500$ psi and $f_y = 60,000$ psi. (Concentrated dead and live loads, 67 and 268 kN, plus girder; columns = 460 mm square and 4.5 m high; wall = 380 mm thick; $f'_c = 24$ N/mm^2; $f_y = 420$ N/mm^2.)

CONCRETE JOIST PROBLEMS:

10.10   Design a concrete joist, using 30-in. wide removable pans, for a typical interior span of 28 ft center to center of supporting girders. Assume a support width of 18 in. Use a live load of 100 psf, $f'_c = 4000$ psi and $f_y = 40,000$ psi. (769-mm wide pans; span = 8.5 m; support width = 460 mm; $f'_c = 28$ N/mm^2; $f_y = 280$ N/mm^2.)

10.11   Determine the service live-load capacity for a single-span joist of 20 ft clear span, using a $2\frac{1}{2}$-in. slab, 20 in. wide and 8-in. deep forms, and 4-in. wide joists with 2-#5 bars. No taper is used. Use $f'_c = 3000$ psi and $f_y = 40,000$ psi.

10.12   Determine the service live-load capacity for an interior span joist of 32-ft span (clear span), using a 2-in. slab, 20-in. wide and 14-in. deep form, and 5-in. wide joists with #7 bars for the bottom, truss, and top steel. The bottom steel is properly embedded in the support to develop its compression capacity at the face of support. The joist has a standard taper. Use $f'_c = 3000$ psi and $f_y = 40,000$ psi.

10.13   Design an end-span joist for a continuous system to carry a live load of 225 psf, using 20-in. wide removable pans, for a clear span of 18 ft. Allow an extra $\frac{1}{2}$ in.

of thickness for dead-load purposes only, since the concrete slab is to serve as the final wearing surface. Use $f'_c = 4500$ psi and $f_y = 60,000$ psi.

MOMENT REDISTRIBUTION PROBLEM:

10.14 Redesign the beam of Prob. 10.1 taking into account permissible moment redistribution. Compare with Prob. 10.1.

11

Monolithic
Beam-to-Column
Joints

11.1 Monolithic Joints

Considerable emphasis has been made concerning design of flexural members for bending, shear, and development of reinforcement in Chaps. 3 through 10. Some attention has been given to development of reinforcement at exterior supports, including the use of hooks (Secs. 6.13 and 6.16). The design of compression members is treated in Chap. 13. Often in design not enough attention is given to the details of connections: how the forces in beams and the forces in columns interact and get transmitted through the joint. The ACI Code provides little guidance specifically directed to joint details.

The state-of-the-art regarding the design of beam-to-column joints has been summarized by ACI-ASCE Committee 352, Joints and Connections in Monolithic Reinforced Concrete Structures [1]. In that report there are detailed provisions for the design of two classes of beam-to-column joints:

Type 1 joints, primarily for static loading, where strength is the primary criterion and no significant inelastic deformations are expected; and
Type 2 joints, usually for earthquake or blast loading, where there is need for sustained strength through stress reversals into the inelastic range.

In general, Type 1 joints require only nominal ductility, whereas Type 2 joints require significant ductility, such as would be required in seismic design. The Committee 352 report [1] has utilized the relatively limited research on joints to establish its recommendations. Some of the more readily available references [2–10] are included at the end of this chapter.

In the following sections of this chapter the general concepts are outlined and two examples are presented using the Committee 352 recommendations.

Construction of tapered rigid frame knee for University of Wisconsin Stadium. (Photo by C. G. Salmon.)

No attempt will be made to provide a complete theoretical treatment or to make a complete statement of the Committee 352 recommendations. The reader should make use of the Committee 352 report for design guidance until such time as rules are incorporated into the ACI Code.

11.2 Forces Acting on a Joint

Just like the members themselves, the joints need to be designed for all types of forces that may act on them: axial load, bending moment, torsion, shear, as well as effects of creep, shrinkage, temperature, or settlement of supports. Assuming that the *members* have themselves been properly designed, the critical factor in joint design is the transmission of the forces that are present at the ends of the members into and through the joint. Figure 11.2.1 shows an interior joint with beams framing into it from all sides of a column.

Referring to Fig. 11.2.2, the forces T_1 and C_1 represent negative bending in a beam framing to a joint from the right side; the forces C_2 and T_2 represent positive bending in a beam framing in from the left side; the forces V_u (col.)

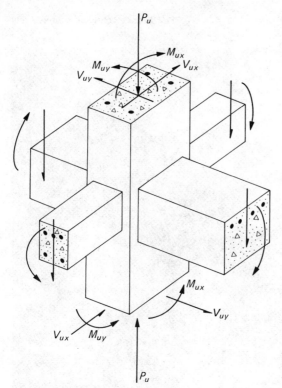

Fig. 11.2.1
Forces on members at a joint.

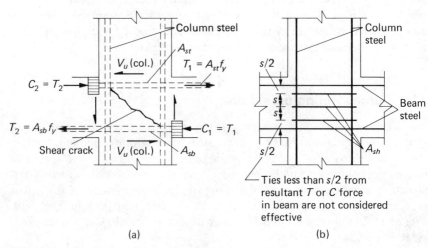

Fig. 11.2.2
Shear in a beam-to-column joint.

(a)

(b)

Ties less than $s/2$ from
resultant T or C force
in beam are not considered
effective

represent the shears in the column just outside the joint. The shear within the joint that potentially may cause the shear crack shown may be expressed

$$V_u = T_1 + T_2 - V_u \text{(col.)} \tag{11.2.1}$$

or

$$V_u = f_y A_{st} + f_y A_{sb} - V_u \text{(col.)} \tag{11.2.2}$$

After obtaining the shear V_u within the joint, that shear is divided by the effective shear area A_{cv} and by the undercapacity factor ϕ for shear to give the nominal ultimate shear stress v_n,

$$v_n = \frac{V_u}{\phi A_{cv}} \tag{11.2.3}$$

Since the forces in Eq. (11.2.1) are those due to the factored loads without reference to the undercapacity factor ϕ, it would seem that the terms $f_y A_{st}$ and $f_y A_{sb}$ in Eq. (11.2.2) should be multiplied by $\phi = 0.90$, the undercapacity factor for bending. However, ACI-ASCE Committee 352 [1] indicates that Eq. (11.2.2), as such, should be used. In this situation as described, of course, it is conservative not to use the undercapacity factor (see Sec. 3.1.1, Ref. 1) in front of the positive quantities in Eq. (11.2.2).

11.3 Confinement at a Joint

In the design or investigation of a joint, the forces in the two orthogonal directions oriented to the longitudinal axes of the horizontal members are examined separately. In that process, joint "confinement" by members transverse to the plane of the forces under consideration is an important factor in the strength of the joint. Referring to Fig. 11.3.1, the *joint core* (shown shaded) is a volume the three dimensions of which are the cross-sectional dimensions of the column and the depth of the deepest beam framing into the column. When the forces in the xz-plane are transferred through or into the joint (i.e., the forces on beam $B2$ are acting on the joint), the spandrel beams $B1$ on each side of the column provide transverse restraint on the joint core. However, the lateral restraint (confinement) provided by the spandrel beam will depend on the proportion of the face of the joint core that is covered by the spandrel beam.

In ACI-12.5.1, relating to hooks, there is provision for a 30% increase in the capacity of a hook when "enclosure is provided perpendicular to the plane of the hook." Enclosure in that context is not defined. ACI-ASCE Committee 352 [1] provides a definition of "confinement" that is specifically related to its design recommendations but could apply as well to ACI-12.5.1.

Confinement by members framing to the face of the joint core (perpendicular to the plane in which the forces are being considered) is considered sufficient if the confining member covers at least three-fourths of the width and three-fourths of the depth of the joint face (see Fig. 11.3.1).

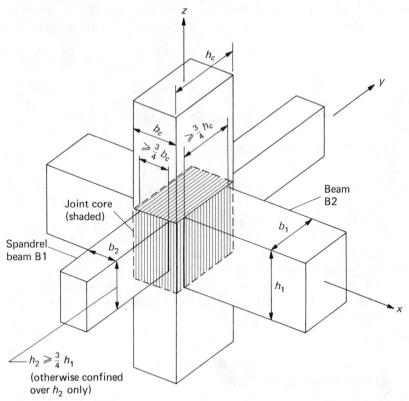

Fig. 11.3.1
Confinement at a joint.

When P_u exceeds $0.4P_b$ on a *Type 1 joint* and where it is *not* confined by a pair of members on opposite faces of the column, special transverse reinforcement should be provided as follows:

1. Where a spiral is used, the requirement is identical with ACI-10.9.3 (see Sec. 13.10),

$$\rho_s = 0.45\left(\frac{A_g}{A_c} - 1\right)\frac{f'_c}{f_y} \qquad (11.3.1)$$

2. Where rectangular hoop and cross-tie reinforcement is used, the required area is (see Fig. 11.3.2)

$$A_{sh} \geq 0.3L_h s_h \left(\frac{A_g}{A_{ch}} - 1\right)\frac{f'_c}{f_y} \qquad (11.3.2)$$

where

A_{sh} = total area of all hoop and extra cross-tie legs crossing middepth of the section in the direction considered

L_h = width, measured to outside of tie reinforcement, in the direction perpendicular to that of shear force being considered

s_h = spacing of tie reinforcement measured along column bars

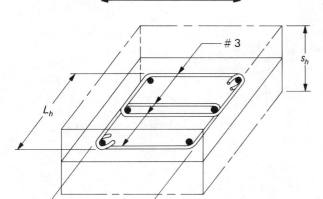

Direction of shear being considered

A_{sh} = 4(0.11) = 0.44 sq in.
L_h = out-to-out of ties
d_h = out-to-out of ties
$A_{ch} = L_h d_h$

Fig. 11.3.2
Rectangular hoop and cross-tie reinforcement in height s_h of column core.

A_g = gross area of column

A_{ch} = area of rectangular core measured to the outside of the hoop or tie

For a *Type 2 joint*, the minimum transverse reinforcement requirements of Eqs. (11.3.1) and (11.3.2) apply whether or not adequate confinement by members is provided. In addition,

$$\min \rho_s \geq 0.12 \frac{f'_c}{f_y} \qquad \text{(11.3.3)}$$

or

$$\min \frac{A_{sh}}{L_h s_h} \geq 0.12 \frac{f'_c}{f_y} \qquad \text{(11.3.4)}$$

11.4 Design Examples

Instead of completely listing all of the requirements indicated in the Committee 352 report, two examples will be presented to illustrate the recommendations as they apply to Type 1 joints used in ordinary building construction. The requirements are similar but more stringent for Type 2 joints where ductility and dissipation of energy into the inelastic range are required.

EXAMPLE 11.4.1 Design the exterior beam-column joint shown in Fig. 11.4.1. The joint is to be a Type 1 joint where strength is the primary criterion. Use $f'_c = 4000$ psi and $f_y = 60,000$ psi.

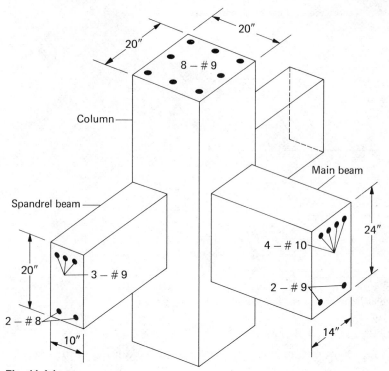

Fig. 11.4.1
Design Example 11.4.1.

Solution: (a) Examine the embedment situation for the 4-#10 bars in the main beam. From Table 6.9.1, the basic L_d required is 48.2 in. which insofar as the beam is concerned would be increased 40% to 67.5 in. for top bars. ACI-ASCE Committee 352 considers embedment into a column as ordinary development and does not consider such bars as top bars. Since the 20-in. column dimension is not enough for straight embedment, regardless of whether or not the bars are considered top bars, the use of a hook is necessary. A standard hook, according to Table 6.13.2 will provide an equivalent straight embedment of 18.3 in. for #10 top bars, or 18.3(1.33) = 24.3 in. if not considered top bars.

According to ACI-12.5.1, hook capacities may be increased 30% when "enclosure is provided perpendicular to the plane of the hook." Since enclosure may consist of external concrete or internal closed ties, spirals, or stirrups, the spandrel beams might be considered to be enclosure by external concrete. Thus, according to ACI-12.5.1, additional straight embedment required becomes:

1. For #10 top bars,

$$\text{required } L_s = 1.4[48.2 - 1.30(18.3)] = 34.2 \text{ in.}$$

2. For #10 ordinary bars,

$$\text{required } L_s = 48.2 - 1.30(24.3) = 16.6 \text{ in.}$$

The same results as shown above may be obtained without using Tables 6.9.1 and 6.13.2, as follows:

1. For #10 top bars,

$$f_h = \xi\sqrt{f'_c} = 360\sqrt{4000} = 22,800 \text{ psi}$$
$$1.3f_h = 1.3(22,800) = 29,600 \text{ psi}$$

$$\text{required } L_s = 1.4\frac{(f_y - f_h)0.04A_b}{\sqrt{f'_c}} = \frac{1.4(60,000 - 29,600)0.04(1.27)}{\sqrt{4000}} = 34.2 \text{ in.}$$

2. For #10 ordinary bars,

$$f_h = \xi\sqrt{f'_c} = 480\sqrt{4000} = 30,300 \text{ psi}$$
$$1.3f_h = 1.3(30,300) = 39,400 \text{ psi}$$

$$\text{required } L_s = \frac{(f_y - f_h)0.04A_b}{\sqrt{f'_c}} = \frac{(60,000 - 39,400)0.04(1.27)}{\sqrt{4000}} = 16.6 \text{ in.}$$

The ACI-ASCE Committee 352 (Sec. 4.2.5.2) recommends the expression developed by Marques and Jirsa [9]

$$f_h = 700(1 - 0.3d_b)\psi\sqrt{f'_c} \qquad\qquad \textbf{(11.4.1)}$$

where $\psi = 1.0$, 1.4, or 1.8.

For $\psi = 1.4$, the hook must meet the following conditions:

1. Bar size is #11 or smaller.
2. Side cover normal to the plane of the hook is not less than 2.5 in.
3. Cover on the free end extension beyond the hook is not less than 2 in., and the extension is contained within the confined core.

For $\psi = 1.8$, the hook must satisfy the requirements for $\psi = 1.4$, and, in addition, the joint must be confined by closed ties at a maximum spacing of $3d_b$ of the anchored bar.

Under item 3 above, it is not clear what is meant by requiring the free end extension to be "contained within the *confined* core." From the work of Marques and Jirsa [9] it is clear that confinement by transverse members is *not* required or necessarily related to Eq. (11.4.1). The requirements of 2.5 in. side cover and 2 in. cover on the tail extension may be sufficient to allow $\psi = 1.4$.

For this example, referring to Fig. 11.4.1, the 4-#10 bars will enter the column *inside* the column bars; thus the side cover will be (1.5 clear + 0.375 tie + 1.128, #9) 3.0 in. in the region containing the hooks. The 2-in. cover will be maintained on the tail of the hook and the hooks will be inside any hoop reinforcement that might be required. Thus for $\psi = 1.4$, Eq. (11.4.1) gives

$$f_h = 700[1 - 0.3(1.27)]1.4\sqrt{4000} = 38,400 \text{ psi}$$

which is almost up to the ACI-12.5.1 value with its 1.3 factor for non-top bars, but falls far short of its value for top bars. ACI-12.5.1 does not define "enclosure"; but common practice would have treated these 10×20 spandrel beams as "enclosure" under ACI-12.5.1.

The required lead-in straight embedment L_s computed by ACI-12.2.2, omitting the 1.4 factor for top bars,

$$L_s = \frac{0.04A_b(f_y - f_h)}{\sqrt{f'_c}}$$

$$= \frac{0.04(1.27)(60,000 - 38,400)}{\sqrt{4000}} = 17.3 \text{ in.}$$

The recommendations [1] (in Sec. 4.2.5.2) permit dividing the above L_s by ψ. Thus

$$\text{required } L_s = \frac{17.3}{1.4} = 12.4 \text{ in.}$$

significantly less than the ACI Code would currently require for non-top bars. The available straight embedment (see Fig. 11.4.2) for #10 bars with hooks is

$$\text{available } L_s = 20 - [2 + 2 + (4 + 1)1.27] = 9.7 \text{ in.} < 12.4 \text{ in.} \quad \text{NG}$$

Note that the straight embedment is measured from the *exterior face of the column steel.*

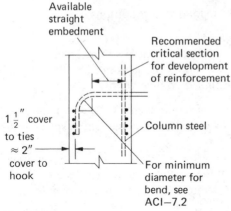

Available straight embedment

Recommended critical section for development of reinforcement

$1\frac{1}{2}''$ cover to ties

Column steel

$\approx 2''$ cover to hook

For minimum diameter for bend, see ACI–7.2

Fig. 11.4.2
Dimensions for embedment into column.

Try 5-#9 bars,

$$f_h = 700[1 - 0.3(1.128)]1.4\sqrt{4000} = 41,000 \text{ psi}$$

$$\text{required } L_s = \frac{0.04(1.0)(60,000 - 41,000)}{1.4\sqrt{4000}} = 8.6 \text{ in.}$$

$$\text{available } L_s = 20 - [2 + 2 + (4 + 1)1.128] = 10.4 \text{ in.} > 8.6 \text{ in.} \quad \text{OK}$$

(b) Examine the shear on the column to be transmitted through the joint. Referring to Fig. 11.4.3, the moment on the columns may be assumed to be zero at midheight (or, preferably, the actual moment diagram would be used).

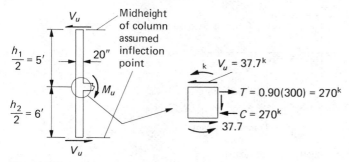

Fig. 11.4.3
Column shear at joint.

In this case, with 12-ft and 10-ft column lengths, the factored column shear times 11 ft equals the factored moment at the end of the beam.

$$V_u \text{ (for column)} \left(\frac{h_1 + h_2}{2}\right) = M_u = 0.90 \, M_n \text{ (for beam)}$$

The strength of the beam (5-#9, $d = 21.6$ in.) is

$$C = 0.85(4)(14)a = 47.6a; \qquad T = 5(1.0)60 = 300 \text{ kips}$$
$$a = 6.30 \text{ in.}$$
$$M_n = 300(21.6 - 3.15)\tfrac{1}{12} = 461 \text{ ft-kips}$$
$$M_u = 0.90(461) = 415 \text{ ft-kips}$$

$$V_u \text{ (for column)} = \frac{415}{11} = 37.7 \text{ kips}$$

Note that in cases where there is lateral loading on the building frames, V_u for column would have been obtained independently from structural analysis; and the V_u value above the joint may be different from the V_u value below the joint. The shear on the column through the joint is, in this case,

$$\text{joint } V_u = 0.90(300) - 37.7 = 232 \text{ kips}$$

The Committee 352 recommendation is

$$\text{joint } V_u = A_{st}f_y - V_u \text{ (for column)}$$
$$= (5.00)(60) - 37.7 = 262 \text{ kips}$$

The shear stress is computed as

$$v_n = \frac{\text{joint } V_u}{\phi A_{cv}} \tag{11.4.2}$$

where A_{cv} is equal to the effective cross-sectional area $b_E d$ resisting the shear (Fig. 11.4.4). For confined sections, the effective width b_E is taken to the outside of the column. For all others, the effective width b_E is measured to the outside of the ties (or the column bars if no ties are used). The effective depth d is measured to the centroid of the column steel. For this example,

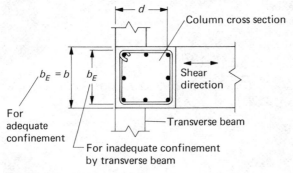

Fig. 11.4.4
Effective shear area in joint core.

the confinement requirement is not satisfied because the 10-in. width of the spandrel beam is less than three fourths of the 20-in. column width; thus

$$b_E = 20 - 2(1.5) = 17 \text{ in.}; \qquad d = 20 - 2.5 = 17.5 \text{ in.}$$

$$v_n = \frac{\text{joint } V_u}{\phi A_{cv}} = \frac{262,000}{0.85(17)(17.5)} = 748 \text{ psi}$$

The Committee 352 report [1] (Sec. 4.2.3.5) indicates the maximum shear stress permitted to be

$$\max v_n \le 20\sqrt{f'_c} = 1260 \text{ psi} > 748 \text{ psi} \qquad\qquad \text{OK}$$

The shear stress attributable to the concrete is given by ACI Formula (11-8) modified to accept a high maximum value. When a Type 1 joint is being designed for a high compressive stress in the column, Committee 352 (Sec. 4.2.3.2) gives

$$v_c = 3.5\beta\gamma\sqrt{f'_c\left(1 + \frac{N_u}{500A_g}\right)} \qquad\qquad \textbf{(11.4.3)}$$

where

$\beta = 1.4$ for a Type 1 joint and 1.0 for a Type 2 joint

$\gamma = 1.4$ if joint is adequately confined laterally by members framing in

$\quad = 1.0$ if joint is not adequately confined

For this example, N_u (includes overload factors) is the column load P_u and is given as 530 kips; thus

$$\frac{N_u}{A_g} = \frac{530,000}{20(20)} = 1325 \text{ psi}$$

The joint is not adequately confined by the spandrel beams; thus

$$v_c = 3.5(1.4)(1.0)\sqrt{4000[1 + 0.002(1325)]} = 592 \text{ psi}$$

Since $v_n > v_c$, transverse reinforcement is required.

When shear reinforcement is required, it can be designed by following ACI-11.5.6.2, except $b_w = b_E$.

$$A_v = \frac{V_s s}{f_y d} = \frac{(v_n - v_c)b_E s}{f_y}$$

$$\frac{A_v}{s} = \frac{(748 - 592)(17)}{60,000} = 0.044$$

For #3 bars, $A_v = A_s$ times number of legs $= 0.11N$. Try two legs ($N = 2$),

$$s = \frac{A_v}{0.044} = \frac{2(0.11)}{0.044} = 5 \text{ in.}$$

Try $s = 5$ in.

(c) Check minimum transverse steel according to Committee 352 (Sec. 4.2.2.2) using Eq. (11.3.2). This provision applies when $P_u > 0.4P_b$. Assume that is the case for this example.

$$A_{sh} \geq 0.3 L_h s_h \left(\frac{A_g}{A_{ch}} - 1 \right) \frac{f_c'}{f_y} \qquad \text{[11.3.2]}$$

For this example, $L_h = 20 - 3 = 17$ in., $A_g = 400$ sq in., $A_{ch} = 17(17) = 289$ sq in.

$$\frac{A_{sh}}{s_h} \geq 0.3(17) \left(\frac{400}{289} - 1 \right) \frac{4}{60} = 0.13$$

This exceeds the amount required for computed shear in part (b) and therefore the 0.13 controls. For four #4 legs,

$$s_h = \frac{4(0.20)}{0.13} = 6.2 \text{ in.}$$

Try 4-#4 legs @ 6-in. spacing.

The placement of these ties must be between the tensile force (300 kips represented by 5-#9 bars) and the compressive force (represented by concrete and the 2-#9 in the compression zone). The distance between the centroids of the bars in the two faces of the 14×24 beam is

$$d - d' \approx 21.6 - 2.5 = 19.1 \text{ in.}$$

Using a 6-in. spacing for the shear reinforcement in the core would indicate three spaces. However, shear reinforcement is not considered effective when closer to the main tension or compression reinforcement than $s/2$ (See Fig. 11.2.2b). In this case, the number of spaces is

$$N = \frac{19.1}{6} = 3.2$$

The final detail is shown in Fig. 11.4.5 with a 5-in. spacing.

It is assumed there is no computed shear in the spandrel beam direction because there are no large unbalanced moments. However, since the spandrels are not adequate to provide confinement, the 4-#4 legs need to be provided in the spandrel direction also, as shown in Fig. 11.4.5.

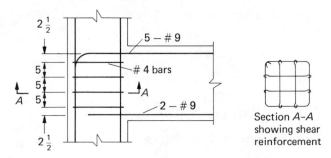

Fig. 11.4.5
Joint for Example 11.4.1.

EXAMPLE 11.4.2   For the interior joint shown schematically in Fig. 11.4.6, determine the shear reinforcement required if the joint is Type 1. Use $f'_c = 4000$ psi and $f_y = 60,000$ psi. Assume P_u of 250 kips exceeds $0.4P_b$ for the column.

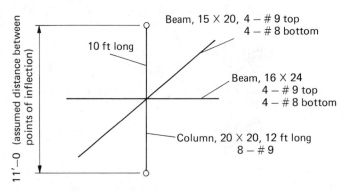

Fig. 11.4.6
Joint for Example 11.4.2.

Solution: (a) Development of reinforcement. All longitudinal steel is to be extended through the joint.

(b) Shear in direction of 16 × 24 beams. Due to lateral loading on the structure, the moments (Fig. 11.4.7a) M_{ut} and M_{ub} have the same rotational direction and give the highest shear through the joint.

The strength M_{ut} based on tension in the 4-#9 bars is

$$C = 0.85f'_c ba = 0.85(4)(16)a = 54.4a$$

$$T = 4(1.0)60 = 240 \text{ kips}$$

$$a = 4.41 \text{ in.}$$

$$M_{nt} = 240(21.5 - 2.20)\tfrac{1}{12} = 386 \text{ ft-kips}$$

$$M_{ut} = \phi M_{nt} = 0.90(386) = 347 \text{ ft-kips}$$

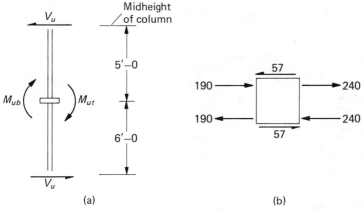

Fig. 11.4.7
Forces in direction of 16 × 24 beams, Example 11.4.2.

The strength M_{ub} based on tension in the 4-#8 bars is

$$C = 54.4a; \qquad T = 4(0.79)60 = 190 \text{ kips}$$
$$a = 3.48 \text{ in.}$$
$$M_{nb} = 190(21.5 - 1.74)\tfrac{1}{12} = 313 \text{ ft-kips}$$
$$M_{ub} = \phi M_{nb} = 0.90(313) = 282 \text{ ft-kips}$$
$$V_u \text{ (on col.)} = \frac{M_{ut} + M_{ub}}{11} = \frac{347 + 282}{11} = 57 \text{ kips}$$

The net shear through the joint (Fig. 11.4.7b) is

$$V_u = 190 + 240 - 57 = 373 \text{ kips}$$

For this joint, the 15 × 20 beams do provide confinement for shear transmitted in the direction of the 16 × 24 beams. The 15-in. width = 0.75 (20-in. column dimension) and the 20-in. depth exceeds 0.75 (24-in. beam depth). Thus confinement is provided; use $b_E = b$.

$$A_{cv} = 20(17.5) = 350 \text{ sq in.}$$
$$v_n = \frac{V_u}{\phi A_{cv}} = \frac{373,000}{0.85(350)} = 1250 \text{ psi}$$
$$\max v_n = 20\sqrt{f'_c} = 1260 \text{ psi} > 1250 \text{ psi} \qquad \text{OK}$$

The shear capacity attributable to the concrete, Eq. (11.4.3)

$$v_c = 3.5\beta\gamma\sqrt{f'_c}(1 + 0.002N_u/A_g)$$

$\beta = 1.4$ for a Type 1 joint, and $\gamma = 1.4$ since lateral confinement is available. Note also that $N_u = P_u = 250$ kips

$$v_c = 3.5(1.4)(1.4)\sqrt{4000}[1 + 0.002(250,000/400)] = 651 \text{ psi}$$
$$v_n - v_c = 1250 - 651 = 599 \text{ psi} < 15\sqrt{f'_c} \quad \text{OK (Committee 352, 4.2.3.5)}$$

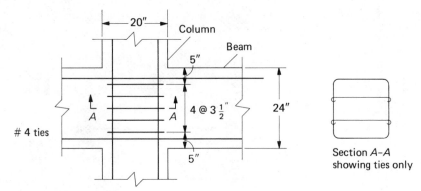

Fig. 11.4.8
Final design for Example 11.4.2.

The transverse steel required in the direction of the 16×24 beam is

$$\frac{A_v}{s} = \frac{(v_n - v_c)b_E}{f_y} = \frac{599(20)}{60,000} = 0.20$$

Try 4 legs with #4 bars,

$$s = \frac{4(0.20)}{0.20} = 4.0 \text{ in.}$$

Try $3\frac{1}{2}$-in. spacing.

(c) Minimum transverse steel requirements. Since $P_u > 0.4P_b$, use Eq. (11.3.2),

$$\frac{A_{sh}}{s_h} \geq 0.3L_h\left(\frac{A_g}{A_{ch}} - 1\right)\frac{f_c'}{f_y}$$

$$\frac{4(0.20)}{3.5} \geq 0.3(17)\left(\frac{400}{289} - 1\right)\frac{4000}{60,000}$$

$$0.23 > 0.13 \qquad\qquad\qquad \text{OK}$$

The ties are shown in Fig. 11.4.8.

(d) Shear in the direction of the 15×20 beam. If the lateral loading on the structure requires unbalanced moments in this direction, similar to the force system shown in Fig. 11.4.7, then the process illustrated in steps (b) and (c) would be repeated for this direction.

The important factors involved in the design of joints intended to resist primarily static loads (Type 1 joints) have been discussed and illustrated in two examples. For the design of Type 2 joints requiring greater ductility, the reader is referred to the Committee 352 report [1]. Other details regarding bar size and spacing limitations are also to be found in the report [1].

SELECTED REFERENCES

1. ACI-ASCE Committee 352. "Recommendations for Design of Beam-Column Joints in Monolithic Reinforced Concrete Structures," *ACI Journal, Proceedings,* **73,** July 1976, 375–393.

2. Norman W. Hanson and Harold W. Connor. "Seismic Resistance of Reinforced Concrete Beams-Columns Joints," *Journal of Structural Division*, ASCE, **93,** October 1967 (ST5), 533–560.

3. John A. Hribar and Raymond C. Vasko. "End Anchorage of High Strength Steel Reinforcing Bars," *ACI Journal, Proceedings*, **66,** November 1969, 875–883.

4. Brian Mayfield, Fung-Kew Kong, Alan Bennison, and Julian C. D. Twiston-Davies. "Corner Joint Details in Structural Lightweight Concrete," *ACI Journal, Proceedings*, **68,** May 1971, 366–372.

5. Eric F. P. Burnett and Rajendra P. Jajoo. "Reinforced Concrete Beam-Column Connections," *Journal of Structural Division*, ASCE, **97,** September 1971 (ST9), 2315–2335.

6. Brian Mayfield, Fung-Kew Kong, and Alan Bennison. "Strength and Stiffness of Lightweight Concrete Corners," *ACI Journal, Proceedings*, **69,** July 1972, 420–427.

7. John Minor and James O. Jirsa. "Behavior of Bent Bar Anchorages," *ACI Journal, Proceedings*, **72,** April 1975, 141–149.

8. James K. Wight and Mete A. Sozen. "Strength Decay of Reinforced Concrete Columns under Shear Reversals," *Journal of Structural Division*, ASCE, **101,** May 1975 (ST5), 1053–1065.

9. Jose G. L. Marques and James O. Jirsa. "A Study of Hooked Bar Anchorages in Beam-Column Joints," *ACI Journal, Proceedings*, **72,** May 1975, 198–209.

10. Ingvar H. E. Nilsson and Anders Losberg. "Reinforced Concrete Corners and Joints Subjected to Bending Moment," *Journal of Structural Division*, ASCE, **102,** June 1976 (ST6), 1229–1254.

PROBLEMS

All problems are to be worked using the ACI Code and the recommendations of ACI Committee 352 [1].

11.1 Check the anchorage of bars and determine the shear reinforcement for the exterior beam-column joint of the accompanying figure. Assume lateral loading provides the critical condition at the joint; assume columns bent in double curvature with an inflection point at midheight. Consider as a Type 1 joint and use $f'_c = 4000$ psi and $f_y = 60,000$ psi. Show detail of shear reinforcement in joint.

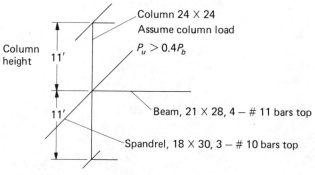

Prob. 11.1

11.2 Repeat Prob. 11.1 except consider the column to be 18 in. square, the spandrel 14 × 24 with 3-#9, and the beam 18 × 28 with 4-#10 bars.

11.3 Repeat Prob. 11.1 except consider the joint to be an interior one with the 21 × 28 beam on both sides of the column. The spandrel then becomes an interior beam. Assume the 21 × 28 beam has 4-#9 in the bottom in addition to the bars in the top and that all bars are continuous through the column. The 18 × 30 beam has 3-#9 in the bottom in addition to the top bars, all bars being continuous through the column. The critical loading condition for the joint is with clockwise moments from the 21 × 28 beam acting on the joint at both sides of the column.

12

Retaining Walls

12.1 Types of Retaining Structures

Retaining structures hold back soil or other loose material and prevent its assuming the natural angle of repose at locations where an abrupt change in ground elevation occurs. The retained material exerts a push on a structure and thus tends to overturn or slide it or both. There may be several types of retaining structures (Fig. 12.1.1) as follows.

1. Gravity Wall. A gravity wall is usually of plain concrete and depends entirely on its weight for stability. It is used for walls up to about 10 ft high.

2. Cantilever Retaining Wall. The cantilever is the most common type of retaining structure and is used for walls in the range of 10 to 25 ft in height. The stem, heel, and toe of such a wall each acts as a cantilever beam.

3. Counterfort Wall. In the counterfort wall the stem and slab are tied together by counterforts, which are transverse walls spaced at intervals and act as tension ties to support the stem wall. Counterfort walls are often economical for heights over about 25 ft.

4. Buttress Wall. A buttress wall is similar to a counterfort wall except that the transverse support walls are located on the side of the stem opposite to the retained material and act as compression struts. Buttresses, as compression elements, are more efficient than the tension counterforts and are economical in the same height range. A counterfort is more widely used

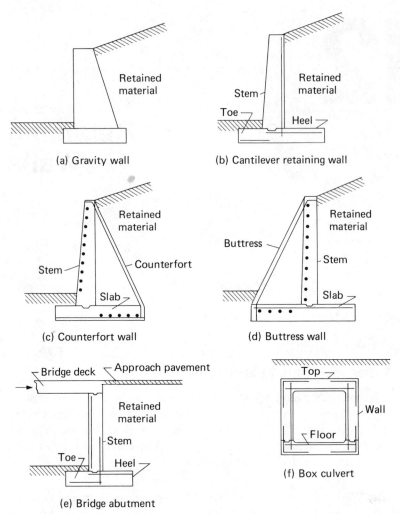

(a) Gravity wall

(b) Cantilever retaining wall

(c) Counterfort wall

(d) Buttress wall

(e) Bridge abutment

(f) Box culvert

Fig. 12.1.1
Types of retaining walls.

than a buttress because the counterfort is hidden beneath the retained material whereas the buttress occupies what may otherwise be usable space in front of the wall.

5. Bridge Abutment. A wall-type bridge abutment acts similarly to a cantilever retaining wall except that the bridge deck provides an additional horizontal restraint at the top of the stem. Thus this abutment is designed as a beam fixed at the bottom and simply supported or partially restrained at the top.

6. Box Culvert. The box culvert, with either single or multiple cells, acts as a closed rigid frame that must not only resist lateral earth pressure but also vertical load from either the soil that it supports or from both the soil and the highway vehicle loads.

12.2 Forces on Retaining Walls

The magnitude and direction of the earth pressure that tends to overturn and slide a retaining wall may be determined by applying the principles of soil mechanics. Excellent texts are available, such as those of Terzaghi and Peck [1] and of Huntington [2], for any extensive study of how to determine the soil pressure to be used in any given situation; thus only a brief summary is provided in this chapter.

The pressure exerted by the retained material is proportional to the distance below the earth surface and to its unit weight. Analogous to the action of a fluid, the unit pressure p at a distance h below the earth surface may be expressed

$$p = Cwh \qquad (12.2.1)$$

where w is the unit weight of the soil and C is a coefficient that depends on the physical properties of the soil. It is the factor C that causes difficulty to designers because it may vary from about 0.3 for loose granular soil to perhaps 1.0 for wet clay.

The factors that may affect the pressure on a wall are as follows:

1. Type of backfill used.
2. Seasonal condition of the backfill material, such as wet, dry, or frozen.
3. Drainage of backfill material.
4. Possibility of backfill overload, such as trucks and equipment near the wall.
5. Degree of care exercised in backfilling.
6. Degree of rotational restraint between various components of the retaining structure.
7. Possibility of vibration in the vicinity of the wall (especially in the case of granular soil).
8. Type of material beneath the footing of the retaining structure.
9. Level of the water table.

Probably the most important single factor is that water must be prevented from accumulating in the backfill material. Walls are rarely designed to retain saturated material, which means that proper drainage must be provided.

When vehicles may travel near and exert their loads or when buildings are constructed near the top of a retaining wall, the lateral pressure against such a wall is increased. In the case of a fixed static load such as a building, the weight of the building can be converted into an additional height (surcharge) of backfill soil material. The effect of a highway or railroad passing over the retained material near the wall causes a dynamic reaction that cannot accurately be converted into a static effect. However, the AASHTO highway bridge specification (Sec. 1.2.19) [3] and the AREA railroad retaining wall specification [4] prescribe an equivalent static surcharge corresponding to a number of additional feet of backfill material.

12.3 Earth Pressure Theories

Since the best backfill against a retaining structure is well-drained cohesionless material (sand and gravel), that is the condition usually specified in design. Although it is true that clay (cohesive material) will frequently exert, under ordinary moist conditions, less pressure against a wall than sand or gravel, under saturated conditions it becomes soft and behaves much as a fluid. Furthermore, some clays are expansive and exert greater pressures than cohesionless material. Drained granular material offers the most reliable situation.

Coulomb Theory. In 1776, Coulomb published the earliest rational solution to the problem of earth pressure against a wall [5]. He considered the *active pressure* against a surface to be the result of the tendency of a wedge of earth to slide against a wall, as shown in Fig. 12.3.1a. The weight W of the wedge of earth is held in equilibrium by the forces P_a and R. The failure plane will assume an angle such that the active pressure force required of the wall is a maximum. In order for the wedge to slide and exert this pressure, the wall must yield or deflect a small amount away from the retained earth. Further, it is assumed that the soil slides along the back of the wall, which requires that it be a plane surface. Thus Coulomb's assumptions require a wedge having a pressure surface (AB of Fig. 12.3.1a) along one side and a failure surface (CB of Fig. 12.3.1a) along the other. In fact the failure surface is curved rather than straight. For active pressure the assumption involves negligible error. Coulomb's equation for *active pressure*, referring to Fig. 12.3.1a, may be written

$$P_a = \frac{wh^2}{2} \frac{\sin^2(\theta - \alpha)}{\sin^2\theta \sin(\theta + \beta)\left[1 + \sqrt{\dfrac{\sin(\alpha + \beta)\sin(\alpha - \delta)}{\sin(\theta + \beta)\sin(\theta - \delta)}}\right]^2} \quad \textbf{(12.3.1)}$$

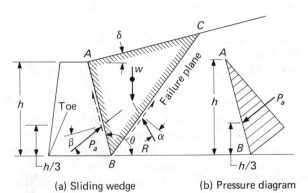

(a) Sliding wedge   (b) Pressure diagram

Fig. 12.3.1
Coulomb theory for active pressure.

where

θ = angle of the pressure surface measured counterclockwise from the horizontal

α = angle of internal friction of the soil

β = angle of friction along the pressure surface (often taken to be that between soil and concrete

δ = angle of retained material with the horizontal

w = unit weight of the retained material

h = vertical projection of the pressure surface

In general, Eq. (12.3.1) may be written

$$P_a = C_a \frac{wh^2}{2} \qquad (12.3.2)$$

and C_a may be referred to as the coefficient of active pressure. When the pressure surface is vertical ($\theta = 90°$) and the friction on that surface is such that $\beta = \delta$, the C_a portion of Eq. (12.3.1) becomes

$$C_a = \cos \delta \left(\frac{\cos \delta - \sqrt{\cos^2 \delta - \cos^2 \alpha}}{\cos \delta + \sqrt{\cos^2 \delta - \cos^2 \alpha}} \right) \qquad (12.3.3)$$

Furthermore, if the backfill is level ($\delta = 0$), the coefficient of active pressure becomes

$$C_a = \frac{1 - \sin \alpha}{1 + \sin \alpha} \qquad (12.3.4)$$

A derivation of Eq. (12.3.1) has been given in considerable detail by Ketchum [7] and in a somewhat abbreviated form by Huntington [2].

Rankine Theory. W. J. M. Rankine presented a theory of earth pressure [6] differing somewhat from that of Coulomb. Rankine's theory applies to a homogeneous incompressible cohesionless soil. The *active pressure* is brought about by considering a lateral expansion of elemental strips in the wedge (Fig. 12.3.2) which are parallel to the earth surface. This lateral

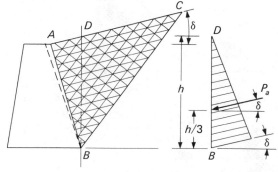

Fig. 12.3.2
Rankine theory for active pressure.

expansion may result from a deflection of surface AB, with the soil moving forward with the back of the wall and not slipping along it. This lateral expansion causes shear planes to develop along AB and CB of Fig. 12.3.2 as well as along the diagonals within the wedge. The Rankine active state of stress is that existing on a vertical plane DB within the soil mass. The Rankine and Coulomb theories yield identical results, Eqs. (12.3.3) and (12.3.4), for a vertical wall when the soil pressure on the vertical plane is assumed to be parallel to the earth surface.

Both Coulomb and Rankine also developed expressions for *passive pressure*—that is, the resistance offered by the soil to an object pushing against it. In such a case the coefficient of passive pressure C_p replaces C_a in Eq. (12.3.2), and the expressions for C_p corresponding to those for C_a in Eqs. (12.3.3) and (12.3.4) become

$$C_p = \cos \delta \left(\frac{\cos \delta + \sqrt{\cos^2 \delta - \cos^2 \alpha}}{\cos \delta - \sqrt{\cos^2 \delta - \cos^2 \alpha}} \right) \qquad (12.3.5)$$

and for $\delta = 0$,

$$C_p = \frac{1 + \sin \alpha}{1 - \sin \alpha} \qquad (12.3.6)$$

12.4 Practical Treatment of Active Soil Pressure

The active soil pressure can, in general, be expressed by

$$P_a = C_a \frac{wh^2}{2} \qquad [12.3.2]$$

where $C_a w$ may be thought of as the density of an equivalent fluid, which depends on the unit weight w of the retained material, the effective angle of internal friction α, and the slope of the backfill δ. As an aid for many common situations, typical values for unit weight and effective internal friction angles are given in Table 12.4.1. Even for clay soils there is widespread practice of estimating an effective α and computing pressures by means of the Coulomb or Rankine formulas, rather than by determining a cohesion value and applying more exact methods.

Table 12.4.1
Ordinary Values for Unit Weight and Internal Friction Angle

Backfill Material	Unit Weight, w(pcf)	Effective Internal Friction Angle, α (degrees)
Soft clay	95–120	0–10
Medium clay	100–120	15–30
Sand and gravel (low permeability)	120–130	25–35
Sand and gravel (high permeability)	110–120	30–40

The active pressure on frictionless vertical walls with level backfill is horizontal in direction and C_a may be computed from the Rankine–Coulomb equation (12.3.4). This formula is valid when the top of the wall can move outward, either by cantilever deflection or by rotation of the entire structure about the toe. The required deflection may practically always be expected to occur.

In a more general situation involving combinations of sloping backfill, surcharge, inclined pressure surface, and friction between the soil and the back of the wall, the Coulomb sliding wedge method should be used. In this case the failure plane that gives the maximum active soil pressure can be obtained by trial and error [2].

12.5 Stability Requirements

The first step in retaining wall design is to establish the proportions such that the stability of the structure (see Fig. 12.5.1) under the action of earth forces is assured. Three requirements must be satisfied: (a) the overturning moment $P_{ah}(h'/3)$ must be more than balanced by the resisting moment $Wx_1 + P_{av}l$, so that an adequate factor of safety against overturning is provided, usually about 2.0; (b) sufficient frictional resistance F in combination with any reliable passive resistance P_p against the toe must provide an adequate factor of safety (usually 1.5) against sliding caused by P_{ah}; and (c) the base width l must be adequate to distribute the load R to the foundation soil without causing excessive settlement or rotation.

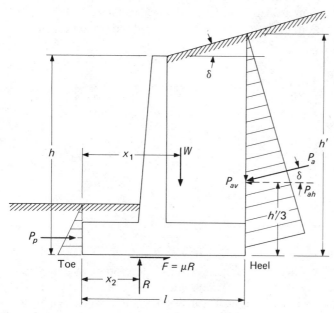

Fig. 12.5.1

Forces on retaining wall—Rankine pressure.

Typically, referring to the Rankine pressure distribution of Fig. 12.5.1, the overturning factor of safety (FS) would be computed

$$\text{FS} = \frac{\text{resisting moment}}{\text{overturning moment}} = \frac{Wx_1 + P_{av}l}{P_{ah}(h'/3)} \qquad (12.5.1)$$

or, perhaps more frequently, neglecting the vertical component of P_a,

$$\text{FS} = \frac{Wx_1}{P_{ah}(h'/3)} \qquad (12.5.2)$$

where W represents the weight of the concrete wall and footing and of the soil resting on the footing.

On the other hand, referring to the Coulomb wedge of Fig. 12.3.1, it may be noted that the resultant force P_a may act on a line that passes to the right of the toe and therefore does not tend to overturn the wall. When the resisting moment of the vertical component of the Rankine active pressure is neglected, the two theories will provide roughly the same overturning factor of safety.

The factor of safety against sliding may be computed, using the notation of Fig. 12.5.1,

$$\text{FS} = \frac{\mu R + P_p}{P_{ah}} \qquad (12.5.3)$$

where μ is the coefficient of friction between the soil and the footing. Table 12.5.1 gives the coefficients of friction as recommended by the 1958 AREA specification [4] and these may serve as a guide to typical values in lieu of more accurate ones. Huntington [2] suggests that when $\tan \alpha < \mu$, the angle of internal friction α of the soil be used, because failure will actually occur in the material rather than between the soil and the concrete.

Table 12.5.1
Values of Coefficient of Friction between
Soil and Concrete, 1958 AREA
Specifications

Soil	μ
Coarse-grained soils (without silt)	0.55
Coarse-grained soils (with silt)	0.45
Silt	0.35
Sound rock (with rough surface)	0.60

The inclusion of some passive resistance P_p on the toe of the footing may or may not be justified. Certainly, to actually develop passive pressure in the soil in front of the wall, the concrete must have been placed without using forms for the toe and without disturbing the soil against which the concrete is placed.

Referring to Fig. 12.5.2, the ordinary passive resistance against the toe is

$$P_{p1} = \tfrac{1}{2}C_p w h_1^2 \tag{12.5.4}$$

but frequently is neglected, and in nearly all cases at least the value of h_1 is reduced under the assumption that during construction, or after, the earth surface cannot be expected to remain undisturbed at its final designated elevation. If when all reliable resistances have been included, the factor of safety remains inadequate, a base key (Fig. 12.5.2) may be used. Essentially, the base key, when placed in an unformed excavation against undisturbed material, may be expected to develop an additional passive force P_{p2} and shift the possible failure plane from line 1 to line 2.

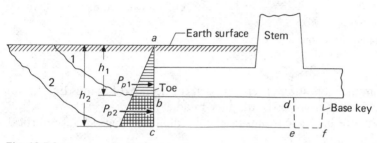

Fig. 12.5.2
Passive resistance and effect of base key.

The base key develops the additional resistance

$$P_{p2} = \tfrac{1}{2}C_p w(h_2^2 - h_1^2) \tag{12.5.5}$$

and also, an inert region, *bced* of Fig. 12.5.2, is created which moves the friction plane from *bd* to *ce*. Thus the frictional force developed along *ce* is based on the internal friction angle α, rather than on the friction angle between soil and concrete. Normally, $\tan\alpha > \mu$ for granular material, so that, by making the base key sufficiently deep to create an inert block, additional frictional resistance is developed.

Finally, the magnitude and distribution of the soil pressure requires investigation. Usual practice is to require the resultant vertical force R to be inside the middle third of the footing for sand and gravel subbases and within the middle half for rock subbase. In addition, the maximum pressure may not exceed the allowable value. Comments regarding allowable bearing capacity as well as some typical safe bearing values are to be found in Chap. 20.

Referring to Fig. 12.5.3a, when the entire footing is under compression, the basic equation for combined bending and axial compression acting on a 1-ft strip along the wall is

$$p = \frac{R}{l} \pm \frac{Re(l/2)}{l^3/12} = \frac{R}{l}\left(1 \pm \frac{6e}{l}\right) \tag{12.5.6}$$

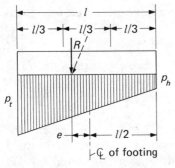

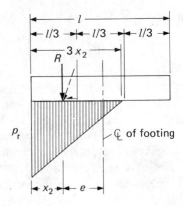

(a) Resultant within middle third

(b) Resultant outside middle third

Fig. 12.5.3
Soil pressure distribution.

For the limiting condition of zero stress at the heel, $e = l/6$; thus Eq. (12.5.6) is valid for all positions of R within the middle third.

When the resultant R is outside the middle third (Fig. 12.5.3b), vertical force equilibrium requires

$$R = \tfrac{1}{2}p_t(3x_2)$$

$$p_t = \frac{2R}{3x_2} \tag{12.5.7}$$

for $0 < 3x_2 < l$.

12.6 Preliminary Proportioning of Cantilever Walls

To begin the design it is necessary to apply certain "rules" along with an approximate use of statics and estimate such dimensions as the length and thickness of the base footing and the relative position of the wall with respect to the footing.

Height of Wall. Since the bottom of the footing must be below the frost penetration depth, say 3 to 4 ft in the northern United States, the overall height equals the desired difference in elevation plus the frost penetration depth.

Position of Stem on the Base Footing. The following demonstration using approximate statics will show that the front face of the wall should coincide with the desired position of the resultant soil pressure beneath the base. Take the most typical situation of a vertical wall with level backfill, as shown in Fig. 12.6.1. Assume an average unit weight w for all material (concrete and earth) enclosed within $abcd$ and neglect entirely the concrete in the toe. Thus

$$R = W = wh\gamma l$$

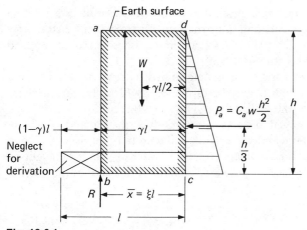

Fig. 12.6.1
Data for economical proportioning of wall.

Satisfying rotational equilibrium about the heel,

$$P_a \frac{h}{3} + W \frac{\gamma l}{2} = R\xi l$$

$$C_a \frac{wh^2}{2}\left(\frac{h}{3}\right) + wh\gamma l \frac{\gamma l}{2} = wh\gamma l(\xi l)$$

Solving for l/h gives

$$\frac{l}{h} = \sqrt{\frac{C_a}{3\gamma(2\xi - \gamma)}} \qquad (12.6.1)$$

The variable ξ must be selected by the designer, based on the type of soil and desired pressure distribution. For good granular soil and acceptance of a triangular pressure distribution with the resultant at the outer edge of the middle third, $\xi = \frac{2}{3}$. For clay where a uniform distribution might be desired, ξ would be $\frac{1}{2}$.

Minimizing the l/h in Eq. (12.6.1) such that the base width is a minimum,

$$\gamma = \xi \qquad (12.6.2)$$

Thus the front face of the wall should line up with the desired position of the soil pressure resultant.

Length of Base. A preliminary value for the length of base may be obtained by the direct application of static moments with respect to point b in Fig. 12.6.1, employing the same assumptions that underlie Eq. (12.6.1). By this direct process a more exact result may be obtained since one could easily estimate the stem thickness and footing thickness as fractions of l or of h.

Thickness of Footing. The base thickness is usually 7 to 10% of the total height h, with a minimum of about 1 ft. It should be about equal to the base thickness of the stem.

Thickness of Stem. The thickness at the top of the wall is arbitrary; however, cover requirements and construction constraints will dictate how thin it may be. Generally 10 or 12 in. minimum is preferred, though no minimum is prescribed by the ACI Code.

The base thickness of the stem is determined as required for bending moment and shear, though it may be estimated as 12 to 16% of the base width or 10 to 12% of the wall height. The stem thickness should not be too skimpy, since a thin wall deflects considerably at the top and savings in reinforcement due to larger effective depth will tend to offset the cost of any extra concrete used. It is recommended that a batter of $\frac{1}{4}$ in./ft of height be provided on the front face to offset deflection or forward tilting of the structure.

12.7 Design Example—Cantilever Retaining Wall

It is required to design a cantilever retaining wall to support a bank of earth 16 ft high above the final level of earth at the toe of the wall. The backfill is to be level, but a building is to be built on the fill. Assume that an 8 ft surcharge will approximate the lateral earth pressure effect. Data: weight of retained material = 120 pcf; angle of internal friction = 35°; coefficient of friction between masonry and soil = 0.40; f'_c = 3000 psi; f_y = 40,000 psi; maximum soil pressure = 5 ksf (kips per square foot). Use the strength method of the ACI Code.

(a) Equivalent fluid pressure. The Rankine-Coulomb Eq. (12.3.4) is applied here for simplicity,

$$C_a = \frac{1 - \sin \alpha}{1 + \sin \alpha} = \frac{0.426}{1.574} = 0.271$$

Equivalent fluid density, $C_a w = 0.271(120) = 32.5$ pcf.

(b) Basic design data. For adequate deflection control on the cantilever wall, choose to use a reinforcement percentage ρ about one-half the maximum permitted by the ACI Code. Choose

$$\rho \approx 0.375\rho_b = 0.0139 \qquad \text{(Table 3.5.1)}$$

This corresponds to $R_u = 495$ psi.

(c) Height of wall. Allowing 4 ft for frost penetration to the bottom of the footing in front of the wall, the total height becomes

$$h = 16 \text{ ft} + 4 \text{ ft} = 20 \text{ ft}$$

(d) Thickness of footing. The thickness may be estimated at this stage of design to be 7 to 10% of the overall height h. Assume a uniform footing thickness, $t = 2$ ft (about 10% of h).

(e) Base length. One could determine the base length by considering the equilibrium of factored loads (using the factor 1.7 for the horizontal earth pressure and using 0.9 for the earth and concrete weight); this practice will give a conservative result. However, it seems within the intent of the ACI

Code to establish base dimensions for foundation structures using actual unfactored loads (see ACI-15.2.4).

Using a 1-ft length of wall and letting the unit weight of material bounded by points a, b, c, and d in Fig. 12.7.1 equal 120 pcf,

$$P_1 = 0.260(20)(1) = 5.2 \text{ kips}$$
$$P_2 = \tfrac{1}{2}(0.650)(20)(1) = 6.5 \text{ kips}$$
$$W = 0.120(20 + 8)x = 3.36x \text{ kips}$$

Summation of moments about point b gives

$$W\left(\frac{x}{2}\right) = P_1(10.0) + P_2(6.67)$$

$$\frac{3.36x^2}{2} = 5.2(10.0) + 6.5(6.67)$$

$$1.68x^2 = 95.3$$

$$x = 7.53 \text{ ft}$$

Since for this granular material the resultant soil pressure is desired to be at the outer edge of the middle third of the footing,

$$\text{base length} = 1.5x = 1.5(7.53) = 11.3 \text{ ft}$$

Try 11 ft 3 in.

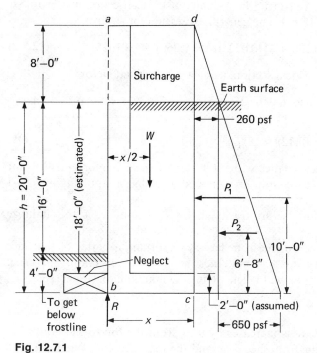

Fig. 12.7.1
Preliminary proportioning for cantilever wall in design example.

(f) Stem thickness. Prior to computing soil pressures and stability factors of safety, a more accurate knowledge of the concrete dimensions is necessary. The thickness of the base of the stem is selected with due regard for the bending moment and shear requirements.

Bending moment will normally provide the governing criterion, for which the general expression (y measured from the top of the wall) is

$$M_y = \frac{0.260y^2}{2} + \frac{0.0325y^3}{6} = 0.130y^2 + 0.00541y^3 \qquad (12.7.1)$$

At the bottom of the assumed 18-ft high stem wall, using a 1.7 overload factor,

$$M_u = 1.7[0.130(18)^2 + 0.00541(18)^3] = 1.7(42.1 + 31.6) = 125 \text{ ft-kips}$$

For a desired $R_u = 495$ psi,

$$\text{required } d = \sqrt{\frac{M_u}{\phi R_u b}} = \sqrt{\frac{125(12,000)}{0.90(495)12}} = 16.8 \text{ in.}$$

Total thickness $= 16.8 + 2$ (cover) $+ 0.5$ (estimated bar radius) $= 19.3$ in. Try 21 in. for the stem base thickness and select 12 in. as the practical minimum for the top of the wall. Note that the selected R_u of 495 psi is a *chosen* guideline value and need not be rigidly adhered to. In this case the 3-in. multiple of 12 in. is preferred to the computed value of 20 in.

The critical section for shear strength is taken at a distance d from the bottom of the stem (ACI-11.1.3.1). Assume the critical section at $y = 16.5$ ft ($d =$ approximately 18 in.). The general expression for shear is

$$V_y = 0.260y + \tfrac{1}{2}(0.0325)y^2 = 0.260y + 0.01625y^2 \qquad (12.7.2)$$

At the approximate critical section, using a 1.7 overload factor

$$V_u = 1.7[0.260(16.5) + 0.01625(16.5)^2] = 1.7(4.29 + 4.42) = 14.8 \text{ kips}$$
$$\phi V_c = \phi(2\sqrt{f'_c})bd$$
$$= 0.85(2\sqrt{3000})(12)(\approx 18)\tfrac{1}{1000} = 20.1 \text{ kips} > 14.8 \text{ kips} \qquad \text{OK}$$

Since $V_u < \phi V_c$, in accordance with ACI-11.5.5.1 shear reinforcement is not required for slabs. The cantilever is treated as a slab in applying any ACI Code limitations.

This thickness will be arbitrarily made 21 in. in order to minimize deflection.

Where appearance on the front face is important, a batter of that face should be provided so as to counteract the effect of deflection. The usual batter is about $\frac{1}{4}$ in./ft of wall height. Thus the minimum batter here is

$$\tfrac{1}{4}(18) = 4\tfrac{1}{2} \text{ in.}$$

In this case the thickness increases by 9 in. from the top to the bottom of the wall, so batter the front face 5 in. and the rear face 4 in. When the wall is in place, it will deflect forward and become nearly vertical; therefore the analysis from this point will consider the front face to be vertical.

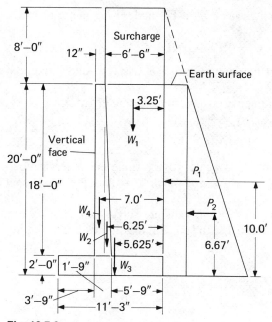

Fig. 12.7.2
Dimensions for computing resultant soil pressure in
design example.

(g) Factor of safety against overturning. Using the dimensions given in
Fig. 12.7.2, locate the resultant of vertical forces (without overload factors)
with respect to the heel, as in Table 12.7.1:

Table 12.7.1

Force	Arm	Moment
$W_1 = 0.120(18 + 8)(6.5) = 20.3$	3.25	66
$W_2 = 0.030(\frac{1}{2})(18)(0.75) = 0.2$	6.25	1
$W_3 = 0.150(11.25)(2.0) = 3.4$	5.63	19
$W_4 = 0.150(1.0)(18) = 2.7$	7.00	19
Totals	26.6	105

$$\text{resultant, from heel} = \frac{105}{26.6} = 3.95 \text{ ft}$$

$$\text{resisting moment} = 26.6(11.25 - 3.95) = 194 \text{ ft-kips}$$

$$\text{overturning moment} = P_1(10) + P_2(6.67)$$
$$= 5.2(10) + 6.5(6.67)$$
$$= 95.3 \text{ ft-kips}$$

$$\text{FS against overturning} = \frac{194}{95.3} = 2.03 > 2.0 \qquad \text{OK}$$

Alternatively, if the stability check is to be made using factored loads, according to ACI-9.2.4,

$$U = 0.9D + 1.7H$$

where H is the horizontal earth pressure. In such a case, it would be required that

$$\text{resisting moment} \geq \text{overturning moment}$$

$$0.9(194) \geq 1.7(95.3)$$

$$175 \geq 162 \qquad\qquad \text{OK}$$

In effect the required factor of safety against overturning under service-load conditions is $1.7/0.9 = 1.89$, which is not much less than the traditional value of 2.0.

(h) Location of resultant and footing soil pressures. Referring to Fig. 12.7.3, and using service loads because the maximum soil pressure limitation is given for that condition,

$$R = 26.6 \text{ kips}$$

$$\bar{x} = \frac{105 + 95.3}{26.6} = 7.53 \text{ ft}$$

$$e = 7.53 - \frac{11.25}{2} = 1.91 \text{ ft}$$

$$\frac{6e}{\text{base length}} = \frac{6(1.91)}{11.25} = 1.02 > 1.0$$

The resultant lies 0.36 in. outside of the middle third; however, it is very close, and the limiting condition of zero stress at the heel is considered adequate.

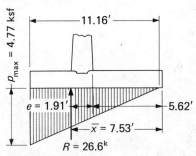

Fig. 12.7.3
Soil pressure and location of resultant
under service load in design example.

The service-load soil pressure diagram is a triangle; thus

$$R = \tfrac{1}{2}(p_{\max})(\text{effective base length})$$

$$26.6 = \tfrac{1}{2}(p_{\max})(11.25 - 7.53)(3)$$

$$p_{\max} = 4.77 \text{ ksf} < 5 \text{ ksf} \qquad\qquad \text{OK}$$

(i) Factor of safety against sliding. Neglecting passive pressure against the toe of the footing and using service loads,

$$\text{force causing sliding} = P_1 + P_2 = 5.2 + 6.5 = 11.7 \text{ kips}$$
$$\text{frictional force} = \mu R = 0.40(26.6) = 10.6 \text{ kips}$$
$$\text{factor of safety} = \frac{10.6}{11.7} = 0.91 < 1.5 \qquad \text{NG}$$

Sliding resistance may also be checked using factored loads, $U = 0.9D + 1.7H$, in which case it is required that

$$\text{resisting force} \geq \text{sliding force}$$
$$0.9(10.6) \geq 1.7(11.7)$$
$$9.55 \text{ kips} < 19.9 \text{ kips} \qquad \text{NG}$$

Thus ACI-9.2.4 would require the same factor of safety against sliding as against overturning, that is, $1.7/0.9 = 1.89$. This exceeds the traditional factor to resist sliding of 1.5.

Since the resistance provided does not give an adequate safety factor, a key (Figs. 12.7.4 and 12.7.5) against sliding is required. Such a key is intended to develop passive pressure in the region in front of and below the bottom of the footing. The procedure for determining the required size of a key is one that is debated by designers. Generally it seems desirable to place the front face of the key about 5 in. in front of the back face of the stem. This will permit anchoring the stem reinforcement in the key.

With full realization of the tendency of practitioners to try to oversimplify this problem, various procedures may reasonably be used for granular cohesionless materials. The maximum effect of a key would be to develop the passive resistance over the depth BC of Fig. 12.7.4, with any resulting failure occurring along a curved path such as $C'C$. Fisher and Mains [8] have advocated the inert-block concept of frictional resistance. In this method, any key used must be extended deep enough below the footing to develop an inert block of soil, $BCDE$ of Fig. 12.7.5; it will then have a failure plane approximately as $C'CDGFH$, so that the passive resistance is developed

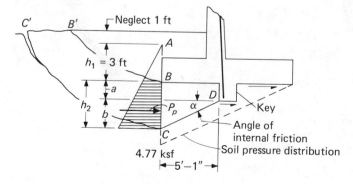

Fig. 12.7.4
Passive resistance concept of frictional resistance.

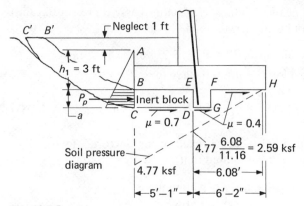

Fig. 12.7.5
Inert block concept of frictional resistance.

over only the depth BC. In determining the passive resistance, the top 1 ft of overburden is usually neglected in the head h_1, of Fig. 12.7.4 or Fig. 12.7.5.

For this design, a factor of safety of 1.5 against sliding under service loads has been considered proper. When passive resistance against the toe is also included, a higher factor of safety, say 2.0, should be used.

Using the inert-block concept, the passive force P_p developed over the distance BC of Fig. 12.7.5 is

$$\text{equivalent fluid pressure} = C_p w = \frac{w}{C_a} = \frac{120}{0.271} = 443 \text{ pcf}$$

$$P_p = \frac{0.443(h_1 + a)^2}{2} - \frac{0.443(h_1)^2}{2}$$

which for $h_1 = 3$ ft gives

$$P_p = 0.222(6a + a^2)$$

By inducing an inert block, the frictional coefficient over the region CD becomes $\tan \alpha = \tan 35° = 0.7$, while the coefficient of 0.40 applies on DG and FH. Thus the frictional resistance

$$F = \mu_1 R_1 + \mu_2 R_2$$
$$= 0.7(\tfrac{1}{2})(4.77 + 2.59)(5.08) + 0.4(\tfrac{1}{2})(2.59)(6.08)$$
$$= 13.1 + 3.15 = 16.2 \text{ kips}$$

Force equilibrium, incorporating a 1.5 factor of safety, gives

$$(P_1 + P_2)1.5 = P_p + F$$
$$11.7(1.5) = 0.222(6a + a^2) + 16.2$$
$$a^2 + 6a - 6.1 = 0$$
$$a = 0.9 \text{ ft}$$

Neglecting the frictional force in front of the key and considering the passive resistance developed below the toe as shown in Fig. 12.7.4, the depth of key required may be computed as

$$b = 5.08 \tan \alpha = 5.08(0.7) = 3.55 \text{ ft}$$

$$P_p = 0.443 \frac{(h_1 + a + b)^2}{2} - \frac{0.443(h_1)^2}{2}$$

$$= 0.222(a^2 + 13.1a + 33.9)$$

Force equilibrium, using a 1.5 safety factor, gives

$$(P_1 + P_2)1.5 = P_p + \mu_2 R_2$$
$$11.7(1.5) = 0.222(a^2 + 13.1a + 33.9) + 0.4(\tfrac{1}{2})(2.59)(6.08)$$
$$a^2 + 13.1a - 31.0 = 0$$
$$a = 2.0 \text{ ft}$$

This would indicate that the latter method is more conservative. The *CRSI Handbook* (Chap. 8, Ref. 4) arbitrarily uses a key whose depth equals two-thirds of the footing thickness. With this discussion and these computations to serve as a guide, make the key depth 18 in. The key may be made square; use 1 ft 6 in. × 1 ft 6 in. Reinforcement will rarely be required, but it is common practice to extend some of the stem steel down into the key.

(j) Design of heel cantilever. The loads considered are included in Fig. 12.7.6, where the effect of the base key is neglected.

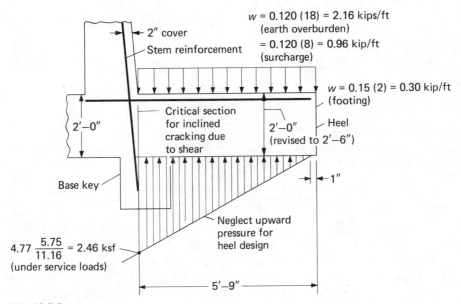

Fig. 12.7.6
Design of heel cantilever in design example.

For bending moment, the critical section is taken at the center of the stem steel. It seems that any possible plane of weakness will occur at the stem steel rather than at the face of support. Thus the downward uniform loading due to earth overburden, surcharge, and footing concrete using an overload factor of 1.4 for the earth and footing concrete and 1.7 for the surcharge is, from Fig. 12.7.6,

$$w_u = 1.4(2.16 + 0.30) + 1.7(0.96) = 5.08 \text{ kips/ft}$$
$$M_u \text{ (downward)} = \tfrac{1}{2}(5.08)(5.96)^2 = 90.2 \text{ ft-kips}$$

The upward soil pressure would reduce this value. However, the upward soil pressure may not actually act in the linear fashion assumed; in fact it might not be there at all. Applying overload conditions under ACI-9.2.4, the most critical situation results when $0.9D$ (i.e., vertical dead load) and $1.7L$ (i.e., horizontal earth pressure) are considered. This would eliminate pressure under the heel entirely.

For shear, ACI-11.1.3 allows the critical section to be taken at the distance d from the face only "When the reaction, in the direction of applied shear, introduces compression into the end region of the member, ..." In this case there is tension induced in the concrete where the heel joins the stem and the inclined crack could extend into the region ahead of the back face of the stem. The shear at the face without including upward soil pressure is

$$V_u = 5.08(5.75) = 29.2 \text{ kips}$$

The design shear strength, unless shear reinforcement is used, is

$$\phi V_c = \phi(2\sqrt{f'_c})bd$$
$$= 0.85(2\sqrt{3000})(12)(21.5)\tfrac{1}{1000} = 24.0 \text{ kips} < 29.2 \text{ kips} \qquad \text{NG}$$

Shear appears to control. The effective depth must be increased in the ratio 29.2/24.0 unless shear reinforcement is to be used.

$$\text{required } d = \frac{21.5(29.2)}{24.0} = 26.2 \text{ in.}$$

Use heel thickness of 30 in. ($d \approx 27.5$ in.).

For flexural strength, using $M_u = 92.0$ ft-kips (corrected for the 30-in. footing weight),

$$\text{required } R_u = \frac{M_u}{\phi bd^2} = \frac{92.0(12,000)}{0.90(12)(27.5)^2} = 135 \text{ psi}$$

This is less than the R_u corresponding to the minimum percentage of reinforcement. Though ACI-10.5 exempts slabs of uniform thickness from the minimum requirement, the retaining wall is a major beamlike structure and the minimum is recommended to apply. Increasing the heel thickness from the preliminary 24 in. to 30 in. reduces the stem height and would permit reducing its thickness. The extra heel thickness will also improve stability against overturning.

From Fig. 3.6.1 or Eq. (3.6.5), the required reinforcement ratio is determined for $R_u = 135$ psi to be 0.00347, which is less than the minimum $200/f_y$ prescribed by ACI-10.5.1. Less than $200/f_y$ may be used provided the amount is one-third more than required for strength; that is, $1.33(0.00347) = 0.0046$.

$$\text{required } A_s = 0.0046(12)(27.5) = 1.52 \text{ sq in./ft}$$

Use #8 @ 6 (A_s = 1.57 sq in./ft).

The development length required for #8 top bars is 23.1(1.4) = 32.4 in. (see Tables 6.9.1 and 6.10.1 based on ACI-12.2). Thus these bars should be embedded at least 32.4 in. into the toe of the footing measured from the stem reinforcement. Use an embedment length of 3 ft from back face of wall.

(k) Design of toe cantilever. The toe of the footing is also treated as a cantilever beam, with the critical section for moment at the front face of the wall and the critical section for shear (inclined cracking) at a distance d from the front face of the wall (one-way action according to ACI-11.11.1.1 will govern). Shear will usually control the required toe thickness. The thickness need not be the same as the heel, though many engineers would make them the same. In this example the heel is unusually thick due to the heavy surcharge. Try a toe thickness somewhat less than the heel, say 2 ft.

Referring to Fig. 12.7.7 and neglecting the earth on the toe, the shear and bending moment (including overload factor) are

$$V_u = 1.7\left(\frac{4.77 + 3.89}{2} - 0.300\right)(2.04) = 13.9 \text{ kips}$$

$$M_u = 1.7[\tfrac{1}{2}(4.77)(3.75)^2(\tfrac{2}{3}) + \tfrac{1}{2}(3.16)(3.75)^2(\tfrac{1}{3}) - \tfrac{1}{2}(0.300)(3.75)^2]$$

$$= 1.7\left[\frac{(3.75)^2}{6}(9.54 + 3.16 - 0.90)\right] = 47.0 \text{ ft-kips}$$

According to ACI-9.2.4, the 1.7 is to be used for the horizontal earth pressure and for live load, while 1.4 may be used for the weights of the concrete and

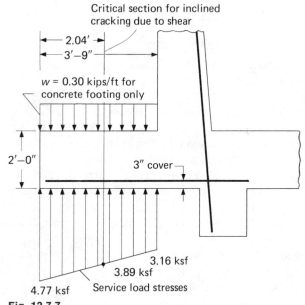

Fig. 12.7.7
Design of toe cantilever in design example.

the earth. Here it has been considered that the toe soil pressure is primarily the result of horizontal earth pressure; hence the conservative procedure of using the 1.7 factor.

$$\text{required } R_u = \frac{47.0(12,000)}{0.90(12)(20.5)^2} = 124 \text{ psi}$$

From Fig. 3.6.1, the required $\rho = 0.00318$ is less than $200/f_y$. Use $1.33(0.00318) = 0.0042$.

$$\text{required } A_s = 0.0042(12)(20.5) = 1.04 \text{ sq in./ft}$$

Use #7 @ 7 $(A_s = 1.03 \text{ sq in./ft})$.
The shear strength is

$$\phi V_c = \phi(2\sqrt{f_c'})bd$$
$$= 0.85(2\sqrt{3000})(12)(20.5)\tfrac{1}{1000} = 22.9 \text{ kips} > 13.9 \text{ kips} \qquad \text{OK}$$

The required development length for the #7 bottom bars is (Tables 6.9.1 and 6.10.1; ACI-12.2)

$$L_d = 17.5(0.8) = 14 \text{ in.}$$

Use embedment of 1 ft 6 in. from front face of wall.

(l) Reinforcement for wall. The wall height (17.5 ft) is now 6 in. less than used in the preliminary design calculations. Retain the 21-in. thickness at the base of the stem. The design moment diagram is shown in Fig. 12.7.8, using Eq. (12.7.1) with maximum $y = 17.5$ ft along with an overload factor of 1.7. The bending moment diagram and the moment capacity diagram of the selected wall steel are shown in Fig. 12.7.8. The steel area required at the base of stem is

$$\text{required } R_u = \frac{117(12,000)}{0.90(12)(18.5)^2} = 380 \text{ psi}$$

$$\text{required } A_s = 0.0103(12)(18.5) = 2.29 \text{ sq in./ft}$$

Use #8 and #9 bars alternated @ $4\tfrac{1}{2}$ $(A_s = 2.38 \text{ sq in./ft})$. The shear has previously been checked and found satisfactory.

The anchorage length of the #9 bars into the footing must be 29.2 in. (according to Table 6.9.1 or computed from equations in ACI-12.2). Use an embedment of 2 ft 6 in. into the footing for both #8 and #9 bars. The base key is available for embedment of stem bars if it might be necessary.

In an endeavor to economize, the quantity of steel per foot of wall should be reduced in the upper parts of the wall so that the capacity provided approximately equals that required. Bar spacing and cutoff are done in accordance with anchorage requirements of the ACI Code, and the resulting design is analyzed by drawing the moment capacity diagram as described in Chap. 6.

In this design, proceeding from the stem base the #9 bars embedded in the footing should not be extended more than about 8 to 10 ft out of the footing, which is placed and cured first. When bars extend out too far, they are often bent or broken off during construction. Thus splice the #8 bars at the base of the stem.

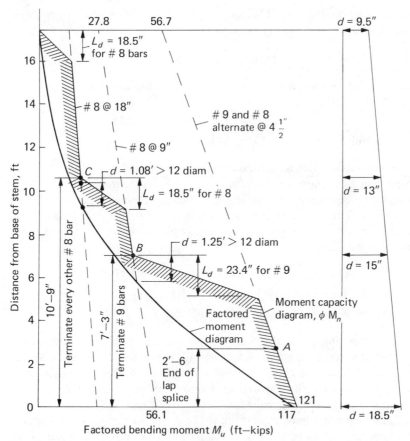

Fig. 12.7.8
Determination of stem reinforcement for design example.

For #8 and #9 alternated at $4\frac{1}{2}$ in., the moment capacity is

$$C = 0.85(3)(12)a = 30.6a$$
$$T = 2.38(40) = 95.2 \text{ kips}$$
$$a = 3.11 \text{ in.}$$

At top of wall,

$$\phi M_n = 0.90(95.2)[9.5 - 0.5(3.11)]\tfrac{1}{12} = 56.7 \text{ ft-kips}$$

At bottom of wall,

$$\phi M_n = 0.90(95.2)[18.5 - 0.5(3.11)]\tfrac{1}{12} = 121 \text{ ft-kips}$$

The two values of moment capacity computed above are used to locate the outer dashed line in Fig. 12.7.8.

Since it is proposed to lap the #8 bars at the base of the wall, ACI-12.16 must be applied to determine the lap distance required. When no more than one-half of the bar area is to be lap spliced within the lap length, the tension splice must meet the requirements for a Class B splice; in this case less than one-half of the total bar area is to be spliced. Referring to Table 6.19.1 (which summarizes ACI-12.16), the lap required is

$$\text{required lap} = 1.3L_d$$

where L_d is the development length required for unspliced bars. In this case for #8 bars,

$$L_d = 23.1 \text{ in. (ACI-12.2 or Table 6.9.1)}$$
$$\text{required lap} = 1.3(23.1) = 30 \text{ in.}$$

Use a splice lap of 2 ft 6 in. terminating at point *A*.

Next, using the moment diagram (Fig. 12.7.8) locate the point where the #9 bars may be terminated, leaving the remaining moment capacity based on #8 @ 9. This moment capacity represented by #8 @ 9 is shown in Fig. 12.7.8 by an inclined dashed line that is plotted by using the following moment capacities:

$$C = 30.6a, \qquad T = 42.0 \text{ kips}, \qquad a = 1.37 \text{ in.}$$
$$\phi M_n \text{ (at top)} = 0.90(42.0)[9.5 - 0.5(1.37)]\tfrac{1}{12} = 27.8 \text{ ft-kips}$$
$$\phi M_n \text{ (at bottom)} = 0.90(42.0)[18.5 - 0.5(1.37)]\tfrac{1}{12} = 56.1 \text{ ft-kips}$$

The termination point *B* is found by extending beyond the intersection of the remaining capacity line (#8 @ 9) with the factored moment diagram a distance of either the effective depth *d* or 12 bar diameters, whichever is greater. In this case the theoretical termination point and the practical location in 3-in. increments coincide.

Whenever tension bars are terminated in the tension zone, stress concentrations occur; therefore a check of ACI-12.11.5 must also be made. Since stirrups are not used in retaining walls, either condition 1 or condition 3 of that section of the code must be satisfied. The conditions, one of which must be satisfied in this case are (1) that the shear at the cutoff point must not exceed two-thirds of the shear capacity; and (2) that the continuing bars must provide at least twice the area required for bending moment at the cutoff point, *and* the shear at the cutoff point must not exceed three-fourths of the shear capacity.

From an inspection of Fig. 12.7.8, it is obvious that item (2) above is not satisfied. Check item (1). Using Eq. (12.7.2), the shear at $y = 10.25$ ft from the top is

$$V_u = 1.7[0.260(10.25) + 0.01625(10.25)^2] = 7.43 \text{ kips}$$
$$\phi V_c = \phi(2\sqrt{f_c'})bd$$
$$= 0.85(2\sqrt{3000})(12)(15)\tfrac{1}{1000} = 16.8 \text{ kips}$$
$$\tfrac{2}{3}(16.8) > 7.43 \qquad\qquad\qquad \text{OK}$$

Thus terminate #9 bars at 7 ft 3 in. from the top of heel.

Additional economy may be achieved by cutting every other #8 bar, leaving #8 @ 18 to extend to the top of the wall. It should be noted that ACI-7.6.5 states that the principal reinforcement shall be spaced not farther apart than 3 times the wall or slab thickness nor more than 18 in. Figure 12.7.8

shows the actual cutoff point C for every other #8. In this case the extension d gives a point slightly below point C. A tension zone cutoff check (ACI-12.11.5) at point C ($y = 6.75$ ft from top) shows

$$V_u = 1.7[0.260(6.75) + 0.01625(6.75)^2] = 4.24 \text{ kips}$$
$$\phi V_c = \phi(2\sqrt{f'_c})bd$$
$$= 0.85(2\sqrt{3000})(12)(13)\tfrac{1}{1000} = 14.5 \text{ kips}$$
$$\tfrac{2}{3}(14.5) > 4.24 \qquad\qquad \text{OK}$$

Terminate every other #8 at 10 ft 9 in. from the top of heel. Actual cut points are located to make bar lengths in the usual 3-in. increments. The complete bar arrangement for the stem is shown in Fig. 12.7.9.

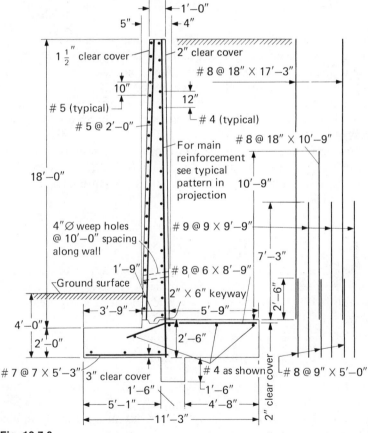

Fig. 12.7.9
Design sketch for cantilever retaining wall.

The reader may note that the moment decreases rapidly from the base of the stem toward the top of the wall. At about 5 ft from the base, the factored moment has decreased about 50%. Somewhere in this vicinity the reinforcement ratio ρ that is required for strength equals the minimum of $200/f_y$.

For the upper portion of the wall, ACI-10.5 would require the actual ρ to be either 0.005 (i.e., $200/f_y$) or four-thirds of the required ρ based on the factored moment. As an example, the moment capacity at point C is indeed approximately equal to four-thirds of the factored moment at C. Thus, in general, wherever actual ρ is less than $200/f_y$, the requirement of ACI–10.5 may be reviewed by seeing that the moment capacity diagram is offset at one-third or more from the factored moment curve.

It is further noted that the stem has been designed for bending moment and shear only. However, the weight of the stem causes compression in it, so that strictly speaking it might be treated as a compression member (under large moment) in accordance with the concepts of Chap. 13. In this design problem the compressive force P_u in the wall under factored loads would be

$$P_u = 1.4\left(\frac{12 + 21}{12}\right)(0.5)(17.5)(0.15) = 5.1 \text{ kips}$$

The combination of this P_u with $M_u = 117$ ft-kips will give a design near the bottom of the "tension controls" region according to Chap. 13 (see Fig. 13.6.2). Although the action of the compressive force increases the theoretical bending strength, the ϕ factor will be slightly decreased from 0.90 toward 0.70. In general, treatment of such walls as compression members is rarely justified but, if done, would permit some slight reduction in reinforcement or thickness of the section.

(m) Temperature and shrinkage reinforcement. Horizontal bars along the length of the wall must be provided, probably with ACI-14.2.10 and 14.2.11 serving as a guide to the amount needed. Accordingly, the total amount required is

$$A_s = 0.0025bh = 0.0025(12)(16.5) = 0.50 \text{ sq in./ft}$$

where the average wall thickness is used for h.

Since it is primarily the front face that is exposed to temperature changes, more of this reinforcement should be placed there. Thus it is suggested that about two-thirds be put in the front face and one-third in the rear face. Accordingly,

$$\tfrac{2}{3}A_s = \tfrac{2}{3}(0.50) = 0.33 \text{ sq in./ft}$$
$$\tfrac{1}{3}A_s = \tfrac{1}{3}(0.50) = 0.17 \text{ sq in./ft}$$

Use on the front face #5 @ 10 ($A_s = 0.37$ sq in./ft). *Use* on the rear face #4 @ 12 ($A_s = 0.20$ sq in./ft).

For vertical reinforcement on the front face, use any nominal amount that is adequate for supporting the horizontal temperature and shrinkage steel in that face.

Use #5 @ 2-ft spacing.

(n) Drainage and other details. Adequate drainage of backfill must be provided since the pressures used are for drained material. A common minimum provision is for weep holes (say 4-in. diameter tile) every 10 to 15 ft along the wall.

Construction of a retaining wall is accomplished in at least two stages; the footing is placed first and then the wall. A shear key is necessary for positive shear transfer between wall and footing (see Fig. 12.7.9). Such a key is made by embedding a beveled 2 × 4 or 2 × 6 timber in the top of the footing. This key may be designed using the shear-friction provisions of ACI-11.7 (discussed in Sec. 5.16). This is a situation in which it is not appropriate to consider shear as a measure of diagonal tension. The nominal ultimate shear strength of the shear key is based on a nominal stress of $0.2f'_c$ but not to exceed 800 psi, as given by ACI-11.7.4.

In this design no bent bars are used. Frequently, the bar arrangement in the toe can be conveniently bent up into the stem and meshed with additional stem reinforcement to give an economical system.

(o) Design sketch. The final details of this design are presented in a design sketch (Fig. 12.7.9) which must accompany any set of design computations.

SELECTED REFERENCES

1. Karl Terzaghi and Ralph B. Peck. *Soil Mechanics in Engineering Practice* (2nd ed.). New York: Wiley, 1968.
2. Whitney Clark Huntington. *Earth Pressures and Retaining Walls.* New York: Wiley, 1957.
3. *Standard Specification of Highway Bridges* (11th ed.). Washington, D.C.: American Association of State Highway and Transportation Officials, 1973.
4. "Retaining Walls and Abutments," *American Railway Engineering Association Manual*, Vol. 1. Chicago: American Railway Engineering Association, 1958 (Chap. 8).
5. C. A. Coulomb. "Essai sur une application des règles des maximis et minimis à quelques problèmes de statique relatifs à l'architecture," *Mem. acad. roy. près divers savants*, **7** (Paris), 1776.
6. W. J. M. Rankine. "On the Stability of Loose Earth," *Philosophical Transactions Royal Society*, **147** (London), 1857.
7. Milo S. Ketchum. *The Design of Walls, Bins, and Grain Elevators* (3rd ed.). New York: McGraw-Hill, 1919 (Chap. 2).
8. G. P. Fisher and R. M. Mains. "Sliding Stability of Retaining Walls," *Civil Engineering*, July 1952, 490.

PROBLEMS

Note: For all problems assume that frost penetration depth is 4 ft.

12.1   Given the cantilever retaining wall of the accompanying figure with Rankine's coefficient for active pressure $C_a = 0.27$, the weight of retained soil = 100 pcf, and the coefficient of friction between concrete and earth = 0.40. Using service load conditions:

(a) Determine the factor of safety provided against overturning. Would you consider this to be adequate?

(b) Determine the factor of safety provided against sliding. Neglect any passive pressure resistance on the toe. Would you consider this factor of safety adequate?

(c) Determine the location of the resultant bearing pressure under footing. Is it within the middle third of the base? Would the position you determined probably be permissible if the foundation material is rock?

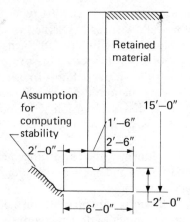

Prob. 12.1

12.2 Determine the adequacy of the retaining wall of the accompanying figure with regard to stability (overturning, sliding, and soil pressure magnitude and distribution). Assume that the wall is on good granular soil with a maximum safe soil pressure of 5000 psf under service-load conditions.

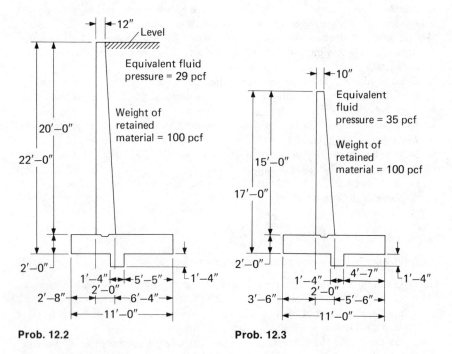

Prob. 12.2

Prob. 12.3

12.3 Determine the adequacy of the retaining wall of the accompanying figure with regard to stability if the backfill is level. Assume an allowable soil pressure of 4000 psf under service-load conditions. Draw a conclusion regarding what would happen if the backfill became saturated to an equivalent fluid pressure of 65 pcf. See the accompanying figure.

12.4   Reconsider the retaining wall conditions of Sec. 12.7 if the surcharge is changed to 10 ft to approximate the effect of a railroad located parallel to and near the top of the wall. Sometimes under such conditions the lateral effect of a surcharge is included but the beneficial stabilizing effect of the vertical surcharge weight is omitted. Compare the wall proportions for both conditions using a minimum length of base and keeping the soil pressure resultant under service-load conditions within the middle third of the base. Verify the adequacy of the dimensions, but do not design the reinforcement. Use $f'_c = 4000$ psi, $f_y = 60,000$ psi, and the ACI Code.

12.5   Assuming that the overall proportioning of the retaining wall of Prob. 12.2 is adequate for earth stability, design the reinforcement for the wall cantilever. Besides dowels at the base, use three changes of reinforcement over the 20-ft wall height. Draw the resulting moment capacity diagram. Use $f'_c = 4000$ psi, $f_y = 60,000$ psi, and the strength method of the ACI Code.

12.6   Design the heel cantilever for the wall of Prob. 12.2 if the backfill is level. Use $f'_c = 4000$ psi, $f_y = 60,000$ psi, and the strength method of the ACI Code. Revise the thickness from that shown if it seems desirable.

12.7   Design the heel cantilever for the wall of Prob. 12.3 if the backfill slopes 30° to the horizontal. Use $f'_c = 4000$ psi. $f_y = 60,000$ psi, and the strength method of the ACI Code. Revise the thickness if it seems desirable.

12.8   Design the toe cantilever for the wall of Prob. 12.2 if the backfill is level. Use $f'_c = 4000$ psi, $f_y = 60,000$ psi and the strength method of the ACI Code. Revise the thickness if it seems desirable.

12.9   Design the toe cantilever for the wall of Prob. 12.3 if the backfill slopes at 30° to the horizontal. Use $f'_c = 4000$ psi, $f_y = 60,000$ psi, and the strength method of the ACI Code. Revise the thickness if it seems desirable.

12.10   Design a cantilever retaining wall to support a bank of earth 17 ft high above the final level of earth at the toe of the wall. The retained material is level, has a weight of 100 pcf and an angle of internal friction of 35°. The allowable soil pressure under service load is 5 ksf and the coefficient of friction between concrete and soil is 0.60. Use $f'_c = 3500$ psi, $f_y = 60,000$ psi, and the strength method of the ACI Code.

12.11   Design a cantilever retaining wall to support a bank of earth 22 ft high above the final level at the toe of the wall. The retained material is level and has a weight of 110 pcf and exerts an equivalent fluid active pressure of 30 pcf and an equivalent fluid passive pressure of 350 pcf. The coefficient of friction is 0.45 between concrete and soil. The maximum soil pressure under service load shall not exceed 3500 psf. Use $f'_c = 3000$ psi, $f_y = 60,000$ psi, and the strength method of the ACI Code.

12.12   Redesign the cantilever retaining wall of Prob. 12.11 if the differential elevation is 24 ft instead of 22 ft.

13

Members in Compression and Bending

13.1 Introduction

The compression member subjected to pure axial load rarely, if ever, exists. All columns are subjected to some moment, which may be due to end restraint arising from the monolithic placement of floor beams and columns or due to accidental eccentricity from imperfect alignment and variable materials.

This chapter considers first the column having minimal bending moment, commonly called "axially" loaded, and later considers the effect of medium and large amounts of bending. Only the basic strength of short compression members is considered, however. The reduction of the strength of compression members due to length effects is treated in Chap. 15.

13.2 Types of Columns

A column has been defined as a member used primarily to support axial compressive load with a ratio of height to least lateral dimension of 3 or greater (ACI-2.1). Shorter concrete compression members may be unreinforced and treated as pedestal footings (ACI-15.11). Reinforced concrete columns are principally of two types, classified according to the manner in which the longitudinal reinforcing bars are laterally supported. A *tied* column is one, usually of square, rectangular, or circular shape, in which the longitudinal reinforcing bars are held in position by separate lateral ties typically spaced about 12 to 18 in. (300 to 450 mm) apart, as shown in Fig. 13.2.1a. A *spirally reinforced* column is one, usually of square or circular shape, in which the longitudinal reinforcing bars are arranged in a circle and

Reinforced concrete tied columns under construction; Engineering Library, University of Wisconsin, Madison, Wis. (Photo by C. G. Salmon.)

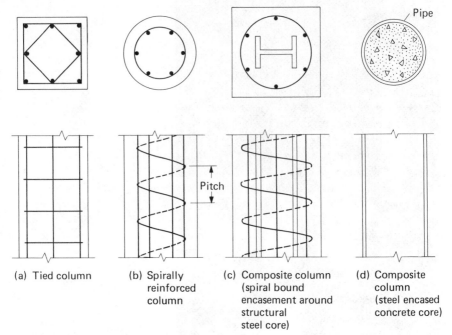

Fig. 13.2.1
Types of columns.

wrapped by a continuous closely spaced spiral typically at a pitch of about 2 to 3 in. (50 to 75 mm), as shown in Fig. 13.2.1b. A *composite* column is one in which a structural steel shape, pipe, or tubing is used, with or without additional longitudinal bars. One common composite column arrangement may contain a structural steel shape completely encased in concrete, which is further reinforced with both longitudinal and lateral reinforcement (spiral or ties) as shown in Fig. 13.2.1c. In a second kind of composite column the steel may encase a concrete core, which may or may not contain longitudinal reinforcing bars, as shown in Fig. 13.2.1d.

The so-called combination column, formerly included in the ACI Code, is one in which a structural steel member, designed to carry most of the load, is wrapped with wire and encased in concrete primarily for fire protection. Since this type of column is usually a member in a steel framework, where no load comes *directly* to the concrete casing, the present ACI Code (ACI-10.14.3) has effectively eliminated it from being included as a reinforced concrete column.

13.3 Behavior of Axially Loaded Columns

Many tests were made in the early 1900s on reinforced concrete columns under axial loads [1–5], but loading was generally of short duration. As early as 1911, however, Withey [5] at the University of Wisconsin observed that when the ultimate load was approached, a transfer of load from concrete to steel took place. In the 1920s and early 1930s extensive investigation of column behavior took place emphasizing long-time loading. Since 1930, significant changes have occurred in column design, primarily influenced by the tests of columns at Lehigh University and at the University of Illinois, summarized by ACI Committee 105 [6]. In this combined study, 564 columns were tested, with attention given to column size, quality of concrete, quality and amount of longitudinal and lateral reinforcement, rate of application of load, and shrinkage and creep under sustained loads. By 1940, design procedures for axially loaded columns became based on the ultimate strength results of the aforementioned extensive investigation. Joint ACI-ASCE Committee 441 has provided an excellent annotated bibliography on reinforced concrete column studies [7].

When concrete and steel act together in compression, the proportion of loading carried by each changes continuously during the time the load is acting. Initially the stress in the steel is E_s/E_c times the stress in the concrete, according to the elastic theory. As the time-dependent effects of creep and shrinkage occur, the concrete gradually takes over relatively more load than its elastic share. Creep and shrinkage deformations have been introduced in Sec. 1.10, discussed in regard to beams in Secs. 4.9 and 4.10, and treated in detail with regard to deflections in Chap. 14.

Members that are subjected to axial compression, either alone or in combination with bending, frequently have a substantial portion of the total load sustained. Consequently the transfer of load to the steel from the concrete due to the time-dependent deformation is more pronounced in these members than in beams. However, even though actual stresses under service loads cannot be meaningfully computed, the ultimate strength can be determined. The experimenters verified that the nominal strength P_n for an axially loaded column may be properly expressed [6] by

$$P_n = k_c f'_c A_c + f_y A_{st} + k_s f_{sy} A_{sp} \qquad (13.3.1)$$

where

> P_n = nominal ultimate strength for a tied column (with third term omitted, i.e., no spiral)

or

> P_n = yield strength for a spirally reinforced column
> k_c = coefficient (0.85) to account for the difference between concrete in the column and that in a test cylinder
> f'_c = standard 28-day cylinder strength
> A_c = net area of concrete, based on gross area for tied column and core area for spirally reinforced column
> A_{st} = area of longitudinal reinforcement
> f_y = yield stress for longitudinal reinforcement
> k_s = constant that varies from 1.5 to 2.5 with an average of 1.95
> f_{sy} = yield stress of spiral steel
> A_{sp} = volume of spiral steel per unit length of column

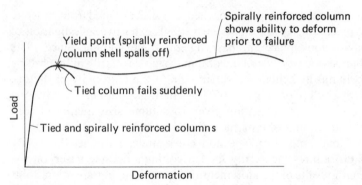

Fig. 13.3.1

Typical load-deformation curves for tied and spirally reinforced columns.

Equation (13.3.1) represents the yield load for the spirally reinforced column that exhibits a marked yielding followed by considerable deformation before complete failure, as shown in Figs. 13.3.1 and 13.3.2. On reaching the yield point, the shell spalls off and the spiral begins to act to confine the crushed concrete in the core. The spiral therefore adds little to the strength prior to reaching yield, but it provides ductility. From Eq. (13.3.1) it may be observed that spiral reinforcing is from 1.5 to 2.5 times as effective in adding ultimate capacity as is the main longitudinal steel, but it does not work at all until the deformation is excessive.

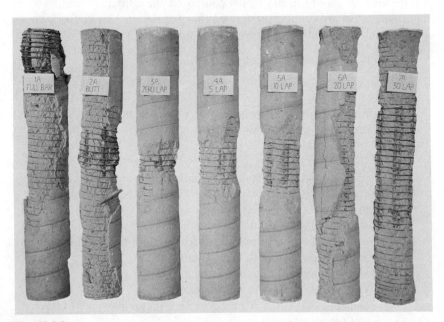

Fig. 13.3.2

Spiral column behavior. (Courtesy of Portland Cement Association.)

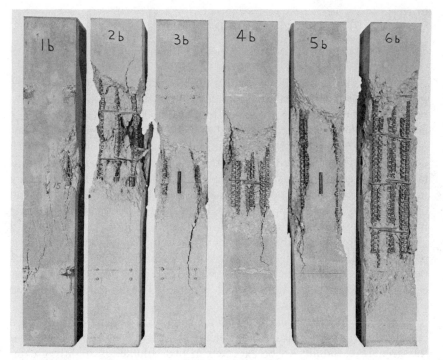

Fig. 13.3.3
Tied column behavior. (Courtesy of Portland Cement Association.)

The tied column behaves exactly as a spirally reinforced column up to the yield point of the spirally reinforced column, at which point failure occurs suddenly in a manner similar to the failure in a compression cylinder test. At that instant the longitudinal bars buckle between points that are restrained by lateral ties. The tied column behavior is illustrated in Figs. 13.3.1 and 13.3.3.

As will be shown later, though both types of column can carry the same ultimate load, a higher factor of safety should be provided for the tied column than for the spirally reinforced column because of the sudden failure and lack of toughness (energy absorption).

13.4 Safety Provisions

The safety provisions for overload in the design of compression members as prescribed by the ACI Code are the same as for any other types of members; these are (ACI-9.2):

For gravity loads,

$$U = 1.4D + 1.7L \tag{13.4.1}$$

For loadings including wind,

$$U = 0.75(1.4D + 1.7L + 1.7W) \tag{13.4.2}$$

or

$$U = 0.9D + 1.3W \qquad (13.4.3)$$

The most severe situation among Eqs. (13.4.1) through (13.4.3) will control the design.

Traditionally, under most building codes, members subject to stresses produced by wind or earthquake forces combined with other loads have been proportioned in the working stress method for unit stresses $33\frac{1}{3}\%$ greater than those specified, provided that the section thus required is not less than that required for the combination of dead and live load. In strength design, the infrequent occurrence of the maximum wind load condition is taken into account by the smaller overload factors when wind effects are included. This reduced safety provision for the temporary effect of wind or earthquake, or both, appears in ACI-Appendix B for the working stress method, and in ACI-9.2.2 and 9.2.3 for the strength method.

Additionally, the possibility of undercapacity is accommodated by the ϕ requirement of ACI-9.3. For spirally reinforced columns $\phi = 0.75$, and for tied columns $\phi = 0.70$, the difference being related partially to the reserve capacity to deform before failure which is exhibited by the spirally reinforced column.

The lower undercapacity factors ϕ for compression members arise from statistical variations in observed strength and are a rough indication that the strength variability to be expected in tied columns is slightly greater than in spiral columns and that the variability expected in columns is greater than in beams. The difference in the behavior of tied and spirally reinforced *axially* loaded columns is further accounted for by the use of a different maximum compression capacity as discussed in Sec. 13.11.

For combined compression and bending, the ϕ value may be variable and increase to 0.90 (for pure flexure) as the axial compression decreases to zero. This variation of ϕ is treated later in Sec. 13.20.

13.5 Concentrically Loaded Short Columns

In accordance with Eq. (13.3.1) without the term representing the contribution of the spiral, the maximum nominal ultimate capacity P_0 on a concentrically loaded short column (Fig. 13.5.1) is

$$P_0 = 0.85f'_c(A_g - A_{st}) + f_y A_{st} \qquad (13.5.1)$$

where A_g is the gross area bh and A_{st} is the total longitudinal reinforcement $(A_1 + A_2)$. This equation is also in agreement with the rectangular stress-block assumptions of Sec. 3.4 where the entire cross section is subject to a failure compressive strain of 0.003. It may also be expressed as

$$P_0 = A_g[0.85f'_c(1 - \rho_g) + f_y \rho_g] \qquad (13.5.2)$$

where $\rho_g = A_{st}/A_g$.

When the terms including ρ_g are combined, Eq. (13.5.2) becomes

$$P_0 = A_g[0.85f'_c + \rho_g(f_y - 0.85f'_c)] \qquad (13.5.3)$$

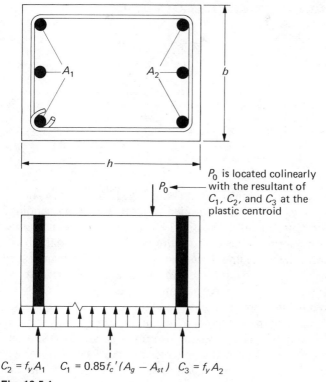

P_0 is located colinearly with the resultant of C_1, C_2, and C_3 at the plastic centroid

$C_2 = f_y A_1$ $C_1 = 0.85 f_c' (A_g - A_{st})$ $C_3 = f_y A_2$

Fig. 13.5.1
A concentrically loaded column.

13.6 General Discussion on Combined Bending and Axial Load

A structural member may be subjected to combined bending and axial load in many ways. It is common in reinforced concrete buildings that bending moments act on all columns. These moments are generally due to unbalanced floor loads on both exterior and interior columns and to eccentric loads such as crane loads in industrial buildings. In determining bending moments in columns due to unbalanced floor loads, ACI-8.8 provides the following simplifying assumptions:

1. The far ends of columns that are monolithic with the structure may be considered fixed in continuity analysis for gravity loading.
2. Maximum bending in a column is due to factored loads on a single adjacent span of the floor under consideration. This bending is in addition to axial forces from factored loads on all floors.
3. The loading condition causing maximum ratio of bending moment to axial load shall also be considered.

Concrete construction is usually monolithic; thus reinforced concrete rigid frames and arches (Fig. 13.6.1) are common and advantageous. All sections in the two structures shown in Fig. 13.6.1 are subjected to combined

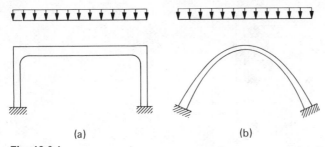

Fig. 13.6.1

Reinforced concrete rigid frame and arch.

bending and axial load. The vertical members in Fig. 13.6.1a and sections near the supports in Fig. 13.6.1b are subjected to more axial than bending stress, while the horizontal member in Fig. 13.6.1a and sections near the crown in Fig. 13.6.1b may be subjected to more bending than axial stress.

It may be seen from the preceding discussion that the relative magnitude of axial and bending stresses may vary to a considerable degree; axial stress is usually compressive, although it may sometimes be tensile.

When combined axial compression and bending act on a section having a low slenderness ratio, from the viewpoint of maximum strength of a section (see Fig. 13.6.2) there may be (1) compression over most or all of the section such that the compressive strain in the concrete reaches 0.003 before the tension steel yields, known as the "compression controls" region, or (2) tension in a large portion of the section such that the strain in the tension steel is greater than the yield point strain when the compressive strain in the concrete reaches 0.003, known as the "tension controls" region. This maximum strength interaction relationship for short members has been verified

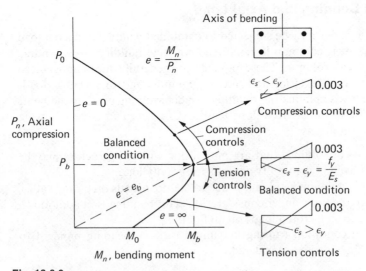

Fig. 13.6.2

Typical ultimate strength interaction diagram for axial conpression and bending moment about one axis.

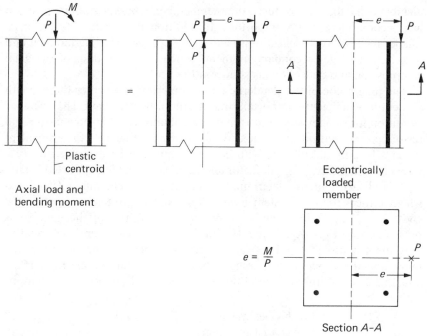

Fig. 13.6.3
Eccentrically loaded column statically equivalent to member subject to axial load and bending moment.

by research [8–12]. The major emphasis for this chapter is the analysis and design of sections whose ultimate strength (P_n and M_n) lies at various points on the interaction diagram (Fig. 13.6.2).

In studying Fig. 13.6.2, the reader may note that radial lines from the origin ($P_n = 0$, $M_n = 0$) represent constant ratios of M_n to P_n; that is, they represent eccentricities e of the load P_n from the *plastic centroid*, which is defined in Fig. 13.5.1. The fact that e is equal to M/P may be observed from Fig. 13.6.3, where it is shown that a column subjected to an eccentric load is statically equivalent to a member under the combined action of an axial load and a bending moment. Thus in Fig. 13.6.2 the vertical axis represents $e = 0$ and the horizontal axis represents $e = \infty$. This concept of replacing axial load and bending moment by a single eccentric load is the practical approach to use in analysis and design computations for a concrete section.

13.7 Length Effects

When the height of an upright compression member does not exceed 3 times its least lateral dimension, it is considered a pedestal and should be designed as such according to ACI-15.11. For longer members, the effect of slenderness ratio (ratio of length to radius of gyration r) must be considered. It is well known that buckling may control the strength of any compression member (see Fig. 15.2.3 for curve typical of reinforced concrete sections). The strength design method, together with better understanding of concrete compression member behavior, has produced slimmer members; thus the stability problem has become increasingly important. In addition to the stability problem, smaller members will deflect more under any primary bending moment and thus have a larger secondary moment, which is the product of the axial compression and deflection (as shown in Fig. 15.1.1).

The magnitude of the slenderness ratio determines whether the strength reduction is sufficiently important that it cannot be neglected. The reference condition for slenderness ratio is that of a column with hinged ends (i.e., no resistance to rotation at either end), as shown in Fig. 15.3.1a. Equivalent pin-end lengths of columns with end restraints can be expressed by kL_u, where k is the effective length factor and L_u is the actual unsupported length.

A vital factor in the determination of the equivalent pin-end length is whether the structural system is *braced* so that relative movement of the ends of a compression member transverse to the axis of the member is prevented (see Figs. 15.3.1 and 15.3.3a,c), or *unbraced* where such relative movement is possible and restraint is provided only by the rigidity of the joints and the stiffness of interacting beams and columns (see Figs. 15.3.2 and 15.3.3b,d). Without general derivation or proof, the following may be stated:

For *braced* systems, $\qquad k \le 1.0$

For *unbraced* systems, $\qquad k \ge 1.0$

A qualitative explanation is available from the study of Figs. 15.3.1 to 15.3.3, but a theoretical development would require a study of structural stability (see Chap. 15 references 26 through 29).

The intent of the ACI Code is to permit the design of compression members as short columns, without strength reduction, when the length effect consideration would result in a strength reduction not exceeding 5%. ACI-10.11.4 permits neglect of length effects when

$$\frac{kL_u}{r} < 34 - 12\frac{M_1}{M_2} \qquad \text{(for \textit{braced systems})} \qquad \textbf{(13.7.1)}$$

where M_1 and M_2 are numerically the smaller and larger bending moments, respectively, at the ends of the member and the ratio M_1/M_2 is positive for single curvature and negative for double curvature; and when

$$\frac{kL_u}{r} < 22 \qquad \text{(for \textit{unbraced systems})} \qquad \textbf{(13.7.2)}$$

These are likely to be exceeded only in a small percentage of compression member designs. Studies of existing (1971) structures have indicated [13] that over 90% of the columns in braced frames and over 40% of the columns in unbraced frames fall within the limits of ACI-10.11.4 and thus strength reduction due to length effects may be ignored.

The remainder of this chapter treats only the basic strength of short compression members. The detailed consideration of the strength reduction due to length effects in both unbraced and braced systems appears separately in Chap. 15.

13.8 Lateral Ties

The lateral ties are used to hold the vertical bars in position, providing lateral support so that individual bars could have the tendency to buckle only *between* the tie supports. Ties do not contribute to the ultimate strength, as indicated by the column studies in the early 1930s [6]. Studies [14–19] have indicated that present tie requirements are conservative for ordinary columns with Grade 40 reinforcement, but may not be conservative for columns with high-strength reinforcement, with large or bundled bars, or of unusual dimensions.

The effect of ties on the ultimate behavior of columns is complex [14]. As a tied column is loaded to failure, the first occurrence is the spalling off of the exterior cover, which in turn causes transfer of load to the concrete core and the longitudinal steel. The loss of stiffness of the longitudinal steel, which begins to yield or to buckle outward, causes additional stress on the concrete core. Once the core achieves its ultimate strength, the column suddenly fails. The above sequence usually takes place rapidly, giving the so-called "sudden" failure.

The following provisions have been prescribed for lateral ties in columns by the ACI Code (ACI-7.10.5):

1. All nonprestressed bars for tied columns shall be enclosed by lateral ties, at least #3 in size for longitudinal bars #10 or smaller, and at least #4 in size for #11, #14, #18, and bundled longitudinal bars.
2. The spacing of the ties shall not exceed 16 longitudinal bar diameters, 48 tie bar diameters, or the least dimension of the column.
3. The ties shall be so arranged that every corner and alternate longitudinal bar shall have lateral support provided by the corner of a tie having an included angle of not more than 135° and no bar shall be farther than 6 in. clear on either side from such a laterally supported bar.
4. Where the bars are located around the periphery of a circle, a complete circular tie may be used.

The ACI *Manual of Standard Practice for Detailing* [20] suggests tie arrangements for various numbers of bars, some common ones being shown in Fig. 13.8.1.

The provisions of ACI-7.10.5.3 permitting the included angle where a tie "corners" the longitudinal reinforcement to be as large as 135° became part of the ACI Code as a result of the Bresler and Gilbert tests [15]. Other pilot tests have justified the liberalization from earlier codes in which a 90° corner was required for every bar [21]. However, since spliced bars and bundled bars have not been included in tests, it is recommended [21] that "it would be prudent to provide at least a set of ties at each end of lap spliced bars, above and below end-bearing splices, and at minimum spacings immediately below sloping regions of offset bent bars."

It may also be noted that ACI-7.10.3 waives the lateral reinforcement requirements "where tests and structural analysis show adequate strength and feasibility of construction."

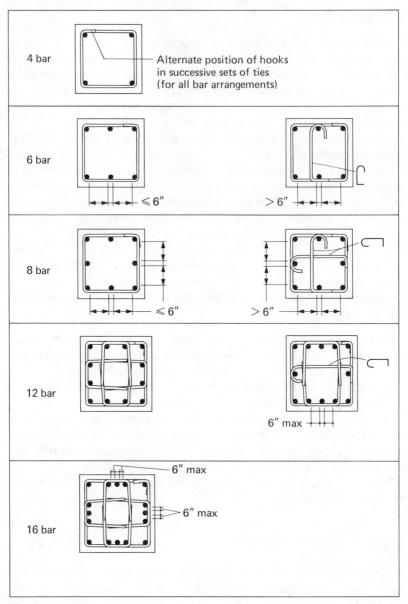

Fig. 13.8.1
Common column tie arrangements (adapted from Ref. 20).

13.9 Spiral Reinforcement and Longitudinal Bar Placement

The spiral provides the column with the ability to absorb considerable deformation prior to failure. This toughness is the principal gain that is achieved by the use of spirally reinforced columns. The knowledge of spiral behavior is based on the column research of the early 1930s [6]. Although the spiral does actually contribute strength to the column (as early as 1903 Considere [1,2] indicated that the spiral was 2.4 times as effective in providing column capacity as was longitudinal reinforcement), the conservative policy of ACI specifications since about 1940 has been to provide spiral reinforcement sufficient to increase the capacity of the core by an amount equal to the capacity of the shell, thus maintaining the column yield capacity when the shell spalls off.

Using the third term of Eq. (13.3.1), with an average k_s of 2, the load capacity as represented by the spiral reinforcement is

$$P_n = 2.0 f_{sy} A_{sp} \qquad (13.9.1)$$

An alternative approach to the acceptance of an experimental value for k_s has been presented by Huang [22], who considers the triaxial loading condition that exists when the spiral is acting in tension.

Let ρ_s be the ratio of the volume of spiral reinforcement to the total volume of the core (out-to-out of spirals), or $\rho_s = A_{sp}/A_c$. Equation (13.9.1) now becomes

$$P_n = 2.0 f_{sy} \rho_s A_c \qquad (13.9.2)$$

Equating Eq. (13.9.2) to the strength of the shell and taking the ultimate concrete strength of the shell as about 90% of that inside the core, or $0.75 f'_c$,

$$2.0 f_{sy} \rho_s A_c = 0.75 f'_c (A_s - A_c)$$

from which

$$\rho_s = 0.375 \left(\frac{A_g}{A_c} - 1 \right) \frac{f'_c}{f_{sy}} \qquad (13.9.3)$$

By providing an additional factor of safety of 1.20 to assure that the spiral effect exceeds the shell capacity, Eq. (13.9.3) becomes

$$\rho_s = 0.45 \left(\frac{A_g}{A_c} - 1 \right) \frac{f'_c}{f_{sy}} \qquad (13.9.4)$$

which is specified in ACI-10.9.3. It should be noted that the yield strength f_{sy} of the spiral may not exceed 60,000 psi.

The design relationship may be obtained by referring to the definition of ρ_s following Eq. (13.9.1).

$$\rho_s = \frac{A_{sp}}{A_c} = \frac{\text{volume of spiral in one loop}}{\text{volume of core for a length } s}$$

$$= \frac{a_s \pi (D_c - d_b)}{(\pi D_c^2/4)s} \qquad (13.9.5)$$

in which D_c is the diameter of the core, a_s is the area of the spiral, and d_b is the diameter of the spiral wire (Fig. 13.9.1).

According to ACI-7.10.4 the clear spacing between spirals must be at least 1 in. but shall not exceed 3 in. The material for the spiral in cast-in-place construction shall have a minimum diameter of $\frac{3}{8}$ in. Anchorage of spiral

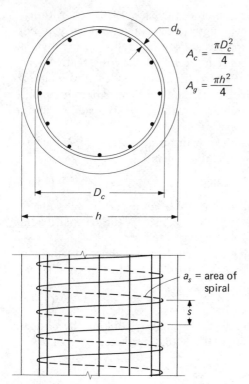

$$A_c = \frac{\pi D_c^2}{4}$$

$$A_g = \frac{\pi h^2}{4}$$

a_s = area of spiral

Fig. 13.9.1
Spirally reinforced column.

reinforcement shall be provided by $1\frac{1}{2}$ extra turns of spiral bar or wire at each end of the spiral unit. Splices, when necessary, shall be made in the spiral bar or wire by welding or by a lap of 48 diameters minimum but not less than 12 in. The spiral reinforcement is to be protected everywhere by a $1\frac{1}{2}$ in. covering of concrete cast monolithically with the core.

In order to hold the spiral in place and maintain the desired pitch, vertical spacer bars with small hooks at the desired pitch are used. These spacer bars support the spiral reinforcement in the forms before the concrete is placed; the spiral is not supported by the main longitudinal bars. ACI-7.10.4 requires spacers in accordance with Table 13.9.1.

Since spirally reinforced columns are usually more heavily reinforced than tied columns, it sometimes becomes necessary at splice points to lap bars inside the main circle of bars. This is done in order to maintain a desirable minimum center-to-center spacing of longitudinal bars at $2\frac{1}{2}$ times the bar diameter and a minimum clear distance (ACI-7.6.3) between individual longitudinal bars of $1\frac{1}{2}$ times the nominal bar diameter, but not less than $1\frac{1}{2}$ in. The preferred and the alternate bar arrangements are shown in Fig. 13.9.2. Bars may also be spliced by butt welding, which permits more utilization of available space. In a large column an inner core of bars wrapped with a spiral or by ties may also be used.

Table 13.9.1
Number of Spacers Required per Spiral (from ACI-7.10.4)

Spiral Core Diameter	Minimum Number of Spacers
Bar or wire smaller than $\frac{5}{8}$-in. (16mm) diameter:	
less than 20 in.	2
20 to 30 in.	3
more than 30 in.	4
Bar or wire $\frac{5}{8}$-in. (16 mm) diameter and larger:	
24 in. or less	3
more than 24 in.	4

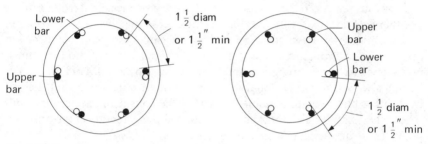

Fig. 13.9.2
Bar arrangement in spiral columns.

13.10 Limits on Percentage of Reinforcement

The percentage of longitudinal reinforcement in terms of the gross cross-sectional area must be between 1 and 8% (ACI-10.9.1). However, ACI-10.8.4 permits basing the percentage on a reduced concrete area A_g in cases where the gross concrete area is in excess of that needed for load considerations, but in no case may the percentage ρ_g be less than 0.005 based on the gross area provided. The primary purpose of these provisions for minimum steel is to prevent the failure mode from becoming that of a plain concrete column, which might be more disastrous than the sudden failure of tied columns previously described. The upper limit on the amount of longitudinal reinforcement is a practical one in that if proper clearances are maintained between bars, little more than $\rho_g = 0.08$ can be put into the section. Thus the maximum ρ_g is, in a way, a double check on the minimum spacing restrictions of ACI-7.6.3.

The detailed minimum requirements on bar size and dimensions for compression members of the 1963 ACI Code and earlier codes have been eliminated. Beginning with the 1971 ACI Code, allowance is made for "wider utilization of reinforced concrete compression members in smaller size and lightly loaded structures, such as low rise residential and light office buildings" [21]. It is recommended [21] that "the engineer should

recognize the need for careful workmanship, as well as the increased significance of shrinkage stresses with small sections."

13.11 Maximum Strength in Axial Compression—ACI Code

Since a truly concentrically loaded column is rare, if not nonexistent, some
minimal eccentricity should be provided for. This accidental eccentricity
may occur due to end conditions, inaccuracy of manufacture, or variation
in materials even when the load is theoretically concentric.

Prior to 1977, the ACI Code provided that no matter how small the
computed e is from the actual loading, compression members had to be
designed for an eccentricity not less than $0.05h$ for spirally reinforced or
composite steel encased columns, or $0.10h$ for tied columns; but at least
1 in. in any case. The minimum eccentricity was measured with respect
to either principal axis, with h defined as the overall dimension of the column.

This minimum eccentricity requirement meant that every compression
member, even though carrying a small computed bending moment, must
be designed to have a strength defined, for example, by point A of Fig. 13.11.1.
In other words, not only could the axial strength not exceed that defined
by point A but a bending moment M_B must be considered as acting simultaneously; that is, the horizontal portion of the strength curve through
point A was not actually available in design.

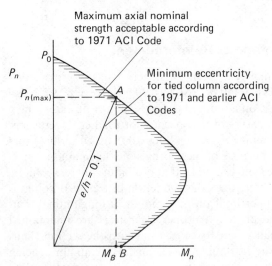

Fig. 13.11.1
Maximum axial strength—1971 ACI Code.

The minimum eccentricity procedure was reasonable as long as the
cross-sectional dimensions were small and the slenderness ratios were relatively large; a moment corresponding to 1 in. or so eccentricity on a 12-in.

column was not unreasonable. However, an $e/h = 0.1$ minimum becomes unreasonable as accidental eccentricity if a column is a power plant machinery pedestal 6 ft square and 20 ft high. A 6-in. accidental eccentricity is unlikely, although a maximum axial nominal strength less than P_0 may be reasonable.

The 1977 ACI Code prescribes (ACI-10.3.5) that for members where the effects of slenderness may be neglected, the maximum axial load nominal strength $P_{n(\max)}$ may not exceed $0.80P_0$ for tied columns and $0.85P_0$ for spirally reinforced columns, with P_0 given by Eq. (13.5.1) or (13.5.2). This procedure makes available for design use the entire horizontal portion of the strength interaction diagram defined by $P_{n(\max)}$. In other words, point C (Fig. 13.11.2a) becomes an acceptable point to use in design, which gives a maximum value of P_n comparable to that corresponding to a minimum $e/h = 0.1$ for tied columns or $e/h = 0.05$ for spirally reinforced columns, but yet not explicitly designed for a bending moment of P_n times $0.1h$ or P_n times $0.05h$.

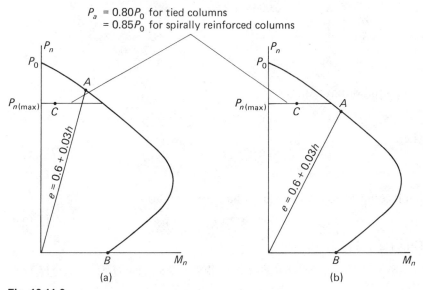

Fig. 13.11.2
Maximum axial strength—1977 ACI Code.

The new procedure is also simpler for those cases that are clearly low bending moment cases (moments less than what corresponds to $e/h = 0.1$ on tied columns, for example). Taking $P_{n(\max)}$ as a proportion of P_0 is a simple calculation; whereas previously the only way $P_{n(\max)}$ could be determined was to solve for point A in Fig. 13.11.1, the intersection of the minimum e/h with the strength interaction diagram.

When the slenderness ratio is high enough to require consideration of the length effects, a minimum eccentricity of $(0.6 + 0.03h)$ is to be used in the evaluation of the magnified factored moment, but in no case may the resulting available nominal strength P_n be taken to exceed $P_{n(\max)}$ (ACI-10.11.5.4).

In an unlikely situation as shown by Fig. 13.11.2b, where $P_{n(max)}$ is vertically higher than point A, the value of P_n at point A on the interaction diagram must be used for design when the effects of slenderness must be considered; but where slenderness may be neglected, the horizontal portion through point C may be used in design for axial compression.

13.12 Balanced Condition—Rectangular Sections

The balanced condition represents the dividing point between the compression controls and tension controls regions of the strength interaction diagram (Fig. 13.6.2). Defined in the same manner as in Chap. 3, it is the loading condition that produces at ultimate strength, simultaneously, a strain of 0.003 in the extreme fiber of concrete and the strain $\epsilon_y = f_y/E_s$ on the tension steel. Referring to the rectangular section in Fig. 13.12.1, the strain relationship gives

$$\frac{x_b}{d} = \frac{0.003}{f_y/E_s + 0.003}$$

$$x_b = \frac{0.003}{f_y/[29(10^6)] + 0.003} d = \frac{87,000d}{f_y + 87,000} \tag{13.12.1}$$

Force equilibrium requires

$$P_b = C_c + C_s - T \tag{13.12.2}$$

where

$$C_c = 0.85f'_c ab = 0.85f'_c \beta_1 x_b b \tag{13.12.3}$$

$$T = A_s f_y \tag{13.12.4}$$

and if compression steel yields at balanced condition,

$$C_s = A'_s(f_y - 85f'_c) \tag{13.12.5}$$

Thus Eq. (13.12.2) becomes

$$P_b = 0.85f'_c \beta_1 x_b b + A'_s(f_y - 0.85f'_c) - A_s f_y \tag{13.12.6}$$

The eccentricity e_b is measured from the plastic centroid, which has been defined in Fig. 13.5.1. For symmetrical sections the plastic centroid is at the middepth of the section.

Rotational equilibrium of the forces in Fig. 13.12.1 is satisfied by taking moments about any point such as the plastic centroid,

$$P_b e_b = C_c\left(d - \frac{a}{2} - d''\right) + C_s(d - d' - d'') + Td'' \tag{13.12.7}$$

Equations (13.12.6) and (13.12.7) may be solved simultaneously to obtain P_b and e_b.

It may be noted that in the case of bending moment without axial load, the balanced condition as defined in Chap. 3 is not permitted by the ACI Code. However, in the case of combined bending and axial load, the balanced condition is only one point on an acceptable interaction diagram.

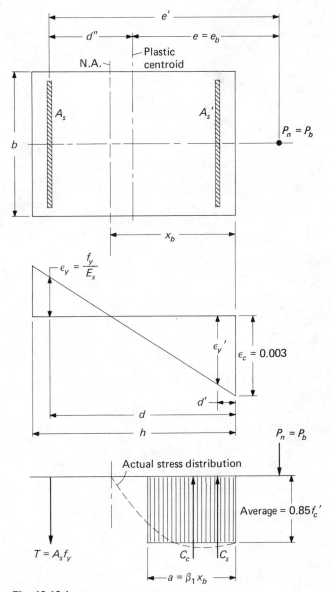

Fig. 13.12.1
Balanced strain condition—rectangular section.

EXAMPLE 13.12.1   Determine the eccentric compressive load P_b and its eccentricity e_b for a balanced strain condition on the section of Fig. 13.12.2. Use $f'_c = 3000$ psi, $f_y = 50,000$ psi, and the ACI Code.

Solution: (a) Locate the neutral axis.

$$x_b = \frac{0.003(21.6)}{0.00172 + 0.003} = 13.72 \text{ in.}$$

$$a_b = \beta_1 x_b = 0.85(13.72) = 11.67 \text{ in.}$$

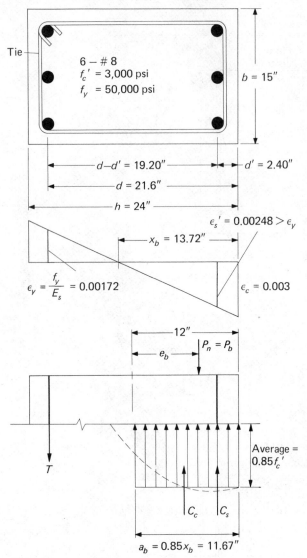

Fig. 13.12.2
Section for Examples 13.12.1 and 13.14.1.

The value β_1 is to be taken at 0.85 for $f'_c \leq 4000$ psi (ACI-10.2.7).
   (b) Compute the forces C_c, C_s, and T.

$$C_c = 0.85(3.0)(11.67)(15) = 446 \text{ kips } (1980 \text{ kN})$$

$$T = 50.0(2.37) = 118 \text{ kips } (527 \text{ kN})$$

$$\epsilon'_s = 0.003\left(\frac{13.72 - 2.4}{13.72}\right) = 0.00248 > \frac{f_y}{E_s}, \qquad \text{compression steel yields}$$

$$C_s = 50.0(2.37) - 0.85(3.0)(2.37) = 118 - 6 = 112 \text{ kips } (500 \text{ kN})$$

(c) Compute P_b and e_b.

$$P_b = C_c + C_s - T = 446 + 112 - 118 = 440 \text{ kips (1960 kN)}$$

For rotational equilibrium about the plastic centroid,

$$P_b e_b = [446(12 - 11.67/2) + 112(12 - 2.4) + 118(12 - 2.4)]\tfrac{1}{12}$$
$$= 229 + 90 + 95 = 414 \text{ ft-kips (562 kN-m)}$$

$$e_b = \frac{414(12)}{440} = 11.3 \text{ in. (287 mm)}$$

On the given section, if $P_n > 440$ kips (or $e < 11.3$ in.), the member is more a column than a beam and is referred to as a case where compression controls; if $P_n < 440$ kips (or $e > 11.3$ in.), the member is more a beam than a column and is referred to as a case where tension controls.

13.13 Balanced Condition—Circular Sections with Round Core

The determination of the values of P_b and e_b at the balanced condition for a circular column is not nearly so simple (Fig. 13.13.1) as for the rectangular column. Of course, formulas can be derived and curves and tables are available for analyzing or designing such circular columns [23–26] as well as for square columns with a circular core [26]. However, these values may be determined by direct application of statics, using coefficients for circular sections (as provided in Fig. 13.13.2) and the rectangular compressive stress distribution as has been used for beams.

EXAMPLE 13.13.1 Determine the load P_b and the eccentricity e_b for a balanced strain condition on the section of Fig. 13.13.1 by using the method of statics and the rectangular stress distribution as for beams. Use $f'_c = 4000$ psi, $f_y = 50,000$ psi and the ACI Code.

Solution: (a) Locate the neutral axis. Referring to Fig. 13.13.1,

$$x_b = \frac{0.003(17.44)}{0.003 + 0.00172} = 11.08 \text{ in. (281 mm)}$$

Assume, as for a rectangular section,

$$a_b = \beta_1 x_b = 0.85(11.08) = 9.41 \text{ in. (239 mm)}$$

(b) Compute forces C_{s1} to C_{s3} and T_1 to T_3. Check strains at the various bars to see whether they yield or not.

For T_1: $\epsilon = \epsilon_y, \qquad f_s = f_y = 50,000 \text{ psi}$

For T_2: $\epsilon = \dfrac{4.93\epsilon_y}{6.36} = 0.00134, \qquad f_s = 38,800 \text{ psi}$

For T_3: $\epsilon = \dfrac{1.22\epsilon_y}{6.36} = 0.00033, \qquad f_s = 9600 \text{ psi}$

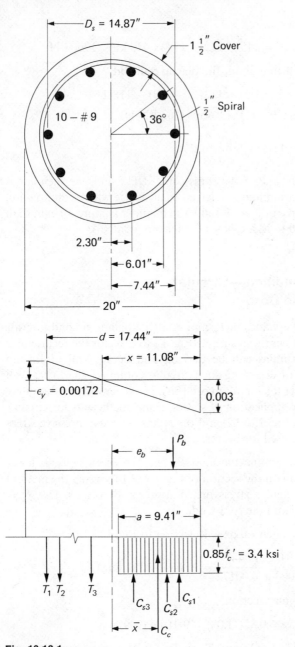

Fig. 13.13.1
Balanced strain condition for section in Examples 13.13.1
and 13.15.1.

For C_{s1}: $\epsilon = 0.003\left(\dfrac{8.52}{11.08}\right) = 0.0023 > \epsilon_y,$ $f'_s = f_y = 50{,}000$ psi

For C_{s2}: $\epsilon = 0.003\left(\dfrac{7.09}{11.08}\right) = 0.0019 > \epsilon_y,$ $f'_s = f_y = 50{,}000$ psi

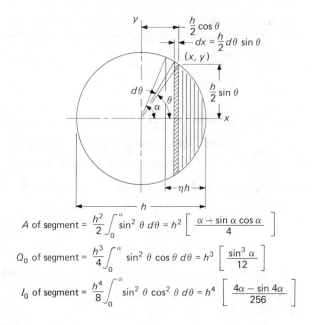

$$A \text{ of segment} = \frac{h^2}{2} \int_0^\alpha \sin^2 \theta \, d\theta = h^2 \left[\frac{\alpha - \sin \alpha \cos \alpha}{4} \right]$$

$$Q_0 \text{ of segment} = \frac{h^3}{4} \int_0^\alpha \sin^2 \theta \cos \theta \, d\theta = h^3 \left[\frac{\sin^3 \alpha}{12} \right]$$

$$I_0 \text{ of segment} = \frac{h^4}{8} \int_0^\alpha \sin^2 \theta \cos^2 \theta \, d\theta = h^4 \left[\frac{4\alpha - \sin 4\alpha}{256} \right]$$

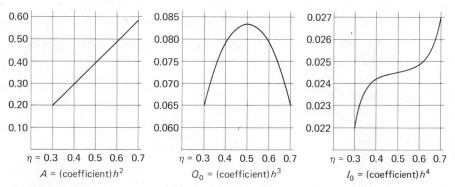

Fig. 13.13.2
Properties of circular segments.

For C_{s3}: $\epsilon = 0.003 \left(\dfrac{3.38}{11.08} \right) = 0.00092$, $f'_s = 26{,}600$ psi

The forces are

$$T_1 = A_s f_y = 1.0(50.0) = 50.0 \text{ kips (222 kN)}$$
$$T_2 = A_s f_s = 2.0(38.8) = 77.6 \text{ kips (345 kN)}$$
$$T_3 = A_s f_s = 2.0(9.6) = 19.2 \text{ kips (85.4 kN)}$$
$$C_{s1} = A'_s(f_y - 0.85f'_c) = 1.0(50.0 - 3.4) = 46.6 \text{ kips (207 kN)}$$
$$C_{s2} = A'_s(f_y - 0.85f'_c) = 2.0(50.0 - 3.4) = 93.2 \text{ kips (415 kN)}$$
$$C_{s3} = A'_s(f'_s - 0.85f'_c) = 2.0(26.6 - 3.4) = 46.4 \text{ kips (206 kN)}$$

Note that the compressive stresses have been corrected by $0.85f'_c$ to account for the concrete that is displaced by steel.

(c) Compute the force C_c, and locate its point of application. Referring to Fig. 13.13.2, which provides data for determining the area, first moment, and moment of inertia of circular segments,

$$\eta = \frac{a}{h} = \frac{9.41}{20} = 0.47$$

Using $\eta = 0.47$ and obtaining the coefficients from Fig. 13.13.2,

$$\text{area of segment} = 0.37(20)^2 = 148 \text{ sq in.}$$
$$Q_0 \text{ of segment} = 0.0825(20)^3 = 660 \text{ in.}^3$$

Computing $\bar{x}$ by dividing Q_0 by the area of the segment,

$$\bar{x} \text{ of segment} = \frac{660}{148} = 4.46 \text{ in.}$$

$$C_c = 0.85 f'_c \text{ (area of segment)}$$
$$= 0.85(4)(148) = 503 \text{ kips (2240 kN)}$$

C_c acts at 4.46 in. (113 mm) from the center of the column.

(d) Compute P_b.

$$P_b = C_c + C_s - T$$
$$= 503 + 186 - 147 = 542 \text{ kips (2410 kN)}$$

(e) Compute e_b. The computations for rotational equilibrium are shown in Table 13.13.1.

Table 13.13.1

	Force	Arm	Moment
C_c	503.0	4.46	2240
C_{s1}	46.6	7.44	347
C_{s2}	93.2	6.01	560
C_{s3}	46.4	2.30	107
T_1	50.0	7.44	372
T_2	77.6	6.01	466
T_3	19.2	2.30	44

Total moment   4136 in.-kips

Therefore

$$M_b = P_b e_b = \frac{4136}{12} = 345 \text{ ft-kips (468 kN-m)}$$

$$e_b = \frac{M_b}{P_b} = \frac{4136}{542} = 7.63 \text{ in. (194 mm)}$$

An alternative method proposed by Whitney [27] is to use an equivalent rectangular column where the depth in the direction of bending is 0.8 of the actual column diameter and the total amount of longitudinal reinforcement is placed one half on each side of the member at $2D_s/3$ apart. The term D_s (Fig. 13.13.1) is the diameter of a circle circumscribing the longitudinal steel of the original column. This equivalent column method gives results that are in good agreement with tests [8].

13.14 Investigation of Strength in Compression Controls Region—Rectangular Sections

When the ultimate eccentric load P_n exceeds the balanced value of P_b or when the eccentricity e is less than the balanced value e_b, the member acts more as a column than as a beam known as "compression controls." In this case the tensile force T (see Fig. 13.12.1) will be based on a stress less than yield stress (see Fig. 13.6.2) and may actually be a compressive force.

The ultimate eccentric load at a given eccentricity $e < e_b$ may be obtained by considering the actual strain variation as the unknown and using the principles of statics. This is the most rational approach.

EXAMPLE 13.14.1   Determine the nominal compressive strength P_n for the section of Fig. 13.12.2 for an eccentricity $e = 8$ in. by direct application of statics. Use $f'_c = 3000$ psi, $f_y = 50,000$ psi, and the ACI Code.

Solution: (a) Estimate whether the eccentricity will be in the compression controls or the tension controls region. Since the balanced condition was determined in Example 13.12.1 as

$$P_b = 440 \text{ kips}, \qquad e_b = 11.3 \text{ in.}$$

it is known that compression controls for $e < 11.3$ in. For $e = 8$ in., the position of the neutral axis x is not known.

(b) Determine the location of the neutral axis. Since the actual x for $e = 8$ in. should exceed the value of $x_b = 13.72$ in. (see Fig. 13.12.2) and the value of ϵ'_s exceeds ϵ_y at the balanced condition, it is certain that $\epsilon'_s > \epsilon_y$ for this present example. Thus, referring to Fig. 13.12.2 for the forces,

$$C_s = A'_s(f_y - 0.85f'_c) = 2.37(50.0 - 2.55) = 112.5 \text{ kips}$$
$$C_c = 0.85f'_c b(0.85x) = 2.55(15)(0.85x) = 32.5x$$
$$T = A_s f_s = 2.37 \frac{(29,000)(0.003)(21.60 - x)}{x} = \frac{4450 - 206x}{x}$$

Taking moments about P_n,

$$0 = 112.5(4.0 - 2.40) - 32.5x\left(\frac{0.85x}{2} - 4\right) + \frac{4450 - 206x}{x}(21.6 - 4.0)$$

$$0 = x^3 - 9.41x^2 + 249.6x - 5673$$

$$x = 16.0 \text{ in. (406 mm)}$$

Then

$$C_s = 112.5 \text{ kips}$$

$$C_c = 32.5(16) = 520 \text{ kips}$$

$$T = \frac{4450 - 206(16)}{16.0} = 72.2 \text{ kips}$$

$$P_n = 520 + 112.5 - 72.4 = 560 \text{ kips } (2490 \text{ kN})$$

Whitney Formula—Compression Controls Case. Approximate procedures may sometimes be desirable, particularly as an aid in selecting section sizes, as will be discussed in Secs. 13.18 and 13.19.

One approximate procedure that may be applied to the case when the reinforcement is symmetrically placed in single layers parallel to the axis of bending is the one proposed by Whitney [27]. Taking moments of the forces in Fig. 13.14.1 about the tension steel gives

$$P_n\left(e + \frac{d - d'}{2}\right) = C_c\left(d - \frac{a}{2}\right) + C_s(d - d') \qquad \textbf{(13.14.1)}$$

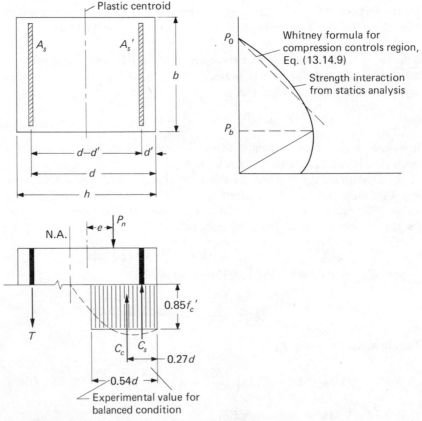

Fig. 13.14.1
Whitney formula—compression controls case.

In estimating the ultimate compressive force C_c in the concrete, Whitney used for the depth of the rectangular stress block an average value based on the balanced condition, $a = 0.54d$. This would give a value for C_c corresponding to the balanced condition; a minimum C_c for the compression controls region. Thus

$$C_c = 0.85f'_c ba = 0.85f'_c b(0.54d) = 0.459bdf'_c$$

and

$$C_c\left(d - \frac{a}{2}\right) = 0.459bdf'_c\left(d - \frac{0.54d}{2}\right) = \frac{1}{3}f'_c bd^2 \qquad (13.14.2)$$

When compression controls, compression steel usually yields at ultimate strength, and neglecting displaced concrete

$$C_s = A'_s f_y \qquad (13.14.3)$$

Substituting Eqs. (13.14.2) and (13.14.3) in Eq. (13.14.1) gives

$$P_n = \frac{\frac{1}{3}f'_c bd^2}{e + \frac{1}{2}(d - d')} + \frac{A'_s f_y(d - d')}{e + \frac{1}{2}(d - d')}$$

from which

$$P_n = \frac{f'_c bh}{\dfrac{3he}{d^2} + \dfrac{3(d - d')h}{2d^2}} + \frac{A'_s f_y}{\dfrac{e}{d - d'} + \dfrac{1}{2}} \qquad (13.14.4)$$

One of the boundary conditions of this interaction relationship is that it must satisfy the condition

$$P_n = P_0 \qquad \text{at } e = 0 \qquad (13.14.5)$$

in which

$$P_0 = 0.85f'_c bh + 2f_y A'_s \qquad (13.14.6)$$

if the correction for the displaced concrete is not made. Substituting the boundary condition as expressed by Eqs. (13.14.5) and (13.14.6) in Eq. (13.14.4) requires

$$\frac{3(d - d')h}{2d^2} = \frac{1}{0.85} = 1.18 \qquad (13.14.7)$$

Making this necessary substitution, Eq. (13.14.4) becomes

$$P_n = \frac{bhf'_c}{\dfrac{3he}{d^2} + 1.18} + \frac{A'_s f_y}{\dfrac{e}{d - d'} + 0.5} \qquad (13.14.8)$$

which is the Whitney formula for symmetrical steel with no correction for concrete displaced by compression steel.

In using an approximate formula such as Eq. (13.14.8), it is desirable to be on the conservative side. This would be the case for small eccentricities, because the actual depth of the compressive stress block would then be larger than the assumed value of $0.54d$.

A more useful expression for Eq. (13.14.8) in terms of dimensionless ratios may be obtained by letting $A_g = bh$, $\xi h = d$, $A_s = A'_s$ (for symmetrical reinforcement), $\rho_g = 2A'_s/A_g$, and $\gamma h = d - d'$; thus

$$P_n = A_g \left[\frac{f'_c}{\left(\dfrac{3}{\xi^2}\right)\left(\dfrac{e}{h}\right) + 1.18} + \frac{\rho_g f_y}{\left(\dfrac{2}{\gamma}\right)\left(\dfrac{e}{h}\right) + 1} \right] \qquad \textbf{(13.14.9)}$$

EXAMPLE 13.14.2   Determine the nominal compressive strength P_n for the section of Fig. 13.12.2 for an eccentricity of 8 in. by using the Whitney formula, Eq. (13.14.8). Use $f'_c = 3000$ psi, $f_y = 50,000$ psi, and the ACI Code.

Solution: Since this loading is in the compression controls region, Eq. (13.14.8) may be used to obtain an approximate strength.

$$
\begin{aligned}
P_n &= \frac{bhf'_c}{3he/d^2 + 1.18} + \frac{A'_s f_y}{e/(d - d') + 0.5} \\[2mm]
&= \frac{360(3.0)}{[3(24)(8)]/(21.6)^2 + 1.18} + \frac{2.37(50)}{8/(19.20) + 0.50} \\[2mm]
&= \frac{1080}{2.415} + \frac{118.5}{0.916} = 448 + 129 = 577 \text{ kips } (2570 \text{ kN})
\end{aligned}
$$

It may be noted that the Whitney formula value (577 kips) is not conservative in this case compared to the more exact statics solution (560 kips). In general, Eq. (13.14.8) is conservative for small eccentricity loading and unconservative as the eccentricity approaches the balanced value, as schematically shown in Fig. 13.14.1.

13.15 Investigation of Strength in Compression Controls Region—Circular Sections

As discussed in detail in the preceding section, a column under eccentric load is in the compression controls region when P_n exceeds P_b or when e is less than e_b. Circular columns are more complicated to analyze than rectangular columns because of the difficulty in treating the circular segments and the steel bars placed around the circumference of a circle.

The most rational approach in the analysis of circular columns lies in the determination of the strain distribution and the use of the principles of statics. This method is illustrated by the following example.

EXAMPLE 13.15.1   Determine the nominal compressive strength P_n for the section of Fig. 13.13.1 for an eccentricity $e = 5$ in., by the direct application of statics. Use $f'_c = 4000$ psi, $f_y = 50,000$ psi, and the ACI Code.

Solution: From the solution for the balanced condition in Example 13.13.1, it is known that compression controls for $e = 5$ in. $< e_b = 7.63$ in.

A relatively exact treatment using the strain diagram for determining the effect of the steel requires several assumptions in order to determine the location of the neutral axis. The forces (see Fig. 13.13.1) on the different bars based on the strain diagram with an unknown value of x instead of x_b are

$$T_1 = \frac{0.003(17.44 - x)}{x}(29,000)(1.0) = \frac{87(17.44 - x)}{x}$$

$$T_2 = \frac{0.003(16.01 - x)}{x}(29,000)(2.0) = \frac{174(16.01 - x)}{x}$$

$$T_3 = \frac{0.003(12.30 - x)}{x}(29,000)(2.0) = \frac{174(12.30 - x)}{x}$$

$$C_{s1} = A'_s(f_y - 0.85f'_c) = 1.0(50.0 - 3.4) = 46.6 \text{ kips}$$
$$C_{s2} = 2.0(50.0 - 3.4) = 93.2 \text{ kips}$$

$$C_{s3} = \left[\frac{0.003(x - 7.70)(29,000)}{x} - 3.4\right](2.0) = \frac{174(x - 7.70) - 6.8x}{x}$$

The values C_{s1} and C_{s2} are based on a strain at least equal to the yield strain ϵ_y at the ultimate condition, while C_{s3} is based on a strain less than yield strain but expressed in terms of x. The reduction has been made for displaced concrete on all bars assumed to be in the compression zone. These assumptions must all be verified after locating the neutral axis x.

The magnitude and location of the force C_c may be expressed as a function of x by using the properties of circular segments in Fig. 13.13.2. The solution for the neutral axis may be obtained by repeated trials in taking moments about P_n as follows:

$$\frac{87(17.44 - x)(12.44)}{x} + \frac{174(16.01 - x)(11.01)}{x} + \frac{174(12.30 - x)(7.30)}{x}$$

$$+ 46.6(2.44) + 93.2(1.01)$$

$$- \left[\frac{174(x - 7.70) - 6.8x}{x}\right](2.70)$$

$$- C_c(5.0 - \bar{x}) = 0$$

from which

$$395.4 - 25.94x - \frac{C_c(5.0 - \bar{x})}{174}x = 0$$

Solving for x by trial computation as shown in Table 13.15.1, gives $x = 13.1$ in. (333 mm).

Table 13.15.1

Trial $a = 0.85x$	Q_0	A	$\bar{x} = Q_0/A$	$C_c = 0.85f'_c A$	x	Derived $a = 0.85x$
10.0	$0.083h^3$	$0.395h^2$	4.20	536	13.9	11.82
10.5	$0.083h^3$	$0.415h^2$	4.00	564	13.5	11.5
11.0	$0.082h^3$	$0.435h^2$	3.77	592	13.1	11.15

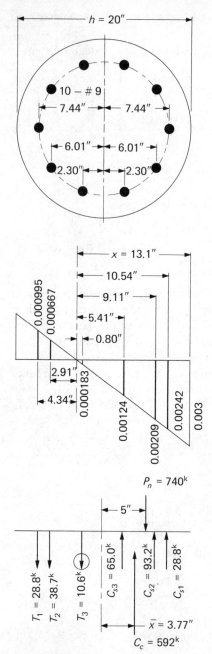

Fig. 13.15.1
Direct application of statics in Example 13.15.1.

The forces then become, after the strain assumptions as shown in Fig. 13.15.1 have been verified,

$$T_1 = 87\left(\frac{4.34}{13.1}\right) = 28.8 \text{ kips}$$

$$T_2 = 174\left(\frac{2.91}{13.1}\right) = 38.7 \text{ kips}$$

$$T_3 = 174\left(\frac{-0.8}{13.1}\right) = -10.6 \text{ kips}, \qquad \text{actually a compression}$$

$$C_{s1} = 46.6 \text{ kips}$$

$$C_{s2} = 93.2 \text{ kips}$$

$$C_{s3} = \frac{174(5.4) - 6.8(13.1)}{13.1} = 65.0 \text{ kips}$$

$$C_c = 592 \text{ kips}$$

The nominal strength P_n is therefore

$$P_n = 592 + 65.0 + 93.2 + 46.6 + 10.6 - 38.7 - 28.8 = 740 \text{ kips } (3290 \text{ kN})$$

A check may be made by taking moments of the forces shown in Fig. 13.15.1 about the centerline of the column; thus

$$P_n(5) = C_c\bar{x} + (C_{s1} + T_1)(7.44) + (C_{s2} + T_2)(6.01)$$
$$+ (C_{s3} + T_3)(2.30)$$
$$740(5) = 592(3.77) + (46.6 + 28.8)(7.44)$$
$$+ (93.2 + 38.7)(6.01) + (65.0 - 10.6)(2.30)$$
$$3700 \approx 2230 + 560 + 793 + 125$$
$$3700 \approx 3708 \qquad\qquad\qquad \text{say, OK}$$

Further trial by revising the expression for T_3 to that of a C_{s4} to include effect of the displaced concrete does not seem warranted and is not shown.

Whitney Formula—Compression Controls Case for Circular Sections.
As mentioned near the end of Sec. 13.13, Whitney proposed an equivalent rectangular column (see Fig. 13.15.2) that could be used for computational purposes to approximate the actual circular section.

The Whitney equation for rectangular columns has been shown to be

$$P_n = \frac{bhf'_c}{3he/d^2 + 1.18} + \frac{A'_s f_y}{e/(d - d') + 0.50} \qquad \textbf{[13.14.8]}$$

Substituting $A_{st}/2$ for A'_s, $2D_s/3$ for $(d - d')$, $0.8h$ for h, $0.4h + D_s/3$ for d, and A_g for bh in Eq. (13.14.8),

$$P_n = \frac{A_g f'_c}{\dfrac{9.6he}{(0.8h + 0.67D_s)^2} + 1.18} + \frac{A_{st} f_y}{\dfrac{3e}{D_s} + 1.00} \qquad \textbf{(13.15.1)}$$

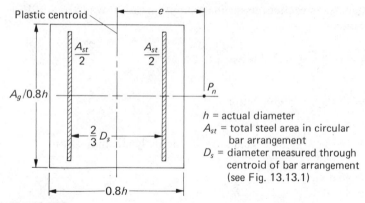

h = actual diameter
A_{st} = total steel area in circular
       bar arrangement
D_s = diameter measured through
       centroid of bar arrangement
       (see Fig. 13.13.1)

Fig. 13.15.2
Whitney's equivalent rectangular section for a circular section in the compression controls region.

For design purposes, Eq. (13.15.1) may be converted into the following, letting $\rho_g = A_{st}/A_g$.

$$P_n = A_g \left[\frac{f'_c}{\dfrac{21.6}{(1.2 + D_s/h)^2} \dfrac{e}{h} + 1.18} + \frac{\rho_g f_y}{\left(\dfrac{3}{D_s/h}\right)\dfrac{e}{h} + 1.0} \right] \qquad \textbf{(13.15.2)}$$

EXAMPLE 13.15.2   Solve Example 13.15.1 using the Whitney formula, Eq. (13.15.1).

Solution: Substituting the properties of the given column section as shown in Fig. 13.13.1 in the Whitney formula for circular sections, Eq. (13.15.1),

$$P_n = A_g f'_c \left/ \left[\frac{9.6he}{(0.8h + 0.67D_s)^2} + 1.18 \right] + A_{st} f_y \left/ \left(\frac{3e}{D_s} + 1.00 \right) \right.\right.$$

$$= \frac{314(4)}{\left\{ \dfrac{9.6(20)(5)}{[0.8(20) + 0.67(14.87)]^2} + 1.18 \right\}} + \frac{10(50)}{\left[\dfrac{3(5)}{14.87} + 1.00 \right]}$$

$$= 482 + 248 = 730 \text{ kips } (3250 \text{ kN})$$

For this problem, this value is in good agreement with the 740 kips obtained by application of statics.

13.16 Investigation of Strength in Tension Controls Region—Rectangular Sections

When the ultimate capacity P_n is less than the balanced value P_b or the eccentricity e is greater than the balanced value e_b, the member acts more as a beam than as a column, known as "tension controls." In this situation the ultimate strain in the steel most distant from the neutral axis will be greater than the yield strain $\epsilon_y = f_y/E_s$ (see Fig. 13.6.2).

The most rational approach is to consider the location of the actual neutral axis distance x as the unknown and use the principles of statics.

EXAMPLE 13.16.1 Determine the nominal compressive strength P_n for the member shown in Fig. 13.16.1 for an eccentricity $e = 20$ in., using the method of statics for $f_c' = 3000$ psi, $f_y = 50{,}000$ psi and the ACI Code.

Solution: From the result of Example 13.12.1 it is known that $e = 20$ in. exceeds the $e_b = 11.3$ in. for the balanced condition; therefore tension controls and the strain on the tension steel exceeds ϵ_y. It is first assumed that the strain on the compression steel is also at least equal to yield strain,

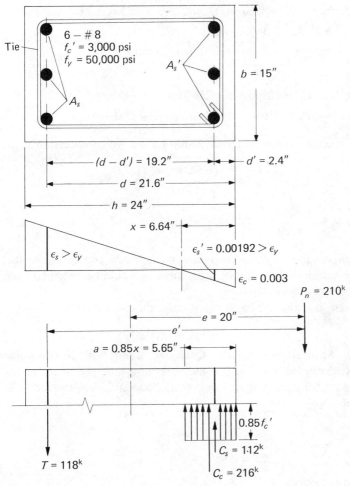

Fig. 13.16.1

Section for Example 13.16.1—tension controls.

although the validity of the assumption must be verified before the solution is accepted. Referring to Fig. 13.16.1, the forces T, C_c, and C_s are

$$T = A_s f_y = 3(0.79)(50.0) = 118 \text{ kips}$$
$$C_c = 0.85f'_c ab = 0.85(3.0)(0.85)(x)(15) = 32.5x$$
$$C_s = A'_s(f_y - 0.85f'_c) = 3(0.79)(50 - 2.55) = 112 \text{ kips}$$

Force equilibrium requires

$$P_n = C_c + C_s - T = 32.5x + 112 - 118 = 32.5x - 6.0$$

Taking moments arbitrarily about the tension steel, rotational equilibrium gives

$$P_n\left(e + \frac{d - d'}{2}\right) = C_c\left(d - \frac{a}{2}\right) + C_s(d - d')$$

$$(32.5x - 6.0)(20 + 9.60) = 32.5x(21.6 - 0.425x) + 112(19.20)$$
$$x^2 + 18.82x - 169.2 = 0$$
$$x = 6.64 \text{ in. (169 mm)}$$

Therefore

$$C_c = 32.5(6.64) = 216 \text{ kips}$$
$$P_n = 216 - 6.0 = 210 \text{ kips (934 kN)}$$

Verifying the correctness of the strain condition on the compression steel,

$$\epsilon'_s = \epsilon_c \frac{x - d'}{x} = 0.003\left(\frac{6.64 - 2.40}{6.64}\right) = 0.00192$$

$$\epsilon_y = \frac{50}{29,000} = 0.00172 < 0.00192 \qquad\qquad \text{OK}$$

Therefore compression steel yields as assumed. When compression steel does yield, the solution using statics is the same as would be obtained from Eq. (13.16.7), which is derived below.

The complete ultimate strength interaction diagram for the section is given in Fig. 13.16.2.

Approximate Formulas—Tension Controls Case for Rectangular Sections. Referring to Fig. 13.16.1 and assuming that the strain in the compression steel is larger than the yield strain, one finds that the forces T, C_s, and C_c are

$$T = A_s f_y$$
$$C_s = A'_s(f_y - 0.85f'_c)$$
$$C_c = 0.85f'_c(\beta_1 x)b$$

From force equilibrium

$$P_n = 0.85f'_c \beta_1 xb + A'_s(f_y - 0.85f'_c) - A_s f_y \qquad\qquad \textbf{(13.16.1)}$$

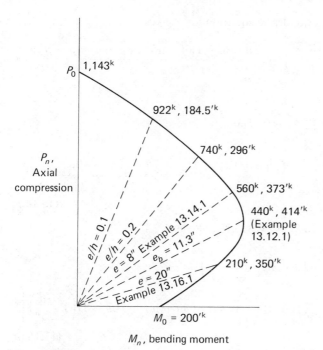

Fig. 13.16.2
Ultimate strength interaction diagram for section of Fig. 13.16.1.

Let $m = f_y/(0.85f'_c)$, $\rho = A_s/bd$, and $\rho' = A'_s/bd$; thus

$$P_n = 0.85f'_c[\beta_1 xb + \rho'(m-1)bd - \rho mbd]$$

$$= 0.85f'_cbd\left[\frac{\beta_1 x}{d} + \rho'(m-1) - \rho m\right] \quad \textbf{(13.16.2)}$$

From moment equilibrium with respect to the tension steel,

$$P_n e' = 0.85f'_c(\beta_1 x)b\left(d - \frac{\beta_1 x}{2}\right) + A'_s(f_y - 0.85f'_c)(d - d') \quad \textbf{(13.16.3)}$$

Making the same substitutions as for Eq. (13.16.1) gives

$$P_n e' = 0.85f'_cbd\left[\beta_1 x - \frac{(\beta_1 x)^2}{2d} + \rho'(m-1)(d-d')\right] \quad \textbf{(13.16.4)}$$

Substituting Eq. (13.16.2) in Eq. (13.16.4) gives

$$e'\left[\frac{\beta_1 x}{d} + \rho'(m-1) - \rho m\right] = \left[\beta_1 x - \frac{(\beta_1 x)^2}{2d} + \rho'(m-1)(d-d')\right]$$

or

$$x^2 + \left(\frac{2\beta_1 e'}{\beta_1^2} - \frac{2\beta_1 d}{\beta_1^2}\right)x + \frac{e'm(\rho' - \rho) - e'\rho' - \rho'(m-1)(d-d')}{\beta_1^2}2d = 0$$

Solving the preceding quadratic equation for x gives

$$x = \frac{d - e'}{\beta_1} + \sqrt{\left(\frac{d - e'}{\beta_1}\right)^2 + \frac{2d[\rho'(m - 1)(d - d') + e'\rho' + e'm(\rho - \rho')]}{\beta_1^2}}$$

or

$$\frac{x}{d} = \frac{1 - e'/d}{\beta_1}$$
$$+ \sqrt{\left(\frac{1 - e'/d}{\beta_1}\right)^2 + \frac{2[\rho'(m - 1)(1 - d'/d) + \rho'(e'/d) + (e'/d)m(\rho - \rho')]}{\beta_1^2}}$$

$$(13.16.5)$$

Substituting Eq. (13.16.5) in Eq. (13.16.2) gives

$$P_n = 0.85f'_c bd \left\{ \rho'(m - 1) - \rho m + \left(1 - \frac{e'}{d}\right) \right.$$
$$\left. + \sqrt{\left(1 - \frac{e'}{d}\right)^2 + 2\left[\left(\frac{e'}{d}\right)(\rho m - \rho'm + \rho') + \rho'(m - 1)\left(1 - \frac{d'}{d}\right)\right]} \right\}$$

$$(13.16.6)$$

For cases where the tension and compression faces are reinforced the same $\rho' = \rho$, Eq. (13.16.6) reduces to

$$P_n = 0.85f'_c bd \left\{ -\rho + 1 - \frac{e'}{d} + \sqrt{\left(1 - \frac{e'}{d}\right)^2 + 2\rho\left[(m - 1)\left(1 - \frac{d'}{d}\right) + \frac{e'}{d}\right]} \right\}$$

$$(13.16.7)$$

When no compression reinforcement is present, Eq. (13.16.6) may be simplified by making $\rho' = 0$; thus

$$P_n = 0.85f'_c bd \left[-\rho m + 1 - \frac{e'}{d} + \sqrt{\left(1 - \frac{e'}{d}\right)^2 + \frac{2e'\rho m}{d}} \right] \quad (13.16.8)$$

13.17 Investigation of Strength in Tension Controls Region—Circular Sections

For this situation, referring to Fig. 13.6.2, the ultimate strain in the steel most distant from the neutral axis will be greater than yield strain $\epsilon_y = f_y/E_s$. The following example illustrates a direct application of statics to obtain the nominal strength P_n.

EXAMPLE 13.17.1 Determine the nominal compressive strength P_n for the section of Fig. 13.17.1 (same section as in Fig. 13.13.1) for an eccentricity $e = 20$ in., by a direct application of statics. Use $f'_c = 4000$ psi, $f_y = 50,000$ psi, and the ACI Code.

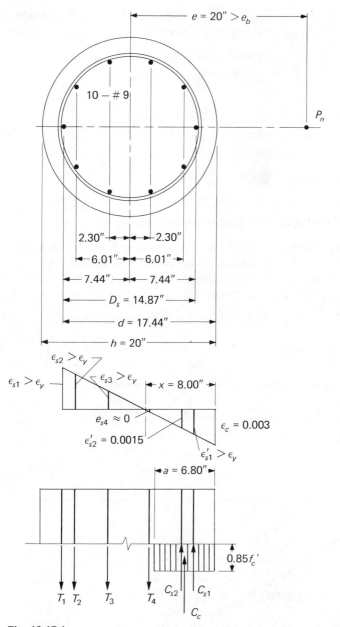

Fig. 13.17.1
Section for Example 13.17.1.

Solution: Because of the solution for the balanced condition (Example 13.13.1), it is known that tension controls for $e = 20$ in. $> e_b = 7.63$ in.

It may be first assumed that the bars contributing the forces T_1, T_2, and T_3 have reached yield strain, that the force T_4 is small enough to be neglected, and that the bars contributing the forces C_{s1} and C_{s2} have also reached yield strain. Of course, once the neutral-axis distance x has been determined, the correctness of these strain assumptions must be verified. The forces are

$$T_1 = 1.0(50.0) = 50.0 \text{ kips}$$
$$T_2 = T_3 = 2.0(50) = 100.0 \text{ kips}$$
$$T_4 = 0$$
$$C_{s2} = 2.0(50.0 - 3.4) = 93.2 \text{ kips}$$
$$C_{s1} = 1.0(50.0 - 3.4) = 46.6 \text{ kips}$$
$$C_c = 0.85f'_c A_{seg}$$

Force equilibrium requires

$$P_n = C_c + C_{s1} + C_{s2} - (T_1 + T_2 + T_3 + T_4)$$
$$= C_c + 93.2 + 46.6 - (50.0 + 100.0 + 100.0) = C_c - 110.2$$

In order to use conveniently the circular section property charts (Fig. 13.13.2 or Fig. 13.17.2), the summation of moments for equilibrium is taken about the plastic centroid, thus illustrating a variation of the method used in Example 13.15.1. The moment equation is

$$P_n(20) = C_c\bar{x} + (C_{s1} + T_1)(7.44) + (C_{s2} + T_2)(6.01) + T_3(2.30)$$

$$P_n = \frac{C_c\bar{x}}{20} + 105.5$$

Replacing P_n in the above equation with $C_c - 110.2$ gives

$$C_c = \frac{4314}{20 - \bar{x}} = 0.85f'_c A_{seg}$$

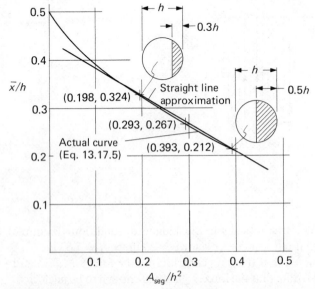

Fig. 13.17.2
Centroid of circular segment versus its area.

Table 13.17.1

A_{seg}	A_{seg}/h^2	$\bar{x}/h$	$\bar{x}$	Computed A_{seg}
120	0.3	0.26	5.2	85.6
100	0.25	0.29	5.8	89.5
92	0.23	0.303	6.06	91.0

$A_{seg} = 1268/(20 - \bar{x})$, which can be solved by trial, using Fig. 13.17.2, to give $A_{seg} = 91$ sq in. See Table 13.17.1.

Therefore

$$P_n = C_c - 110.2 = 3.4(91) - 110.2 = 199 \text{ kips (885 kN)}$$

From Fig. 13.13.2, $a = 0.34(20) = 6.8$ in. and $x = 6.8/0.85 = 8.00$ in.

To verify the correctness, the steel strains must be checked. Thus

$$\epsilon_{s1} = \frac{9.44}{8.00}(0.003) > \epsilon_y \qquad\qquad \text{OK}$$

$$\epsilon_{s2} = \frac{8.01}{8.00}(0.003) > \epsilon_y \qquad\qquad \text{OK}$$

$$\epsilon_{s3} = \frac{4.30}{8.00}(0.003) = 0.00161 \approx \epsilon_y = 0.0017 \qquad\qquad \text{OK}$$

$$\epsilon_{s4} = \frac{8.00 - 7.70}{8.00}(0.003) \approx 0 \qquad\qquad \text{OK}$$

$$\epsilon'_{s2} = \frac{8.00 - 3.99}{8.00}(0.003) = 0.0015 < \epsilon_y, \qquad f_s = 43.5 \text{ ksi}$$

$$\epsilon'_{s1} = \frac{8.00 - 2.56}{8.00}(0.003) = 0.00204 > \epsilon_y \qquad\qquad \text{OK}$$

C_{s2} is found to have been taken at too high a value, though it is not expected that the result will change significantly. If a second trial is desired, it will be as follows:

$$C_{s2} = 2.0(43.5 - 3.4) = 80.2 \text{ kips}$$

$$P_n = C_c - 123.2$$

$$P_n = \frac{C_c\bar{x}}{20} + 105.5 - 3.9 = \frac{C_c\bar{x}}{20} + 101.6$$

$$C_c = \frac{224.8(20)}{20 - \bar{x}} = 0.85f'_c A_{seg} = 3.4A_{seg}$$

$$A_{seg} = \frac{1323}{20 - \bar{x}}, \qquad A_{seg} = 94 \text{ sq in.}, \qquad a = 6.9 \text{ in.} \qquad \text{OK}$$

$$P_n = 3.4(94.0) - 123.2 = 196 \text{ kips (872 kN)}$$

This value of P_n may be compared with 177 kips obtained by using the approximate formula, Eq. (13.17.12), developed later in this section.

Whitney-Hognestad Formula—Tension Controls Case for Circular Sections. As shown above, treatment of circular columns by the direct application of statics involves complicated calculations. A formula for this case is at best approximate; however, Whitney [27] and Hognestad [8] have indicated that the use of an equivalent column gives results in reasonable agreement with test results. Since less of the circular cross section is under compression in this condition than for the condition in which compression controls, it is considered that the equivalent rectangle as used for the latter case (small eccentricity) is not sufficiently accurate. Therefore the circular section is still used for computing C_c, while the equivalent steel effect is obtained by placing 40% of the total steel area on each side of the plastic centroid at a distance apart equal to 75% of the core diameter, as shown in Fig. 13.17.3.

The development of the approximate formula follows. Referring to Fig. 13.17.3, it is assumed that a uniform compressive stress of $0.85f_c'$ acts over a portion of the area on the compression side of the neutral axis. The internal forces are

$$C_c = 0.85f_c'A_{seg} \qquad (A_{seg} = \text{area of crosshatched section}) \qquad \textbf{(13.17.1)}$$
$$C_s = 0.4A_{st}f_y \qquad \textbf{(13.17.2)}$$
$$T = 0.4A_{st}f_y \qquad \textbf{(13.17.3)}$$

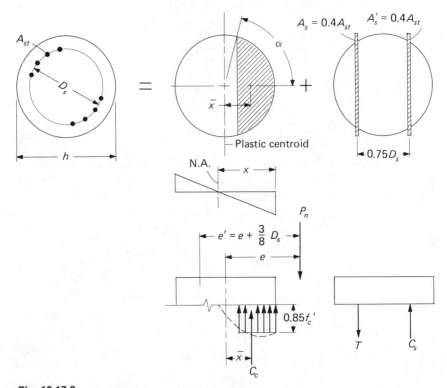

Fig. 13.17.3
Whitney-Hognestad formula for circular columns with round core—tension controls.

The properties of circular segments (Fig. 13.13.2) indicate

$$Q_0 = A_{seg}\bar{x} = \frac{h^3}{12}\sin^3\alpha \qquad (13.17.4)$$

or

$$\frac{\bar{x}}{h} = \frac{h^2\sin^3\alpha}{12A_{seg}} \qquad (13.17.5)$$

Since a simple expression for $\bar{x}$ is desired, Hognestad shows [on page 90 of Ref. 8] that a straight-line approximation can be used. Figure 13.17.2 shows the plot of Eq. (13.17.5).

The most useful portion of the actual curve in that figure is for the compression area extending from $0.3h$ to $0.5h$, which part is essentially a straight line. Thus a straight line can be used,

$$\frac{\bar{x}}{h} = 0.212 + \left(0.393 - \frac{A_{seg}}{h^2}\right)\frac{0.324 - 0.212}{0.393 - 0.198}$$

or

$$\bar{x} = 0.212h + 0.576\left(0.393 - \frac{A_{seg}}{h^2}\right)h \qquad (13.17.6)$$

When it is assumed that $C_s = T$, which means that no correction is to be made for concrete displaced by steel,

$$P_n = C_c$$

which from Eq. (13.17.1) means

$$A_{seg} = \frac{P_n}{0.85f'_c} \qquad (13.17.7)$$

Substitution in Eq. (13.17.6) gives

$$\bar{x} = 0.212h + 0.576\left(0.393h - \frac{P_n}{0.85f'_ch}\right) \qquad (13.17.8)$$

which is essentially the equation used by Whitney and Hognestad.

The solution for P_n can finally be obtained by satisfying moment equilibrium of the two couples: one made of P_n and C_c, the other of T and C_s.

$$0.40A_{st}f_y(0.75D_s) = P_n(e - \bar{x}) \qquad (13.17.9)$$

or

$$0.30A_{st}f_yD_s = P_n\left[e - 0.212h - 0.576\left(0.393h - \frac{P_n}{0.85f'_ch}\right)\right]$$

$$P_ne = 0.30A_{st}f_yD_s + 0.438P_nh - \frac{0.678P_n^2}{f'_ch}$$

$$P_n^2 + P_n\frac{(e - 0.438h)f'_ch}{0.678} - \frac{0.30A_{st}f_yD_sf'_ch}{0.678} = 0 \qquad (13.17.10)$$

Solving the quadratic equation gives

$$P_n = 0.833f'_c h^2 \left[\sqrt{\left(\frac{0.85e}{h} - 0.37\right)^2 + \frac{\rho_g m D_s}{2.55h}} - \left(\frac{0.85e}{h} - 0.37\right) \right]$$

$$(13.17.11)$$

By arbitrarily changing some of the coefficients in Eq. (13.17.11) or by slightly altering the straight line for $\bar{x}$, the following equation is obtained,

$$P_n = 0.85f'_c h^2 \left[\sqrt{\left(\frac{0.85e}{h} - 0.38\right)^2 + \frac{\rho_g m D_s}{2.5h}} - \left(\frac{0.85e}{h} - 0.38\right) \right]$$

$$(13.17.12)$$

which is the Whitney-Hognestad formula in the form given by the 1963 ACI Code and which may serve as an approximate formula for design.

13.18 Design for Ultimate Strength—Region I, Minimum Eccentricity

The approach to design of compression members in bending in accordance with the strength design method of the ACI Code may be divided into three categories (see Fig. 13.18.1): (a) design in Region I for a member having small or negligible bending moment (i.e., maximum axial capacity governs); (b) design for Region II in which compression controls but the strength P_n is less than the $0.80P_0$ (tied) or $0.85P_0$ (spirally reinforced) maximum; and (c) design for Region III in which tension controls.

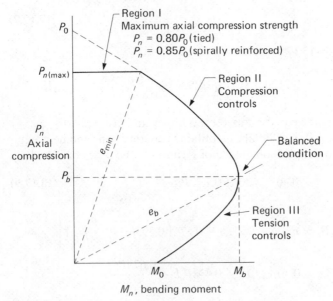

Fig. 13.18.1
Design categories for strength of section under combined axial compression and bending moment.

Design in Region I occurs under the following conditions:

1. For members having low slenderness ratio kL_u/r such that the *effects of slenderness may be neglected* according to ACI-10.11.4 (see also Sec. 13.7):
   (a) The member is subject to axial compression where the bending moment is considered negligible and is not computed.
   (b) The bending moment on the member is computed, but the corresponding eccentricity $e = M_u/P_u$ is less than e_{min} (Fig. 13.18.1) corresponding to the maximum axial capacity.
2. For members where the *effects of slenderness must be considered*, computation of bending moment is required, with the result magnified by the factor δ in accordance with ACI-10.11.5 (see Chap. 15).
   (a) When the eccentricity $e = M_u/P_u$ at any end of a member is computed and found to be less than the code-specified $(0.6 + 0.03h)$ in., the value $(0.6 + 0.03h)$ is to be used as the basic value to be magnified by the factor δ. When $\delta(0.6 + 0.03h)$ is less than e_{min} (Fig. 13.18.1), design is in Region I.
   (b) When computed end eccentricity $e = M_u/P_u$ exceeds $(0.6 + 0.03h)$ in., the computed e is magnified to give δe. When δe is less than e_{min} (Fig. 13.18.1), design is in Region I.

The reader may note particularly that the member designed in Region I has its axial compression force P_u limited by the maximum given by ACI-10.3.5, but need not be explicitly designed to carry the moment based on e_{min} as was required by the 1971 ACI Code. When slenderness effects can be neglected, there is no requirement for bending strength if design bending moment was not computed, or the *actual* design bending moment must be capable of being carried if design bending moment was computed.

When design is in Region I and slenderness must be considered, the required bending strength for the section is based on the magnified actual eccentricity δe or the magnified minimum $\delta(0.6 + 0.03h)$, whichever is greater. Ordinarily any reasonable arrangement of steel will provide sufficient bending strength when design in Region I is based on just using the maximum axial strength prescribed by ACI-10.3.5.

EXAMPLE 13.18.1 Design an axially loaded spirally reinforced circular column for a gravity dead load of 220 kips and a live load of 238 kips using approximately $3\frac{1}{2}\%$ of reinforcement. The column is of average height, and it will be assumed that there is no reduction in strength due to the effects of slenderness. Use $f'_c = 3000$ psi, $f_y = 40,000$ psi, and the ACI Code.

Solution: (a) Determine the required nominal strength P_n.

$$P_u = 1.4(220) + 1.7(238) = 308 + 405 = 713 \text{ kips}$$

$$P_n = \frac{P_u}{\phi} = \frac{713}{0.75} = 950 \text{ kips}$$

(b) Determine the column size. ACI-10.3.5 gives the maximum axial compression nominal strength as

$$P_{n(max)} = 0.85P_0$$

where P_0 is given by Eqs. (13.5.1) or (13.5.3). Thus

$$P_{n(max)} = 0.85A_g[0.85f'_c + \rho_g(f_y - 0.85f'_c)]$$
$$950 = 0.85A_g[0.85(3) + 0.035(40 - 2.55)]$$

$$\text{required } A_g = \frac{950}{3.28} = 289 \text{ sq in.,} \qquad h \text{ (diameter)} = 19.2 \text{ in.}$$

Try $h = 20$ in. with $A_g = 314$ sq in.

(c) Determine reinforcement. Solve the $P_{n(max)}$ equation for ρ_g.

$$950 = 0.85(314)[2.55 + \rho_g(40 - 2.55)]$$
$$\text{required } \rho_g = 0.0270$$
$$\text{required } A_{st} = \rho_g A_g = 0.0270(314) = 8.46 \text{ sq in.}$$

Use 20-in. diameter column with 9-#9 bars.

No further check is required since no moment has been computed and the maximum axial capacity given by ACI-10.3.5 governs in this case.

(d) Design the spiral reinforcement. Using Eq. (13.9.4) which is ACI Formula (10-5),

$$\rho_s = 0.45\left(\frac{A_g}{A_c} - 1\right)\frac{f'_c}{f_{sy}}$$

$$A_g = 314 \qquad \text{and} \qquad A_c = \frac{(20 - 3)^2\pi}{4} = 227$$

$$\rho_s = 0.45\left(\frac{314}{227} - 1\right)\frac{3.0}{40.0} = 0.013$$

Applying Eq. (13.9.5) gives

$$s_{max} = \frac{a_s\pi(D_c - d_b)}{\rho_s A_c} = \frac{a_s\pi(17 - d_b)}{0.013(227)}$$

which gives the data in Table 13.18.1 Limitations (ACI-7.10.4.3):

1. Clear spacing ≤ 3 in.
2. Clear spacing ≥ 1 in.

Use #3 spiral at 2 in. spacing.

Table 13.18.1

Bar	a_s (sq in.)	s_{max} (in.)	Maximum Clear Spacing (in.)
#3	0.11	1.95	1.57
#4	0.20	3.52	3.02

13.19 Design for Ultimate Strength—Region II, Compression Controls ($e_{min} < e < e_b$)

EXAMPLE 13.19.1   Design a square tied column with about 3% reinforcement for a dead-load axial load of 214 kips and bending moment of 47 ft-kips, and a live-load axial load of 132 kips and bending moment of 23 ft-kips. Use $f'_c = 3000$ psi, $f_y = 40,000$ psi, and the ACI Code.

Solution: (a) Determine the required nominal strength.

$$P_n = \frac{P_u}{\phi} = \frac{1.4(214) + 1.7(132)}{0.70} = 750 \text{ kips}$$

$$M_n = \frac{M_u}{\phi} = \frac{1.4(47) + 1.7(23)}{0.70} = 150 \text{ ft-kips}$$

(b) Eccentricity.

$$e = \frac{M_n}{P_n} = \frac{150(12)}{750} = 2.4 \text{ in.}$$

Although it cannot be certain that $e = 2.4$ in. exceeds e_{min}, it is expected that e_{min} corresponding to $0.80P_0$ (Fig. 13.18.1) will be approximately $0.1h$. Thus for a section smaller than 24 in. the design will be in Region II.
(c) Determine approximate size if $P_n = 750$ kips equals P_b.

$$x_b = \left(\frac{\epsilon_c}{\epsilon_c + \epsilon_y}\right)d = \left(\frac{0.003}{0.003 + 40/29,000}\right)d = 0.685d$$

$$P_b = C_c + C_s - T$$
$$= 0.85f'_c b\beta_1 x_b + A'_s f_y(\text{approx}) - A_s f_y$$

If the column is made symmetrical, then $A'_s = A_s$; therefore

$$P_b \approx 0.85f'_c b\beta_1 x_b = 0.85(3.0)b(0.85)(0.685d) = 1.483bd$$

For $P_b = 750$ kips,

$$\text{balanced } bd \approx \frac{750}{1.483} = 506 \text{ sq in.}$$

Assuming $d \approx 0.9h$,

$$A_g \text{ (balanced)} = \frac{506}{0.9} = 562 \text{ sq in. (23.7 in. square)}$$

which means (referring to Fig. 13.19.1) that if an area larger than 562 sq in. is used, tension will probably control; and if an area less than 562 sq in. is provided, compression will probably control.

Since it is preferred to use a column smaller than the approximate balanced size, this design will probably be within Region II, in which compression

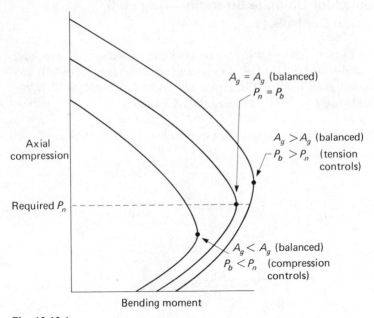

Fig. 13.19.1
Variation of ultimate strength with gross concrete area, assuming constant
percentage of steel reinforcement.

controls. For the purpose of estimating dimensionless ratios, assume a
section about 22 in. square.

(d) Select size for about 3% reinforcement. Assuming compression controls for this small eccentricity and using Eq. (13.14.9),

$$P_n = A_g \left[\frac{f'_c}{(3/\xi^2)(e/h) + 1.18} + \frac{\rho_g f_y}{(2/\gamma)(e/h) + 1} \right]$$

$$\left(\frac{e}{h} \right)_{approx} = \frac{2.4}{22} = 0.109, \quad \text{estimated} \frac{e}{h} \approx 0.12$$

$$(d - d')_{approx} = 19.5 - 2.5 = 17.0, \quad \gamma \approx \frac{17}{22} \approx 0.77$$

$$\xi = \frac{d}{h} \approx \frac{19.5}{22} = 0.89$$

$$P_n = A_g \left[\frac{3.0}{(3/0.792)(0.12) + 1.18} + \frac{0.03(40)}{(2/0.77)(0.12) + 1} \right]$$

$$750 = A_g(1.845 + 0.915) = 2.76 A_g$$

$$A_g = \frac{750}{2.76} = 272 \text{ sq in.}$$

Try 17-in. square column.

(e) Estimate reinforcement.

$$A_{st} = 0.03(272) = 8.2 \text{ sq in.}$$

Try 10-#9 bars.

(f) Check design. An analysis may be made any one of the three ways: statics, approximate Eq. (13.14.8), or a handbook, such as the *ACI Strength Design Handbook*, [25].

If an approximate formula is to be used as a check, one must be certain that the formula correctly applies. To do this, the balanced condition (P_b and e_b) must be determined for the selected section. In this example, following the procedure of Sec. 13.12, the balanced condition is

$$P_b = 354.7 \text{ kips}, \qquad e_b = 11.03 \text{ in.}$$

Since $P_n > 354.7$ and $e < 11.03$, it is verified that compression controls. The approximate equation (13.14.8) gives for the nominal strength,

$$P_n = \frac{bhf'_c}{3he/d^2 + 1.18} + \frac{A'_s f_y}{e/(d - d') + 0.5}$$

$$= \frac{289(3)}{3(17)(2.4)/(14.56)^2 + 1.18} + \frac{5(40)}{2.4/12.12 + 0.5}$$

$$= 493 + 286 = 779 \text{ kips} > 750 \text{ kips required} \qquad\qquad \text{OK}$$

An analysis using basic statics on the section of Fig. 13.19.2, in the same manner as illustrated in Example 13.14.1, gives $P_n = 809$ kips for $e = 2.4$ in. *Use* 17-in. square column and 10-#9 bars, with 5 bars in each face. (Fig. 13.19.2).

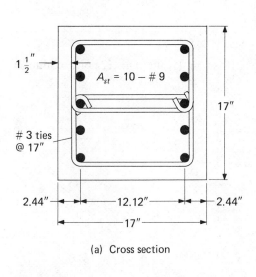

(a) Cross section

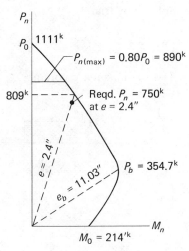

(b) Ultimate strength interaction diagram

Fig. 13.19.2
Section for Example 13.19.1.

Note that a better arrangement of bars, especially when the eccentricity is small as in this case, is to distribute them on all four faces, preferably the same arrangement on all four faces to minimize construction errors.

(g) Select lateral ties. Applying the provisions of ACI-7.10.5.2, try #3 ties. Spacing limitations:

1. Least lateral dimension = 17 in.
2. 16 bar diameters = 16(1.128) = 18 in.
3. 48 ties diameters = 48($\frac{3}{8}$) = 18 in.

Use #3 ties, 2 ties per set, at 17 in. spacing. The final cross section and the strength interaction diagram are shown in Fig. 13.19.2.

EXAMPLE 13.19.2   Redesign the column of Example 13.19.1 to be the smallest square tied column permitted by the ACI Code.

Solution: Use Eq. (13.14.9) to estimate size. Since $A_g < A_g$ (balanced), compression controls (see Fig. 13.19.1). In this equation assume that $\xi^2 = (d/h)^2 \approx 0.65$ and $\gamma = (d - d')/h \approx 0.70$, which are reasonable values for $h < 16$ in. For the smallest column, the maximum ρ_g of 0.08 has been assumed.

$$\text{required } P_n = 750 \text{ kips}, \qquad e = 2.4 \text{ in.}$$

$$750 = A_g \left[\frac{3.0}{(3/0.65)(e/h) + 1.18} + \frac{0.08(40)}{(2/0.70)(e/h) + 1} \right]$$

$$750 = A_g \left[\frac{3.0}{4.6(e/h) + 1.18} + \frac{3.2}{2.9(e/h) + 1} \right]$$

Solving by trial:

for $\dfrac{e}{h} = \dfrac{2.4}{14} = 0.17,$ $\qquad A_g = \dfrac{750}{3.665} = 204,$ $\qquad h = 14.3$ in.

Try $14\frac{1}{2}$-in. square column, $A_g = 210$ sq in. (Note: This is not a common

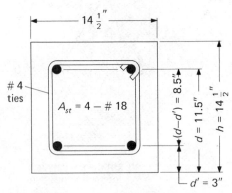

Fig. 13.19.3
Trial section for Example 13.19.2.

size for columns and is used here only to illustrate the procedure.)

$$\text{required } A_{st} = 0.08(204) = 16.3 \text{ sq in.}$$

The only arrangement that can be used to get the steel into the two opposite faces is 4-#18. Try 4-#18, $A_s = 16.00$ sq in.
   Check (see Fig. 13.19.3):

$$\frac{e}{h} = \frac{2.4}{14.5} = 0.165$$

$$\xi^2 = \left(\frac{d}{h}\right)^2 = \left(\frac{11.50}{14.5}\right)^2 = 0.628$$

$$\gamma = \frac{d - d'}{h} = \frac{11.50 - 3.00}{14.5} = 0.586$$

$$P_n = A_g\left(\frac{f'_c}{(3/\xi^2)(e/h) + 1.18} + \frac{\rho_g A_g}{(2/\gamma)(e/h) + 1}\right)$$

$$= 210\left[\frac{3.0}{(3/0.628)(0.165) + 1.18} + \frac{0.0763(40)}{(2/0.586)(0.165) + 1}\right]$$

$$= 210(1.525 + 1.95) = 210(3.475) = 730 \text{ kips}$$

This is about 2.7% under the required capacity. If this is not acceptable, a more exact statics check could be made in an attempt to verify the adequacy. The practical solution is to increase the column size to 15 in. For ties, #4 size is minimum with #18 bars (ACI-7.10.5),

$$16 \text{ bar diameters} = 16(2.25) = 36 \text{ in.}$$

$$\text{least column dimension} = 15 \text{ in.}$$

$$48 \text{ tie diameters} = 48(\tfrac{1}{2}) = 24 \text{ in.}$$

Use a 15 × 15 in. square column, with 4-#18 bars, symmetrically placed. Provide #4 ties spaced at 15 in.

Practical Design Approach. In design practice, compression member design is rarely done in the detailed manner illustrated throughout this chapter. Instead, use is usually made of design aids giving the strength interaction diagram in nondimensional format. Various design aids are available such as the *ACI Strength Design Handbook* (Vol. 1 containing information in tabular form; Vol. 2 containing nondimensional interaction diagrams) [25] and the *CRSI Handbook* [26]. One typical interaction chart is given as Fig. 13.19.4.

EXAMPLE 13.19.3   Design a square tied column containing about 2% reinforcement to carry a dead-load axial compression of 750 kN and bending moment of 65 kN-m, and a live-load axial compression of 530 kN and bending moment of 35 kN-m. Use $f'_c = 28$ N/mm², $f_y = 415$ N/mm², and the ACI Code.

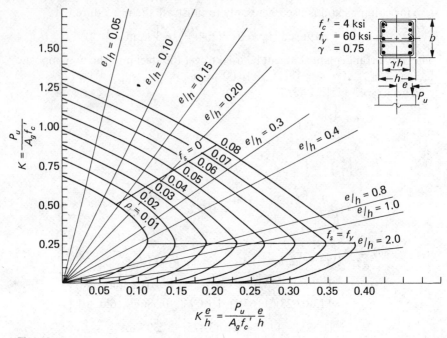

Fig. 13.19.4

Typical nondimensional strength interaction diagram (adapted from Ref. 25).

Solution: (a) Apply the overload factors and compute the eccentricity.

$$P_u = 1.4(750) + 1.7(530) = 1950 \text{ kN}$$
$$M_u = 1.4(65) + 1.7(35) = 151 \text{ kN-m}$$
$$e = \frac{151(1000)}{1950} = 77.4 \text{ mm}$$

(b) Estimate e/h and use interaction chart, Fig. 13.19.4. The chart has $P_u = \phi P_n = 0.70 P_n$ already included. Note that the chart values of $f'_c = 4000$ psi and $f_y = 60,000$ psi correspond closely to the given metric data. This chart is for $\gamma = 0.75$. Try $e/h = 0.2$ with $\rho_g = 0.02$. From the chart, obtain

$$K = \frac{P_u}{f'_c bh} = 0.52$$

$$\text{required } bh = \frac{1950(1000)}{28(0.52)} = 134,000 \text{ mm}^2$$

Try a section 400-mm square ($A_g = 160,000 \text{ mm}^2$).

$$\frac{e}{h} = \frac{7.74}{40} = 0.19$$

$$\gamma = \frac{40 - 13}{40} = 0.675 < 0.75$$

The result so far obtained is slightly on the nonconservative side since it is based on a chart for which the bars at the faces are placed at a relatively farther distance apart than they actually are in this design.

$$\text{actual } K = \frac{P_u}{f'_c b h} = \frac{1950}{28(160)} = 0.435$$

$$\text{actual } K\frac{e}{h} = 0.435(0.19) = 0.0842$$

Enter Fig. 13.19.4 with these two coordinates; find $\rho_g = 0.013$.

$$\text{required } A_{st} = 0.013(160,000) = 2080 \text{ mm}^2$$

Select 6-22 mm diameter bars from Table 1.12.2, $A_{st} = 2280 \text{ mm}^2$

(c) Check by statics. Based on the e/h ratio and the curves of Fig. 13.19.4, the solution is expected to be in the compression controls region. Referring to Fig. 13.19.5,

$$C_c = 0.85f'_c b a = 0.85(28)(400)a\frac{1}{1000} = 9.52a$$
$$a = \beta_1 x = 0.85x \text{ (since 28 N/mm}^2 \approx 4000 \text{ psi)}$$
$$C_c = 8.09x$$

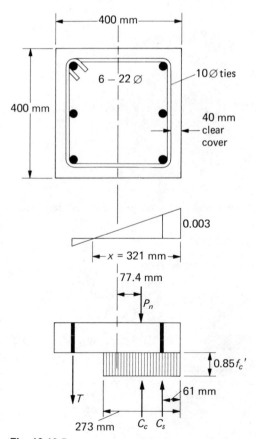

Fig. 13.19.5
Section for Example 13.19.3.

Assume compression steel yields,

$$C_s = 3(380)[415 - 0.85(28)]\tfrac{1}{1000} = 446 \text{ kN}$$

Taking $E_s = 200,000 \text{ N/mm}^2$,

$$T = 3(380)\left(\frac{339 - x}{x}\right)(0.003)(200,000)\tfrac{1}{1000}$$

$$T = \frac{232,000 - 684x}{x}$$

Taking moments about P_n gives

$$T(339 - 122.6) + C_s(122.6 - 61.0) + C_c(122.6 - 0.425x) = 0$$

$$\frac{232,000 - 684x}{x}(216.4) + 446(61.6) + 8.09x(122.6 - 0.425x) = 0$$

$$x^3 - 288x^2 + 3500x - 14,600,000 = 0$$

$$x = 321 \text{ mm}$$

Check strains:

$$\epsilon_y = \frac{f_y}{E_s} = \frac{415}{200,000} = 0.00208$$

At C_s,

$$\epsilon'_s = 0.003\left(\frac{321 - 61}{321}\right) = 0.00243 > \epsilon_y \text{ (compression steel yields)}$$

At T,

$$\epsilon_s = 0.003\left(\frac{339 - 321}{321}\right) = 0.00017 < \epsilon_y$$

This steel is in tension, but does not yield; the strength of the section is in the compression controls region.

Compute forces:

$$\begin{aligned}
C_c &= 8.09x = 8.09(321) &&= 2600 \\
C_s & &&= 446 \\
T &= 3(380)(0.00017)(200) &&= -39 \\
& P_n &&= 3007 \text{ kN}
\end{aligned}$$

$$\phi P_n = 0.70(3007) = 2100 \text{ kN} > P_u = 1950 \text{ kN required} \qquad \text{OK}$$

Check by taking moments about plastic centroid:

$$3007(77.4) = 2600[200 - 0.5(273)] + 446(139) + 39(139)$$

$$232,700 \approx 232,500 \qquad \text{OK}$$

Use 400-mm square column with 6-22-mm diameter bars, as shown in Fig. 13.19.5.

13.20 Design for Ultimate Strength—Region III, Tension Controls ($e > e_b$)

The "tension controls" region contains the transition in ultimate strength from the condition of crushing failure of concrete as a column to that of ductile flexural failure as a beam. It follows that the safety provisions should logically provide for a gradual increase in the undercapacity factor from that of columns to that of beams.

The ACI Code requires the use of ϕ factors of 0.70 and 0.75 for tied and spirally reinforced columns, respectively, so long as the eccentric compressive-load design strength P_u (not P_n) is $0.10f'_cA_g$ or larger. Then as the magnitude of the axial compression decreases from $0.10f'_cA_g$ to zero, the ϕ factor may be linearly increased to 0.90.

In order to be safe, however, it is necessary that the value $0.10f'_cA_g$ is within Region III; in other words, one must be certain this compression is less than the design strength ϕP_b at the balanced condition. This will usually be the case when f_y does not exceed 60,000 psi, there is symmetrical reinforcement, and the distance $(h - d' - d_s)$ (see Fig. 13.12.1) between tension and compression reinforcement is not less than $0.70h$. Under these conditions the undercapacity factors ϕ are (ACI-9.3.2)

$$\phi = 0.90 - \frac{1.5P_u}{f'_cA_g} \geq 0.75 \qquad \text{(for spirally reinforced members)} \qquad \textbf{(13.20.1)}$$

and

$$\phi = 0.90 - \frac{2.0P_u}{f'_cA_g} \geq 0.70 \qquad \text{(for tied members)} \qquad \textbf{(13.20.2)}$$

The relationships are shown in Fig. 13.20.1.

In the relatively few cases where the balanced load ϕP_b is smaller than $0.10f'_cA_g$, the liberalization of the ϕ factor would have to start from where

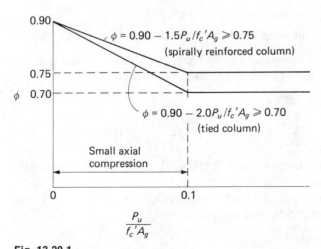

Fig. 13.20.1
Variation in ϕ for beam-columns having symmetrical reinforcement, $f_y \leq 60,000$ psi, and $(d - d')/h \geq 0.70$.

the axial compressive load is equal to ϕP_b. Using ϕP_b for $0.10f'_c A_g$ in Eqs. (13.20.1) and (13.20.2) gives

$$\phi = 0.90 - \frac{0.15P_u}{0.75P_b} \geq 0.75 \qquad \text{(for spirally reinforced members)} \qquad \textbf{(13.20.3)}$$

and

$$\phi = 0.90 - \frac{0.20P_u}{0.70P_b} \geq 0.70 \qquad \text{(for tied members)} \qquad \textbf{(13.20.4)}$$

EXAMPLE 13.20.1   Design a rectangular tied column, not over 14 in. wide with about 3% reinforcement, to carry a service dead load of $P = 43$ kips and $M = 96$ ft-kips and a service live load of $P = 32$ kips and $M = 85$ ft-kips. Use symmetrical reinforcement with $f'_c = 4500$ psi, $f_y = 50{,}000$ psi, and the ACI Code.

Solution: (a) Required nominal strengths and eccentricity. Assuming that $P_u \geq 0.10f'_c A_g$, the value of ϕ is 0.70.

$$P_n = \frac{P_u}{\phi} = \frac{1.4(43) + 1.7(32)}{0.70} = 164 \text{ kips}$$

$$M_n = \frac{M_u}{\phi} = \frac{1.4(96) + 1.7(85)}{0.70} = 398 \text{ ft-kips}$$

$$e = \frac{398(12)}{164} = 29.1 \text{ in.}$$

(b) Find the approximate size such that $P_n = P_b$ (see Fig. 13.19.1 and discussion relating to Example 13.19.1).

$$x_b = \frac{0.003d}{0.003 + 0.00172} = 0.635d$$

$$a = \beta_1 x_b = 0.825(0.635)d = 0.524d$$

$$P_b = 0.85(4.5)(0.524)bd + A'_s(f_y - 0.85f'_c) - A_s f_y.$$

For $A'_s = A_s$, it is conservative and probably reasonable to assume that the two terms involving steel approximately cancel each other. Therefore

$$P_b \approx 2.00bd$$

$$\text{balanced } bd \approx \frac{164}{2.00} = 82.0 \text{ sq in.} \left(A_g \approx \frac{82.0}{0.8} = 103 \text{ sq in.} \right)$$

It is reasonably certain that an area larger than this must be used; therefore tension would control.

(c) Determine size required for reinforcement ratio ρ_g about 0.03. Using Eq. (13.16.7) to obtain preliminary size requirement,

$$P_n = 0.85f'_c bd$$

$$\times \left\{ -\rho + 1 - \frac{e'}{d} + \sqrt{\left(1 - \frac{e'}{d}\right)^2 + 2\rho\left[(m-1)\left(1 - \frac{d'}{d}\right) + \frac{e'}{d}\right]} \right\}$$

$$[\textbf{13.16.7}]$$

Estimate

$$\rho = 0.015 \text{ (one-half total percentage)}$$

$$\frac{e'}{d} = \frac{d - h/2 + e}{d} \approx 2.0$$

$$\frac{d'}{d} \approx 0.1$$

Also

$$m = \frac{f_y}{0.85f'_c} = \frac{50,000}{0.85(4500)} = 13.08$$

Thus

$$P_n = 3.82bd\{-0.015 + 1 - 2 + \sqrt{(-1.0)^2 + 0.03[12.08(0.9) + 2.00]}\}$$
$$= 3.82bd(-1.015 + \sqrt{1.00 + 0.386})$$
$$= 3.82(0.163)bd = 0.623bd$$

$$\text{required } bd = \frac{164}{0.623} = 263 \text{ sq in.}$$

Try 14 × 18 column, $A_g = 252$ sq in. Rechecking several variables,

$$\frac{e'}{d} = \frac{d - h/2 + e}{d} = \frac{15.5 - 9 + 29.1}{15.5} = 2.30$$

$$\frac{d'}{d} = \frac{2.5}{15.5} = 0.16$$

$$P_n = 3.82bd(-1.315 + 1.445)$$

$$\text{required } bd = \frac{164}{0.497} = 330 \text{ sq in.}$$

Try 14 × 20 column, $A_g = 280$ sq in.

$$\frac{e'}{d} = \frac{17.5 - 10.0 + 29.1}{17.5} = 2.09$$

$$\frac{d'}{d} = \frac{2.5}{17.5} = 0.14$$

$$P_n = 3.82bd(-1.105 + 1.252)$$

$$\text{required } bd = \frac{164}{0.562} = 292 \text{ sq in.} \approx 280 \text{ sq in.}$$

The 14 × 20 section will be further investigated, and reinforcement will be determined by statics.

(d) Use approximate statics to determine reinforcement. Assuming that C_s and T are equal in Fig. 13.20.2,

$$P_n = C_c = 0.85f'_c ab$$
$$164 = 0.85(4.5)a(14)$$
$$a = 3.06 \text{ in.}$$

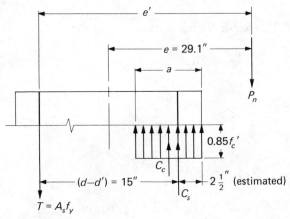

Fig. 13.20.2
Statics for Example 13.20.1.

Equating the moments of the two couples,

$$P_n\left(19.1 + \frac{3.06}{2}\right) = A_s f_y(d - d')$$

$$A_s = \frac{164(20.63)}{50(15)} = 4.51 \text{ sq in.}$$

$$A_{st} = 9.02 \text{ sq in.}$$

$$\rho = \frac{9.02}{14(20)} = 0.0322$$

Try 6-#11 bars, $A_{st} = 9.36$ sq in.

(e) Check by statics (see Fig. 13.20.3). A statics check may be made (1) by determining the neutral-axis location to satisfy $\Sigma F_y = 0$ for $P_n = 164$ kips and then comparing the allowable eccentricity of this load with the known eccentricity, or (2) by determining the neutral-axis location to satisfy the condition $e = 29.1$ in. and then comparing the allowable P_n at this eccentricity with the known eccentric load. The first approach is taken here to illustrate an alternative procedure not previously used in this chapter.

Assuming that the neutral axis is at $x = 3.75$ in. from the extreme compressive face,

$$\epsilon'_s \approx 0.003\left(\frac{3.75 - 2.5}{3.75}\right) \approx 0.001 \qquad \text{say } f'_s = 30 \text{ ksi}$$

$P_n = 164$ kips
$T = 4.68(50) = 234$ kips
$C_s = 4.68[30 - 0.85(4.5)] = 122.5$ kips
$C_c = 164 + 234 - 122.5 = 275.5$ kips
$C_c = 0.85 f'_c ab$

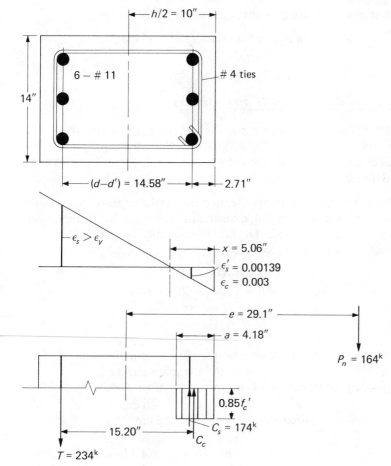

Fig. 13.20.3
Section for Example 13.20.1.

$$a = \frac{275.5}{0.85(4.5)14} = 5.14 \text{ in.}$$

$$x = \frac{a}{0.825} = 6.23 \text{ in.}$$

$$\epsilon_s' = 0.003\left(\frac{6.23 - 2.71}{6.23}\right) = 0.00169, \qquad f_s' = 49 \text{ ksi}$$

Revise $f_s' = 40$ ksi, $C_s = 169.0$ kips, $C_c = 229$ kips

    $a = 4.27$ in., $x = 5.17$ in., $\epsilon_s' = 0.00143$

    $f_s' = 41.5$ ksi

Revise $f_s' = 41$ ksi, $C_s = 174.0$ kips, $C_c = 224$ kips

    $a = 4.18$ in., $x = 5.06$ in., $\epsilon_s' = 0.00139$

    $f_s' = 40.4$ ksi   say OK

Taking summation of moments about the center of the column,

$$164e = 224[10 - 0.5(4.18)] + (234 + 174)(7.29)$$

from which

$$e = 28.9 \text{ in.} \approx 29.1 \text{ in.} \qquad\qquad \text{OK}$$

Use 14 × 20 column, with 6-#11 bars, 3 bars in each face.

EXAMPLE 13.20.2   Design a rectangular tied column, not over 14 in. wide, to carry a service dead load of $P = 12$ kips and $M = 80$ ft-kips and a service live load of $P = 10$ kips and $M = 85$ ft-kips. Use $f'_c = 4500$ psi, $f_y = 50,000$ psi, and the ACI Code.

Solution: (a) Obtain eccentricity. Because the axial compression is of small magnitude relative to the bending moment, the correct ϕ factor quite likely will be between 0.70 and 0.90. The eccentricity may be obtained by considering only the overload factors U; thus

$$P_u = 1.4(12) + 1.7(10) = 33.8 \text{ kips}$$
$$M_u = 1.4(80) + 1.7(85) = 256 \text{ ft-kips}$$

$$e = \frac{256(12)}{33.8} = 91.0 \text{ in.}$$

With this large eccentricity, the section is clearly near the bottom of the "tension controls" region on the strength interaction diagram.

(b) Approach the design as a compression member. Assuming $\phi \approx 0.80$,

$$\text{required } P_n = \frac{P_u}{\phi} = \frac{33.8}{0.8} = 42.2 \text{ kips}$$

Estimate size required using Eq. (13.16.7) for Region III (tension controls).

$$P_n = 0.85 f'_c bd$$

$$\times \left\{ -\rho + 1 - \frac{e'}{d} + \sqrt{\left(1 - \frac{e'}{d}\right)^2 + 2\rho \left[(m - 1)\left(1 - \frac{d'}{d}\right) + \frac{e'}{d}\right]} \right\}$$

Estimate a depth of say 20 in. and $\rho \approx 0.015$ ($\rho_g \approx 0.03$),

$$\frac{e'}{d} = \frac{d - h/2 + e}{d} \approx \frac{17.5 - 10 + 91}{17.5} = 5.6$$

$$\frac{d'}{d} \approx \frac{2.5}{17.5} = 0.143$$

$$m = 13.08 \qquad \text{(see Example 13.20.1)}$$

$$P_n = 0.85(4.5)bd\{-0.015 + 1 - 5.6$$
$$+ \sqrt{(1 - 5.6)^2 + 0.03[(13.08 - 1)(1 - 0.143) + 5.6]}\}$$
$$= 0.134bd$$

$$\text{required } bd = \frac{P_n}{0.134} = \frac{42.2}{0.134} = 314 \text{ sq in.}$$

which would indicate a section about 14 × 25.

(c) Alternative approach considering the member as a beam. Try about one-half the maximum percentage of reinforcement allowed by ACI Code. From Table 3.5.1, $0.75\rho_b$ is about 0.03. Using Eq. (3.6.4), or Fig. 3.6.1, find

$$R_u \approx 650 \text{ psi}$$

Estimate ϕ again at 0.80.

$$\text{required } M_n = \frac{M_u}{\phi} = \frac{256}{0.80} = 320 \text{ ft-kips}$$

$$\text{required } bd^2 = \frac{M_n}{R_u} = \frac{320(12,000)}{650} = 5900 \text{ in.}^3$$

If $b = 14$ in., required $d = 21$ in. and $h = d + 2.5 = 21 + 2.5 = 23.5$, say 24 in. It appears from (b) and (c) that a section about 14×24 will work.

(d) Compute the correct value of ϕ to be used assuming that the 14×24 section is satisfactory.

$$0.10f'_c A_g = 0.10(4.5)(14)(24) = 151 \text{ kips} > P_u$$

Assuming one layer of steel in each face,

$$\gamma = \frac{d - d'}{h} \approx \frac{21.5 - 2.5}{24} = 0.79 > 0.70 \qquad\qquad \text{OK}$$

and

$$f_y < 60,000 \text{ psi}$$

Using Eq. (13.20.2),

$$\phi = 0.90 - 2.0\left(\frac{P_u}{f'_c A_g}\right)$$

$$= 0.90 - 2.0\left(\frac{33.8}{4.5(14)(24)}\right) = 0.90 - 0.04 = 0.86$$

A statics check may now be made to be certain the nominal strength of the section is at least

$$\text{required } P_n = \frac{P_u}{\phi} = \frac{33.8}{0.86} = 39.3 \text{ kips}$$

$$\text{required } M_n = \frac{M_u}{\phi} = \frac{256}{0.86} = 298 \text{ ft-kips}$$

Selection of bars and the check procedure offer no feature that has not already been treated elsewhere.

13.21 Axial Tension and Bending Moment

In the relatively uncommon situation of axial tension in combination with bending moment, the strength interaction diagram can be considered to extend on the negative P_n side of the axis, as shown in Fig. 13.21.1. The strength analysis for tension values of P_n is similar to that used for compression loading in the "tension controls" region. When the eccentric load is tensile, the neutral-axis distance x will be smaller than it is under pure

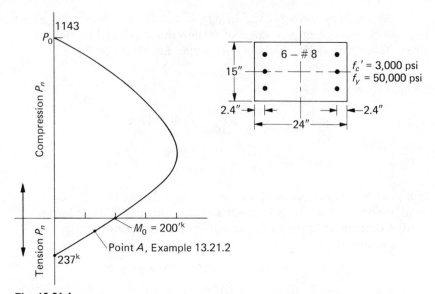

Fig. 13.21.1
Strength interaction diagram showing both axial compression and axial tension.

bending (M_0). The following examples illustrate the calculation of points on the tension side of the interaction diagram (Fig. 13.21.1).

EXAMPLE 13.21.1 Determine the maximum value for the tensile force P_n when no bending moment is acting on the section shown in Fig. 13.21.1.

Solution: Since the concrete will crack before the steel yields, only the steel participates in carrying axial tension. Thus

$$P_n = A_{st}f_y = 6(0.79)50 = 237 \text{ kips}$$

This is plotted on Fig. 13.21.1.

EXAMPLE 13.21.2 Determine the axial tensile strength P_n on the section of Fig. 13.21.1 when the eccentricity is 20 in.

Solution: Referring to Fig. 13.21.2, the eccentric tensile force P_n must be acting on the tensile side of the plastic centroid. In this case the neutral-axis distance x is smaller than its value for pure bending. For bending alone,

$$C_c = 0.85f'_cba = 0.85(3)(15)a = 38.3a$$
$$T = A_sf_y = 3(0.79)50 = 118.5 \text{ kips}$$

Assuming the compression steel yields,

$$C_s = 3(0.79)(50 - 2.55) = 112.5 \text{ kips}$$
$$C = T$$

$$a = \frac{118.5 - 112.5}{38.3} = 0.16, \qquad x = \frac{0.16}{0.85} < 2.4 \text{ in.}$$

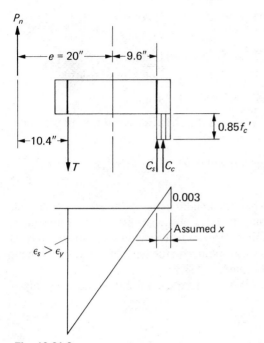

Fig. 13.21.2
Free-body diagram and assumed strain diagram
for Example 13.21.2.

The above computation shows that compression steel does not yield under
bending alone; thus it likely will not yield when P_n is tension at $e = 20$ in.

Thus for axial tension estimate C_s to be in compression but at less than
yield stress. Neglecting any displaced concrete effect,

$$C_s = A'_s\epsilon'_s E_s = 3(0.79)\left(\frac{x - 2.4}{x}\right)(0.003)(29{,}000) = \frac{206x - 495}{x}$$

$$C_c = 0.85f'_c b(0.85x) = 0.85(3)(15)(0.85x) = 32.5x$$
$$T = A_s f_y = 3(0.79)50 = 118.5 \text{ kips}$$

Taking moments about P_n (refer to Fig. 13.21.2) gives

$$T(20 - 12 + 2.4) - C_c(20 + 12 - 0.425x) - C_s(20 + 9.6) = 0$$
$$x^3 - 75.3x^2 - 352x + 1060 = 0$$
$$x = 2.10 \text{ in.}$$

Check assumptions,

$$\epsilon'_s = \left(\frac{2.10 - 2.40}{2.10}\right)0.003 = -0.000429 < \epsilon_y$$

The steel represented by C_s actually is in tension and does not yield; there
is no displaced concrete effect.

$$C_s = 3(0.79)(-0.000429)29,000 = -\ 29.4 \text{ kips}$$
$$C_c = 32.5(2.10) \qquad\qquad = +\ 68.3 \text{ kips}$$
$$T = \qquad\qquad\qquad\qquad = -118.5 \text{ kips}$$
$$P_n = -\ 79.6 \text{ kips (tension)}$$

$$M_n = 79.6(20)\tfrac{1}{12} = 133 \text{ ft-kips}$$

This value is plotted as point A on Fig. 13.21.1. Check by taking moments about the plastic centroid:

$$133 = [(118.5 - 29.4)(9.6) + 68.3(12 - 0.89)]\tfrac{1}{12}$$
$$133 \approx 134 \qquad\qquad\qquad\qquad\qquad\qquad\qquad\qquad\qquad \text{OK}$$

The reader may note that when the axial tension is sufficiently high such that the neutral axis falls beyond the edge of the section, there is no longer a compression face of the member. However, the method illustrated in this example seems sufficient to show how points on the tension–bending moment interaction diagram may be obtained.

Note also that a ϕ factor of 0.90 is to be used for this entire region of axial tension.

13.22 Working Stress Method

In the working stress method, or "alternate method" of the ACI Code, the service-load moment and axial force are used without applying the overload factors U or the undercapacity factors ϕ.

The allowable service-load capacity (ACI-Appendix B.6.1) is taken as 40% of the ultimate strength—that is, $0.40M_n$ and $0.40P_n$, subject to possible further reduction due to the effects of slenderness.

Note that limiting the service-load capacity to 40% of the ultimate strength is equivalent to using a U/ϕ value of 2.5. Even at the higher value of $U = 1.70$ for live load only, combined with the lower value of $\phi = 0.70$ for tied columns, the resulting U/ϕ value is $1.70/0.70 = 2.43$. This shows that design of columns by the ACI "alternate method" will always be more conservative than by the strength method, thus offering no advantage.

13.23 Biaxial Bending and Compression

The investigation or design of a square or rectangular section subjected to an axial compression in combination with bending moments about both the x and y axes has received considerable attention [28–44].

One method of analysis is to use the basic principles of equilibrium with the same ultimate strength assumptions as were used earlier in this chapter for the case of axial compression and bending about only one axis. This method essentially involves a trial and error process for obtaining the position of an inclined neutral axis; hence any such method is sufficiently complex that no formula may be developed for practical use.

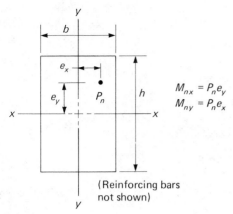

Fig. 13.23.1
Notation.

Failure Surfaces. The concept of using failure surfaces has been presented by Bresler [29] and Pannell [31]. The nominal ultimate strength of a section under biaxial bending and compression is a function of three variables, P_n, M_{nx}, and M_{ny}, which may also be expressed in terms of the axial force P_n acting at eccentricities $e_y = M_{nx}/P_n$ and $e_x = M_{ny}/P_n$ with respect to the x and y axes, respectively, as shown in Fig. 13.23.1.

Three types of failure surfaces may be defined. In the first type S_1, the variables used along the three orthogonal axes are P_n, e_x, and e_y, as shown in Fig. 13.23.2; in the second type S_2, the variables are $1/P_n$, e_x, and e_y, as shown in Fig. 13.23.3; and in the third type S_3, the variables are P_n, M_{nx}, and M_{ny}, as shown in Fig. 13.23.4. Bresler has developed a very useful analysis procedure [29] using the reciprocal surface S_2. The third type of failure surface S_3 is a three-dimensional extension of the interaction diagram

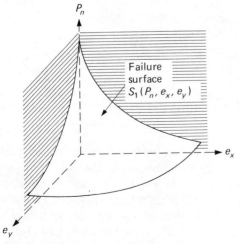

Fig. 13.23.2
Failure surface $S_1(P_n, e_x, e_y)$ (from Ref. 29).

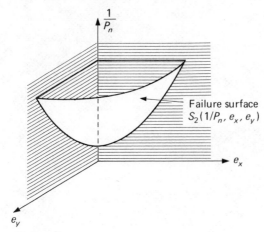

Fig. 13.23.3
Reciprocal failure surface $S_2(1/P_n, e_x, e_y)$ (from Ref. 29).

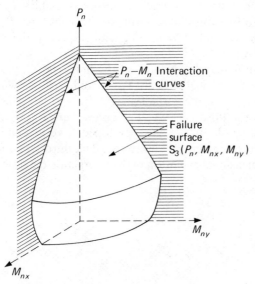

Fig. 13.23.4
Failure surface $S_3(P_n, M_{ny}, M_{nx})$ (from Ref. 29).

for uniaxial bending and compression as has been used in the earlier part of this chapter. A number of investigators have made approximations to S_3 for use in design and analysis [29,30,32,35,36]. Bresler [29] and Parme, Nieves, and Gouwens [36] have suggested practical approaches to the use of the surface S_3. In the presentation that follows, two analysis methods are presented; the first using the reciprocal $1/P_n$–e_x–e_y surface S_2 that gives a simple tool for analysis, and the second using the $P_n - M_{ny} - M_{nx}$ surface S_3 which is very helpful in design.

Bresler Reciprocal Load Method. Bresler, in an attempt to develop a realistic procedure for analysis, suggested [29] approximating a point $(1/P_{n1}, e_{xA}, e_{yB})$ on the reciprocal failure surface S_2 by a point $(1/P_i, e_{xA}, e_{yB})$ on a *plane* S_2' passing through points A, B, and C (Fig. 13.23.5). Each point on the true surface is approximated by a different plane; that is, the entire failure surface is defined by an infinite number of planes.

The problem then is to determine the load capacity P_{n1} which may act with biaxial eccentricities e_{xA} and e_{yB} by assuming that P_{n1} equals the value P_i lying on the plane S_2' specifically established for it. The specific plane is defined by passing it through three points A, B, and C known to lie on the true failure surface S_2,

$$A\left(e_{xA}, \quad 0, \quad \frac{1}{P_y}\right)$$

$$B\left(0, \quad e_{yB}, \quad \frac{1}{P_x}\right)$$

$$C\left(0, \quad 0, \quad \frac{1}{P_0}\right)$$

where P_0 is the nominal ultimate capacity under axial compression alone without any eccentricity; P_x is the nominal ultimate compression load capacity at the uniaxial eccentricity e_{yB} ($M_{nx} = P_x e_{yB}$); and P_y is the nominal ultimate compression load capacity at the uniaxial eccentricity e_{xA} ($M_{ny} = P_y e_{xA}$).

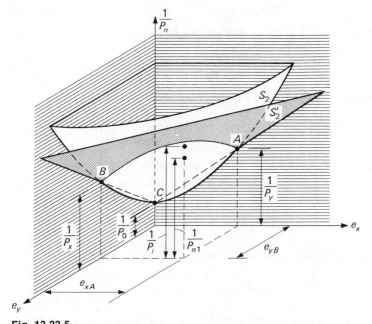

Fig. 13.23.5
Graphical representation of the reciprocal load method (from Ref. 29).

In other words, point A represents a point (P_y, M_{ny}) on the uniaxial P–M interaction diagram, such as Fig. 13.6.2, for bending about the y axis; point B represents a point (P_x, M_{nx}) on the uniaxial P–M interaction diagram for bending about the x axis; and point C is a point that is common to both of the uniaxial P–M interaction diagrams.

The equation of the plane S_2' may be defined in terms of the three points A, B, and C. By letting $x = e_x$, $y = e_y$, and $z = 1/P_n$, the general equation of a plane is

$$A_1 x + A_2 y + A_3 z + A_4 = 0 \qquad (13.23.1)$$

Substitution of the coordinates of points A, B, and C (see Fig. 13.23.5) into Eq. (13.23.1) gives

$$A_1 e_{xA} + \quad 0 \quad + A_3 \frac{1}{P_y} + A_4 = 0 \qquad (13.23.2a)$$

$$0 \quad + A_2 e_{yB} + A_3 \frac{1}{P_x} + A_4 = 0 \qquad (13.23.2b)$$

$$0 \quad + \quad 0 \quad + A_3 \frac{1}{P_0} + A_4 = 0 \qquad (13.23.2c)$$

Solving Eqs. (13.23.2abc) for A_1, A_2, and A_3 in terms of A_4,

$$A_1 = \frac{1}{e_{xA}}\left(\frac{P_0}{P_y} - 1\right) A_4 \qquad (13.23.3a)$$

$$A_2 = \frac{1}{e_{yB}}\left(\frac{P_0}{P_x} - 1\right) A_4 \qquad (13.23.3b)$$

$$A_3 = -P_0 A_4 \qquad (13.23.3c)$$

Substitution of Eqs. (13.23.3abc) into Eq. (13.23.1) gives

$$A_4 \left[\frac{x}{e_{xA}}\left(\frac{P_0}{P_y} - 1\right) + \frac{y}{e_{yB}}\left(\frac{P_0}{P_x} - 1\right) - P_0 z + 1 \right] = 0 \qquad (13.23.4)$$

Dividing the above equation by P_0, the equation of the plane S_2' becomes

$$\frac{x}{e_{xA}}\left(\frac{1}{P_y} - \frac{1}{P_0}\right) + \frac{y}{e_{yB}}\left(\frac{1}{P_x} - \frac{1}{P_0}\right) - z + \frac{1}{P_0} = 0 \qquad (13.23.5)$$

At the point $(x = e_{xA}, y = e_{yB}, z = 1/P_i)$ on the plane that approximates the point $(x = e_{xA}, y = e_{yB}, z = 1/P_{n1})$ on the true failure surface, Eq. (13.23.5) becomes

$$\left(\frac{1}{P_y} - \frac{1}{P_0}\right) + \left(\frac{1}{P_x} - \frac{1}{P_0}\right) - \frac{1}{P_i} + \frac{1}{P_0} = 0$$

which reduces to the following expression for the value of P_i:

$$\frac{1}{P_i} = \frac{1}{P_x} + \frac{1}{P_y} - \frac{1}{P_0} \qquad (13.23.6)$$

Bresler [29] has found the computed values of P_i from using Eq. (13.23.6) to be "in excellent agreement with test results, the maximum deviation being

9.4%, and the average deviation being 3.3%." Ramamurthy [35] also reported test results and concluded that Eq. (13.23.6) "can be used to predict ultimate loads with reasonable accuracy." Pannell has presented additional test results in his discussion of Ref. 29 and indicated that Eq. (13.23.6) may be inappropriate when small values of axial load are involved, such as when P_n/P_0 is in the range of 0.06 or less. For such cases the member should be designed for flexure only.

EXAMPLE 13.23.1   Determine the adequacy of a 16-in. square column section containing 8-#10 bars as shown in Fig. 13.23.6a. The section is to carry ultimate loads, $P_n = P_u/\phi = 200$ kips, $M_{nx} = M_{ux}/\phi = 167$ ft-kips, and $M_{ny} = M_{uy}/\phi = 75$ ft-kips. The tied column has $f'_c = 3000$ psi and $f_y = 40,000$ psi.

Solution: The eccentricities of P_n are

$$e_y = \frac{M_{nx}}{P_n} = \frac{167(12)}{200} = 10.0 \text{ in.}$$

$$e_x = \frac{M_{ny}}{P_n} = \frac{75(12)}{200} = 4.5 \text{ in.}$$

In order to determine the values of P_x and P_y, the P_n–M_{nx} and P_n–M_{ny} interaction diagrams in uniaxial bending are needed for bending about the x and y axes, respectively. Because of the symmetry in this case, a single $P_n - M_{nx}$ or M_{ny} diagram valid for both bending axes is all that is required, as shown in Fig. 13.23.6b. The interaction information may be obtained by using equilibrium, by the use of approximate formulas such as developed in Secs. 13.14 through 13.17, or by means of nondimensionalized P–M diagrams such as provided in ACI publication SP–17A [25].

From the P_n–e_x or e_y interaction diagram, Fig. 13.23.6c, determine P_x and P_y for uniaxial bending,

$$e_x = \ 4.5 \text{ in.}, \qquad \text{find } P_y = 480 \text{ kips}$$
$$e_y = 10.0 \text{ in.}, \qquad \text{find } P_x = 260 \text{ kips}$$

Then, using Eq. (13.23.6),

$$\frac{1}{\text{provided } P_n} \approx \frac{1}{P_i} = \frac{1}{P_x} + \frac{1}{P_y} - \frac{1}{P_0}$$

Multiplying by 1000 for convenience,

$$\frac{1000}{P_i} = \frac{1000}{260} + \frac{1000}{480} - \frac{1000}{952}$$

$$\frac{1000}{P_i} = 3.85 + 2.08 - 1.05 = 4.88$$

$$\text{provided } P_n \approx P_i = \frac{1000}{4.88} = 205 \text{ kips} > \text{required } P_n = 200 \text{ kips} \quad \text{OK}$$

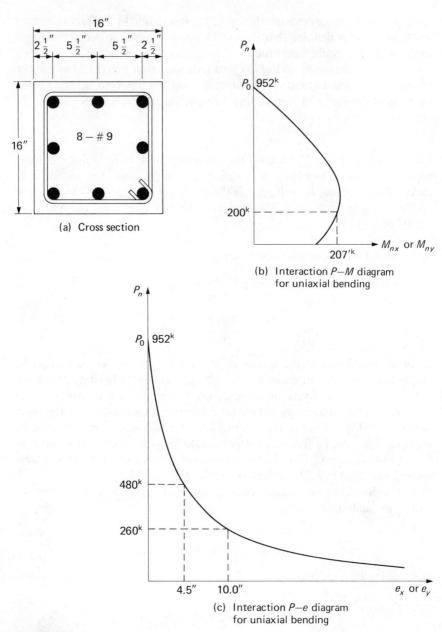

Fig. 13.23.6
Section and interaction diagrams for Example 13.23.1.

The more exact analysis of this section may be made by using statics on the assumption that there is a uniformly stressed compression zone, in the same way as for uniaxial bending and compression. In biaxial bending and compression, the uniform compressive stress $0.85f'_c$ is considered to act on a compression zone bounded by the edges of the cross section and a straight line at a distance $a = \beta_1 x$ from the fiber of maximum strain (corner of section) and parallel to the neutral axis. Such an analysis gives the capacity $P_n = 216.7$ kips with the neutral axis inclined at an angle of $29.23°$ clockwise with the x axis and the distance a equal to 9.65 in. from the extreme fiber in compression. This kind of exact analysis is usually practical only with the aid of a computer.

Load Contour Method—Bresler Approach. The load contour method involves cutting the failure surface S_3 (Fig. 13.23.4) at a constant value of P_n to give a so-called "load contour" interaction relating M_{nx} and M_{ny}. In other words, the entire surface S_3 may be considered to include a family of curves (load contours) corresponding to constant values of P_n, which if drawn superimposed on one another in a single plane would be analogous to a contour map. A typical plane at constant P_n along with its load contour is shown in Fig. 13.23.7.

The general nondimensional equation for the load contour at constant P_n may be expressed [29] in the form

$$\left(\frac{M_{nx}}{M_{0x}}\right)^{\alpha_1} + \left(\frac{M_{ny}}{M_{0y}}\right)^{\alpha_2} = 1.0 \qquad (13.23.7)$$

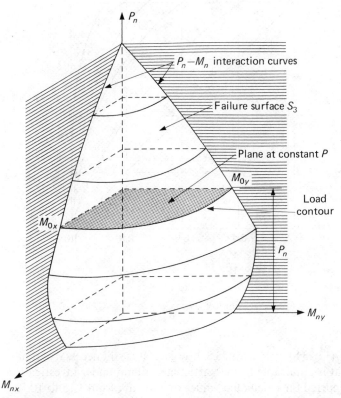

Fig. 13.23.7
Load contours for constant P_n on failure surface S_3(from Ref. 29).

where

$$M_{nx} = P_n e_y; \; M_{ny} = P_n e_x$$
$M_{0x} = M_{nx}$ capacity at axial load P_n when M_{ny} (or e_x) is zero
$M_{0y} = M_{ny}$ capacity at axial load P_n when M_{nx} (or e_y) is zero

and α_1 and α_2 are exponents that depend on the dimensions of the cross section, the reinforcement amount and location, concrete strength, steel yield stress, and amount of concrete cover.

Bresler [29] suggests that it is acceptable to take $\alpha_1 = \alpha_2 = \alpha$; then

$$\left(\frac{M_{nx}}{M_{0x}}\right)^{\alpha} + \left(\frac{M_{ny}}{M_{0y}}\right)^{\alpha} = 1 \qquad \textbf{(13.23.8)}$$

which is shown graphically in Fig. 13.23.8.

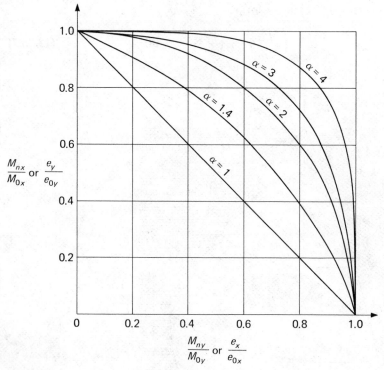

Fig. 13.23.8
Interaction curves for Eq. (13.23.8) (from Ref. 29).

In using Eq. (13.23.8) or Fig. 13.23.8, however, it is still necessary to have a value of α that is applicable to the particular column under investigation. Bresler [29] reported the calculated values of α to vary from 1.15 to 1.55.

For practical purposes, it seems satisfactory to take α as 1.5 for rectangular sections and between 1.5 and 2.0 for square sections.

Load Contour Method—Parme Approach.[†] The approach described herein has been developed by Parme et al. [36], as an extension of the Bresler load contour method. The Bresler interaction equation (13.23.8) is assumed to be the basic strength criterion to define the typical load contour representing the intersection of the failure surface S_3 (Fig. 13.23.7) with a horizontal plane at a height P_n. Such a typical load contour is shown in Fig. 13.23.9. A change in the orientation of the M_{nx} and M_{ny} axes has been made in Fig. 13.23.9 to suit the two-dimensional representation.

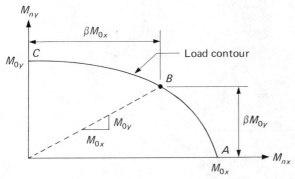

Fig. 13.23.9
Load contour at plane of constant P_n cut through failure surface S_3 (Fig. 13.23.7).

In the Parme approach, a point B on the load contour is defined such that the biaxial moment capacities M_{nx} and M_{ny} at this point are in the same ratio as the uniaxial moment capacities M_{0x} and M_{0y}; thus at point B

$$\frac{M_{ny}}{M_{nx}} = \frac{M_{0y}}{M_{0x}} \qquad (13.23.9)$$

or

$$M_{nx} = \beta M_{0x}; \qquad M_{ny} = \beta M_{0y} \qquad (13.23.10)$$

When the load contour of Fig. 13.23.9 is adjusted to take the nondimensional form of Fig. 13.23.10, the point B will have the ratio β defined by Eq. (13.23.10) as its x and y coordinates. In the physical sense, the ratio β is that constant portion of the uniaxial moment capacities which may be permitted to act simultaneously on the column section. The actual value of β depends on the ratio of P_n to P_0, as well as the material and cross-sectional properties; however, the usual range is between 0.55 and 0.70 [36]. An average value of $\beta = 0.65$ is suggested for design. More accurate values of β have been computed using basic principles of equilibrium and charts for

---

[†] This approach may also be referred to as the Portland Cement Association (PCA) method since Ref. 36 is also available as PCA Advanced Engineering Bulletin No. 18.

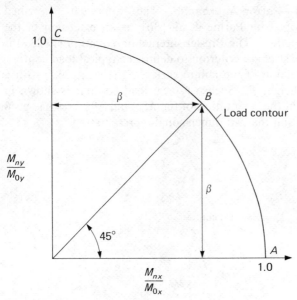

Fig. 13.23.10
Nondimensional load contour at constant P_n.

β values have been presented in Ref. 36. These β-value charts appear as Fig. 13.23.11.

Once an empirical value of β has been ascertained for a given cross section and loading, the complete nondimensional load contour is defined if Eq. (13.23.8) is accepted as the correct relationship. The relationship between the α of Eq. (13.23.8) and β is obtained by using the coordinates of point B, which is known to lie on the contour. Thus substituting the coordinates of B into Eq. (13.23.8) gives

$$\left(\frac{\beta M_{0x}}{M_{0x}}\right)^{\alpha} + \left(\frac{\beta M_{0y}}{M_{0y}}\right)^{\alpha} = 1$$

$$\beta^{\alpha} = \tfrac{1}{2}$$

$$\alpha \log \beta = \log 0.5$$

$$\alpha = \frac{\log 0.5}{\log \beta}$$

(13.23.11)

Thus Eq. (13.23.8) may be written

$$\left(\frac{M_{nx}}{M_{0x}}\right)^{\log 0.5/\log \beta} + \left(\frac{M_{ny}}{M_{0y}}\right)^{\log 0.5/\log \beta} = 1$$ (13.23.12)

Plots of Eq. (13.23.12) for different values of β are shown in Fig. 13.23.12.

Gouwens [43] has presented equations that may be used in place of the curves of Fig. 13.23.12.

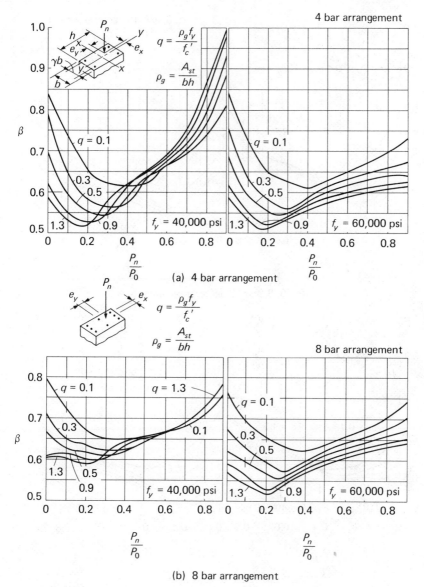

Fig. 13.23.11

Biaxial bending design constants β (from Ref. 36). For $0.6 \le \gamma \le 1.0$; $3000 \le f'_c \le 6000$; and $1.0 \le h/b \le 4.0$. (Figure is continued on page 462.)

For design purposes, the nondimensionalized load contour of Fig. 13.23.10 may be approximated by two straight lines AB and BC as shown in Fig. 13.23.13. When M_{ny}/M_{0y} exceeds M_{nx}/M_{0x},

$$\frac{M_{ny}}{M_{0y}} + \frac{M_{nx}}{M_{0x}}\left(\frac{1-\beta}{\beta}\right) = 1 \qquad (13.23.13)$$

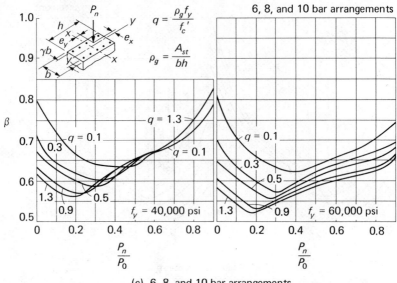

(c) 6, 8, and 10 bar arrangements

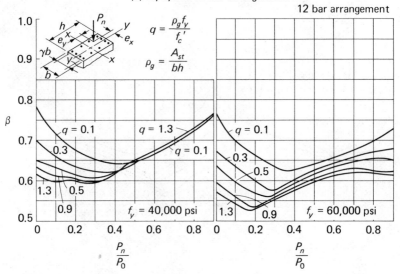

(d) 12 bar arrangement

Fig. 13.23.11 continued
Biaxial bending design constants β (from Ref. 36). For $0.6 \leq \gamma \leq 1.0$; $3000 \leq f'_c \leq 6000$; and $1.0 \leq h/b \leq 4.0$.

When M_{ny}/M_{0y} is less than M_{nx}/M_{0x}, the straight-line approximation equation for AB is

$$\frac{M_{nx}}{M_{0x}} + \frac{M_{ny}}{M_{0y}}\left(\frac{1-\beta}{\beta}\right) = 1 \qquad (13.23.14)$$

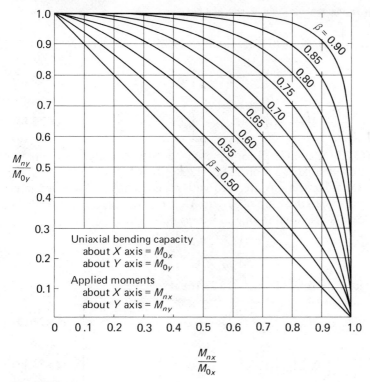

Fig. 13.23.12
Biaxial bending interaction relationship (load contour) in terms of β values (from Ref. 36).

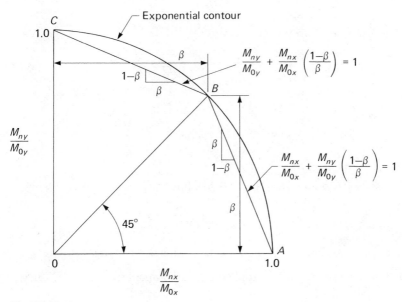

$$\frac{M_{ny}}{M_{0y}} + \frac{M_{nx}}{M_{0x}}\left(\frac{1-\beta}{\beta}\right) = 1$$

$$\frac{M_{nx}}{M_{0x}} + \frac{M_{ny}}{M_{0y}}\left(\frac{1-\beta}{\beta}\right) = 1$$

Fig. 13.23.13
Straight-line approximation of load contour for design (from Ref. 36).

For design purposes, Eqs. (13.23.13) and (13.23.14) may be written

$$M_{ny} + M_{nx}\left(\frac{M_{0y}}{M_{0x}}\right)\left(\frac{1-\beta}{\beta}\right) = M_{0y}; \qquad \left[\text{for } \frac{M_{ny}}{M_{nx}} \geq \frac{M_{0y}}{M_{0x}}\right] \qquad \textbf{(13.23.15)}$$

$$M_{nx} + M_{ny}\left(\frac{M_{0x}}{M_{0y}}\right)\left(\frac{1-\beta}{\beta}\right) = M_{0x}; \qquad \left[\text{for } \frac{M_{ny}}{M_{nx}} \leq \frac{M_{0y}}{M_{0x}}\right] \qquad \textbf{(13.23.16)}$$

Thus Eqs. (13.23.15) and (13.23.16) represent the alternate algebraic expressions to the exponential equation of Eq. (13.23.12) or Fig. 13.23.12.

When rectangular sections are used with reinforcement distributed uniformly along all faces, the ratio of M_{0y} to M_{0x} (i.e., M_{ny}/M_{nx} of Fig. 13.23.1) will be approximately equal to that of b to h; thus

$$\frac{M_{0y}}{M_{0x}} \approx \frac{b}{h}$$

which gives for Eqs. (13.23.15) and (13.23.16), respectively,

$$M_{ny} + M_{nx}\left(\frac{b}{h}\right)\left(\frac{1-\beta}{\beta}\right) \approx M_{0y} \qquad \left[\text{for } \frac{M_{ny}}{M_{nx}} \geq \frac{b}{h}\right] \qquad \textbf{(13.23.17)}$$

$$- \quad M_{nx} + M_{ny}\left(\frac{h}{b}\right)\left(\frac{1-\beta}{\beta}\right) \approx M_{0x} \qquad \left[\text{for } \frac{M_{ny}}{M_{nx}} \leq \frac{b}{h}\right] \qquad \textbf{(13.23.18)}$$

EXAMPLE 13.23.2   Investigate the section of Example 13.23.1 (Fig. 13.23.6) using the Parme load contour method.

Solution: (a) Use Eq. (13.23.12) or Fig. 13.23.12. In order to make a check by this method, the correct β value must be determined.

$$\frac{P_n}{P_0} = \frac{200}{952} = 0.21 \qquad (P_0 \text{ from Fig. 13.23.6b})$$

$$q = \rho_g \frac{f_y}{f_c'} = \frac{8(1.0)}{16(16)}\left(\frac{40}{3}\right) = 0.42$$

Find $\beta = 0.615$ from Fig. 13.23.11.

$$\frac{M_{nx}}{M_{0x}} = \frac{167}{207} = 0.806$$

where M_{0x} is from Fig. 13.23.6b.

Using $\beta = 0.615$ and $M_{nx}/M_{0x} = 0.806$, find from Fig. 13.23.12,

$$\frac{M_{ny}}{M_{0y}} = 0.39$$

$$\text{max } M_{ny} = 0.39(207) = 81 \text{ ft-kips} > 75 \text{ ft-kips} \qquad \text{OK}$$

(b) Use Eq. (13.23.14). The applied biaxial moments M_{nx} and M_{ny} give

$$\frac{M_{nx}}{M_{0x}} = \frac{167}{207} = 0.806; \qquad \frac{M_{ny}}{M_{0y}} = \frac{75}{207} = 0.362$$

Substituting $\beta = 0.615$ from part (a) in Eq. (13.23.14),

$$\frac{M_{nx}}{M_{0x}} + \frac{M_{ny}}{M_{0y}}\left(\frac{1-\beta}{\beta}\right) \le 1$$

$$0.806 + 0.362\left(\frac{1-0.615}{0.615}\right) = 0.806 + 0.227 = 1.033$$

which would indicate a small overstress. As is expected, the straight-line relationship is conservative.

Design Procedure. The design procedure may be summarized as follows:

1. Estimate the value of β at 0.65, or use Fig. 13.23.11 to make an estimate.
2. If M_{ny} is larger than M_{nx}, compute the approximate equivalent uniaxial bending moment M_{0y} using Eq. (13.23.17); if M_{nx} is larger than M_{ny}, compute the approximate equivalent uniaxial bending moment M_{0x} using Eq. (13.23.18).
3. Design the section using the methods treated in Secs. 13.18 through 13.20.
4. Check by using any one of the three approaches of this section: (a) the Bresler reciprocal load method, Eq. (13.23.6); (b) the Bresler load contour method, Eq. (13.23.8); (c) the Parme load contour method: Eq. (13.23.12), which is the same as Fig. 13.23.12; or Eqs. (13.23.13) and (13.23.14) which are straight-line approximations to the load contour.

Several additional comments in regard to the design of compression members in biaxial bending may be made as follows:

1. Whenever possible, columns subjected to biaxial bending should be circular in cross section.
2. If rectangular or square columns are necessary, the reinforcement should be uniformly spread around the perimeter.
3. Circular or square columns can reasonably be designed to satisfy for a given P_u by using the equation [29],

$$\left(\frac{M_{nx}}{M_{0x}}\right)^{1.75} + \left(\frac{M_{ny}}{M_{0y}}\right)^{1.75} = 1.0 \qquad \textbf{(13.23.19)}$$

4. Rectangular columns can be approximately designed to satisfy for a given P_u by using the equation [29],

$$\left(\frac{M_{nx}}{M_{0x}}\right)^{1.5} + \left(\frac{M_{ny}}{M_{0y}}\right)^{1.5} = 1.0 \qquad \textbf{(13.23.20)}$$

EXAMPLE 13.23.3 Select a rectangular cross section for a compression member subjected to biaxial bending, to take the following service loads: dead load, $P = 100$ kips, $M_x = 50$ ft-kips, and $M_y = 25$ ft-kips; live load, $P = 40$ kips, $M_x = 60$ ft-kips, and $M_y = 20$ ft-kips. Use $f'_c = 4000$ psi and $f_y = 60,000$ psi.

Solution: (a) Determine required nominal strengths. Assume $\phi = 0.70$.

$$P_n = \frac{P_u}{\phi} = \frac{1.4(100) + 1.7(40)}{0.70} = 297 \text{ kips}$$

$$M_{nx} = \frac{M_{ux}}{\phi} \qquad \text{(for bending about } x \text{ axis)}$$

$$= \frac{1.4(50) + 1.7(60)}{0.70} = 246 \text{ ft-kips}$$

$$M_{ny} = \frac{M_{uy}}{\phi} \qquad \text{(for bending about } y \text{ axis)}$$

$$= \frac{1.4(25) + 1.7(20)}{0.70} = 98.5 \text{ ft-kips}$$

(b) Estimate equivalent uniaxial bending moment. Estimate $\beta = 0.65$ and use Eq. (13.23.18),

$$\text{equivalent } M_{0x} \approx M_{nx} + M_{ny}\left(\frac{h}{b}\right)\left(\frac{1-\beta}{\beta}\right)$$

Assume h/b proportional to $M_{nx}/M_{ny} = 246/98.5 \approx 2.5$

$$\text{equivalent } M_{0x} \approx 246 + 98.5(2.5)\left(\frac{1 - 0.65}{0.65}\right) = 378 \text{ ft-kips}$$

(c) Determine equivalent eccentricity for uniaxial bending and compression.

$$P_n = 297 \text{ kips}$$
$$M_n = 378 \text{ ft-kips}$$

$$\text{equivalent } e_y = \frac{378(12)}{297} = 15.3 \text{ in.}$$

(d) Determine approximate requirements for a balanced section.

$$x_b = \left(\frac{\epsilon_c}{\epsilon_c + \epsilon_y}\right)d = \left[\frac{0.003}{0.003 + (60/29,000)}\right]d = 0.592d$$

If symmetrical reinforcement is used, $\rho = \rho'$,

$$P_b \approx C_c = 0.85f_c'b\beta_1 x_b$$
$$= 0.85(4)b(0.85)(0.592d) = 1.71bd$$

For $P_b = 297$ kips,

$$\text{balanced } bd \approx \frac{297}{1.71} = 173 \text{ sq in.}$$

$$\text{balanced } A_g \approx \frac{173}{0.9} = 192 \text{ sq in.}$$

If $h/b = 2.5$,

$$\text{balanced } b = \sqrt{\frac{192}{2.5}} = 8.8$$

which gives a section about 9 × 22. Since a 9-in. section is narrower than generally desired, the section to be chosen will probably be larger than the balanced cross section. Thus, according to Fig. 13.19.1, the section will probably be in Region III where tension controls.

(e) Determine required size assuming tension controls. Use Eq. (13.16.7), and assume $\rho_g \approx 0.04$,

$$P_n = 0.85f_c'bd\left\{-\rho + 1 - \frac{e'}{d}\right.$$

$$\left. + \sqrt{\left(1 - \frac{e'}{d}\right)^2 + 2\rho\left[(m-1)\left(1 - \frac{d'}{d}\right) + \frac{e'}{d}\right]}\right\}$$

Estimate

$$\rho = 0.02 \text{ (one-half total in each face)}$$

$$\frac{e'}{d} = \frac{d - h/2 + e}{d} \approx 1.2 \qquad \text{(assuming } h \text{ as 20 to 24 in.)}$$

$$\frac{d'}{d} \approx 0.13$$

$$m = \frac{f_y}{0.85f_c'} = \frac{6.0}{0.85(4)} = 17.7$$

Thus

$$P_n = 3.4bd\{-0.22 + \sqrt{(-0.2)^2 + 0.04[16.7(0.87) + 1.2]}\}$$
$$= 3.4bd(-0.22 + 0.82)$$
$$= 2.04bd$$

If $b = 12$ in.,

$$\text{required } d = \frac{297}{2.04(12)} = 12.1; \qquad h = 15 \text{ in.}$$

Revise equivalent M_{0x} to assume $h/b \approx 1.33$ (say 12 × 16),

$$\text{equivalent } M_{0x} = 317 \text{ ft-kips}$$

$$e_y = \frac{317(12)}{297} = 12.8 \text{ in.}$$

Revise e'/d to 1.35 (assume $h \approx 16$ in.), and d'/d to 0.185,

$$P_n = 3.4bd\{-0.37 + \sqrt{(-0.35)^2 + 0.04[16.7(0.815) + 1.35]}\}$$
$$= 3.4bd(-0.37 + 0.85) = 1.63bd$$

If $b = 12$ in.,

$$\text{required } d = \frac{297}{1.63(12)} = 15.2 \text{ in.}; \qquad h = 18 \text{ in.}$$

Try a section 12×18.

$$A_s \approx 0.04(12)(15.2) = 7.3 \text{ sq in.}$$

(f) Check the section of Fig. 13.23.14a using the Bresler reciprocal-load method.

$$\text{required } e_y = \frac{M_{nx}}{P_n} = \frac{246(12)}{297} = 9.95 \text{ in.}$$

$$\text{required } e_x = \frac{M_{ny}}{P_n} = \frac{98.5(12)}{297} = 4.02 \text{ in.}$$

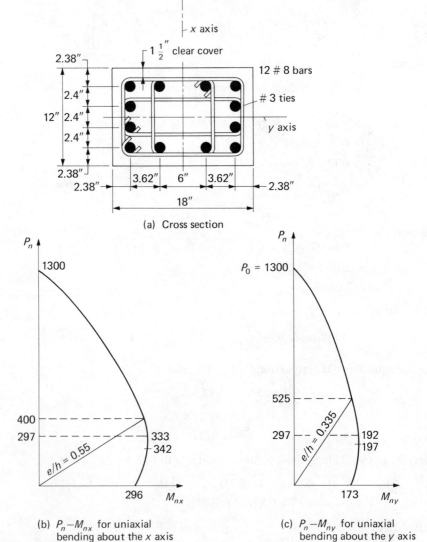

(a) Cross section

(b) $P_n - M_{nx}$ for uniaxial bending about the x axis

(c) $P_n - M_{ny}$ for uniaxial bending about the y axis

Fig. 13.23.14
Data for Example 13.23.3.

Establish the strength P_n for the required values of e_y and e_x from uniaxial P_n–M_n interaction diagrams as in Fig. 13.23.14. The values of P_x and P_y for $e/h = 0.55$ and $e/b = 0.335$ may also be obtained directly using the *ACI Strength Handbook*, Vol. 2 [25]. Thus

$$\text{for } e_y = 9.95 \text{ in.,} \qquad \text{find } P_x = 400 \text{ kips}$$
$$\text{for } e_x = 4.02 \text{ in.,} \qquad \text{find } P_y = 525 \text{ kips}$$

Using Eq. (13.23.6), with $P_0 = 1300$ kips (Fig. 13.23.15),

$$\frac{1}{P_i} = \frac{1}{P_x} + \frac{1}{P_y} - \frac{1}{P_0}$$

$$\frac{1000}{P_i} = \frac{1000}{400} + \frac{1000}{525} - \frac{1000}{1300}$$

$$= 2.50 + 1.90 - 0.77 = 2.63$$

$$\text{provided } P_n \approx P_i = \frac{1000}{2.63} = 380 \text{ kips} > 297 \text{ kips required} \qquad \text{OK}$$

Section should perhaps be reduced. Reduce the amount of steel and recheck. Try 10-#8 instead of 12-#8 (3 in the 12 in. width instead of 4).

Find $P_x = 358$ kips; $P_y = 482$ kips; $P_0 = 1145$ kips.

$$\frac{1000}{P_i} = \frac{1000}{358} + \frac{1000}{482} - \frac{1000}{1145}$$

$$= 2.79 + 2.08 - 0.87 = 4.00$$

$$P_i = \frac{1000}{4.00} = 250 \text{ kips} < 297 \text{ kips} \qquad \text{NG}$$

Use 12 × 18 section with 12-#8 bars, as in Fig. 13.23.14.

(g) Check using the Parme load contour method. Using Fig. 13.23.11d,

$$q = \rho_g \frac{f_y}{f_c'} = \frac{9.48}{12(18)} \left(\frac{60}{4} \right) = 0.66$$

$$\frac{P_n}{P_0} = \frac{297}{1300} = 0.23$$

Find $\beta = 0.56$ from Fig. 13.23.11d.
Next, enter Fig. 13.23.12 with $M_{nx}/M_{0x} = 246/233 = 0.74$ and $\beta = 0.56$.

$$\text{Find capacity} \frac{M_{ny}}{M_{0y}} = 0.38$$

$$\text{capacity } M_{ny} = 0.38(192) = 73 \text{ ft-kips} < 98.5 \text{ ft-kips}$$

By this approach the design appears unsafe. The basic statics analysis for this section gives a capacity P_n for $e_y = 9.95$ in. and $e_x = 4.02$ in. of 291 kips.

SELECTED REFERENCES

1. A. Considère. "Compressive Resistance of Concrete Steel and Hooped Concrete, Part I," *Engineering Record*, December 20, 1902, 581–583; Part II, December 27, 1902, 605–606.

2. A. Considère. "Concrete-Steel and Hooped Concrete," *Reinforced Concrete*, 1903, p. 119.

3. A. N. Talbot. "Tests of Concrete and Reinforced Concrete Columns." *Bulletin*, No. 10, 1906, and No. 20, 1907, University of Illinois, Urbana.

4. M. O. Withey. "Tests of Plain and Reinforced Concrete Columns," *Engineering Record*, July 1909, 41.

5. M. O. Withey. "Tests on Reinforced Concrete Columns," *Bulletin*, No. 300, 1910, and No. 466, 1911, *University of Wisconsin*.

6. Committee 105. "Reinforced Concrete Column Investigation," *ACI Journal*, *Proceedings*, **26,** April 1930, 601–612; **27,** February 1931, 675–676; **28,** November 1931, 157–158; **29,** September 1932, 53–56; February 1933, 275–284; **30,** September–October 1933, 78–90; November–December 1933, 153–156.

7. Joint ACI-ASCE Committee 441. *Reinforced Concrete Columns* (annotated bibliography), *ACI Bibliography* No. 5. Detroit: American Concrete Institute, 1965.

8. E. Hognestad. "A Study of Combined Bending and Axial Load in Reinforced Concrete Members," *Bulletin* No. 399, November 1951, Engineering Experiment Station, University of Illinois, Urbana (117 references).

9. ACI-ASCE Committee 327. "Report on Ultimate Strength Design," *Proceedings ASCE*, **81,** October 1955, Paper No. 809. See also *ACI Journal, Proceedings*, **52,** January 1956, 505–524.

10. A. H. Mattock, L. B. Kriz, and Eivind Hognestad, "Rectangular Concrete Stress Distribution in Ultimate Strength Design," *ACI Journal, Proceedings*, **57,** February 1961, 875–928.

11. E. O. Pfrang, C. P. Siess, and M. A. Sozen. "Load-Moment-Curvature Characteristics of Reinforced Concrete Cross Sections," *ACI Journal, Proceedings*, **61,** July 1964, 763–778. Disc. 1673–1683.

12. German Gurfinkel and Arthur Robinson. "Determination of Strain Distribution and Curvature in a Reinforced Concrete Section Subjected to Bending Moment and Longitudinal Load," *ACI Journal, Proceedings*, **64,** July 1967, 398–403.

13. James G. MacGregor, John E. Breen, and Edward O. Pfrang. "Design of Slender Concrete Columns," *ACI Journal, Proceedings*, **67,** January 1970, 6–28.

14. F. E. Richart, J. O. Draffin, T. A. Olson, and R. H. Heitman. "The Effect of Eccentric Loading, Protective Shells, Slenderness Ratios, and Other Variables in Reinforced Concrete Columns," *Bulletin* No. 368, 1947 (130 pp.), Engineering Experiment Station, University of Illinois, Urbana.

15. B. Bresler and P. H. Gilbert. "Tie Requirements for Reinforced Concrete Columns," *ACI Journal, Proceedings*, **58,** Nov. 1961, 555–570; Disc., **58,** 897–907.

16. James F. Pfister, "Influence of Ties on the Behavior of Reinforced Concrete Columns," *ACI Journal, Proceedings*, **61,** May 1964, 521–537.

17. Fred M. Hudson. "Reinforced Concrete Columns: Effects of Lateral Tie Spacing on Ultimate Strength," *Symposium on Reinforced Concrete Columns*, Publication SP-13. Detroit, Michigan: American Concrete Institute, 1966, (pp. 235–244).

18. Edwin G. Burdette and Hubert K. Hilsdorf. "Behavior of Laterally Reinforced Concrete Columns," *Journal of Structural Division*, ASCE, **97,** February 1971 (ST2), 587–602.

19. N. G. Bunni. "Rectangular Ties in Reinforced Concrete Columns," *Reinforced Concrete Columns* (SP–50). Detroit: American Concrete Institute, 1975 (pp. 193–210).

20. ACI Committee 315. *Manual of Standard Practice for Detailing Reinforced Concrete Structures* (6th ed.). Detroit: American Concrete Institute, 1974.

21. ACI Committee 318. *Commentary on the Building Code Requirements for Reinforced Concrete (ACI 318–77)*, Detroit: American Concrete Institute, 1977.

22. Ti Huang. "On the Formula for Spiral Reinforcement," *ACI Journal, Proceedings*, **61**, March 1964, 351–353. Disc., 1241–1248.

23. Charles S. Whitney and Edward Cohen. "Guide for Ultimate Strength Design of Reinforced Concrete," *ACI Journal, Proceedings*, **53**, November 1956, 455–490.

24. *Ultimate Load Tables for Circular Columns*. Chicago: Portland Cement Association, 1960.

25. ACI Committee 340. *Design Handbook in Accordance with Strength Design Method of ACI 318–71*, Vol. 1 (1973), Vol. 2 (1978), (SP–17A), Detroit: American Concrete Institute.

26. *CRSI Handbook* (2nd ed.). Chicago: Concrete Reinforcing Steel Institute, 1975.

27. Charles S. Whitney. "Plastic Theory of Reinforced Concrete Design," *Transactions ASCE*, **107**, 1942, 251–326.

28. K. H. Chu and A. Pabarcius. "Biaxially Loaded Reinforced Concrete Columns," *Proceedings ASCE*, **84**, ST8, December 1958, 1–27.

29. Boris Bresler. "Design Criteria for Reinforced Columns under Axial Load and Biaxial Bending," *ACI Journal, Proceedings*, **57**, November 1960, 481–490. Disc. 1621–1638.

30. Richard W. Furlong. "Ultimate Strength of Square Columns under Biaxially Eccentric Loads," *ACI Journal, Proceedings*, **57**, March 1961, 1129–1140.

31. F. N. Pannell. "Failure Surfaces for Members in Compression and Biaxial Bending," *ACI Journal, Proceedings*, **60**, January 1963, 129–140.

32. J. L. Meek. "Ultimate Strength of Columns With Biaxially Eccentric Loads," *ACI Journal, Proceedings*, **60**, August 1963, 1053–1064.

33. A. Aas-Jakobsen. "Biaxial Eccentricities in Ultimate Load Design," *ACI Journal, Proceedings*, **61**, March 1964, 293–315.

34. John F. Fleming and Stuart D. Werner. "Design of Columns Subjected to Biaxial Bending," *ACI Journal, Proceedings*, **62**, March 1965, 327–342. Disc., 1217–1224.

35. L. N. Ramamurthy. "Investigation of the Ultimate Strength of Square and Rectangular Columns under Biaxially Eccentric Loads," *Symposium on Reinforced Concrete Columns* (SP–13). Detroit: American Concrete Institute, 1966 (pp. 263–298).

36. Alfred L. Parme, Jose M. Nieves, and Albert Gouwens. "Capacity of Reinforced Rectangular Columns Subject to Biaxial Bending," *ACI Journal, Proceedings*, **63**, September 1966, 911–923.

37. Donald C. Weber. "Ultimate Strength Design Charts for Columns with Biaxial Bending," *ACI Journal, Proceedings*, **63**, November 1966, 1205–1320. Disc., 1583–1586.

38. Anis Farah and M. W. Huggins. "Analysis of Reinforced Concrete Columns Subjected to Longitudinal Load and Biaxial Bending," *ACI Journal, Proceedings*, **66**, July 1969, 569–575.

39. K. N. Smith and W. H. Nelles. "Columns Subjected to Biaxial Bending—Preliminary Selection of Reinforcing," *ACI Journal, Proceedings*, **71**, August 1974, 411–413.

40. Peter D. Heimdahl and Albert C. Bianchini. "Ultimate Strength of Biaxially Eccentrically Loaded Concrete Columns Reinforced With High Strength Steel," *Reinforced Concrete Columns* (SP–50). Detroit: American Concrete Institute, 1975 (pp. 93–117).

41. S. I. Abdel-Sayed and N J. Gardner. "Design of Symmetric Square Slender Reinforced Concrete Columns Under Biaxially Eccentric Loads," *Reinforced*

Concrete Columns (SP–50). Detroit: American Concrete Institute, 1975 (pp. 149–164).

42. A. K. Basu and P. Suryanarayana. "Analysis of Restrained Reinforced Concrete Columns Under Biaxial Bending," *Reinforced Concrete Columns* (SP–50). Detroit: American Concrete Institute, 1975 (pp. 211–232).

43. Albert J. Gouwens. "Biaxial Bending Simplified," *Reinforced Concrete Columns* (SP–50). Detroit: American Concrete Institute, 1975 (pp. 233–261).

44. W. F. Chen and M. T. Shoraka. "Tangent Stiffness Method for Biaxial Bending of Reinforced Concrete Columns," *Publications*, International Association for Bridge and Structural Engineering, 35–1, 1975, 23–44.

PROBLEMS

All problems[†] are to be worked in accordance with the strength method of the ACI Code unless otherwise indicated, and all stated loads are service loads. Note that eccentricities e_x and e_y are measured along the x- and y-axes, respectively (see Fig. 13.23.1).

13.1 Determine the compressive service load that the column of the accompanying figure may be permitted to carry at an eccentricity $e_y = 0.1h = 1.8$ in. according to ultimate strength procedures. Assume that dead load and live load are equal. Use $f'_c = 3000$ psi and $f_y = 40,000$ psi. Use basic principles of statics to obtain solution, considering the effect of compression concrete displaced by steel; compare the result (P_n) with that obtained by the Whitney formula (Eq. 13.14.8) and compare with the maximum P_n given by ACI-10.3.5. ($e = 46$ mm; $f'_c = 21$ N/mm²; $f_y = 280$ N/mm².)

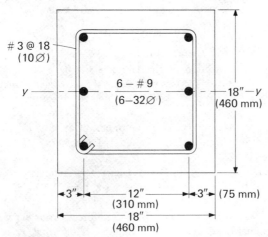

Probs. 13.1 and 13.2

13.2 Same as Prob. 13.1 except $f'_c = 5000$ psi and $f_y = 60,000$ psi. ($f'_c = 35$ N/mm²; $f_y = 420$ N/mm².)

[†] Many problems may be solved either as problems stated in U.S. Customary units, or as problems in metric units using quantities in parenthesis at the end of the statement. The metric conversions are approximate to avoid implying higher precision for the given information in metric units than that for the U.S. Customary units.

13.3 Determine the ultimate capacity $P_n = P_u/\phi$ of the spirally reinforced column of the accompanying figure when the loading has an eccentricity $e = 0.05h = 0.9$ in. Use $f'_c = 3000$ psi and $f_y = 40,000$ psi. Use **(a)** basic statics with the circular section including the effect of compression concrete displaced by steel, **(b)** basic statics with Whitney's equivalent rectangle, and **(c)** the Whitney formula. Compare with maximum P_n obtained from ACI-10.3.5. ($e = 23$ mm; $f'_c = 21$ N/mm^2; $f_y = 280$ N/mm^2.)

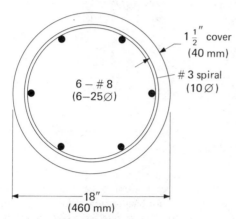

$1\frac{1}{2}''$ cover
(40 mm)

3 spiral
(10 Ø)

6 – # 8
(6–25Ø)

18"
(460 mm)

Probs. 13.3 and 13.4

13.4 Same as Prob. 13.3 except use $f'_c = 5000$ psi and $f_y = 60,000$ psi. ($f'_c = 35$ N/mm^2; $f_y = 420$ N/mm^2.)

13.5 Determine the balanced condition $P_b = U/\phi$ in addition to e_b with respect to bending about the strong axis (measured as e_y) for the column of the accompanying figure. Use the basic statics method with $f'_c = 3000$ psi and $f_y = 40,000$ psi. ($f'_c = 21$ N/mm^2; $f_y = 280$ N/mm^2.)
(a) Consider the effect of the compression concrete displaced by steel.
(b) Neglect the effect of the compression concrete displaced by steel.

13.6 Using the basic statics method and taking account of the compression concrete displaced by steel, calculate and plot the P_n versus M_n interaction capacity diagram for the column of Prob. 13.5. Take bending with respect to the strong axis ($h = 24$ in.). To obtain points for the diagram, compute P_n for the following cases in addition to e_b (see Prob. 13.5):
(a) $e = 0(P_0)$
(b) $e = 0.1h$
(c) $e = 0.3h$
(d) $e = 0.7h$
(e) $e = h$
(f) $e = \infty(M_0)$

13.7 Same as Prob. 13.5 except use $f'_c = 4000$ psi and $f_y = 60,000$ psi. ($f'_c = 28$ N/mm^2; $f_y = 420$ N/mm^2.)

13.8 Same as Prob. 13.6 except use $f'_c = 4000$ psi and $f_y = 60,000$ psi. (For e_b, see Prob. 13.7).

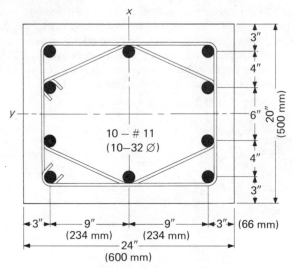

Probs. 13.5, 13.6, 13.7, and 13.8

13.9 For the section of the accompanying figure, using basic statics determine and plot the interaction diagram of $P_n - M_n$ for bending about the x axis. Compute the balanced condition in addition to those points indicated for Prob. 13.6. Use $f'_c = 3000$ psi and $f_y = 40,000$ psi. ($f'_c = 21$ N/mm^2; $f_y = 280$ N/mm^2.)

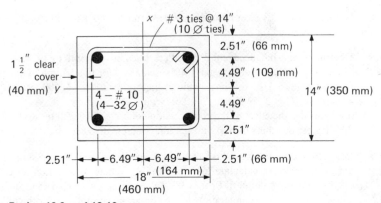

Probs. 13.9 and 13.10

13.10 Repeat Prob. 13.9 except consider bending about the y axis.

13.11 For the section of Prob. 13.9, determine the nominal ultimate capacity P_n for an eccentricity e_y of 5 in. with respect to the x axis. Use $f'_c = 5000$ psi and $f_y = 60,000$ psi. ($e = 125$ mm; $f'_c = 35$ N/mm^2; $f_y = 420$ N/mm^2.)

13.12 Repeat Prob. 13.11, except use an eccentricity e_y of 22 in. with respect to the x axis. ($e = 560$ mm.)

13.13 For the section in the accompanying figure, determine the nominal ultimate capacity P_n for an eccentricity e_y of 6 in. with respect to the x axis. Use $f'_c = 3000$ psi and $f_y = 40,000$ psi. ($e = 150$ mm; $f'_c = 21$ N/mm^2; $f_y = 280$ N/mm^2.)

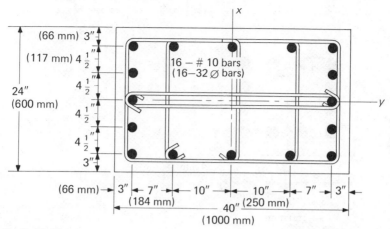

Prob. 13.13

13.14 For the section of the accompanying figure, determine the nominal ultimate capacity P_n for an eccentricity e_y of 32 in. with respect to the x axis. Use $f'_c = 3000$ psi and $f_y = 40,000$ psi.

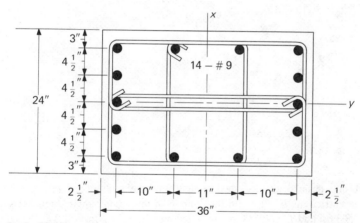

Prob. 13.14

13.15 For the section of the accompanying figure, using basic statics determine and plot the interaction diagram of $P_n - M_n$ for bending about the x axis. Compute the balanced condition in addition to those points indicated for Prob. 13.6. Use $f'_c = 4000$ psi and $f_y = 60,000$ psi. ($f'_c = 28$ N/mm²; $f_y = 420$ N/mm².)

13.16 For the column of the accompanying figure, determine the nominal ultimate load P_n at an eccentricity of 21 in. Use $f'_c = 4000$ psi and $f_y = 50,000$ psi. Apply the basic principles of statics. ($e = 530$ mm; $f'_c = 28$ N/mm²; $f_y = 350$ N/mm².)
(a) Use the Whitney-Hognestad equivalent system for the reinforcement along with the circular concrete section.
(b) Use more exact treatment of the reinforcement in its correct position in the cross section.

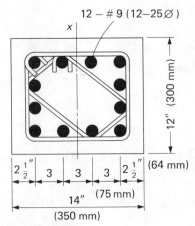

12 – # 9 (12–25∅)

x

12" (300 mm)

$2\frac{1}{2}$" | 3 | 3 | 3 | $2\frac{1}{2}$" (64 mm)

14" (75 mm)

(350 mm)

Prob. 13.15

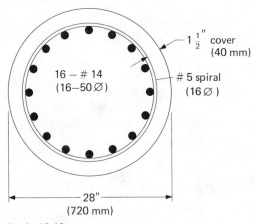

16 – # 14 (16–50∅)

$1\frac{1}{2}$" cover (40 mm)

5 spiral (16∅)

28" (720 mm)

Prob. 13.16

13.17 Using basic principles, determine the nominal ultimate capacity P_n or an eccentricity e_y of 30 in. on the column of the accompanying figure. Use $f'_c = 3500$ psi and $f_y = 40,000$ psi. ($e = 760$ mm; $f'_c = 24$ N/mm²; $f_y = 280$ N/mm².)

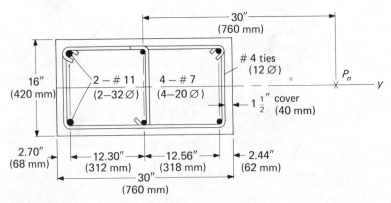

30" (760 mm)

16" (420 mm)

2 – # 11 (2–32∅)

4 – # 7 (4–20∅)

4 ties (12∅)

P_n

x

y

$1\frac{1}{2}$" cover (40 mm)

2.70" (68 mm)

12.30" (312 mm)

12.56" (318 mm)

2.44" (62 mm)

30" (760 mm)

Prob. 13.17

13.18 Design the smallest (in whole inches) square tied column with not over 4% reinforcement to carry an axial compression of 200 kips dead load and 160 kips live load. For the member selected, determine the capacity when $e = 0.10h$ as was required under earlier ACI Codes. Comment. Use $f'_c = 3500$ psi and $f_y = 40,000$ psi. (DL = 900 kN; LL = 700 kN; $f'_c = 24$ N/mm²; $f_y = 280$ N/mm².)

13.19 Same as Prob. 13.18, except use a spirally reinforced circular column.

13.20 Design the smallest (in whole inches) square tied column permitted by the ACI Code to carry an axial compression of 350 kips dead load and 150 kips live load. Assume that the column is short enough so that no splicing of reinforcement is necessary. For the member selected, determine whether or not the capacity would have been adequate if a minimum $e = 0.1h$ had been required. Use $f'_c = 3750$ psi and $f_y = 40,000$ psi. (DL = 160 tons; LL = 70 tons; $f'_c = 265$ kgf/cm²; $f_y = 2800$ kgf/cm².)

13.21 Same as Prob. 13.19, except use a spirally reinforced circular column.

13.22 Design a square tied column with symmetrical reinforcement of about $3\frac{1}{2}\%$ to carry a dead load of $P = 200$ kips and $M = 75$ ft-kips and a live load of $P = 175$ kips and $M = 65$ ft-kips. Check final answer using basic statics. Use 1-in. (or 20-mm) increments with $f'_c = 4000$ psi and $f_y = 50,000$ psi. (DL: $P = 890$ kN, $M = 100$ kN-m; LL: $P = 780$ kN; $M = 88$ kN-m; $f'_c = 28$ N/mm²; $f_y = 350$ N/mm².)

13.23 Redesign the column of Prob. 13.22 using a rectangular column not over 15 in. (380 mm) wide instead of a square column.

13.24 Redesign the column of Prob. 13.22 as a spirally reinforced circular column.

13.25 Design a square tied column with symmetrical reinforcement of about 4% to carry a dead load of $P = 225$ kips and $M = 220$ ft-kips and a live load of $P = 200$ kips and $M = 190$ ft-kips. Check final answer using basic statics. Use 1-in. (or 20-mm) increments with $f'_c = 4000$ psi and $f_y = 40,000$ psi. (DL: $P = 102$ tons, $M = 30$ t-m; LL: $P = 90$ tons, $M = 26$ t-m; $f'_c = 280$ kgf/cm²; $f_y = 2800$ kgf/cm².)

13.26 Redesign the column of Prob. 13.25 using a rectangular column not over 16 in. (400 mm) wide instead of a square column.

13.27 Redesign the column of Prob. 13.25 as a spirally reinforced circular column.

13.28 Design a square tied column with about 4% reinforcement to carry a dead load of $P = 250$ kips and $M = 90$ ft-kips, and a live load of $P = 185$ kips and $M = 70$ ft-kips. Use 1-in. (or 20-mm) increments with $f'_c = 4000$ psi and $f_y = 60,000$ psi. (DL: $P = 1100$ kN, $M = 120$ kN-m; LL: $P = 820$ kN, $M = 95$ kN-m; $f'_c = 28$ N/mm²; $f_y = 420$ N/mm².)

13.29 Design a circular spirally reinforced column for the conditions given in Prob. 13.28. Make statics check using the designed circular section; also check using equivalent rectangle.

13.30 Design a square tied column with symmetrical reinforcement of about 2% to carry a dead load of $P = 25$ kips and $M = 125$ ft-kips and a live load of $P = 10$ kips and $M = 50$ ft-kips. Use 1-in. (or 20-mm) increments with $f'_c = 4000$ psi and $f_y = 60,000$ psi. (DL: $P = 110$ kN, $M = 170$ kN-m; LL: $P = 45$ kN, $M = 68$ kN-m; $f'_c = 28$ N/mm²; $f_y = 420$ N/mm².)

13.31 Redesign the column of Prob. 13.30 as a rectangular column having a depth-to-width ratio of between 1.5 and 2.0 along with unsymmetrical reinforcement with respect to the bending axis.

13.32 Design a square tied column with symmetrical reinforcement of about $2\frac{1}{2}\%$ to carry a dead load of $P = 75$ kips and $M = 125$ ft-kips and a live load of $P = 30$ kips and $M = 50$ ft-kips. Use 1-in. (or 20-mm) increments with $f'_c = 4000$ psi and $f_y = 60,000$ psi. (DL: $P = 34$ t, $M = 17$ t-m; LL: $P = 14$ t, $M = 7$ t-m; $f'_c = 280$ kgf/cm^2; $f_y = 4200$ kgf/cm^2.)

13.33 Redesign the column of Prob. 13.32 using a rectangular member but still using symmetrical reinforcement.

13.34 Redesign the column of Prob. 13.32 as a spirally reinforced circular column.

PROBLEMS ON BIAXIAL BENDING AND COMPRESSION

13.35 Determine the nominal ultimate capacity P_n for the column of Prob. 13.5 under an eccentricity e_y of 8 in. about the strong axis and an eccentricity e_x of 5 in. about the weak axis. (Hint: Use the interaction curve of Prob. 13.6 and calculate a similar interaction curve for the weak axis; then use basic statics, employing the two interaction curves as a guide.) Use $f'_c = 3000$ psi and $f_y = 40,000$ psi. ($e_y = 200$ mm; $e_x = 130$ mm; $f'_c = 21$ N/mm^2; $f_y = 280$ N/mm^2.)

13.36 Determine the adequacy of the rectangular tied column section of Prob. 13.9 when subjected to an axial load of 90 kips, applied with an eccentricity e_y of 5 in. with respect to the x axis and with an eccentricity e_x of 3 in. with respect to the y axis. Use $f'_c = 3000$ psi and $f_y = 40,000$ psi (use information developed in Probs. 13.9 and 13.10). Compare results using **(a)** Bresler reciprocal load method and **(b)** Parme load contour method.

13.37 Repeat Prob. 13.36, except the axial load is 45 kips applied with eccentricities of 10 in. with respect to the x axis and 6 in. with respect to the y axis.

13.38 Design a square tied column with about 4% reinforcement uniformly distributed around its sides. The loads are dead load, $P = 225$ kips, $M_x = 236$ ft-kips, and $M_y = 108$ ft-kips, and live load, $P = 200$ kips, $M_x = 204$ ft-kips, $M_y = 64$ ft-kips. Select size in whole inches that are multiples of two, using $f'_c = 4000$ psi and $f_y = 40,000$ psi.

13.39 Repeat Prob. 13.38, except use $f_y = 60,000$ psi.

13.40 Repeat Prob. 13.38, except reduce moments M_x about the x axis to 215 ft-kips dead load and 162 ft-kips live load, and increase f_y to 60,000 psi.

14

Deflections

14.1 Deflections—General

Throughout the period from 1910 to 1956, while the working stress method was used nearly exclusively, concrete with a compressive strength f'_c from 1500 to 3000 psi (approximately 10.5 to 21 N/mm^2) and reinforcement with a yield stress from 33 ksi to 40 ksi (approximately 230 to 280 N/mm^2) were predominant. The use of these materials with conservative allowable stresses, along with the straight-line working stress method, resulted in large stiff sections having small deflections. Ordinary reinforced concrete design involved little concern for deflections.

With the widespread use of the strength method and the realistic acceptance of the additional strength of concrete in compression according to the nonlinear relationship between stress and strain, sections could be made smaller. Such smaller sections deflect a greater amount than those designed under the working stress method.

The common use of 60,000 psi (420 N/mm^2) yield strength steel and of concrete having strengths f'_c ranging from the ordinary value of 4000 psi (28 N/mm^2) up to 9000 psi (63 N/mm^2) permits smaller sections than those resulting from the use of lower strength materials.

The permissible deflection is governed by the serviceability requirements for the structure, such as the amount of deformation that can be tolerated by the interacting components of the structure. Excessive deflection of the member may not in itself be detrimental, but the effect on structural components that are supported by the deflecting member frequently determines the acceptable amount. Both the short-time (instantaneous or immediate) and the long-time effects must be considered. The acceptable deflection depends on many factors, among which are the type of building (warehouse, school, factory, residence, etc.), the presence of plastered ceilings, the type and arrangement of partitions, the sensitivity of equipment to deflection, and the mangitude and duration of live load. Vibration and noise transmission are also serviceability concerns that depend on the stiffness of flexural members just as does deflection.

The maximum acceptable immediate deflections due to live load, for flat roofs or floors that do not support and are not attached to nonstructural elements such as plastered ceilings or frangible partitions likely to be damaged by large deflections, are prescribed by ACI-Table 9.5(b) to be (a) for flat roofs, $L/180$ and (b) for floors, $L/360$. Further, in recognition of the increase of deflection with time, ACI-Table 9.5(b) also prescribes limits for the sum of the *creep and shrinkage deflection due to all sustained loads plus any additional live-load deflection*. The two stated limits for this deflection combination are (a) when nonstructural elements are likely to be damaged, $L/480$, and (b) when no damage to nonstructural elements is likely, $L/240$.

Limitations on deflection are somewhat arbitrary; historically, $L/360$ has been the accepted limit to prevent the cracking of plastered ceilings. Other limits should be considered as guidelines, with the designer having the responsibility for evaluating the possible adverse effects of excessive deflection in any given situation.

ACI Committee 435 has reported recommendations for allowable deflections for a great variety of situations [1].

The general concepts dealt with in this chapter are applicable to both one-way (beams and slabs) and two-way systems. Specific examples are applied only to one-way systems. The reader is referred to Sec. 16.14 for a brief discussion of two-way system deflections, along with specific references.

14.2 Deflections for Elastic Sections

Various methods are available in structural analysis for computing deflections on uniform and variable moment of inertia sections in statically determinate and indeterminate structures. In general, using any of the several methods, the maximum deflection in an elastic member may be expressed as

$$\Delta_{max} = \beta_a \frac{ML^2}{EI_c} . \qquad (14.2.1)$$

where

> M = a reference value of bending moment such as the maximum positive value
> L = span length
> E = modulus of elasticity
> I_c = moment of inertia of a standard section in the member
> β_a = a coefficient that depends on the degree of fixity at supports, the variation in moment of inertia along the span, and the distribution of loading

The deflection coefficient β_a for simple cases may be found in handbooks, such as *Handbook of Concrete Engineering* [2].

The following example will demonstrate one elastic method, the conjugate-beam method, while also deriving one of the most useful deflection expressions.

EXAMPLE 14.2.1   Using the conjugate-beam method, derive the general expression for the elastic midspan deflection for a uniformly loaded span with unequal end moments, as shown in Fig. 14.2.1.

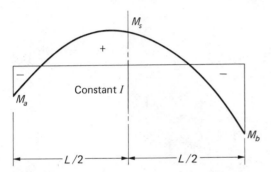

Fig. 14.2.1
Typical bending moment diagram for a uniformly loaded span.

Solution: In the conjugate-beam method, the deflection at a given point equals the bending moment at that point for a beam loaded with the M/EI diagram. Thus the system of Fig. 14.2.1 may be regarded as being composed of three separate conjugate beams as shown in Fig. 14.2.2.

The midspan deflections, or the bending moments on the three conjugate beams, are

$$\text{uniform load, } \Delta_s = \frac{2}{3}\left(\frac{L}{2}\right)\left(\frac{M_0}{EI}\right)\left[\frac{L}{2} - \frac{3}{8}\left(\frac{L}{2}\right)\right] = \frac{5M_0L^2}{48EI}$$

$$\text{left-end moment, } \Delta_a = \frac{1}{3}\left(\frac{-M_a}{EI}\right)\left(\frac{L}{2}\right)\left(\frac{L}{2}\right) - \frac{1}{2}\left(\frac{-M_a}{2EI}\right)\left(\frac{L}{2}\right)\left(\frac{1}{3}\right)\left(\frac{L}{2}\right)$$

$$= \frac{-M_aL^2}{16EI}$$

$$\text{right-end moment, } \Delta_b = \frac{-M_bL^2}{16EI}$$

The total midspan deflection is

$$\Delta_m = \Delta_s + \Delta_a + \Delta_b$$

$$= \frac{5M_0L^2}{48EI} - \frac{M_aL^2}{16EI} - \frac{M_bL^2}{16EI}$$

$$= \frac{L^2}{48EI}[5M_0 - 3(M_a + M_b)] \qquad (14.2.2)$$

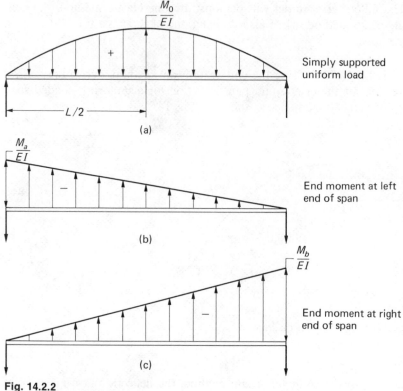

Fig. 14.2.2
Component conjugate beams.

The net positive midspan moment M_s is

$$M_s = M_0 - \tfrac{1}{2}(M_a + M_b) \tag{14.2.3}$$

Then, upon substituting Eq. (14.2.3) in Eq. (14.2.2), one obtains

$$
\begin{aligned}
\Delta_m &= \frac{L^2}{48EI}\left[5M_s + \frac{5}{2}(M_a + M_b) - 3(M_a + M_b)\right] \\
&= \frac{5L^2}{48EI}\left[M_s - \frac{1}{10}(M_a + M_b)\right] \tag{14.2.4}
\end{aligned}
$$

Equation (14.2.4) may be used with satisfactory results for practically all uniform section cases, even though the absolute maximum deflection will be obtained only when the loading is uniform and the end moments are equal.

Continuous Beams Having Variable Flexural Rigidity. When significant changes of gross cross section along the span length are involved, such changes should be included when performing the statically indeterminate analysis for end moments. When deflections are desired for such cases, the best approach is to account for the variable flexural rigidity EI exactly, either mathematically in the component conjugate beams (see Fig. 14.2.2), or by the use of numerical integration.

As an *approximation*, it is suggested to use Eq. (14.2.4) even when variable flexural rigidity is involved, particularly when the variable EI results from the variation in the extent of tension concrete cracking. In such cases, one may use a single adjusted value of flexural rigidity EI. Three methods have been suggested [3].

1. *Midspan value alone.* With this assumption the EI for Eq. (14.2.4) is

$$EI = (EI)_c \tag{14.2.5}$$

where $(EI)_c$ is the flexural rigidity at midspan. This is the simplest method and when the inflection point is between about $0.2L$ and the support, the results are within $\pm 20\%$ of those obtained using variable EI, as long as $0.33 \le \alpha \le 1.0$ [where $\alpha = (EI$ at midspan$)/(EI$ at end$)$]. When α lies between 0.50 and 1.0, the results are within $\pm 5\%$ of those obtained using variable EI. A recent study [4] suggests this method to be satisfactory for ordinary design situations.

2. *Simple average.* With this assumption the EI used for Eq. (14.2.4) is the average EI

$$EI = \frac{\frac{1}{2}[(EI)_{e1} + (EI)_{e2}] + (EI)_c}{2} \tag{14.2.6}$$

where $(EI)_{e1}$ and $(EI)_{e2}$ are the flexural rigidities at the two ends of the span. It is suggested that the use of both $(EI)_{e1}$ and $(EI)_{e2}$ is appropriate only when there are end moments at both ends. For end moment at one end, it is appropriate to use $EI = \frac{1}{2}[(EI)_e + (EI)_c]$.

3. *Weighted average.* In this method the adjusted EI is obtained by weighting the flexural rigidities in accordance with the magnitudes of the end moments [3]. The following weighted-average expression has been recommended by ACI Committee 435 [5] as giving a somewhat improved result over the use of the midspan value alone. For spans with *both* ends continuous,

$$EI = 0.70(EI)_c + 0.15[(EI)_{e1} + (EI)_{e2}] \tag{14.2.7}$$

For spans with *one* end continuous,

$$EI = 0.85(EI)_c + 0.15(EI)_e \tag{14.2.8}$$

For a single heavy concentrated load, only the midspan value $(EI)_c$ should be used.

14.3 Modulus of Elasticity

As discussed in Sec. 1.9, variance in interpretation is encountered when referring to the modulus of elasticity of concrete. Ordinary beam theory presumes the modulus in tension to be the same as in compression for a homogeneous material. In a reinforced concrete section, creep affects the apparent modulus primarily on the compression side. Even the short-time loading modulus, measured as the secant modulus, is considerably more variant than the compressive strength f'_c. On the tension side there are cracks in the concrete in regions of high bending moment, while at low-moment sections the concrete may not crack. The secant modulus in tension is essentially the same as in compression when the stress magnitude is low, but the modulus reduces markedly as the stress nears the cracking level. In other words, in both tension and compression the actual modulus of elasticity varies not only with the magnitude of stress from top to bottom at a section, but also along the span.

Further, creep and shrinkage over a period of time effectively reduce the modulus in compression and will generally magnify deflections by a factor of two or three. Referring to Fig. 1.10.1 one may note that the true elastic strain decreases with time, indicating that the modulus of elasticity increases. The modulus increases because it is dependent on f'_c which increases with age. In design practice, usually the apparent elastic strain is used as computed with a code-specified E_c, presumably corresponding to the 28-day age at loading. Beyond 28 days, however, the increase in modulus of elasticity is relatively slight. The concept of using a reduced effective modulus of elasticity to account for creep and shrinkage is merely a device for obtaining the larger total deflections (elastic + creep + shrinkage) when loading is sustained for a period of time.

14.4 Moment of Inertia

The other property which, in addition to the modulus of elasticity, determines the flexural rigidity and therefore the deflection of a member is the moment of inertia. The effective moment of inertia, even for sections whose external dimensions are constant, varies considerably along a span. Consider a span with a T-shaped section in a continuous beam or frame, as shown in Fig. 14.4.1. In such a continuous structure, at or near the support the concrete slab is cracked, and the effective section is as shown in section $A-A$; while in the positive moment zone the stem is cracked, with the resulting effective section as shown in section $B-B$. Furthermore, near the points of inflection the stresses may be low enough so that nearly the entire section may be uncracked and fully effective, as shown in section $C-C$.

In an elastic continuity analysis as discussed in Chaps. 7 and 10, only relative stiffness values are required; but in deflection computations, the absolute magnitudes for E_c and I must first be determined or assumed. Moreover, the amount of deflection under each increment of load is not constant. The flexural rigidity E_cI is greater under low stress, since the fully uncracked section provides the greatest effective moment of inertia.

The subject of effective moment of inertia for computing deflections due to short-term loading has received significant study in the past several years [6–8]. It is known that the flexural rigidity E_cI varies with the magnitude of bending moment in the general manner shown in Fig. 14.4.2. Of course, the moment of inertia of the cracked transformed section increases roughly

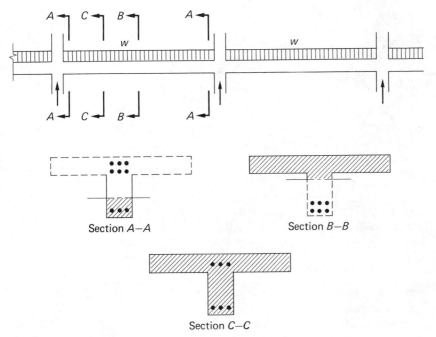

Fig. 14.4.1
Effective moment of inertia for continuous T-shaped sections.

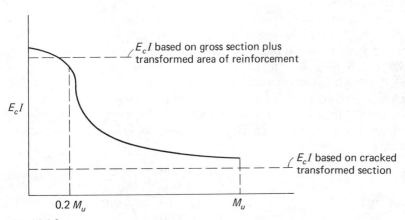

Fig. 14.4.2
Typical variation of flexural rigidity with applied bending moment.

proportionally with an increase in the percentage of reinforcement. Sections with higher percentages of reinforcement exhibit less change in rigidity under increasing load than those with low percentages of reinforcement.

For loads below the cracking load (see Fig. 14.4.3), deflections may be based on the gross concrete section, with generally a small difference arising from whether or not the transformed area of reinforcement is also included. However, as the load increases above the cracking load, the moment of

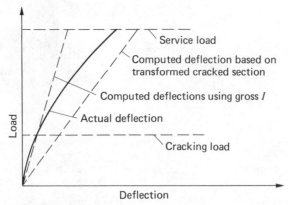

Fig. 14.4.3
Typical load-deflection curve for reinforced concrete beams.

inertia approaches that of the cracked transformed section, although it may be greater between cracks.

Prior to 1971, either gross moment of inertia or transformed cracked section moment of inertia was used. Generally, as shown by the typical load deflection curve in Fig. 14.4.3, the use of gross section underestimated the deflection, and the use of cracked transformed section overestimated the deflection. However, the degree of accuracy was affected by the magnitude of the service load compared to the load to cause cracking.

The 1963 ACI Code prescribed using gross section when ρf_y did not exceed 500, and using transformed cracked section when ρf_y exceeded 500, where $\rho = A_s/(bd)$. This procedure provided satisfactory results when ρf_y was either well below or well above 500. However, it gave an abrupt discontinuity instead of a gradual transition for the moment of inertia.

Since 1971 the ACI Code (Formula 9-7) has used the expression proposed by Branson [7] in 1963 that includes the effects of load level and degree of cracking:

$$I_e = \left(\frac{M_{cr}}{M_{max}}\right)^3 I_g + \left[1 - \left(\frac{M_{cr}}{M_{max}}\right)^3\right] I_{cr} \leq I_g \qquad (14.4.1)$$

where

$M_{cr} = f_r I_g / y_t =$ cracking moment

$M_{max} =$ maximum service-load moment acting at the condition under which deflection is computed

$I_g =$ gross moment of inertia (neglecting reinforcement)

$I_{cr} =$ cracked transformed section moment of inertia

$f_r =$ modulus of rupture (unit tensile stress capacity at cracking in flexure), taken by ACI Code as $7.5\sqrt{f'_c}$ for normal-weight concrete; in general may be taken [5] as $0.65\sqrt{wf'_c}$, where w is the unit weight of concrete

$y_t =$ distance from neutral axis to extreme fiber of concrete in tension

Equation (14.4.1) is intended to be calculated at the location of maximum moment as a single value for the entire span in the case of simply supported beams, or as a single value between points of inflection in continuous beams. If one wishes to recognize the continuous variation of the moment of inertia along the span, Branson proposed using the fourth power instead of the third power in Eq. (14.4.1). In this case M_{cr} and M_{max} are the cracking moment and the applied moment, respectively, at each section along the span. The span may be broken into segments with each segment having a different moment of inertia and numerical integration used to compute the deflection.

Equation (14.4.1) was developed from a statistical study of 54 test specimens which had M_{max}/M_{cr} values from 2.2 to about 4 and I_g/I_{cr} values from 1.3 to 3.5. The study included simple-span rectangular beams [10], T-beams [6], and two-span continuous rectangular beams [11]. Branson has provided an excellent summary [8,9,22] of background material relating to Eq. (14.4.1).

14.5 Instantaneous Deflections in Design

Throughout the history of reinforced concrete construction, computation of instantaneous (short-time) deflection has usually involved using either cracked transformed section or gross uncracked section [12]. In either case, Eq. (14.2.1) is suitable after it is slightly rewritten using E_c and I_e

$$\Delta = \beta_a \left(\frac{ML^2}{E_c I_e} \right) \tag{14.5.1}$$

where

β_a = coefficient based on load and support conditions
I_e = effective moment of inertia
E_c = modulus of elasticity of concrete

For instantaneous (elastic) deflection and also generally for long-time deflection under sustained loads, the basic value of modulus of elasticity to be used for concrete is (ACI-8.5.1)

$$E_c = 33w^{1.5}\sqrt{f'_c}$$

for concrete having a unit weight between 90 and 155 pcf. For normal-weight concrete,

$$E_c = 57,000\sqrt{f'_c}$$

The effective moment of inertia for Eq. (14.5.1) may be obtained using various methods [12] but the generally accepted expression is Eq. (14.4.1).

In order to compute deflection at different load levels, such as dead load or dead load plus live load, the effective moment of inertia I_e should be computed using Eq. (14.4.1) for that total load level in each case. The incremental deflection, such as for live load only, is then computed as the difference between the deflections due to dead plus live load and dead load only. It should be assumed that the live load cannot act in the absence of dead load.

Computation of the live-load deflection as $\Delta_{D+L} - \Delta_D$ gives the live-load deflection occurring during the *first* application of live load. Figure 14.5.1 shows the typical idealized load or moment versus deflection relationship [14]. For repeated loadings, the upper envelope of load-deflection curves is nearly the same as the single-loading curve for both reinforced and pre-stressed concrete members, even though increasing residual deflections occur due to creep and cracking effects [5]. Thus it seems reasonable to compute short-time deflections using I_e as described above and the residual deflection separately as discussed in the sections on creep and shrinkage.

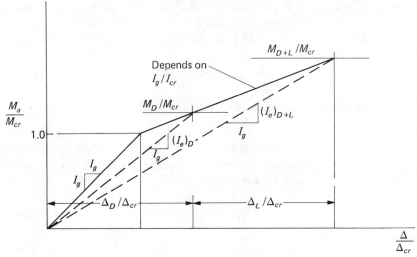

Fig. 14.5.1
Typical idealized moment-deflection diagram for short-time loading (from Refs. 5, 14, and 22).

A comparison of the measured short-time deflections with the deflections computed by various methods [12] is shown in Fig. 14.5.2. A recent study [13] indicates that by using the present ACI Code criteria for deflection for simply supported beams under *controlled laboratory conditions* "there is approximately a 90% chance that the deflections of a particular beam will be within the range of 20% less than to 30% more than the calculated value."

The following two examples demonstrate the computation of instantaneous deflection.

EXAMPLE 14.5.1 Investigate the instantaneous (short-time loading) deflection for the simply supported beam of Fig. 14.5.3 over a span of 40 ft. Assume that the member has been designed by the ultimate strength method using $f'_c = 4000$ psi, $f_y = 60,000$ psi, and the ACI Code.

Solution: According to ACI-Table 9.5(a) the minimum depth unless deflection is computed is $L/16 = 40(12)/16 = 30$ in. Thus a deflection computation is required.

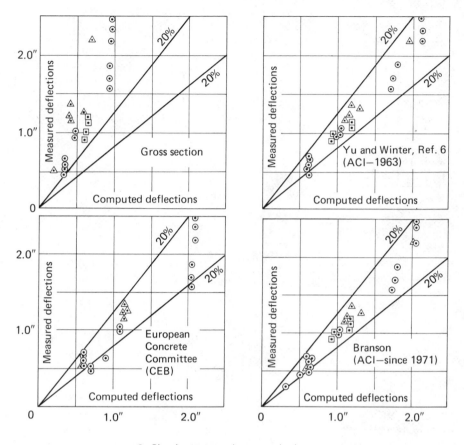

⊙ Simply supported rectangular beams

△ Simply supported T beams

⊡ 2 span continuous rectangular beams

Fig. 14.5.2
Comparison of computed and measured short-time deflections (from Ref. 12).

(a) Total dead- plus live-load short-time deflection. The gross moment of inertia is

$$I_g = \tfrac{1}{12}(14)(24)^3 = 16,100 \text{ in.}^4 \ (671,000 \text{ cm}^4)$$

$$M_{max} = \frac{28(40)}{4} + \frac{0.35(40)^2}{8} = 280 + 70 = 350 \text{ ft-kips} \ (475 \text{ kN-m})$$

For the cracked transformed section, as shown in Fig. 14.5.3b, the neutral-axis position is

$$\frac{14x^2}{2} = 57.3(21.5 - x)$$

$$x^2 + 8.19x = 176.0$$

$$x = 9.78 \text{ in.}$$

$$I_{cr} = \tfrac{1}{3}(14)(9.78)^3 + 57.3(21.5 - 9.78)^2 = 12,200 \text{ in.}^4 \ (509,000 \text{ cm}^4)$$

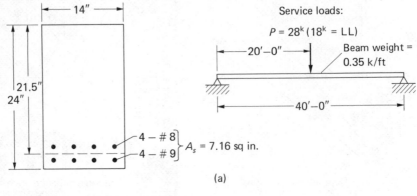

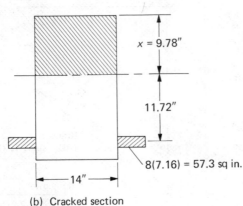

(b) Cracked section

Fig. 14.5.3
Beam for Example 14.5.1.

The effective moment of inertia I_e is dependent on the bending moment M_{cr} that causes cracking at the extreme tension fiber.

$$M_{cr} = \frac{f_r I_g}{y_t} = \frac{0.474(16,100)}{12}\left(\frac{1}{12}\right) = 53 \text{ ft-kips}$$

$$f_r = 7.5\sqrt{f_c'} = 7.5\sqrt{4000} = 474 \text{ psi} \qquad (\text{ACI-9.5.2.3})$$

$$\frac{M_{cr}}{M_{max}} = \frac{53}{350}(\text{dead load + live load}) = 0.151; \qquad \left(\frac{M_{cr}}{M_{max}}\right)^3 = 0.0035$$

From ACI Formula (9-7), Eq. (14.4.1), the effective moment of inertia is

$$I_e = \left(\frac{M_{cr}}{M_{max}}\right)^3 I_g + \left[1 - \left(\frac{M_{cr}}{M_{max}}\right)^3\right] I_{cr}$$

$$= 0.0035(16,100) + 0.9965(12,200) = 12,200 \text{ in.}^4$$

For practical purposes, $I_e = I_{cr}$.

$$E_c = 33w^{1.5}\sqrt{f_c'} = 33(145)^{1.5}\sqrt{4000} = 3.64 \times 10^6 \text{ psi}$$

$$\Delta \text{ (beam weight)} = \frac{5WL^3}{384EI} = \frac{5(0.35)(40)(40)^3(1728)}{384(3.64)(10^3)(12,200)} = 0.45 \text{ in. (11 mm)}$$

$$\Delta \text{ (concentrated load)} = \frac{PL^3}{48EI} = \frac{28(40)^3(1728)}{48(3.64)(10^3)(12,200)} = 1.45 \text{ in. (37 mm)}$$

The total instantaneous deflection under dead load and live load is

$$(\Delta_i)_{D+L} = 0.45 + 1.45 = 1.90 \text{ in. (48 mm)}$$

(b) Dead-load short-time deflection.

$$M_{max} = \frac{10(40)}{4} + 70 = 170 \text{ ft-kips (for dead load only)}$$
$$(231 \text{ kN-m})$$

$$\frac{M_{cr}}{M_{max}} = \frac{53}{170}\left(\frac{\text{dead}}{\text{load}}\right) = 0.312; \qquad \left(\frac{M_{cr}}{M_{max}}\right)^3 = 0.030$$

$$I_e = (0.030)(16,100) + (0.970)(12,200) = 12,300 \text{ in.}^4$$

Even under dead load alone, $I_e \approx I_{cr}$; so the answer may be obtained by proportion.

$$(\Delta_i)_D = 0.45 + 1.45\left(\frac{10}{28}\right) = 0.97 \text{ in. (25 mm)}$$

This deflection may not be harmful because the part represented by the beam weight plus the dead-load portion from the concentrated load may be accommodated by using a negative deflection (camber) in construction. Even if camber is not used, such dead-load instantaneous deflection will not affect plastered ceilings or other items that are put into place after the immediate dead-load deflection has taken place. Concern is primarily with the instantaneous deflection from live load and the long-term creep and shrinkage deflection from sustained loads.

(c) Live-load short-time deflection. Though in this example it makes no appreciable difference, consistent logic dictates that live-load deflection must be obtained indirectly as

$$(\Delta_i)_L = (\Delta_i)_{D+L} - (\Delta_i)_D$$
$$= 1.90 - 0.97 = 0.93 \text{ in. (24 mm)}$$

It is assumed that live load cannot act in the absence of dead load. Thus if the effective moment of inertia when dead load alone is acting is considerably different from that when dead load plus live load is acting, the live-load deflection is properly obtained only by subtracting Δ_D from Δ_{D+L}.

From a practical viewpoint, $I_e = I_{cr}$ may be used whenever $(M_{cr}/M_{max})^3$ is less than about 0.1, in which case live-load deflection may be obtained directly by proportion instead of indirectly as illustrated above. Assuming this to be a floor beam not supporting partitions, the acceptable immediate live-load deflection from ACI-Table 9.5(b) is

$$\text{allowable } (\Delta_i)_L = \frac{L}{360} = \frac{40(12)}{360} = 1.33 \text{ in.} > 0.93 \text{ in. (34 mm} > 24 \text{ mm)}$$

· OK

If plastered ceilings or frangible partitions are to be supported, the deflection due to long-time creep and shrinkage must be added to that due to live loads; the acceptable limit for this deflection is $L/480$ (ACI-Table 9.5b).

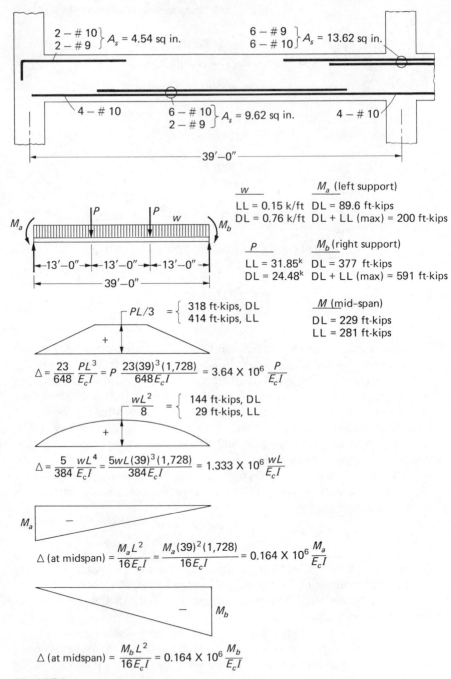

$$\frac{w}{} \qquad \underline{M_a \text{ (left support)}}$$

LL = 0.15 k/ft   DL = 89.6 ft-kips
DL = 0.76 k/ft   DL + LL (max) = 200 ft-kips

$$\frac{P}{} \qquad \underline{M_b \text{ (right support)}}$$

LL = 31.85^k DL = 377 ft-kips
DL = 24.48^k DL + LL (max) = 591 ft-kips

$PL/3 = \begin{cases} 318 \text{ ft-kips, DL} \\ 414 \text{ ft-kips, LL} \end{cases}$

$\underline{M \text{ (mid-span)}}$

DL = 229 ft-kips
LL = 281 ft-kips

$$\Delta = \frac{23}{648}\frac{PL^3}{E_cI} = P\,\frac{23(39)^3(1,728)}{648E_cI} = 3.64 \times 10^6\,\frac{P}{E_cI}$$

$\dfrac{wL^2}{8} = \begin{cases} 144 \text{ ft-kips, DL} \\ 29 \text{ ft-kips, LL} \end{cases}$

$$\Delta = \frac{5}{384}\frac{wL^4}{E_cI} = \frac{5wL(39)^3(1,728)}{384E_cI} = 1.333 \times 10^6\,\frac{wL}{E_cI}$$

$$\Delta \text{ (at midspan)} = \frac{M_aL^2}{16E_cI} = \frac{M_a(39)^2(1,728)}{16E_cI} = 0.164 \times 10^6\,\frac{M_a}{E_cI}$$

$$\Delta \text{ (at midspan)} = \frac{M_bL^2}{16E_cI} = 0.164 \times 10^6\,\frac{M_b}{E_cI}$$

Fig. 14.5.4
Data for Example 14.5.2.

EXAMPLE 14.5.2 Investigate the instantaneous deflection on the continuous beam of Fig. 14.5.4. Use $f'_c = 3000$ psi, $f_y = 40,000$ psi, and the ACI Code.

Solution: This continuous girder supports two smaller beams that frame to it and some uniform loading that comes directly to it. ACI-9.5.2.4 indicates that I_e is to be computed as an average value for the positive- and negative-moment regions. The more recent recommendations of ACI Committee 435 [5] is that use of the positive-moment region I_e is adequate for most situations and is likely to be more accurate than using the average when the loading is largely concentrated, as it is in this case.

(a) Section at the left support. For the gross section neglecting reinforcement (see Fig. 14.5.5),

$$x = \frac{36(18)18 + 90(4.5)38.25}{36(18) + 90(4.5)} = \frac{27,160}{1053} = 25.79 \text{ in.}$$

$$I_g = \tfrac{1}{3}(18)[(25.79)^3 + (14.71)^3] + 72(4.5)(12.46)^2 + \tfrac{1}{12}(72)(4.5)^3$$
$$= 173,000 \text{ in.}^4$$

Had reinforcement been included, $x = 25.29$ in. and $I_g = 200,000$ in.^{4} It is generally accepted that I_g for use in ACI Formula (9-7) should not include steel reinforcement.

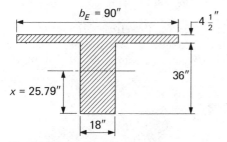

Fig. 14.5.5
Gross section of beam for Example 14.5.2.

For the transformed cracked section (see Fig. 14.5.6a),

$$18x\left(\frac{x}{2}\right) + 40.6(x - 2.6) = 40.9(36.7 - x)$$

$$x^2 + 9.05x = 178.2$$

$$x = 9.56 \text{ in.}$$

$$I_{cr} = \tfrac{1}{3}(18)(9.56)^3 + 40.6(9.56 - 2.6)^2 + 40.9(36.7 - 9.56)^2$$
$$= 37,200 \text{ in.}^4$$

It is noted that the modular ratio n is used to transform the steel in the compression zone, instead of $2n$ which would be used in working stress method to check stresses. The use of n is believed to give the more accurate short-time deflection result, though using $2n$ also gives answers believed to

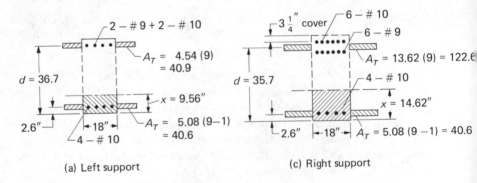

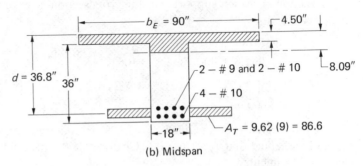

Fig. 14.5.6

Transformed cracked sections for Example 14.5.2.

be sufficiently accurate. If one has used $2n$ for the stress calculation, it is recommended the same I_{cr} be used for the deflection calculation.

Compute the cracking moment capacity of the beam with tension on the flange.

$$f_r = 7.5\sqrt{f_c'} = 7.5\sqrt{3000} = 411 \text{ psi}$$

$$M_{cr} = \frac{f_r I_g}{y_t} = \frac{0.411(173,000)}{14.71}\left(\frac{1}{12}\right) = 402 \text{ ft-kips}$$

$$\frac{M_{cr}}{M_{max}} = \frac{402}{89.6}\left(\frac{\text{dead}}{\text{load}}\right) > 1; \quad \text{use } I_e = I_g = 173,000 \text{ in.}^4$$

$$\frac{M_{cr}}{M_{max}} = \frac{402}{200}\left(\frac{\text{dead load}}{+ \text{ live load}}\right) > 1; \quad \text{use } I_e = I_g = 173,000 \text{ in.}^4$$

(b) Midspan section (Fig. 14.5.6b). Determine whether or not the neutral axis occurs in the flange by taking moments about the bottom of the flange,

$$90(4.5)(2.25) < 86.6(32.3)$$

Locate the neutral axis, including the effect of compression in the stem.

$$90(4.5)(x - 2.25) + 18(x - 4.5)^2(\tfrac{1}{2}) = 86.6(36.8 - x)$$

$$x^2 + 45.6x = 435$$

$$x = 8.09 \text{ in.}$$

$$I_{cr} = \tfrac{1}{12}(72)(4.5)^3 + 72(4.5)(5.84)^2 + \tfrac{1}{3}(18)(8.09)^3 + 86.6(36.8 - 8.09)^2$$

$$= 86,200 \text{ in.}^4$$

The cracking moment capacity of the beam with tension in the stem is

$$M_{cr} = \frac{f_r I_g}{y_t} = \frac{0.411(173{,}000)}{25.79}\left(\frac{1}{12}\right) = 229.5 \text{ ft-kips}$$

$$\frac{M_{cr}}{M_{max}} = \frac{229.5}{229}\left(\frac{\text{dead}}{\text{load}}\right) > 1; \qquad \text{use } I_e = I_g = 173{,}000 \text{ in.}^4$$

$$\frac{M_{cr}}{M_{max}} = \frac{229.5}{510}\left(\frac{\text{dead load}}{+ \text{ live load}}\right) = 0.45; \qquad \left(\frac{M_{cr}}{M_{max}}\right)^3 = 0.091$$

$$I_e = \left(\frac{M_{cr}}{M_{max}}\right)^3 I_g + \left[1 - \left(\frac{M_{cr}}{M_{max}}\right)^3\right] I_{cr}$$

$$= 0.091(173{,}000) + 0.909(86{,}200) = 94{,}000 \text{ in.}^4$$

(c) Section at the right support (Fig. 14.5.6c). Use transformed cracked section and locate the neutral axis,

$$18x\left(\frac{x}{2}\right) + 40.6(x - 2.6) = 122.6(35.7 - x)$$

$$x^2 + 18.13x = 498$$

$$x = 15.02 \text{ in.}$$

$$I_{cr} = \tfrac{1}{3}(18)(15.02)^3 + 122.6(35.7 - 15.02)^2 + 40.6(15.02 - 2.60)^2$$

$$= 79{,}000 \text{ in.}^4$$

$$M_{cr} = 402 \text{ ft-kips (same as left support)}$$

$$\frac{M_{cr}}{M_{max}} = \frac{402}{377}\left(\frac{\text{dead}}{\text{load}}\right) > 1; \qquad \text{use } I_e = I_g = 173{,}000 \text{ in.}^4$$

$$\frac{M_{cr}}{M_{max}} = \frac{402}{591}\left(\frac{\text{dead load}}{+ \text{ live load}}\right) = 0.68; \qquad \left(\frac{M_{cr}}{M_{max}}\right)^3 = 0.314$$

$$I_e = 0.314(173{,}000) + 0.686(79{,}000) = 109{,}000 \text{ in.}^4$$

(d) Summary of values for I_e. The values of effective moment of inertia are

	For DL	For DL + LL
Left end	$I_e = 173{,}000 \text{ in.}^4$	$I_e = 173{,}000 \text{ in.}^4$
Midspan	$I_e = 173{,}000 \text{ in.}^4$	$I_e = 94{,}000 \text{ in.}^4$
Right end	$I_e = 173{,}000 \text{ in.}^4$	$I_e = 109{,}000 \text{ in.}^4$

Having obtained the above values, usual practice is to use a single adjusted value of flexural rigidity as discussed in Sec. 14.2. Here the simple average will be used as suggested by ACI-9.5.2.4.
   For dead load,

$$I_{avg} = 173{,}000 \text{ in.}^4$$

For dead load plus live load,

$$I_{avg} = \frac{1}{2}\left(\frac{173{,}000 + 109{,}000}{2} + 94{,}000\right) = 118{,}000 \text{ in.}^4$$

The task of determining the immediate deflection is actually one of analyzing a continuous beam with variable moment of inertia. Because the most "exact" computations at best give deflections within probably $\pm 20\%$, procedures more complex than the one illustrated here are not justified.

(e) Immediate dead-load deflection.

$$M_a = 89.6 \text{ ft-kips} \qquad M_b = 377 \text{ ft-kips}$$
$$w = 0.76 \text{ kip/ft} \qquad P = 24.48 \text{ kips}$$

It is to be noted that the span is taken as that measured between the center-lines of supports, and the end moments are those computed for the same locations. Equally acceptable results are obtained by using the clear span and the face-of-support moments. Referring to Fig. 14.5.4 the total midspan deflection is

$$\Delta = \frac{10^6}{E_c I_e}(3.64P + 1.333wL - 0.164M_a - 0.164M_b)$$

$$E_c = 33w^{1.5}\sqrt{f_c'} = 57,000\sqrt{3000} = 3.15 \times 10^6 \text{ psi (ACI-8.5.1)}$$

$$(\Delta_i)_D = \frac{1}{3.15(173)}[3.64(24.48) + 1.333(0.76)(39) - 0.164(89.6 + 377.0)]$$

$$= \frac{89.2 + 39.5 - 76.4}{545} = \frac{52.3}{545} = 0.10 \text{ in. (2.5 mm)}$$

As previously mentioned, dead-load deflection will usually cause no difficulty, as most of it may be compensated for by the construction. However, it is used as a basis for determining the long-time creep and shrinkage deflection which is discussed in the next section.

(f) Immediate dead- plus live-load deflection.

$$M_a = 200 \text{ ft-kips} \qquad M_b = 591 \text{ ft-kips}$$
$$w = 0.91 \text{ kip/ft} \qquad P = 56.33 \text{ kips}$$

$$(\Delta_i)_{D+L} = \frac{1}{3.15(118)}[3.64(56.33) + 1.333(0.91)(39) - 0.164(200 + 591)]$$

$$= \frac{205.0 + 47.0 - 129.7}{372} = \frac{122.3}{372} = 0.33 \text{ in. (8.4 mm)}$$

(g) Immediate live-load deflection.

$$(\Delta_i)_L = (\Delta_i)_{D+L} - (\Delta_i)_D = 0.33 - 0.10 = 0.23 \text{ in. (5.8 mm)}$$

If this is a floor that does not support frangible partitions, the limiting permissible deflection is $L/360$, or

$$\frac{L}{360} = \frac{39(12)}{360} = 1.3 \text{ in.} > 0.23 \text{ in. (33 mm} > 5.8 \text{ mm)} \qquad \text{OK}$$

By making use of the moment envelope, using the maximum positive moment of 555 ft-kips (at right-hand concentrated load) and the associated end moments, $M_a = 200$ ft-kips and $M_b = 591$ ft-kips, Eq. (14.2.4) may be directly applied to give 0.35 in. as the approximate immediate deflection due to dead load plus maximum live load.

(h) Alternate computation using I_e only at midspan instead of an average value.

For dead load, $I_e = 173,000$ in.^{4} [see part (b)]
For dead load plus live load, $I_e = 94,000$ in.^{4} [see part (b)]

$$(\Delta_i)_D = 0.10 \text{ in. (2.5 mm)}$$

There was no difference here because the I_e was the same at midspan as at the two supports.

$$(\Delta_i)_{D+L} = 0.33 \left(\frac{118,000}{94,000}\right) = 0.41 \text{ in. (10 mm)}$$

$$(\Delta_i)_L = 0.41 - 0.10 = 0.31 \text{ in. (7.9 mm)}$$

As stated earlier, it is likely that this result is at least as accurate as averaging because the loads are primarily concentrated loads. Even if the loading is uniform, the slight improvement in accuracy by averaging probably does not justify computing I_e at three locations instead of one.

14.6 Creep Effect on Deflections under Sustained Load

The total long-term deflection includes the instantaneous elastic deflection plus the contributions from creep and shrinkage. Creep is inelastic deformation with time under sustained loads at unit stresses within the accepted elastic range (say, below $0.5f'_c$), as shown in Fig. 14.6.1. This inelastic deformation increases at a decreasing rate during the time of loading. The internal

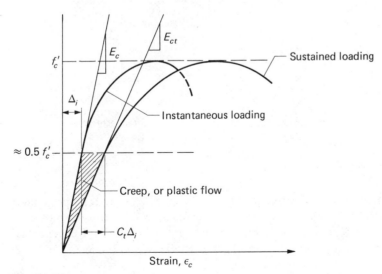

Fig. 14.6.1
Typical stress-strain curves for instantaneous and long-time loading.

mechanics of creep, or plastic flow, has been the subject of considerable study for many years [15–19]. Creep deformation is believed to be the result of a combination of the following: (1) closing of internal voids, (2) viscous flow of the cement-water paste, (3) crystalline flow in the aggregate, and (4) the flow of water out of the cement gel due to external load and drying. Factors that affect the magnitude of creep deformation are (1) the constituents—such as the composition and fineness of the cement, the admixtures, and the size, grading, and mineral content of the aggregates; (2) proportions, such as water content and water-cement ratio; (3) curing temperature and humidity; (4) relative humidity during storage; (5) size of the concrete member, particularly the ratio of span length to beam depth [10]; (6) age at loading; (7) duration of loading; and (8) magnitude of stress.

Since, as seen from Fig. 14.6.1, the result of creep is an increase in strain with constant stress, one of the ways of accounting for it is by the use of a modified modulus of elasticity E_{ct}. An alternative and more recently preferred procedure is to apply a multiplier C_t to the elastic deflection Δ_i.

In order to help understand the qualitative effect of creep on beam deformation, consider the singly reinforced beam of Fig. 14.6.2. It is noted that the strain at the tension steel is essentially unchanged because the concrete contributes little in taking tension and ordinary deformed steel reinforcement exhibits little creep. Since the neutral axis moves down, two observations may be made: (1) The concrete stress reduces at the compression face (i.e., same compressive force acting and x_{cp} exceeds x_i); and (2) the increase in compressive strain is much greater than the increase in curvature (ϕ).

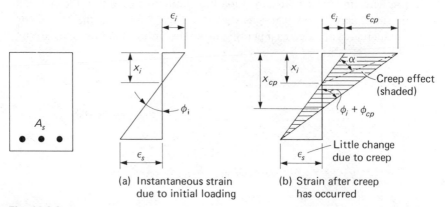

(a) Instantaneous strain due to initial loading

(b) Strain after creep has occurred

Fig. 14.6.2
Creep effect on beam curvature.

Many mathematical expressions for the creep effect have been presented, the majority of which involve exponential functions and thus do not give creep magnitude that approaches a finite limit [20]. The most generally accepted expressions have been of the hyperbolic type in the form

$$\epsilon_{cp} = \frac{t^{\alpha}}{a + bt^{\alpha}} \tag{14.6.1}$$

where ϵ_{cp} is the creep strain due to an applied stress of 1 psi; a and b are experimental constants; t is the time after application of load; and α is an experimentally determined exponent.

For deflection purposes it is frequently desirable to use a creep coefficient C_t defined as the ratio of creep strain to elastic strain,

$$C_t = \frac{\epsilon_{cp}}{\epsilon_i} \tag{14.6.2}$$

ACI Committee 209 has recommended [21] the equation of Branson et al. [20–22] for the creep coefficient, as follows:

$$C_t = \left(\frac{t^{0.60}}{10 + t^{0.60}}\right)C_u \tag{14.6.3}$$

where

C_t = ratio of creep strain to elastic strain at any time t after a basic curing period

t = time in days after loading

C_u = ultimate creep coefficient: recommended *average* value is 2.35 for 40% humidity.

The general relationship of C_t/C_u appears in Fig. 1.10.2.

Equation (14.6.3) applies to the standard condition of 40% ambient relative humidity, 4 in. (75 mm) or less slump, minimum thickness of member 6 in. (150 mm) or less, and loading age of 7 days for moist-cured concrete or 1 to 3 days for steam-cured concrete. For other conditions, the standard condition value is to be multiplied by the following correction factors (CF):

(a) Age at loading. For moist-cured concrete,

$$(CF)_a = 1.25t_a^{-0.118} \tag{14.6.4a}$$

For steam-cured concrete,

$$(CF)_a = 1.13t_a^{-0.095} \tag{14.6.4b}$$

In the above two equations, t_a is the age at loading, in days after the initial period of curing. Several useful values of Eq. (14.6.4ab) appear in Table 14.6.1.

Table 16.14.1
Creep Correction Factor, $(CF)_a$ for Age at Loading, Eq. (14.6.4ab)

	Correction Factor, $(CF)_a$	
t_a, Age in Days after Initial Curing Period	Moist Cured for 7 days Initial Curing Period	Steam Cured for 1–3 Days Initial Curing Period
10	0.95	0.90
20	0.87	0.85
30	0.83	0.82
60	0.77	0.76
90	0.74	0.74

Table 14.6.2

Creep Correction Factor, $(CF)_h$ for Humidity, Eq. (14.6.5)

Ambient Relative Humidity, H, Percent	Correction Factor $(CF)_h$
40 or less	1.00
50	0.94
60	0.87
70	0.80
80	0.73
90	0.67
100	0.60

(b) Humidity. For $H \geq 40\%$,

$$(CF)_h = 1.27 - 0.0067H \qquad (14.6.5)$$

where H is the ambient relative humidity in percent. Values for this correction factor appear in Table 14.6.2.

(c) Minimum thickness of member. Where the minimum thickness of the member in inches exceeds 6 in. (150 mm), a correction factor (reduction factor) may be applied. However, for most design purposes such a correction may be neglected. For members whose minimum thickness greatly exceeds 12 in. (300 mm), Ref. 23 provides a chart that may be used to correct for the effect of minimum thickness.

(d) Other correction factors. Additional correction factors are available to account for variations in slump, cement content, percent of fine aggregate, and air content [20]; however, these tend to be either small or offset one another and may generally be neglected. Reference 23 provides a simple chart for these additional correction factors if they are desired.

Compression Steel Effect on Creep. The presence of compression steel decreases the deformation due to creep (and shrinkage as discussed in the next section). Evaluation of the effect of compression steel has been reported by Washa and Fluck [10], Yu and Winter [6], and Hollington [24], and a multiplier factor has been given by Committee 435 [12], as follows:

$$k_r = 0.85 - 0.45 \left(\frac{A'_s}{A_s} \right) \geq 0.40 \qquad (14.6.6)$$

Thus from Fig. 14.6.1, $C_t \Delta_i$ would become $k_r C_t \Delta_i$ when the compression steel effect is included.

14.7 Shrinkage Effect on Deflections under Sustained Load

Shrinkage of concrete in beams may have a similar effect on the deflection as creep. Shrinkage of an isolated plain concrete member would merely shorten it without causing curvature. When steel reinforcement is added, however, bond between concrete and steel restrains the shrinkage. Thus, a singly reinforced beam, having its shrinkage restrained at the reinforced face and unrestrained at the unreinforced face, will have considerable curvature. Generally it is difficult to separate the effects of creep and shrinkage. Shrinkage occurs more pronounced during the first few months than does creep. Typically, 90% of the shrinkage will have occurred at the end of 1 year, whereas not until the end of 5 years will 90% of the creep have occurred. A number of investigators have studied shrinkage effects separately from those of creep [19–23,26–28].

If the free shrinkage strain is known, shrinkage curvature ϕ_{sh} must be determined as a function of shrinkage strain. Such curvature will be dependent on the relative amounts of compression and tension steel just as creep is so affected. Finally, the shrinkage deflection will involve the geometry of the support system. Shrinkage deflection Δ_{sh} may be expressed [12,21] as

$$\Delta_{sh} = \alpha_1 \phi_{sh} L^2 \qquad (14.7.1)$$

where α_1 is a factor relating to the geometry of the support system and may be taken as the following:

$$\alpha_1 = 0.50 \text{ cantilever beams}$$
$$= 0.125 \text{ simply supported beams}$$
$$= 0.086 \text{ beams continuous at one end only}$$
$$= 0.063 \text{ beams continuous at both ends}$$

and L is the span length of the beam.

Shrinkage Strain, ϵ_{sh}. Shrinkage strain ϵ_{sh} may also be expressed in the form of Eq. (14.6.1) given for creep. ACI Committee 209 has recommended [21] that the following expressions by Branson et al. [20,22] may be used for shrinkage strain:
For any time after age 7 days for moist-cured concrete,

$$\epsilon_{sh} = \frac{t}{35 + t}(\epsilon_{sh})_u \qquad (14.7.2a)$$

For any time after age 1 to 3 days for steam-cured concrete,

$$\epsilon_{sh} = \frac{t}{55 + t}(\epsilon_{sh})_u \qquad (14.7.2b)$$

where

ϵ_{sh} = shrinkage strain at any time t after initial curing
t = time in days after initial curing
$(\epsilon_{sh})_u$ = ultimate shrinkage strain: average value suggested is 800×10^{-6} in./in. for 40% humidity.

Equation (14.7.2a) is shown graphically in Fig. 1.10.4. For conditions other than those of 40% ambient relative humidity, 4 in. (75 mm) or less slump, and minimum thickness of members 6 in. (150 mm) or less, the standard condition value of Eqs. (14.7.2ab) is to be multiplied by the following correction factors (CF):

(a) Humidity. For $H \geq 40\%$,

$$(CF)_h = 1.40 - 0.010H, \qquad 40 \leq H \leq 80\% \qquad (14.7.3)$$

$$(CF)_h = 3.00 - 0.030H, \qquad H \geq 80\% \qquad (14.7.4)$$

where H is the relative humidity in percent. Values for $(CF)_h$ appear in Table 14.7.1.

Table 14.7.1
Shrinkage Correction Factor $(CF)_h$ for Humidity, Eqs. (14.7.3) and (14.7.4)

Ambient Relative Humidity, H, Percent	Correction Factor $(CF)_h$
40 or less	1.00
50	0.90
60	0.80
70	0.70
80	0.60
90	0.30
100	0

Other corrections such as for minimum thickness greater than 6 in. and slump greater than 4 in. normally can be neglected.

Shrinkage Curvature, ϕ_{sh}. Several investigators [7,12,21,28] have developed expressions for curvature due to warping that arises from nonuniform shrinkage. Reinforcement of different amounts in the two faces of a beam is the principal cause of shrinkage warping.

Miller [28] established the following relationship for the singly reinforced beam. Referring to Fig. 14.7.1, by straight-line proportion,

$$\phi_{sh} = \frac{\epsilon_{sh} - \epsilon_s}{d} = \frac{\epsilon_{sh}}{d}\left(1 - \frac{\epsilon_s}{\epsilon_{sh}}\right) \qquad (14.7.5)$$

where ϵ_s is the compressive strain induced in the steel from shrinkage; ϵ_{sh} is the free shrinkage strain at the unreinforced face. Miller established empirically values for ϵ_s/ϵ_{sh} as a function of the percentage of reinforcement ρ.

Branson [7] modified Miller's equation and empirically extended the results to give equations including the effects of compression steel.

$$\phi_{sh} = 0.7\frac{\epsilon_{sh}}{h}(\rho - \rho')^{1/3}\left(\frac{\rho - \rho'}{\rho}\right)^{1/2} \qquad \text{for } (\rho - \rho') \leq 3\% \quad (14.7.6)$$

$$\phi_{sh} = \frac{\epsilon_{sh}}{h} \qquad \text{for } (\rho - \rho') > 3\% \qquad (14.7.7)$$

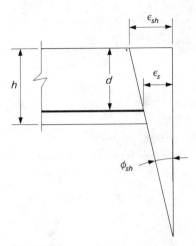

Fig. 14.7.1
Shrinkage strain related to beam
curvature for a singly reinforced
beam (after Miller, Ref. 28).

Note that ρ and ρ' are in percent, 100 (A_s or A'_s)/(bd). Equations (14.7.6) and (14.7.7) are recommended [12,21] as the most accurate relationships available.

Geometry of Warping from Shrinkage. In order to establish the factor α_1 in Eq. (14.7.1) for the four typical cases, the well-known moment-area theorems for beam deflections may be used. Since the quantity $M/(EI)$ is in fact the curvature due to bending moment, the ϕ_{sh} diagrams in Fig. 14.7.2 may be regarded as the equivalent $M/(EI)$ diagrams. For the cantilever beam (Fig. 14.7.2a),

$$\Delta_{sh} = BB' = \text{moment of } \phi_{sh} \text{ diagram between } A \text{ and } B \text{ about } B$$

$$= (\phi_{sh}L)\left(\frac{L}{2}\right) = 0.50\phi_{sh}L^2$$

For the simply supported beam (Fig. 14.7.2b),

$$\theta_A = \text{area of } \phi_{sh} \text{ diagram between } A \text{ and } C$$

$$= \phi_{sh}\left(\frac{L}{2}\right)$$

$$\Delta_{sh} = CC' = CC_1 - C_1C'$$

$$= \theta_A\left(\frac{L}{2}\right) - (\text{moment of } \phi_{sh} \text{ diagram between } A \text{ and } C \text{ about } C)$$

$$= \phi_{sh}\left(\frac{L}{2}\right)\left(\frac{L}{2}\right) - \phi_{sh}\left(\frac{L}{2}\right)\left(\frac{L}{4}\right) = 0.125\phi_{sh}L^2$$

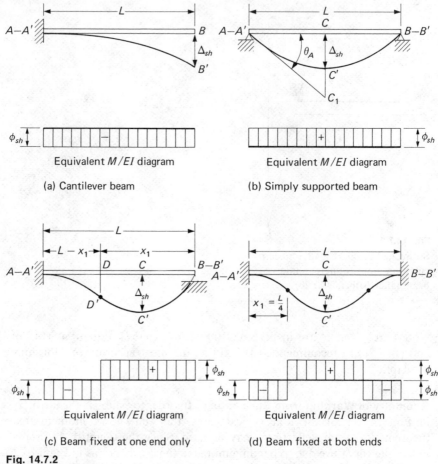

Fig. 14.7.2
Geometry of warping due to shrinkage.

For the beam fixed at one end only (Fig. 14.7.2c),

deflection of B from tangent at A

$$= \text{moment of } \phi_{sh} \text{ diagram between } A \text{ and } B \text{ about } B$$

$$= -\phi_{sh}(L - x_1)\left(x_1 + \frac{L - x_1}{2}\right) + \phi_{sh}\left(\frac{x_1^2}{2}\right) = 0$$

from which

$$x_1 = \frac{\sqrt{2}L}{2}$$

In order that the tangent at C' be horizontal, the distances AD and DC must be equal; thus

$$AD = DC = L - x_1 = \left(1 - \frac{\sqrt{2}}{2}\right)L$$

$$\Delta_{sh} = CC' = \text{moment of } \phi_{sh} \text{ diagram between } A \text{ and } C \text{ about } C$$
$$= \text{moment of a couple} = \phi_{sh}(L - x_1)^2$$
$$= \phi_{sh}L^2(1 - \tfrac{1}{2}\sqrt{2})^2 = \phi_{sh}L^2(1 - \sqrt{2} + \tfrac{1}{2})$$
$$= 0.086\phi_{sh}L^2$$

For the beam fixed at both ends (Fig. 14.7.2d), in order that the slope be horizontal at midspan for symmetry,

$$x_1 = \frac{L}{4}$$

Then

$$\Delta_{sh} = CC' = \text{moment of } \phi_{sh} \text{ diagram between } A \text{ and } C \text{ about } C$$

$$= \text{moment of a couple} = \phi_{sh}\left(\frac{L}{2}\right)^2$$

$$= 0.063\phi_{sh}L^2$$

Compression Steel Effect on Combined Shrinkage and Creep. Whenever shrinkage is to be considered *in combination with creep* in the computation for the deflection due to sustained load, a multiplier similar to that given by Eq. (14.6.6) may be applied [21] to the short-time deflection; in this case,

$$k_r = 1.0 - 0.60\left(\frac{A'_s}{A_s}\right) \geq 0.40 \qquad (14.7.8)$$

The $C_t\Delta_i$ in Fig. 14.6.1 would become $k_rT\Delta_i$, where both k_r and T (see Table 14.9.1) include shrinkage as well as creep. Alternate expressions for k_r have been suggested by Shaikh [29], and the general relationship has been discussed by Branson [25]. Based on additional data involving flanged sections as well as rectangular sections, Branson [25] recommends as more logical Eq. (14.7.9), which is a function of the compression steel percentage ρ' rather than the steel area ratio, A'_s/A_s.

$$k_r = \frac{1}{1 + 50\rho'} \qquad (14.7.9)$$

where $\rho' = A'_s/bd$. This equation has been recommended [5] by ACI Committee 435 for inclusion in the ACI Code.

14.8 Creep and Shrinkage Deflection—ACI Code Method

In the ACI Code method, the creep and shrinkage deflection due to sustained load is obtained by multiplying the short-time (instantaneous) deflection by a single factor (ACI-9.5.2.5). Thus

$$\Delta_{cp+sh} = k_rT(\Delta_i)_D \qquad (14.8.1)$$

where

$$k_rT = 2 - 1.2\left(\frac{A'_s}{A_s}\right) \geq 0.6 \qquad (14.8.2)$$

and $(\Delta_i)_D$ is the instantaneous deflection due to all sustained loads (usually dead load).

EXAMPLE 14.8.1 For the beam of Example 14.5.1 determine the creep and shrinkage deflection according to the ACI Code. Assume only the dead load is sustained.

Solution: First it is necessary to compute the short-time (instantaneous) deflection due to all sustained loads, in this case the dead load. From Example 14.5.1, part (b) of the solution,

$$(\Delta_i)_D = 0.97 \text{ in. (25 mm)}$$

Since no compression steel is used, Eq. (14.8.2) gives

$$k_r T = 2.0$$

Then from Eq. (14.8.1)

$$\Delta_{cp+sh} = k_r T (\Delta_i)_D = 2.0(0.97) = 1.94 \text{ in. (49 mm)}$$

If part of the live load were considered as sustained, such as certain types of equipment whose placement or installation is not expected to change for a period of 5 years or more, then it would be necessary to compute Δ_i for the dead load plus the sustained live load. Under the ACI Code, an additional effective moment of inertia I_e would be computed using M_{cr}/M_{max} where M_{max} is due to dead load plus sustained live load.

14.9 Creep and Shrinkage Deflection — Alternate Procedures

Separate Creep and Shrinkage Multiplier Procedure. A procedure for computing the deflections due to creep and shrinkage separately was recommended by ACI Committee 435 [12,30], based on the work of Branson [7], as modified by recent improvement in the prediction of creep and shrinkage [21]. Thus

$$\Delta_{cp+sh} = \Delta_{cp} + \Delta_{sh} \tag{14.9.1}$$

where, using Eq. (14.7.1),

$$\Delta_{sh} = \alpha_1 \phi_{sh} L^2 \tag{14.9.2}$$

and

$$\Delta_{cp} = k_r C_t (\Delta_i)_D \tag{14.9.3}$$

For evaluation of Eqs. (14.9.2) and (14.9.3),

$\alpha_1 = $ constant (see Eq. 14.7.1)
$\phi_{sh} = $ shrinkage curvature [Eqs. (14.7.6) and (14.7.7)]
$L = $ span length
$k_r = $ compression steel factor [Eq. (14.6.6)] or $0.85/(1 + 50\rho')$[†]

[†] This is 0.85 of Eq. (14.7.9) and is analogous to Eq. (14.6.6) being 0.85 of Eq. (14.7.8).

C_t = creep coefficient, originally given in tabular form [12], but more recently [21] and more accurately as Eq. (14.6.3) with correction factors of Eqs. (14.6.4) and (14.6.5)

$(\Delta_i)_D$ = instantaneous deflection due to all sustained loads

Combined Creep and Shrinkage Multiplier Procedure. This method is similar to the ACI Code method, except the time-dependent factor T can be more accurately evaluated [21,25,30]. It may be stated as

$$\Delta_{cp+sh} = k_r T(\Delta_i)_D \qquad (14.9.4)$$

where

$$k_r = 1/(1 + 50\rho') \qquad (14.9.5)$$

T = time-dependent coefficient (creep plus shrinkage), which may be taken from Table 14.9.1.

Table 14.9.1
Time-Dependent Coefficient T Including Both Creep and Shrinkage Effects, for Both Normal Weight and Lightweight Concrete Members of Common Types, Sizes, and Composition [from Branson (30)][a]

Concrete Strength f'_c at 28 days	Average Relative Humidity, Age when Loaded								
	100%			70%			50%		
	≤7d	14d	≥28d	≤7d	14d	≥28d	≤7d	14d	≥28d
2500 to 4000 psi (17 to 28 N/mm²)	2.0	1.5	1.0	3.0	2.0	1.5	4.0	3.0	2.0
>4,000 psi (28 N/mm²)	1.5	1.0	0.7	2.5	1.8	1.2	3.5	2.5	1.5

[a] It is suggested that the following percentages of the values in the table be used for sustained loads that are maintained for the periods indicated:

25% for 1 month or less
50% for 3 months
75% for 1 year
100% for 5 years or more

The 50% values may normally be used for average relative humidities lower than 50%, which might be the case in heated buildings, for example.

EXAMPLE 14.9.1 For the beam of Example 14.5.1 determine the ultimate (i.e., 5 years duration of load) creep and shrinkage deflection using methods more accurate than the basic ACI method. Assume only the dead load is sustained, the ambient relative humidity is 70%, the age at loading is 20 days after the initial moist-curing period.

Solution: It is noted that ACI-9.5.2.5 permits computation of long-time deflection by a "more comprehensive analysis," which could include either of these alternate methods.

(a) Separate creep and shrinkage multiplier procedure.

$$\Delta_{cp+sh} = \Delta_{cp} + \Delta_{sh}$$

Using Eq. (14.9.3),

$$\Delta_{cp} = k_r C_t (\Delta_i)_D$$

$$k_r = 0.85 - 0.45\left(\frac{A'_s}{A_s}\right) = 0.85 \qquad \text{for } A'_s = 0$$

or

$$k_r = \frac{0.85}{1 + 50\rho'} = 0.85 \qquad \text{for } \rho' = 0$$

and from Eq. (14.6.3), for $t = 5(365)$ days,

$$C_t = \left(\frac{t^{0.60}}{10 + t^{0.60}}\right) C_u = 0.90 \, C_u$$

which for $C_u = 2.35$ as recommended for average conditions gives the basic value of C_t as

$$C_t = 2.12$$

Adjusting for 70% humidity, $(CF)_h = 0.80$ from Eq. (14.6.5) or Table 14.6.2, and for 20-day age of loading after initial moist-curing period, $(CF)_a = 0.87$. Thus the adjusted C_t is

$$C_t = 2.12(0.80)(0.87) = 1.47$$

From Example 14.5.1 using the ACI Code method,

$$(\Delta_i)_D = 0.97 \text{ in. (25 mm)}$$

Then

$$\Delta_{cp} = k_r C_t (\Delta_i)_D = 0.85(1.47)0.97 = 1.21 \text{ in. (31 mm)}$$

For shrinkage, from Eq. (14.7.1),

$$\Delta_{sh} = \alpha_1 \phi_{sh} L^2$$

where

$$\alpha_1 = 0.125 \qquad \text{for simply supported beams}$$

For this beam, since $\rho = 2.38\%$ and $\rho' = 0$, Eq. (14.7.6) gives

$$\phi_{sh} = 0.7\left(\frac{\epsilon_{sh}}{h}\right)\sqrt[3]{\rho}$$

Using ϵ_{sh} from Eq. (14.7.2a),

$$\epsilon_{sh} = \frac{t}{35 + t}(\epsilon_{sh})_u$$

which for $t = 5(365)$ days is, for average conditions,

$$\epsilon_{sh} \approx (\epsilon_{sh})_u = 800 \times 10^{-6} \text{ in./in.}$$

Adjusting for 70% humidity, $(CF)_h = 0.70$, from Eq. (14.7.3) or Table 14.7.1, the adjusted ϵ_{sh} is

$$\epsilon_{sh} = (800 \times 10^{-6})0.70 = 560 \times 10^{-6} \text{ in./in.}$$

Then,

$$\phi_{sh} = 0.7 \left(\frac{560 \times 10^{-6}}{24} \right) \sqrt[3]{2.38} = 25.2 \times 10^{-6} \text{ in.}$$

$$\Delta_{sh} = \alpha_1 \phi_{sh} L^2 = 0.125(25.2 \times 10^{-6})(480)^2 = 0.73 \text{ in. (19 mm)}$$

$$\Delta_{cp+sh} = 1.21 + 0.73 = 1.94 \text{ in. (49 mm)}$$

(b) Combined creep and shrinkage multiplier procedure. Using Eq. (14.9.4),

$$\Delta_{cp+sh} = k_r T (\Delta_i)_D$$

$$k_r = \frac{1}{1 + 50\rho'} = 1.0$$

$$T = \text{value from Table 14.9.1} \approx 1.8$$

Note that age at loading is *after* initial curing period.

$$(\Delta_i)_D = 0.97 \text{ in. (25 mm)} \qquad \text{(from Example 14.5.1)}$$

$$\Delta_{cp+sh} = 1.0(1.8)0.97 = 1.75 \text{ in. (44 mm)}$$

A comparison of computation methods for creep and shrinkage deflection may be obtained from the following summary.

Method	Δ_{sh+cp}
1. ACI, using $k_r T = 2.0$	1.94 in. (Example 14.8.1)
2. Separate creep and shrinkage as per Eqs. (14.9.1) to (14.9.3), etc.	1.94 in. (Example 14.9.1a)
3. Combined creep and shrinkage using $k_r T = 1.8$	1.75 in. (Example 14.9.1b)

14.10 ACI Minimum Depth of Flexural Members

According to the ACI Code the minimum depths specified in ACI-9.5.2.1 shall apply to all cases of "one-way construction . . . unless computation of deflection indicates a lesser thickness may be used without adverse effects." The minimum depth (thickness) values apply to members where large deflection is *not* likely to damage partitions, ceilings, or other frangible attachments. When large deflection may cause such damage, deflections must be computed whether or not the minimum thickness requirement is satisfied.

The minimum depths prescribed by any such table are arbitrary and not necessarily conservative. The following logic may be used to explain the limitation on span-depth ratio as an attempt to control deflection.

The deflection at midspan of a simply supported beam is

$$\Delta = \frac{5wL^4}{384EI} \qquad \qquad \textbf{(14.10.1)}$$

The maximum bending moment is

$$M = \frac{wL^2}{8} = \frac{fI}{c} \qquad (14.10.2)$$

Substituting Eq. (14.10.2) in Eq. (14.10.1) gives

$$\Delta = \frac{5L^2 f}{48 Ec} \qquad (14.10.3)$$

Assuming that cracked section is effective at service-load conditions,

$$\frac{f}{c} = \frac{f_s}{n(d-x)} = \frac{f_c}{x} \qquad (14.10.4)$$

where x is the distance between the neutral axis and the extreme compression fiber. Assume the beam is fully stressed at $f_s = 24{,}000$ psi for Grade 60 steel, and that $x \approx 0.4h$.

$$\frac{f}{c} \approx \frac{24{,}000}{(E_s/E_c)(0.6h)} = \frac{40{,}000 E_c}{hE_s} = \frac{E_c}{725h} \qquad (14.10.5)$$

for $E_s = 29 \times 10^6$ psi. Substituting Eq. (14.10.5) in Eq. (14.10.3) and calling $E = E_c$.

$$\frac{\Delta}{L} = \frac{5}{48}\left(\frac{1}{725}\right)\frac{L}{h}$$

$$\min h = \frac{1}{6950}\left(\frac{L}{\Delta}\right)L \qquad (14.10.6)$$

Equation (14.10.6) represents an approximate relationship between depth, span, and span-to-deflection ratio for a fully stressed section under *short-time loading*. If the member is under a reduced stress, the depth may be decreased proportionally to give the same short-time deflection. To account for the sustained load creep and shrinkage deflection, the depth must be increased. Table 14.10.1 shows the application of Eq. (14.10.6) to give the minimum depth required for various deflection limitations under fully and partially stressed conditions. The last two columns in Table 14.10.1 assume that total

Table 14.10.1
Minimum Depths for Various Equivalent Immediate Deflections and Percentage Stressed[a]

Percent Stressed	$\Delta = L/300$	$\Delta = L/360$	$\Delta = L/480$	$2\Delta = L/300$	$2\Delta = L/360$
100	$L/23.2$	$L/19.3$	$L/14.5$	$L/11.5$	$L/9.7$
67	$L/35$	$L/29$	$L/21.5$	$L/17.5$	$L/14.5$
60	$L/39$	$L/32$	$L/24$	$L/19.5$	$L/16$
50	$L/46.5$	$L/38.5$	$L/29$	$L/23$	$L/19.5$

[a] Assumes $f_s = 24{,}000$ psi at 100% stressed.

deflection including creep and shrinkage effects is twice the immediate deflection.

Any selection of limiting values for minimum depth from Table 14.10.1 can only be a crude attempt to control deflection. Table 14.10.2 (ACI-Table 9.5a) is the result of a compromise between the relative conservative recommendations of ACI Committee 435 and the values practicing engineers believe suitable on the basis of experience.

Table 14.10.2
Minimum Depth h for Beams and One-Way Slabs, for Members *Not* Supporting or Attached to Partitions or Other Construction Likely to Be Damaged by Large Deflections (from ACI-Table 9.5a)

Type of Members		Simple Support	One End Continuous	Both Ends Continuous	Cantilever
Beams	$f_y = 60$ ksi	$L/16$	$L/18.5$	$L/21$	$L/8$
	$f_y = 40$ ksi	$L/20$	$L/23$	$L/26$	$L/10$
One-way slabs	$f_y = 60$ ksi	$L/20$	$L/24$	$L/28$	$L/10$
(solid)	$f_y = 40$ ksi	$L/25$	$L/30$	$L/35$	$L/12.5$

NOTE: For structural lightweight concrete having unit weights w from $90 - 120$ pcf, multiply table values by $1.65 - 0.005 w$ but not less than 1.09. (60 ksi $= 420$ N/mm^2; 40 ksi $= 280$ N/mm^2, approximately.)

When large deflections may cause cracking of partitions and other frangible attachments, the total deflection (ACI-9.5.2.6) that occurs after installation of such elements is limited to $L/480$. This shows that the minimum depths of ACI-Table 9.5a are likely to be too low; hence that table *does not apply for such cases*, and deflection computations must be made.

In general, minimum depth as a proportion of span is an inadequate criterion for controlling deflection; computation of deflection should be made whenever deflection is of concern.

14.11 Span-to-Depth Ratio to Account for Cracking and Sustained Load Effects

In order to illustrate the effects of the many variables on the span-to-depth ratio, the following general development, similar to that of Branson [30], is presented.

The short-time deflection Δ_i may be expressed, according to Eq. (14.5.1), as

$$\Delta_i = \beta_a \left(\frac{M_{max} L^2}{E_c I_e} \right) \tag{14.11.1}$$

where

M_{max} = maximum moment at the stage for which deflection is desired
I_e = Eq. (14.4.1), [which is ACI Code Formula (9-7)]
$\quad = (M_{cr}/M_{max})^3 I_g + [1 - (M_{cr}/M_{max})^3] I_{cr} \leq I_g$

M_{cr} = maximum moment to cause a beam to crack at the extreme fiber in tension = $f_r I_g / y_t$

f_r = modulus of rupture = $0.65\sqrt{wf'_c}$ (ACI uses $7.5\sqrt{f'_c}$ for ordinary weight concrete)

y_t = distance from neutral axis to extreme fiber in tension

Multiplying Eq. (14.11.1) by $f_r I_g / (y_t M_{cr})$, which is equal to unity, gives

$$\Delta_i = \beta_a \left(\frac{M_{max} L^2}{E_c I_e} \right) \frac{f_r I_g}{y_t M_{cr}} \tag{14.11.2}$$

Solving Eq. (14.11.2) for L/y_t gives

$$\frac{L}{y_t} = \frac{\Delta_i}{L} \left(\frac{E_c}{f_r \beta_a} \right) \left(\frac{M_{cr}}{M_{max}} \right) \frac{I_e}{I_g} \tag{14.11.3}$$

Since both E_c and f_r are proportional to $\sqrt{f'_c}$, let

$$\beta_w = \frac{E_c}{f_r} = \frac{33w^{1.5}\sqrt{f'_c}}{0.65w^{0.5}\sqrt{f'_c}} = 50.8w \tag{14.11.4}$$

For normal weight concrete

$$\beta_w = 50.8w = 50.8(145) = 7370$$

Conversion from normal-weight concrete to lightweight concrete may be made by multiplying L/y_t by the ratio of the unit weight of lightweight concrete to 145 pcf (2330 kg/m^3).

Letting $\gamma = I_e/I_g$ and $\beta_w = E_c/f_r$ in Eq. (14.11.3),

$$\frac{L}{y_t} = \frac{\Delta_i}{L} \left(\frac{\beta_w}{\beta_a} \right) \left(\frac{M_{cr}}{M_{max}} \right) \gamma \tag{14.11.5}$$

where

$$\gamma = \frac{I_e}{I_g} = \left(\frac{M_{cr}}{M_{max}} \right)^3 + \left[1 - \left(\frac{M_{cr}}{M_{max}} \right)^3 \right] \frac{I_{cr}}{I_g} \tag{14.11.6}$$

Using the methods of Chap. 4, the ratio of the moment of inertia of the cracked section to that of the gross section may be computed for various shapes of beams. As an example, for a singly reinforced rectangular beam assuming $d = 0.9h$,

$$\frac{I_{cr}}{I_g} = \frac{bx^3/3 + nA_s(d-x)^2}{bh^3/12}$$

$$= 8.75 \left[\frac{(x/d)^3}{3} + n\rho \left(1 - \frac{x}{d} \right)^2 \right] \tag{14.11.7}$$

where

$$x/d = \sqrt{(\rho n)^2 + 2\rho n} - \rho n. \tag{14.11.8}$$

Approximate expressions of $\gamma = I_e/I_g$ for the positive- and negative-moment regions of a T-shaped beam are given by Branson [30].

For dead-load deflection, $M_{\max} = M_D$, which makes $\gamma = \gamma_D$; Eq. (14.11.5) then becomes

$$\frac{(\Delta_i)_D}{L} = \frac{\beta_a}{\beta_w}\left(\frac{M_D}{M_{cr}}\right)\left(\frac{L}{y_t}\right)\left(\frac{1}{\gamma_D}\right) \tag{14.11.9}$$

For dead load plus live load,

$$\frac{(\Delta_i)_{D+L}}{L} = \frac{\beta_a}{\beta_w}\left(\frac{M_{D+L}}{M_{cr}}\right)\left(\frac{L}{y_t}\right)\left(\frac{1}{\gamma_{D+L}}\right) \tag{14.11.10}$$

As discussed in Sec. 14.5, since live load cannot act in the absence of dead load, the live-load deflection must be obtained indirectly,

$$\frac{(\Delta_i)_L}{L} = \frac{(\Delta_i)_{D+L}}{L} - \frac{(\Delta_i)_D}{L} \tag{14.11.11}$$

which, using Eqs. (14.11.9) and (14.11.10), and letting $C_L = M_L/M_D$, gives

$$\frac{(\Delta_i)_L}{L} = \frac{\beta_a}{\beta_w}\left(\frac{L}{y_t}\right)\left(\frac{M_{D+L}}{M_{cr}}\right)\left[\frac{1}{\gamma_{D+L}} - \frac{1}{\gamma_D(1 + C_L)}\right] \tag{14.11.12}$$

When excessive deflection may cause damage to partitions and other nonstructural construction, it is the sum of deflections due to live load plus creep and shrinkage that is of concern. The instantaneous (short-time) dead-load deflection will have occurred when forms are removed and before any breakable attachments are put in place. Thus using Eq. (14.8.1),

$$\Delta_{cp+sh} = k_r T(\Delta_i)_D$$

Finally, the deflection to be controlled to minimize possible damage is

$$\frac{(\Delta_i)_L}{L} + \frac{\Delta_{cp+sh}}{L} = \frac{\beta_a}{\beta_w}\left(\frac{L}{y_t}\right)\left(\frac{M_{D+L}}{M_{cr}}\right)\left[\frac{1}{\gamma_{D+L}} + \frac{(k_r T - 1)}{\gamma_D(1 + C_L)}\right]$$

$$= \frac{\beta_a}{\beta_w}\left(\frac{L}{y_t}\right)\left(\frac{M_{D+L}}{M_{cr}}\right)\left[\frac{1 + C_L + (k_r T - 1)(\gamma_{D+L}/\gamma_D)}{1 + C_L}\right]\frac{1}{\gamma_{D+L}} \tag{14.11.13}$$

Solving for L/y_t gives

$$\left(\frac{L}{y_t}\right)_{\substack{\text{limit for} \\ L + cp + sh}} = \left(\frac{\Delta}{L}\right)\left(\frac{\beta_w}{\beta_a}\right)\left(\frac{M_{cr}}{M_{D+L}}\right)\left[\frac{C_L + 1}{C_L + 1 + (k_r T - 1)(\gamma_{D+L}/\gamma_D)}\right]\gamma_{D+L} \tag{14.11.14}$$

For instantaneous dead load plus live load, Eq. (14.11.10) gives

$$\left(\frac{L}{y_t}\right)_{\substack{\text{limit for} \\ D+L}} = \left(\frac{\Delta}{L}\right)\left(\frac{\beta_w}{\beta_a}\right)\left(\frac{M_{cr}}{M_{D+L}}\right)\gamma_{D+L} \tag{14.11.15}$$

As shown below if the span-to-depth ratio limit is available for short-time deflection under dead load plus live load, such as from Table 14.10.1, the effect of creep and shrinkage can be obtained by the use of a multiplier. Comparing Eqs. (14.11.14) and (14.11.15), in which Δ/L may be taken as a stated limit,

$$\left(\frac{L}{y_t}\right)_{L+cp+sh} = \left(\frac{L}{y_t}\right)_{D+L}\left[\frac{C_L+1}{C_L+1+(k_rT-1)(\gamma_{D+L}/\gamma_D)}\right] \quad \textbf{(14.11.16)}$$

For the situation in which the I_e under dead load only is approximately the same as I_e under dead plus live load, $\gamma_{D+L} \approx \gamma_D$, in which case Eq. (14.11.16) becomes

$$\left(\frac{L}{y_t}\right)_{L+cp+sh} = \left(\frac{L}{y_t}\right)_{D+L}\left(\frac{C_L+1}{C_L+k_rT}\right) \quad \textbf{(14.11.17)}$$

Charts are available [30] for the L/h ratio for short-time effects of dead load plus live load, Eq. (14.11.10). The chart for singly reinforced rectangular beams ($y_t = 0.5h$) is given in Fig. 14.11.1.

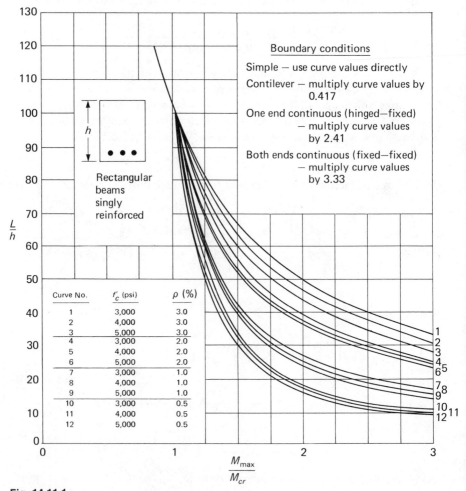

Fig. 14.11.1

L/h versus M_{max}/M_{cr} curves for the conditions: $\Delta = L/360$, normal-weight concrete, and uniformly distributed short-time loading, and for different boundary conditions, steel percentages, and concrete strengths (from Ref. 30).

EXAMPLE 14.11.1 Determine the depth of beam required for the loading conditions of Example 14.5.1 (Fig. 14.5.3) if the sum of the immediate live load plus creep and shrinkage deflection must not exceed $L/480$. Assume only the dead load is sustained and the sustained load factor $k_r T = 2$ as given by ACI-9.5.2.5.

Solution: (a) Use ACI-Table 9.5a.

$$\frac{L}{h} = 16$$

This considers average conditions and includes some effect of sustained load deflection.

$$\min h = \frac{480}{16} = 30 \text{ in.}$$

(b) Use more accurate procedure with Fig. 14.11.1.

$$\rho = 0.0238$$

$$M_{cr} = \frac{f_r I_g}{y_t} = \frac{7.5\sqrt{4000}(16,100)}{12(12)} = 53 \text{ ft-kips}$$

$$\frac{M_{max}}{M_{cr}} = \frac{180 + 100 + 70}{53} = 6.1 > 3; \quad \text{use 3}$$

$$C_L = \frac{M_L}{M_D} = \frac{180}{170} = 1.06$$

From Fig. 14.11.1 for $M_{max}/M_{cr} = 3$ and $\rho = 0.0238$, find

$$\left(\frac{L}{h}\right)_{D+L} = 29, \quad \text{for } \frac{\Delta}{L} = \frac{1}{360}$$

$$\left(\frac{L}{h}\right)_{D+L} = 29\left(\frac{360}{480}\right) = 21.8, \quad \text{for } \frac{\Delta}{L} = \frac{1}{480}$$

$$\left(\frac{L}{h}\right)_{L+cp+sh} = 21.8\left(\frac{C_L + 1}{C_L + k_r T}\right) = 21.8\left(\frac{1.06 + 1}{1.06 + 2}\right) = 14.7$$

$$\min h = \frac{480}{14.7} = 32.6 \text{ in.}$$

which is somewhat more severe than ACI-Table 9.5a.

(c) Required depth and adequacy of beam in Example 14.5.1. For the given beam with $h = 24$ in.,

$$(\Delta_i)_L = 0.93 \text{ in.} \quad \text{(Example 14.5.1)}$$

$$\Delta_{cp+sh} = 1.94 \text{ in.} \quad \text{(Example 14.8.1)}$$

$$\text{allowable } \Delta = \frac{L}{480} = \frac{480}{480} = 1 \text{ in.}$$

$$\text{actual } \Delta = 0.93 + 1.94 = 2.87 \text{ in.}$$

If the beam were 28 in. deep, with the same loading it would be approximately carrying only $(24/28 = 0.855)$ 85.5% of its capacity, that is, stressed to only 85.5%. In which case,

$$\min h = 32.6(0.855) = 27.9 \text{ in.}$$

It would appear that 28 or perhaps 29 in. is required to satisfy deflection limit. Unless the width is reduced, which seems undesirable here, increasing the depth will increase dead-load moment, so the 30-in. minimum given by ACI-Table 9.5a seems in this case to be about right.

14.12 ACI Code Deflection Provisions—Beam Examples

The ACI Code provisions (ACI-9.5) regarding deflection computations may be summarized as follows. In both the strength method and the working stress method (ACI "alternate" method), deflections *under service-load conditions* must be computed

1. Whenever excessive deflection may adversely affect the strength or serviceability of the structure at service loads (ACI-9.5.1).
2. When minimum thickness used is *less* than that given by ACI-Table 9.5a for beams and one-way slabs (see also Table 14.10.2 in this chapter).

The use of minimum thicknesses from ACI-Table 9.5a eliminates the need for computation of deflection *only for those cases where partitions, ceilings, and other nonstructural elements are not being supported.* Beams or one-way slabs supporting such frangible elements are in category (1) above, and deflections must be computed whether or not the minimum thickness limits of Table 9.5a have been met.

EXAMPLE 14.12.1 Investigate the deflection for the beam of Fig. 14.12.1 (same as obtained in Example 3.6.1) used on a simple span of 25 ft. The maximum bending moments under service load are 158 ft-kips dead load

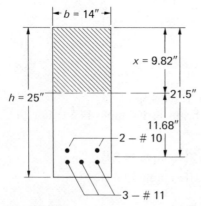

Fig. 14.12.1
Section for Example 14.12.1.

and 105 ft-kips live load, which correspond to $M_u = 400$ ft-kips as used for design by the strength method. Assume that all loading is uniformly distributed and that none of the live load is sustained. The beam supports partitions and other construction likely to be damaged by large deflections. Use $f'_c = 4000$ psi, $f_y = 40,000$ psi, and the ACI Code. (Approximate $f'_c = 28$ N/mm²; $f_y = 280$ N/mm².)

Solution: (a) Check minimum thickness (ACI-Table 9.5a), or from Table 14.10.2 for $f_y = 40$ ksi,

$$\min h = \frac{L}{20} = \frac{25(12)}{20} = 15 \text{ in.} < 25 \text{ in. used}$$

This would make it seem that deflection is not likely to be excessive; however, deflection computations must be made because of the frangible items the beam supports.

(b) Examine reinforcement ratio ρ

$$\rho = \frac{A_s}{bd} = \frac{7.22}{14(21.5)} = 0.024$$

This exceeds $0.5\rho_{max} = 0.375\rho_b = 0.0185$ suggested in Chap. 3 as a guideline for deflection control; thus from this check one may predict that deflection may be a problem.

(c) Determine the moment of inertia I_g for gross uncracked section without steel and I_{cr} for the cracked transformed section.

For gross uncracked section,

$$I_g = \tfrac{1}{12}(14)(25)^3 = 18,200 \text{ in.}^4$$

For cracked section, locate neutral axis under service loads,

$$\frac{14x^2}{2} = 7.22(8)(21.5 - x)$$

$$x = 9.81 \text{ in.}$$
$$I_{cr} = \tfrac{1}{3}(14)(9.81)^3 + 7.22(8)(11.69)^2 = 12,300 \text{ in.}^4$$

(d) Determine effective moment of inertia I_e (ACI Formula 9-7). The cracking moment is

$$M_{cr} = \frac{f_r I_g}{y_t} = \frac{7.5\sqrt{4000}(18,200)}{12.5(12)} = 57.6 \text{ ft-kips } (78.2 \text{ kN-m})$$

For dead-load deflection,

$$\frac{M_{cr}}{M_{max}} = \frac{57.6}{158} = 0.365; \qquad \left(\frac{M_{cr}}{M_{max}}\right)^3 = 0.05$$

$$I_e = \left(\frac{M_{cr}}{M_{max}}\right)^3 I_g + \left[1 - \left(\frac{M_{cr}}{M_{max}}\right)^3\right] I_{cr}$$

$$= 0.05(18,200) + 0.95(12,300) = 12,600 \text{ in.}^4 \ (524,000 \text{ cm}^4)$$

For dead- plus live-load deflection,

$$\frac{M_{cr}}{M_{max}} = \frac{57.6}{263} = 0.22; \qquad \left(\frac{M_{cr}}{M_{max}}\right)^3 = 0.01$$

$$I_e \approx I_{cr} = 12,300 \text{ in.}^4 \ (512,000 \text{ cm}^4)$$

(e) Compute immediate deflections.

$$E_c = 57,000\sqrt{f_c'} = 57,000\sqrt{4000} = 3.6 \times 10^6 \text{ psi}$$

For dead load,

$$(\Delta_i)_D = \frac{5wL^4}{384EI} = \frac{5ML^2}{48EI} = \frac{5(158)(12)(300)^2}{48(3.6)(10^3)(12,600)} = 0.39 \text{ in. (9.9 mm)}$$

For dead load plus live load,

$$(\Delta_i)_{D+L} = \frac{5(263)(12)(300)^2}{48(3.6)(10^3)(12,300)} = 0.67 \text{ in. (17 mm)}$$

Then immediate live-load deflection is

$$(\Delta_i)_L = (\Delta_i)_{D+L} - (\Delta_i)_D = 0.67 - 0.39 = 0.28 \text{ in. (7.1 mm)}$$

(f) Compute creep and shrinkage deflection. From ACI-9.5.2.5 the multiplier is

$$k_r T = 2 - 1.2\left(\frac{A_s'}{A_s}\right) = 2.0$$

$$\Delta_{cp+sh} = k_r T(\Delta_i)_D = 2.0(0.39) = 0.78 \text{ in. (20 mm)}$$

(g) Check limitation of ACI-Table 9.5b. For roof or floor construction supporting or attached to nonstructural elements likely to be damaged by large deflection,

$$(\Delta_i)_L + \Delta_{cp+sh} \le \frac{L}{480}$$

This limit is for the deflection that is estimated to occur *after* the nonstructural elements are put in place. Whatever portion, if any, of the live load or creep and shrinkage deflection has occurred prior to the placement of nonstructural elements may be excluded from the $L/480$ limitation. Further, if adequate measures are taken to prevent damage to supported or attached elements, the $L/480$ limit may be exceeded (footnote, ACI-Table 9.5b).

For this example,

$$0.28 + 0.78 = 1.06 \text{ in. (27 mm)} > \frac{L}{480} = \frac{300}{480} = 0.63 \text{ in. (16 mm)}$$

which is not acceptable. This shows that the minimum thickness indicated by ACI-Table 9.5a was not even close.

EXAMPLE 14.12.2 Investigate the deflection for the one-way continuous slab shown in Fig. 14.12.2. The slab is $4\frac{1}{2}$ in. thick. Assume that 60% of the 100 psf live load is sustained. Use $f_c' = 3000$ psi and $f_y = 40,000$ psi.

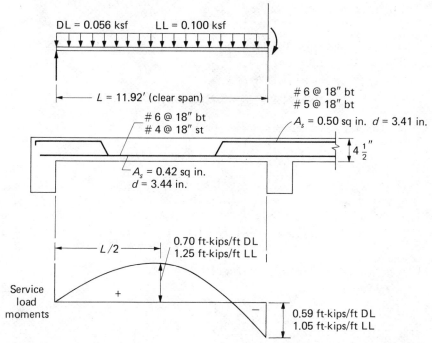

Fig. 14.12.2
End-span details for continuous slab of Example 14.12.2. (See also Fig. 7.5.1a.)

Solution: Use may be made of Eq. (14.2.4) to compute midspan deflection:

$$\Delta_m = \frac{5L^2}{48EI}\left[M_s - \frac{1}{10}(M_a + M_b)\right] \qquad \textbf{[14.2.4]}$$

Note that clear span is used with a conservative assumption of zero end moment at the exterior support. Thus

M_s = net midspan moment
$\quad = \frac{1}{8}(0.156)(11.92)^2 - \frac{1}{2}(1.64) = 2.77 - 0.82 = 1.95$ ft-kips/ft
$E_c = 57,000\sqrt{f'_c} = 57,000\sqrt{3000} = 3.12 \times 10^6$ psi

(a) Determine I_g and I_{cr}, using a 1-ft width of section.

$$I_g = \tfrac{1}{12}(12)(4.5)^3 = 91.1 \text{ in.}^4$$

For negative-moment region, $d = 3.41$ in., $n = 9$

$$\frac{12x^2}{2} = 9(0.50)(3.41 - x)$$

$$x = 1.27 \text{ in.}$$
$$I_{cr} = \tfrac{1}{3}(12)(1.27)^3 + 9(0.50)(3.41 - 1.27)^2 = 28.7 \text{ in.}^4$$

For positive-moment region, $d = 3.44$ in.,

$$\frac{12x^2}{2} = 9(0.42)(3.44 - x)$$

$$x = 1.19 \text{ in.}$$
$$I_{cr} = \tfrac{1}{3}(12)(1.19)^3 + 9(0.42)(2.44 - 1.19)^2 = 25.9 \text{ in.}^4$$

(b) Determine effective moment of inertia I_e.

$$f_r = 7.5\sqrt{f'_c} = 7.5\sqrt{3000} = 411 \text{ psi}$$

$$M_{cr} = \frac{f_r I_g}{y_t} = \frac{0.411(91.1)}{2.25(12)} = 1.39 \text{ ft-kips}$$

$$I_e = \left(\frac{M_{cr}}{M_{max}}\right)^3 I_g + \left[1 - \left(\frac{M_{cr}}{M_{max}}\right)^3\right] I_{cr}$$

In negative-moment region, for dead load

$$\frac{M_{cr}}{M_D} = \frac{M_{cr}}{M_{max}} = \frac{1.39}{0.59} > 1; \qquad I_e = I_g = 91.1 \text{ in.}^4$$

and for dead plus live load,

$$\frac{M_{cr}}{M_{D+L}} = \frac{M_{cr}}{M_{max}} = \frac{1.39}{1.64} = 0.848; \qquad \left(\frac{M_{cr}}{M_{max}}\right)^3 = 0.609$$
$$I_e = 0.609(91.1) + 0.391(28.7) = 66.7 \text{ in.}^4$$

In positive-moment region, for dead load

$$\frac{M_{cr}}{M_D} = \frac{M_{cr}}{M_{max}} = \frac{1.39}{0.70} > 1; \qquad I_e = I_g = 91.1 \text{ in.}^4$$

and for dead plus live load,

$$\frac{M_{cr}}{M_{D+L}} = \frac{M_{cr}}{M_{max}} = \frac{1.39}{1.95} = 0.713; \qquad \left(\frac{M_{cr}}{M_{max}}\right)^3 = 0.362$$
$$I_e = 0.362(91.1) + 0.638(25.9) = 49.5 \text{ in.}^4$$

(c) Consider the effect of sustained live load that contributes to the creep and shrinkage deflection. The immediate deflection due to all sustained loads is required as the base value on which to apply the time-dependent multiplier.

For negative-moment region, using sustained load moment of $0.59 + 0.6(1.05) = 1.22$ ft-kips/ft.

$$\frac{M_{cr}}{M_{max}} = \frac{1.39}{1.22} > 1; \qquad I_e = I_g = 91.1 \text{ in.}^4$$

For positive-moment region, using sustained load moment of $0.70 + 0.6(1.25) = 1.46$ ft-kips/ft,

$$\frac{M_{cr}}{M_{max}} = \frac{1.39}{1.46} = 0.952; \qquad \left(\frac{M_{cr}}{M_{max}}\right)^3 = 0.863$$

$$I_e = 0.863(91.1) + 0.137(25.9) = 82.2 \text{ in.}^4$$

(d) Immediate live-load deflection.

$$(\Delta_i)_L = (\Delta_i)_{D+L} - (\Delta_i)_D$$

$$\text{avg } I_e \text{ (dead load)} = 91.1 \text{ in.}^4$$

$$\text{avg } I_e \text{ (dead + live load)} = \frac{66.7 + 49.5}{2} = 58.1 \text{ in.}^4$$

$$(\Delta_i)_{D+L} = \frac{5(11.92)^2 144}{48(3.12)(10^3)58.1}\left(1.95 - \frac{1.64}{10}\right)(12) = 0.25 \text{ in.}$$

$$(\Delta_i)_D = \frac{5(11.92)^2 144}{48(3.12)(10^3)91.1}\left(0.70 - \frac{0.59}{10}\right)(12) = 0.06 \text{ in.}$$

$$(\Delta_i)_L = 0.25 - 0.06 = 0.19 \text{ in.}$$

(e) Creep and shrinkage deflection. The immediate deflection due to sustained loads,

$$\text{avg } I_e = \frac{82.2 + 91.1}{2} = 86.7 \text{ in.}^4$$

$$(\Delta_i)_{D + \text{sust } L} = \frac{5(11.92)^2 144}{48(3.12)(10^3)86.7}\left(1.45 - \frac{1.22}{10}\right)(12) = 0.13 \text{ in.}$$

$$(\Delta_i)_{cp+sh} = k_r T (\Delta_i)_{D + \text{sust } L}$$
$$= 2.0(0.13) = 0.26 \text{ in.}$$

(f) Check deflection if the limit of $L/480$ in ACI-Table 9.5b applies,

$$(\Delta_i)_L + \Delta_{cp+sh} = 0.19 + 0.26 = 0.45 \text{ in.}$$

$$\text{allowable } \Delta = \frac{L}{480} = \frac{11.92(12)}{480} = 0.30 \text{ in.}$$

which appears unacceptable. If none of the live load was considered sustained,

$$(\Delta_i)_L + \Delta_{cp+sh} = 0.19 + 2(0.06) = 0.31 \text{ in.} \approx 0.30 \text{ in.} \qquad \text{OK}$$

The decision regarding whether or not part of the live load is sustained should be made by considering the actual loading and its duration. For instance, a floor system supporting library stacks as the live load might well be considered to have a significant part of the live load treated as being sustained. In most situations it is acceptable to consider that only the dead load is sustained and thereby affects the magnitude of creep and shrinkage deflection.

In spite of the fact the deflection calculations have been illustrated throughout this chapter without shortcutting any steps in the formal procedure, deflection computations should be made keeping practicality in mind. The effective moment of inertia I_e theoretically should be computed at each total load level for which deflection is of concern: usually dead load, dead load plus live load, and dead load plus sustained live load. I_e should be computed at each end and at the midspan region in order to obtain an average as is encouraged by the ACI Code.

However, when the true accuracy obtainable from a deflection computation is recognized, the designer should use the I_e equation only when the result will be significantly different from using either I_{cr} or I_g. Further, for most situations only the midspan I_e need be computed; an average does not measurably improve accuracy. The authors believe these practical suggestions satisfy the spirit of the ACI Code.

SELECTED REFERENCES

1. ACI Committee 435, Subcommittee 1. "Allowable Deflections," *ACI Journal, Proceedings*, **65,** June 1968, 433–444. Disc. 1037–1038.
2. Mark Fintel (Ed.). *Handbook of Concrete Engineering*. New York: Van Nostrand, 1974 (801 pp.) (Chap. 2, "Deflections," p. 49).
3. ACI Committee 435, Subcommittee 7. "Deflections of Continuous Beams," *ACI Journal, Proceedings*, **70,** December 1973, 781–787.
4. P. D. Zuraski, C. G. Salmon, and A. Fattah Shaikh. "Calculation of Instantaneous Deflections for Continuous Reinforced Concrete Beams," *Deflections of Concrete Structures* (SP–43). Detroit: American Concrete Institute, 1974 (pp. 315–331).
5. ACI Committee 435, Building Code Subcommittee. *Revised ACI Code and Commentary Provision on Deflections*. Report of recommendations approved by Committee 435, November 1975.
6. Wei-Wen Yu and George Winter. "Instantaneous and Long-Time Deflections of Reinforced Concrete Beams Under Working Loads," *ACI Journal, Proceedings*, **57,** July 1960, 29–50. Disc. 1165–1171.
7. Dan E. Branson. "Instantaneous and Time-Dependent Deflections of Simple and Continuous Reinforced Concrete Beams," Part 1, Report No. 7. Alabama Highway Research Report, Bureau of Public Roads, August 1963, (1965) (pp. 1–78).
8. Dan E. Branson. Discussion of "Variability of Deflections of Simply Supported Reinforced Concrete Beams," by ACI Committee 435, *ACI Journal, Proceedings*, **69,** July 1972, 449–451.
9. Dan E. Branson Discussion of "Proposed Revision of ACI 318–63 Building Code Requirements for Reinforced Concrete," *ACI Journal, Proceedings*, **67,** September 1970, 692–693.
10. G. W. Washa and P. G. Fluck. "Effect of Compressive Reinforcement on the Plastic Flow of Reinforced Concrete Beams," *ACI Journal, Proceedings*, **49,** October 1952, 89–108.
11. G. W. Washa and P. G. Fluck. "Plastic Flow (Creep) of Reinforced Concrete Continuous Beams," *ACI Journal, Proceedings*, **52,** January 1956, 549–561.
12. ACI Committee 435. "Deflections of Reinforced Concrete Flexural Members," *ACI Journal, Proceedings*, **63,** June 1966, 637–674.
13. ACI Committee 435. "Variability of Deflections of Simply Supported Reinforced Concrete Beams," *ACI Journal, Proceedings*, **69,** January 1972, 29–35.

14. N. H. Burns and C. P. Siess. "Repeated and Reverse Loading in Reinforced Concrete," *Journal of Structural Division*, ASCE, **92,** October 1966 (ST5), 65–78.
15. J. R. Shank. "The Mechanics of Plastic Flow of Concrete," *ACI Journal, Proceedings*, **32,** November–December 1935, 149–180.
16. P. G. Fluck and G. W. Washa. "Creep of Plain and Reinforced Concrete," *ACI Journal, Proceedings*, **54,** April 1958, 879–895.
17. A. D. Ross. "Creep of Concrete Under Variable Stress," *ACI Journal, Proceedings*, **54,** March 1958, 739–758.
18. Adam Neville and Bernard Meyers. "Creep of Concrete: Influencing Factors and Prediction," *Symposium on Creep of Concrete*, (SP–9). Detroit: American Concrete Institute, 1964 (pp. 1–33).
19. ACI Committee 209. "Effects of Concrete Constituents, Environment, and Stress on the Creep and Shrinkage of Concrete," *Designing for Effects of Creep, Shrinkage, and Temperature in Concrete Structures* (SP–27). Detroit: American Concrete Institute, 1971 (pp. 1–42).
20. D. E. Branson and M. L. Christiason. "Time Dependent Concrete Properties Related to Design—Strength and Elastic Properties, Creep, and Shrinkage," *Designing for Effects of Creep, Shrinkage, and Temperature in Concrete Structures*, (SP–27). Detroit: American Concrete Institute, 1971 (pp. 257–277).
21. ACI Committee 209. "Prediction of Creep, Shrinkage, and Temperature Effects in Concrete Structures," *Designing for Effects of Creep, Shrinkage, and Temperature in Concrete Structures* (SP–27). Detroit: American Concrete Institute, 1971 (pp. 51–93).
22. Dan E. Branson. *Deformation of Concrete Structures*. New York: McGraw-Hill, 1977.
23. B. L. Meyers and D. E. Branson. "Design Aid for Predicting Creep and Shrinkage Properties of Concrete," *ACI Journal, Proceedings*, **69,** September 1972, 551–555.
24. M. R. Hollington. *A Series of Long-Term Tests to Investigate the Deflection of a Representative Precast Concrete Floor Component*, Technical Report TRA 442. London; Cement and Concrete Association, April 1970 (43 pp.).
25. Dan E. Branson. "Compression Steel Effect on Long-Time Deflection," *ACI Journal, Proceedings*, **68,** August 1971, 555–559.
26. T. C. Hansen and A. H. Mattock. "Influence of Size and Shape of Member on Shrinkage and Creep of Concrete," *ACI Journal, Proceedings*, **63,** February 1966, 267–289.
27. Hans Gesund. "Shrinkage and Creep Influence on Deflections and Moments of Reinforced Concrete Beams," *ACI Journal, Proceedings*, **59,** May 1962, 689–704.
28. Alfred L. Miller. "Warping of Reinforced Concrete Due to Shrinkage," *ACI Journal, Proceedings*, **54,** May 1958, 939–950.
29. A. F. Shaikh. Discussion of "Proposed Revision of ACI 318–63: Building Code Requirements for Reinforced Concrete," *ACI Journal, Proceedings*, **67,** September 1970, 722–723.
30. Dan E. Branson. "Design Procedures for Computing Deflections," *ACI Journal, Proceedings*, **65,** September 1968, 730–742.

PROBLEMS

All problems[†] are to be done in accordance with the ACI Code unless otherwise indicated.

[†] Most problems may be solved as problems stated in U.S. Customary units, or as problems in metric units using quantities in parenthesis at the end of the statement. The metric conversions are approximate to avoid implying higher precision for given information in metric units than that for the U.S. Customary units.

14.1 Compute the immediate deflections due to dead and live load on the beam of the accompanying figure. The span of the uniformly loaded, simply supported beam is 30 ft, and the maximum service-load moments are 80 ft-kips for dead load and 95 ft-kips for live load. Use $f'_c = 3500$ psi $(n = 8.5)$ and $f_y = 60,000$ psi. (Span $= 9.2$ m; $M_D = 110$ kN-m; $M_L = 130$ kN-m; $f'_c = 24$ N/mm^2; 420 N/mm^2.)

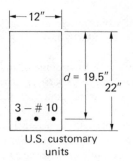
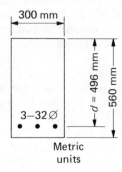

U.S. customary units

Metric units

Probs. 14.1, 14.7, and 14.8

14.2 Compute the immediate deflections due to dead and live load on the beam of the accompanying figure. The uniformly loaded, simply supported beam on a span of 29 ft must resist maximum service-load moments of 300 ft-kips dead load and 500 ft-kips live load. Use $f'_c = 4000$ psi $(n = 8)$ and $f_y = 40,000$ psi. (Span $= 8.9$ m; $M_D = 407$ kN-m; $M_L = 680$ kN-m; $f'_c = 28$ N/mm^2; $f_y = 280$ N/mm^2.)

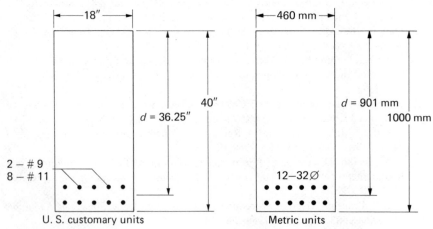

U. S. customary units

Metric units

Probs. 14.2, 14.9, and 14.10

14.3 Compute the immediate deflections due to dead and live load on the beam of the accompanying figure. The uniformly loaded, simply supported beam on a span of 30 ft must resist maximum service-load moments of 20 ft-kips dead load and 14 ft-kips live load. Use $f'_c = 3000$ psi $(n = 9)$ and $f_y = 40,000$ psi. (Span $= 9.1$ m; $M_D = 27$ kN-m; $M_L = 19$ kN-m; $f'_c = 21$ N/mm^2; $f_y = 280$ N/mm^2.)

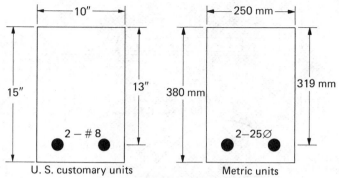

Probs. 14.3, 14.4, 14.11, and 14.12

14.4 Repeat Prob. 14.3 except the service-load moments are 29 ft-kips dead load and 19 ft-kips live load, and $f_y = 60,000$ psi. ($M_D = 40$ kN-m; $M_L = 26$ kN-m; $f_y = 420$ N/mm^2.)

14.5 Investigate the acceptability of the beam of the accompanying figure for immediate live-load deflection if the limitation is $L/360$. Use $f'_c = 3500$ psi ($n = 8.5$) and $f_y = 40,000$ psi.

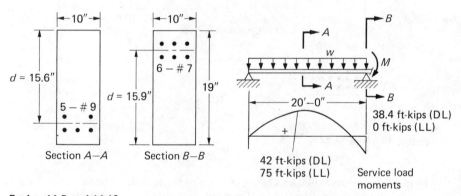

Probs. 14.5 and 14.13

14.6 Investigate the acceptability of the beam of the accompanying figure for immediate live-load deflection if the limitation is $L/360$. Use $f'_c = 3000$ psi ($n = 9$) and $f_y = 60,000$ psi.

14.7 Investigate the acceptability of the beam of Prob. 14.1, if the limit for live load plus creep and shrinkage deflection is $L/360$. Consider that none of the live load is sustained. Use data computed in Prob. 14.1 if that problem was previously assigned.

14.8 Repeat Prob. 14.7 except use the separate creep and shrinkage multiplier procedure instead of ACI method. Assume humidity is 80%, age at loading is 28 days after initial curing period, and duration of sustained load is 5 years.

14.9 Investigate the acceptability of the beam of Prob. 14.2 if the beam supports partitions and other nonstructural construction likely to be damaged by large deflection. Consider that 20% of the live load is sustained.

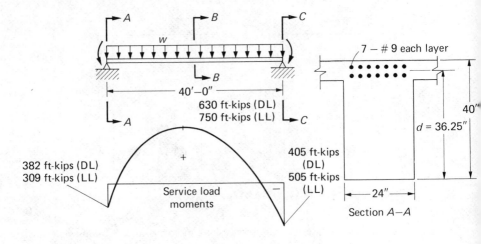

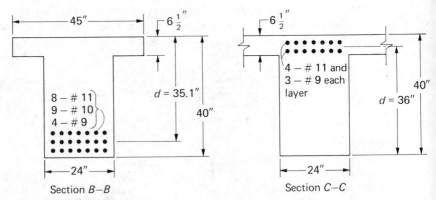

Probs. 14.6 and 14.14

14.10 Repeat Prob. 14.9 except use the separate creep and shrinkage multiplier procedure instead of the ACI method. The deflection limit is the same as for ACI Code, however. Assume humidity is 90%, age at loading is 60 days after initial curing period, and duration of sustained load is 5 years.

14.11 Investigate the acceptability of the beam of Prob. 14.3 if the beam supports partitions, etc., which limit the maximum deflection due to live load plus creep and shrinkage to $L/360$. Assume none of the live load is sustained, the relative humidity is 50%, age at loading is 20 days after initial curing, and sustained load will be in place for 1 year.
 (a) Use ACI method.
 (b) Use separate creep and shrinkage multiplier procedure.
 (c) Use combined creep and shrinkage multiplier procedure.

14.12 Investigate the acceptability of the beam of Prob. 14.4 if the beam supports partitions, etc., which limit the maximum deflection due to live load plus creep and shrinkage to $L/480$. Assume none of the live load is sustained, the relative humidity is 90%, age at loading is 30 days after initial curing period, and duration of sustained load is 5 years or more.

(a) Use ACI method.

(b) Use separate creep and shrinkage multiplier procedure.

14.13 Investigate the acceptability of the beam of Prob. 14.5 if the live load plus creep and shrinkage deflection is limited to $L/250$ and 10% of the live load is considered sustained. Assume relative humidity is 50%, age at leading is 10 days after initial curing period, and duration of sustained loading is 1 year.

(a) Use ACI Code method.

(b) Use separate creep and shrinkage multiplier procedure.

14.14 Investigate the acceptability of the beam of Prob. 14.6 if the beam supports partitions and other nonstructural construction likely to be damaged by large deflections. Assume that 10% of the live load is sustained.

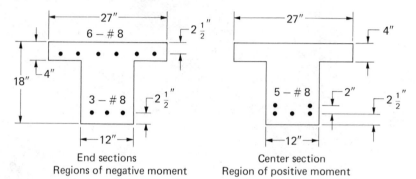

End sections
Regions of negative moment

Center section
Region of positive moment

Prob. 14.15

14.15 Investigate the acceptability of an interior 45-ft span (see the accompanying figure) of a continuous T-section with regard to deflection. The service-load moments at midspan are 40 ft-kips dead load and 100 ft-kips live load; and at both supports are 50 ft-kips dead load and 114 ft-kips live load. Assume that the $L/480$ limit of ACI-Table 9.5b applies and that none of the live load should be considered as sustained. Use $f'_c = 3500$ psi $(n = 8.5)$ and $f_y = 60,000$ psi.

15

Length
Effects
on Columns

15.1 General

In the basic treatment of compression members in Chap. 13, the assumption was made that the effects of buckling and lateral deflection on strength were small enough to be neglected. Short compression members—that is, those having a low slenderness ratio L/r (L = column height and r = radius of gyration = $\sqrt{I/A}$)—are not in danger of buckling prior to achieving their ultimate strength based on the properties of the cross section. Further, the lateral deflections of short compression members subjected to bending moments are small, thus contributing little secondary bending moment $P\Delta$ as shown in Fig. 15.1.1. It is these buckling and deflection effects that reduce the ultimate strength of a compression member below the value computed according to the principles of Chap. 13.

The adoption of the strength method for design, along with the use of higher strength steel and concrete, has led to the increased use of slender members. A stocky member having an L/r less than 20 will achieve essentially the strength discussed in Chap. 13, whereas a member having L/r greater than about 70 will have a considerable reduction in strength, both due to the likelihood of buckling and because of secondary bending moment. To permit the greatest flexibility in structural design, specifications should provide for adequate determination of strength with any slenderness ratio. Thus the provisions of ACI 10.10 and 10.11 take into account the length effects on long compression members.

Hotel Americana, Houston, Texas. (Courtesy of Portland Cement Association.)

In computing r, ACI-10.11.3 endorses a simple value for the rectangular column with b as the long dimension,

$$r = \sqrt{\frac{I}{A}} = \sqrt{\frac{\frac{1}{12}bh^3}{bh}} = 0.288h \approx 0.30h$$

and for the circular column,

$$r = \sqrt{\frac{I}{A}} = \sqrt{\frac{\pi h^4(4)}{64\pi h^2}} = 0.25h$$

These values actually should be slightly larger due to the effect of the reinforcement.

In the ACI Code, the evaluation of the effect of slenderness is approximated by using the moment magnifier approach, whereby the sum of the primary and secondary moments (Fig. 15.1.1) is treated as being equal to the product of the primary moment and a magnification factor δ. The general idea relating to this approach is derivable from the differential equation of the beam-column.

In the next several sections, the general concepts relating to the effect of slenderness on the strength of compression members are presented.

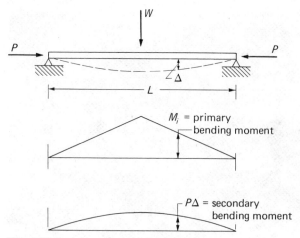

Fig. 15.1.1
Primary and secondary moment for beam-columns.

15.2 Buckling of Concentrically Loaded Columns

Over 200 years ago Leonhard Euler derived the well-known Euler formula [1] for concentrically loaded columns stressed below the proportional limit. Engesser [2] in 1889 proposed the tangent modulus modification of the Euler formula. In 1910 von Kármán [3] performed a series of careful tests verifying Engesser's assumptions. The tangent modulus formula has now been accepted as representing the lower bound for buckling strength of concentrically loaded columns,

$$P_c = \frac{\pi^2 E_t I}{(kL_u)^2} \tag{15.2.1}$$

where

P_c = buckling load
E_t = tangent modulus of elasticity of concrete at buckling
I = moment of inertia of the effective section (taken as the uncracked transformed section)
kL_u = equivalent pin-end length (L_u = actual unbraced length)

Although von Kárman was the first to use a rational analytical method for the inelastic buckling of long slender columns, his work did not consider reinforced concrete. More recent investigations on concentrically loaded reinforced concrete columns have been summarized and extended by Broms and Viest [4,5], whose design recommendations [6] formed the basis for the 1963 ACI Code provisions.

The fact that concentrically loaded columns rarely, if ever, exist in reinforced concrete structures led investigators [7–22] to focus attention since 1963 on the interaction of long columns with beams in frame structures, resulting in the more rational provisions for length effects on compression members beginning with the 1971 ACI Code.

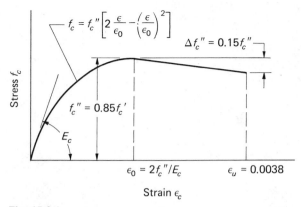

Fig. 15.2.1
Hognestad's stress-strain diagram for flexure (Ref. 23).

The basic design limitation of a maximum axial strength equal to 80 or 85% of the concentric capacity P_0 (see Fig. 13.11.2) means, of course, that from a practical viewpoint the concentrically loaded column is considered not to exist. However, to help the reader understand the effect of the slenderness ratio on the behavior of beam-columns over the entire range from $P_n = P_0$ with $M_n = 0$ to $P_n = 0$ with $M_n = M_0$ (see Fig. 13.16.2), the limiting case of the concentrically loaded column will be considered first.

In order to apply Eq. (15.2.1), a realistic expression for E_t of concrete must be used. Since buckling may occur at practically any value of concrete strain, it is necessary to know as accurately as possible the stresses at all strain levels.

One of the more realistic stress-strain diagrams for concrete in compression is that of Hognestad [23] shown in Fig. 15.2.1. The idealized stress-strain curve for steel is shown in Fig. 15.2.2. The initial modulus of elasticity for concrete is taken [23] as

$$E_c = 1,800,000 + 500f_c'' \text{ psi}$$

in which $f_c'' = 0.85f_c'$, while the modulus for steel is taken at 29,000,000 psi. These stress-strain relationships have been used by researchers [4,5,7] along with the assumptions that (1) concrete resists no tensile stress, (2) linear strain exists across the section, and (3) the deflected shape is part of a sine wave. On the basis of these assumptions, evaluation of Eq. (15.2.1) gives the typical column strength curves, such as those of Fig. 15.2.3.

A study of Fig. 15.2.3 shows that in the curves for $f_y = 40,000$ psi there occurs a flat leveling off (such as portion BC of Fig. 15.2.3) of the curve, indicating yielding of the steel with a sudden drop in E_s from 29×10^6 psi to zero. In such cases where $\epsilon_y < \epsilon_0$, the concrete may still increase the capacity (such as portion AB in Fig. 15.2.3) with an increased strain up to ϵ_0. For $f_y = 50,000$ psi and $f_c' = 4000$ psi, the strains $\epsilon_y = 0.00173$ and $\epsilon_0 = 0.00194$ are nearly equal so that little increase above the plateau of yielding in the steel can occur. The effect of creep on long-time loading may be noted by the crosshatched region.

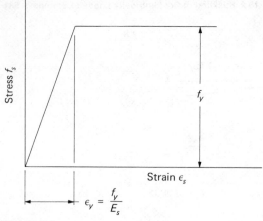

Fig. 15.2.2
Idealized stress-strain relationship for steel.

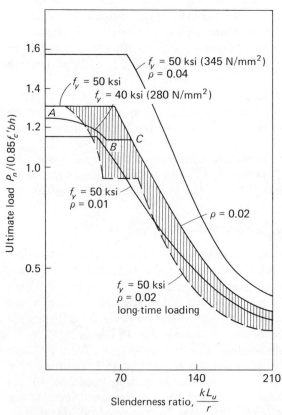

Fig. 15.2.3
Strength curves for reinforced concrete ($f'_c = 4000$ psi) (28 N/mm^2) concentrically loaded pin-end columns (adapted from Ref. 4).

EXAMPLE 15.2.1 Calculate the ordinate and abscissa of points A, B, and C of Fig. 15.2.3. Use $f'_c = 4000$ psi, $f_y = 40{,}000$ psi, and the steel area of $A_s = 0.02bh$ ($0.01bh$ in each face located at $0.45h$ from the center). Use the stress-strain diagrams of Figs. 15.2.1 and 15.2.2.

Solution:

$$f''_c = 0.85f'_c = 0.85(4) = 3.4 \text{ ksi}$$
$$E_c = 1800 + 500f''_c = 1800 + 500(3.4) = 3500 \text{ ksi}$$

$$\epsilon_0 = \frac{2f''_c}{E_c} = 2\left(\frac{3.4}{3500}\right) = 0.00194$$

$$\epsilon_y = \frac{f_y}{E_s} = \frac{40}{29{,}000} = 0.00138$$

(a) Point A, maximum strength of section according to the principles of Chap. 13 (upper limit, $\epsilon_c = \epsilon_0 > \epsilon_y$),

$$P_n = 0.85f'_c bh + A_s f_y$$

without correcting for the displaced concrete.

$$P_n = 0.85f'_c bh + 0.02bh(40)$$

$$= 0.85f'_c bh\left[1 + \frac{0.02(40)}{0.85(4)}\right]$$

$$\frac{P_n}{0.85f'_c bh} = 1.235 \qquad \text{(ordinate of point } A\text{)}$$

(b) Point B, $\epsilon_c = \epsilon_y = 0.00138 < \epsilon_0$, $E_s = 0$.

$$f_c = f''_c\left[2\left(\frac{\epsilon}{\epsilon_0}\right) - \left(\frac{\epsilon}{\epsilon_0}\right)^2\right]$$

$$= 3.4\left[2\left(\frac{1.38}{1.94}\right) - \left(\frac{1.38}{1.94}\right)^2\right]$$

$$= 3.4[2(0.712) - 0.508] = 3.12 \text{ ksi}$$
$$P_n = f_c bh + A_s f_y = 3.12bh + 0.02bh(40) = 3.92bh$$

$$\frac{P_n}{0.85f'_c bh} = \frac{3.92}{3.4} = 1.153 \qquad \text{(ordinate of point } B\text{)}$$

Using Eq. (15.2.1),

$$(kL_u)^2 = \frac{\pi^2 E_t I}{P_c} \qquad\qquad \textbf{[15.2.1]}$$

$$I = \frac{bh^3}{12} + 0.02bh\left(\frac{E_s}{E_t}\right)(0.45h)^2$$

$$= bh^3\left[\frac{1}{12} + 0.02\left(\frac{0}{1008}\right)(0.45)^2\right] = 0.0833bh^3$$

$$E_t = \frac{df_c}{d\epsilon} = f''_c \left(\frac{2}{\epsilon_0} - \frac{2\epsilon}{\epsilon_0^2} \right) = E_c - \frac{E_c\epsilon}{\epsilon_0}$$

$$= 3500 \left(1 - \frac{1.38}{1.94} \right) = 1008 \text{ ksi}$$

$$(kL_u)^2 = \frac{\pi^2(1008)(0.0833bh^3)}{3.92bh} = 212h^2$$

$$\frac{kL_u}{h} = 14.55$$

For a rectangular section, $r = h/\sqrt{12}$,

$$\frac{kL_u}{r} = 14.55\sqrt{12} = 50.3 \qquad \text{(abscissa of point } B)$$

(c) Point C, ϵ_c at an infinitesimal amount less than ϵ_y; $E = 29{,}000$ ksi.

$$I = bh^3 \left[\frac{1}{12} + 0.02 \left(\frac{29{,}000}{1008} \right)(0.45)^2 \right]$$

$$= bh^3(0.0833 + 0.1167) = 0.2000bh^3$$

$$(kL_u)^2 = \frac{\pi^2(1008)(0.200bh^3)}{3.92bh} = 507h^2$$

$$\frac{kL_u}{h} = 22.5$$

$$\frac{kL_u}{r} = 22.5\sqrt{12} = 78 \qquad \text{(abscissa of point } C)$$

15.3 Equivalent Pin-End Lengths

For conditions other than pin ends where the factor k in Eq. (15.2.1) is 1.0, the equivalent pin-end length factor k must be determined for various rotational and translational end restraint conditions. Where translation at both ends is adequately prevented, the distance between points of inflection is shown in Fig. 15.3.1. For all such cases the equivalent pin-end length is less than the actual unbraced length (i.e., k is less than one).

If sidesway or joint translation is possible, as in the case of the unbraced frame, the equivalent pin-end length exceeds the actual unbraced length (i.e., k is greater than one), as shown in Fig. 15.3.2.

As reinforced concrete columns are in general part of a larger frame, it is necessary to understand the concepts of a *braced frame* (where joint translation is prevented by rigid bracing, shear walls, or attachment to an adjoining structure) and the *unbraced frame* (where buckling stability is dependent on the stiffness of the beams and columns that constitute the frame). As shown

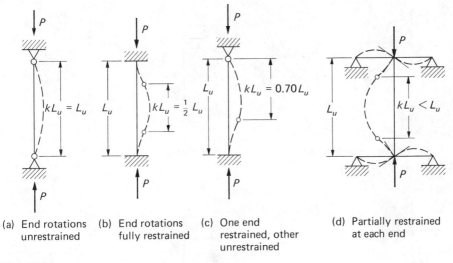

(a) End rotations unrestrained   (b) End rotations fully restrained   (c) One end restrained, other unrestrained   (d) Partially restrained at each end

Fig. 15.3.1
Equivalent pin-end lengths; no joint translation.

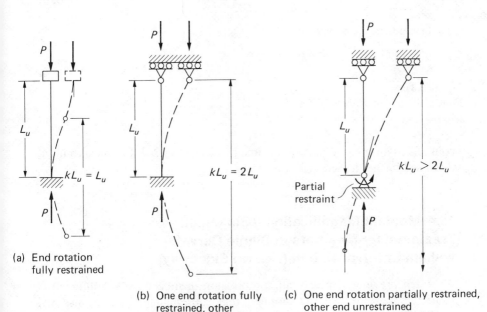

(a) End rotation fully restrained

(b) One end rotation fully restrained, other unrestrained

(c) One end rotation partially restrained, other end unrestrained

Fig. 15.3.2
Equivalent pin-end lengths; joint translation possible.

in Fig. 15.3.3a and c, the equivalent length kL_u for cases where joint translation is prevented may never exceed the actual length L_u. In an unbraced frame (Fig. 15.3.3b and d) instability results in a sidesway type of buckling with the equivalent length kL_u always exceeding the actual length L_u. Some research has been done to investigate the behavior of long reinforced concrete

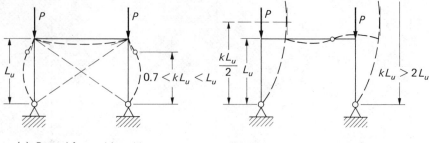

(a) Braced frame, hinged base   (b) Unbraced frame, hinged base

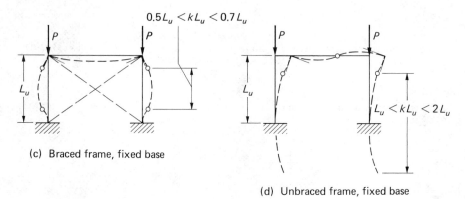

(c) Braced frame, fixed base

(d) Unbraced frame, fixed base

Fig. 15.3.3
Equivalent pin-end lengths for frames.

columns as an integral part of a frame [9,10,13,14,19,20]. Frame stability is discussed further in Secs. 15.7 and 15.8.

15.4 Moment Magnification—Simplified Treatment for Members in Single Curvature without End Translation (i.e., No Sidesway)

As stated previously, nearly all compression members are simultaneously subjected to some bending moment that causes lateral deflections. Any deflected compression member is further subjected to a secondary bending moment $P\Delta$, as shown in Fig. 15.1.1. One may consider this as a magnification of the applied bending moment. An approximate determination of the amplifying effect may be made by considering the member as finally achieving a deflection Δ_{max}, which is composed of the deflection Δ_0 due to the primary applied bending moment and the additional deflection Δ_1 due to the secondary moment from axial compression (see Fig. 15.4.1). It may be assumed that the secondary bending moment takes the shape of a sine curve (very nearly exact for members with no end restraint and whose primary bending moment and deflection are both maximum at midspan). The midspan

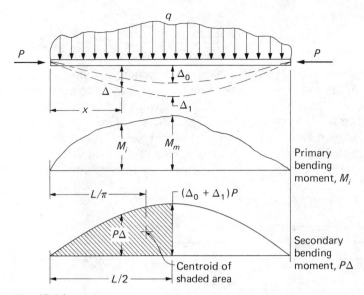

Fig. 15.4.1
Primary and secondary bending moment.

deflection Δ_1 equals the moment of the $M/(EI)$ diagram (for secondary bending moment) between the support and midspan taken about the support, according to the moment-area principle. Thus

$$\Delta_1 = \frac{P}{EI}(\Delta_0 + \Delta_1)\left(\frac{L}{2}\right)\frac{2}{\pi}\left(\frac{L}{\pi}\right) = (\Delta_0 + \Delta_1)\frac{PL^2}{\pi^2 EI} \qquad (15.4.1)$$

from which

$$\Delta_1 = \Delta_0\left[\frac{PL^2/(\pi^2 EI)}{1 - PL^2/(\pi^2 EI)}\right] = \Delta_0\left(\frac{\alpha}{1-\alpha}\right) \qquad (15.4.2)$$

where $\alpha = PL^2/(\pi^2 EI)$. Since Δ_{max} is the sum of Δ_0 and Δ_1,

$$\Delta_{max} = \Delta_0 + \Delta_1 = \Delta_0 + \Delta_0\left(\frac{\alpha}{1-\alpha}\right) = \frac{\Delta_0}{1-\alpha} \qquad (15.4.3)$$

The maximum bending moment, including the effect of axial load, becomes

$$M_{max} = M_m + P\Delta_{max} \qquad (15.4.4)$$

Substituting the expression for Δ_{max} of Eq. (15.4.3) and making $P = \alpha\pi^2 EI/L^2$, Eq. (15.4.4) becomes

$$M_{max} = M_m\left(\frac{C_m}{1-\alpha}\right) = M_m\delta \qquad (15.4.5)$$

where

$$\delta = \frac{C_m}{1-\alpha} = \text{magnification factor} \qquad (15.4.6)$$

and

$$C_m = 1 + \left(\frac{\pi^2 EI \Delta_0}{M_m L^2} - 1 \right) \alpha \qquad (15.4.7)$$

Thus, for common cases of single curvature deflection, the amplification factor to be applied to the primary bending moment is equal to $C_m/(1 - \alpha)$. Typical values of C_m are shown in Table 15.4.1 which is adapted from the AISC Commentary [24] to the 1969 AISC Specification. One may note that for all cases shown in Table 15.4.1 this C_m value will generally be close to 1.0. In actual concrete structures α rarely exceeds about 0.3, which would make C_m as low as 0.82 for the cases shown. The approximate treatment of slender-

Table 15.4.1

Values of C_m for Common Situations with No Joint Translation[a]

	Case	C_m	Primary Bending Moment
1	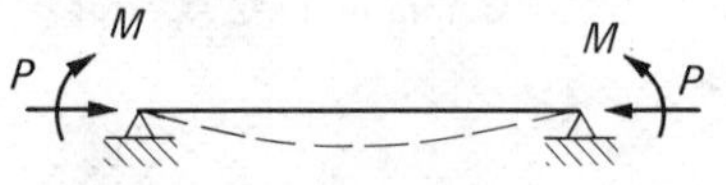 M P ... M P	$1.0 + 0.2\alpha$	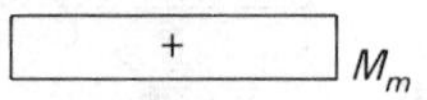 $+$ M_m
2	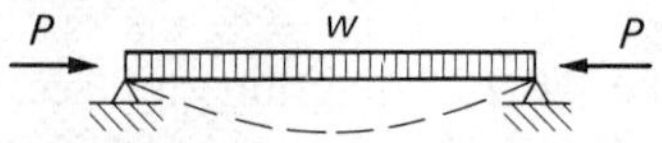 P w P	1.0	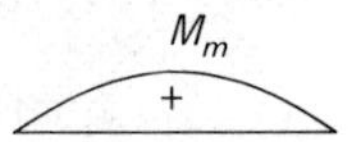 M_m $+$
3	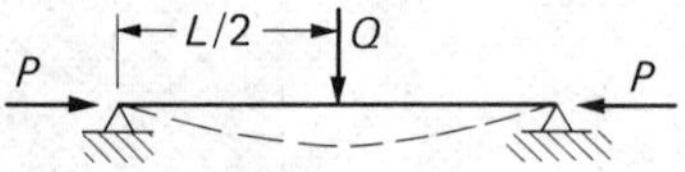 P $\vdash L/2 \dashv Q$ P	$1.0 - 0.2\alpha$	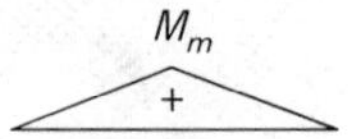 M_m $+$
4	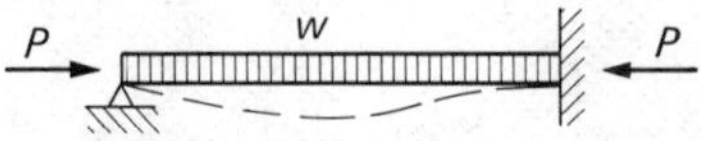 P w P	$1.0 - 0.3\alpha$	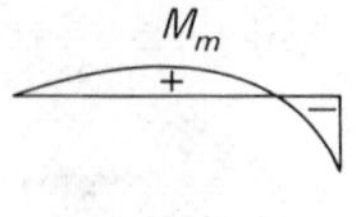 M_m $+$ $-$
5	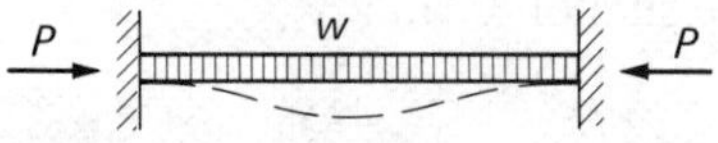 P w P	$1.0 - 0.4\alpha$	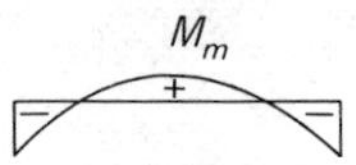 M_m $+$
6	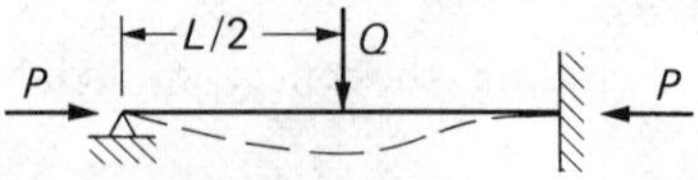 P $\vdash L/2 \dashv Q$ P	$1.0 - 0.4\alpha$	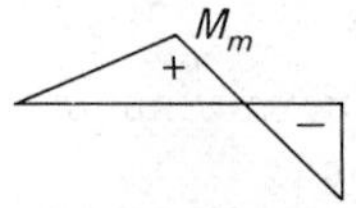 M_m $+$ $-$
7	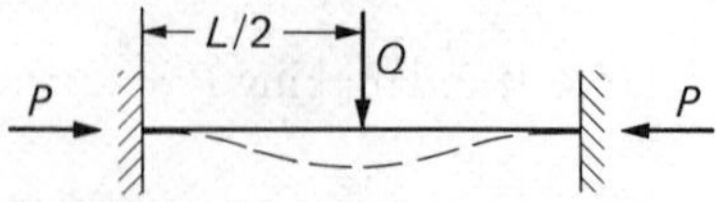 P $\vdash L/2 \dashv Q$ P	$1.0 - 0.6\alpha$	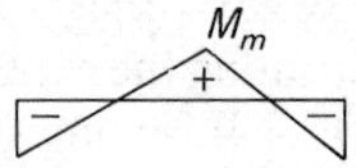 M_m $-$ $+$ $-$
8	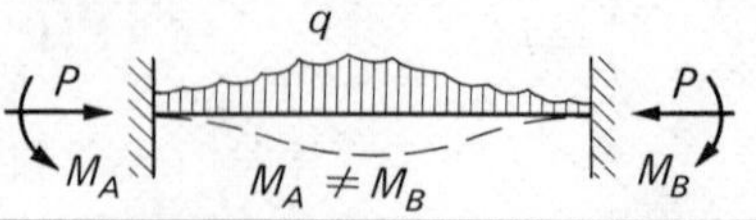 P q P M_A $M_A \neq M_B$ M_B	Eq.(15.4.7)	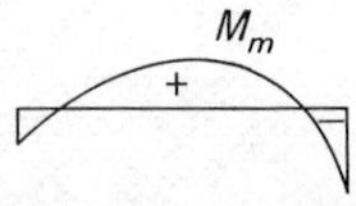 M_m $+$

[a] Adapted from Ref. 24.

ness in ACI-10.11.5 conservatively requires that C_m shall be taken as 1.0 for all cases with transverse loading between supports.

15.5 Moment Magnification—Members Subjected to End Moments Only; No Joint Translation

Consider the general case shown in Fig. 15.5.1 wherein the end moments M_1 and M_2 constitute the primary bending moment M_i which is a function of z. The sum of primary and secondary moments causes the member to have a deflection y which gives rise to the secondary moment Py. Stating the total moment M_z at the section z of Fig. 15.5.1 gives

$$M_z = M_i + Py = -EI\frac{d^2y}{dz^2} \tag{15.5.1}$$

for sections with constant EI; and dividing by EI gives

$$\frac{d^2y}{dz^2} + \frac{P}{EI}y = -\frac{M_i}{EI} \tag{15.5.2}$$

For design purposes, the general expression for moment M_z is of greater importance than the deflection y. Differentiating Eq. (15.5.2) twice gives

$$\frac{d^4y}{dz^4} + \frac{P}{EI}\frac{d^2y}{dz^2} = -\frac{1}{EI}\frac{d^2M_i}{dz^2} \tag{15.5.3}$$

From Eq. (15.5.1),

$$\frac{d^2y}{dz^2} = -\frac{M_z}{EI} \quad \text{and} \quad \frac{d^4y}{dz^4} = -\frac{1}{EI}\frac{d^2M_z}{dz^2}$$

Substitution into Eq. (15.5.3) gives

$$-\frac{1}{EI}\frac{d^2M_z}{dz^2} + \frac{P}{EI}\left(-\frac{M_z}{EI}\right) = -\frac{1}{EI}\frac{d^2M_i}{dz^2}$$

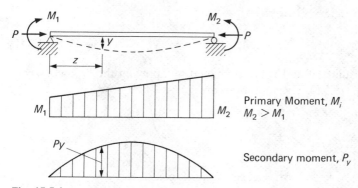

Fig. 15.5.1
Beam-column having end moments without transverse loading.

or, simplifying and letting $\lambda^2 = P/EI$.

$$\frac{d^2 M_z}{dz^2} + \lambda^2 M_z = \frac{d^2 M_i}{dz^2} \tag{15.5.4}$$

which is the same form as the deflection differential equation, Eq. (15.5.2). The homogeneous solution for Eq. (15.5.4) is

$$M_z = A \sin \lambda z + B \cos \lambda z \tag{15.5.5}$$

To this must be added the particular solution that will satisfy the right-hand side of the differential equation. In the special case of unequal end moments acting alone,

$$M_i = M_1 + \frac{M_2 - M_1}{L} z \tag{15.5.6}$$

Since

$$\frac{d^2 M_i}{dz^2} = 0$$

Equation (15.5.4) becomes a homogeneous equation, in which case Eq. (15.5.5) represents the entire solution.

In order to determine the maximum moment,

$$\frac{dM_z}{dz} = 0 = A\lambda \cos \lambda z - B\lambda \sin \lambda z \tag{15.5.7}$$

or

$$\tan \lambda z = \frac{A}{B} \tag{15.5.8}$$

At maximum M_z,

$$\sin \lambda z = \frac{A}{\sqrt{A^2 + B^2}}, \qquad \cos \lambda z = \frac{B}{\sqrt{A^2 + B^2}} \tag{15.5.9}$$

Substitution of Eq. (15.5.9) in Eq. (15.5.5) gives

$$M_{max} = \frac{A^2}{\sqrt{A^2 + B^2}} + \frac{B^2}{\sqrt{A^2 + B^2}}$$

$$= \sqrt{A^2 + B^2} \tag{15.5.10}$$

Now the constants A and B are evaluated by applying the boundary conditions to Eq. (15.5.5). The conditions are

(1) at $z = 0$, $\qquad M_z = M_1$

$\qquad \therefore B = M_1$

(2) at $z = L$, $\qquad M_z = M_2$

$\qquad M_z = A \sin \lambda L + M_1 \cos \lambda L$

$$\therefore A = \frac{M_2 - M_1 \cos \lambda L}{\sin \lambda L}$$

so that

$$M_z = \left(\frac{M_2 - M_1 \cos \lambda L}{\sin \lambda L}\right) \sin \lambda z + M_1 \cos \lambda z \qquad (15.5.11)$$

and

$$M_{max} = \sqrt{\left(\frac{M_2 - M_1 \cos \lambda L}{\sin \lambda L}\right)^2 + M_1^2}$$

$$= M_2 \sqrt{\frac{1 - 2(M_1/M_2)\cos \lambda L + (M_1/M_2)^2}{\sin^2 \lambda L}} \qquad (15.5.12)$$

For the general case of a beam-column subjected to end moments, the maximum moment may be either (1) the larger end moment M_2 at the braced (supported) location, (Fig. 15.5.2a) or (2) the magnified moment given by Eq. (15.5.12) that occurs at a variable location out along the span (Fig. 15.5.2b), depending on the ratio M_1/M_2 and the value of α, since $\lambda L = \pi \sqrt{\alpha}$. In order to investigate the strength of a beam-column, one needs to know whether the maximum moment occurs at a location away from the support, and if so, the correct *distance*. To eliminate the need for such information, the concept of equivalent uniform moment (Fig. 15.5.2c) is used. Thus, for the case with unequal end moments, use of the equivalent moment assumes M_{max} to be at midspan.

To establish the equivalent moment, let $M_1 = M_2 = M_{equiv}$ in Eq. (15.5.12),

$$M_{max} = M_{equiv} \sqrt{\frac{2(1 - \cos \lambda L)}{\sin^2 \lambda L}} \qquad (15.5.13)$$

Equate Eq. (15.5.12) and Eq. (15.5.13),

$$M_{equiv} = M_2 \sqrt{\frac{(M_1/M_2)^2 - 2(M_1/M_2)\cos \lambda L + 1}{2(1 - \cos \lambda L)}} \qquad (15.5.14)$$

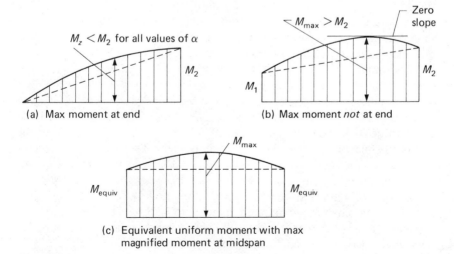

(a) Max moment at end

(b) Max moment *not* at end

(c) Equivalent uniform moment with max magnified moment at midspan

Fig. 15.5.2

Combined primary and secondary bending-moment diagrams for beam-columns having end moments without transverse loading.

Use the procedure of Sec. 15.4 where the approximate expression for maximum moment was shown to be

$$M_{max} = M_m \delta = M_m \left(\frac{C_m}{1 - \alpha} \right) \qquad (15.5.15)$$

For the case of uniform moment ($M_1 = M_2 = M_{equiv}$),

$$\Delta_0 = \frac{M_{equiv} L^2}{8EI}$$

$$M_m = M_{equiv}$$

$$C_m = 1 + \left[\left(\frac{\pi^2 EI}{L^2} \right) \frac{M_{equiv} L^2}{8EI M_{equiv}} - 1 \right] \alpha \approx 1$$

Thus

$$M_{max} = M_{equiv} \left(\frac{1}{1 - \alpha} \right) \qquad (15.5.16)$$

Substitution of Eq. (15.5.14) into Eq. (15.5.16) gives

$$M_{max} = M_2 \left(\frac{C_m}{1 - \alpha} \right) \qquad (15.5.17)$$

in which

$$C_m = \sqrt{\frac{(M_1/M_2)^2 - 2(M_1/M_2)\cos \lambda L + 1}{2(1 - \cos \lambda L)}} \qquad (15.5.18)$$

Comparing Eq. (15.5.17) with Eq. (15.5.16), $C_m M_2$ may be considered to be the equivalent uniform moment along the span.

Equation (15.5.18) assumes that the strength of the beam-column is limited by excessive deflection *in the plane of bending*. Also, it does not fully cover the double-curvature cases where M_1/M_2 lies between -0.5 and -1.0. The actual failure mode of members bent in double curvature with such bending-moment ratios is generally one of "unwinding" from double to single curvature in a sudden type of buckling.

Massonnet [25] and the AISC steel design specification [24] have suggested expressions for C_m to be used for design in place of Eq. (15.5.18). The comparison of Eq. (15.5.18) with the recommendations of Massonnet and the AISC is shown in Fig. 15.5.3. The reader should note that for a given value of α, the curve shown terminates when the moment M_2 at the end of the member exceeds the magnified moment. The straight line recommended by AISC, and adopted by ACI-10.11.5.3, falls near the upper limit for C_m at any given bending-moment ratio, and thus seems to be a realistic and simple approximation. In the ACI strength method α is computed by using for P the required nominal ultimate capacity, $P_n = P_u/\phi$. Thus ACI-10.11.5.3, Formula (10-11), for members braced against sidesway and without transverse loads between supports, is

$$C_m = 0.6 + 0.4 \frac{M_1}{M_2} \geq 0.4 \qquad (15.5.19)$$

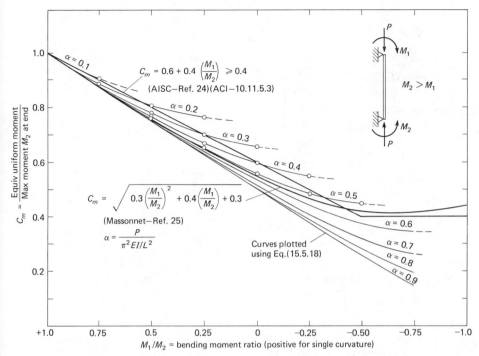

Fig. 15.5.3

Comparison of theoretical C_m with design recommendations for members subject to end moments only, without joint translation.

15.6 Moment Magnification—
Members with Sidesway Possible

The unbraced frame, or the frame where joint translation may occur when instability arises due to the slenderness of the compression elements, does not lend itself to the simple but relatively accurate treatment presented in the last two sections. More complete treatment of the braced and unbraced elastic frames may be found elsewhere [26,27].

A simple approximation of C_m for this case may be obtained by starting with Eq. (15.4.5) which applies for the single-curvature case,

$$M_{max} = M_m \left(\frac{C_m}{1 - \alpha} \right) \tag{15.6.1}$$

Next consider the situation of Fig. 15.6.1. Whatever the degree of restraint at the top and bottom of the two-story member, the deflection curve, and therefore the secondary bending moment (P times deflection), may be reasonably assumed to be a sine curve, in which case the development used when no sidesway occurs (Fig. 15.4.1) is also valid here. Since $2L$ from Fig. 15.6.1 equals L for Fig. 15.4.1, Eq. (15.4.7) for C_m becomes

$$C_m = 1 + \left(\frac{\pi^2 E I \Delta_0}{4 L^2 M_m} - 1 \right) \alpha \tag{15.6.2}$$

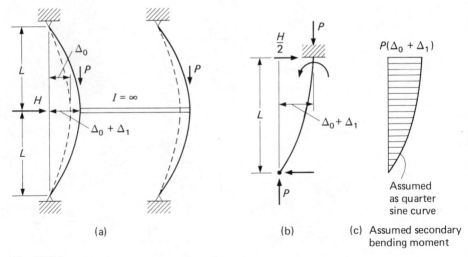

Fig. 15.6.1
Beam-column with sidesway instability.

The larger effective length ($2L$ instead of L) is also used in the computation of α. Next, referring to Fig. 15.6.1,

$$\Delta_0 = \frac{(H/2)L^3}{3EI} \tag{15.6.3}$$

$$M_m = \frac{HL}{2} \tag{15.6.4}$$

Substitution of Eqs. (15.6.3) and (15.6.4) into Eq. (15.6.2) gives

$$C_m = 1 + \left[\frac{\pi^2 EI}{4L^2} \left(\frac{HL^3}{6EI} \right) \left(\frac{2}{HL} \right) - 1 \right] \alpha$$

$$C_m = 1 + \left(\frac{\pi^2}{12} - 1 \right) \alpha = 1 - 0.18\alpha \tag{15.6.5}$$

which is suggested for the unbraced frame by the AISC Commentary [24]. Again, it will be conservative to take $C_m = 1$ for unbraced frames, as required in the approximate evaluation of slenderness effects in ACI-10.11.5.3.

15.7 Beam-Columns in Rigid Frames

Most reinforced concrete members subjected to combined axial compression and bending moment occur as parts of rigid frames, rather than as isolated members. A correct rational treatment of long members in such frames must include the actual end restraints afforded by the contiguous members, as well as whether or not the frame is braced to prevent joint translation. The formal procedures for determination of elastic buckling loads in a frame subjected to primary axial forces only are well known [27–30]. Generally, the solutions must be obtained by trial from an implicit expression and become complicated for situations other than a single story, one- or two-bay frame. More recently, computer programs have become available for individual case solutions [31]. Moment magnification due to the secondary moment ($P\Delta$) effect for members of a rigid frame is a situation different from elastic buckling. The inclusion of $P\Delta$ effect is often called *second-order analysis*. Again, for individual irregular elastic frames, braced or unbraced, computer programs exist to give maximum bending moment everywhere in the structure [31].

Design of the compression members in rigid frames has traditionally been done by estimating the relative sizes of members and performing a nominal elastic analysis to determine moments, shears, and axial loads. The nominal analysis is one using a conventional method such as moment distribution wherein stiffnesses are determined from gross uncracked sections and the secondary effects of deflection and reduction in stiffness due to axial load are neglected. Each member of the frame is then designed or investigated individually using the loading from the nominal analysis.

In the absence of a convenient second-order analysis for obtaining moment magnification, a compression member restrained by adjoining members at its ends may be considered removed from the frame and replaced by an equivalent pin-end column (see Fig. 15.3.3) whose length is equal to the effective length kL_u for axial compression on the real column. The equivalent column is then analyzed for compression plus the end moments carried by the member. The equivalent length kL_u would be used both for the axial effect as in Eq. (15.2.1) and for determining any magnified bending moment by Eq. (15.4.5).

One of the difficulties that arises in using the nominal analysis for the reinforced concrete frame is that when the gross moment of inertia is used for the beam stiffness, the restraining effect of the beams on the columns is overestimated [32,33]. If a beam is cracked under service load but assumed uncracked, the amount of moment transmitted to the column will be underestimated. This is the common situation.

15.8 Alignment Charts for Effective Length Factor *k*

The most commonly used procedure for obtaining effective length is to use the alignment charts from the Structural Stability Research Council Guide [26], originally developed by O. J. Julian and L. S. Lawrence, and presented in detail by T. C. Kavanagh [34]. The charts are shown in Fig. 15.8.1, the complete derivations of which appear in Chap. 14 of Ref. 27.

The equivalent pin-end (hinged) length factor k is a function of the end restraint factors ψ_A and ψ_B, at the top and bottom of the member, respectively, defined as

$$\psi = \frac{\Sigma\, EI/L \text{ for column members in the plane of bending}}{\Sigma\, EI/L \text{ for beam members in the plane of bending}} \qquad \textbf{(15.8.1)}$$

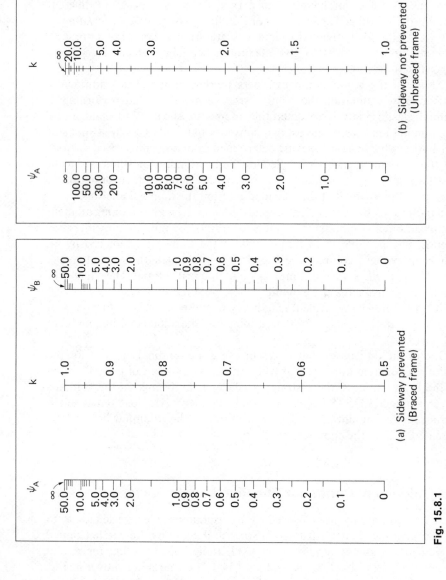

Fig. 15.8.1

Alignment charts for effective length factor for columns in continuous frames (from Ref. 34), where

$$\psi = \frac{\Sigma EI/L, \text{ columns}}{\Sigma EI/L, \text{ beams}}$$

(a) Sideway prevented (Braced frame)

(b) Sideway not prevented (Unbraced frame)

which for a hinged end gives $\psi = \infty$ and for a fixed end, $\psi = 0$. Since a frictionless hinge cannot exist in practical construction, ψ is to be taken equal to 10 for an end assumed as hinged in the analysis.

One nomogram (or alignment chart), Fig. 15.8.1a, is for braced frames where sidesway (joint translation) is prevented, and the other, Fig. 15.8.1b, is for the unbraced frame where sidesway is possible, being restrained only by the stiffness of interacting beams and columns.

This effective length procedure has been adopted by ACI-10.11 in the approximate evaluation of slenderness effects. The alignment charts are implicitly endorsed for determining the *k* factor by their inclusion in the ACI Commentary [35].

The assumptions inherent in the development of the alignment chart for the braced frame (Fig. 15.8.1a) are as follows [27]:

1. All columns reach their respective critical loads simultaneously.
2. The structure is assumed to consist of symmetrical rectangular frames.
3. At any joint, the restraining moment provided by the girders is distributed among the columns in proportion to their stiffnesses.
4. The girders are elastically restrained at their ends by the columns, and at the onset of buckling the rotations of the girder at its ends are equal and opposite (i.e., the girders are deflected in single curvature).
5. The girders carry no axial loads.

For the unbraced frame alignment chart (Fig. 15.8.1b) the assumptions (1) through (3) and (5) are unchanged; however, the girders are assumed to be deflected in double curvature, where the rotations of the ends are equal in magnitude and direction.

By means of the alignment charts one may determine the *k* factor for a column of constant cross section in a multibay frame. With steel frames where the material is homogeneous and isotropic, the modulus of elasticity E is constant for all members, and the moment of inertia I is computed for the gross cross section. In reinforced concrete, E varies with concrete strength and magnitude of loading, while I also varies depending on the degree of cracking and the reinforcement percentage. ACI-10.11.2.2 requires that the effective length factor *k* for the *unbraced* frame "shall be determined with due consideration of cracking and reinforcement on relative stiffness." For the *braced* frame, ACI-10.11.2.1 merely says the effective length factor "shall be taken as 1.0, unless analysis shows that a lower value may be used." It is believed that an appropriate use of the alignment chart would constitute an "analysis" as required by the ACI Code.

Thus, for the purpose of evaluating the end restraint factor ψ, cracked section moment of inertia should be used for the beams whereas gross moment of inertia is probably satisfactory for the columns [36] (or ACI Formula 10-9 with $\beta_d = 0$, as discussed in Sec. 15.11). Particularly recognition of different behavior in beams and columns is necessary when the percentage of reinforcement is significantly different, such as with 0.08 in the columns and 0.005 in the beams.

As an alternative to actually using the nomograms of Fig. 15.8.1 some approximate formulas for the effective length factor k have been proposed and are endorsed by the ACI Commentary.

For members in *braced* frames, the 1972 British Code of Standard Practice [38] gives

$$k = 0.7 + 0.05(\psi_A + \psi_B) \leq 1.0 \tag{15.8.2}$$

$$k = 0.85 + 0.05\psi_{min} \leq 1.0 \tag{15.8.3}$$

For members in *unbraced* frames, Furlong [39] proposed for members restrained at both ends,

when $\psi_{avg} < 2$ (i.e., high end restraint),

$$k = \frac{20 - \psi_{avg}}{20}\sqrt{1 + \psi_{avg}} \tag{15.8.4}$$

when $\psi_{avg} > 2$ (i.e., moderate to low end restraint),

$$k = 0.9\sqrt{1 + \psi_{avg}} \tag{15.8.5}$$

Equations (15.8.4) and (15.8.5) give k values that are within 2% of those obtained by the nomograms.

For members in *unbraced* frames, when hinged at one end, the British Code of Standard Practice [38] proposes

$$k = 2.0 + 0.3\psi \tag{15.8.6}$$

15.9 Interaction Diagrams—Effect of Slenderness

In order to understand the ACI Code procedure and its approximations as discussed in Sec. 15.11, the general approach is presented for determining a point on the P_n–M_n interaction diagram for kL/r not equal to zero. In Chap. 13 the basic strength of a section with zero kL/r was treated, giving an interaction diagram such as Fig. 13.6.2, and designated by $kL/r = 0$ in Fig. 15.9.1.

Points A and B represent combinations of P_n and M_n with the neutral axes (NA) located at x_A and x_B, respectively, from the extreme compression fiber whose strain is taken as the ACI Code prescribed value 0.003. In the following development it will be shown that when kL/r is not zero, the ultimate capacity, including primary and secondary moment contributions to M_n, may be achieved when the strain at the extreme compression fiber is less than 0.003. The curve labeled $kL/r \approx 60$ in Fig. 15.9.1 represents a typical strength interaction curve that includes slenderness effects.

Pfrang and Siess [11], Pfrang [18], and MacGregor, Breen, and Pfrang [37] have provided excellent discussions of the slenderness effects on interaction diagrams. A long column may fail in one of two ways: (1) it may fail by reaching a combined P_n–M_n that exceeds the cross-section strength computed by the methods of Chap. 13; (2) it may fail by instability when

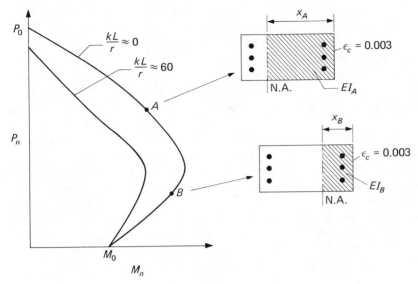

Fig. 15.9.1
Beam-column strength interaction diagram, including effective cross section for moment of inertia.

an infinitesimal increase in axial load results in additional deflection such that equilibrium cannot be achieved.

Referring to Fig. 15.9.2a, the member of large slenderness, say $kL/r = 100$, will generally follow the loading path up to point D where the material strength is reached. Point D is on the short column ($kL/r = 0$) interaction diagram but is at a smaller axial load P_{long} than it would be (P_{short} in Fig. 15.9.2a) if kL/r were actually zero. If the column fails by instability, it would

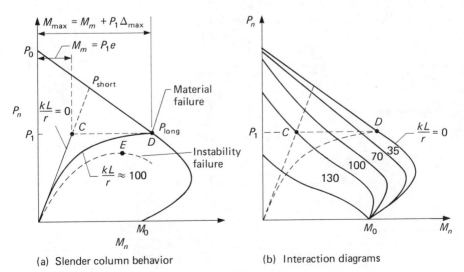

(a) Slender column behavior

(b) Interaction diagrams

Fig. 15.9.2
Slender column interaction diagrams (adapted from Ref. 37).

follow the path (dashed) up to point E; that is, it would be unable to reach the material strength interaction diagram (for $kL/r = 0$).

Generally, columns in braced frames are capable of achieving a "material failure," while the "instability failure" is not common but may occur in unbraced frames.

In the construction of interaction diagrams, as shown in Fig. 15.9.2b, a material failure occurring at D on the $kL/r = 0$ curve due to an axial load P_1 plus a magnified moment $M_m\delta$ (equal to $M_m + P_1\Delta_{max}$) may be plotted *for the particular loading arrangement* at point C on the primary moment radial line. Whatever the primary moment loading arrangement—such as equal end eccentricities of axial load, unequal end eccentricities of axial load, or lateral transverse loading—the deflection of the member will differ so that the secondary bending moment $P\Delta$ will differ. This means that different types of primary moments will cause a member of $kL/r = 100$ to follow a curved path to intersect the $kL/r = 0$ material strength interaction diagram at different locations such as point D. The radial line through point C is a function of only the primary moment, which is the same for all slenderness ratios.

The development of a correct interaction diagram for members of large slenderness, such as Fig. 15.9.2b, would require an elaborate analysis for each structure taking into account such factors as the following: (1) a realistic moment-curvature relationship; (2) the time-dependent and cracking effects on deflections; and (3) the influence of axial load on the flexural stiffness of members.

EXAMPLE 15.9.1 Illustrate qualitatively the determination of the long column strength, indicating the process of computing point D (material failure) or point E (instability failure) of Fig. 15.9.2a. Assume that the loading condition is a simply supported member with axial load P_1 and subjected to a primary bending moment M_i which arises from uniform lateral loading. The Hognestad stress-strain curve for concrete (Fig. 15.2.1) is to be used (see also Fig. 15.9.3).

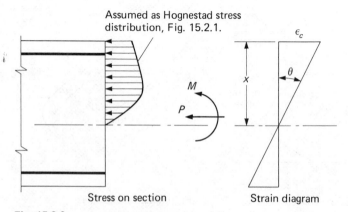

Fig. 15.9.3
Basic stress and strain relationships for beam-columns.

Solution: (a) Compute M–θ curve. For the *constant* value of axial load P_1, a series of moment capacities M may be determined for various values of the extreme fiber strain ϵ_c. The principles of Chap. 13 are used except M is computed for other values of ϵ_c in addition to 0.003, which is the ACI prescribed maximum. Points A and B of Fig. 15.9.1 correspond to using 0.003. When ϵ_c is less than 0.003, the neutral axis distances x will also change. The determination of M involves solving also for x. Then, using the strain geometry relationship,

$$\theta = \frac{\epsilon_c}{x} = \frac{M}{EI} \qquad (15.9.1)$$

the M–θ curve may be plotted as in Fig. 15.9.4. For determining values of M and x for a given P, the Hognestad compressive stress distribution should be used for good results, and this will be more complicated than using the Whitney rectangular stress block though the principles are the same.

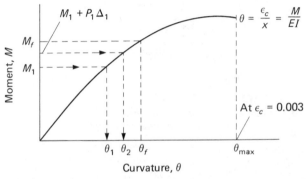

Fig. 15.9.4
Moment-rotation characteristics for a section.

(b) Compute deflection under primary bending moment. For the constant P_1 select a value of maximum primary moment M_1 that is not expected to cause failure. For the uniform lateral loading condition (parabolic variation) the values of θ for values of M (such as θ_1 for M_1 in Fig. 15.9.5) are obtained from the relationship of Fig. 15.9.4. Using the conjugate beam with the θ loading, compute the deflections (including Δ_1 at midspan).

(c) Compute deflection under primary plus secondary bending moment. The secondary bending moment $P\Delta$ is computed and added to the primary moment, as in Fig. 15.9.6. For this first approximation of total moment, the θ variation is determined from Fig. 15.9.4. The conjugate beam with the θ loading is used to compute the second approximation of deflection.

(d) Iteration. The newly computed deflection means increased secondary moment which will result in increased deflection. The process in (c) is repeated until the newly computed deflection agrees with that used for computing the secondary bending moment. These iterations then yield one combination of P_1 and M for which the beam-column is stable. If the maximum value of ϵ_c computed from Eq. (15.9.1) exceeds 0.003, the applied moment is too large,

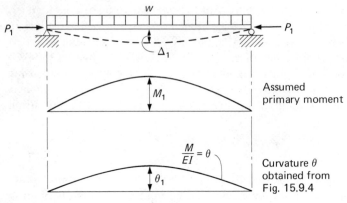

Fig. 15.9.5
Loading and first approximation for Δ.

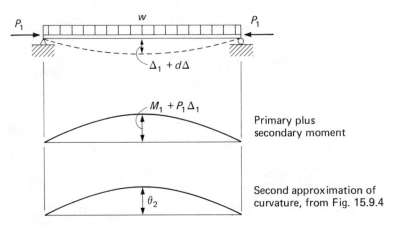

Fig. 15.9.6
Second approximation for deflection.

resulting in a material failure. Generally the initial value of M applied will result in maximum ϵ_c well below 0.003.

(e) Apply a larger value of M_1 and repeat the entire process of (b) through (d). The entire process is repeated for larger and larger values of M_1 until one of two situations results. One is that the maximum ϵ_c computed from maximum θ, when the structure is in equilibrium under primary plus secondary moment, equals the prescribed failure limit 0.003 (or whatever other value is decided on); or two, the equilibrium situation cannot be achieved due to the fact that each succeeding moment increment due to $P_1\Delta$ results in successively larger deflection increments. The former corresponds to point D and the latter to point E of Fig. 15.9.2a.

In either failure mode, the multiple iteration processes give for each axial load level a *single* point on the strength interaction curve (such as Fig. 15.9.2b) for whatever value of slenderness ratio was used.

Except for the initial computation of the M–θ relationship, the process is identical to the numerical computation of such a point described on pp. 629–634 of Ref. 27.

When the maximum moment (primary plus secondary) M_f has been determined *for which the member is stable*, it will frequently be that θ_f (see Fig. 15.9.4) is less than $\theta_{\max}$, particularly for the unbraced frame where the problem of instability is greatest. It has already been shown from Eq. (15.4.4) that in general

$$M_f = M_{\max} = M_m + P\Delta_{\max}$$

or

$$M_f = M_m\delta$$

where

$$\delta = \text{magnification factor} = \frac{M_f}{M_m}$$

Of course, for a design situation the maximum primary moment M_m is known; however, M_f can only be determined by the effort described in this example. Thus if the magnifier concept is to be used in practical design, simpler approaches, such as presented in Secs. 15.4 through 15.6, are necessary.

15.10 Strength Reduction Factors

For many years prior to the 1971 ACI Code adoption, the usual approach to the strength of long columns was to apply a strength reduction factor R to the short column strength computed according to the procedures of Chap. 13. Such a reduction factor depended primarily on the type of loading and the effective slenderness ratio. Generally speaking the reduction factor expressions were simple linear equations, included only a few types of loading, and gave overly conservative results for most situations. Referring to Fig. 15.9.2a, the reduction factor was intended to arrive at point C from the capacity P_{short} by reducing both the P_n and M_n. The reduction factor R would equal $P_{\text{long}}/P_{\text{short}}$.

The reduction factor approach was based on the studies by Broms and Viest [4–6] and Chang and Ferguson [7] of hinged and restrained columns with eccentrically applied loads. The greatest reduction in strength as a function of kL/r occurs under conditions of high concrete strength, low reinforcement percentage, high steel yield point, low eccentricity ratio e/h, and long-time loading. Taking a lower bound value for R as affected by material strengths (f_y and f_c') and reinforcement ratio (ρ), but keeping eccentricity ratio e_1/e_2 (i.e., moment gradient along the length of the column) as the primary variable in addition to slenderness ratio (kL_u/r), Broms and Viest [6] recommended the following design expression:

$$R = \frac{P_{\text{long}}}{P_{\text{short}}} = 1.20 - 0.0075\frac{kL_u}{r} - 0.13\frac{e_1}{e_2} \leq 1.0 \qquad \textbf{(15.10.1)}$$

where

kL_u = equivalent pin-end length

r = radius of gyration (taken approximately as $0.3h$ for rectangular sections and $0.25h$ for circular sections)

e_1 = smaller of the end eccentricities of load

e_2 = larger of the end eccentricities of load.

Equation (15.10.1) is shown in Fig. 15.10.1 along with the curves computed analytically.

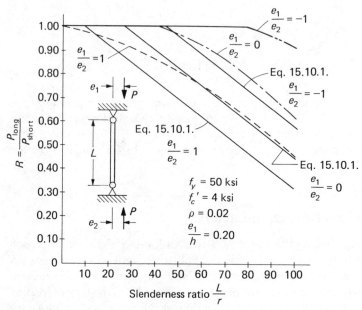

Fig. 15.10.1

Effect of moment gradient on hinged columns as represented by eccentricity ratio (adapted from Ref. 6).

Since little investigation had been made for reinforced concrete columns subject to transverse loading, a conservative recommendation [6] was to use for such cases an eccentricity e applied at both ends such that the bending moment of the compressive loads equals the maximum moment due to lateral loads.

Though the moment magnifier procedure has been explicitly used since 1971, the strength reduction factor approach of the 1963 ACI Code has been retained in a modified fashion in the ACI Commentary [35]. The following equations used to present the method are those of the Commentary modified version based on computer studies [19,20]. According to the Commentary, these equations, within the limits noted, lead to an accuracy equal to that of the moment magnifier method of ACI-10.11.5.

Basically the reduction factors apply to members in the "compression controls" region (see Fig. 13.6.2); however, for simplicity the Commentary suggests "no increase in R is justified where tension governs the design, unless axial load is less than $0.10f'_cbh$." Of course, as axial load approaches zero and the problem approaches that of a beam, neither buckling nor moment magnification should apply.

Braced Frame (No Relative Lateral Displacement of Ends of Member)— Single Curvature. For the case where the nominal eccentricity does not exceed $0.10h$,

$$R = 1.23 - 0.008\frac{L_u}{r} \le 1.0 \qquad (15.10.2)$$

which agrees closely with Eq. (15.10.1) if the eccentricity term can be neglected.

When the eccentricity exceeds $0.10h$,

$$R = 1.07 - 0.008\frac{L_u}{r} \le 1.0 \qquad (15.10.3)$$

which agrees closely with Eq. (15.10.1) if $e_1/e_2 = +1$.

Braced Frame (No Relative Lateral Displacement of Ends of Member)— Double Curvature. Whenever a point of contraflexure occurs between the ends, the effect of both moment magnification and buckling is markedly less; thus

$$R = 1.0 \qquad \text{for}\ \frac{L_u}{r} \le 54 \qquad (15.10.4)$$

and

$$R = 1.32 - 0.006\frac{L_u}{r} \le 1.0 \qquad \text{for}\ 54 < \frac{L_u}{r} \le 100 \qquad (15.10.5)$$

which agrees closely with Eq. (15.10.1) if $e_1/e_2 = -1$.

Unbraced Frame (Relative Lateral Displacement of Ends of Member Not Prevented). Equation (15.10.3) for single curvature may be used for all such cases, except the equivalent pin-end length kL_u will exceed the actual unbraced length L_u; thus for kL_u/r not exceeding 40,

$$R = 1.07 - 0.008\frac{kL_u}{r} \le 1.0 \qquad (15.10.6)$$

Further, Eq. (15.10.6) is recommended only when the beams framing into the ends of the compression member have a reinforcement percentage ρ equal to at least 0.01 based on negative moment at the end of the beam.

A further restriction to Eq. (15.10.6) is that it is to be used only for short-duration loading; such as loading including live load, wind, or earthquake. When other loads of sustained duration are considered, Eq. (15.10.6) should be reduced to

$$R = 0.97 - 0.008\frac{kL_u}{r} \le 1.0 \qquad (15.10.7)$$

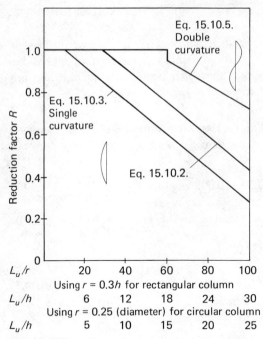

Fig. 15.10.2

Reduction factor for compression members *without* relative lateral displacement of ends.

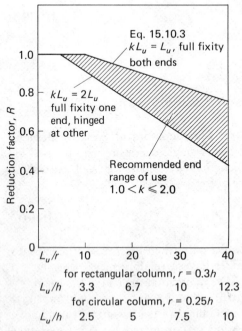

Fig. 15.10.3

Reduction factor for compression member *with* relative lateral displacement possible (short duration loading).

Effective Length Factor k. For the reduction-factor approach k should be taken as 1.0 for the braced frame cases, and should be computed by the following for the unbraced frame situation,

$$k = 0.78 + 0.22\psi \geq 1.0 \tag{15.10.8}$$

where $\psi = (\Sigma EI/L, \text{columns})/(\Sigma EI/L, \text{beams})$, with the average value for the two ends of the member to be used in Eq. (15.10.8).

The reduction factor R is to be applied to *both* the axial load and the bending moment that act simultaneously. Graphical representations of the reduction-factor expressions are shown in Figs. 15.10.2 and 15.10.3. Examples illustrating the use of the reduction-factor method appear in Sec. 15.15 where the method is compared with the ACI magnifier method.

15.11 ACI Code—Moment Magnifier Approximate Method

It has been shown in Secs. 15.4 through 15.6 that the maximum moment in an elastic beam-column is given by Eq. (15.4.4)

$$M_{\max} = M_m + P\Delta_{\max} = M_m + \frac{P\Delta_0}{1 - \alpha} \tag{15.4.4}$$

where $\alpha = P/P_c$ and $P_c = \pi^2 EI/L^2$. Furthermore, Eqs. (15.4.5), (15.5.17), and (15.6.1), applicable to braced or unbraced frames, indicated that the maximum moment may also be expressed as the maximum primary moment M_m times a magnification factor δ,

$$M_{\max} = M_m\left(\frac{C_m}{1 - \alpha}\right) \tag{15.11.1}$$

$$= M_m\delta \tag{15.11.2}$$

A number of studies have shown [37,40,47] that this approach is acceptable for reinforced concrete compression members using the strength design method. Design of the members is based on the required P_u combined with $M_{\max} = M_m\delta$, where P_u and M_m are obtained from a nominal elastic analysis using factored loads. M_m is the maximum moment acting on the member and it may occur at either end, or if there is transverse loading, in the midspan region. The nominal ultimate capacity of the designed section must be

$$P_n = \frac{P_u}{\phi} \quad \text{and} \quad M_n = \frac{M_m}{\phi}\left(\frac{C_m}{1 - P_n/P_c}\right) \tag{15.11.3}$$

For practical purposes the strength reduction factor ϕ in the denominator may be treated as shown, or as a multiplier on the other side of the equation. However, since P_n appears in the magnifier, the expression for δ contains ϕ in any case,

$$\delta = \frac{C_m}{1 - P_u/(\phi P_c)} \tag{15.11.4}$$

which is ACI Formula 10-7.

Factor C_m. The quantity C_m has two basic meanings: (1) for braced frames with transverse loading and single-curvature deflection, and for unbraced frames, it is truly a part of the moment magnifier; (2) for braced frames with end moments alone acting, the factor C_m is really not part of the magnifier, rather $C_m M_m$ gives an equivalent uniform moment which is then magnified by multiplying by $1/[1 - P_u/(\phi P_c)]$. For the first meaning of C_m, given by Eqs. (15.4.6) or (15.6.5), ACI-10.11.5.3 states "C_m shall be taken as 1.0." This is a conservative approach since the correct C_m will usually be between 0.9 and 1.0. Thus the use of C_m under ACI-10.11.5 may be summarized as follows:

For braced frames:

(a) Transverse loading,

$$C_m = 1.0 \qquad (15.11.5)$$

(b) End moments only, use Eq. (15.5.19)

$$C_m = 0.6 + 0.4\frac{M_1}{M_2} \geq 0.4 \qquad (15.11.6)$$

which is ACI Formula 10-11. Note that M_2 is larger than M_1 and the ratio M_1/M_2 is positive when the member is bent in single curvature.

For unbraced frames: All cases

$$C_m = 1.0 \qquad (15.11.7)$$

Stiffness Parameter EI. The other quantity required for evaluating the moment magnifier δ is

$$P_c = \frac{\pi^2 EI}{(kL_u)^2} \qquad (15.11.8)$$

which is slightly modified from the form used in Secs. 15.4 through 15.6 by the term kL_u, which is the unsupported length L_u of the member in a reinforced concrete frame modified for the pinned condition by the equivalent pin-end length factor k.

The principal difficulty with the magnifier method is that it requires a value for EI, as illustrated by its general development in Sec. 15.9. EI correctly varies due to cracking, time-dependent effects, and nonlinearity of the concrete stress-strain curve. MacGregor, Breen, and Pfrang [37] proposed two simple expressions to use *when more precise values are not available.* These appear in ACI-10.11.5.2 as Formulas 10-9 and 10-10, respectively,

$$EI = \frac{0.2E_cI_g + E_sI_s}{1 + \beta_d} \qquad (15.11.9)$$

or

$$EI = \frac{0.4E_cI_g}{1 + \beta_d} \qquad (15.11.10)$$

where

E_c = concrete modulus of elasticity = $57{,}000\sqrt{f'_c}$ for normal-weight concrete (ACI-8.5)

I_g = gross moment of inertia of concrete section, neglecting reinforcement

I_s = moment of inertia of reinforcement

β_d = proportion of the total design load that is considered sustained so as to contribute to time-dependent deformations—usually the ratio of factored dead load to total factored loads.

The larger of Eqs. (15.11.9) and (15.11.10) is appropriate for use and is still an underestimate of the correct EI.

The relative accuracy of these EI expressions is shown in Fig. 15.11.1 from Ref. 37. The theoretical values were for the case of no sustained load $(\beta_d = 0)$ [37]. In the study of Eqs. (15.11.9) and (15.11.10), Design Subcommittee of ASCE-ACI Committee 441 [37] estimated EI values for about 100 cases using theoretical load-moment-curvature diagrams computed in a manner similar to that discussed in Sec. 15.9, considering columns of various dimensions, strengths, and steel percentages. Effective EI values were also computed for the University of Texas frame tests [9,13,14], and for a series of frames simulated by the computer.

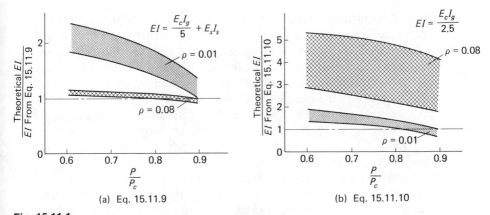

Fig. 15.11.1

Comparison of equations for EI with EI values from moment-curvature diagrams, for short-duration loading $(\beta_d = 0)$ (adapted from Ref. 37.)

Since 1971, MacGregor et al. [41] and Medland and Taylor [42] have reexamined the accuracy of the EI expressions and found that the treatment of the creep effect using the denominator term $(1 + \beta_d)$ tends to be overly conservative. The more accurate formulas for EI are

$$EI = \frac{0.2E_cI_g}{\alpha} + E_sI_s \qquad (15.11.11)$$

or

$$EI = \frac{0.2E_cI_g}{\alpha} + 1.2\rho_gE_sI_s \qquad (15.11.12)$$

where $\alpha = 0.75 + 1.8\beta_d$.

Equations (15.11.11) and (15.11.12) are not explicitly included as part of the ACI Code; however, ACI-10.11.5.2 presumably would permit use of these equations since they are more precise than ACI Formulas (10-9) and (10-10). The sustained-load effect on slender columns has also been studied by Goyal and Jackson [43] and Drysdale and Huggins [44].

Unbraced Frames—Multiple Columns. If sideway instability is to occur in a given story, all columns in the story must become unstable simultaneously. In other words, an individual column cannot become unstable in a sideway mode independently of the other columns in the same story. Thus in applying Eq. (15.11.4) P_u and P_c must be the total for all columns in the story,

$$\delta = \frac{C_m}{1 - \Sigma P_u/(\phi \Sigma P_c)} \qquad (15.11.13)$$

in accordance with ACI-10.11.6.2. However, if a given column within a story is more slender or more heavily loaded than the rest, such a column should also be checked individually as a member in a braced frame.

Minimum Eccentricity Design. When computations indicate only a small moment to be acting on a member such that the eccentricity M_u/P_u is less than $(0.6 + 0.03h)$ in., the primary moment M_m in Eq. (15.11.2) is to be computed as $P_u(0.6 + 0.03h)$ (ACI-10.11.5.4). Although ACI-10.11.5.4 refers only to *end* eccentricities, the authors believe the intent is to use this code-stated minimum e as the basis for applying the magnifier whether the small primary moment actually acts at the end of a member or at some point between the ends. When the minimum eccentricity requirements control, the provisions are intended to be applied to bending about only one axis at a time, *not* as a case of biaxial bending.

Further, when computed *end* moments are small (or zero) for a *braced* frame member having only end moments acting, there arises some question regarding what value should be taken for the ratio M_1/M_2 in the C_m equation, Eq. (15.11.6). ACI-10.11.5.4 specifies determining the ratio M_1/M_2 for that C_m equation by either of the following:

1. When actual computed end moments give eccentricities less than a minimum of $(0.6 + 0.03h)$ in., such actual end moments may be used for M_1/M_2 in Eq. (15.11.6).
2. If computations indicate essentially no moment at both ends—that is, the member is considered to be axially loaded—single curvature is to be assumed with $C_m = 1$.

Biaxial Bending. For compression members subjected to bending about both principal axes, the moment about *each* axis is to be magnified by the factor δ which is computed from the restraint conditions for that axis (ACI-10.11.7). In general, the effective length factor k, the stiffness factor EI, and C_m may differ for each bending axis. The member may also be considered as part of a braced system in one direction and unbraced in the other. Additional data on biaxial bending of slender members may be found in Refs. 44 and 45.

15.12 ACI Code—Slenderness Ratio Limitations

Although the slenderness ratio is never zero in actual structures, there are certain limits for kL_u/r below which the reduction in strength may reasonably be neglected. The ACI Code provisions are based on the assumption that a strength loss of up to 5% can be tolerated without the designer having to consider the slenderness effect; thus a significant number of ordinary columns can be designed considering only the provisions of Chap. 13.

ACI-ASCE Committee 441 surveyed typical reinforced concrete buildings to determine the normal range of variables found in columns of such buildings [37]. A great variety of buildings were studied, including towers (braced frames) as high as 33 stories and an unbraced frame 20 stories high. The total number of columns exceeded 20,000. The following results were reported [37]. For braced frames, 98% of the columns had L/h less than 12.5 ($L/r \approx 42$) and e/h less than 0.64. For unbraced frames, 98% of the columns had L/h less than 18 ($L/r \approx 60$) and e/h less than 0.84. Further, it was found that the practical upper limit on the slenderness ratio kL/r is about 70 in building columns. In general, these limits for the variables provide a guide to the range of variables that are used in any approximate method.

Taking the idea that attainment of at least 95% of the material strength of a short column is acceptable, the effects of slenderness may be neglected when:

For braced frame members (ACI-10.11.4.1),

$$\frac{kL_u}{r} < 34 - 12\frac{M_1}{M_2} \tag{15.12.1}$$

where M_1 is the smaller and M_2 the larger of end moments on the member.

For single curvature cases the ratio M_1/M_2 is positive, while for double curvature the ratio is negative. When the member is subject to large transverse loading (other than end moments alone), the ratio M_1/M_2 should probably be taken as $+1$.

For unbraced frame members (ACI-10.11.4.2),

$$\frac{kL_u}{r} < 22 \tag{15.12.2}$$

For all compression members with kL_u/r exceeding 100, a more elaborate analysis as discussed in Sec. 15.13 is required (ACI-10.11.4.3).

Comparison of the slenderness limits of Eqs. (15.12.1) and (15.12.2) with actual columns in existing buildings indicates [37] that over 90% of the columns in braced frames and over 40% of the columns in unbraced frames will fall within the limits of those equations and allow neglect of the slenderness effect.

15.13 ACI Code—General Analysis

As an alternative to the approximate methods involving the moment magnifier (Sec. 15.11) or the reduction factor (Sec. 15.10), the ACI Code actually gives the highest priority to a general frame analysis taking into account "the influence of axial loads and variable moment of inertia on member stiffness and fixed-end moments, the effect of deflections on the moments and forces, and the effects of duration of loads" (ACI-10.10.1). The resulting moments, shears, and axial forces from such an analysis would be used to design the members, instead of those resulting from a nominal elastic analysis with additional approximate adjustments, such as the application of a magnification factor.

In recognition of the fact that the general analysis is practical only with aid of a high-speed computer, the ACI Code prescribes an approximate method. ACI Committee 441, Columns, recommends [35], however, that improved structural analysis should be used to overcome weaknesses in the conventional methods of nominal analysis. Many analysis shortcomings affect not only long columns but in fact affect short columns as much or more [35].

The following requirements are suggested by the ACI Commentary [35] as minimum for an adequate rational analysis as prescribed by ACI-10.10.1.

1. The structure may be idealized as a planar frame consisting of linear elements. This is customary for even the nominal frame analysis. Additionally, when structural walls exist, their stiffness should be included in the analysis.
2. Realistic moment-curvature relationships must be used to obtain accurate values of deflections and secondary bending moments. The Commentary accepts as satisfying this requirement, the ACI Code approximate EI expression, Eq. (15.11.9). However, the use of a more accurate EI relationship is encouraged. Hognestad's stress-strain curve (Fig. 15.2.1) could be used along with Branson's effective moment of inertia, Eq. (14.4.1) with the fourth power used instead of the cube, and applied as a continuously varying function along the span. The effects of sustained load on deflection must be included; this can be done using methods of Chap. 14.
3. The influence of axial load on the flexural stiffness of the members must be considered. For instance, the flexural stiffness of a member without axial load is $4EI/L$. When axial load is present, the 4 becomes greatly reduced. The general ideas relating to the effect of axial load on flexural stiffness of elastic members may be found in Ref. 27.
4. The maximum moments in the compression members must include the effects of member deflections and rotations in braced as well as unbraced systems. The maximum moment (primary plus secondary) may occur either at a support or out in the span away from a support.
5. Any proposed analysis method (i.e., computer program in all likelihood) should be checked against available test results and the accuracy achieved should be at least equal to that obtained by the ACI Code moment magnifier approximate method.

Rational Method for Unbraced Frames under Lateral Loading. Furlong [46] has proposed guidelines for a rational analysis that may satisfy the intent of ACI-10.10.1 within the complexity implied by the five requirements of the ACI Commentary referred to above. The recommended procedure applies to *unbraced* frames. For such frames, the slenderness effects are the products of the column load P_u times the sway deflection Δ. Furlong shows that acceptable estimates of the lateral deflection Δ can be obtained if the cracked-section moment of inertia, I_{cr}, is used for the beam stiffness and the gross-section moment of inertia, I_g (without steel), is used for the column stiffness. The value of I_{cr} for beams can be reasonably approximated as $0.5I_g$. Such computations will underestimate the column stiffness (because the stiffening effect of the reinforcement is neglected) until cracking starts or until the compression load reaches the range where deformation is non-linear; that is, when applied moment is 70 to 80% of the flexural capacity of the column.

Thus the recommended [46] procedure for unbraced frames is as follows:

1. Estimate lateral deflection Δ using an elastic analysis that involves inten-tionally "soft" (i.e., low) stiffness values for moment of inertia in both beams and columns.
2. Proportion column reinforcement using the *larger* of the following:
   (a) $M_m + P_u\Delta$ (primary moment plus the product of thrust P_u and the story displacement Δ);
   (b) $2M_m$ (twice the design primary moment M_u).
3. Primary moments (M_m) cannot exceed one-third of column moment capacity M_u (computed according to the principles of Chap. 13 as the value of moment M_u capable of being carried simultaneously with P_u).
4. Moments at the ends of beams must be increased by the $P_u\Delta$ amount (see discussion in Sec. 15.14).

For unbraced frames this rational method will eliminate the need for evaluating restraint factors ψ, effective length factors k, and magnification factors δ. Design by this procedure may even be simpler than using the approximate magnifier procedure of ACI-10.11.5.

15.14 Restraining Effect of Beams

The restraining effect of beams has a major effect on column behavior. The problem is discussed in detail in Refs. 19, 20, 32, 33 and 37.

Braced Frames. Consider the portion of a braced frame shown in Fig. 15.14.1. The primary moment M_c on the column depends on the relative stiffnesses of beam and column. The moment M_{ext} applied to the cantilever at A is resisted by the beam and the column; thus

$$M_{ext} = M_b + M_c \qquad (15.14.1)$$

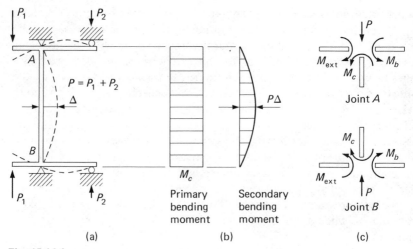

Fig. 15.14.1
Braced frame—restraining effect of beam.

Since the column deflects, there will be an additional moment $P\Delta$ on it, such that

$$M_{\max} = M_c + P\Delta \qquad (15.14.2)$$

Solving for M_c in Eq. (15.14.1) and substituting into Eq. (15.14.2) gives

$$M_{\max} = M_{\text{ext}} - M_b + P\Delta \qquad (15.14.3)$$

As the column deflects laterally due to $M_c + P\Delta$, joint A rotates forcing more and more of the applied moment to be resisted by the beam. This effect is further increased by the reduction in column stiffness due to axial load. However, beam deflection due to creep and shrinkage gives the reverse effect by putting moment back on the column.

When the beam is relatively stiff (high percentage ρ) compared to the column (i.e., slender column), the primary moment on the column is overestimated by the nominal analysis and the moment on the beam is underestimated. This is not a problem because the slender column will be conservatively designed, and underestimating the beam end moment will increase the positive moment and also the chance that beam deflection will control.

When the beam is relatively flexible (low percentage ρ) compared to the column (i.e., short stiff column), the primary moment on the column is underestimated by the nominal analysis and the beam end moment overestimated. In this case the column could be significantly underdesigned. For the beam design, it makes little difference because with a low percentage ρ the beam is ductile and redistribution of moments (see Sec. 10.11) can occur. In other words, on the ductile beam it is not too essential whether the moment capacity is somewhat larger at the support or at midspan as long as the total load is capable of being carried.

A multiplier to increase the design moment on short columns has been suggested [33]. For the *single-curvature* case in *braced* frames, the nominal

e/h should be multiplied by

$$\text{multiplier} = 1.38 + 5.5(\rho_g - 5.5\rho) \tag{15.14.4}$$

where

ρ_g = ratio of column steel to gross area bh
ρ = ratio of tension beam steel to effective area bd

The relationship of Eq. (15.14.4) was developed for an average end restraint factor ψ for the column equal to 1.0, which corresponds to an effective length factor k about 0.8. It would seem Eq. (15.14.4) could be used for any short column in a braced frame.

Unbraced Frames. In unbraced frames, the beam may be inadequately designed for moment at its junction with the column, when a lateral shear load such as wind is applied. The beam moment must be equal to the magnified moment on the column. When the moment magnifier method or the general analysis is used, no problem arises as long as one recognizes that the moment, $M_m + P_u\Delta$, or δM_m, acting at the end of the column must be carried by the beams in a manner such that equilibrium of the joint is maintained. However, when a reduction-factor procedure is used, only the primary moment is known. Although the reduction-factor approach may give an adequately designed column, the primary moment alone is improper to use for the beam moment.

Figure 15.14.2 shows the geometry relationship necessary to obtain an approximation of the magnified moment for use in the design of the beam

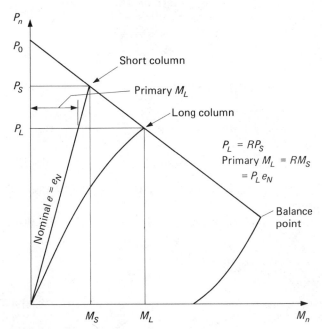

Fig. 15.14.2
Approximation for long-column end moment (adapted from Ref. 20).

Table 15.15.1

Length Effects on Columns—Summary of Useful Formulas

1. *Definitions*

$$\psi = \frac{\Sigma EI/L \text{ of columns}}{\Sigma EI/L \text{ of beams}};\qquad \begin{array}{l}\psi = 0 \text{ (fixed end)}\\ \psi = 10 \text{ (column end supported on footing)}\\ \psi = \infty \text{ (theoretical hinged end)}\end{array}$$ [15.8.1]

$$P_c = \frac{\pi^2 EI}{(kL_u)^2}$$ [15.11.8]

$$\delta = \frac{C_m}{1 - P_n/P_c} = \frac{C_m}{1 - P_u/(\phi P_c)} = \frac{C_m}{1 - \alpha}$$ [15.11.4]

2. *Slenderness Ratio Limitation (No Length Effect)*

Braced frames
$$\frac{kL_u}{r} < 34 - 12\frac{M_1}{M_2}$$ [15.12.1]

$$|M_1| < |M_2|;\qquad M_1/M_2 \text{ positive for single curvature}$$

Unbraced frames
$$\frac{kL_u}{r} < 22$$ [15.12.2]

3. *1963 ACI Strength Reduction Method*

Braced frames
(single curvature)
$$R = 1.23 - 0.008\frac{L_u}{r} \le 1.0;\quad \frac{e}{h} \le 0.10$$ [15.10.2]

$$R = 1.07 - 0.008\frac{L_u}{r} \le 1.0;\quad \frac{e}{h} > 0.10$$ [15.10.3]

Braced frames
(double curvature)
$$R = 1.0;\quad \frac{L_u}{r} \le 54$$ [15.10.4]

$$R = 1.32 - 0.006\frac{L_u}{r} \le 1.0;\quad 54 < \frac{L_u}{r} \le 100$$ [15.10.5]

Unbraced frames
(short duration loading)
$$R = 1.07 - 0.008\frac{kL_u}{r} \le 1.0;\quad \frac{kL_u}{r} \le 40$$ [15.10.6]

$$k = 0.78 + 0.22\psi_{\text{avg}} \ge 1.0$$ [15.10.8]

Unbraced frames
(sustained duration loading)
$$R = 0.97 - 0.008\frac{kL_u}{r} \le 1.0;\quad \frac{kL_u}{r} \le 40$$ [15.10.7]

$$k = 0.78 + 0.22\psi_{\text{avg}} \ge 1.0$$ [15.10.8]

4. *Effective Length Factor k in Moment Magnifier Method*

Braced frames
(a) Nomogram (alignment chart) [Fig. 15.8.1a]
(b) 1972 British Code $k = 0.7 + 0.05(\psi_A + \psi_B) \le 1.0$ [15.8.2]
  $k = 0.85 + 0.05\psi_{\min} \le 1.0$ [15.8.3]

(c) ACI Code $k = 1.0$ (on safe side) [Sec. 15.8]

Table 15.15.1 (*cont.*)

4. *Effective Length Factor k in Moment Magnifier Method* (*cont.*)

Unbraced frames

(a) Nomogram (alignment chart)   [Fig. 15.8.1b]

(b) Furlong $k = \dfrac{20 - \psi_{avg}}{20} \sqrt{1 + \psi_{avg}}; \quad \psi_{avg} < 2$ [15.8.4]

$k = 0.9\sqrt{1 + \psi_{avg}}; \quad \psi_{avg} > 2$ [15.8.5]

(c) 1972 British Code $k = 2.0 + 0.3\psi; \quad$ one hinged end   [15.8.6]

---

5. *C_m Factor in Moment Magnifier Method*

Braced frames

Transverse loading, $C_m = 1.0$ [15.11.5]

End moments only, $C_m = 0.6 + 0.4 \dfrac{M_1}{M_2} \geq 0.4$ [15.11.6]

$$|M_1| < |M_2|; \quad M_1/M_2 \text{ positive for single curvature}$$

Unbraced frames $C_m = 1.0$ [15.11.7]

---

6. *Stiffness Parameter EI in Moment Magnifier Method*

Larger of $\begin{cases} EI = \dfrac{0.2E_cI_g + E_sI_s}{1 + \beta_d} & \text{[15.11.9]} \\[3mm] EI = \dfrac{0.4E_cI_g}{1 + \beta_d} & \text{[15.11.10]} \end{cases}$

$$E_c = 57{,}000\sqrt{f_c'}; \quad \beta_d = \frac{\text{factored sustained load}}{\text{factored total load}}$$

Larger of $\begin{cases} EI = \dfrac{0.2E_cI_g}{\alpha} + E_sI_s & \text{[15.11.11]} \\[3mm] EI = \dfrac{0.2E_cI_g}{\alpha} + 1.2\rho_gE_sI_s & \text{[15.11.12]} \end{cases}$

$$\alpha = 0.75 + 1.8\beta_d; \quad \beta_d = \frac{\text{factored sustained load}}{\text{factored total load}}$$

EI_{cr} of beam $\approx EI_g/2$ [Sec. 15.13]

---

7. *Restraining Effect of Beams*

Braced frames   multiplier for $\dfrac{e}{h} = 1.38 + 5.5(\rho_g - 5.5\rho)$ [15.14.4]
$\left(\begin{array}{c}\text{single curvature} \\ \text{short columns}\end{array}\right)$

ρ_g (column) $= A_{st}/(bh); \quad \rho$ (beam) $= A_s/(bd)$

Unbraced frames $M_L = P_L e_N \left(\dfrac{1 - P_L/P_0}{R - P_L/P_0}\right)$ [15.14.9]
(when R method is used)

---

when the reduction-factor method is used. A materials failure situation is assumed and the interaction diagram in the "compression controls" zone is assumed to be a straight line. From similar triangles,

$$\frac{M_L}{M_S} = \frac{P_0 - P_L}{P_0 - P_S} \tag{15.14.5}$$

or

$$M_L = M_S\left(\frac{1 - P_L/P_0}{1 - P_S/P_0}\right) \tag{15.14.6}$$

also

$$M_S = \frac{\text{primary } M_L}{R}; \qquad P_S = \frac{P_L}{R} \tag{15.14.7}$$

$$M_L = \frac{\text{primary } M_L}{R}\left(\frac{1 - P_L/P_0}{1 - P_L/(RP_0)}\right) \tag{15.14.8}$$

and primary $M_L = P_L e_N$, in which case,

$$M_L = P_L e_N\left(\frac{1 - P_L/P_0}{R - P_L/P_0}\right) \tag{15.14.9}$$

where $P_0 = 0.85 f'_c(A_g - A_{st}) + A_{st} f_y$. The beam must be designed to carry the moment M_L. If the column failure is in the tension controls zone, the approximation is invalid, though if it is used, it will be excessively conservative. "Tension controls" cases may be avoided if Eq. (15.14.9) is used only for kL/r up to about 50[20].

This adjustment to obtain M_L when using the reduction-factor method applies only to the unbraced frame, where the critical magnified moment is at the end of the column. In braced frames the end moments are not magnified because the deflection at the joint is zero.

Moment of Inertia for Restraining Beam. Even though gross section is used for a nominal elastic frame analysis, the adjustment to the nominal e/h may be eliminated if cracked transformed section is used for the moment of inertia in computing the end restraint factor ψ [20]. In general, more accurate results are obtained by using Eq. (15.11.9) with $\beta_d = 0$ for the column members and transformed cracked section for the beam members in determining the effective length factor k.

15.15 Examples

In the preceding sections of this chapter, basic concepts underlying the ACI Code provisions relating to length effects on columns have been discussed. Details are given for the moment magnifier method of the present ACI Code as well as the strength reduction method used prior to the 1971 ACI Code and retained as an option for some situations in the present ACI Commentary. In order to facilitate easy reference to the actual quantitative procedures or formulas, most of which appear in the ACI Code or Commentary, Table 15.15.1 is presented summarizing the information needed

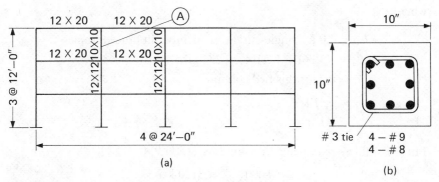

Fig. 15.15.1
Rigid frame for Examples 15.15.1 and 15.15.2.

for solving practical problems. For illustration, the following eight examples are presented.

EXAMPLE 15.15.1 Determine the adequacy of the interior top floor column (column A) of the *braced* frame of Fig. 15.15.1. The column is 10×10 with 4-#8 and 4-#9 bars ($f_y = 50$ ksi and $f'_c = 3$ ksi) and is to carry a service axial compression of 108 kips live load and 36 kips dead load. The bending moments that may act in combination with the axial load have been computed and found to be negligible. If the member is not adequate, revise the design so that it satisfies the moment magnifier method of the ACI Code.

Solution: (a) Determine slenderness ratio. Unless a rational evaluation of end restraint is made, ACI-10.11.2.1 requires taking the effective length factor k for a braced frame equal to 1.0. The radius of gyration may be taken as $0.3h$ according to ACI-10.11.3. The clear height L_u is

$$L_u = 12 - \frac{20}{12} = 10.33 \text{ ft}$$

Then

$$\frac{kL_u}{r} = \frac{1.0(10.33)(12)}{0.3(10)} = 41.3$$

(b) Slenderness ratio limits. Since the end moments are negligible, the minimum eccentricity provisions of ACI-10.11.5.4 govern the design. Accordingly, the deformation should be considered as single curvature with $M_1/M_2 = 1.0$. The slenderness limit is

$$\left(\frac{kL_u}{r}\right)_{\text{limit}} = 34 - 12\frac{M_1}{M_2} = 22 < 41.3$$

Thus slenderness effects must be considered.
(c) Moment magnifier δ.

$$\delta = \frac{C_m}{1 - \dfrac{P_u}{\phi P_c}}$$

where

$$C_m = 1.0 \text{ for single-curvature member in braced frame}$$
$$P_u = 1.4(36) + 1.7(108) = 234 \text{ kips}$$
$$\phi = 0.7 \text{ for this tied column}$$

$$P_c = \frac{\pi^2 EI}{(kL_u)^2}$$

For the stiffness parameter EI using Eqs. (15.11.9) or (15.11.10),

$$E_c = 57{,}000\sqrt{f_c'} = 3120 \text{ ksi}$$

$$I_g = \frac{10(10)^3}{12} = 833 \text{ in.}^4$$

$$E_s = 29{,}000 \text{ ksi}$$

$$I_s = 2(2.79)(2.59)^2 = 37.4 \text{ in.}^4$$

$$0.2E_cI_g + E_sI_s = 0.2(3120)(833) + 29{,}000(37.4)$$
$$= 520{,}000 + 1{,}090{,}000 = 1{,}610{,}000 \text{ kip in.}^2$$

$$0.4E_cI_g = 1{,}040{,}000 \text{ kip in.}^2$$

The EI values are to be divided by $(1 + \beta_d)$ to account for time-dependent deflection due to creep and shrinkage. Using the larger of the two values of EI, and dividing by $(1 + \beta_d)$, where β_d is the proportion of factored load that is sustained,

$$\beta_d = \frac{36(1.4)}{108(1.7) + 36(1.4)} = 0.215$$

$$EI = \frac{1{,}610{,}000}{1 + 0.215} = 1{,}330{,}000 \text{ kips in.}^2$$

$$P_c = \frac{\pi^2(1{,}330{,}000)}{[1.0(10.33)(12)]^2} = 854 \text{ kips}$$

$$\frac{P_u}{\phi P_c} = \frac{234}{0.7(854)} = 0.391$$

$$\delta = \frac{1.0}{1 - 0.391} = 1.64$$

In this case, the minimum eccentricity $(0.6 + 0.03h)$ should be magnified so that

$$\text{required } e = 1.64(e_{\min}) = 1.69(0.6 + 0.03h) = 0.98 + 0.049h \text{ in.}$$

Note that even the magnified eccentricity might not exceed the eccentricity corresponding to the maximum axial compressive strength of $0.80P_0$ ($P_{n(\max)}$ of Fig. 13.11.2). When this happens as it does in this case, there is still no reduction in strength due to the slenderness effect.

(d) Rational analysis for effective length factor k. For the beam the cracked-section moment of inertia is recommended. An approximation is $I_{cr} = I_g/2 = 4000$ in.[4]

$$(EI)_{bm} = E_c I_{cr} = 3120(4000) = 12,500,000 \text{ kip in.}^2$$
$$(EI)_{col} = 1,610,000 \text{ kip in.}^2$$

End restraint factors,

$$\psi_A(\text{top}) = \frac{\Sigma EI/L \text{ for cols}}{\Sigma EI/L \text{ for beams}} = \frac{1610/12}{2(12,500)/24} = 0.13$$

$$\psi_B(\text{bottom}) = \frac{(1610 + 3230)/12}{2(12,500)/24} = 0.39$$

Since the 12×12 column below has not been designed, its EI value is taken as $0.6 E_c I_g$, which is approximately the general expression obtained for the 10×10 column by the ACI formula. From Fig. 15.8.1a, $k = 0.62$. The more correct effective slenderness ratio is

$$\frac{kL}{r} = \frac{0.62(10.33)12}{0.3(10)} = 25.6$$

The magnification factor is also affected,

$$P_c = \frac{\pi^2(1,330,000)}{[0.62(10.33)(12)]^2} = 2220 \text{ kips}$$

$$\frac{P_u}{\phi P_c} = \frac{234}{0.7(2220)} = 0.151$$

$$\delta = \frac{1.0}{1 - 0.151} = 1.18$$

$$\text{required } e = 1.18(e_{min}) = 0.71 + 0.035h \text{ in.}$$

In this case the beams are very stiff compared to the columns. Using cracked section for the beams and the ACI EI formula for the columns gave little different result than would be obtained by using gross section.

(e) Check capacity. The strength of the section may be checked by the methods of Chap. 13.

$$\text{required } P_n = \frac{P_u}{\phi} = \frac{234}{0.7} = 334 \text{ kips}$$

$$\text{required } e = 0.71 + 0.035(10) = 1.06 \text{ in. } (0.106h)$$
$$[\text{according to (d) above}]$$

The actual nominal strength P_n at $e = 1.06$ in. is 431 kips (a convenient source is Ref. 25 of Chap. 13). Even when $e = 0.98 + 0.049h = 1.47$ in. as obtained in (c), the capacity P_n is 382 kips. So this section is adequate as a braced frame column.

Note that the strength P_n may not be taken in design greater than $0.80P_0$ according to ACI-10.3.5,

$$P_{n(max)} = 0.80[0.85f'_c(A_g - A_{st}) + f_yA_{st}]$$
$$= 0.80[0.85(3)(100 - 7.16) + 50(7.16)] = 476 \text{ kips} > 431 \text{ kips} \quad \text{OK}$$

EXAMPLE 15.15.2 Repeat Example 15.15.1 except consider the frame as unbraced.

Solution: In general, members in unbraced frames will have end moments on the members. One might assume that this case was the result of gravity load analysis that happened to give negligible column moment. In some cases where beams are unusually stiff, the behavior of the unbraced frame is little different from that of the braced frame.

(a) Effective pin-end length. From part (d) of Example 15.15.1 the end restraint factors are

$$\psi_A \text{ (top)} = 0.13 \qquad \psi_B \text{ (bottom)} = 0.39$$

From Fig. 15.8.1b, $k = 1.07$. From part (c) of Example 15.15.1,

$$EI = 1,330,000 \text{ kip in.}^2 \qquad \text{(for column)}$$

which includes the effect of 21.5% sustained factored load.

$$P_c = \frac{\pi^2 EI}{(kL_u)^2} = \frac{\pi^2(1,330,000)}{[1.07(10.33)(12)]^2} = 746 \text{ kips}$$

$$\frac{P_n}{P_c} = \frac{334}{746} = 0.448$$

For C_m, ACI-10.11.5.3 says to use 1.0.

$$\delta = \frac{C_m}{1 - P_n/P_c} = \frac{1.0}{1 - 0.448} = 1.81$$

If design is to be nominally based on minimum eccentricities, in this case ($h = 10$ in.)

$$\text{required } e = 1.81(e_{min}) = 1.81(0.6 + 0.03h) = 1.63 \text{ in.}$$

The capacity P_n for the member with $e = 1.63$ in. is 364 kips which exceeds the requirement of 334 kips, and is acceptable.

EXAMPLE 15.15.3 Determine the adequacy of the square tied column (17 in. square, with 10-#9 bars, $f'_c = 3000$ psi, $f_y = 40,000$ psi) which is an exterior first-floor column in the frame of Fig. 15.15.2. Assume that this frame is braced sufficiently to prevent relative translation of its joints. Also assume 40% of the design (factored) load is sustained.

Solution: (a) Effective length. In accordance with ACI-10.11.2.1, neglecting an analysis to determine a k value less than 1.0 for a braced frame, use

$$kL_u = L_u = 10 \text{ ft}$$

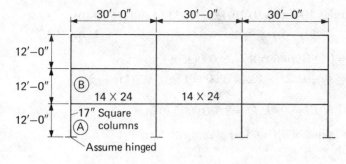

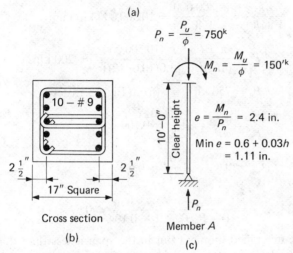

Fig. 15.15.2
Rigid frame for Example 15.15.3.

(b) Slenderness ratio limits. The actual column slenderness ratio is

$$\frac{kL_u}{r} = \frac{120}{0.3(17)} = 23.6$$

Slenderness effects may be neglected when

$$\frac{kL_u}{r} < 34 - 12\frac{M_1}{M_2}$$

In this case, $M_1/M_2 = 0$,

$$\left(\frac{kL_u}{r}\right)_{\text{limit}} = 34 > 23.6$$

Slenderness effects may be neglected. In the following sections, the method will be illustrated even though it would not be required by the ACI Code.

(c) Moment magnifier δ.

$$E_c = 57,000\sqrt{f_c'} = 3120 \text{ ksi}$$
$$I_g = \tfrac{1}{12}(17)(17)^3 = 6950 \text{ in.}^4$$
$$I_s = 2(5)(6)^2 = 360 \text{ in.}^4$$

Using ACI Formulas 10-9 and 10-10, Eqs. (15.11.9) and (15.11.10),

$$EI = 0.2E_cI_g + E_sI_s$$
$$= 0.2(3120)(6950) + 29,000(360)$$
$$= 4,340,000 + 10,440,000 = 14,800,000 \text{ kip in.}^2$$

or

$$EI = 0.4E_cI_g = 8,680,000 \text{ kip in.}^2$$

Using the larger value of EI and applying the factor $(1 + \beta_d)$ to account for sustained load,

$$\frac{EI}{1 + \beta_d} = \frac{14,800,000}{1.40} = 10,500,000 \text{ kip in.}^2$$

$$P_c = \frac{\pi^2 EI}{(kL_u)^2} = \frac{\pi^2(10,500,000)}{[1.0(10.0)(12)]^2} = 7200 \text{ kips}$$

$$P_n = 750 \text{ kips} \qquad \text{(from Fig. 15.15.2c)}$$

$$\frac{P_n}{P_c} = \frac{P_u}{\phi P_c} = \frac{750}{7200} = 0.104$$

$$C_m = 0.6 + 0.4\frac{M_1}{M_2} = 0.6$$

$$\delta = \frac{C_m}{1 - P_n/P_c} = \frac{0.6}{1 - 0.104} = 0.67 < 1.0$$

In this case the magnified moment out in the span is less than that at the braced point. The design must be based on $P_n = 750$ kips and $M_n = 150$ ft-kips at the top of the column. The capacity is found to be $P_n = 808$ kips at $e = 2.4$ in.

EXAMPLE 15.15.4   Reexamine the adequacy of the 17-in. square column of Example 15.15.3 (Fig. 15.15.2) if the frame is unbraced instead of braced.

Solution: (a) Effective length and slenderness ratio. The end restraint factors ψ must be determined. Assuming the cracked-section moment of inertia for the beam to be half of the gross moment of inertia,

$$I_{cr} \approx \frac{I_g}{2} = \frac{14(24)^3/12}{2} = 8070 \text{ in.}^4$$

When the beam reinforcement is known, the actual I_{cr} for the beam should be used here. For the column, either I_g or the EI from ACI Formulas 10-9 or 10-10 should be used. From Example 15.15.3, part (c)

$$EI = 14,800,000 \text{ kip in.}^2$$

without sustained load effect. Then

$$\psi_A \text{ (top)} = \frac{\Sigma EI/L \text{ cols}}{\Sigma EI/L \text{ bms}} = \frac{2(14,800,000)/12}{3120(8070)/30} = 2.94$$

For this calculation the use of center-to-center span distances is recommended as being consistent with the nominal frame analysis using those distances.

$$\psi_B \text{ (bottom)} = 10.0 \text{ (hinged)}$$

The Structural Stability Research Council [26] recommends that for column ends supported by, but not rigidly connected to, a footing or foundation, ψ may be taken as 10.0 unless designed as a true friction free pin. Using Fig. 15.8.1b, find

$$k = 2.25$$

The effective slenderness ratio is

$$\frac{kL_u}{r} = \frac{2.25(10.0)12}{0.3(17)} = 53$$

which exceeds the limit of 22 given by ACI-10.11.4.2 for unbraced frames. Slenderness effects must be considered.

(b) Magnification factor.

$$C_m = 1.0 \text{ for unbraced frames}$$

From Example 15.15.3, part (c),

$$EI = \frac{14,800,000}{1 + \beta_d} = \frac{14,800,000}{1.40} = 10,500,000 \text{ kip in.}^2$$

$$P_c = \frac{\pi^2 EI}{(kL_u)^2} = \frac{\pi^2(10,500,000)}{[2.25(10)(12)]^2} = 1420 \text{ kips}$$

$$\frac{P_n}{P_c} = \frac{P_u}{\phi P_c} = \frac{750}{1420} = 0.528$$

$$\delta = \frac{C_m}{1 - P_n/P_c} = \frac{1.0}{1 - 0.528} = 2.12$$

The section must have adequate material strength to carry

$$P_n = 750 \text{ kips}$$

and

$$M_n = M_m \delta = 150(2.12) = 318 \text{ ft-kips}$$

$$\text{required } e = \frac{M_n}{P_n} = \frac{318(12)}{750} = 5.1 \text{ in.}$$

For $f'_c = 3000$ psi and $f_y = 40,000$ psi, the 17-in. section is inadequate. Try 20 in. square with 8-#9 (see Fig. 15.15.3).

(c) Check magnification factor for 20-in. column.

$$I_g = \tfrac{1}{12}(20)(20)^3 = 13,300 \text{ in.}^4$$

$$I_s = 6.0(7.5)^2 = 337 \text{ in.}^4$$

$$EI = 0.2E_c I_g + E_s I_s$$

$$= 0.2(3120)(13,300) + 29,000(337) = 18,100,000 \text{ kip in.}^2$$

$$\psi_A \text{ (top)} = \frac{2(18,100,000)/12}{3120(8070)/30} = 3.6$$

$$\psi_B \text{ (bottom)} = 10.0 \text{ (hinged)}$$

Using Fig. 15.8.1b, find $k = 2.4$

$$C_m = 1.0$$

$$\frac{EI}{1 + \beta_d} = \frac{18,100,000}{1.40} = 12,900,000 \text{ kip in.}^2$$

$$P_c = \frac{\pi^2 EI}{(kL_u)^2} = \frac{\pi^2(12,900,000)}{[2.4(10)(12)]^2} = 1530 \text{ kips}$$

$$\frac{P_n}{P_c} = \frac{750}{1530} = 0.490$$

$$\delta = \frac{C_m}{1 - P_n/P_c} = \frac{1.0}{1 - 0.490} = 1.96$$

The section must have adequate material strength to carry

$$P_n = 750 \text{ kips}$$

$$M_n = M_m\delta = 150(1.96) = 294 \text{ ft-kips}$$

$$\text{required } e = \frac{M_n}{P_n} = \frac{294(12)}{750} = 4.70 \text{ in.}$$

The 20-in. square section shown in Fig. 15.15.3 is adequate, having a capacity P_n of 760 kips at $e = 4.70$ in. (based on statics using Whitney rectangular stress block).
Use 20-in. square with 8-#9.

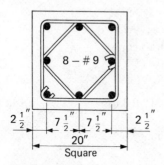

Fig. 15.15.3
Cross section for Example 15.15.4.

EXAMPLE 15.15.5 Check the 17-in. square column in the braced frame of Example 15.15.3 using the strength reduction-factor method of the ACI Commentary.

Solution: The slenderness ratio, as computed in Example 15.15.3, is (since $k = 1.0$)

$$\frac{L_u}{r} = 23.6$$

Since this is a single-curvature situation, and the nominal eccentricity is

$$e = \frac{150(12)}{750} = 2.4 \text{ in.}$$

which exceeds $0.1h$, the reduction factor, Eq. (15.10.3), is

$$R = 1.07 - 0.008\frac{L_u}{r}$$

$$= 1.07 - 0.008(23.6) = 0.88$$

The material strength required for the section is

$$\text{required } P_n = \frac{750}{0.88} = 852 \text{ kips}$$

$$\text{required } M_n = \frac{150}{0.88} = 171 \text{ ft-kips}$$

Because the reduction-factor procedure does not recognize the moment gradient, this case where the maximum moment occurs at the top of the column is treated the same as if the maximum primary moment of 150 ft-kips were acting at midspan. In Example 15.15.3 it was shown that the magnified moment out in the span did not exceed the moment at the top; thus the top conditions controlled. If the reduction factor of 0.88 were used for this column, the 17-in. square would appear inadequate (P_n capacity $= 808$ kips $<$ 852 kips required).

EXAMPLE 15.15.6 Check the 20-in. column selected for the unbraced frame column of Example 15.15.4, using the reduction-factor method of the ACI Commentary.

Solution: Using the reduction-factor procedure, the effective length is given by

$$k = 0.78 + 0.22\psi_{avg}$$

$$\psi_{avg} = \frac{3.6 + 10.0}{2} = 6.8$$

$$k = 0.78 + 0.22(6.8) = 0.78 + 1.50 = 2.28$$

This is close to the value of 2.4 obtained by using the alignment chart (Fig. 15.8.1b). Using this value of k, the slenderness ratio is

$$\frac{kL_u}{r} = \frac{2.28(10)(12)}{0.3(20)} = 45.6$$

The reduction factor, for loads of short duration, is

$$R = 1.07 - 0.008\frac{kL_u}{r}$$

$$= 1.07 - 0.008(45.6) = 0.70$$

The use of this reduction factor assumes that beams have a negative-moment reinforcement ratio $\rho \geq 0.01$ and that kL_u/r does not exceed 40. In this case since kL_u/r exceeds 40, the reduction-factor method is not applicable and the magnifier method of ACI-10.11.5, or some more exact method, must be used.

Investigation of the 20-in. square section with 8-#9 shows that P_n (short)= 1010 kips at $e = 2.4$ in. Applying the reduction factor 0.70, P_n (long) = 707 kips, which is less than the actual P_n of 750 kips.

When using the reduction-factor method for the unbraced frame, one must also determine the approximate magnified moment that must be provided for in the design of the restraining beams. Thus using Eq. (15.14.9)

$$M_L = P_L e_N \left(\frac{1 - P_L/P_0}{R - P_L/P_0} \right)$$

$$P_L = 750 \text{ kips}$$
$$P_0 = 0.85 f'_c (A_g - A_{st}) + A_{st} f_y$$
$$= 0.85(3)(400 - 8) + (8.0)40 = 1320 \text{ kips}$$

$$M_L = 750 \left(\frac{2.4}{12} \right) \left(\frac{1 - 750/1320}{0.70 - 750/1320} \right)$$

$$= 491 \text{ ft-kips}$$

For a sidesway type of deformation, the sum of the beam restraining moments equals the sum of the column moments above and below a joint. Thus the 491 ft-kips is an approximation of the column moment at the top of column A (Fig. 15.15.2). The approximate magnified moment in column B could have been determined in a similar manner after that member had been designed. The negative moment capacity of the 14×24 beam must equal at least the sum of the two column moments.

The reader may note that the approximate value of 491 ft-kips computed on the basis of a reduction factor $R = 0.70$ and a linear interaction diagram (Fig. 15.14.2) is high compared to the more exact value of 294 ft-kips computed by the moment magnifier method in Example 15.15.4. The moment magnifier method is considered more rational than the reduction-factor method.

EXAMPLE 15.15.7   Determine the adequacy of the 14×20 in. compression member designed without regard to length effects in Sec. 13.20, Example 13.20.1 (6-#11 bars, $f'_c = 4500$ psi, and $f_y = 50,000$ psi). The member serves as an exterior column in a braced frame, with loading as shown in Fig. 15.15.4, and having a clear height of 22 ft 6 in.

Solution: It is logical and proper to determine primary bending moment by any elastic method such as moment distribution. Assume that the maximum nominal ultimate moment at an intermediate point is 398 ft-kips. Design as a short column neglecting slenderness, as demonstrated in Example 13.20.1, has resulted in a member that is controlled by tension. For this braced frame member, $kL_u = L_u = 22.5$ ft.

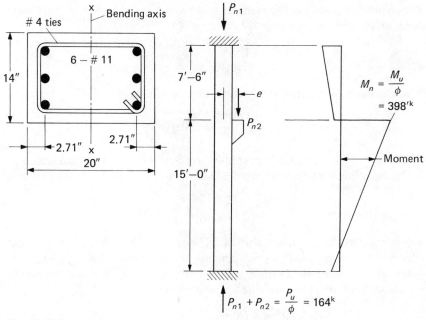

Fig. 15.15.4
Member and loading for Example 15.15.7.

(a) For possible instability in the plane of the frame,

$$\frac{kL_u}{r_x} = \frac{1.0(22.5)12}{0.3(20)} = 45$$

which exceeds the maximum value of 22 for which slenderness effects may be neglected according to ACI-10.11.4. When the bending moment diagram has the largest moment at a location other than at an end, M_1/M_2 should be taken conservatively as 1.0. Note that the moment diagram is similar to the case of transverse loading and should be similarly treated.

$$I_g = \tfrac{1}{12}(14)(20)^3 = 9330 \text{ in.}^4$$
$$I_s = 2(3)(1.56)(7.29)^2 = 497 \text{ in.}^4$$
$$E_c = 57,000\sqrt{4500} = 3820 \text{ ksi}$$

Assuming no sustained load, $\beta_d = 0$,

$$EI = 0.2E_c I_g + E_s I_s$$
$$= 0.2(3820)(9330) + 29,000(497) = 21,500,000 \text{ kip in.}^2$$

or,

$$EI = 0.4E_c I_g = 0.4(3820)(9330) = 14,300,000 \text{ kip in.}^2$$
$$C_m = 1.0$$

$$P_c = \frac{\pi^2 EI}{(kL_u)^2} = \frac{\pi^2(21,500,000)}{[1.0(22.5)(12)]^2} = 2910 \text{ kips}$$

$$\delta = \frac{C_m}{1 - P_n/P_c} = \frac{1.0}{1 - 164/2910} = 1.06$$

The required capacity of the member *in the plane of the frame* (i.e., the strong orientation of the member) is

$$P_n = 164 \text{ kips}$$
$$M_n = M_m\delta = 398(1.06) = 423 \text{ ft-kips}$$

A statics analysis of this section using an eccentricity of

$$e = \frac{423(12)}{164} = 30.9 \text{ in.}$$

gives $P_n = 151$ kips, which is probably not close enough to be acceptable.

(b) Buckling transverse to the plane of the frame. The slenderness ratio is

$$\frac{kL_u}{r_y} = \frac{22.5(12)}{0.3(14)} = 64.4$$

which exceeds the limiting value of 22 for which the effect of slenderness may be neglected. Again, as in part (a), M_1/M_2 should be conservatively taken as 1.0. Since slenderness effects must be considered, the minimum $e = 0.6 + 0.03h$ must be magnified by the factor δ.

$$I_g = \tfrac{1}{12}(20)(14)^3 = 4570 \text{ in.}^4$$
$$I_s = 2(2)(1.56)(4.29)^2 = 115 \text{ in.}^4$$
$$EI = 0.2E_cI_g + E_sI_s$$
$$= 0.2(3820)(4570) + 29{,}000(115) = 6{,}830{,}000 \text{ kip in.}^2$$

or

$$EI = 0.4E_cI_g = 0.4(3820)(4570) = 6{,}980{,}000 \text{ kip in.}^2$$
$$C_m = 1.0$$

$$P_c = \frac{\pi^2 EI}{(kL_u)^2} = \frac{\pi^2(6{,}980{,}000)}{[1.0(22.5)(12)]^2} = 945 \text{ kips}$$

$$\delta = \frac{C_m}{1 - P_n/P_c} = \frac{1.0}{1 - 164/945} = 1.21$$

Thus, in the weaker direction the member must have the capacity $P_n = 164$ kips at an eccentricity

$$e = 1.21(0.6 + 0.03h) = 0.72 + 0.036h$$
$$= 0.72 + 0.036(14) = 1.22 \text{ in.}$$

A statics analysis indicates that the capacity P_n is 1205 kips at this eccentricity with respect to the weaker axis.

The capacity P_n may not be taken greater than $0.80P_0$,

$$P_{n(max)} = 0.80[0.85(4.5)(280 - 9.36) + 50(9.36)] = 1200 \text{ kips}$$

which is approximately the same as the capacity at the minimum eccentricity of 1.22 in.

EXAMPLE 15.15.8 Design column A for the unbraced frame of Fig. 15.15.5 to carry service axial compression and bending moment of 160 kips

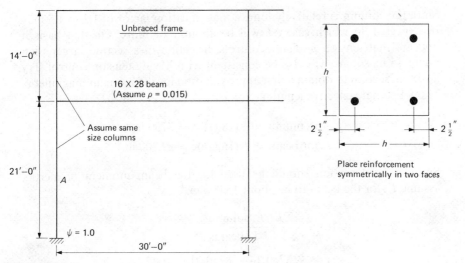

Fig. 15.15.5
Data for Example 15.15.8.

and 170 ft-kips, respectively. Consider 50% of the load to be dead load. Select a square member to contain approximately $2\frac{1}{2}\%$ reinforcement. Use $f'_c = 5000$ psi, $f_y = 60,000$ psi, and the strength method of the ACI Code.

Solution: (a) Design loads,

$$P_u = 1.4(80) + 1.7(80) = 248 \text{ kips}$$
$$M_u = 1.4(85) + 1.7(85) = 264 \text{ ft-kips}$$

(b) Estimate size at balanced condition. Using the procedure described in Secs. 13.19 and 13.20, assume that the axial force contributions of the steel in the two faces are approximately equal, $T \approx C_s$; then

$$C_c \approx P_b = \text{required } P_n$$

$$0.85f'_c\beta_1 x_b b = \frac{248}{\phi}$$

$$x_b = \left(\frac{0.003}{0.003 + 60/29,000}\right)d = 0.592d$$

$$0.85(5)(0.8)(0.592d)b = \frac{248}{0.7} = 354$$

$$\text{balanced } bd = \frac{354}{2.01} = 176 \text{ sq in.}$$

Assume $d \approx 0.85h$

$$\text{balanced } bh = \frac{176}{0.85} = 208 \text{ sq in.}, \qquad \text{say 15 in. square}$$

$$\text{required } e = \frac{264(12)}{248}\delta = 12.78\delta \text{ in.}$$

Since the column is relatively long, a magnification factor of 1.2 to 1.5 may be expected, in which case e/h will be about 1 or more. On that basis it appears that tension *probably* controls. Selection of a section larger than about 15 in. square will also be consistent with having tension control. Try an 18-in. section to obtain a first approximation for the moment magnifier δ.

(c) Estimate effective length factor k.

$$I_g \text{ for column} = \tfrac{1}{12}(18)(18)^3 = 8750 \text{ in.}^4$$
$$I_g \text{ for beam} = \tfrac{1}{12}(16)(28)^3 = 29{,}200 \text{ in.}^4$$

Since cracked section should be used for the beam moment of inertia, assume I_{cr} for the beam to be about 15,000 in.^{4}.

$$\psi \text{ (top)} = \frac{\Sigma EI/L, \text{ columns}}{\Sigma EI/L, \text{ beams}}$$

$$= \frac{8750/14 + 8750/21}{15{,}000/30} = \frac{1042}{500} \approx 2.0$$

Using the alignment chart of Fig. 15.8.1b, with ψ (bottom) = 1.0 (given), find $k \approx 1.45$.

(d) Estimate magnification factor δ. Since reinforcement is not yet selected, the following approximation is used,

$$EI \approx \frac{0.5 E_c I_g}{1 + \beta_d}$$

$$= \frac{0.5(57\sqrt{5000})8750}{1.45} = 12{,}200{,}000 \text{ kip in.}^2$$

where

$$\beta_d = \frac{1.4(80)}{1.4(80) + 1.7(80)} = 0.45$$

assuming only dead load is sustained.

$$P_c = \frac{\pi^2 EI}{(kL_u)^2}$$

$$= \frac{\pi^2(12{,}200{,}000)}{[1.45(18.67)(12)]^2} = 1140 \text{ kips}$$

where

$$L_u = 21.0 - 2.33 = 18.67 \text{ ft}$$

$$\delta = \frac{C_m}{1 - P_n/P_c}$$

$$= \frac{1.0}{1 - 354/1140} = 1.45$$

required $e = 12.78\delta = 12.78(1.45) = 18.5$ in.

(e) Determine column size considering $e = 18.5$ in. and $\rho_g = 0.025$, and assuming tension controls. Use Eq. (13.16.7),

$$P_n = 0.85f'_c bd\left\{-\rho + 1 - \frac{e'}{d} + \sqrt{\left(1 - \frac{e'}{d}\right)^2 + 2\rho\left[(m-1)\left(1 - \frac{d'}{d}\right) + \frac{e'}{d}\right]}\right\}$$

Estimate (see Fig. 13.16.1 for e') using $h = 18$ in.,

$$\frac{e'}{d} = \frac{18.5 + 6.5}{15.5} = 1.61$$

$$\frac{d'}{d} = \frac{2.5}{15.5} = 0.16$$

$$m = \frac{f_y}{0.85f'_c} = \frac{60}{0.85(5)} = 14.1$$

$$\rho = 0.5\rho_g = 0.0125$$

$$P_n = 0.85(5)bd\{-0.0125 + 1 - 1.61$$
$$+ \sqrt{(1 - 1.61)^2 + 2(0.0125)[13.1(1 - 0.16) + 1.61]}\}$$
$$= 4.25bd\{-0.6225 + \sqrt{0.372 + 0.315}\}$$
$$= 4.25(0.206)bd = 0.876bd$$

Assuming $d \approx 0.85h$

$$\text{required } bh = \frac{354}{0.876(0.85)} = 475 \text{ sq in.}$$

An 18-in. square section is not acceptable; a 19-in. square section might be acceptable but is an uncommon size. Try 20 in. square with 10-#9 bars ($\rho_g = 0.025$).

(f) Recheck effective length factor k. Use ACI formula without sustained load factor β_d for EI.

$$EI \text{ for column} = 0.2E_cI_g + E_sI_s$$
$$I_g = \tfrac{1}{12}(20)(20)^3 = 13,300 \text{ in.}^4$$
$$E_c = 57\sqrt{5000} = 4030 \text{ ksi}$$
$$I_s = 2(4)(7.5)^2 = 450 \text{ in.}^4$$
$$EI = 0.2(4030)(13,300) + 29,000(450) = 23,800,000 \text{ kips in.}^2$$

For the beam, cracked transformed section should be used. In lieu of using the general method of Chap. 4, Eqs. (14.11.7) and (14.11.8) may be used with $n = 7$ for $f'_c = 5000$ psi.

$$\frac{x}{d} = \sqrt{(\rho n)^2 + 2\rho n} - \rho n$$

$$\rho n = 0.015(7) = 0.105$$

$$\frac{x}{d} = \sqrt{(0.105)^2 + 0.21} - 0.105 = 0.365$$

$$\frac{I_{cr}}{I_g} = 8.75\left[\frac{(x/d)^3}{3} + \rho n\left(1 - \frac{x}{d}\right)^2\right]$$

$$= 8.75\left[\frac{(0.365)^3}{3} + 0.105(0.635)^2\right] = 0.512$$

EI for beam $= 0.512 E_c I_g$

$$= 0.512(4030)(29,200) = 60,300,000 \text{ kip in.}^2$$

$$\psi \text{ (top)} = \frac{23.9/14 + 23.9/21}{60.3/30} = 1.4$$

Using Fig. 15.8.1b, find $k = 1.37$ for $\psi_A = 1.4$ and $\psi_B = 1.0$.

(g) Recompute magnification factor.

$$\frac{EI}{1 + \beta_d} = \frac{23,800,000}{1.45} = 16,400,000 \text{ kip in.}^2$$

$$P_c = \frac{\pi^2 EI}{(kL_u)^2} = \frac{\pi^2(16,400,000)}{[1.37(18.67)(12)]^2} = 1720 \text{ kips}$$

$$\delta = \frac{C_m}{1 - P_n/P_c} = \frac{1.0}{1 - 354/1720} = 1.26$$

(h) Recheck capacity by approximate formula, Eq. (13.16.7). Using the 20-in. square section with 10-#9 (4 in each face), the more accurate distance from face of concrete to center of bars is

$$d' = d_s = 1.5 \text{ (cover)} + 0.375 \text{ (#3 tie)} + 0.564 \text{ (bar radius)} = 2.44 \text{ in.}$$

instead of 2.5 in. used in the preliminary computations.

$$\text{required } e = 12.78\delta = 12.78(1.26) = 16.1 \text{ in.}$$

$$\frac{e'}{d} = \frac{16.1 + 7.56}{17.56} = 1.35$$

$$\frac{d'}{d} = \frac{2.44}{17.56} = 0.139$$

$\rho = 0.01$ (using only the bars in one face)

$m = 14.1$

$m' = m - 1 = 13.1$

$$P_n = 4.25bd\{-0.01 + 1 - 1.35$$
$$+ \sqrt{(1 - 1.35)^2 + 2(0.01)[13.1(1 - 0.139) + 1.35]}\}$$
$$= 4.25bd(-0.36 + \sqrt{0.1225 + 0.253})$$
$$= 4.25(0.253)bd = 1.075bd$$

$$P_n = 1.075(20)(17.56) = 378 \text{ kips} > 354 \text{ kips required} \qquad \text{OK}$$

A statics analysis of the selected section indicates a capacity $P_n = 439$ kips at $e = 16.1$ in.

Use 20-in. square section with 10-#9 bars as shown in Fig. 15.15.6.

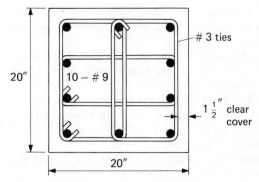

Fig. 15.15.6
Section selected for Example 15.15.8.

SELECTED REFERENCES

1. L. Euler. *DeCurvis Elasticis, Additamentum I, Methodus Inveniendi Lineas Curvas Maximi Minimive Proprietate Gaudentes.* Lausanne and Geneva: 1744, (pp. 267–268); and "Sur la Force des Colonnes," *Mémoires de l'Académie de Berlin,* Vol. 13. Berlin: 1759 (pp. 252–282).
2. F. Engesser. "Ueber die Knickfestigkeit gerader Stäbe," *Zeitschrift für Architektur und Ingenieurwesen,* Vol. 35. Hannover: 1889 (p. 455). Also "Die Knickfestigkeit gerader Stäbe," *Zentralblatt der Bauverwaltung,* Berlin, Dec. 5, 1891, p. 483.
3. T. von Kármán. "Die Knickfestigkeit gerader Stäbe," *Physikalische Zeitschrift,* Vol. 9. 1908 (p. 136). Also, "Untersuchungen über Knickfestigkeit," *Mitteilungen über Forschungsarbeiten auf dem Gebiete des Ingenieurwesens,* No. 81. Berlin: 1910.
4. Bengt Broms and I. M. Viest. "Ultimate Strength Analysis of Long Hinged Reinforced Concrete Columns," *Journal of Structural Division,* ASCE, **84,** (ST1) January 1958 (Paper No. 1510).
5. Bengt Broms and I. M. Viest. "Ultimate Strength Analysis of Long Restrained Reinforced Concrete Columns," *Journal of Structural Division,* ASCE, **84,** (ST3) May 1958 (Paper No. 1635).
6. Bengt Broms and I. M. Viest. "Design of Long Reinforced Concrete Columns," *Journal of Structural Division,* ASCE, **84,** (ST4) July 1958 (Paper No. 1694).
7. Wen F. Chang and Phil M. Ferguson. "Long Hinged Reinforced Concrete Columns," *ACI Journal, Proceedings,* **60,** January 1963, 1–25.
8. Luis P. Sáenz and Ignacio Martín. "Test of Reinforced Concrete Columns with High Slenderness Ratios," *ACI Journal, Proceedings,* **60,** May 1963, 589–616.
9. John E. Breen and Phil M. Ferguson. "The Restrained Long Concrete Column As a Part of A Rectangular Frame," *ACI Journal, Proceedings,* **61,** May 1964, 563–587.
10. John E. Breen. "Computer Use In Studies of Frames with Long Columns," *International Symposium on Flexural Mechanics of Reinforced Concrete* (SP–12). Detroit: American Concrete Institute, 1965 (pp. 535–556).
11. Edward O. Pfrang and Chester P. Siess. "Behavior of Restrained Reinforced Concrete Columns," *Journal of Structural Division,* ASCE, **90,** (ST5) October 1964, 113–135; Disc. **91,** (ST3) June 1965, 280–287.
12. J. G. MacGregor. Discussion of "Behavior of Restrained Reinforced Concrete Columns," by E. O. Pfrang and C. P. Siess, *Journal of Structural Division,* ASCE, **91,** (ST3) June 1965, 280–287.

13. Richard W. Furlong and Phil M. Ferguson. "Tests of Frames with Columns in Single Curvature," *Symposium on Reinforced Concrete Columns* (SP–13). Detroit: American Concrete Institute, 1966 (pp. 55–73).

14. Phil M. Ferguson and John E. Breen. "Investigation of the Long Column in a Frame Subject to Lateral Loads," *Symposium on Reinforced Concrete Columns* (SP–13). Detroit: American Concrete Institute, 1966 (pp. 75–119).

15. Ignacio Martín and Elmer Olivieri. "Test of Slender Reinforced Concrete Columns Bent in Double Curvature," *Symposium on Reinforced Concrete Columns* (SP–13). Detroit: American Concrete Institute, 1966 (pp. 121–138).

16. J. G. MacGregor and S. L. Barter. "Long Eccentrically Loaded Concrete Columns Bent in Double Curvature," *Symposium on Reinforced Concrete Columns* (SP–13). Detroit: American Concrete Institute, 1966 (pp. 139–156).

17. Alfred L. Parme. "Capacity of Restrained Eccentrically Loaded Long Columns," *Symposium on Reinforced Concrete Columns* (SP–13). Detroit: American Concrete Institute, 1966 (pp. 325–367).

18. Edward O. Pfrang. "Behavior of Reinforced Concrete Columns with Sidesway," *Journal of Structural Division*, ASCE, **92**, (ST3) June 1966, 225–252.

19. Phil M. Ferguson and Hajime Okamura. "Long Columns in Frames—Computer Analyses—Part 2, Columns in Braced Frames." Report to Reinforced Concrete Research Council, University of Texas, Austin, July 1968.

20. Phil M. Ferguson, Hajime Okamura, and S. N. Pagay. "Long Columns in Frames—Computer Analyses—Part 3, Columns in Unbraced Frames—Shear Loading." Report of Reinforced Concrete Research Council, University of Texas, Austin, September 1968.

21. R. Green and John E. Breen. "Eccentrically Loaded Concrete Columns Under Sustained Load," *ACI Journal, Proceedings*, **66**, November 1969, 866–874.

22. John E. Breen and Phil M. Ferguson. "Long Cantilever Columns Subject to Lateral Forces," *ACI Journal, Proceedings*, **66**, November 1969, 884–893.

23. E. Hognestad. *A Study of Combined Bending and Axial Load in Reinforced Concrete Members* (Bulletin No. 399). Urbana: University of Illinois Engineering Experiment Station, November 1951, (128 pp.).

24. *Specification for the Design, Fabrication and Erection of Structural Steel for Buildings* (adopted February 12, 1969). Also, *Commentary* on 1969 Specification. New York: American Institute of Steel Construction, 1970.

25. Charles Massonnet. "Stability Considerations in the Design of Steel Columns," *Journal of Structural Division*, ASCE, **85**, (ST7) September 1959, 75–111.

26. Bruce G. Johnston (Ed.). *Guide to Stability Design Criteria for Metal Structures* (3rd ed.) (Structural Stability Research Council). New York: Wiley, 1976 (Chap. 15).

27. Charles G. Salmon and John E. Johnson. *Steel Structures: Design and Behavior.* New York and London: Intext Educational Publishers (Harper & Row), 1971 (Chap. 14).

28. S. P. Timoshenko and J. M. Gere. *Theory of Elastic Stability* (2nd ed.). New York: McGraw-Hill, 1961 (pp. 17–19, 59–70).

29. Friedrich Bleich. *Buckling Strength of Metal Structures*, New York: McGraw-Hill, 1952 (Chaps. 6 and 7).

30. William McGuire. *Steel Structures.* Englewood Cliffs, N.J.: Prentice-Hall, 1968 (pp. 424–520).

31. C. K. Wang. *Computer Methods in Advanced Structural Analysis.* New York: Intext Educational Publishers (Harper & Row), 1973.

32. Shriniwas N. Pagay, Phil M. Ferguson, and John E. Breen. "Importance of Beam Properties on Concrete Column Behavior," *ACI Journal, Proceedings*, **67**, October 1970, 808–815.

33. Hajime Okamura, Shriniwas N. Pagay, John E. Breen, and Phil M. Ferguson. "Elastic Frame Analysis—Corrections Necessary for Design of Short Concrete Columns in Braced Frames," *ACI Journal, Proceedings*, **67**, November 1970, 894–897.

34. Thomas C. Kavanagh. "Effective Length of Framed Columns," *Transactions ASCE*, **127**, Part II, 1962, 81–101.

35. *Commentary on Building Code Requirements for Reinforced Concrete* (ACI 318–77). Detroit: American Concrete Institute, 1977 (Sections 10.8–10.11).

36. John E. Breen, James G. MacGregor, and Edward O. Pfrang. "Determination of Effective Length Factors for Slender Concrete Columns," *ACI Journal, Proceedings*, **69**, November 1972, 669–672.

37. James G. MacGregor, John E. Breen, and Edward O. Pfrang. "Design of Slender Concrete Columns," *ACI Journal, Proceedings*, **67**, January 1970, 6–28.

38. *Code of Practice for the Structural Use of Concrete*, Part I. *Design, Materials and Workmanship*. London: British Standards Institute, 1972.

39. Richard W. Furlong. "Column Slenderness and Charts for Design," *ACI Journal, Proceedings*, **68**, January 1971, 9–18.

40. G. A. Blomier and J. E. Breen. "Effect of Yielding of Restraints on Slender Concrete Columns With Sidesway Prevented," *Reinforced Concrete Columns* (SP–50). Detroit: American Concrete Institute, 1975 (pp. 41–65).

41. J. G. MacGregor, U. H. Oelhafen, and S. E. Hage. "A Reexamination of the *EI* Value for Slender Columns," *Reinforced Concrete Columns* (SP–50). Detroit: American Concrete Institute, 1975 (pp. 1–40).

42. Ian C. Medland and Donald A. Taylor. "Flexural Rigidity of Concrete Column Sections," *Journal of Structural Division*, ASCE, **97**, February 1971 (ST2), 573–586.

43. Brij B. Goyal and Neil Jackson. "Slender Concrete Columns under Sustained Load," *Journal of Structural Division*, ASCE, **97**, November 1971 (ST11), 2729–2750.

44. Robert G. Drysdale and Mark W. Huggins. "Sustained Biaxial Load on Slender Concrete Columns," *Journal of Structural Division*, ASCE, **97**, May 1971 (ST5), 1423–1443.

45. S. I. Abdel-Sayed and N. J. Gardner. "Design of Symmetric Square Slender Reinforced Concrete Columns under Biaxially Eccentric Loads," *Reinforced Concrete Columns* (SP–50). Detroit: American Concrete Institute, 1975 (pp. 149–164).

46. Richard W. Furlong. "Guidelines for Analyzing Column Slenderness by a Rational Analysis of an Elastic Frame," *ACI Journal, Proceedings*, **73**, March 1976, 138–140.

47. James Colville. "Slenderness Effects in Reinforced Concrete Square Columns," *Reinforced Concrete Columns* (SP–50). Detroit: American Concrete Institute, 1975 (pp. 165–191).

PROBLEMS

All problems[†] are to be done in accordance with the strength method of the ACI Code unless otherwise specified.

15.1 Determine the required material strength, including length effect, for a 16-in. square tied column that has a clear height of 18 ft and serves as an interior

---

[†] Most problems may be solved as problems stated in US Customary units, or as problems in metric units using quantities in parenthesis at the end of the statement. The metric conversions are approximate to avoid implying higher precision for the given information in metric units than that given for the US Customary units.

member of a braced frame. The member is designed as axially loaded with the following service loads: live load, 130 kips; dead load, 200 kips. Use $f'_c = 3000$ psi and $f_y = 50,000$ psi. Without actually selecting bars, assume about $2\frac{1}{2}\%$ total reinforcement equally divided in the opposite faces of the member. (400 mm square section; 5.5 m clear height; LL = 580 kN; DL = 890 kN; $f'_c = 21$ N/mm²; $f_y = 350$ N/mm².)

(a) Use ACI moment magnifier method.

(b) Use ACI Commentary reduction factor method, if applicable.

15.2 Determine the adequacy, including length effects, for a 14-in. diameter spirally reinforced column (assume about $2\frac{1}{2}\%$ reinforcement) which is an interior second-floor column (column A) in the braced frame of the accompanying figure. The member is to carry an ultimate axial load $P_n = P_u/\phi = 500$ kips. The 14×22 beams contain $\rho = 0.015$ for negative-moment tension steel. Use $f'_c = 5000$ psi and $f_y = 40,000$ psi. Assume no sustained load. (350 mm diameter; $P_n = 2200$ kN; 350 mm × 560 mm beams; $f'_c = 35$ N/mm²; $f_y = 280$ N/mm².)

(a) Use the ACI moment magnifier method.

(b) Use the ACI Commentary reduction-factor method, if applicable.

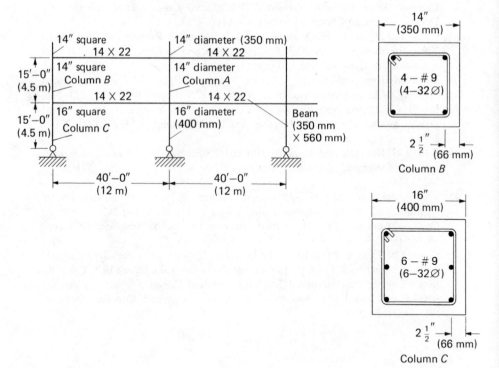

Probs. 15.2 to 15.8

15.3 Repeat Prob. 15.2, except consider that the frame is *unbraced* instead of braced.

15.4 Determine the adequacy of the exterior square column (column B) of the figure for Prob. 15.2, if the member is carrying an ultimate axial compression $P_n = P_u/\phi = 750$ kips and an ultimate primary bending moment $M_n = M_u/\phi = 94$ ft-kips with 60% of the loads assumed to be dead load. Assume that the primary bending moment varies from $+M$ at the top of the member linearly

to $-M/2$ at the bottom, with joint translation adequately prevented (i.e., a braced frame). Use $f'_c = 5000$ psi and $f_y = 40,000$ psi. The 14×22 beams contain $\rho = 0.015$ for negative moment tension steel. ($P_n = 340$ tons; $M_n = 13$ t.-m; $f'_c = 350$ kgf/cm^2; $f_y = 2800$ kgf/cm^2; 350 mm $\times$ 560 mm beams.)
(a) Use ACI moment magnifier method.
(b) Use ACI Commentary reduction factor method, if applicable.

15.5 Repeat Prob. 15.4, except consider that the frame is *unbraced* instead of braced.

15.6 Repeat Prob. 15.4, except consider the primary bending moment constant over the height of the column.

15.7 Determine the adequacy of the 16-in. square first-floor column (column C) of the figure for Prob. 15.2, which is carrying service axial load of 350 kips and a primary bending moment of 115 ft-kips (assume loads 70% dead load). The primary bending moment varies from a maximum at the top to zero at the bottom and joint translation is adequately prevented. Use $f'_c = 5000$ psi and $f_y = 40,000$ psi. ($P = 1550$ kN; $M = 156$ kN-m; $f'_c = 35$ N/mm^2; $f_y = 280$ N/mm^2.)
(a) Use ACI moment magnifier method.
(b) Use ACI Commentary reduction factor method, if applicable.

15.8 Repeat Prob. 15.7, except consider that sidesway is possible (i.e., unbraced frame). Assume 14×22 beams contain negative-moment reinforcement $\rho = 0.015$.

15.9 Determine the adequacy of an 18-in. square tied member in a braced frame where the member has end flexibilities $\psi = 2.0$ at its top and 10.0 at its bottom and has a clear height of 16 ft. The member is required to carry an ultimate axial load $P_n = P_u/\phi = 100$ kips, and the maximum ultimate primary bending moment $M_n = M_u/\phi = 240$ ft-kips. Assume primary bending moment is constant over the height of the member, and that 70% of the loads are dead load, and remainder live load. Use $f'_c = 3000$ psi and $f_y = 40,000$ psi. The member reinforcement consists of 8-#9 bars, four in each face centered $2\frac{1}{2}$ in. (or 64 mm) from edge of member. (460 mm square member; clear height = 5 m; $P_n = 445$ kN; $M_n = 325$ kN-m; $f'_c = 21$ N/mm^2; $f_y = 280$ N/mm^2; reinforcement, 4–25 mm diam. and 4–32 mm diam. bars.)
(a) Use ACI moment magnifier method.
(b) Use ACI Commentary reduction factor method, if applicable.

15.10 Repeat Prob. 15.9 if bending moment arises from uniform lateral load, and apply rational analysis to determine k (less than 1.0) and for determination of C_m (assume the member fixed at one end and simply supported at the other). Use only moment magnifier method.

15.11 Repeat Prob. 15.9, except consider the frame *unbraced* instead of braced.

15.12 Using the concepts developed in Sec. 15.2 for the axially loaded column,
(a) Compute critical ordinates and plot carefully the column curve P_n vs kL_u/r for the 14-in. diameter column (column A) of Prob. 15.2, assuming $\rho_g = 0.02$ and $2\frac{1}{2}$ in. as the distance from the face of the column to the center of the longitudinal bars. Use Figs. 15.2.1 and 15.2.2 as the accurate stress-strain relationships. Particularly, compute and plot points for kL_u/r below 50, in addition to the critical values.
(b) Assuming that the strength curve of part (a) is "exact," determine therefrom the reduction factor R for the situation of Prob. 15.2, using the alignment chart (Fig. 15.8.1a) for establishing the effective length.

(c) Repeat part (b) except follow the ACI Code for establishing the effective length.

(d) Compare with Prob. 15.2 results and comment on your comparison.

15.13 (a) Redesign the column used in Example 15.15.8 except for service loads use an axial compression of 200 kips and bending moment of 140 ft-kips with a length for column A of 20 ft instead of 21 ft. ($P = 890$ kN; $M = 190$ kN-m; length of column above $= 4.3$ m; length of column $A = 6.1$ m; beam $= 400$ mm $\times$ 700 mm on 9-m span; $f'_c = 35$ N/mm^2; $f_y = 420$ N/mm^2.)

(b) How much smaller could the member have been if the frame were adequately braced to prevent joint translation?

15.14 (a) Redesign the columns used in Example 15.15.8 except use 18 ft (5.5 m) instead of 21 ft for the length of column A.

(b) How much smaller could the member have been if the frame were adequately braced to prevent joint translation?

16

Design of Two-Way Systems— Slabs Supported on Beams

16.1 General Description

In reinforced concrete buildings, a basic and common type of floor is the slab–beam–girder construction, which has been treated in Chaps. 8 and 10. As shown in Fig. 16.1.1a the shaded slab area is bounded by the two adjacent beams on the sides and portions of the two girders at the ends. When the length of this area is two or more times its width, almost all of the floor load goes to the beams, and very little, except some near the edge of the girders, goes directly to the girders. Thus the slab may be designed as a one-way slab, with the main reinforcement parallel to the girder and the shrinkage and temperature reinforcement parallel to the beams. The deflected surface of a one-way slab is primarily one of single curvature.

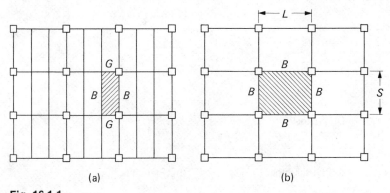

Fig. 16.1.1
One-way versus two-way slabs.

When the ratio of the long span L to the short span S as shown in Fig. 16.1.1b is less than about 2, the deflected surface of the shaded area becomes one of double curvature. The floor load is carried in both directions to the four supporting beams around the panel, hence the name "two-way slab." Obviously, when S is equal to L, the four beams around a typical interior panel should be identical; for other cases the long beams take more load than the short beams.

In the flat-slab or flat-plate type (Fig. 16.1.2) of floor construction, the concrete slab is reinforced in two or more directions, generally without beams or girders to transfer the loads to the columns. Thus the *slab itself* becomes a grid of *two-way* shallow beams supported directly on columns. In such cases the column tends to punch upward through the slab, and the inclined cracking arising from the punching shear must be prevented. The necessary shear resistance may be obtained (see Chap. 17) by several procedures: (1) enlarge the top of the column in the shape of an inverted frustum, known as the column "capital," thus lengthening the section over which the shear can be carried from the column perimeter to the capital perimeter; (2) thicken the slab in the vicinity of the column, using what is referred to as a "drop panel," thus providing an increased shear-resisting area along the perimeter of the column; (3) provide both a column capital and a drop panel, thus combining an increased length of resisting section with an increased thickness; and (4) use special shear reinforcement consisting of steel rolled section devices [11] or multiple bar stirrups to increase the shear resistance at the junction of the slab and the column.

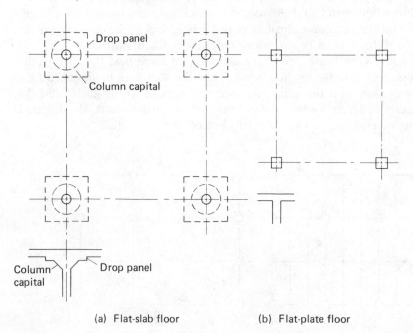

(a) Flat-slab floor   (b) Flat-plate floor

Fig. 16.1.2
Flat-slab and flat-plate floor construction.

Actually the terms *two-way* slab (Fig. 16.1.1b), *flat slab* (Fig. 16.1.2a), and *flat-plate* floor (Fig. 16.1.2b) are arbitrary, because there is in fact two-way action in all three types and a flat (usually nearly square) ceiling area usually exists within the panel in all three types. Following tradition, the implication is that there are beams between columns in two-way slabs; but no such beams, except edge beams along the exterior sides of the entire floor area, are used in flat slabs or flat plates. From the viewpoint of structural analysis, however, the distinction as to whether or not there are beams between columns is not pertinent, because if beams of any relative size could be designed to interact with the slab, use of beams of zero size would be only the limit condition.

Thus if methods of structural analysis and design are developed for two-way slabs with beams, many of these general provisions should apply equally well to flat slabs or plates. Until 1971 the design of two-way slabs supported on beams has, historically, been treated separately from the flat slabs or flat plates without beams. Various empirical procedures have been proposed and used [1–3]. The present ACI Code takes an integrated view and Chap. 13 of the Code refers to two-way slab *systems* with or without beams. In addition to solid slabs, hollow slabs with interior voids to reduce dead weight, slabs (such as waffle slabs) with recesses made by permanent or removable fillers between joists in two directions, and slabs with paneled ceilings near the central portion of the panel are also included in this category (ACI-13.1.3 and 4).

16.2 General Design Concept of ACI Code

The basic approach to the design of two-way systems involves imagining that vertical cuts are made through the entire building along lines midway between the columns. The cutting creates a series of frames whose width centerlines lie along the column lines. The resulting series of rigid frames, taken separately in the longitudinal and transverse directions of the building, may be treated floor by floor as would generally be acceptable for a rigid frame structure consisting of beams and columns, in accordance with ACI-8.9.1. A typical rigid frame would consist of (1) the columns above and below the floor, and (2) the floor system, with or without beams, bounded laterally between the centerlines of the two panels (one panel for an exterior line of columns) adjacent to the line of columns as shown in Fig. 16.2.1.

Thus the design of a two-way slab system (including two-way slab, flat slab, and flat plate) is reduced to that of a rigid frame; hence the name "equivalent-frame method."

As in the case of design of actual rigid frames consisting of beams and columns, approximate methods of analysis may be suitable for many usual slab systems, spans, and story heights. As treated in Chap. 7 the analysis for actual frames could be (a) approximate using the moment and shear coefficients of ACI-8.3, or (b) more accurate using structural analysis after assuming the relative stiffnesses of the members. In slab systems the moments and shears on these equivalent frames may be determined (a) approximately

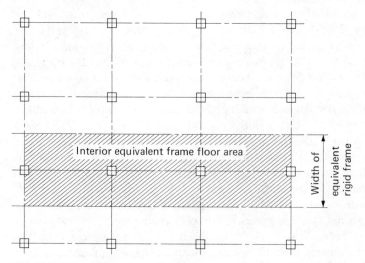

Fig. 16.2.1
Tributary floor area for an interior equivalent frame of a two-way slab system.

using moment and shear coefficients prescribed by the "direct-design method" of ACI-Chapter 13, or (b) by structural analysis in a manner similar to that for actual frames using the special provisions of the "equivalent-frame method" of ACI-Chapter 13.

The equivalent frame is the structure being dealt with whether the moments are determined by the "direct-design method (DDM)" or by the "equivalent-frame method (EFM)." These two ACI Code terms describe two ways of obtaining the longitudinal variation of bending moments and shears.

When the "equivalent-frame method" is used for obtaining the longitudinal variation of moments and shears, the relative stiffness of the columns, as well as that of the floor system, can be assumed in the preliminary analysis and then reviewed, as is the case for design of any statically indeterminate structure. Design moment envelopes may be obtained for dead load in combination with various patterns of live load, as described in Chap. 7 (Sec. 7.2).

Once the longitudinal variation in design moments and shears has been obtained, whether by ACI "DDM" or "EFM," the moment across the entire width of the floor system being considered is distributed laterally to the beam, if used, and to the slab. The lateral distribution procedure and the remainder of the design is essentially the same whether "DDM" or "EFM" has been used. The accuracy of the methods utilizing the concept of dividing the structure into equivalent frames has been verified by experimental [4–8, see also Chap. 17, Refs. 5–11] and analytical [9,10] research.

For convenience in treatment, the more general case of slabs supported on beams (two-way slabs) is taken up first in this chapter. The special cases of flat plates or flat slabs in which no beams are used at all, along with situations where only edge beams are used around the exterior sides of the floor, are presented in the next chapter.

16.3 Total Factored Static Moment

Consider two typical interior panels *ABCD* and *CDEF* in a two-way slab floor, as shown in Fig. 16.3.1a. Let L and S be the panel size in the long and short directions, respectively. Let lines 1–2 and 3–4 be center lines of panels *ABCD* and *CDEF*, both parallel to the long direction. Isolate as a free body (see Fig. 16.3.1b) the floor slab and the included beam bounded by the lines 1–2 and 3–4 in the long direction and the transverse lines $1'$–$3'$ and $2'$–$4'$ at the faces of the beams in the short direction. The load acting on this free body (see Fig. 16.3.1c) is wS per unit distance in the long direction. The total upward force acting on lines $1'$–$3'$ or $2'$–$4'$ is $wSL_n/2$, where L_n is the clear span in the long direction between faces of supports.

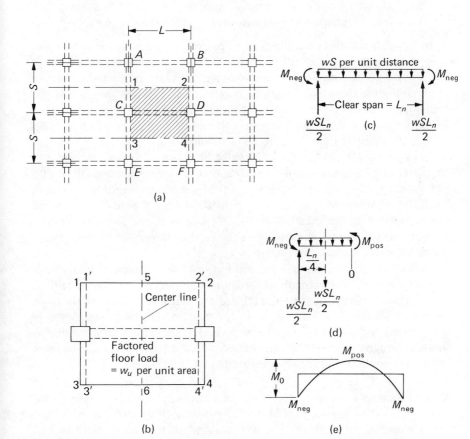

Fig. 16.3.1
Statics of a typical interior panel in a two-way slab.

If M_{neg} and M_{pos} are the numerical values of the total negative and positive bending moments along lines 1'–3' and 5–6, then moment equilibrium of the free body of Fig. 16.3.1d requires

$$M_0 = M_{neg} + M_{pos} = \frac{wSL_n^2}{8} \tag{16.3.1}$$

ACI-13.6.2 uses the symbol M_0 to mean $M_{neg} + M_{pos}$ and calls M_0 the *total factored static moment*. It states, "The absolute sum of the positive and average negative factored moments in each direction shall not be less than M_0"; or

$$\frac{M_{neg} \text{ (left)} + M_{neg} \text{ (right)}}{2} + M_{pos} \geq M_0 = \frac{wL_2L_n^2}{8} \tag{16.3.2}$$

in which

w = factored load per unit area
L_n = clear span in the direction moments are being determined, measured face to face of supports, but not less than $0.65L_1$
L_1 = span length in the direction moments are being determined, measured center to center of supports
L_2 = transverse span length, measured center to center of supports

In flat-slab construction, the floor slabs are supported at the round (but sometimes square) column capitals. ACI-13.6.2.5 suggests the treatment of circular supports as square supports having the same area for the purpose of obtaining the clear span length L_n. Later in Sec. 17.2 it is shown that this technique is not as conservative as the more exact expression for M_0 derived by directly using the round supports. It is noted that ACI-13.6.2.2 does express its intent in Eq. (16.3.2) in an inequality form.

In two-way slab design, then, the value of M_0 must first be divided into M_{neg} and M_{pos}, if the restraints at each end of the span are identical; or into $[M_{neg} \text{ (left)} + M_{neg} \text{ (right)}]/2$ and M_{pos} if the span end restraints are different. Then the moments M_{neg} (left), M_{neg} (right), and M_{pos} should be distributed transversely along the lines 1–3 or 1'–3', 2–4 or 2'–4', and 5–6, respectively. This last distribution is a function of the relative flexural stiffness between the slab and the included beam.

In an effort to present, explain, and illustrate the design procedure for a two-way slab floor system in accordance with the ACI Code, it will be necessary to assume that preliminary dimensions and sizes of the slab, beams, and columns are available. In the usual design processes, not only the preliminary sizes may need to be revised as they are found unsuitable, but also designs based on two or three different relative beam sizes to slab thickness should be made and compared.

Design Example. Figure 16.3.2 shows a two-way slab floor with a total area of 12,500 sq ft. It is divided into 25 panels with a panel size of 25 ft × 20 ft. Concrete strength is $f'_c = 3000$ psi and steel yield strength is $f_y = 40,000$ psi. Service live load is to be taken as 120 psf. Story height is 12 ft. The preliminary sizes are as follows: slab thickness is $6\frac{1}{2}$ in.; long beams are 14 × 28 in. overall; short beams are 12 × 24 in. overall; upper and lower

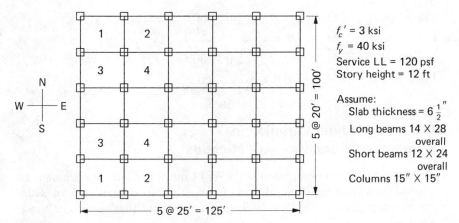

Fig. 16.3.2
Floor plan for design example.

columns are 15×15 in. The four kinds of panels (corner, long-sided edge, short-sided edge, and interior) are numbered 1, 2, 3, and 4 in Fig. 16.3.2.

In the subsequent sections of this chapter, design procedures are described and explained; then the design example as given above is used for numerical illustration.

EXAMPLE 16.3.1   For the design example just described, determine the total factored static moment in any one span of the equivalent rigid frames whose widths are designated A, B, C, and D in Fig. 16.3.3.

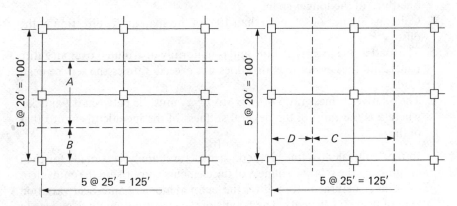

Fig. 16.3.3
Equivalent rigid frame notations in design example.

Solution: The factored load w_u per unit floor area is

$$w_u = w_D + w_L = 1.4(6.5)\left(\frac{150}{12}\right) + 1.7(120)$$

$$= 114 + 204 = 318 \text{ psf}$$

For frame A, $M_0 = \frac{1}{8}wL_2L_n^2 = \frac{1}{8}(0.318)(20)(24)^2 = 458$ ft-kips

For frame B, $M_0 = 229$ ft-kips

For frame C, $M_0 = \frac{1}{8}wL_2L_n^2 = \frac{1}{8}(0.318)(25)(18.83)^2 = 352$ ft-kips

For frame D, $M_0 = 176$ ft-kips

16.4 Longitudinal Variation in Moments and Shears—ACI Methods

Two methods are recommended in the ACI Code for obtaining the moments and shears to be used in the design of two-way slab systems with or without beams; they are the *"direct-design method"* and the *"equivalent-frame method."*

In the "direct-design method," the distribution between positive- and negative-moment zones of the total factored static moment along the span, as computed from Eq. (16.3.2), is made approximately using a set of coefficients prescribed by the ACI Code. This is done for each equivalent frame, including long and short directions, into which the structure is divided. As applied to two-way slabs, this method may be used under the following limitations on continuity, dimensions, live-load to dead-load ratios, and relative stiffness ratios of beams to slabs (ACI-13.6.1).

1. There is a minimum of three continuous spans in each direction.
2. Panels must be rectangular with the ratio of longer to shorter span within a panel not greater than 2.0.
3. The successive span lengths in each direction do not differ by more than one-third of the longer span.
4. Columns are not offset more than 10% of the span in the direction of the offset.
5. The load is due to gravity only and is uniformly distributed over an entire panel, and the service live load does not exceed 3 times the service dead load.
6. The relative stiffness ratio of L_1^2/α_1 to L_2^2/α_2 must lie between 0.2 and 5.0, where α is the ratio of the flexural stiffness of the included beam to that of the slab.

In the "equivalent-frame method," a structural analysis is made for each frame utilizing the relative stiffness of the elements comprising the equivalent frame. This structural analysis gives the factored moment and shear variation instead of using coefficients. The details of the structural analysis appear in Sec. 16.14.

When a typical horizontal span in a rigid frame is subjected to a total factored dead and live load of w_uL_2 per foot, as shown in Fig. 16.4.1a, equilibrium requires that the sum of the absolute average value of the negative moments at the center of supports and the positive moment at midspan be equal to $w_uL_2L_1^2/8$, where L_1 is the span length between centerlines of supports; thus

$$M_{pos} + \frac{1}{2}(M_{ni} + M_{nj}) = \frac{1}{8}w_uL_2L_1^2 \tag{16.4.1}$$

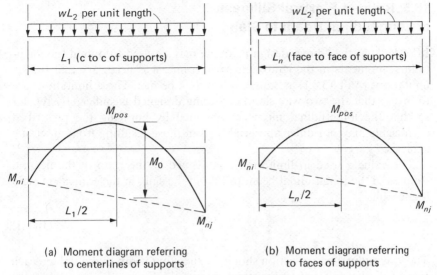

(a) Moment diagram referring
to centerlines of supports

(b) Moment diagram referring
to faces of supports

Fig. 16.4.1
Typical moment diagram of a horizontal span.

In the "equivalent-frame method" the moment envelopes of such moment diagrams obtained for various live-load patterns are used; consequently the left side of Eq. (16.4.1), using the *maximum* values of the envelope, should be larger than $w_u L_2 L_1^2/8$—more so as the live-load to dead-load ratio increases. Although the maximum envelope value at midspan can be used directly in design, the value at centerlines of support can be used only as a basis for obtaining the reduced value at the face of support, at which location the slab thickness is investigated and reinforcement designed. In the "direct-design method," the reacting shears are assumed to act on the clear span at the faces of support, as shown in Fig. 16.4.1b. For one particular loading condition, in which the clear span is subjected to the factored dead and live load, Eq. (16.4.1) becomes

$$M_{pos} + \tfrac{1}{2}(M_{ni} + M_{nj}) = \tfrac{1}{8}w_u L_2 L_n^2 = M_0 \qquad (16.4.2)$$

where L_n is the clear span and M_{ni} and M_{nj} are the negative moments at the faces of supports. The difference between the theoretical moment envelope and the clear span moment diagram of Fig. 16.4.1b is small as long as the six limitations as stated earlier are satisfied.

Thus the ACI Code "direct-design method" uses the total factored static moment M_0, which is then distributed using coefficients to M_{pos} at midspan and M_{ni} and M_{nj} at the faces of supports. In the ACI "equivalent-frame method," the total static moment is also used (the center-to-center span L_1 is used instead of the clear span L_n in the expression for M_0); however, the distribution to the positive and negative regions is to be made according to the results from the elastic frame analysis (such as the moment-distribution method). Then, of course, the reduced moments at the face of support, obtained from the moment envelope, are to be used in the design.

16.5 Ratio of Flexural Stiffness of Longitudinal Beam to Slab

In order that the "direct-design method" may be used to obtain the longitudinal moments in the equivalent rigid frame, it is necessary that the six limitations (ACI-13.6.1) as stated in Sec. 16.4 be met. These limitations are to insure that the two-way slab floor being designed is sufficiently regular so that the longitudinal moments obtained by applying the prescribed coefficients may not differ appreciably from those resulting from an elastic analysis.

The value α used in limitation 6 is defined as the ratio of the flexural stiffness of the longitudinal beam to that of the slab, in the equivalent rigid frame; thus

$$\alpha = \frac{E_{cb}I_b}{E_{cs}I_s} \tag{16.5.1}$$

The longitudinal beam section should include that width of the slab on each side of the beam equal to the projection of the beam above or below the slab, whichever is greater, but not greater than 4 times the slab thickness (ACI-13.2.4). The moment of inertia of such a flanged section about its own centroidal axis (Fig. 16.5.1) may be shown to be

$$I_g = k \frac{b_w h^3}{12} \tag{16.5.2a}$$

in which

$$k = \frac{1 + \left(\dfrac{b_E}{b_w} - 1\right)\left(\dfrac{t}{h}\right)\left[4 - 6\left(\dfrac{t}{h}\right) + 4\left(\dfrac{t}{h}\right)^2 + \left(\dfrac{b_E}{b_w} - 1\right)\left(\dfrac{t}{h}\right)^3\right]}{1 + \left(\dfrac{b_E}{b_w} - 1\right)\left(\dfrac{t}{h}\right)} \tag{16.5.2b}$$

where
$$h = \text{overall beam depth}$$
$$t = \text{overall slab thickness}$$
$$b_E = \text{effective width of flange}$$
$$b_w = \text{width of web}$$

Table 16.5.1
Values of k in Terms of (b_E/b_w) and (t/h) in Eq. (16.5.2b)

b_E/b_w	t/h									
	0.1	0.2	0.3	0.4	0.5	0.6	0.7	0.8	0.9	1.0
2	1.222	1.328	1.366	1.372	1.375	1.396	1.454	1.565	1.743	2.000
3	1.407	1.564	1.605	1.608	1.625	1.694	1.844	2.098	2.477	3.000
4	1.564	1.744	1.777	1.781	1.825	1.956	2.212	2.621	3.209	4.000

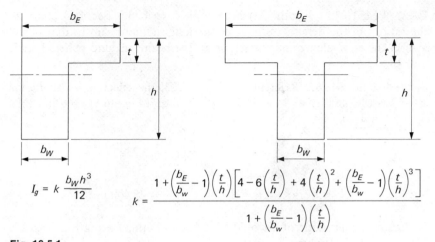

$$I_g = k \frac{b_w h^3}{12}$$

$$k = \frac{1 + \left(\frac{b_E}{b_w} - 1\right)\left(\frac{t}{h}\right)\left[4 - 6\left(\frac{t}{h}\right) + 4\left(\frac{t}{h}\right)^2 + \left(\frac{b_E}{b_w} - 1\right)\left(\frac{t}{h}\right)^3\right]}{1 + \left(\frac{b_E}{b_w} - 1\right)\left(\frac{t}{h}\right)}$$

Fig. 16.5.1

Moment of inertia of a flanged section.

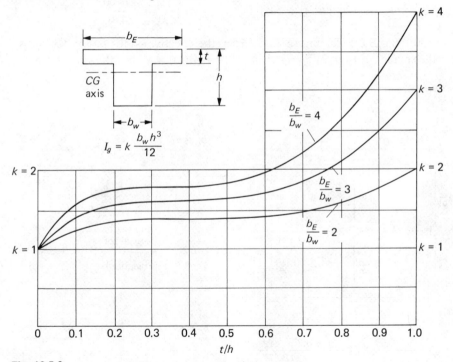

Fig. 16.5.2

Values of k in terms of b_E/b_w and t/h.

Equation (16.5.2b) expresses the nondimensional constant k in terms of (b_E/b_w) and (t/h). Typical values of k are tabulated in Table 16.5.1 and three curves are plotted in Fig. 16.5.2. The values of k are about 1.4, 1.6, and 1.8, respectively, for b_E/b_w values of 2, 3, and 4, when t/h values are between 0.2 and 0.5. Thus

$$k \approx 1.0 + 0.2\left(\frac{b_E}{b_w}\right) \quad \text{for} \quad 2 < \frac{b_E}{b_w} < 4 \quad \text{and} \quad 0.2 < \frac{t}{h} < 0.5 \quad \textbf{(16.5.2c)}$$

EXAMPLE 16.5.1   For the design example described in Sec. 16.3, compute the ratio α of the flexural stiffness of the longitudinal beam to that of the slab in the equivalent rigid frame, for all the beams around panels 1, 2, 3, and 4.

Solution: (a) B1–B2. Referring to Fig. 16.5.3, the effective width b_E for B1–B2 is the smaller of $14 + 2(21.5) = 57$ in. or $14 + 8(6.5) = 66$ in.; thus $b_E = 57$ in. Using Eq. (16.5.2b),

$$\frac{b_E}{b_w} = \frac{57}{14} = 4.07, \qquad \frac{t}{h} = \frac{6.5}{28} = 0.232$$

$$k = 1.774, \qquad I_b = 1.774\,\frac{14(28)^3}{12} = 45,400 \text{ in.}^4$$

A slightly higher value of k would have been obtained using Eq. (16.5.2c). Using Eq. (16.5.1), where $E_{cb} = E_{cs}$,

$$I_s = \tfrac{1}{12}(240)(6.5)^3 = 5490 \text{ in.}^4, \qquad \alpha = \frac{E_{cb}I_b}{E_{cs}I_s} = \frac{45,400}{5490} = 8.27$$

(b) B3–B4. Referring to Fig. 16.5.3, the effective width b_E for B3–B4 is the smaller of $14 + 21.5 = 35.5$ in. or $14 + 4(6.5) = 40$ in.; thus $b_E = 35.5$ in.

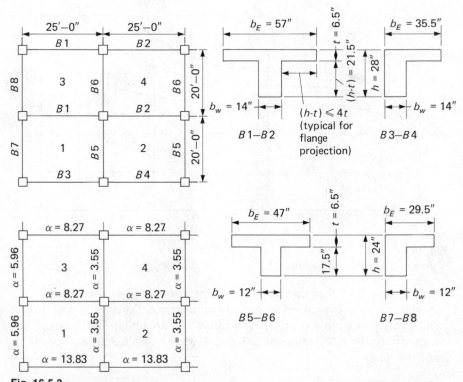

Fig. 16.5.3
Computation of α values in design example.

Using Eq. (16.5.2b),

$$\frac{b_E}{b_w} = \frac{35.5}{14} = 2.54, \qquad \frac{t}{h} = \frac{6.5}{28} = 0.232$$

$$k = 1.484, \qquad I_b = 1.484 \frac{14(28)^3}{12} = 38,000 \text{ in.}^4$$

Using Eq. (16.5.1),

$$I_s = \tfrac{1}{12}(120)(6.5)^3 = 2745 \text{ in.}^4, \qquad \alpha = \frac{E_{cb}I_b}{E_{cs}I_s} = \frac{38,000}{2745} = 13.83$$

(c) $B5-B6$. Referring to Fig. 16.5.3, the effective width b_E for $B5-B6$ is the smaller of $12 + 2(17.5) = 47$ in. or $12 + 8(6.5) = 64$ in.; thus $b_E = 47$ in. Using Eq. (16.5.2b),

$$\frac{b_E}{b_w} = \frac{47}{12} = 3.92, \qquad \frac{t}{h} = \frac{6.5}{24} = 0.271$$

$$k = 1.762, \qquad I_b = 1.762 \frac{12(24)^3}{12} = 24,400 \text{ in.}^4$$

Using Eq. (16.5.1),

$$I_s = \tfrac{1}{12}(300)(6.5)^3 = 6870 \text{ in.}^4, \qquad \alpha = \frac{E_{cb}I_b}{E_{cs}I_s} = \frac{24,400}{6870} = 3.55$$

(d) $B7-B8$. Referring to Fig. 16.5.3, the effective width b_E for $B7-B8$ is the smaller of $12 + 17.5 = 29.5$ in. or $12 + 4(6.5) = 38$ in.; thus $b_E = 29.5$ in. Using Eq. (16.5.2b),

$$\frac{b_E}{b_w} = \frac{29.5}{12} = 2.46, \qquad \frac{t}{h} = 0.271$$

$$k = 1.480, \qquad I_b = 1.480 \frac{12(24)^3}{12} = 20,500 \text{ in.}^4$$

Using Eq. (16.5.1),

$$I_s = \tfrac{1}{12}(150)(6.5)^3 = 3435 \text{ in.}^4, \qquad \alpha = \frac{E_{cb}I_b}{E_{cs}I_s} = \frac{20,500}{3435} = 5.96$$

The resulting α values for $B1$ through $B8$ around panels 1, 2, 3, and 4 are shown in Fig. 16.5.3.

EXAMPLE 16.5.2   Show that for the design example described in Sec. 16.3 the six limitations of the direct-design method are satisfied.

Solution: The first four limitations are satisfied by inspection. For the fifth limitation,

$$\text{service dead load} = 6.5\left(\frac{150}{12}\right) = 81 \text{ psf}$$

$$\text{service live load} = 120 \text{ psf}$$

$$\text{ratio of service LL to service DL} = \frac{120}{81} < 3 \qquad\qquad \text{OK}$$

For the sixth limitation, referring to Fig. 16.5.3 and taking L_1 and L_2 in the long and short directions, respectively,

Panel 1,
$$\frac{L_1^2}{\alpha_1} = \frac{625}{0.5(13.83 + 8.27)} = 56.6,$$

$$\frac{L_2^2}{\alpha_2} = \frac{400}{0.5(5.96 + 3.55)} = 84.0$$

Panel 2,
$$\frac{L_1^2}{\alpha_1} = \frac{625}{0.5(13.83 + 8.27)} = 56.6,$$

$$\frac{L_2^2}{\alpha_2} = \frac{400}{3.55} = 112.7$$

Panel 3,
$$\frac{L_1^2}{\alpha_1} = \frac{625}{8.27} = 75.6,$$

$$\frac{L_2^2}{\alpha_2} = \frac{400}{0.5(5.96 + 3.55)} = 84.0$$

Panel 4,
$$\frac{L_1^2}{\alpha_1} = \frac{625}{8.27} = 75.6,$$

$$\frac{L_2^2}{\alpha_2} = \frac{400}{3.55} = 112.7$$

All ratios of L_1^2/α_1 to L_2^2/α_2 lie between 0.2 and 5.

16.6 Minimum Slab Thickness for Deflection Control

Semiempirical equations are prescribed by the ACI Code (ACI-9.5.3.1) to give a minimum thickness for use in the design of two-way slab systems in order to control deflections. These equations give a minimum thickness that from experience has been found to be satisfactory.

The slab thickness t (ACI uses h) in two-way slab systems must be at least

$$\min t = \frac{L_n(0.8 + 0.2f_y/40,000)}{36 - 2.5(1 - \beta_s)(1 + L_n/S_n) + 5\alpha_m L_n/S_n}, \text{ ACI Formula (9-10)}$$

(16.6.1)

or

$$\min t = \frac{L_n(0.8 + 0.2f_y/40,000)}{36 + 5(1 + \beta_s)L_n/S_n}, \text{ ACI Formula (9-11)} \quad (16.6.2)$$

but it need not be more than

$$t = \frac{L_n(0.8 + 0.2f_y/40,000)}{36}, \text{ ACI Formula (9-12)} \quad (16.6.3)$$

Also, the thickness for two-way slabs supported on beams must be at least $3\frac{1}{2}$ in. when α_m is at least equal to 2.0.

The rationale for these ACI formulas may be examined by observing the plot of the formulas in Fig. 16.6.1. The quantity obtained is the long direction clear span to thickness ratio L_n/t, similar to the span to depth ratio limitations that are used for beams (see Secs. 14.10 and 14.11).

Figure 16.6.1 includes the full feasible range of variables: (1) the panel proportions ranging from square to two-to-one rectangular, (2) the β_s from a maximum of 1.0 for an interior panel continuous over all four edges to a minimum of 0.5 for a corner panel continuous over only two sides, and (3) the α_m ranging from zero with no edge beams to 2.5 or so for very stiff edge beams.

The following logical results are indicated from a study of Fig. 16.6.1:

1. The stiffness of edge beams is the predominant factor; the no-edge-beam condition requires the thickest slab ($L_n/t = 36$ min), from which the thickness required decreases until the edge beams provide an average stiffness corresponding to $\alpha_m = 1.50 + 0.50S_n/L_n + 0.50\beta_s(1 - S_n/L_n)$, which has a maximum value of 2.0 for combinations of variables within the applicable range.

2. The proportion β_s of the perimeter of the panel that is continuous affects the required thickness; an interior panel with β_s at maximum of 1.0 allows

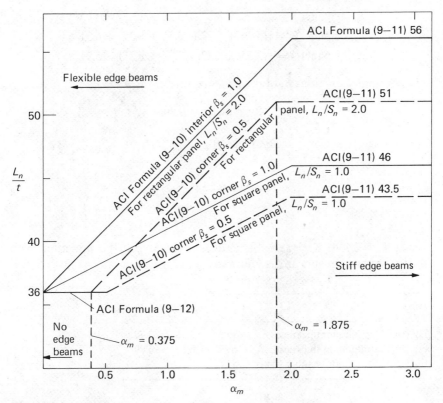

Fig. 16.6.1
ACI minimum slab-thickness formulas (for Grade 40 steel). For Grade 60, divide L_n/t by 1.1 (adapted from Ref. 12).

a higher L_n/t value, 5% higher for a square panel and 10% higher for a two-to-one rectangular panel.

3. The ratio L_n/S_n of the plan dimensions of the panel affects the thickness by requiring the thickest slab (lowest L_n/t) for the square panel. As the panel becomes more rectangular, more load is transferred to the supports in the short direction; thus with the shorter span becoming more effective the thickness can be reduced (L_n/t increased).

4. The steel yield strength f_y influences the thickness, since the higher the yield stress, the higher the stress and strain at service load, the more the cracking, and the greater the deflection. The L_n/t values of Fig. 16.6.1 are for Grade 40 steel and are to be divided by 1.1 for Grade 60 steel.

EXAMPLE 16.6.1   For the design example described in Sec. 16.3, determine the minimum thickness of the two-way slab for deflection control; and compare it with preliminary thickness of $6\frac{1}{2}$ in.

Solution: The average ratios α_m for panels 1, 2, 3, and 4 may be computed from the α values shown in Fig. 16.5.3; thus

$$\alpha_m \text{ for panel } 1 = \tfrac{1}{4}(5.96 + 8.27 + 3.55 + 13.83) = 7.90$$
$$\alpha_m \text{ for panel } 2 = \tfrac{1}{4}(3.55 + 8.27 + 3.55 + 13.83) = 7.30$$
$$\alpha_m \text{ for panel } 3 = \tfrac{1}{4}(5.96 + 8.27 + 3.55 + 8.27) = 6.51$$
$$\alpha_m \text{ for panel } 4 = \tfrac{1}{4}(3.55 + 8.27 + 3.55 + 8.27) = 5.91$$

The continuity fractions β_s of the panel perimeters are

$$\beta_s \text{ for panel } 1 = 0.50$$
$$\beta_s \text{ for panel } 2 = \frac{65}{90}$$
$$\beta_s \text{ for panel } 3 = \frac{70}{90}$$
$$\beta_s \text{ for panel } 4 = 1.0$$

Using $L_n = 24$ ft, $S_n = 18.83$ ft, and $f_y = 40{,}000$ psi, the minimum slab thickness requirements are as follows:

Panel	1	2	3	4
Eq. (16.6.1), minimum thickness	3.45	3.56	3.78	3.91
Eq. (16.6.2), minimum thickness	6.32	6.13	6.09	5.91
Eq. (16.6.3), need not be more than	8	8	8	8

If a uniform slab thickness for the entire floor area is to be used, the minimum for deflection control is 6.32 in., which compares well with the $6\frac{1}{2}$ in. preliminary thickness.

One may note from Fig. 16.6.1 that it is necessary only to use ACI Formula (9-11) or Eq. (16.6.2), since this requirement governs when α_m equals or exceeds 2.0. Figure 16.6.1 illustrates that it will rarely be necessary to utilize more than *one* of the three minimum thickness expressions.

16.7 Direct-Design Method—Longitudinal Distribution of Total Static Moment

In the "direct-design method," moment curves in the direction of span length need not be computed by an elastic analysis (such as the moment-distribution method) of the equivalent rigid frame subjected to various pattern loadings; instead they are nominally defined for regular situations, with additional prescribed adjustments for pattern loading effects.

Referring to Fig. 16.7.1, L_1 and L_2 are the centerline spans in the longitudinal and transverse directions, while L_n is the clear span in the longitudinal direction. The total static moment in the longitudinal direction has been defined by Eq. (16.3.2) to be

$$M_0 = \tfrac{1}{8} w_u L_2 L_n^2 = M_{\text{pos}} + \tfrac{1}{2}(M_{ni} + M_{nj}) \qquad \text{[16.3.2]}$$

in which M_{pos} is the positive moment at midspan, and M_{ni} and M_{nj} are absolute values of the negative moments at the faces of supports. To avoid the use of excessively small values of M_0 in the case of short spans and large columns or column capitals, the clear span L_n to be used in Eq. (16.3.2) is not to be less than $0.65L_1$ (ACI-13.6.2.5).

In the "direct-design method," wherein the six limitations described in Sec. 16.4 are satisfied, the design (factored) moment curves as shown in Fig. 16.7.1c may be "directly used for design" for the exterior and interior spans, except in cases where the positive moment should be adjusted upward for pattern loading effects (ACI-13.6.3 and ACI-13.6.10). Of course, these moments are yet to be distributed in some manner across the entire width L_2 in the transverse direction. This latter distribution will be treated in Sec. 16.10.

For a span that is completely fixed at both ends, the negative moment at the fixed end is twice as large as the positive moment at midspan. For a typical interior span satisfying the limitations for the direct-design method, the specified negative moment of $0.65M_0$ is a little less than twice the specified positive moment of $0.35M_0$, which is fairly reasonable because the restraining effect of the columns and adjacent panels is definitely less than that of a completely fixed-ended beam.

If the exterior edge of an exterior span is a simple support (i.e., slab is simply supported on a wall), the moment there is, of course, zero. In the meantime, as has been demonstrated in Chap. 7 on continuity analysis, the positive moment at midspan and the negative moment at the interior end become higher than their corresponding values for the interior span. These values are to be taken as $M_{\text{pos}} = 0.63M_0$ and $M_n = 0.75M_0$, respectively; they satisfy the statics equation

$$M_0 = M_{\text{pos}} + \tfrac{1}{2}(M_{ni} + M_{nj}) = 0.63M_0 + \tfrac{1}{2}(0 + 0.75M_0)$$

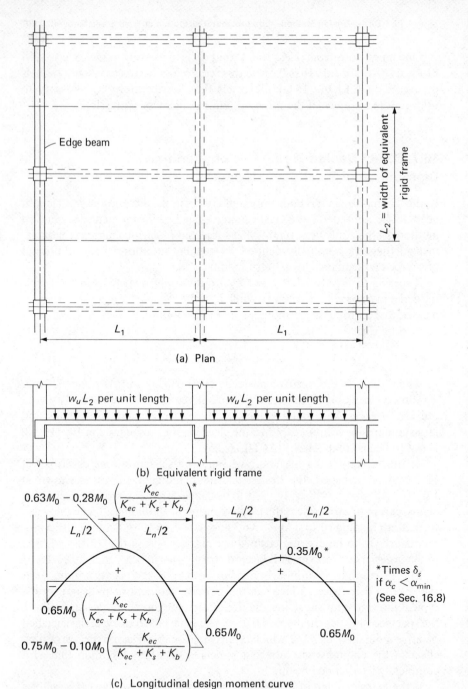

(a) Plan

(b) Equivalent rigid frame

(c) Longitudinal design moment curve

Fig. 16.7.1

Direct-design method: longitudinal distribution of moments.

Equivalent-Column Concept. At the exterior end of the equivalent rigid frame (Fig. 16.7.2) the slab is normally built monolithically with columns above and below the floor being considered, and since an edge beam at least equal in size to the width of the column by the depth of the slab is always present, these two types of structural elements (columns and edge beam) will give a combined stiffness K_{ec} defined as the flexural stiffness of the equivalent column. The method of determining K_{ec} is shown later in this section.

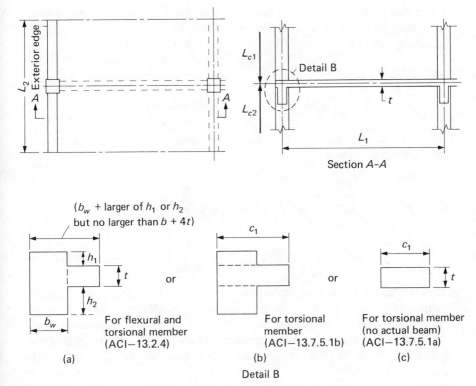

Fig. 16.7.2
Effective edge-beam section of equivalent rigid frame.

Referring to the exterior joint in section A-A of Fig. 16.7.2, the flexural stiffnesses of the slab and the included beam, for use in the direct-design method, may be taken as

$$K_s = \frac{4EI_s}{L_1} = \frac{4E_{cs}L_2t^3/12}{L_1}, \qquad K_b = \frac{4E_{cb}I_b}{L_1} \qquad \textbf{(16.7.1)}$$

wherein I_b is the gross moment of inertia of the longitudinal beam section defined by ACI-13.2.4. When an elastic analysis is made instead of the direct-design method for longitudinal distribution of moments, the stiffness coefficient in Eq. (16.7.1) should be taken more accurately larger than 4 because the moment of inertia of the slab or the beam between the column centerline and the edge of the column is to be taken much larger (ACI-13.7.3.3).

Using the distribution-factor concept of the moment-distribution method and taking $0.65M_0$ as the full restraining moment, the reduced restraining moment on the slab and beam owing to the presence of an equivalent column of flexural stiffness K_{ec} becomes

$$M_{\text{neg}} \text{ at exterior support} = 0.65M_0\left(\frac{K_{ec}}{K_{ec} + K_s + K_b}\right) \qquad (16.7.2)$$

which becomes zero if $K_{ec} = 0$. The moment at the interior end of an exterior span may be taken as a linear variation from $0.65M_0$ for a large value of K_{ec} at the exterior end to $0.75M_0$ for a zero value of K_{ec}; thus

$$M_{\text{neg}} \text{ at interior end of exterior span} = 0.75M_0 - 0.10M_0\left(\frac{K_{ec}}{K_{ec} + K_s + K_b}\right)$$

$$(16.7.3)$$

Using the statics equation (Eq. 16.3.2), the positive moment at the middle of the exterior span is

$$
\begin{aligned}
M_{\text{pos}} &= M_0 - \tfrac{1}{2}(M_{ni} + M_{nj}) \\
&= M_0 - \frac{1}{2}\left[\frac{0.65M_0(K_{ec})}{K_{ec} + K_s + K_b} + 0.75M_0 - \frac{0.10M_0(K_{ec})}{K_{ec} + K_s + K_b}\right] \\
&= 0.63M_0 - 0.28M_0\left(\frac{K_{ec}}{K_{ec} + K_s + K_b}\right) \qquad (16.7.4)
\end{aligned}
$$

After the moments have been established by these "direct-design" coefficients, ACI-13.6.7 permits any moment to be modified by 10% provided the total factored static moment M_0 for the panel is statically accommodated.

The flexural stiffness of the equivalent column at the exterior end of the equivalent frame is to be obtained from the equation (ACI Formula 13-6)

$$\frac{1}{K_{ec}} = \frac{1}{\Sigma K_c} + \frac{1}{K_t} \qquad (16.7.5)$$

ΣK_c is defined as the sum of the flexural stiffnesses of the columns above and below the floor. For use in the direct-design method, ΣK_c is permitted (ACI Commentary-13.7.4) to be taken as

$$\Sigma K_c = \frac{4EI_{c1}}{L_{c1}} + \frac{4EI_{c2}}{L_{c2}} \qquad (16.7.6)$$

in which the subscripts 1 and 2 refer to the upper and lower columns, respectively. K_t is the torsional stiffness of the spandrel beam and may be taken as (ACI Formula 13-7)

$$K_t = \Sigma \frac{9E_{cs}C}{L_2(1 - c_2/L_2)^3} \qquad (16.7.7)$$

where c_2 and L_2 relate to the transverse spans on each side of the column, and E_{cs} is the modulus of elasticity of the slab concrete. C is the torsional constant (see Chap. 19, Sec. 19.3) for the spandrel beam as shown in detail B of Fig. 16.7.2; it is equal to (ACI Formula 13-8)

$$C = \sum \left(1 - 0.63\frac{x}{y}\right)\left(\frac{x^3 y}{3}\right) \tag{16.7.8}$$

where

x = shorter dimension of each component rectangle
y = longer dimension of each component rectangle

and the component rectangles should be taken in such a way that the largest value of C is obtained (ACI Commentary-13.7.5).

The nature of Eq. (16.7.5) for the equivalent column stiffness may be explained by examining Fig. 16.7.3. The stiffness K_{ec} is defined as the moment per unit rotation about axis z that can be considered the value for the entire width of the equivalent frame. Along the length c_2, the rotation equals the

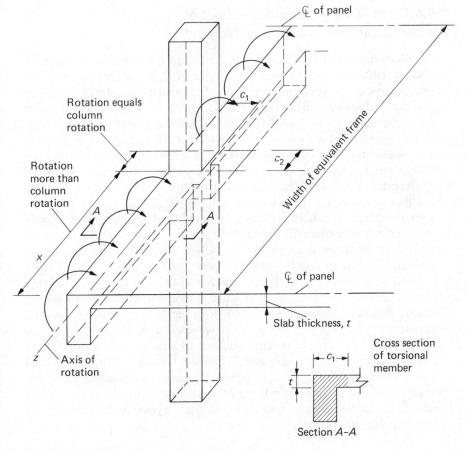

Fig. 16.7.3
Equivalent column concept.

rotation of the column; whereas along the lengths x on either side of the column, the rotation is different (usually much more). Since the rotation per unit moment (flexibility) is different for the torsional element (edge beam) than it is for the column, the ACI Code adds the flexibility of the torsional members to that of the column to obtain the equivalent column flexibility. This gives the logical result that if the column is infinitely stiff ($K_c = \infty$) and therefore does not rotate about axis z, the equivalent column stiffness K_{ec} equals the torsional stiffness since rotation will still occur everywhere except over the width c_2 at the column. Only when the torsional element has very high stiffness will the K_{ec} approach K_c. If the exterior support were a wall, the rotation about the z axis would be relatively the same along the width; for such a case, K_{ec} would be ΣK_c (the flexural stiffness of the wall above and below the floor). The adding of flexibilities ($1/K$) to find K_{ec} conforms to the findings of both three-dimensional analysis [9] and experimental work [5,6,10] in that the spandrel beam can rotate even though the columns are infinitely stiff.

16.8 Direct-Design Method—Effect of Pattern Loadings on Positive Moment

To understand the effect of pattern loadings on the longitudinal moment values in multiple panel two-way slab systems, it is convenient to review some aspects of the continuity analysis of the usual column-beam type of rigid frames discussed earlier in Chap. 7. Some of the findings, which might be visualized by those knowledgeable in influence lines and maximum moment envelopes due to dead- and live-load combinations, are as follows: (1) the higher the ratio of column stiffness to beam stiffness, the smaller the effect of pattern loadings, because the ends of the span are closer to the fixed condition and less effect is exerted on the span by loading patterns on adjacent spans; (2) the lower the ratio of dead load to live load, the larger the effect of pattern loadings, because dead load exists constantly on all spans and the pattern is related to live load only; and (3) maximum negative moments at supports are less affected by pattern loadings than maximum positive moments within the span.

Based on studies by Jirsa, Sozen, and Siess [13], it is recommended that in order to limit the increase in positive moment within the slab system caused by pattern loadings to such a tolerance (33% according to ACI Commentary–13.6.10) that the moment values in Fig. 16.7.1c (ACI-13.6.3) may be used, the ratio of column stiffness to slab stiffness must have at least the values shown in Table 16.8.1 (from ACI-Table 13.6.10). If the ratio α_c of column stiffness to slab and beam stiffness is less than the minimum value α_{min} shown in Table 16.8.1, then the positive moments in Fig. 16.7.1c must be multiplied by the coefficient δ_s given by the following formula (ACI Formula 13–5),

$$\delta_s = 1 + \frac{2 - \beta_a}{4 + \beta_a}\left(1 - \frac{\alpha_c}{\alpha_{min}}\right) \tag{16.8.1}$$

Table 16.8.1

Minimum Ratio α_{min} of Column Stiffness to Combined Beam and Slab Stiffness to Qualify for Positive-Moment Multiplier $\delta_s = 1$ (α = ratio of beam to slab stiffness)[a]

$\beta_a = \dfrac{DL}{LL}$	Aspect Ratio L_2/L_1	Ratio of Beam to Slab Stiffness, α				
		0	0.5	1.0	2.0	4.0
2.00	0.50–2.00	0	0	0	0	0
1.00	0.50	0.6	0	0	0	0
	0.80	0.7	0	0	0	0
	1.00	0.7	0.1	0	0	0
	1.25	0.8	0.4	0	0	0
	2.00	1.2	0.5	0.2	0	0
0.50	0.50	1.3	0.3	0	0	0
	0.80	1.5	0.5	0.2	0	0
	1.00	1.6	0.6	0.2	0	0
	1.25	1.9	1.0	0.5	0	0
	2.00	4.9	1.6	0.8	0.3	0
0.33	0.50	1.8	0.5	0.1	0	0
	0.80	2.0	0.9	0.3	0	0
	1.00	2.3	0.9	0.4	0	0
	1.25	2.8	1.5	0.8	0.2	0
	2.00	13.0	2.6	1.2	0.5	0.3

[a] From ACI-Table 13.6.10.

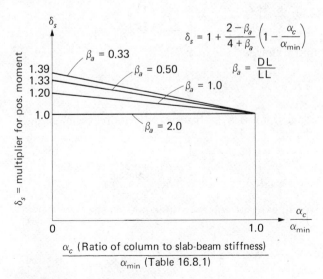

$$\delta_s = 1 + \frac{2 - \beta_a}{4 + \beta_a}\left(1 - \frac{\alpha_c}{\alpha_{min}}\right)$$

$$\beta_a = \frac{DL}{LL}$$

δ_s = multiplier for pos. moment

$\beta_a = 0.33$

$\beta_a = 0.50$

$\beta_a = 1.0$

$\beta_a = 2.0$

1.39
1.33
1.20
1.0

0

1.0

$\dfrac{\alpha_c}{\alpha_{min}}$

$\dfrac{\alpha_c \text{ (Ratio of column to slab-beam stiffness)}}{\alpha_{min} \text{ (Table 16.8.1)}}$

Fig. 16.8.1
Direct-design method: effect of pattern loadings.

in which

> β_a = ratio of service dead load to service live load
> α_c = ratio of column stiffness to slab and beam stiffness
>   = $\Sigma K_c / (\Sigma K_s + \Sigma K_b)$
> α_{min} = value shown in Table 16.8.1

For the half column strip parallel to an exterior edge, it is conservative, and therefore permissible to use the value of α_c computed for the adjacent interior column if it is equal in size to the exterior column. The graph shown in Fig. 16.8.1 is not so much to save the arithmetic involved in Eq. (16.8.1) as to show the variation of δ_s with respect to α_c / α_{min} and β_a.

16.9 Direct-Design Method—Procedure for Computation of Longitudinal Moments

The background explanation for the distribution of the total static moment M_0 in the longitudinal direction and for the modification of positive moment due to the effect of pattern loadings has been presented in the two preceding sections. Utilizing this information the procedure for the computation of longitudinal moments by the "direct-design method" may be summarized as follows:

1. Check if the six limitations for the "direct-design method" listed in Sec. 16.4 are satisfied.
2. Compute the total static moment $M_0 = w_u L_2 L_n^2 / 8$ as stated by Eq. (16.3.2).
3. Compute the slab stiffness

$$K_s = \frac{4EI_s}{L_1}, \qquad I_s = \Sigma \frac{1}{2} L_2 \left(\frac{t^3}{12} \right)$$

4. Compute the column stiffness

$$\Sigma K_c = K_{c1} + K_{c2} = \frac{4EI_{c1}}{L_{c1}} + \frac{4EI_{c2}}{L_{c2}}$$

5. Compute the torsional stiffness K_t of transverse spandrel beam defined by detail B in Fig. 16.7.2,

$$K_t = \Sigma \frac{9E_{cs}C}{L_2(1 - c_2/L_2)^3}, \qquad C = \Sigma \left(1 - 0.63 \frac{x}{y} \right) \left(\frac{x^3 y}{3} \right)$$

6. Compute the equivalent exterior column stiffness K_{ec} from

$$\frac{1}{K_{ec}} = \frac{1}{\Sigma K_c} + \frac{1}{K_t}$$

7. Compute the ratio α of the longitudinal beam (ACI-13.2.4) stiffness to that of the slab by $\alpha = (E_{cb}I_b)/(E_{cs}I_s)$ and with the value of β_a = (service

DL/service LL), obtain the value of α_{min} from Table 16.8.1 or ACI-Table 13.6.10.

8. Compute for the exterior and interior spans the ratio α_c of the flexural stiffnesses of the upper and lower columns to the combined flexural stiffnesses of the slab and beam by the following:

$$\alpha_c = \frac{K_{c1} + K_{c2}}{\Sigma K_s + \Sigma K_b}$$

9. If the value of α_c computed in step 8 does not reach the α_{min} shown in Table 16.8.1, the positive moments M_{pos} must be increased for pattern loading effects by the multiplier δ_s, Eq. (16.8.1). If α_c/α_{min} exceeds one, $\delta_s = 1$ (i.e., no pattern loading effect).

10. Compute negative moment at face of exterior support equal to

$$0.65M_0 \left(\frac{K_{ec}}{K_{ec} + K_s + K_b} \right)$$

11. Compute positive moment in exterior span equal to

$$\delta_s \left[0.63M_0 - 0.28M_0 \left(\frac{K_{ec}}{K_{ec} + K_s + K_b} \right) \right]$$

12. Compute negative moment at exterior face of first interior support equal to

$$0.75M_0 - 0.10M_0 \left(\frac{K_{ec}}{K_{ec} + K_s + K_b} \right)$$

13. Compute negative moment at interior face of interior support equal to

$$0.65M_0.$$

14. Compute positive moment in interior span equal to

$$\delta_s(0.35M_0).$$

EXAMPLE 16.9.1 For the design example described in Sec. 16.3, determine the longitudinal moments in frames A, B, C, and D, as shown in Figs. 16.3.3 and 16.9.2.

Solution: (a) Torsional constants C. The transverse edge beam effective sections in the short and long directions of the two-way slab floor system are shown in Fig. 16.9.1. The slab width beyond the beam stem is in each case equal to the projection of the beam stem below the slab, 17.5 and 21.5 in., respectively, because 4 times the slab thickness would be 26 in. In addition, ACI-13.7.5.1b indicates that the column dimension may also control the effective slab width; in this case the column is only 15 in. wide, whereas to control it would have to exceed 35.5 and 29.5 in. in the long and short dimensions, respectively. The column dimension may control in situations where the column is actually a shear wall.

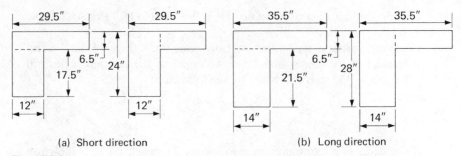

(a) Short direction (b) Long direction

Fig. 16.9.1

Transverse edge-beam sections in design example.

The cross section may be divided into component rectangles in two different ways and the larger value of C is to be used. For the short direction,

$$C = \left[1 - \frac{0.63(6.5)}{29.5}\right]\frac{29.5(6.5)^3}{3} + \left[1 - \frac{0.63(12)}{17.5}\right]\frac{17.5(12)^3}{3} = 8050 \text{ in.}^4$$

or

$$C = \left[1 - \frac{0.63(6.5)}{17.5}\right]\frac{17.5(6.5)^3}{3} + \left[1 - \frac{0.63(12)}{24}\right]\frac{24(12)^3}{3} = 10,700 \text{ in.}^4 \quad Use$$

For the long direction,

$$C = \left[1 - \frac{0.63(6.5)}{35.5}\right]\frac{35.5(6.5)^3}{3} + \left[1 - \frac{0.63(14)}{21.5}\right]\frac{21.5(14)^3}{3} = 14,500 \text{ in.}^4$$

or

$$C = \left[1 - \frac{0.63(6.5)}{21.5}\right]\frac{21.5(6.5)^3}{3} + \left[1 - \frac{0.63(14)}{28}\right]\frac{28(14)^3}{3} = 19,100 \text{ in.}^4 \quad Use$$

(b) Torsional stiffness K_t. The torsional stiffnesses K_t of the transverse edge beam sections are

For frame A, $\qquad K_t = \dfrac{2(9)E(10,700)}{240(1 - 15/240)^3} = 974E^\dagger$

For frame B, $\qquad K_t = 487E^\dagger$

For frame C, $\qquad K_t = \dfrac{2(9)E(19,100)}{300(1 - 15/300)^3} = 1340E^\dagger$

For frame D, $\qquad K_t = 670E^\dagger$

(c) Equivalent exterior column stiffnesses K_{ec}. Since all columns are of the same size, 15 × 15 in. and 12 ft long,

$$K_{c1} = K_{c2} = \frac{4E15(15)^3/12}{144} = 117E$$

[†] Increase in torsional stiffness is permitted, but not required, to account for beams that frame into the column in the direction moments are determined. Such increase is neglected here, as allowed in the direct-design method (ACI Commentary-13.7.5).

For frame A, $\quad \dfrac{1}{K_{ec}} = \dfrac{1}{K_{c1} + K_{c2}} + \dfrac{1}{K_t} = \dfrac{1}{234E} + \dfrac{1}{974E}$

$$K_{ec} = \frac{1000E}{1000/234 + 1000/974} = \frac{1000E}{4.27 + 1.03} = 189E$$

For frame B, $\quad \dfrac{1}{K_{ec}} = \dfrac{1}{234E} + \dfrac{1}{487E}$

$$K_{ec} = \frac{1000E}{1000/234 + 1000/487} = \frac{1000E}{4.27 + 2.05} = 158E$$

For frame C, $\quad \dfrac{1}{K_{ec}} = \dfrac{1}{234E} + \dfrac{1}{1340E}$

$$K_{ec} = \frac{1000E}{1000/234 + 1000/1340} = \frac{1000E}{4.27 + 0.75} = 199E$$

For frame D, $\quad \dfrac{1}{K_{ec}} = \dfrac{1}{234E} + \dfrac{1}{670E}$

$$K_{ec} = \frac{1000E}{1000/234 + 1000/670} = \frac{1000E}{4.27 + 1.49} = 173E$$

(d) Minimum ratio α_{min}. The ratio β_a of service dead to live load is

$$\beta_a = \frac{6.5(150/12)}{120} = \frac{81}{120} = 0.67$$

The minimum ratios α_{min} required for making positive-moment multiplier $\delta_s = 1.0$ are tabulated below

Frame	A	B	C	D
$\alpha = \dfrac{E_{cb}I_b}{E_{cs}I_s}$ from Fig. 16.5.3	8.27	13.83	3.55	5.96
L_2/L_1	0.80	0.80	1.25	1.25
α_{min} from Table 16.8.1	0	0	0	0

(e) Ratio α_c of $(K_{c1} + K_{c2})$ to $(K_s + K_b)$. In the present design example, the ratio α_c of $(K_{c1} + K_{c2})$ to $(K_s + K_b)$ is the same for exterior and interior spans.

For frame A,

$$K_s = \frac{4E(240)(6.5)^3/12}{300} = 73.2E$$

$$K_b = \frac{4EI_b \text{ of B1-B2 (Example 16.5.1)}}{300} = \frac{4E(45,400)}{300} = 606E$$

$$\alpha_c = \frac{234E}{606E + 73.2E} = 0.344$$

For frame B,

$$K_s = 36.6E$$

$$K_b = \frac{4EI_b \text{ of } B3\text{-}B4 \text{ (Example 16.5.1)}}{300} = \frac{4E(38,000)}{300} = 507E$$

$$\alpha_c = \frac{234E}{507E + 36.6E} = 0.430$$

For frame C,

$$K_s = \frac{4E(300)(6.5)^3/12}{240} = 114E$$

$$K_b = \frac{4EI_b \text{ of } B5\text{-}B6 \text{ (Example 16.5.1)}}{240} = \frac{4E(24,400)}{240} = 406E$$

$$\alpha_c = \frac{234E}{406E + 114E} = 0.450$$

For frame D,

$$K_s = 57E$$

$$K_b = \frac{4EI_b \text{ of } B7\text{-}B8 \text{ (Example 16.5.1)}}{240} = \frac{4E(20,500)}{240} = 341E$$

$$\alpha_c = \frac{234E}{341E + 57E} = 0.587$$

Actually the above computations for α_c are unnecessary because values of α_{min} (or the minimum value of α_c required to make $\delta_s = 1.0$) are zero for all frames. However, the values of K_s and K_b are still needed in computing the distribution factor DF at the exterior joint.

(f) Positive moment multiplier δ_s. Since there is sufficient stiffness in the columns to minimize the pattern loading effects for all frames, $\delta_s = 1.0$ in all cases.

(g) Distribution factors DF at exterior joint.

For frame A, $\quad DF = \dfrac{K_{ec}}{K_{ec} + K_b + K_s} = \dfrac{189E}{189E + 606E + 73.2E} = 0.218$

For frame B, $\quad DF = \dfrac{158E}{158E + 507E + 36.6E} = 0.225$

For frame C, $\quad DF = \dfrac{199E}{199E + 406E + 114E} = 0.277$

For frame D, $\quad DF = \dfrac{173E}{173E + 341E + 57E} = 0.303$

(h) Longitudinal moments in the frames. The longitudinal moments in frames A, B, C, and D are computed below and shown in Fig. 16.9.2.

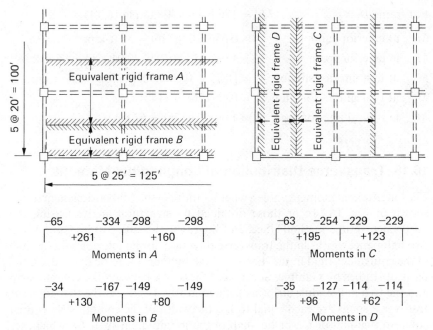

Fig. 16.9.2
Longitudinal moments for two-way slab floor of Example 16.9.1.

For frame A, $\quad\quad\quad\quad\quad$ $M_0 = 458$ ft-kips (Example 16.3.1)

M_{neg} at exterior support $\quad\quad = 0.65(0.218)(458) = 65$ ft-kips

M_{pos} in exterior span $\quad\quad\quad = 1.0[0.63 - 0.28(0.218)](458) = 261$ ft-kips

M_{neg} at first interior support $\quad = [0.75 - 0.10(0.218)](458) = 334$ ft-kips

M_{neg} at typical interior support $= 0.65(458) = 298$ ft-kips

M_{pos} in typical interior span $\quad = 1.0(0.35)(458) = 160$ ft-kips

For frame B, $\quad\quad\quad\quad\quad$ $M_0 = 229$ ft-kips (Example 16.3.1)

M_{neg} at exterior support $\quad\quad = 0.65(0.225)(229) = 34$ ft-kips

M_{pos} in exterior span $\quad\quad\quad = 1.0[0.63 - 0.28(0.225)](229) = 130$ ft-kips

M_{neg} at first interior support $\quad = [0.75 - 0.10(0.225)](229) = 167$ ft-kips

M_{neg} at typical interior support $= 0.65(229) = 149$ ft-kips

M_{pos} in typical interior span $\quad = 1.0(0.35)(229) = 80$ ft-kips

For frame C, $\quad\quad\quad\quad\quad$ $M_0 = 352$ ft-kips (Example 16.3.1)

M_{neg} at exterior support $\quad\quad = 0.65(0.277)(352) = 63$ ft-kips

M_{pos} in exterior span $\quad\quad\quad = 1.0[0.63 - 0.28(0.277)](352) = 195$ ft-kips

M_{neg} at first interior support $\quad = [0.75 - 0.10(0.277)](352) = 254$ ft-kips

M_{neg} at typical interior support $= 0.65(352) = 229$ ft-kips

M_{pos} in typical interior span $\quad = 1.0(0.35)(352) = 123$ ft-kips

For frame D, $\qquad M_0 = 176$ ft-kips (Example 16.3.1)

M_{neg} at exterior support $\qquad = 0.65(0.303)(176) = 35$ ft-kips

M_{pos} in exterior span $\qquad = 1.0[0.63 - 0.28(0.303)](176) = 96$ ft-kips

M_{neg} at first interior support $\quad = [0.75 - 0.10(0.303)](176) = 127$ ft-kips

M_{neg} at typical interior support $= 0.65(176) = 114$ ft-kips

M_{pos} in typical interior span $\quad = 1.0(0.35)(176) = 62$ ft-kips

16.10 Transverse Distribution of Longitudinal Moment

The longitudinal moment values, whether those of the "direct-design method" shown in Fig. 16.7.1c or those obtained by structural analysis using the "equivalent-frame method" (Sec. 16.14), are for the entire width (sum of the two half panel widths in the transverse direction, for an interior column line) of the equivalent rigid frame. Each of these moments is to be divided, on the basis of studies by Gamble, Sozen, and Siess [4], between the column strip and the two half middle strips as defined in Fig. 16.10.1. If the two adjacent transverse spans are each equal to L_2, the width of the column strip is then equal to one-half of L_2, or one-half of the longitudinal span L_1, whichever is smaller (ACI-13.2.1). This seems reasonable, since when the longitudinal span is shorter than the transverse span, a larger portion of the moment across the width of the equivalent frame might be expected to concentrate near the column centerline.

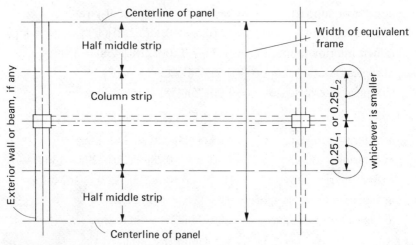

Fig. 16.10.1
Definition of column and middle strips.

The transverse distribution of the longitudinal moment to column and middle strips is a function of three parameters, using L_1 and L_2 for the longitudinal and transverse spans, respectively: (1) the aspect ratio L_2/L_1; (2) the ratio $\alpha_1 = E_{cb}I_b/(E_{cs}I_s)$ of the longitudinal beam stiffness to slab

Table 16.10.1
Percentage of Longitudinal Moment in Column Strip (ACI-13.6.4)

Aspect Ratio L_2/L_1			0.5	1.0	2.0
Negative moment at exterior support	$\alpha_1 L_2/L_1 = 0$	$\beta_t = 0$	100	100	100
		$\beta_t \geq 2.5$	75	75	75
	$\alpha_1 L_2/L_1 \geq 1.0$	$\beta_t = 0$	100	100	100
		$\beta_t \geq 2.5$	90	75	45
Positive moment	$\alpha_1 L_2/L_1 = 0$		60	60	60
	$\alpha_1 L_2/L_1 \geq 1.0$		90	75	45
Negative moment at interior support	$\alpha_1 L_2/L_1 = 0$		75	75	75
	$\alpha_1 L_2/L_1 \geq 1.0$		90	75	45

stiffness; and (3) the ratio $\beta_t = E_{cb}C/(2E_{cs}I_s)$ of the torsional rigidity of edge beam section [as defined by Detail B of Fig. 16.7.2 and Eq. (16.7.8)] to the flexural rigidity of a width of slab equal to the span length of the beam. According to ACI-13.6.4, the column strip is to take the percentage of the longitudinal moment as shown in Table 16.10.1.

Regarding the distributing percentages shown in Table 16.10.1, the following observations may be made:

1. In general, the column strip takes more than 50% of the longitudinal moment.
2. The column strip takes a larger share of the negative longitudinal moment than the positive longitudinal moment.
3. When no longitudinal beams are present, the column strip takes the same share of the longitudinal moment, irrespective of the aspect ratio. The reader may note, however, that the column strip width is a fraction of L_1 or L_2, whichever is smaller.
4. In the presence of longitudinal beams, the larger the aspect ratio, the smaller the distribution to the column strip. This seems consistent because the same reduction in the portion of moment going into the slab is achieved by restricting the column strip width to a fraction of L_1 when L_2/L_1 is greater than one.
5. The column strip takes a smaller share of the exterior moment as the torsional rigidity of the edge beam section increases.

When the exterior support consists of a column or wall extending for a distance equal to or greater than three-fourths of the transverse width, the exterior negative moment is to be uniformly distributed over the transverse width (ACI-13.6.4.3).

The procedure for distributing the longitudinal moment across a transverse width to the column and middle strips may be summarized as follows:

1. Divide the total transverse width applicable to the longitudinal moment into a column strip width and two half middle strip widths, one adjacent

to each side of the column strip. For an exterior column line, the column strip width is $\frac{1}{4}L_1$ or $\frac{1}{4}L_2$, whichever is smaller; for an interior column line, the column strip width is $\Sigma(\frac{1}{4}L_1$ or $\frac{1}{4}L_2$, whichever is smaller, of the panels on both sides).

2. Determine the ratio $\beta_t = E_{cb}C/(2E_{cs}I_s)$ of edge beam torsional rigidity to slab flexural rigidity. (Note: The 2 arises from approximating the shear modulus of elasticity in the numerator as $E_{cb}/2$.)

3. Determine the ratio $\alpha_1 = E_{cb}I_b/(E_{cs}I_s)$ of longitudinal beam flexural stiffness to slab flexural stiffness.

4. Divide the longitudinal moment at each critical section into two parts according to the percentage shown in Table 16.10.1: one part to the column strip width; and the remainder to the half middle strip for an exterior column line, or to the half middle strips on each side of an interior column line.

5. If there is an exterior wall instead of an exterior column line, the strip ordinarily called the exterior column strip will not deflect and therefore no moments act. In this case there can be no longitudinal distribution of moments; thus there is no computed moment to distribute laterally to the half middle strip adjacent to the wall. This half middle strip should be combined with the next adjacent half middle strip, which itself receives a lateral distribution in the frame of the first interior column line. The total middle strip in this situation is designed for twice the moment in the half middle strip from the first interior column line (ACI-13.6.6.3).

Distribution of Moment in Column Strip to Beam and Slab.

When a longitudinal beam exists in the column strip along the column centerline, the column strip moment as determined by the percentages in Table 16.10.1 (ACI-13.6.4) should be divided to the beam and the slab. ACI-13.6.5 states that 85% of this moment be taken by the beam if $\alpha L_2/L_1$ is equal to or greater than 1.0, and for values of $\alpha L_2/L_1$ between 1.0 and 0, the proportion of moment to be resisted by the beam is to be obtained by linear interpolation between 85 and 0%.

EXAMPLE 16.10.1 For the design example described in Sec. 16.3, distribute the longitudinal moments computed for frames A, B, C, and D (see Fig. 16.9.2) into three parts—namely, for the longitudinal beam, for the column strip slab, and for the middle strip slab.

Solution: The values for the total longitudinal moments in frames A, B, C, and D at the five critical sections are taken from Example 16.9.1 and shown again in Table 16.10.2. The results of transverse distribution of these moments are also shown in this table.

(a) Negative moment at face of exterior support. For frame A, $L_2/L_1 = 0.80$; $\alpha_1 = 8.27$ (Fig. 16.5.3); $\alpha_1 L_2/L_1 = 6.61$; $C = 10,700$ in.^{4} (Example 16.9.1); $I_s = 240(6.5)^3/12 = 5490$ in.^{4}; and $\beta_t = C/(2I_s) = 10,700/[2(5490)] = 0.98$. Table 16.10.3 shows the linear interpolation for obtaining the column strip percentage from the prescribed limits of Table 16.10.1. The total moment of 65 ft-kips is divided into three parts, 92.6% to column strip (of

Table 16.10.2 (also see Fig. 16.9.2)

Transverse Distribution of Longitudinal Moments in Design Example

Frame A

Total Width = 20 ft, Column Strip Width = 10 ft, Middle Strip Width = 10 ft

	Exterior Span			Interior Span	
	Exterior Negative	Positive	Interior Negative	Negative	Positive
Total moment	−65	+261	−334	−298	+160
Moment in beam	−51	+179	−229	−205	+110
Moment in column strip slab	−9	+32	−41	−36	+20
Moment in middle strip slab	−5	+50	−64	−57	+30

Frame B

Total Width = 10 ft, Column Strip Width = 5 ft, Half Middle Strip Width = 5 ft

	Exterior Span			Interior Span	
	Exterior Negative	Positive	Interior Negative	Negative	Positive
Total moment	−34	+130	−167	−149	+80
Moment in beam	−26	+89	−115	−103	+55
Moment in column strip slab	−5	+16	−20	−18	+10
Moment in middle strip slab	−3	+25	−32	−28	+15

Frame C

Total Width = 25 ft, Column Strip Width = 10 ft, Middle Strip Width = 15 ft

	Exterior Span			Interior Span	
	Exterior Negative	Positive	Interior Negative	Negative	Positive
Total moment	−63	+195	−254	−229	+123
Moment in beam	−44	+112	−145	−132	+70
Moment in column strip slab	−8	+20	−26	−23	+13
Moment in middle strip slab	−11	+63	−83	−74	+40

Frame D

Total Width = 12.5 ft, Column Strip Width = 5 ft, Half Middle Strip Width = 7.5 ft

	Exterior Span			Interior Span	
	Exterior Negative	Positive	Interior Negative	Negative	Positive
Total moment	−35	+96	−127	−114	+62
Moment in beam	−24	+55	−73	−65	+36
Moment in column strip slab	−5	+10	−13	−12	+6
Moment in middle strip slab	−7	+31	−41	−37	+20

Table 16.10.3

Linear Interpolation for Column Strip Percentage of
Exterior Negative Moment—Frame A

L_2/L_1		0.5	0.8	1.0
	$\beta_t = 0$	100%	100%	100%
$\alpha_1 L_2/L_1 = 6.61$	$\beta_t = 0.98$	96.1%	92.6%	90.2%
	$\beta_t \geq 2.50$	90%	81%	75%

which 85% goes to the beam and 15% to the slab since $\alpha_1 L_2/L_1 = 6.61 \geq 1.0$)
and 7.4% to the middle strip slab. The results are shown in Table 16.10.2.

For frame B, $L_2/L_1 = 0.80$; $\alpha_1 = 13.83$ (Fig. 16.5.3); $\alpha_1 L_2/L_1 = 11.1$;
$\beta_t = 0.98$ same as for frame A; and column strip moment percentage $= 92.6\%$,
the same as for frame A.

For frame C, $L_2/L_1 = 1.25$; $\alpha_1 = 3.55$ (Fig. 16.5.3); $\alpha_1 L_2/L_1 = 4.44$; $C = 19,100$ in.^{4}; $I_s = 300(6.5)^3/12 = 6870$ in.^{4}; and $\beta_t = C/(2I_s) = 19,100/[2(6870)] = 1.39$. Table 16.10.4 shows the linear interpolation for obtaining the column

Table 16.10.4

Linear Interpolation for Column Strip Percentage of
Exterior Negative Moment—Frame C

L_2/L_1		1.0	1.25	2.0
	$\beta_t = 0$	100%	100%	100%
$\alpha_1 L_2/L_1 = 4.44$	$\beta_t = 1.39$	86.1%	81.9%	69.4%
	$\beta_t \geq 2.50$	75%	67.5%	45%

strip percentage from the prescribed limits of Table 16.10.1. The total
moment of 63 ft-kips is divided into three parts, 81.9% to column strip (of
which 85% goes to the beam and 15% to the slab since $\alpha_1 L_2/L_1 = 4.44 \geq 1.0$)
and 18.1% to the middle strip slab.

For frame D, $L_2/L_1 = 1.25$; $\alpha_1 = 5.96$ (Fig. 16.5.3), $\alpha_1 L_2/L_1 = 7.45$; $\beta_t = 1.39$ same as for frame C; and column strip moment percentage $= 81.9\%$, the
same as for frame C.

(b) Negative moments at exterior face of first interior support and at face
of typical interior support. For frame A, $L_2/L_1 = 0.80$ and $\alpha_1 L_2/L_1 = 6.61 > 1.0$. Using the prescribed values in Table 16.10.1, the proportion of
moment going to the column strip is determined to be 81% by linear inter-
polation:

L_2/L_1	0.5	0.8	1.0
$\alpha_1 L_2/L_1 = 6.61$	90%	81%	75%

For frame B, $L_2/L_1 = 0.80$ and $\alpha_1 L_2/L_1 = 11.1$. The proportion of moment is again 81% for the column strip, the same as for strip A.

For frame C, $L_2/L_1 = 1.25$ and $\alpha_1 L_2/L_1 = 4.44$. Using the prescribed values in Table 16.10.1, the proportion of moment going to the column strip is determined to be 67.5% by linear interpolation:

L_2/L_1	1.0	1.25	2.0
$\alpha_1 L_2/L_1 = 4.44$	75%	67.5%	45%

For frame D, $L_2/L_1 = 1.25$ and $\alpha_1 L_2/L_1 = 7.47$. The proportion of moment is again 67.5% for the column strip, the same as for frame C.

(c) Positive moments in exterior and interior spans. Since the prescribed limits for $\alpha_1 L_2/L_1 \geq 1.0$ are the same for positive moment and for negative moment at interior support, the percentages of column strip moment for positive moments in exterior and interior spans are identical to those for negative moments as determined in part (b) of this example.

16.11 Slab Thickness Requirement in Flexure and Shear

The slab thickness must be sufficient for resisting the bending moment and shear at the critical sections.

First it is necessary to search for the location where the intensity of bending moment is the largest per unit width of slab. With the preliminary thickness already assumed, the percentage of tension reinforcement required may be compared with $0.75\rho_b$. Deflection control is usually satisfactory if the percentage of reinforcement is less than one-half of $0.75\rho_b$. Crack control for the two-way slab is usually not a problem and is not covered by the ACI Code; however, when Grade 60 steel or higher strength is used and crack control is of concern, the possible crack width may be predicted by referring to the work of Nawy and others [14–17].

The shear requirement may be investigated by observing strips 1-1 and 2-2 in Fig. 16.11.1. Beams with $\alpha_1 L_2/L_1$ values larger than 1.0 are assumed to carry the loads acting on the tributary floor areas bounded by 45° lines drawn from the corners of the panel and the centerline of the panel parallel to the long side (ACI-13.6.8.1). If this is the case, the loads on the trapezoidal areas E and F of Fig. 16.11.1 go to the long beams; and those on the triangular areas G and H go to the short beams. The shear per unit width of slab along the beam is highest at ends of slab strips 1-1 and 2-2, which, considering the increased shear at the exterior face of the first interior support, is approximately equal to

$$V_u = 1.15\left(\frac{w_u S}{2}\right) \tag{16.11.1}$$

If $\alpha_1 L_2/L_1$ is equal to zero, there is, of course, no load on the beams (because there are no beams). When the value of $\alpha_1 L_2/L_1$ is between 0 and 1.0, the percentage of the floor load going to the beams should be obtained by

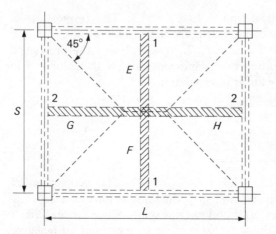

Fig. 16.11.1
Load transfer from floor area to beams.

linear interpolation. In such a case, the shear expressed by Eq. (16.11.1) would be reduced, but the shear around the column due to the portion of the floor load going directly to the columns by two-way action should be investigated as for flat-plate floors (see Sec. 17.8).

EXAMPLE 16.11.1   Investigate if the preliminary slab thickness of $6\frac{1}{2}$ in. in the design example described in Sec. 16.3 is sufficient for resisting flexure and shear.

Solution: For each of the equivalent frames *A, B, C,* and *D,* the largest bending moment in the slab occurs at the exterior face of the first interior support in the middle strip slab. From Table 16.10.2, this moment is observed to be 64/10, 32/5, 83/15, or 41/7.5 ft-kips per ft of width in frames *A, B, C,* and *D,* respectively. Taking the effective depth to the contact level between the reinforcing bars in the two directions, and assuming #5 bars,

$$\text{average } d = 6.50 - 0.75 - 0.63 = 5.12 \text{ in.}$$

The largest R_u required is

$$R_u = \frac{M_u}{\phi bd^2} = \frac{6400(12)}{0.90(12)(5.12)^2} = 271 \text{ psi}$$

From Fig. 3.6.1, the percentage of reinforcement ρ for this value of R_u is 0.007, which is well below $0.375\rho_b = 0.0139$. Hence excessive deflection should not be expected; this is further verification of the minimum thickness formulas given in ACI-9.5.3.
   The factored floor load w_u is

$$w_u = 1.4w_D + 1.7w_L = 318 \text{ psf}$$

Since all $\alpha L_2/L_1$ values are well over 1.0, take V from Eq. (16.11.1) as

$$V_u = \frac{1.15wS}{2} = \frac{1.15(0.318)(20)}{2} = 3.66 \text{ kips}$$

$$V_c = 2\sqrt{f'_c}b_w d = 2\sqrt{3000}(12)(5.12)\tfrac{1}{1000} = 6.73 \text{ kips}$$

$$V_u = 3.66 \text{ kips} < \phi V_c = 0.85(6.73) = 5.72 \text{ kips} \qquad \text{OK}$$

Note that the shear 3.66 kips is the maximum at strip 1-1 of Fig. 16.11.1; actually the average for all such strips will be lower.

16.12 Beam Size Requirement in Flexure and Shear

The size of the beams along the column centerlines in a two-way slab panel should be sufficient to take the bending moments and shears at the critical sections.

For approximately equal spans, the largest bending moment should occur at the exterior face of the first interior column where the available section for strength computation is rectangular in nature because the effective slab projection is on the tension side. Then with the preliminary beam size the required reinforcement ratio ρ may be determined and compared with $0.75\rho_b$, the maximum value permitted. Deflection is unlikely to be a problem with T-sections, but must be investigated if excessive deflection may cause difficulty.

The maximum shear in the beam should also occur at the exterior face of the first interior column. The shear diagram for the exterior span may be obtained by placing the negative moments already computed for the beam by the "direct-design method" at the face of the column at each end and loading the span with the percentage of floor load interpolated between $\alpha_1 L_2/L_1 = 0$ and $\alpha_1 L_2/L_1 \geq 1.0$. The maximum nominal shear stress v_n should stay below, say, $6\sqrt{f'_c}$, as discussed in Sec. 10.2.

EXAMPLE 16.12.1 Investigate if the preliminary overall sizes of 14 × 28 in. for the long beam and 12 × 24 in. for the short beam are suitable for the two-way slab system of the design example described in Sec. 16.3.

Solution: Since the values of α, or of $\alpha_1 L_2/L_1$, are considerably larger than 1.0 for all beam spans, there is to be no reduction of the floor load going into the beams from the tributary areas (ACI-13.6.8). As shown in Fig. 16.12.1, the most critical span is $B1$ for the long direction and $B5$ for the short direction. Actually the load acting on the clear span of the beam should include the floor load (including the weight of the beam stem itself or any other load) directly over the beam stem width plus the floor load on the tributary areas bounded by the 45° lines from the corner of the panel. Also for practical purposes it is acceptable to consider the shear due to floor load at the face of column equal to one half of the floor load on the tributary areas between column centerlines, as shown in Fig. 16.12.1.

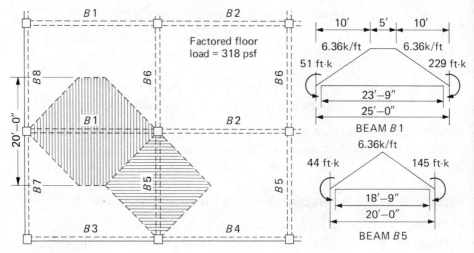

Fig. 16.12.1
Beams around the two-way slab panel.

(a) Size of long beam $B1$. The negative moments at the face of supports, 51 and 229 ft-kips, are taken from Table 16.10.2, frame A.

$$\text{weight of beam stem} = \frac{14(21.5)}{144}(150) = 314 \text{ lb/ft}$$

$$\text{maximum negative moment} = \tfrac{1}{10}(1.4)(0.314)(23.75)^2 + 229$$
$$= 25 + 229 = 254 \text{ ft-kips}$$

$b = 14$ in. $d = 28 - 2.5$ (assume one layer of steel) $= 25.5$ in.

$$R_u = \frac{M_u}{\phi b_w d^2} = \frac{254(12,000)}{0.90(14)(25.5)^2} = 372 \text{ psi}$$

From Fig. 3.6.1, $\rho = 0.010$, which is well below $0.75\rho_b = 0.027$. Perhaps the beam size should be reduced. From Fig. 16.12.1,

$$\text{total design (factored) floor load on } B1 = 6.36(15) = 95.4 \text{ kips}$$

$$\max V_u = 1.15(1.4)(0.314)\frac{23.75}{2} + \frac{1}{2}(95.4) + \frac{229 - 51}{23.75}$$

$$= 6.0 + 47.7 + 7.5 = 61.2 \text{ kips}$$

$$v_n = \frac{V_u}{\phi b_w d} = \frac{61,200}{0.85(14)(25.5)} = 202 \text{ psi} = 3.7\sqrt{f_c'} \qquad \text{OK}$$

(b) Size of short beam $B5$. The negative moments at the face of supports, 44 and 145 ft-kips, are taken from Table 16.10.2, frame C.

$$\text{weight of beam stem} = \frac{12(17.5)}{144}(150) = 219 \text{ lb/ft}$$

maximum negative moment $= \frac{1}{10}(1.4)(0.219)(18.75)^2 + 145$

$$= 11 + 145 = 156 \text{ ft-kips}$$

$b = 12$ in. $d = 24 - 2.5$ (assume one layer of steel) $= 21.5$ in.

$$R_u = \frac{M_u}{\phi b_w d^2} = \frac{156(12{,}000)}{0.90(12)(21.5)^2} = 376 \text{ psi}$$

From Fig. 3.6.1, $\rho = 0.0105$, which is well below $0.75\rho_b = 0.027$. From Fig. 16.12.1,

total design (factored) floor load on $B5 = 6.36(10) = 63.6$ kips

$$\max V_u = 1.15(1.4)(0.219)\frac{18.75}{2} + \frac{1}{2}(63.6) + \frac{145 - 44}{18.75}$$

$$= 3.3 + 31.8 + 5.4 = 40.5 \text{ kips}$$

$$v_n = \frac{V_u}{\phi b_w d} = \frac{40{,}500}{0.85(12)(21.5)} = 185 \text{ psi} = 3.4\sqrt{f_c'} \qquad \text{OK}$$

Both beams probably should have been made smaller.

16.13 Reinforcement in Slab

The reinforcement in two-way slab systems may be expressed either in size and spacing of bars or in total number of bars within a definite width of slab. As noted in ACI-13.4.2, the spacing of reinforcement must be not more than 2 times the slab thickness except for those portions of the slab area that may be of cellular or ribbed construction; and the reinforcement ratio shall be at least equal to that for shrinkage and temperature effects as stated in ACI-7.12.

It is well known from plate bending theory that a transversely loaded slab simply supported along four edges will tend to develop corner reactions as shown in Fig. 16.13.1, for which reinforcement must be provided. Thus

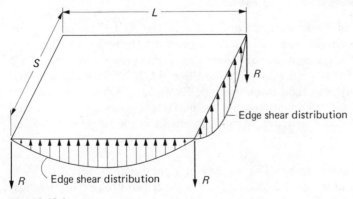

Fig. 16.13.1
Edge reactions for simply supported slab.

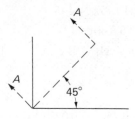

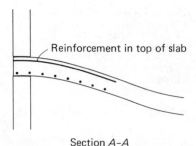

Section *A-A*

Fig. 16.13.2
Corner reinforcement in two-way slab.

in slabs supported on beams having a value of α greater than 1.0, special reinforcement (Fig. 16.13.2) shall be provided at exterior corners in both the bottom and top of the slab. This reinforcement (ACI-13.4.6) is to be provided for a distance in each direction from the corner equal to one-fifth the longer span. The reinforcement in both the top and bottom of the slab must be sufficient to resist a moment equal to the maximum positive moment per foot of width in the slab, and it may be placed in a single band parallel to the diagonal in the top of the slab and perpendicular to the diagonal in the bottom of the slab, or in two bands parallel to the sides of the slab.

16.14 Equivalent-Frame Method

The "equivalent-frame method" prescribed by the ACI Code differs from the "direct-design method" only in the way by which the longitudinal moments along the spans of the equivalent rigid frame (as defined in Sec. 16.2) are obtained. In the "equivalent-frame method" (ACI-13.7) the elastic analysis of the equivalent rigid frame is made for various vertical or lateral or both critical load combinations, and the maximum positive moments (and reversals) within the span and negative moments at the supports are determined.

Equivalent Rigid Frame. The equivalent rigid frame is taken on both longitudinal and transverse column lines as described in Sec. 16.2. For vertical loading each floor of such a frame may be analyzed separately with its attached upper and lower columns which are assumed to be fixed at their far ends; and the slab-beam may be assumed to be fixed at any support two panels distant from the support or the span where critical moments are being obtained.

Moments of Inertia. When an elastic analysis is to be made, the moments of inertia are treated in a more accurate manner than when moment coefficients are used in the "direct-design method." The moment of inertia of the slab-beam between the center of the column and the face of the column, bracket, or capital is to be assumed equal to that of the slab-beam at the face of the column, bracket, or capital, divided by the quantity $(1 - c_2/L_2)^2$ (ACI-13.7.3.3). The moment of inertia of the column is to be assumed infinite from the top of the slab to the bottom of the slab-beam at the joint (ACI-13.7.4.5).

Fixed-End Moments, Stiffness, and Carry-Over Factors. The stiffness and carry-over factors of the slab-beam and of the columns, with variable moments of inertia along their respective lengths, may be conveniently computed by the column-analogy method [18]. The fixed-end moments due to uniform load acting on the slab-beam can be computed by the same method [18]; ACI Commentary Table 13-1 provides values of fixed-end moments, as well as stiffness and carry-over factors, for slabs with various support widths.

Equivalent Column Stiffness. The equivalent column stiffness K_{ec} is to be computed from

$$\frac{1}{K_{ec}} = \frac{1}{\Sigma K_c} + \frac{1}{K_t}$$

wherein

ΣK_c = stiffness K_{c1} of the upper column + stiffness K_{c2} of the lower column

$$K_t = \Sigma \frac{9EC}{L_2(1 - c_2/L_2)^3}\left(\frac{I_{sb}}{I_s}\right)$$

$$C = \Sigma \left(1 - \frac{0.63x}{y}\right)\frac{x^3 y}{3}$$

C is the torsional constant of the transverse torsional member having a section that consists of the larger of (a) a portion of slab having width equal to that of the column dimension in the direction of the span, (b) the portion of slab in (a) plus the transverse beam above and below the slab, or (c) the transverse beam stem plus portion of slab on each side of the beam extending a distance equal to the projection of the beam above or below the slab, whichever is greater, but not greater than 4 times the slab thickness. I_{sb} is the moment of inertia of width of slab used for the calculation of I_s but including the contribution of that portion of the beam stem extending above or below the slab.

Loads on the Equivalent Frame. When the loading pattern is definitely known, the equivalent frame should be analyzed for that load. When the service live load does not exceed three-quarters of the service dead load, the maximum bending may be assumed to occur at all sections under full factored live load (ACI-13.7.6.2). For other conditions, maximum positive bending near midspan of a panel may be assumed to occur under three-quarters of the full factored live load in the panel and in alternate panels, and maximum negative bending in the slab at a support may be assumed to occur under three-quarters of the full factored live load in the adjacent panels only. In no case, however, may the factored moments be taken as less than those occurring with full factored live load on all panels.

Reduction of Negative Moment to Face of Support. The factored negative moment at any support is to be taken at the face of the column. When capitals (or brackets) are used, as described in Sec. 16.1, the face of capital is considered the face of support (ACI-13.7.7.3) and special conditions regarding reduction of negative moment apply (ACI-13.7.7). Section 17.13 considers this in detail.

Column Moments. Moments determined for the equivalent column in the frame analysis should be apportioned to the lower end of the upper column and the upper end of the lower column in the ratio of their respective stiffnesses, with the resulting values further reduced to the top of the slab or the bottom of the slab-beam for design use.

Sum of Positive and Average Negative Moments. Two-way slab systems that satisfy the limitations of the "direct-design method," but yet have the longitudinal moments determined by means of the "equivalent-frame method," may have the resulting factored moments reduced in such proportion that the numerical sum of the positive and the average negative moments at face of supports need not exceed the total statical moment M_0.

Deflections. When the deflection must be calculated for a two-way slab system, the ACI Code (ACI-9.5.3.4) provides little guidance other than that one should take into account "the size and shape of the panel, conditions of support, and nature of restraints at the panel edges." The effective moment of inertia I_e (Eq. 14.4.1) is required to be used in such calculations. Although a number of techniques have been proposed [19-22], adaption of the equivalent-frame concept seems to have the most promise of being relatively simple to apply and giving reasonable results. This equivalent-frame application has been developed by Nilson and Walters [21] for essentially uncracked systems and extended by Kripanarayanan and Branson [23] for partially cracked load ranges.

EXAMPLE 16.14.1 Assuming the "equivalent-frame method" is to be applied to the design example described in Sec. 16.3, obtain the distribution and carry-over factors at the exterior and interior joints of the equivalent rigid frames A, B, C, and D as shown by the notations in Fig. 16.3.3. Also determine the longitudinal moments in equivalent rigid frame A by the moment-distribution method and compare them with the results of the "direct-design method" in Example 16.9.1, Part (h).

Solution: (a) Flexural properties of slab-beam. The variations in the moment of inertia of the slab-beam in the long and short directions are shown in Fig. 16.14.1. For the long slab-beam, the ratio of moment of inertia between the center and the face of the column to the moments of inertia of the rest of the span is $1.0/(1 - 15/240)^2 = 1.137$; and it is $1.0/(1 - 15/300)^2 = 1.11$ for the short slab-beam (ACI-13.7.3.3). The stiffness, carry-over, and fixed-end moment coefficients may be computed by the column-analogy method [18].

For the long direction, referring to Fig. 16.14.1a,

$$A = 23.75 + 2(0.879)(0.625) = 23.75 + 1.10 = 24.85$$

$$I = \tfrac{1}{12}(23.75)^3 + 1.10(12.1875)^2 = 1117 + 164 = 1281$$

$$S_{ii} = \frac{25}{24.85} + \frac{25(12.5)^2}{1281} = 1.005 + 3.045 = 4.05$$

$$S_{ij} = -(1.005 - 3.045) = 2.04$$

$$\text{COF} = \frac{2.04}{4.05} = 0.503$$

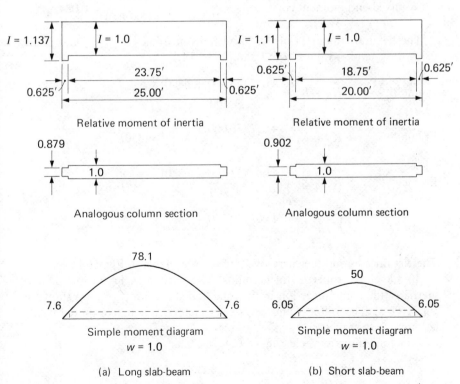

Relative moment of inertia   Relative moment of inertia

Analogous column section   Analogous column section

Simple moment diagram   Simple moment diagram
$w = 1.0$ $w = 1.0$

(a) Long slab-beam   (b) Short slab-beam

Fig. 16.14.1
Flexure properties of slab-beam strip, Example 16.14.1.

load on analogous column for uniform load ($w = 1.0$)

$$= \tfrac{2}{3}(78.1 - 7.6)(23.75) + 7.6(23.75) + 0.879(7.6)(0.625)$$
$$= 1117 + 180 + 4 = 1301$$

$$\text{fixed-end moment coefficient} = \frac{1301}{24.85L_1^2} = \frac{1301}{24.85(625)} = 0.084$$

For the short direction, referring to Fig. 16.14.1b,

$$A = 18.75 + 2(0.902)(0.625) = 18.75 + 1.13 = 19.88$$
$$I = \tfrac{1}{12}(18.75)^3 + 1.13(9.6875)^2 = 550 + 106 = 656$$

$$S_{ii} = \frac{20}{19.88} + \frac{20(10)^2}{656} = 1.01 + 3.05 = 4.06$$

$$S_{ij} = -(1.01 - 3.05) = 2.04$$

$$\text{COF} = \frac{2.04}{4.06} = 0.502$$

load on analogous column for uniform load ($w = 1.0$)

$$= \tfrac{2}{3}(50 - 6.05)(18.75) + 6.05(18.75) + 0.902(6.05)(0.625)$$
$$= 550 + 113.5 + 3.4 = 666.9$$

$$\text{fixed-end moment coefficient} = \frac{666.9}{19.88L_1^2} = \frac{666.9}{19.88(400)} = 0.084$$

The flexural stiffnesses of the slab-beams in frames A, B, C, and D are, using the I_b and I_s values from Example 16.5.1,

Frame A, $\qquad K_b + K_s = \dfrac{4.05E(45{,}400 + 5490)}{300} = 687E$

Frame B, $\qquad K_b + K_s = \dfrac{4.05E(38{,}000 + 2745)}{300} = 550E$

Frame C, $\qquad K_b + K_s = \dfrac{4.06E(24{,}400 + 6870)}{240} = 529E$

Frame D, $\qquad K_b + K_s = \dfrac{4.06E(20{,}500 + 3435)}{240} = 405E$

These stiffnesses and the carry-over factors are shown in Fig. 16.14.4.

(b) Flexural properties of columns. The variations in the moment of inertia of the column section in the long and short directions are shown in Fig. 16.14.2. The stiffness and carry-over factors may be computed by the column-analogy method.

For the long direction, referring to Fig. 16.14.2a,

$$A = 9.67, \qquad I = \tfrac{1}{12}(9.67)^3 = 75.3$$

$$S_{TT} = \frac{12}{9.67} + \frac{12(6.90)^2}{75.3} = 1.24 + 7.60 = 8.84$$

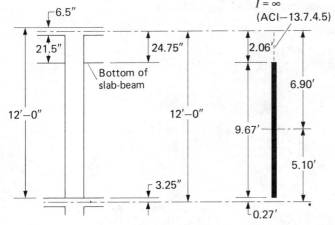

(a) Column section in long direction

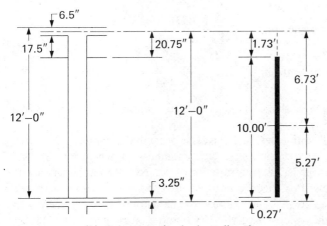

(b) Column section in short direction

Fig. 16.14.2

Flexure properties of columns, Example 16.14.1.

$$S_{BB} = \frac{12}{9.67} + \frac{12(5.10)^2}{75.3} = 1.24 + 4.15 = 5.39$$

$$S_{TB} = S_{BT} = -\left[\frac{12}{9.67} - \frac{12(6.90)(5.10)}{75.3}\right] = -1.24 + 5.60 = 4.36$$

$$C_{TB} = \frac{4.36}{8.84} = 0.493$$

$$C_{BT} = \frac{4.36}{5.39} = 0.809$$

Stiffness at top, $\quad K_{c2} = S_{TT}\dfrac{EI}{L} = \dfrac{8.84E(15)^4/12}{144} = 259E$

Stiffness at bottom, $\quad K_{c1} = S_{BB}\dfrac{EI}{L} = \dfrac{5.39E(15)^4/12}{144} = 158E$

For the short direction, referring to Fig. 16.14.2b,

$$A = 10.00, \qquad I = \tfrac{1}{12}(10)^3 = 83.3$$

$$S_{TT} = \frac{12}{10} + \frac{12(6.73)^2}{83.3} = 1.20 + 6.53 = 7.73$$

$$S_{BB} = \frac{12}{10} + \frac{12(5.27)^2}{83.3} = 1.20 + 4.01 = 5.21$$

$$S_{TB} = S_{BT} = -\left[\frac{12}{10} - \frac{12(6.73)(5.27)}{83.3} \right] = -1.20 + 5.12 = 3.92$$

$$C_{TB} = \frac{3.92}{7.73} = 0.507$$

$$C_{BT} = \frac{3.92}{5.21} = 0.752$$

$$\text{Stiffness at top,} \qquad K_{c2} = \frac{7.73E(15)^4/12}{144} = 226E$$

$$\text{Stiffness at bottom,} \qquad K_{c1} = \frac{5.21(15)^4/12}{144} = 153E$$

These stiffnesses and the carry-over factors obtained above are summarized in Fig. 16.14.4.

(c) The torsional stiffnesses of transverse torsional members. The torsional constants C for the transverse edge members shown in Fig. 16.14.3 are taken from Example 16.9.1, but those for the transverse members through the interior columns have been computed in the same manner with the results shown in Fig. 16.14.3. The values for the ratio of I_{sb} to I_s needed to amplify the torsional stiffness K_t (ACI Code and Commentary-13.7.5.4) for each direction are also shown in Fig. 16.14.3.
For frame A,

$$\text{edge } K_t = \frac{18E(10,700)}{240(1 - 15/240)^3}(12.13) = 974E(12.13) = 11,800E$$

$$\text{interior } K_t = \frac{18E(11,900)}{240(1 - 15/240)^3}(12.13) = 1084E(12.13) = 13,200E$$

For frame B, using $I_{sb}/I_s = 19.9$ for 14×21.5 projection below 127×6.5 slab,

$$\text{edge } K_t = 487E(19.9) = 9680E$$
$$\text{interior } K_t = 542E(19.9) = 10,800E$$

For frame C,

$$\text{edge } K_t = \frac{18E(19,100)}{300(1 - 15/300)^3}(5.76) = 1340E(5.76) = 7720E$$

$$\text{interior } K_t = \frac{18E(20,700)}{300(1 - 15/300)^3}(5.76) = 1450E(5.76) = 8350E$$

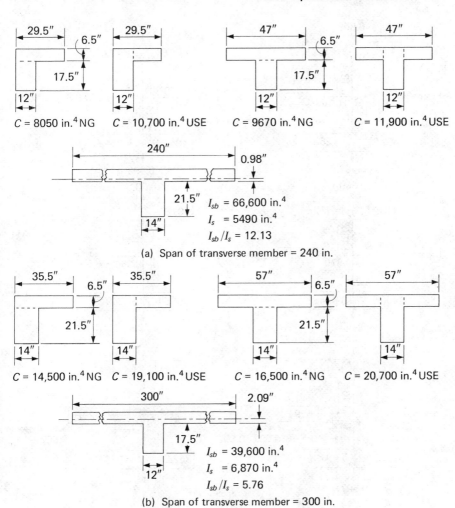

Fig. 16.14.3
Properties of transverse torsional members, Example 16.14.1.

For frame D, using $I_{sb}/I_s = 9.51$ for 12×17.5 projection below 156×6.5 slab,

$$\text{edge } K_t = 670E(9.51) = 6370E$$
$$\text{interior } K_t = 725E(9.51) = 6890E$$

(d) The equivalent column stiffness K_{ec} and distribution factors. The equivalent column stiffness is computed from the formula

$$\frac{1}{K_{ec}} = \frac{1}{\Sigma K_c} + \frac{1}{K_t}$$

For frame A,

$$\text{exterior } K_{ec} = \frac{E}{1/417 + 1/11,800} = 402E$$

$$\text{interior } K_{ec} = \frac{E}{1/417 + 1/13,200} = 404E$$

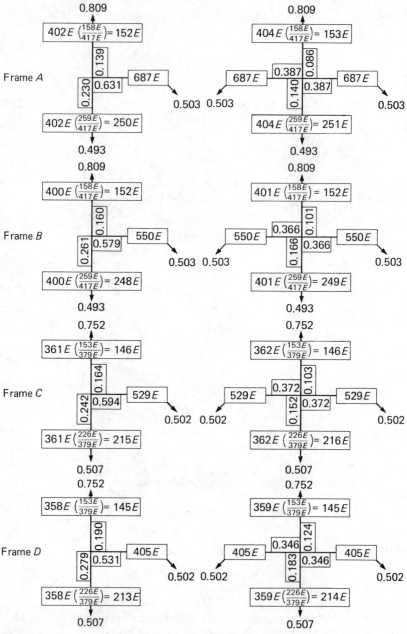

Fig. 16.14.4

Distribution factors at exterior and interior joints, Example 16.14.1.

For frame B,

$$\text{exterior } K_{ec} = \frac{E}{1/417 + 1/9680} = 400E$$

$$\text{interior } K_{ec} = \frac{E}{1/417 + 1/10,800} = 401E$$

For frame C,

$$\text{exterior } K_{ec} = \frac{E}{1/379 + 1/7720} = 361E$$

$$\text{interior } K_{ec} = \frac{E}{1/379 + 1/8350} = 362E$$

For frame D,

$$\text{exterior } K_{ec} = \frac{E}{1/379 + 1/6370} = 358E$$

$$\text{interior } K_{ec} = \frac{E}{1/379 + 1/6890} = 359E$$

These equivalent stiffnesses K_{ec} are apportioned to the upper and lower columns in the ratio of their respective stiffnesses, as shown in Fig. 16.14.4. The distribution factors at the exterior and interior joints for each of the four frames, as well as carry-over factors, are also shown in Fig. 16.14.4. It may be noted that the effect of the torsional member stiffness on the equivalent column stiffness is relatively small.

(e) Fixed-end moments for frame A

$$\text{factored dead load } w_D = 1.4(\tfrac{150}{12})(6.5) = 1.4(81) = 114 \text{ psf}$$

$$\text{factored live load } w_L = 1.7(120) = 204 \text{ psf}$$

$$\text{FEM due to } (w_D + w_L) = 0.084(0.318)(20)(25)^2 = 334 \text{ ft-kips}$$

$$\text{FEM due to } (w_D + \tfrac{3}{4}w_L) = 0.084(0.267)(20)(25)^2 = 280 \text{ ft-kips}$$

$$\text{FEM due to } w_D \text{ only} = 0.084(0.114)(20)(25)^2 = 120 \text{ ft-kips}$$

(f) Moment distribution for frame A. Moment distribution for five loading conditions is shown in Table 16.14.1. Although only two cycles of moment distribution are needed, a third cycle is added for little extra work. The positive moments at midspan are computed from the formula

$$M_{pos} = \tfrac{1}{8}wL_1^2 - \tfrac{1}{2}(M_{ni} + M_{nj})$$

where M_{ni} and M_{nj} are the negative moments at the center of supports. Summarizing the results of moment distribution in Table 16.14.1.

Maximum positive moment at center of first span = the larger of 232 and 225 = 232 ft-kips

Maximum positive moment at center of second span = the larger of 149 and 180 = 180 ft-kips

Maximum positive moment at center of third span = the larger of 171 and 195 = 195 ft-kips

Maximum negative moment at 0–1 = the larger of 131 and 123 = 131 ft-kips

Maximum negative moment at 1–0 = the larger of 399 and 349 = 399 ft-kips

Maximum negative moment at 1–2 = the larger of 375 and 337 = 375 ft-kips

Table 16.14.1

Moment Distribution

Joint	0	1		2		3		4		5
Member	0–1	1–0	1–2	2–1	2–3	3–2	3–4	4–3	4–5	5–4
DF	0.631	0.387	0.387	0.387	0.387	0.387	0.387	0.387	0.387	0.631
COF	0.503	0.503	0.503	0.503	0.503	0.503	0.503	0.503	0.503	0.503

All Spans Loaded with Full Live Load

FEM	−334	+334	−334	+334	−334	+334	−334	+334	−334	+334
Balance	+211	0	0	0	0	0	0	0	0	−211
CO	0	+106	0	0	0	0	0	0	−106	0
Balance	0	−41	−41	0	0	0	0	+41	+41	0
CO	−21	0	0	−21	0	0	+21	0	0	+21
Balance	+13	0	0	+8	+8	−8	−8	0	0	−13
Total	−131	+399	−375	+321	−326	+326	−321	+375	−399	+131
Moment at ℄ of Span	232			149		171		149		232

First, Third, and Fifth Spans Loaded with Three-Fourths Live Load

FEM	−280	+280	−120	+120	−280	+280	−120	+120	−280	+280
Balance	+177	−62	−62	+62	+62	−62	−62	+62	+62	−177
CO	−31	+89	+31	−31	−31	+31	+31	−31	−89	+31
Balance	+20	−46	−46	+24	+24	−24	−24	+46	+46	−20
CO	−23	+10	+12	−23	−12	+12	+23	−12	−10	+23
Balance	+14	−8	−8	+14	+14	−14	−14	+8	+8	−14
Total	−123	+263	−193	+166	−223	+223	−166	+193	−263	+123
Moment at ℄ of Span	225		2 (reversal)		195		2 (reversal)		225	

$$\frac{\text{Maximum negative moment}}{\text{at } 2-1} = \text{the larger of 321 and 308} = 321 \text{ ft-kips}$$

$$\frac{\text{Maximum negative moment}}{\text{at } 2-3} = \text{the larger of 326 and 312} = 326 \text{ ft-kips}$$

(g) Reduction of negative moment to face of support for frame A. The shear diagram consistent with the maximum negative moments at supports is shown in Fig. 16.14.5b. When the negative moments in Fig. 16.14.5a are leveled off between the center and the face of the column, the resulting moment diagram takes the shape in Fig. 16.14.5c.

(h) Sum of positive and average negative moments for frame A. The sum of positive and average negative moments in each span of Fig. 16.14.5c may

Table 16.14.1 (*cont.*)

Second and Fourth Spans Loaded with Three-Fourths Live Load

FEM	−120	+120	−280	+280	−120	+120	−280	+280	−120	+120
Balance	+76	+62	+62	−62	−62	+62	+62	−62	−62	−76
CO	+31	+38	−31	+31	+31	−31	−31	+31	−38	−31
Balance	−20	−3	−3	−24	−24	+24	+24	+3	+3	+20
CO	−2	−10	−12	−2	+12	−12	+2	+12	+10	+2
Balance	+1	+8	+8	−4	−4	+4	+4	−8	−8	−1
Total	−34	+215	−256	+219	−167	+167	−219	+256	−215	+34
Moment at ₵ of Span	53 (no reversal)		180		13 (no reversal)		180		53 (no reversal)	

First, Second, and Fourth Spans Loaded with Three-Fourths Live Load

FEM	−280	+280	−280	+280	−120	+120	−280	+280	−120	+120
Balance	+177	0	0	−62	−62	+62	+62	−62	−62	−76
CO	0	+89	−31	0	+31	−31	−31	+31	−38	−31
Balance	0	−22	−22	−12	−12	+24	+24	+3	+3	+20
CO	−11	0	−6	−11	+12	−6	−2	+12	+10	+2
Balance	+7	+2	+2	0	0	+1	+1	−8	−8	−1
Total		+349	−337							

Second, Third, and Fifth Spans Loaded with Three-Fourths Live Load

FEM	−120	+120	−280	+280	−280	+280	−120	+120	−280	+280
Balance	+76	+62	+62	0	0	−62	−62	+62	+62	−177
CO	+31	+38	0	+31	−31	0	+31	−31	−89	+31
Balance	−20	−15	−15	0	0	−12	−12	+46	+46	−20
CO	−8	−10	0	−8	−6	0	+23	−6	−10	+23
Balance	+5	+4	+4	+5	+5	−9	−9	+6	+6	−14
Total				+308	−312					

be obtained as

$$232 + \tfrac{1}{2}(89 + 344) = 449 \text{ ft-kips for the first span}$$
$$180 + \tfrac{1}{2}(325 + 274) = 480 \text{ ft-kips for the second span}$$
$$195 + 278 = 473 \text{ ft-kips for the third span}$$

Because the present system satisfies the limitations of the "direct-design method" and the total static moment is 458 ft-kips, the moments in the second and third spans may be scaled down by the ratios 458/480 and 458/473, respectively.

(i) Comparison with longitudinal moments in the "direct-design method" for frame A. The longitudinal moments obtained by the "direct-design

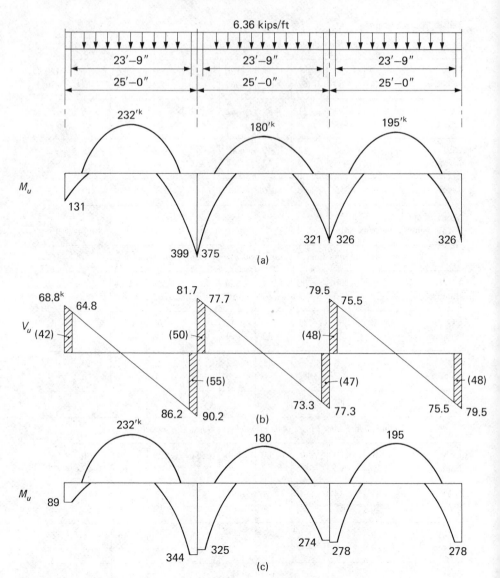

Fig. 16.14.5
Maximum shears and moments for frame A.

method" are -65, $+261$, -334, -298, $+160$ ft-kips; these values compare well with -89, $+232$, -344, -278 (or -270 scaled down), $+195$ (or $+189$ scaled down) in Fig. 16.14.5.

SELECTED REFERENCES

1. Joseph DiStasio and M. P. Van Buren. "Slabs Supported on Four Sides," *ACI Journal, Proceedings*, **32**, January–February 1936, 350–364.
2. R. L. Bertin, Joseph DiStasio, and M. P. Van Buren. "Slabs Supported on Four Sides," *ACI Journal, Proceedings*, **41**, June 1945, 537–556.

3. C. P. Siess and N. M. Newmark. "Rational Analysis and Design of Two-Way Concrete Slabs," *ACI Journal, Proceedings*, **45**, December 1948, 273–316.
4. W. L. Gamble, M. A. Sozen, and C. P. Siess. "Measured and Theoretical Bending Moments in Reinforced Concrete Floor Slabs," Civil Engineering Structural Research Series No. 246. Urbana: University of Illinois, June 1962.
5. M. A. Sozen and C. P. Siess. "Investigation of Multi-Panel Reinforced Concrete Floor Slabs," *ACI Journal, Proceedings*, **60**, August 1963, 999–1028.
6. S. A. Guralnick and R. W. LaFraugh. "Laboratory Study of a 45-Foot Square Flat Plate Structure," *ACI Journal, Proceedings*, **60**, September 1963, 1107–1185.
7. W. L. Gamble, M. A. Sozen, and C. P. Siess. "Tests of a Two-Way Reinforced Concrete Floor Slab," *Journal of Structural Division*, ASCE, **95**, (ST6) June 1969, 1073–1096.
8. M. Daniel Vanderbilt, Mete A. Sozen, and Chester P. Siess. "Tests of a Modified Reinforced Concrete Two-Way Slab," *Journal of Structural Division*, ASCE, **95**, (ST6) June 1969, 1097–1116.
9. W. G. Corley and J. O. Jirsa. "Equivalent Frame Analysis for Slab Design," *ACI Journal, Proceedings*, **67**, November 1970, 875–884.
10. William L. Gamble. "Moments in Beam Supported Slabs," *ACI Journal, Proceedings*, **69**, March 1972, 149–157.
11. "Shearhead Reinforcement for Flat-Plate Floors," *Modern Developments in Reinforced Concrete* (No. 22). Chicago: Portland Cement Association, 1948.
12. *Notes on ACI 318-71 Building Code Requirements with Design Applications*. Skokie, Illinois: Portland Cement Association, 1972.
13. J. O. Jirsa, M. A. Sozen, and C. P. Siess. "Pattern Loadings on Reinforced Concrete Floor Slabs," *Journal of Structural Division*, ASCE, **95**, (ST6) June 1969, 1117–1137.
14. Edward G. Nawy. "Crack Width Control in Welded Fabric Reinforced Centrally Loaded Two-Way Concrete Slabs," *Causes, Mechanism, and Control of Cracking in Concrete* (SP-20). Detroit: American Concrete Institute, 1968 (pp. (211–235).
15. Edward G. Nawy and G. S. Orenstein. "Crack Width Control in Reinforced Concrete Two-Way Slabs," *Journal of Structural Division*, ASCE, **96**, (ST3) March 1970, 701–721.
16. Edward G. Nawy and Kenneth W. Blair. "Further Studies on Flexural Crack Control in Structural Slab Systems," *Cracking, Deflection, and Ultimate Load of Concrete Slab Systems* (SP-30). Detroit: American Concrete Institute, 1971, (pp. 1–41).
17. Edward G. Nawy. "Crack Control Through Reinforcement Distribution in Two-Way Acting Slabs and Plates," *ACI Journal, Proceedings*, **69**, April 1972, 217–219.
18. C. K. Wang. *Statically Indeterminate Structures*. New York: McGraw-Hill, 1953 (Chap. 9).
19. Mortimer D. Vanderbilt, Mete A. Sozen, and Chester P. Siess, "Deflections of Multiple-Panel Reinforced Concrete Floor Slabs", *Journal of Structural Division*, ASCE, **91**, (ST4) August 1965, 77–101.
20. ACI Committee 435, "State-of-the-Art Report, Deflection of Two-Way Reinforced Concrete Floor Systems", *Deflections of Concrete Structures*, (SP-43). Detroit: American Concrete Institute, 1974, (pp. 55–81).
21. Arthur H. Nilson and Donald B. Walters, Jr., "Deflection of Two-Way Floor Systems by the Equivalent Frame Method", *ACI Journal, Proceedings*, **72**, May 1975, 210–218.
22. B. Vijaya Rangan, "Prediction of Long-Term Deflections of Flat Plates and Slabs", *ACI Journal, Proceedings*, **73**, April 1976, 223–226.

23. K. M. Kripanarayanan and D. E. Branson, "Short Time Deflections of Flat Plates, Flat Slabs, and Two-Way Slabs", *ACI Journal, Proceedings*, **73,** December 1976, 686–690.

PROBLEMS

16.1 Design the typical interior frame along columns 2-5-7 for the two-way slab system shown. The 13-ft long columns are connected by beams, and no column capitals or drop panels are used. As an initial trial, assume all beams (interior) are 12 × 24 in. overall. Revise beam size as necessary during the design. Determine slab thickness based on ACI-9.5.3, then use the "direct-design method" for longitudinal distribution of moments. Show design sketch giving all your decisions, including dimensions, bar sizes, bar lengths, and stirrups for the two spans from column 2 to column 7. The live load is 150 psf, $f'_c = 4000$ psi, and $f_y = 60,000$ psi.

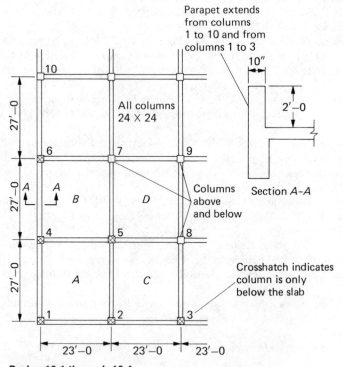

Probs. 16.1 through 16.4

16.2 Design the interior frame of Prob. 16.1, except that a 12-in. wall exists at the lower-story level and contains the 24-in. square columns at locations 1, 2, 3, 4, 6, and 10.

16.3 Design the typical interior frame along column lines 4-5-8 for the two-way slab system of Prob. 16.1.

16.4 Design the exterior half-frame along column lines 1-2-3 for the two-way slab system of Prob. 16.1.

16.5 Design an interior frame in the long direction for a floor system of slabs supported on beams which has 5 panels at 21 ft in one direction and 5 panels at 27 ft in the other direction. The live load is 175 psf and the dead load is 40 psf in addition to the slab weight. Assume that all panels are bounded by beams that are 14 in. wide. Columns 15 in. square and 13 ft long are located at the corners of all panels. Use $f'_c = 4000$ psi, $f_y = 50,000$ psi, and the "direct-design method" of the ACI Code.

16.6 Design a floor system of slabs supported on beams which has two panels at 16 ft in one direction and two panels at 21 ft in the other direction. Assume that all panels are bounded by beams 12 in. wide and the columns are 14 in. square and 11 ft long. The live load is 200 psf, and the dead load is 50 psf in addition to the slab weight. Use $f'_c = 3000$ psi, $f_y = 60,000$ psi, and the ACI Code.

16.7 Design a simply supported sidewalk slab for an 18-ft square panel to carry a live load of 250 psf. The panel is supported by beams 12 in. wide on all four sides. There are no walls or columns above the slab. Use $f'_c = 4000$ psi, $f_y = 60,000$ psi, and the ACI Code.

17

Design of Two-Way Systems— Flat-Slabs and Flat-Plate Floors

17.1 General Description

Both the flat-slab and flat-plate floors, as shown by Fig. 17.1.1ab (same as Fig. 16.1.2ab), are characterized by the absence of beams along the interior column lines, but edge beams may or may not be used at the exterior edges of the floor. Flat-slab floors differ from flat-plate floors in that flat-slab floors provide adequate shear strength by having either or both of the following: (a) drop panels (i.e., increased thickness of slab) in the region of the columns; or (b) column capitals (i.e., tapered enlargement of the upper ends of columns). In flat-plate floors a uniform slab thickness is used and the shear strength is obtained by the embedment of multiple-U stirrups or structural steel devices known as *shearhead reinforcement* within the slab of uniform thickness. Relatively speaking, flat slabs are more suitable for larger panel size or heavier loading than flat plates.

The design procedures for flat-slab and flat-plate floors without beams are essentially identical to those for two-way slab floors with beams, because the nonexistence of beams along interior column lines can be considered as the existence of such beams but with zero flexural stiffness. Thus the two-way slab system without beams is a special case.

Historically, flat slabs predate both two-way slabs on beams and flat plates. Flat-slab floors were originally patented by O. W. Norcross [1] in the United States on April 29, 1902. Several systems of placing reinforcement have been developed and patented since then—the four-way system, the two-way system, the three-way system, and the circumferential system. Mr. C. A. P. Turner [1] was one of the early advocates of a flat-slab system known as the "mushroom" system. About 1908 the flat slab began being

Flat slab (waffle slab) with capitals in the Fisher Cleveland Plant. (Courtesy of Portland Cement Association.)

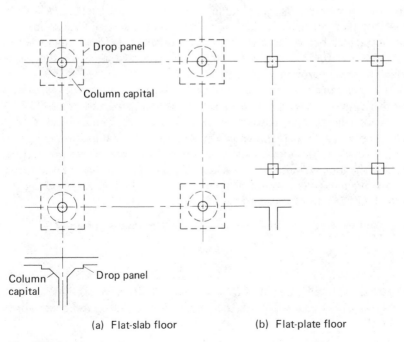

(a) Flat-slab floor   (b) Flat-plate floor

Fig. 17.1.1
Flat-slab and flat-plate floor construction.

recognized as an acceptable floor system, but for many years designers were confronted with difficulties of patent infringements.

17.2 General Design Concept of ACI Code

The general procedure of cutting up the structure into equivalent rigid frames in the long and short directions of the structure has been described in detail in Sec. 16.2. As described in that section, longitudinal moments on these equivalent rigid frames may be determined by the "direct-design method" using code prescribed coefficients or by the "equivalent-frame method" using structural analysis.

17.3 Total Static Moment

The ability of flat-slab floor systems to carry load has been substantiated by numerous tests of actual structures [1]. However, the amount of reinforcement used, say, in a typical interior panel, was less than what it should be to satisfy an analysis by statics, as is demonstrated in this section. This led to some controversy [2], but after studies by Westergaard and Slater [3], a provision was adopted (about 1921) into the code that a reduction of moment coefficient from the statically required value of $0.125(wL^2/8)$ to 0.09 may be made. This reduction was not regarded as a violation of statics but it was used as a way of permitting an increase in the allowable unit stresses. The reduction, moreover, was applicable only to flat slabs that satisfied the limitations then specified in the code. Over the years these limitations had been liberalized, but at the same time the moment coefficient was raised to values closer to 0.125. The present ACI Code logically stipulates the use of the full statically required coefficient of 0.125.

The statical analysis of a typical interior panel was first made in 1914 by Nichols [2] and further developed later by Westergaard and others [3,4,5].

Consider the typical interior panel of a flat-slab floor subjected to a load of w per unit area, as shown in Fig. 17.3.1a. The total load on the panel area (rectangle minus four quadrantal areas) is supported by the vertical shears at the four quandrantal arcs. Let M_{nL} and M_{pL} be the total negative and positive moments about a horizontal axis in the S direction along the edges of $ABCD$ and EF, respectively. Then

$$\text{load on area } ABCDEF = \text{sum of reactions at arcs } AB \text{ and } CD$$

$$= w\left(\frac{SL}{2} - \frac{\pi c^2}{8}\right)$$

Considering the half panel $ABCDEF$ as a free body, recognizing that there is no shear at the edges BC, DE, EF, and FA, and taking moments about axis 1-1,

$$M_{nL} + M_{pL} + w\left(\frac{SL}{2} - \frac{\pi c^2}{8}\right)\left(\frac{c}{\pi}\right) - \frac{wSL}{2}\left(\frac{L}{4}\right) + \frac{w\pi c^2}{8}\left(\frac{2c}{3\pi}\right) = 0$$

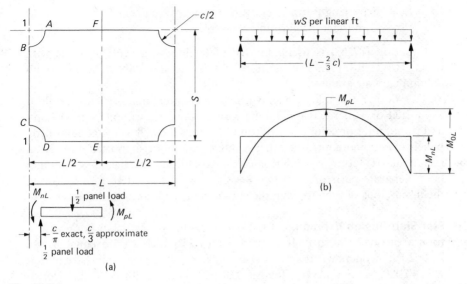

Fig. 17.3.1
Statics of a typical interior panel in a flat slab.

Letting $M_{OL} = M_{nL} + M_{pL}$,

$$M_{OL} = \frac{1}{8}wSL^2\left(1 - \frac{4c}{\pi L} + \frac{c^3}{3SL^2}\right) \approx \frac{1}{8}wSL^2\left(1 - \frac{2c}{3L}\right)^2 \quad \textbf{(17.3.1a)}$$

Similarly, in the other direction,

$$M_{OS} = M_{nS} + M_{pS}$$

$$= \frac{1}{8}wLS^2\left(1 - \frac{4c}{\pi S} + \frac{c^3}{3LS^2}\right) \approx \frac{1}{8}wLS^2\left(1 - \frac{2c}{3S}\right)^2 \quad \textbf{(17.3.1b)}$$

Actually Eqs. (17.3.1a and b) may be more easily visualized by inspecting the equivalent interior span as shown in Fig. 17.3.1b.

ACI Formula (13-3) states that the minimum value for the full factored statical moment is to be

$$M_0 = \frac{w_u L_2 L_n^2}{8} \quad \textbf{(17.3.2)}$$

in which

M_0 = total factored static moment
w_u = factored load per unit area
L_n = clear span length in the direction moments are being determined, measured face to face of supports but not less than $0.65L_1$, where L_1 is the center to center of supports (columns or column capitals) distance in the direction moments are being determined

$L_2 =$ span length transverse to L_1, measured center to center of supports for typical interior panels

Equation (17.3.2) is useful for flat-plate floors or two-way slabs with beams, while Eq. (17.3.1ab) is more suitable to flat slabs, wherein round column capitals are used.

Two design examples are shown in this chapter: one is a flat-slab floor supported on square edge columns with rectangular capitals, edge beams, and round interior columns with round capitals, as well as rectangular drop panels over all columns; the other is a flat-plate floor supported directly on rectangular exterior and interior columns without any beams on column lines. Separate parts of these two design examples are described following the discussions of each topic in the subsequent sections of this chapter.

Flat-Slab Design Example. Figure 17.3.2 shows a flat-slab floor with a total area of 12,500 sq ft. It is divided into 25 panels with a panel size of 25×20 ft. Concrete strength is $f'_c = 3000$ psi and steel yield strength is $f_y = 40,000$ psi. Service live load is 120 psf. Story height is 10 ft. Exterior columns are 16 in. square and interior columns are 18 in. round. Edge beams are 14×24 in. overall. Thickness of slab is $7\frac{1}{2}$ in. outside of drop panel and $10\frac{1}{2}$ in. through the drop panel. Sizes of column capitals and drop panels are as shown in Fig. 17.3.2.

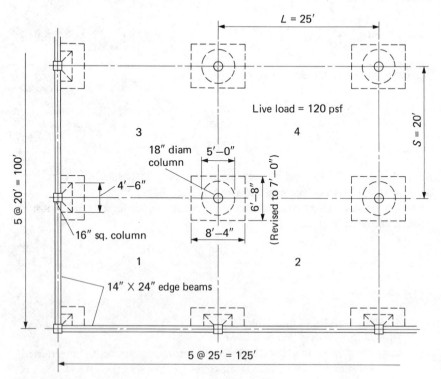

Fig. 17.3.2
Flat-slab design example.

Flat-Plate Design Example. Figure 17.3.3 shows a flat-plate floor with a total area of 4500 sq ft. It is divided into 25 panels with a panel size of 15×12 ft. Concrete strength is $f'_c = 4000$ psi and steel yield strength is $f_y = 50{,}000$ psi. Service live load is 60 psf. Story height is 9 ft. All columns are rectangular, 12 in. in the long direction and 10 in. in the short direction. Preliminary slab thickness is set at $5\frac{1}{2}$ in. No edge beams are used along the exterior edges of the floor.

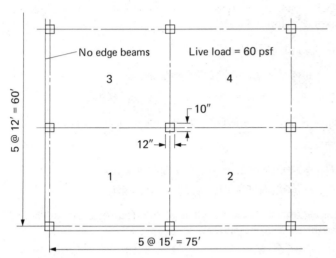

Fig. 17.3.3
Flat-plate design example.

EXAMPLE 17.3.1 Compute the total factored static moment in the long and short directions of an interior panel in the flat-slab design example as shown in Fig. 17.3.2. Compare the results obtained by using Eqs. (17.3.1ab) and (17.3.2).

Solution: Neglecting the weight of the drop panel, the service dead load is $(150/12)(7.5) = 94$ psf; thus

$$w_u = 1.4w_D + 1.7w_L = 1.4(94) + 1.7(120) = 132 + 204 = 336 \text{ psf}$$

Using Eqs. (17.3.1ab),

$$M_{OL} = \frac{1}{8}wSL^2\left(1 - \frac{2c}{3L}\right)^2 = \frac{1}{8}(0.336)(20)(25)^2\left[1 - \frac{2(5)}{3(25)}\right]^2 = 395 \text{ ft-kips}$$

$$M_{OS} = \frac{1}{8}wLS^2\left(1 - \frac{2c}{3S}\right)^2 = \frac{1}{8}(0.336)(25)(20)^2\left[1 - \frac{2(5)}{3(20)}\right]^2 = 292 \text{ ft-kips}$$

The equivalent square area for the column capital (ACI-13.6.2.5) has its side equal to 4.43 ft; then, using Eq. (17.3.2),

$$M_{OL} = \tfrac{1}{8}wSL_n^2 = \tfrac{1}{8}(0.336)(20)(25 - 4.43)^2 = 356 \text{ ft-kips}$$

$$M_{OS} = \tfrac{1}{8}wLS_n^2 = \tfrac{1}{8}(0.336)(25)(20 - 4.43)^2 = 255 \text{ ft-kips}$$

Insofar as flat slabs with column capitals are concerned, it appears that the larger values of 395 ft-kips and 292 ft-kips should be used because Eqs. (17.3.1ab) are specially suitable; in particular, ACI-13.6.2.2 states that the total factored static moment shall not be less than that given by Eq. (17.2.2).

EXAMPLE 17.3.2 Compute the total factored static moment in the long and short directions of a typical panel in the flat-plate design example as shown in Fig. 17.3.3, which is to support a service live load of 60 psf. Assume that the thickness of the slab is $5\frac{1}{2}$ in.

Solution: The dead load for a $5\frac{1}{2}$ in. slab is

$$DL = (5.5/12)(150) = 69 \text{ psf}$$

The factored load is

$$w_u = 1.4w_D + 1.7w_L = 1.4(69) + 1.7(60) = 96 + 102 = 198 \text{ psf}$$

Using Eq. (17.3.2),

$$M_{OL} = \tfrac{1}{8}(0.198)(12)(15 - 1)^2 = 58.2 \text{ ft-kips}$$
$$M_{OS} = \tfrac{1}{8}(0.198)(15)(12 - 0.83)^2 = 46.3 \text{ ft-kips}$$

These moment values obtained on the basis of the clear spans of 14 ft and 11 ft 2 in. are appropriate for flat-plate floors.

17.4 Nominal Requirements for Slab Thickness and Size of Edge Beams, Column Capital, and Drop Panel

Whether the ACI "direct-design method" or the "equivalent-frame method" is used for determining the longitudinal distribution of moments, certain nominal requirements for slab thickness and size of edge beams, column capital, and drop panel must be fulfilled. These requirements are termed "nominal" because they are code prescribed. It should be realized, of course, that the code provisions are based on a combination of experience, judgment, tests, and theoretical analysis.

Slab Thickness. The minimum thickness for deflection control is given by semi-empirical ACI Code Formulas (9-10), (9-11), and (9-12) stated and shown graphically in Sec. 16.6. From Fig. 16.6.1, one may note that for slab panels *without* edge beams, Eq. (16.6.3) controls:

$$\min t \geq \frac{L_n(0.8 + 0.2f_y/40,000)}{36}, \text{ ACI Formula (9-12)} \quad \textbf{[16.6.3]}$$

Additional minimum thickness requirements relating to flat-slab and flat-plate construction are as follows:

For slabs without beams or drop panels, 5 in.
For slabs without beams but with properly sized drop panels, 4 in.

Edge Beams. Even though beams are not used in flat slabs or flat plates between columns inside the floor plan, they are frequently used at discontinuous edges, hence the name "edge beams." The stiffness of a beam is proportional to EI/L; when E and L of different beams are identical, the stiffness is measured by $I = bh^3/12$ in which b and h are overall dimensions of the concrete. In two-way slabs with beams the relative stiffness of the beam to the slab adjacent to the beam on both sides of it is denoted by α; the stiffness of the slab is measured by $Bt^3/12$ where B is the total width of the slab in the equivalent frame bounded laterally by the centerline of the adjacent panel. When edge beams are not used, or if the edge beam is so small that α is less than 0.80, ACI-9.5.3.3 states that the requirement for slab thickness expressed by Eqs. (16.6.1) to (16.6.3) must be increased by 10% in the panel having the discontinuous edge.

Column Capital. As shown in Fig. 17.1.1 the column capital is an enlargement of the top of the column as it meets the floor slab or drop panel. The purpose of the capital is to gain increased perimeter around the column to transmit shear from the floor loading and to provide increasing thickness as the perimeter decreases near the column. Assuming a maximum 45° line for distribution of the shear into the column, ACI-13.1.2 requires that the effective column capital for strength considerations be within the largest circular cone or pyramid with a 90° vertex that can be included within the outlines of the actual supporting element (see Fig. 17.4.1). The diameter of the column capital is usually about 20 to 25% of the average span length between columns.

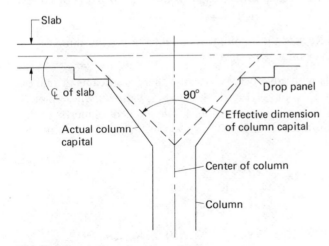

Fig. 17.4.1
Effective dimension of column capital.

Drop Panel. As shown in Fig. 17.1.1 the drop panel is an area of increased slab thickness surrounding the column. When drop panels extend from the centerline of supports a minimum distance of one-sixth of the span length measured from center to center in each direction, and when the projection below the slab is at least one-fourth of the slab thickness outside of the drop, ACI-9.5.3.2 permits the minimum slab thickness required by Eqs. (16.6.1) to (16.6.3) to be reduced by 10%. For determining reinforcement, ACI-13.4.7.3 requires that the thickness of the drop below the slab be assumed at a value no larger than one-fourth of the distance between the edge of the drop panel and the edge of the column capital.

Summary of Nominal Requirements. The nominal requirements for flat slabs may be summarized as follows:

1. The minimum slab thickness (ACI-9.5.3.1) shall be that of Eq. (16.6.1), but not less than that of Eq. (16.6.2), and need not be more than that of Eq. (16.6.3).
2. The minimum slab thickness shall be 5 in. for flat slabs without drop panels; and 4 in. for flat slabs with drop panels.
3. In edge panels when the ratio α of edge beam stiffness to slab stiffness is less than 0.80, the ACI minimum thickness requirement must be increased by 10% (ACI-9.5.3.3).
4. When the size of a drop panel is at least one-third of the span length and its projection below the slab is at least one-fourth of the thickness outside of the drop, the values expressed by Eqs. (16.6.1) to (16.6.3) may be reduced by 10% (ACI-9.5.3.2).
5. Since the reinforcement within the drop panel must be computed on the assumption that its projection below the slab is not more than one-fourth of the distance between the edges of the column capital and the drop panel (ACI-13.4.7.3), there is little reason to use a drop panel of larger thickness.

EXAMPLE 17.4.1 Review the nominal requirements for the dimensions in the flat-slab design example described in Sec. 17.3.

Solution: (a) Panels with edge beams. Because there are beams at one or more sides of panels 1, 2, and 3 (Fig. 17.4.2), the α_m value for these panels will not be zero, as it is for the interior panel 4. The moment of inertia of the edge-beam section shown in Fig. 17.4.2 is 22,900 in.[4] Thus the α value for the long edge beam is

$$\alpha = \frac{I_b}{I_s} = \frac{22,900}{120(7.5)^3/12} = \frac{22,900}{4220} = 5.42$$

and for the short edge beam, it is

$$\alpha = \frac{I_b}{I_s} = \frac{22,900}{150(7.5)^3/12} = \frac{22,900}{5270} = 4.34$$

These α values are entered on Fig. 17.4.2. The average α (i.e., α_m) for panels 1, 2, and 3 are, respectively, 2.4, 1.4, and 1.1.

An examination of Fig. 16.6.1 showing the ACI minimum thickness equations reveals that ACI Formula (9-11) [Eq. (16.6.2)] governs for panel 1, whereas Formula (9-10) [Eq. (16.6.1)] governs for panels 2 and 3.

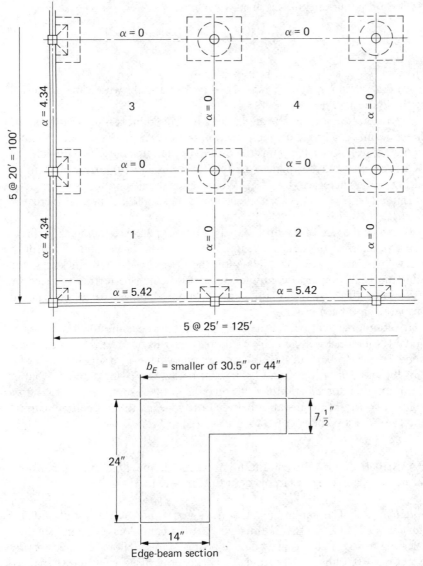

Fig. 17.4.2
Computation of α values in Example 17.4.1.

(b) Interior panel. Panel 4 having no beams along its perimeter has $\alpha_m = 0$. Figure 16.6.1 shows for $\alpha_m = 0$ ACI Formula (9-12) [Eq. (16.6.3)] controls.

(c) Minimum thickness. Assuming the entire slab is to have a uniform thickness, ACI Formula (9-12) applied to the interior panel gives $L_n/t = 36$, a lower value than obtained for the panels 1, 2, or 3. This, of course, is the primary reason for using edge beams—that is, to stiffen the edges of exterior panels and thus make the interior panel govern the thickness. The longest clear span L_n is $(25 - 4.43) = 20.57$ ft.

The minimum thickness is, from Eq. (16.6.3),

$$\min t = \frac{L_n(0.8 + 0.2f_y/40{,}000)}{36} = \frac{20.57(12)(0.8 + 0.2)}{36} = 6.86 \text{ in.}$$

Thus the $7\frac{1}{2}$-in. slab as used is ample.

(d) The minimum slab thickness of 4 in. for flat slabs with drop is satisfied by the $7\frac{1}{2}$-in. slab used here.

(e) The ratio α of edge-beam stiffness to slab stiffness is 4.34 in the short direction and 5.42 in the long direction, as shown in Fig. 17.4.2. These α values are well above 0.8. Thus the minimum slab thickness requirements of ACI Formula (9-11) for panel 1 and ACI Formula (9-10) for panels 2 and 3 need not be increased by 10%. When α_m is small enough so that ACI Formula (9-12) would govern, then that value would be the one increased by 10%.

(f) Since the size of the drop panel (see Fig. 17.3.2) is equal in each direction to one-third of the span length, and the 3-in. projection of the drop below the slab is more than one-fourth of the $7\frac{1}{2}$-in. slab thickness, the minimum slab thickness computed in part (a) could be further reduced by 10%. Thus the $7\frac{1}{2}$-in. slab thickness is more than ample; $6\frac{1}{2}$-in. should probably have been used.

(g) Reinforcement within the drop panel must be computed on the basis of the $10\frac{1}{2}$-in. thickness actually used or $7\frac{1}{2}$-in. plus one-fourth of the projection of the drop beyond the column capital, whichever is smaller. In order that the full 3-in. projection of the drop below the $7\frac{1}{2}$-in. slab is usable in computing reinforcement, the 6 ft 8 in. side of the drop is revised to 7 ft so that one-fourth of the distance between the edges of the 5-ft column capital and the 7-ft drop is just equal to $(10.5 - 7.5) = 3$ in.

EXAMPLE 17.4.2 Review the nominal requirements for the dimensions in the flat-plate design example described in Sec. 17.3.

Solution: (a) The minimum slab thickness from ACI Formulas (9-10) through (9-12) [Eqs. (16.6.1) through (16.6.3)] can be easily established by referring to Fig. 16.6.1. Since no edge beams are used along the sides of any panel, $\alpha_m = 0$. Thus ACI Formula (9-12) governs. The longest clear span L_n is $(15 - 1) = 14$ ft.

$$\min t = \frac{L_c(0.8 + 0.2f_y/40{,}000)}{36}$$

$$= \frac{14(1.05)(12)}{36} = 4.90 \text{ in.} < 5\frac{1}{2} \text{ in. used} \qquad \text{OK}$$

(b) The minimum slab thickness of 5 in. for flat slabs without drop panels is satisfied by the $5\frac{1}{2}$-in. slab used here.

(c) Since no edge beams are used, $\alpha = E_{cb}I_b/(E_{cs}I_s) = 0$, which is less than 0.8. Thus the minimum slab thickness becomes 1.1 times the controlling

4.90 in. computed from ACI Formula (9-12) [Eq. (16.6.3)] in part (a); or

$$\min t = 1.10(4.90) = 5.39 \text{ in.} < 5\tfrac{1}{2}\text{-in. used.}$$

Thus the $5\tfrac{1}{2}$-in. slab is appropriate.

17.5 Direct-Design Method—Longitudinal Distribution of Total Static Moment

Same as for two-way slabs supported on beams, two methods are specified by the ACI Code for determining the longitudinal moments in flat-slab and flat-plate floors. In order that the "direct-design method" may be used rather than the "equivalent-frame method," the first five of the six limitations (ACI-13.6.1) as stated in Sec. 16.4 must be satisfied, because the sixth limitation relates to the relative stiffnesses of the included beam and the slab. The first five limitations are restated below:

1. There is a minimum of three continuous spans in each direction.
2. Panels must be rectangular with the ratio of longer to shorter span within a panel not greater than 2.0.
3. The successive span lengths in each direction do not differ by more than one-third of the longer span.
4. Columns are not offset more than 10% of the span in the direction of the offset.
5. The load is due to gravity only and is uniformly distributed over an entire panel, and the service live load does not exceed 3 times the service dead load.

Though the design of two-way slab systems is to a large extent empirical, the ACI limitations conform to the experimental results that are available [6–11] and to many years of experience with slabs in actual structures. The "direct-design method" can also be used when it can be demonstrated that variations from any of the five limitations will still produce a slab system that satisfies the conditions of equilibrium and geometric compatibility and provides adequate strength and serviceability. Van Buren [36] has provided such an analysis for staggered columns in flat plates.

The longitudinal distribution of the total factored static moment M_0 depends on three important parameters: (1) the flexural stiffness K_{ec} of the equivalent exterior column, which in turn is a function of the torsional stiffness K_t of the transverse edge-beam section, if there is such a beam, and the flexural stiffnesses K_{c1} and K_{c2} of the upper and lower exterior columns; (2) the ratio α of the flexural stiffness K_b of the longitudinal beam section (in flat slabs or flat plates there may be longitudinal beams along exterior column lines but not interior column lines) to the flexural stiffness K_s of the slab in the width of the equivalent frame; and (3) the ratio β_a of the service dead to live loads. The first parameter affects the distribution of M_0 to M_{ni}, M_{pos}, and M_{nj} (see Fig. 16.4.1) in the exterior span, while the second and third parameters affect the increase in the positive moment M_{pos} for the exterior and interior spans due to pattern loading effects. The background explanation has been presented in Secs. 16.7 and 16.8; the complete procedure for longitudinal distribution in the "direct-design method" may be summarized as follows:

1. Compute the torsional constant C (see Chap. 19, Sec. 19.3) of the transverse edge-beam section by dividing it into component rectangles such that the value of C is the largest obtainable

$$C = \sum \left(1 - 0.63 \frac{x}{y}\right)\left(\frac{x^3 y}{3}\right)$$

in which x and y are the short and long sides of each rectangle, respectively. The transverse edge-beam section (see Fig. 16.7.2) is taken as the largest of (a) a portion of slab having a width equal to the column dimension c_1 in the longitudinal direction, (b) the portion of slab in part (a) plus that part of the transverse beam above and below the slab, or (c) the transverse beam including a portion of slab on each side extending a distance equal to the projection of the beam above or below the slab, whichever is greater, but not greater than 4 times the slab thickness.

2. Compute the torsional stiffness K_t of the transverse edge-beam section by

$$K_t = \sum \frac{9E_{cs}C}{L_2(1 - c_2/L_2)^3}$$

where the summation sign refers to the panels on both sides of the column centerline and L_2 is the full panel dimension (center to center) in the transverse direction.

3. Compute the stiffness K_{ec} of the *equivalent* exterior column from

$$\frac{1}{K_{ec}} = \frac{1}{\sum K_c} + \frac{1}{K_t}$$

where $\sum K_c$ is the sum of the flexural stiffnesses of the upper and lower exterior columns.

4. Compute the ratio α of longitudinal beam stiffness (such beam may exist along the exterior edges of flat slabs or flat plates) to that of the slab by

$$\alpha = \frac{E_{cb}I_b}{E_{cs}I_s}$$

and with the value of $\beta_a = $ (service DL)/(service LL), obtain the value of α_{min} from Table 16.8.1 (or ACI-Table 13.6.10).

5. Compute for the exterior and interior spans the ratio α_c of the flexural stiffnesses of upper and lower columns to the combined flexural stiffnesses of the slab and beam by

$$\alpha_c = \frac{K_{c1} + K_{c2}}{\sum K_s + \sum K_b}$$

6. If the computed value of α_c does not reach the α_{min} shown in Table 16.8.1, the positive moments M_{pos} must be increased for pattern loading effects by multiplying by the factor δ_s, where

$$\delta_s = 1 + \frac{2 - \beta_a}{4 + \beta_a}\left(1 - \frac{\alpha_c}{\alpha_{min}}\right) \qquad \text{for } \alpha_c < \alpha_{min}$$

otherwise,

$$\delta_s = 1.0 \qquad \text{for } \alpha_c \geq \alpha_{min}$$

7. Determine the distribution factor DF at the exterior joint by

$$DF = \frac{K_{ec}}{K_{ec} + K_b + K_s}$$

8. Obtain the longitudinal moments in the frame as follows:

Negative moment at face of exterior support $= 0.65(DF)M_0$.
Positive moment in exterior span $= \delta_s[0.63 - 0.28(DF)]M_0$.
Negative moment at exterior face of first interior support
$\quad = [0.75 - 0.10(DF)]M_0$.
Negative moment at face of typical interior support $= (0.65)M_0$.
Positive moment in typical interior span $= \delta_s(0.35)M_0$.

In the "direct-design method," the flexural stiffnesses K_b, K_s, K_{c1}, and K_{c2} may be computed by using the general expression $4EI/L$; that is, the member is assumed to have constant moment of inertia along its entire length.

In the "equivalent-frame method" wherein elastic analyses are made, the moment of inertia of the horizontal span and of the columns should be modified in regions near the supports so that the stiffness coefficients and the carry-over factors are no longer 4 and 0.5, respectively. Also, the torsional stiffness K_t must be modified to K_{ta}, where $K_{ta} = K_t I_{sb}/I_s$, in which I_{sb} is the moment of inertia of the slab-beam combination, using the same width of slab used for computing I_s along with the actual beam, including any beam stem above and below the slab. Further, not only is the equivalent column stiffness K_{ec} of the exterior column needed, as in the "direct-design method"; but the values of K_{ec} for all exterior and interior columns are required to compute the distribution and carry-over factors at all exterior and interior joints.

EXAMPLE 17.5.1 By the "direct-design method" compute the longitudinal moments in the exterior and interior spans of the equivalent rigid frames A, B, C, and D (Fig. 17.5.1) in the flat-slab design example described in Sec. 17.3.

Solution: (a) The five limitations required for using the "direct-design method" are all satisfied.

(b) Total factored static moment. Referring to the equivalent rigid frames A, B, C, and D in Fig. 17.5.1, the total static moment may be taken from the

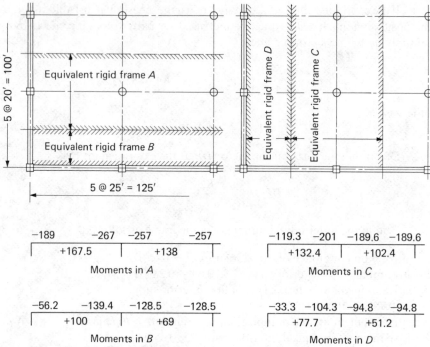

Fig. 17.5.1
Longitudinal moments for flat-slab design example.

results of Example 17.3.1; thus

$$M_0 \text{ for } A = 395 \text{ ft-kips}$$
$$M_0 \text{ for } B = \tfrac{1}{2}(395) = 197.5 \text{ ft-kips}$$
$$M_0 \text{ for } C = 292 \text{ ft-kips}$$
$$M_0 \text{ for } D = \tfrac{1}{2}(292) = 146 \text{ ft-kips}$$

(c) Slab stiffness K_s.

$$K_s \text{ for } A = \frac{4EI_s}{L_1} = \frac{4E(240)(7.5)^3/12}{25(12)} = 112.5E$$

$$K_s \text{ for } B = 56.25E$$

$$K_s \text{ for } C = \frac{4EI_s}{L_1} = \frac{4E(300)(7.5)^3/12}{20(12)} = 176E$$

$$K_s \text{ for } D = 88E$$

(d) Column stiffness K_c.

$$K_c \text{ (upper and lower interior columns)} = \frac{2(4EI_c)}{L} = \frac{2(4E)\pi(18)^4/64}{10(12)} = 343E$$

$$K_c \text{ (upper and lower exterior columns)} = \frac{2(4EI_c)}{L} = \frac{2(4E)(16)^4/12}{10(12)} = 364E$$

(e) Torsional stiffness K_t. Since all edge beams are of the same size, the torsional constant C is computed on the basis of the cross section shown in Fig. 17.4.2, which is repeated here in Fig. 17.5.2. Using alternate A in Fig. 17.5.2,

$$C = \left[1 - \frac{0.63(7.5)}{30.5}\right]\frac{(7.5)^3(30.5)}{3} + \left[1 - \frac{0.63(14)}{16.5}\right]\frac{(14)^3(16.5)}{3}$$

$$= 3625 + 7025 = 10{,}700 \text{ in.}^4$$

Using alternate B in Fig. 17.5.2,

$$C = \left[1 - \frac{0.63(14)}{24}\right]\frac{(14)^3(24)}{3} + \left[1 - \frac{0.63(7.5)}{16.5}\right]\frac{(7.5)^3(16.5)}{3}$$

$$= 13{,}860 + 1660 = 15{,}500 \text{ in.}^4$$

Use the larger value of $C = 15{,}500$ in.^{4}

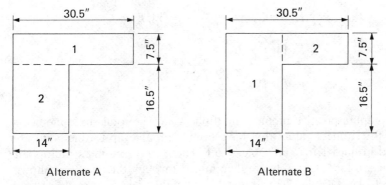

Fig. 17.5.2
Edge section for torsion, Example 17.5.1.

The size of the rectangular exterior column capital in the direction of the edge beam is 4.5 ft (Fig. 17.3.2).

$$K_t \text{ for } A = \frac{2(9E)(15{,}500)}{240(1 - 4.5/20)^3} = 2500E$$

$$K_t \text{ for } B = \tfrac{1}{2}(2500E) = 1250E^\dagger$$

$$K_t \text{ for } C = \frac{2(9E)(15{,}500)}{300(1 - 4.5/25)^3} = 1690E$$

$$K_t \text{ for } D = \tfrac{1}{2}(1690E) = 845E^\dagger$$

[†] Increase in torsional stiffness, to account for the higher flexural stiffness occurring where beams frame into columns in the direction moments are being determined, has been neglected. Such increase is required by ACI-13.7.5.4 for the "equivalent-frame method" but may be waived for the "direct design method" (ACI Commentary-13.6.3.3(2)).

(f) Equivalent column stiffness K_{ec}.

$$K_{ec} \text{ for } A = \frac{E}{1/364 + 1/2500} = \frac{1000E}{2.75 + 0.400} = 317E$$

$$K_{ec} \text{ for } B = \frac{E}{1/364 + 1/1250} = \frac{1000E}{2.75 + 0.800} = 281E$$

$$K_{ec} \text{ for } C = \frac{E}{1/364 + 1/1690} = \frac{1000E}{2.75 + 0.592} = 299E$$

$$K_{ec} \text{ for } D = \frac{E}{1/364 + 1/845} = \frac{1000E}{2.75 + 1.19} = 253E$$

(g) Beam stiffness K_b. From Example 17.4.1, the gross moment of inertia of the edge beam (longitudinal beam for frames B and D) shown in Fig. 17.4.2 about the centroidal axis is 22,900 in.[4]

$$K_b \text{ for } A = 0$$

$$K_b \text{ for } B = \frac{4E(22,900)}{300} = 305E$$

$$K_b \text{ for } C = 0$$

$$K_b \text{ for } D = \frac{4E(22,900)}{240} = 381E$$

(h) Compute positive moment multipliers δ_s. The total static moments M_0 and the stiffness values that have been computed up to this point are tabulated in lines 1 to 7 of Table 17.5.1. The positive moment multipliers δ_s for pattern loading effects are determined through the processes shown in lines 8 to 12 of Table 17.5.1. It may be noted that, with the small live-load to dead-load ratio of 120 to 94 and with the fairly large 18-in. round interior and 16-in. square exterior columns, the α_c furnished is larger than the α_{min} specified so that there is virtually no pattern loading effect for all equivalent rigid frames (except δ_s of 1.06 for frame C).

(i) Compute longitudinal moments at all critical locations. The longitudinal moments at all critical sections are computed and shown in lines 13 to 18 of Table 17.5.1. Note that the value shown in line 13 is the distribution factor at the exterior column, according to the terminology of the moment-distribution method. These longitudinal moments are again shown in Fig. 17.5.1 for equivalent rigid frames A, B, C, and D, respectively.

EXAMPLE 17.5.2 By the "direct-design method" compute the longitudinal moments in the exterior and interior spans of the equivalent rigid frames A, B, C, and D (Fig. 17.5.3) in the flat-plate design example described in Sec. 17.3.

Solution: (a) The five limitations required for using the "direct-design method" are all satisfied.

Table 17.5.1

Longitudinal Moments for the Flat-Slab Design Example

Line Number	Equivalent Rigid Frame	A	B	C	D
1	M_0 (ft-kips)	395	197.5	292	146
2	K_s (in.^{3})	112.5E	56.25E	176E	88E
3	ΣK_c (in.^{3}) interior	343E	364E	343E	364E
4	K_t (in.^{3})	2500E	1250E	1690E	845E
5	K_c at edge (in.^{3})	364E	364E	364E	364E
6	K_{ec} (in.^{3})	317E	281E	299E	253E
7	K_b (in.^{3})	0	305E	0	381E
8	$\alpha = K_b/K_s$	0	5.42	0	4.34
9	$\alpha_c = \Sigma K_c/\Sigma(K_b + K_s)$ interior[a]	1.52	0.51	0.97	0.39
10	L_2/L_1	0.80	0.80	1.25	1.25
11	$\alpha_{min}(\beta_a = 0.78)$ (from Table 16.8.1)	1.05	0	1.28	0
12	δ_s	1.0	1.0	1.06	1.0
13	$K_{ec}/(K_{ec} + K_b + K_s)$	0.737	0.438	0.629	0.351
14	$0.65M_0$ times (13)	189.0	56.2	119.3	33.3
15	$\delta_s M_0[0.63 - 0.28$ times (13)]	167.5	100.0	140.5	77.7
16	$M_0[0.75 - 0.10$ times (13)]	267	139.4	201	104.3
17	$0.65M_0$	257	128.5	189.6	94.8
18	$\delta_s[0.35M_0]$	138	69.0	108.3	51.2

[a] α_c should be computed for both interior and exterior columns. It is conservative to use the smaller (in this case interior column values) for comparing with α_{min}.

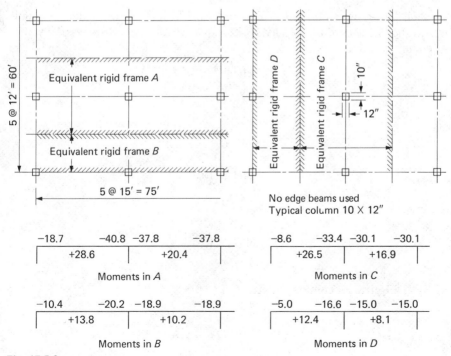

5 @ 12' = 60'

Equivalent rigid frame A

Equivalent rigid frame B

5 @ 15' = 75'

Equivalent rigid frame D

Equivalent rigid frame C

10"

12"

No edge beams used
Typical column 10 × 12"

−18.7   −40.8 −37.8   −37.8
      +28.6   +20.4

Moments in A

−10.4   −20.2 −18.9   −18.9
      +13.8   +10.2

Moments in B

−8.6   −33.4 −30.1   −30.1
      +26.5   +16.9

Moments in C

−5.0   −16.6 −15.0   −15.0
      +12.4   +8.1

Moments in D

Fig. 17.5.3

Longitudinal moments for flat-plate design example.

(b) Total factored static moment from the results of Example 17.3.2.

$$M_0 \text{ for } A = 58.2 \text{ ft-kips}$$
$$M_0 \text{ for } B = \tfrac{1}{2}(58.2) = 29.1 \text{ ft-kips}$$
$$M_0 \text{ for } C = 46.3 \text{ ft-kips}$$
$$M_0 \text{ for } D = 23.1 \text{ ft-kips}$$

(c) Slab stiffness K_s.

$$K_s \text{ for } A = \frac{4EI_s}{L_1} = \frac{4E(144)(5.5)^3/12}{15(12)} = 44.4E$$

$$K_s \text{ for } B = 22.2E$$

$$K_s \text{ for } C = \frac{4EI_s}{L_1} = \frac{4E(180)(5.5)^3/12}{12(12)} = 69.4E$$

$$K_s \text{ for } D = 34.7E$$

(d) Column stiffness K_c.

$$K_c \text{ for } A \text{ and } B = \frac{2(4EI_c)}{L} = \frac{2(4E)(10)(12)^3/12}{9(12)} = 106.7E$$

$$K_c \text{ for } C \text{ and } D = \frac{2(4EI_c)}{L} = \frac{2(4E)(12)(10)^3/12}{9(12)} = 74.1E$$

(e) Torsional stiffness K_t. Since no edge beams are used, the torsional member is, according to Fig. 16.7.2, equal to the slab thickness t by the column width c_1

$$C \text{ for } A \text{ or } B = \left[1 - \frac{0.63(5.5)}{12}\right]\frac{(5.5)^3(12)}{3} = 474 \text{ in.}^4$$

$$C \text{ for } C \text{ or } D = \left[1 - \frac{0.63(5.5)}{10}\right]\frac{(5.5)^3(10)}{3} = 363 \text{ in.}^4$$

$$K_t \text{ for } A = \frac{2(9E)(474)}{144(1 - 10/144)^3} = 73.6E$$

$$K_t \text{ for } B = 36.8E$$

$$K_t \text{ for } C = \frac{2(9E)(363)}{180(1 - 12/180)^3} = 44.7E$$

$$K_t \text{ for } D = 22.4E$$

(f) Equivalent column stiffness K_{ec}.

$$K_{ec} \text{ for } A = \frac{E}{1/106.7 + 1/73.6} = \frac{1000E}{9.33 + 13.6} = 43.6E$$

$$K_{ec} \text{ for } B = \frac{E}{1/106.7 + 1/36.8} = \frac{1000E}{9.33 + 27.2} = 27.4E$$

$$K_{ec} \text{ for } C = \frac{E}{1/74.1 + 1/44.7} = \frac{1000E}{13.5 + 22.4} = 27.8E$$

$$K_{ec} \text{ for } D = \frac{E}{1/74.1 + 1/22.4} = \frac{1000E}{13.5 + 44.7} = 17.2E$$

(g) Compute positive moment multipliers δ_s. The total static moment M_0 and the stiffness values that have been computed up to this point are tabulated in lines 1 to 5 of Table 17.5.2. The positive-moment multipliers δ_s for pattern loading effects are determined through the processes shown in lines 6 to 9 of Table 17.5.2. Alternate equations for the multiplier δ_s have been proposed by Jofriet and McNeice [12]. Since there are no beams at all, K_b and α are zero in all cases. The values of α_{min} are taken from Table 16.8.1. Note again that except for frame C, $\delta_s = 1.0$, in Table 17.5.2.

Table 17.5.2
Longitudinal Moments for the Flat-Plate Design Example

Line Number	Equivalent Rigid Frame	A	B	C	D
1	M_0 (ft-kips)	58.2	29.1	46.3	23.1
2	K_s (in.^{3})	44.4E	22.2E	69.4E	34.7E
3	ΣK_c (in.^{3})	106.7E	106.7E	74.1E	74.1E
4	K_t (in.^{3})	73.6E	36.8E	44.7E	22.4E
5	K_{ec} (in.^{3})	43.6E	27.4E	27.8E	17.2E
6	$\alpha_c = \Sigma K_c / \Sigma K_s$ interior	1.20	2.40	0.53	1.07
7	L_2/L_1	0.80	0.80	1.25	1.25
8	α_{min} ($\beta_a = 1.15$) (Table 16.8.1)	0.60	0.60	0.68	0.68
9	δ_s	1.0	1.0	1.04	1.0
10	$K_{ec}/(K_{ec} + K_s)$	0.495	0.552	0.286	0.332
11	$0.65M_0$ times (10)	18.7	10.4	8.6	5.0
12	$\delta_s M_0[0.63 - 0.28$ times (10)]	28.6	13.8	26.5	12.4
13	$M_0[0.75 - 0.10$ times (10)]	40.8	20.2	33.4	16.6
14	$0.65M_0$	37.8	18.9	30.1	15.0
15	$\delta_s[0.35M_0]$	20.4	10.2	16.9	8.1

(h) Compute longitudinal moments at all critical sections. The longitudinal moments are computed in lines 10 to 15 of Table 17.5.2 and shown also in Fig. 17.5.3.

17.6 Transverse Distribution of Longitudinal Moment

The longitudinal moments as computed in the preceding section are for the entire transverse width of the frame being considered. Each of these moments is to be proportioned into two parts, the greater percentage to the column strip and the remainder to the two half middle strips at each side of an interior column strip or to the only half middle strip adjacent to an exterior column strip. The actual distinction of half middle strips is only necessary when adjacent equivalent frames are not identical, such as along the first interior column line from the edge of the structure. The width of the column strip is $\frac{1}{4}S$ for a frame along the exterior column line of the structure, for either the long or short direction, where S is the short panel dimension; and it is $\frac{1}{4}S_1 + \frac{1}{4}S_2$ for an interior frame, again in either the long or short direction, where S_1 and S_2 are the short spans of the two adjacent panels. The remainder of the total strip width on one side (for an edge frame) or each side (for an interior frame) of the column strip constitutes the width of the half middle strip.

The transverse distribution of the longitudinal moment to column and middle strips depends on three parameters: (1) the aspect ratio L_2/L_1; (2) the factor $\alpha_1 L_2/L_1$ which is the product of the ratio α_1 of longitudinal beam to slab stiffnesses and the aspect ratio; and (3) the ratio $\beta_t = E_{cb}C/(2E_{cs}I_s)$ of torsional stiffness of edge-beam section to flexural stiffness of a slab width equal to the span length of the edge beam. As may be seen from Table 16.10.1, only the first two parameters affect the transverse distribution of the negative moments at the first and typical interior supports as well as the positive moments in exterior and interior spans; but all three parameters are involved in the transverse distribution of the negative moment at the exterior support.

Where the exterior support consists of a column or wall of a length equal to or greater than three-fourths of the transverse width, the exterior negative moment is to be uniformly distributed in the transverse direction (ACI-13.6.4.3).

If a longitudinal edge beam exists in an exterior column strip, the longitudinal moment that goes into the column strip should be again divided into two parts, one for the longitudinal edge beam and the other for the slab in the column strip. The percentage of the column strip moment that goes into the longitudinal edge beam may be taken as 85% if $\alpha L_2/L_1$ is equal to or greater than 1.0, with this proportion to be adjusted by linear interpolation between 85% and 0% for values of $\alpha L_2/L_1$ between 1.0 and 0.

Finally, it may be noted that the middle strip adjacent and parallel to an edge supported by a wall should be proportioned to resist twice the moment assigned to the half middle strip corresponding to the first row of interior supports (ACI-13.6.6.3).

EXAMPLE 17.6.1   Divide the five critical moments in each of the equivalent rigid frames A, B, C, and D in the flat-slab design example, as shown in Fig. 17.5.1, into two parts: one for the half column strip (for frames B and D) or the full column strip (for frames A and C), and the other for the half middle strip (for frames B and D) or the two half middle strips on both sides of the column line (for frames A and C).

Solution: The percentages of the longitudinal moments going into the column strip width are shown in lines 10 to 12 of Table 17.6.1. Note that the column strip width shown in line 2 is one-half of the shorter panel dimension for both frames A and C, and one-fourth of this value for frames

B and D. Note also the sum of the values on lines 2 and 3 should be equal to that on line 1, for each respective frame.

The moment of inertia of the slab equal in width to the transverse span of the edge beam is

$$I_s \text{ in } \beta_t \text{ for } A \text{ and } B = \frac{240(7.5)^3}{12} = 8440 \text{ in.}^4$$

and

$$I_s \text{ in } \beta_t \text{ for } C \text{ and } D = \frac{300(7.5)^3}{12} = 10{,}600 \text{ in.}^4$$

These values are shown in line 5 of Table 17.6.1.

Table 17.6.1
Transverse Distribution of Longitudinal Moment, Example 17.6.1

Line Number	Equivalent Rigid Frame	A	B	C	D
1	Total transverse width (in.)	240	120	300	150
2	Column strip width (in.)	120	60	120	60
3	Half middle strip width (in.)	2@60	60	2@90	90
4	C (in.^{4}) from Example 17.5.1, Part (e)	15,500	15,500	15,500	15,500
5	I_s (in.^{4}) in β_t	8,440	8,440	10,600	10,600
6	$\beta_t = E_{cb}C/(2E_{cs}I_s)$	0.920	0.920	0.735	0.735
7	α_1 from Table 17.5.1, line 8	0	5.42	0	4.34
8	L_2/L_1	0.80	0.80	1.25	1.25
9	$\alpha_1 L_2/L_1$	0	4.33	0	5.43
10	Exterior negative moment, percent to column strip	90.8%	93.0%	92.6%	90.4%
11	Positive moment, percent to column strip	60.0%	81.0%	60.0%	67.5%
12	Interior negative moment, percent to column strip	75.0%	81.0%	75.0%	67.5%

The percentages shown in lines 10 to 12 are obtained from Table 16.10.1, by interpolation if necessary. Having had these percentages, the separation of each of the longitudinal moment values shown in Fig. 17.5.1 into two parts is a simple matter and thus is not shown further.

EXAMPLE 17.6.2   Divide the five critical moments in each of the equivalent rigid frames A, B, C, and D in the flat-plate design example, as shown in Fig. 17.5.3, into two parts: one for the half column strip (for frames B and D) or the full column strip (for frames A and C), and the other for the half middle strip (for frames B and D) or the two half middle strips on both sides of the column line (for frames A and C).

Solution: The percentages of the longitudinal moments going into the column strip width are shown in lines 10 to 12 of Table 17.6.2. Explanations are identical to those for the preceding example.

Table 17.6.2
Transverse Distribution of Longitudinal Moment, Example 17.6.2

Line Number	Equivalent Rigid Frame	A	B	C	D
1	Total transverse width (in.)	144	72	180	90
2	Column strip width (in.)	72	36	72	36
3	Half middle strip width (in.)	2@36	36	2@54	54
4	C (in.^{4}) from Example 17.5.2, Part (e)	474	474	363	363
5	I_s (in.^{4}) in β_t	2,000	2,000	2,500	2,500
6	$\beta_t = E_{cb}C/(2E_{cs}I_s)$	0.118	0.118	0.073	0.073
7	α_1	0	0	0	0
8	L_2/L_1	0.80	0.80	1.25	1.25
9	$\alpha_1 L_2/L_1$	0	0	0	0
10	Exterior negative moment, percent to column strip	98.8%	98.8%	99.3%	99.3%
11	Positive moment, percent to column strip	60%	60%	60%	60%
12	Interior negative moment, percent to column strip	75%	75%	75%	75%

17.7 Design of Slab Thickness and Reinforcement for Flexure

Slab Thickness. The slab thickness outside of the drop panel, if any, and the total thickness through the drop must both be investigated so that under the most severe bending moment the maximum ratio of tension reinforcement satisfies ACI-10.3.3 (i.e., less than $0.75\rho_b$ for flexural members with tension steel only). With the minimum thickness requirements of ACI-9.5.3 already satisfied, however, the maximum reinforcement ratio is more likely to be well below $0.375\rho_b$. In evaluating the drop-panel thickness for flexure, the drop width should be used as the transverse width of the compression area, since the drop is usually narrower than the width of the column strip. Also, the effective depth to be used for computing the reinforcement should not be more than what would be furnished by a drop thickness below the slab equal to one-fourth the distance from the edge of drop to the edge of column capital.

Reinforcement. When the nominal requirements for slab thickness as discussed in Sec. 17.4 are satisfied, no compression reinforcement will likely be required. The tension steel area required within the strip being considered can then be obtained by the following steps:

1. $M_n = \dfrac{\text{factored moment } M_u \text{ in the strip}}{(\phi = 0.90)}$

2. $m = \dfrac{f_y}{0.85 f'_c}, \qquad R_u = \dfrac{M_n}{bd^2}, \qquad \rho = \dfrac{1}{m}\left(1 - \sqrt{1 - \dfrac{2mR_u}{f_y}}\right), \qquad A_s = \rho bd$

Instead of using the equation for ρ in step 2, the curves in Fig. 3.6.1 may be used. Note also that the values of b and d to be used in step 2 for negative moment in a column strip with drop are the drop width for b, and for d the smaller of the actual effective depth through the drop and that provided by a drop thickness below the slab at no more than one-fourth the distance between the edges of the column capital and the drop. For positive-moment computation the full column strip width should be used for b, and the effective depth in the slab for d. After obtaining the steel area A_s required within the strip, a number of bars may be chosen so that they provide either the area required for strength or the area required for shrinkage and temperature reinforcement, which is $0.002bt$ for Grades 40 and 50 steel, but somewhat less for higher grades (see ACI-7.12). The spacing of reinforcing bars must not exceed 2 times the slab thickness (ACI-13.4.2), except in slabs of cellular or ribbed construction where the requirement for shrinkage and temperature reinforcement governs (i.e., 5 times the slab thickness or 18 in.).

Crack Control. In addition to deflection control, crack control is the other major serviceability requirement usually considered in the design of flexural members. ACI-10.6 gives criteria for beams and one-way slabs to insure distribution of flexural reinforcement to minimize crack width under service loads. No ACI Code provisions are given for two-way slab systems; however, ACI Committee 224, Cracking, has suggested a formula to predict the possible crack width in two-way acting slabs, flat slabs, and flat plates. The recommendations are based on the work of Nawy et al. (see Ref. 14–17 of Chap. 16). When the predicted crack width is considered excessive (there are no ACI Code limits for slabs), the distribution (size and spacing) of flexural reinforcement may be adjusted [Ref. 17 of Chap. 16] to decrease predicted crack width. Ordinarily crack width is not a problem on two-way acting slabs, but when steel with f_y equal to 60,000 psi or higher is used, crack control should be considered.

Development Lengths and Bar Cutoffs and Bends. General guidance for laying out the reinforcement within the slab is provided by ACI-Fig. 13.4.8, which shows in detail the minimum lengths of straight and bent bars in column as well as middle strips. The determination of minimum lengths is similar to that for bars in one-way slabs, as discussed in Chap. 8. Specifically all positive reinforcement perpendicular to a discontinuous edge should extend at least 6 in. into the edge beam, wall, or column; and all negative reinforcement perpendicular to such an edge should be bent, hooked, or in some way anchored in the edge beam, wall, or column. Development lengths required for all negative reinforcement should be provided on either side of the face of support, in the manner treated in Chap. 6.

Example. For purpose of illustration the design of reinforcement in a typical column strip and a typical middle strip in the flat-slab design example first described in Sec. 17.3 is shown in the following example. Note that the total static moment for a typical panel in this flat-slab floor has been computed in Example 17.3.1, the nominal requirements for the dimensions have

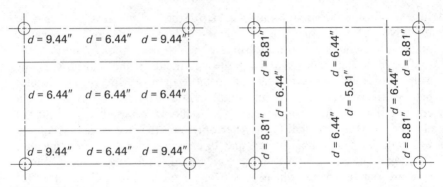

Fig. 17.7.1
Effective depths provided at critical sections for flat-slab floor, Example 17.7.1.

been investigated in Example 17.4.1, the longitudinal moments have been computed in Example 17.5.1, and the transverse distribution of these longitudinal moments has been determined in Example 17.6.1.

EXAMPLE 17.7.1   Design the reinforcement in the exterior and interior spans of a typical column strip and a typical middle strip in the short direction of the flat-slab floor dealt with earlier in Examples 17.3.1, 17.4.1, 17.5.1, and 17.6.1. As described earlier in Sec. 17.3, $f'_c = 3000$ psi and $f_y = 40,000$ psi.

Solution: (a) Moments in column and middle strips. The typical column strip is the column strip of equivalent rigid frame C of Fig. 17.5.1; but the typical middle strip is the sum of two half middle strips, taken from each of the two adjacent equivalent rigid frames C. The factored moments in the typical column and middle strips are shown in Table 17.7.1.

(b) Slab thickness for flexure. For $f'_c = 3000$ psi and $f_y = 40,000$ psi, the maximum percentage for tension reinforcement only is $0.75\rho_b = 0.0278$

Table 17.7.1
Factored Moments in a Typical Column Strip and Middle Strip, Example 17.7.1 (Flat Slab)

Line Number	Moments at Critical Section (*ft-kips*)	Exterior Span			Interior Span		
		Negative Moment	*Positive Moment*	*Negative Moment*	*Negative Moment*	*Positive Moment*	*Negative Moment*
1	Total M in column and middle strips (Fig. 17.5.1) (rigid frame C)	-119.3	$+140.5$	-201	-189.6	$+108.3$	-189.6
2	Percentage to column strip (Table 17.6.1)	92.6%	60%	75%	75%	60%	75%
3	Moment in column strip	-110.5	$+84.3$	-150.7	-142.2	$+65.0$	-142.2
4	Moment in middle strip	-8.8	$+56.2$	-50.3	-47.4	$+43.3$	-47.4

Table 17.7.2

Design of Reinforcement in Column Strip, Example 17.7.1 (Flat Slab) ($f_y = 40{,}000$ psi, $f'_c = 3000$ psi)

Line Number	Critical Section	Exterior Span			Interior Span		
		Negative Moment	Positive Moment	Negative Moment	Negative Moment	Positive Moment	Negative Moment
1	Moment, Table 17.7.1, line 3 (ft-kips)	−110.5	+84.3	−150.7	−142.2	+65.0	−142.2
2	Width b of drop or strip (in.)	100	120	100	100	120	100
3	Effective depth d (in.)	8.81	6.44	8.81	8.81	6.44	8.81
4	$M_n = M_u/0.90$ (ft-kips)	−123	+94	−166	−158	+72	−158
5	R_u (psi) $= M_n/(bd^2)$	190	226 *	257	244	174	244
6	ρ, Eq. (3.6.5) or Fig. 3.6.1	0.50%	0.59%	0.67%	0.64%	0.45%	0.64%
7	$A_s = \rho bd$	4.40	4.57	5.90	5.63	3.47	5.63
8	$A_s = 0.002bt^*$	2.40	1.80	2.40	2.40	1.80	2.40
9	N = larger of (7) or (8)/0.31	14.2	14.7	19.0	18.2	11.2	18.2
10	N = width of strip/(2t)	5	8	5	5	8	5
11	N required, larger of (9) or (10)	15	15	19	19	12	19
12	Use #5 bars	15 st†	6 st 9 bt	3 st 16 bt	3 st 16 bt	5 st 7 bt	5 st 14 bt

* $bt = 100(10.5) + 20(7.5) = 1200$ in.² for negative moment region.
† Bent bars at exterior supports may be used if a general analysis is made (ACI-Fig. 13.4.8).

Table 17.7.3

Design of Reinforcement in Middle Strip, Example 17.7.1 (Flat Slab) ($f_y = 40{,}000$ psi, $f'_c = 3000$ psi)

Line Number	Critical Section	Exterior Span			Interior Span		
		Negative Moment	Positive Moment	Negative Moment	Negative Moment	Positive Moment	Negative Moment
1	Moment, Table 17.7.1, line 4 (ft-kips)	−8.8	+56.2	−50.3	−47.4	+43.3	−47.4
2	Width of strip, b (in.)	180	180	180	180	180	180
3	Effective depth d (in.)	6.44	5.81	6.44	6.44	5.81	6.44
4	$M_n = M_u/0.90$ (ft-kips)	−9.8	+62	−56	−53	+48	−53
5	R_u (psi) $= M_n/(bd^2)$	16	123	90	85	95	85
6	ρ, Eq. (3.6.5) or Fig. 3.6.1	0.04%	0.32%	0.23%	0.22%	0.24%	0.22%
7	$A_s = \rho bd$	0.46	3.30	2.67	2.53	2.51	2.53
8	$A_s = 0.002bt$	2.70	2.70	2.70	2.70	2.70	2.70
9	N = larger of (7) or (8)/0.31*	8.7	10.6	8.7	8.7	8.7	8.7
10	N = width of strip/(2t)	12	12	12	12	12	12
11	N required, larger of (9) or (10)	12	12	12	12	12	12
12	Use #5 bars	12 st†	6 st 6 bt	12 bt	12 bt	6 st 6 bt	12 bt

* A mixture of #5 and #4 bars could have been selected.
† Bent bars at exterior supports may be used if a general analysis is made (ACI-Fig. 13.4.8).

(Table 3.5.1). The actual percentages used (line 6 of Tables 17.7.2 and 17.7.3) are nowhere near this maximum. Thus there is ample compressive strength in the slab. This phenomenon is usual because of the deflection control exerted by the minimum slab thickness requirements.

(c) Design of reinforcement. The design of reinforcement for the typical column strip is shown in Table 17.7.2; for the typical middle strip, it is shown in Table 17.7.3. Because the moments in the long direction are larger than those in the short direction, the larger effective depth is assigned to the long direction wherever the two layers of steel are in contact. This contact at crossing occurs in the top steel at the intersection of column strips and in the bottom steel at the intersection of middle strips. Assuming #5 bars and $\frac{3}{4}$ in. clear cover, the effective depths provided at various critical sections of the long and short directions are shown in Fig. 17.7.1.

17.8 Shear Strength in Two-Way Slab Systems

The shear strength of a flat-slab or flat-plate floor around a typical interior column under dead and full live loads is analogous to that of a square or rectangular spread footing subjected to a concentrated column load, except each is an inverted situation of the other. The area enclosed between the parallel pairs of centerlines of the adjacent panels of the floor is like the area of the footing, because there is no shear force along the panel centerline of a typical interior panel in a floor system. Consequently the discussion here is essentially identical to what is included in Chap. 20 on footings.

The shear strength of two-way slab systems without shear reinforcement has been studied by many investigators [13–20]. An excellent summary is provided by ASCE-ACI Task Committee 426 under Chairman N. M. Hawkins [21].

The shear strength of the flat slab should be first investigated for wide-beam action and then for two-way action (ACI-11.11). In the wide-beam action, the critical section is parallel to the panel centerline in the transverse direction and extends across the full distance between two adjacent longitudinal panel centerlines. As in one-way beams, this critical section of width b_w times the effective depth d is located at a distance d from the face of the equivalent square column capital or from the face of the drop panel, if any. The nominal strength in usual cases where no shear reinforcement is used is

$$V_n = V_c = v_c b_w d \qquad (17.8.1a)$$

where v_c according to the simplified method of ACI-11.3.1.1 is

$$v_c = 2\sqrt{f'_c} \qquad (17.8.1b)$$

Alternatively, V_c may be determined using the more detailed expression (ACI-11.3.2.1) involving $\rho V_u d/M_u$, Eq. (5.10.10).

In the two-way action, potential diagonal cracking may occur along a truncated cone or pyramid around the column. Thus the critical section is located so that its periphery b_0 is at a distance equal to one-half of the effective depth through the drop from the periphery of the column capital, and also at a distance equal to one-half of the effective depth outside of the drop from the periphery of the drop. Where no drop is used, of course, there would be only one critical section for two-way action. If shear reinforcement is not used, the nominal shear strength is

$$V_n = V_c = v_c b_0 d \tag{17.8.2a}$$

where from ACI-11.11.2,

$$v_c = \left(2 + \frac{4}{\beta_c}\right)\sqrt{f'_c} \le 4\sqrt{f'_c} \tag{17.8.2b}$$

where for a rectangular column capital or drop, β_c is the ratio of the long side to the short side of the rectangle. Unless β_c is larger than 2.0, the expression involving β_c does not control and v_c is limited to $4\sqrt{f'_c}$.

Even when shear reinforcement is used (ACI-11.11.4), the nominal strength is limited to a maximum of

$$V_n = V_c + V_s = (v_c + v_s)b_0 d \le 6\sqrt{f'_c} b_0 d \tag{17.8.3}$$

Further, in the design of any shear reinforcement, the portion of the strength $V_c = v_c b_0 d$ may not exceed that with $v_c = 2\sqrt{f'_c}$ (ACI-11.11.3.4). If shearhead reinforcement such as described in Sec. 17.9 is used (ACI-11.11.4), the maximum $(v_c + v_s)$ in Eq. (17.8.3) is $7\sqrt{f'_c}$, but in the design of such shearhead the strength contribution V_c is neglected.

The investigation of the shear strength of the flat-slab floor and the flat-plate floor in the two design examples will be shown.

EXAMPLE 17.8.1   Investigate the shear strength in wide-beam and two-way actions in the flat-slab design example. Note that $f'_c = 3000$ psi.

Solution: (a) Wide-beam action. Investigation for the wide-beam action is made for sections 1-1 and 2-2 in the long direction, as shown in Fig. 17.8.1a. The short direction has a wider critical section and shorter span; thus it does not control. For section 1-1, if the entire width of 20 ft is conservatively assumed to have an effective depth of 6.12 in.,

$$V_u = 0.336(20)(9.52) = 64 \text{ kips} \qquad \text{(section 1-1)}$$
$$V_n = V_c = v_c b_w d = 2\sqrt{f'_c}(240)(6.12)\tfrac{1}{1000} = 161 \text{ kips}$$
$$V_u = 64 \text{ kips} < \phi V_n = 0.85(161) = 137 \text{ kips} \qquad\qquad \text{OK}$$

If, however, b_w is taken as 84 in. and d as 9.12 in. on the contention that the increased depth d is only over a width of 84 in.,

$$V_n = V_c = 2\sqrt{f'_c}(84)(9.12)\tfrac{1}{1000} = 84 \text{ kips}$$

This latter value is probably unrealistically low. For section 2-2, the shear resisting section has a constant d of 6.12 in.; thus

$$V_u = 0.336(20)(7.82) = 53 \text{ kips} \qquad \text{(section 2-2)}$$
$$V_u = 53 \text{ kips} < \phi V_n = 161 \text{ kips} \qquad\qquad \text{OK}$$

It will be rare that wide-beam (one-way) action will govern.

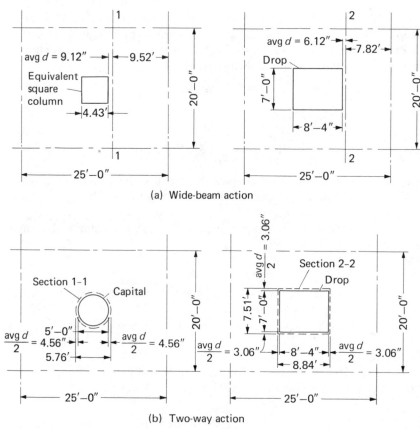

(a) Wide-beam action

(b) Two-way action

Fig. 17.8.1
Critical sections for shear in flat-slab design of Fig. 17.3.2.

(b) Two-way action. The critical sections for two-way action are the circular section 1-1 at $d/2 = 4.56$ in. from the edge of the column capital and the rectangular section 2-2 at $d/2 = 3.06$ in. from the edge of the drop, as shown in Fig. 17.8.1b. Since there are no shearing forces at the centerlines of the four adjacent panels, the shear forces around the critical sections 1-1 and 2-2 in Fig. 17.8.1b are

$$V_u = 0.336\left[500 - \frac{\pi(5.76)^2}{4}\right] + 1.4(0.038)\left[7(8.33) - \frac{\pi(5.76)^2}{4}\right]$$

$$= 159.2 + 1.7 = 161 \text{ kips} \quad \text{(section 1-1)}$$

In the second term, the 0.038 is the weight of the 3-in. drop in ksf.

$$V_u = 0.336[500 - 8.84(7.51)] = 146 \text{ kips} \quad \text{(section 2-2)}$$

The corresponding shear strengths are

$$\phi V_n = \phi V_c = \phi v_c b_0 d = \phi(4\sqrt{f_c'})b_0 d$$

$$= 0.85(4\sqrt{f_c'})(69.12)(9.12)\tfrac{1}{1000} = 369 \text{ kips} \quad \text{(section 1-1)}$$

$$= 0.85(4\sqrt{f_c'})(2)(106.12 + 90.12)(6.12)\tfrac{1}{1000} = 447 \text{ kips} \quad \text{(section 2-2)}$$

The value of v_c is $4\sqrt{f'_c}$ since β_c is less than 2.0. For both sections, V_u is well below ϕV_n; thus shear reinforcement is not required.

EXAMPLE 17.8.2   Investigate nominal shear stresses in wide-beam and two-way actions in the flat-plate design example. Note that $f'_c = 4000$ psi.

Solution: (a) Wide-beam action. Assuming $\frac{3}{4}$ in. clear cover and #4 bars, the average effective depth when bars in two directions are in contact is

$$\text{avg } d = 5.50 - 0.75 - 0.50 = 4.25 \text{ in.}$$

Referring to Fig. 17.8.2a,

$$v_n = \frac{V_u}{\phi b_w d} = \frac{198(12)(6.65)}{0.85(144)(4.25)} = 30.4 \text{ psi} < (2\sqrt{f'_c} = 126 \text{ psi})\quad \text{(section 1-1)}$$

(b) Two-way action. Referring to Fig. 16.11.2b,

$$v_n = \frac{V_u}{\phi b_o d} = \frac{198[180 - 1.35(1.19)]}{0.85(61)(4.25)} = 160 \text{ psi} < (4\sqrt{f'_c} = 253 \text{ psi})\text{(section 2-2)}$$

Thus shear reinforcement is not required for this flat-plate floor.

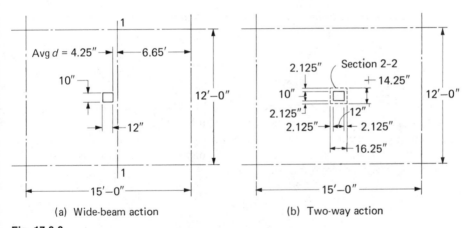

(a) Wide-beam action   (b) Two-way action

Fig. 17.8.2
Shear stresses in flat-plate design example of Fig. 17.3.3.

17.9 Shear Reinforcement in Flat-Plate Floors

In flat-plate floors where neither column capitals nor drop panels are used, shear reinforcement is frequently necessary. In such cases two-way action usually controls. The shear reinforcement may take the form of properly anchored bars or wires placed in vertical sections around the column (Fig. 17.9.1a), or consist of shearheads, which are steel I or channel shapes fabricated by welding into four identical arms at right angles and continuous through the column section (Fig. 17.9.1b). The strength of two-way slab systems with shear reinforcement has been summarized by Hawkins [22]. Corley and Hawkins [23] have studied shearhead reinforcement.

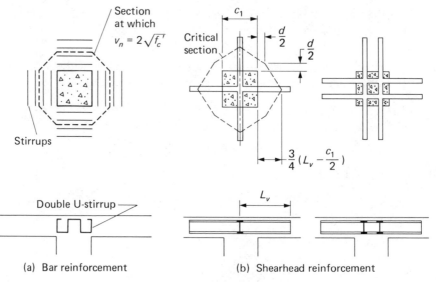

Fig. 17.9.1
Bar and shearhead reinforcement in flat-plate floors.

When *bar or wire shear reinforcement* is used, the nominal strength is

$$V_n = V_c + V_s$$

$$= v_c b_0 d + \frac{A_v f_y d}{s} \qquad \text{(17.9.1a)}$$

where b_0 is the periphery around the critical section for two-way shear action, A_v is the total stirrup bar area around b_0, and $v_c = 2\sqrt{f'_c}$.

The provided design strength ϕV_n must exceed the factored load shear V_u acting on the periphery b_0. For design it may be convenient to use nominal stress $v_n = V_n/(b_0 d)$, making Eq. (17.9.1a)

$$v_n = v_c + \frac{A_v f_y}{s b_0} \qquad \text{(17.9.1b)}$$

Such bar or wire reinforcement is required wherever the loading $V_n = V_u/\phi$ exceeds V_c based on v_c of $(2 + 4/\beta_c)\sqrt{f'_c}$ (or $4\sqrt{f'_c}$ maximum); however, in the design of shear reinforcement V_c for Eq. (17.9.1a) is based on $v_c = 2\sqrt{f'_c}$, and the maximum strength V_s from the shear reinforcement may not exceed a value based on $v_s = 4\sqrt{f'_c}$ (i.e., $v_c + v_s \leq 6\sqrt{f'_c}$) according to ACI-11.11.3.2.

Shear strength may be provided by *shearheads* under ACI-11.11.4 whenever the nominal stress $v_n = V_u/(\phi b_0 d)$ at the critical section is between $(2 + 4/\beta_c)\sqrt{f'_c}$ and $7\sqrt{f'_c}$. These provisions, based on the tests of Corley and Hawkins [23], apply only where shear is transferred at an interior column.

With regard to the size of the shearhead, it must furnish a ratio α_v of 0.15 or larger (ACI-11.11.4.5) between the stiffness for each shearhead arm $(E_s I_x)$ and that for the surrounding composite cracked slab section of width

$(c_2 + d)$; or

$$\min \alpha_v = \frac{E_s I_x}{E_c(\text{composite } I_s)} = 0.15 \tag{17.9.2}$$

The steel shape used must not be deeper than 70 times its web thickness; and the compression flange must be located within $0.3d$ of the compression surface of the slab (ACI-11.11.4.2 and 11.11.4.4). In addition, the plastic moment capacity M_p of the shearhead arm must be at least (ACI-11.11.4.6).

$$\min M_p = \frac{V_u}{8\phi}\left[h_v + \alpha_v\left(L_v - \frac{c_1}{2}\right)\right] \tag{17.9.3}$$

where

V_u = shear force around the periphery of column face, due to factored loads
h_v = depth of shearhead
L_v = length of shearhead measured from column centerline
ϕ = 0.90, the capacity reduction factor for flexure

Equation (17.9.2) is to assure that the required shear capacity of the slab is reached before the flexural capacity of the shearhead is exceeded.

The length of the shearhead should be such that the nominal ultimate shear stress v_n will not exceed $4\sqrt{f'_c}$ computed at a peripheral section located at $\frac{3}{4}(L_v - c_1/2)$ along the shearhead but no closer elsewhere than $d/2$ from the column face (ACI-11.11.4.7 and 11.11.4.8). This length requirement is shown in Fig. 17.9.1b.

When a shearhead is used, it may be considered to contribute a resisting moment

$$M_v = \frac{\phi \alpha_v V_u}{8}\left(L_v - \frac{c_1}{2}\right) \tag{17.9.4}$$

to each column strip, but not more than 30% of the total moment resistance required in the column strip, nor the change in column strip moment over the length L_v, nor the required M_p given by Eq. (17.9.3).

EXAMPLE 17.9.1 Using the dimensions of the flat-plate floor described in Sec. 17.3 (Fig. 17.3.3) but changing the live load to 200 psf, investigate the shear strength for wide-beam and two-way actions around an interior column. If the maximum nominal shear stress v_n for two-way action is between $4\sqrt{f'_c}$ (which controls since β_c is less than 2.0) and $6\sqrt{f'_c}$, determine the A_v/s requirement for shear reinforcement at the peripheral critical section and show the nominal shear-stress variation from the critical section to the panel centerline. Use $f'_c = 4000$ psi and $f_y = 50,000$ psi; assume #5 slab reinforcement.

Solution: (a) Wide-beam action.

$$w_u = 1.4w_D + 1.7w_L = 1.4(150)(5.5/12) + 1.7(200)$$
$$= 96 + 340 = 436 \text{ psf}$$
$$\text{avg } d \text{ in column strip} = 5.50 - 0.75 - 0.63 = 4.12 \text{ in.}$$

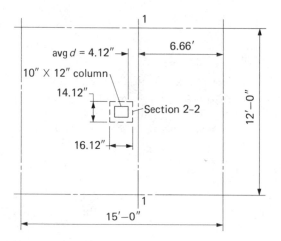

Fig. 17.9.2
Critical sections for shear, Example 17.9.1.

For a 12-in. wide strip along section 1-1 of Fig. 17.9.2,

$$v_n = \frac{V_u}{\phi b_w d} = \frac{436(6.66)}{0.85(12)(4.12)} = 69 \text{ psi} < (2\sqrt{f_c'} = 126 \text{ psi}) \qquad \text{OK}$$

(b) Two-way action. Referring to section 2-2 of Fig. 17.9.2,

$$v_n = \frac{V_u}{\phi b_o d} = \frac{436[180 - 1.34(1.18)]}{0.85(60.48)(4.12)} = 368 \text{ psi}$$

Since the maximum nominal shear stress of 368 psi is between $4\sqrt{f_c'} = 253$ psi and $6\sqrt{f_c'} = 380$ psi, shear reinforcement is required to take the excess stress v_n which exceeds $2\sqrt{f_c'} = 126$ psi. The shear reinforcement in this case may consist of properly anchored bars or wires and need not be a shearhead. The variation of the nominal shear stress from the maximum value of 368 psi to zero at the panel centerline over the equally spaced points 1 to 5 is shown in Fig. 17.9.3. The A_v/s requirement around the critical section of 60.48 in.

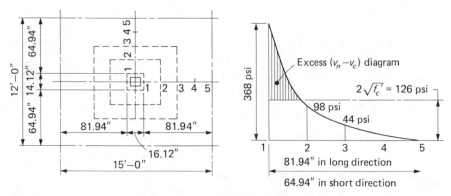

Fig. 17.9.3
Variation of two-way shear stress, Example 17.9.1.

periphery is, from applying Eq. (17.9.1b),

$$\frac{A_v}{s} = \frac{(v_n - v_c)b_0}{f_y} = \frac{(368 - 126)(60.48)}{50,000} = 0.292 \text{ in.}$$

Assuming $s = d/2 \approx 2$ in. spacing,

$$A_v = 0.58 \text{ sq in.}$$

If two double #3 U stirrups are used at each of the four sides,

$$\text{provided } A_v = 4(4)(0.11) = 1.76 \text{ sq in.}$$

As shown in Fig. 17.9.3, the nominal shear stress drops to 126 psi in a rather steep manner so that the number and spacing of these U stirrups can be laid out by the aid of the excess $(v_n - v_c)$ diagram.

EXAMPLE 17.9.2   Design the shearhead reinforcement for the two-way shear action of Example 17.9.1.

Solution: (a) Two-way action nominal shear stress. Since the maximum nominal shear stress v_n of 368 psi is between $4\sqrt{f_c'} = 253$ psi and $7\sqrt{f_c'} = 442$ psi, shearhead reinforcement for the interior column may be designed according to ACI-11.11.4.

(b) Length of shearhead. The length of shearhead should be such that the shear stress be less than $4\sqrt{f_c'}$, computed around a periphery passing through points at $\frac{3}{4}(L_v - c_1/2)$ from but no closer than $d/2$ to the column faces. Assuming a square as the critical periphery since the shearhead must have four identical arms (ACI-11.11.4.1), the required b_0 (ft) may be computed from (Fig. 17.9.4),

$$4\sqrt{4000} = \frac{436[180 - (b_0/4)^2]}{0.85(12b_0)(4.12)}$$

Neglecting the $(b_0/4)^2$ in the numerator,

$$b_0 = \frac{436(180)}{253(0.85)(4.12)(12)} = 7.4 \text{ ft (88.5 in.)}$$

The distance L_v may be computed from the following:

$$4\left[\frac{3}{4}\left(L_v - \frac{c_1}{2}\right) + \frac{c_1}{2}\right]\sqrt{2} = b_0$$

which gives

$$L_v = \left(\frac{88.5}{4\sqrt{2}} - 5\right)\frac{4}{3} + 5 = 19.2 \text{ in.}$$

$$L_v = \left(\frac{88.5}{4\sqrt{2}} - 6\right)\frac{4}{3} + 6 = 18.8 \text{ in.}$$

or, based on a periphery approaching no closer than $d/2$ to the periphery of the column section,

$$L_v = (8.06 + 2.06)\tfrac{4}{3} + 5 = 18.5 \text{ in.}$$
$$L_v = (7.06 + 2.06)\tfrac{4}{3} + 6 = 18.2 \text{ in.}$$

Use $L_v = 20$ in.

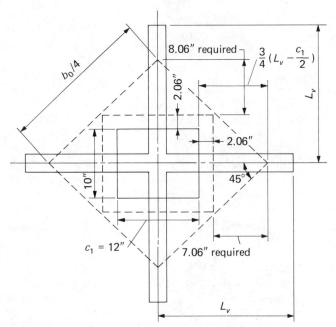

Fig. 17.9.4

Required length of shearhead, Example 17.9.2.

(c) Size of shearhead. The shearhead stiffness must be at least 0.15 of that of the composite cracked slab section of width $(c_2 + d)$. It can be shown that 14-#5 bars and 10-#5 bars are required for negative slab reinforcement in the 72-in. wide column strips of the long and short directions, respectively. The composite cracked section across width AA in Fig. 17.9.5 should be used because there is more steel in the slab in the long direction. The steel

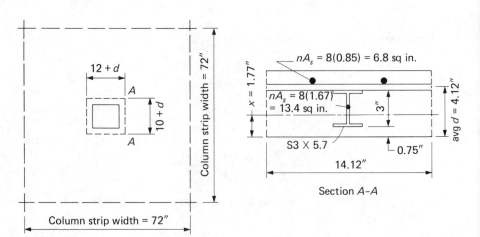

Fig. 17.9.5

Cracked slab section of width $(c_2 + d)$, Example 17.9.2.

area A_s in section AA is

$$A_s = \frac{10 + d}{72}(14)(0.31) = \frac{14.12}{72}(14)(0.31) = 0.85 \text{ sq in.}$$

Assume a $S3 \times 5.7$ section for the shearhead placed as shown in Fig. 17.9.5. The centroidal axis of the composite cracked section may be obtained by equating the static moments of the compression and tension transformed areas,

$$\frac{14.12x^2}{2} = 13.4(2.25 - x) + 6.8(4.12 - x)$$

$$x = 1.77 \text{ in.}$$

$$\text{composite } I_s = \frac{14.12(1.77)^3}{3} + n(I_x \text{ of steel section}) + 13.4(0.48)^2 + 6.8(2.35)^2$$

$$= 26.1 + 8(2.52) + 3.0 + 37.6 = 86.8 \text{ in.}^3$$

$$\text{provided } \alpha_v = \frac{E_s(2.52)}{E_c(\text{composite } I_s)} = \frac{8(2.52)}{86.8} = 0.23 > 0.15 \qquad \text{OK}$$

The plastic section modulus of the $S3 \times 5.7$ is given by the *AISC Manual*[†] as 1.95 in.[3] Using A36 steel, the provided M_p is

$$\text{provided } M_p = 36(1.95) = 70.2 \text{ in.-kips}$$

The required M_p is computed from using Eq. (17.9.4) as

$$\text{required } M_p = \frac{V_u}{8\phi}\left[h_v + \alpha_v\left(\text{required } L_v - \frac{c_1}{2}\right)\right]$$

$$= \frac{0.436(180)}{8(0.90)}[3 + 0.23(19.2 - 5)]$$

$$= 68.3 \text{ in.-kips} < 70.2 \text{ in-kips} \qquad \text{OK}$$

(d) Shearhead contribution to resist negative moment in slab. The negative moments at the face of column in the 72-in. column strip width in the long and short directions are $(436/198)(0.75)$ times those for equivalent rigid frames A and C in Fig. 17.5.3, wherein $(436/198)$ is the ratio of factored loads (using 200 psf compared to using 60 psf live load) on the slab and 0.75 is the factor for transverse distribution shown in line 12 of Table 17.6.2. Thus

$$\text{column strip moment in long direction} = \frac{436}{198}(0.75)(37.8) = 62.4 \text{ ft-kips}$$

$$\text{column strip moment in short direction} = \frac{436}{198}(0.75)(30.1) = 49.7 \text{ ft-kips}$$

[†] See *Manual of Steel Construction* (7th ed.). New York: American Institute of Steel Construction, 1970.

The resisting moment of the shearhead may be computed from Eq. (17.9.4),

$$M_v = \frac{\phi \alpha_v V_u}{8}\left(L_v - \frac{c_1}{2}\right)$$

$$= \frac{0.90(0.23)(0.436)(180)}{8(12)}[(20-6) \text{ or } (20-5)]$$

$$= 2.37 \text{ or } 2.54 \text{ ft-kips}$$

Thus the contribution is rather small and the revision of slab reinforcement is unnecessary.

17.10 Direct-Design Method—Moments in Columns

The moments in columns due to unbalanced loads on adjacent panels are readily available when an elastic analysis is performed on the equivalent rigid frame for the various pattern loadings. In the "direct-design method," wherein the five limitations listed in Sec. 17.5 are satisfied, the longitudinal moments in the slab are prescribed by the provisions of the Code (ACI-13.6.3). In a similar manner, the Code prescribes the unbalanced moment at an interior column as follows (ACI Formula 13-4):

$$M = 0.08\left[\left(w_D + \frac{1}{2}w_L\right)L_2L_n^2 - w'_D L'_2(L'_n)^2\right]\left(\frac{K_{ec}}{K_{ec} + \Sigma(K_s + K_b)}\right) \quad \textbf{(17.10.1)}$$

where

$$w_D = \text{factored dead load per unit area}$$
$$w_L = \text{factored live load per unit area}$$
$$w'_D, L'_2, L'_n = \text{quantities referring to shorter span}$$
$$K_{ec} = \text{flexural stiffness of equivalent column, defined by Eq.}$$
$$(16.7.5)$$
$$K_s = \text{flexural stiffness of slab}$$
$$K_b = \text{flexural stiffness of beam, if any}$$

The moment is yet to be distributed between the two ends of the upper and lower columns meeting at the joint.

The rationale for Eq. (17.10.1) may be observed from the stiffness ratios at a typical interior joint shown in Fig. 17.10.1a, wherein the distribution factor for the sum of the column end moments is $K_{ec}/[K_{ec} + \Sigma(K_b + K_s)$ of adjacent spans] and the unbalanced moment in the column strip is taken to be 0.080/0.125 times the difference in the total static moments due to dead plus half live load on the longer span and dead load only on the shorter span.

There is no suggestion made in the code in regard to the moment in the exterior column. One possible approximation is to apply Eq. (17.10.1) also to an exterior column by taking the shorter span as zero, as shown in Fig. 17.10.1b. In such a case the distribution factor becomes $K_{ec}/[K_{ec} + \Sigma(K_b + K_s)$ of exterior span only].

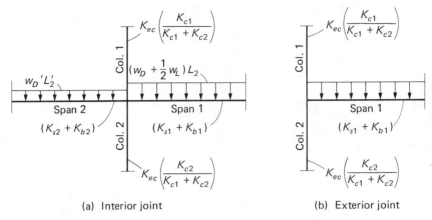

(a) Interior joint   (b) Exterior joint

Fig. 17.10.1
Direct-design method: relative stiffness for members framing a joint for use in determining moments in columns.

EXAMPLE 17.10.1. Obtain the moments in the interior and exterior columns in each direction for the flat-plate design example. Refer to Examples 17.3.2 and 17.5.2.

Solution: (a) Flexural stiffnesses. The flexural stiffnesses shown on the two equivalent rigid frames in Fig. 17.10.2 are taken from columns A and C in Table 17.5.2 of Example 17.5.2. Note that the stiffness of the horizontal span contains that of the slab only, since there are no beams between columns in this structure. The value of K_{ec} in Table 17.5.2 is divided equally between the upper and lower columns because K_{c1} of the upper column and K_{c2} of the lower column are equal in this case.

(b) Exterior column, long direction.

$$w_D = 1.4(150)(5.5/12) = 1.4(69) = 96 \text{ psf}$$
$$w_L = 1.7(60) = 102 \text{ psf}$$

The unbalanced moment acting on the exterior joint is

$$0.08(0.096 + 0.051)(12)(15 - 1)^2 = 27.7 \text{ ft-kips}$$

The distribution factor to *both* column ends is, from Fig. 17.10.2,

$$\frac{43.6E}{43.6E + 44.4E} = 0.495$$

The moment to be transferred to the columns is $0.495(27.7) = 13.7$ ft-kips, divided between upper and lower columns in proportion to their stiffnesses (in this case, equally).

(c) Interior column, long direction. The unbalanced moment acting on the interior joint is

$$0.08[(0.096 + 0.051)(12)(15 - 1)^2 - 0.096(12)(15 - 1)^2]$$
$$= 0.08(0.051)(12)(14)^2 = 9.6 \text{ ft-kips}$$

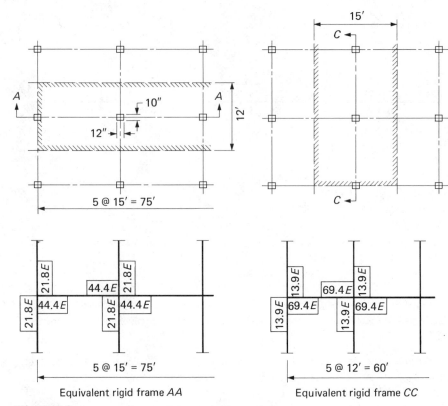

Equivalent rigid frame *AA*   Equivalent rigid frame *CC*

Fig. 17.10.2

Stiffness of equivalent rigid frames, Example 17.10.1.

The distribution factor at both column ends is, from Fig. 17.10.2,

$$\frac{43.6E}{43.6E + 88.8E} = 0.330$$

The moment to be transferred to the columns is $0.330(9.6) = 3.16$ ft-kips, divided between upper and lower columns.

(d) Exterior column, short direction. The unbalanced moment acting on the exterior joint is

$$0.08(0.096 + 0.051)(15)(12 - 0.83)^2 = 22.0 \text{ ft-kips}$$

The distribution factor to both column ends is, from Fig. 17.10.2,

$$\frac{27.8E}{27.8E + 69.4E} = 0.286$$

The moment to be transferred to the columns is $0.286(22.0) = 6.30$ ft-kips, divided between upper and lower columns.

(e) Interior column, short direction. The unbalanced moment acting on the interior joint is

$$0.08(0.051)(15)(12 - 0.83)^2 = 7.64 \text{ ft-kips}$$

The distribution factor to both column ends is, from Fig. 17.10.2,

$$\frac{27.8E}{27.8E + 138.8E} = 0.167$$

The moment to be transferred to the columns is $0.167(7.64) = 1.28$ ft-kips, divided between upper and lower columns.

17.11 Transfer of Moments to Columns

Inasmuch as the columns meet the slab at monolithic joints, there should be moment transfer between the slab and the column ends. The moments may arise out of lateral loads due to wind or earthquake effects acting on the multistory frame, or they may be due to unbalanced gravity loads as considered in Sec. 17.10. In addition, the shear forces at the column ends and throughout the columns must be considered in the design of lateral reinforcement (ties or spiral) in the columns (ACI-11.12.1.1). The transfer of moment and shear at the slab-column interface is extremely important in the design of flat plates and has been the subject of numerous research studies [24–31].

Let M be the total moment that is to be transferred to both ends of the columns meeting at an exterior or an interior joint. Test results by Hanson and Hanson [25] have shown that about 60% of the moment is transferred by flexure and the remainder by unbalanced shear stresses around the critical periphery located at $d/2$ from the column faces. The ACI Code requires the division of the total factored moment M_u into M_b transferred by flexure (ACI-13.3.4) and M_v transferred by shear (ACI-11.12.2.3) such that

$$M_b = \frac{M_u}{1 + \dfrac{2}{3}\sqrt{\dfrac{c_1 + d}{c_2 + d}}} \tag{17.11.1}$$

and

$$M_v = M_u - M_b \tag{17.11.2}$$

The moment M_b is considered to be transferred through a slab width equal to $(c_2 + 3t)$ at the column (ACI-13.3.4), where t is the slab or drop panel thickness. Concentration of reinforcement in this width by closer spacing or additional reinforcement may be used to resist this moment.

If $c_1 = c_2$, Eq. (17.11.1) becomes

$$M_b = 0.60M_u$$

If $c_2 = 2c_1$ and $c_1 = d$, Eq. (17.11.1) becomes

$$M_b = 0.648M_u$$

It appears reasonable that when c_2 is larger than c_1, the moment transferred by flexure is greater because the effective slab width $(c_2 + 3t)$ resisting the moment is relatively larger.

The moment M_v transferred by shear acts with the associated shear force V_u at the centroid of the shear area around the critical periphery located at $d/2$ from the column faces, as shown in Fig. 17.11.1. Referring to Fig. 17.11.1,

$$v_1 = \frac{V_u}{\phi A_c} - \frac{M_v x_1}{\phi J_c} \tag{17.11.3}$$

$$v_2 = \frac{V_u}{\phi A_c} + \frac{M_v x_2}{\phi J_c} \tag{17.11.4}$$

It is noted that in order to be consistent with the strength design method, the capacity reduction factor ϕ is included in the denominators of Eqs. (17.11.3) and (17.11.4). By using a section property J_c analogous to the polar moment of inertia about the z-z axis (perpendicular to the column and located at the centroid of the shear area) of the shear areas around the critical periphery, it is assumed that there are both horizontal and vertical shear stresses on the shear areas with dimensions a by d in Fig. 17.11.1. For an exterior column, x_1 and x_2 are obtained by locating the centroid of the channel-shaped vertical shear area represented by the dashed line $(a + b + a)$ shown in Fig. 17.11.1a, and

$$A_c = (2a + b)d \tag{17.11.5}$$

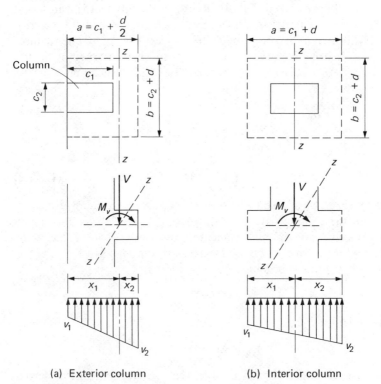

(a) Exterior column   (b) Interior column

Fig. 17.11.1
Shear transfer of moment to columns.

$$J_c = d\left[\frac{2a^3}{3} - (2a + b)(x_2)^2\right] + \frac{ad^3}{6} \tag{17.11.6}$$

For an interior column, referring to Fig. 17.11.1b,

$$A_c = 2(a + b)d \tag{17.11.7}$$

$$J_c = d\left[\frac{a^3}{6} + \frac{ba^2}{2}\right] + \frac{ad^3}{6} \tag{17.11.8}$$

According to ACI-11.12.2.4, the larger shear stress v_2 shown in Fig. 17.11.1 must be less than $4\sqrt{f_c'}$ (or less if shear area dimension ratio is larger than 2), otherwise shear reinforcement as described in Sec. 17.9 is required.

EXAMPLE 17.11.1   Investigate the transfer of the unbalanced gravity load moments in the long direction, as already computed in Example 17.10.1, to the exterior and interior columns, respectively. Compare the moment transferred by flexure in the critical slab width with the total moment in the column strip computed in Examples 17.5.2 and 17.6.2. Compute the shear stresses around the critical periphery due to the moment transferred by shear.

Solution: (a) Exterior column, transfer by flexure. From Example 17.10.1, the moment to be transferred is

$$M_u = 13.7 \text{ ft-kips}$$

From Eq. (17.11.1), using the average effective depth for #4 slab reinforcement of 4.25 in.,

$$M_b = \frac{M_u}{1 + \dfrac{2}{3}\sqrt{\dfrac{c_1 + d}{c_2 + d}}} = \frac{13.7}{1 + \dfrac{2}{3}\sqrt{\dfrac{12 + 4.25}{10 + 4.25}}} = 0.584(13.7)$$

$$= 8.0 \text{ ft-kips}$$

As shown by Fig. 17.11.2, this moment is in a critical slab width of 26.5 in. From Table 17.6.2 and Fig. 17.5.3, the total amount in the 72-in. wide column strip is

$$M \text{ in column strip} = 0.988(18.7) = 18.5 \text{ ft-kips}$$

If the slab reinforcement is placed at equal spacing in the column strip, additional reinforcement is needed in the 26.5 in. width for a moment of

$$M_b - 18.5\left(\frac{26.5}{72}\right) = 8.0 - 6.8 = 1.2 \text{ ft-kips}$$

(b) Exterior column, transfer by shear. The shear force V is taken as $(w_D + w_L)$ times the floor area of 12×7.5 ft around the exterior column.

$$V_u = (96 + 102)(12)(7.5) = 17,800 \text{ lb}$$
$$M_v = M_u - M_b = 13.7 - 8.0 = 5.7 \text{ ft-kips}$$

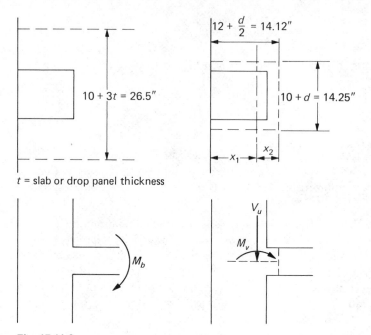

Fig. 17.11.2
Transfer of moments at exterior column, Example 17.11.1.

From Fig. 17.11.2,

$$x_2 = \frac{2(14.12)(7.06)}{28.24 + 14.25} = 4.70 \text{ in.}$$

$$A_c = 4.25(28.24 + 14.25) = 180 \text{ in.}^2$$

$$J_c = 4.25\left[\frac{2(14.12)^3}{3} - 42.49(4.70)^2\right] + \frac{14.12(4.25)^3}{6}$$

$$= 3990 + 180 = 4170 \text{ in.}^4$$

$$v_1 = \frac{17,800}{0.85(180)} - \frac{5700(12)(9.42)}{0.85(4170)} = 116 - 182 = -66 \text{ psi}$$

$$v_2 = \frac{17,800}{0.85(180)} + \frac{5700(12)(4.70)}{0.85(4170)} = 116 + 91 = 207 \text{ psi}$$

The capacity v_c is $4\sqrt{f'_c} = 253$ psi when no shear reinforcement is provided.

(c) Interior column, transfer by flexure. From Example 17.10.1, the moment to be transferred is

$$M_u = 3.16 \text{ ft-kips}$$
$$M_b = 0.584M_u = 0.584(3.16) = 1.85 \text{ ft-kips}$$

From Table 17.6.2 and Fig. 17.5.3, the total moment in the 72-in. wide column strip is

$$M \text{ in column strip} = 0.75(37.8) = 28.4 \text{ ft-kips}$$

Since the column strip moment in the 26.5 in. width of $26.5(28.4)/72 = 10.5$ ft-kips is larger than 1.85 ft-kips, no additional reinforcement is needed.

(d) Interior column, transfer by shear. The shear force is taken as $(w_D + w_L)$ times the floor area of 12×15 ft.

$$V_u = (96 + 102)(12)(15) = 35,600 \text{ lb}$$
$$M_v = 3.16 - 1.85 = 1.31 \text{ ft-kips.}$$

From Fig. 17.11.3,

$$A_c = 4.25(32.50 + 28.50) = 259 \text{ in.}^2$$

$$J_c = 4.25 \left[\frac{2(16.25)^3}{12} + 2(14.25)(8.12)^2 \right] + \frac{16.25(4.25)^3}{6}$$

$$= 11,040 + 210 = 11,250 \text{ in.}^4$$

$$v_1 = \frac{35,600}{0.85(259)} - \frac{1310(12)(8.12)}{0.85(11,250)} = 162 - 13 = 149 \text{ psi}$$

$$v_2 = \frac{35,600}{0.85(259)} + \frac{1310(12)(8.12)}{0.85(11,250)} = 162 + 13 = 175 \text{ psi}$$

The capacity v_c is $4\sqrt{f'_c} = 253$ psi when no shear reinforcement is provided.

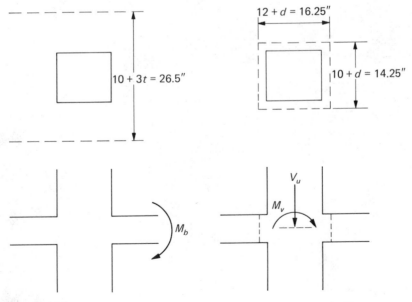

Fig. 17.11.3
Transfer of moments at interior column, Example 17.11.1.

17.12 Openings and Corner Connections in Flat Slabs

When openings and corner connections are present in flat-slab floors, designers must make sure that adequate provisions for them are made. The ASCE-ACI Joint Task Committee [21] has summarized available information. Recent tests by Roll, et al. [32] have provided additional data for treating openings, while Zaghlool et al. [33,34] have provided data for corner connections.

ACI-13.5.1 first prescribes in general that openings of any size may be provided if it can be shown by analysis that all strength and serviceability conditions including the limits on the deflections are satisfied. However, in common situations (ACI-13.5.2) a special analysis need not be made for slab systems not having beams when (1) openings are within the middle half of the span in each direction, provided the total amount of reinforcement required for the panel without the opening is maintained; (2) openings in the area common to two column strips do not interrupt more than one-eighth of the column strip width in either span, and the equivalent of reinforcement interrupted is added on all sides of the openings; (3) openings in the area common to one column strip and one middle strip do not interrupt more than one-fourth of the reinforcement in either strip, and the equivalent of reinforcement interrupted be added on all sides of the openings.

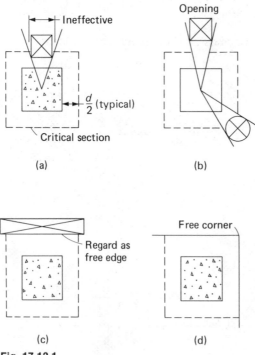

Fig. 17.12.1

Effect of openings and free edges on critical periphery of two-way shear action (from ACI Commentary–11.11.5).

In regard to two-way action nominal shear stress, the critical section for slabs without shearhead is not to include that part of the periphery which is enclosed by radial projections of the openings to the center of the column (ACI-11.11.5). For slabs with shearhead, the critical periphery is to be reduced only by one-half of what is cut away by the radial lines from the center of the column to the edges of the opening. Some critical sections with cutaways by openings are shown in Fig. 17.12.1.

17.13 The Equivalent-Frame Method

In the "equivalent-frame method," which differs from the "direct-design method" only in the way by which the longitudinal moments along the spans of the equivalent rigid frame are obtained, the elastic analysis is made for various critical vertical or lateral load combinations. Regarding the method, the following may be stated:

1. Each equivalent rigid frame consists of the slab (with or without beam along column line) bounded laterally by the centerline of the panel on each side of the centerline of the column. The moment of inertia of the slab-beam between the center of the column and the face of the column, bracket, or capital, is to be assumed equal to that of the slab-beam at the face of the column divided by the quantity $(1 - c_2/L_2)^2$ where c_2 and L_2 are measured in the transverse direction (ACI-13.7.3.3). An equivalent square may be used for column capitals of nonrectilinear shape, provided, of course, the column capital lies inside the largest right circular cone or pyramid with a 90° vertex that can be included within the outlines of the supporting element (see Fig. 17.4.1). The stiffness assumptions prescribed for this method have been studied by Cardenas et al. [35].

2. The moment of inertia of the column is to be assumed infinite from the top of the slab to the bottom of the column capital or slab-beam (ACI-13.7.4.5).

3. The equivalent column stiffness K_{ec} can be computed from

$$\frac{1}{K_{ec}} = \frac{1}{\Sigma K_c} + \frac{1}{K_t}$$

wherein

$\Sigma K_c = (K_{c1}$, stiffness at lower end of upper column)
$\qquad + (K_{c2}$, stiffness at upper end of lower column)

$$K_t = \Sigma \frac{9EC}{L_2(1 - c_2/L_2)^3}\left(\frac{I \text{ of slab with beam stem, if any}}{I \text{ of slab}}\right)$$

$$C = \Sigma\left(1 - 0.63\frac{x}{y}\right)\left(\frac{x^3 y}{3}\right) \qquad \text{of section defined in Fig. 16.7.2}$$

4. When the service live load does not exceed three-quarters of the service dead load, the maximum bending may be assumed to occur at all

sections under full factored live load. For other conditions, maximum positive bending near midspan of a panel may be assumed to occur under three-quarters of the full factored live load in the panel and in alternate panels; and maximum negative bending in the slab at a support may be assumed to occur under three-quarters of the full factored live load in the adjacent panels only. In no case, however, may the design moments be taken as less than those occurring with full factored live load on all panels (ACI-13.7.6).

5. The factored negative moments are to be taken at the face of the rectilinear supports but in no case at a distance greater than $0.175L_1$ from the center of columns. The factored negative moment at an exterior support is to be taken at a section halfway between the face of the column and the edge of the capital or bracket (ACI-13.7.7).

6. Moments determined for the equivalent column in the frame analysis should be apportioned to the upper and lower columns in the ratio of their respective stiffnesses, with the resulting values further reduced to the top of the slab or the bottom of the column capital or slab-beam for design use.

7. Two-way slab systems satisfying the limitations of the "direct-design method," but still analyzed by means of the "equivalent-frame method," may have the resulting factored moments reduced in such proportion that the numerical sum of the positive and the average negative moments need not exceed the total statical moment M_0 (ACI-13.7.7).

EXAMPLE 17.13.1   By the "equivalent-frame method" determine the longitudinal moments in the long direction through a line of interior columns in the flat-slab design example as described in Sec. 17.3. Compare these moments resulting from elastic analysis with those obtained by the "direct-design method" as shown in Fig. 17.5.1. Available data include $f'_c = 3000$ psi; $f_y = 40,000$ psi; thickness of slab = $7\frac{1}{2}$ in.; thickness through drop = $10\frac{1}{2}$ in.; diameter of interior column capital = 5 ft (side of equivalent square = 4.43 ft); edge column capital = 4 ft 6 in. × 2 ft 3 in. (to column centerline); drop panel = 8 ft 4 in. × 7 ft; interior column = 18 in. round; exterior column = 16 in. square; story height = 10 ft; edge-beam section = 14 × 24 in. overall depth; long direction = 5 panels at 25 ft; short direction = 5 panels at 20 ft; and service live load = 120 psf.

Solution: (a) Flexural properties of slab strip. The stiffnesses, carry-over factors, and fixed-end moments may be determined by various analysis methods. The column-analogy method (see Chap. 16, Ref. 18, for example) is used in this example. Simmonds and Misic [37] have provided design aids to meet the ACI Code assumptions of the "equivalent-frame method."

The variation in the moment of inertia along an exterior span of the slab strip is shown in Fig. 17.13.1a. Taking the moment of inertia through the $7\frac{1}{2}$-in. slab as the reference value of 1, the moment of inertia through the drop is $(10.5/7.5)^3 = 2.742$, and the moment of inertia between the column centerline and the face of the equivalent square column capital is $2.742/(1 - 4.43/20)^2 = 2.742/0.607 = 4.52$.

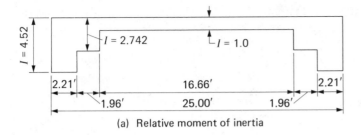

(a) Relative moment of inertia

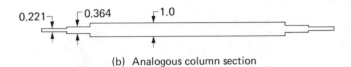

(b) Analogous column section

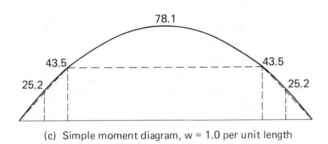

(c) Simple moment diagram, w = 1.0 per unit length

Fig. 17.13.1
Flexure properties of slab strip, Example 17.13.1.

The variation in the width of the analogous column section is $1/I$, which is shown in Fig. 17.13.1b. The area of the analogous column section is

$$A = 16.66 + 2(0.364)(1.96) + 2(0.221)(2.21)$$
$$= 16.66 + 1.43 + 0.98 = 19.07$$

The moment of inertia about the midspan, neglecting the moments of inertia of the short segments about their own centroidal axes, is

$$I = \tfrac{1}{12}(16.66)^3 + 1.43(9.31)^2 + 0.98(11.40)^2 = 385 + 124 + 128 = 637$$

$$\text{stiffness factor} = L\left(\frac{1}{A} + \frac{Mc}{I}\right) = 25\left[\frac{1}{19.07} + \frac{12.5(12.5)}{637}\right]$$

$$= 1.31 + 6.14 = 7.45$$

$$\text{carry-over factor} = \frac{6.14 - 1.31}{7.45} = \frac{4.83}{7.45} = 0.649$$

$$\text{stiffness at end of 20-ft wide slab strip} = \frac{7.45E(7.5)^3/12}{300}(240) = 210E$$

The load on the analogous column is equal to the summation of the product of the width of the analogous column section and the area of the simple-beam moment diagram of Fig. 17.13.1c. Considering the moment areas over the short segments as being trapezoidal, the load on the analogous column is

$$P = \tfrac{2}{3}(78.1 - 43.5)(16.66) + 43.5(16.66)$$
$$+ 2(0.364)(\tfrac{1}{2})(43.5 + 25.2)(1.96)$$
$$+ 2(0.221)(\tfrac{1}{2})(25.2)(2.21)$$
$$= 385 + 725 + 49 + 12 = 1171$$

$$\text{FEM coefficient} = \frac{P}{AL^2} = \frac{1171}{19.07(25)^2} = 0.0985$$

Since the edge column capital is almost equal in size to the equivalent square of the interior column capital, the FEM coefficient, stiffness, and carry-over factor obtained above for the interior span will also be used for the exterior span.

(b) Flexure properties of columns. The length of the column is measured between the centerlines of slab thickness, as shown in Fig. 17.13.2. The moment of inertia is assumed to be infinite from the top of the slab to the bottom of the column capital.

The properties of the analogous column section for the interior column is, from Fig. 17.13.2a,

$$A = 0.725L, \qquad I = \tfrac{1}{12}(0.725L)^3 = (31.73 \times 10^{-3})L^3$$

The stiffness factors at the top and bottom are

$$S_{TT} = \frac{1}{0.725} + \frac{(0.606)^2}{31.73 \times 10^{-3}} = 1.38 + 11.58 = 12.96$$

$$S_{BB} = \frac{1}{0.725} + \frac{(0.394)^2}{31.73 \times 10^{-3}} = 1.38 + 4.89 = 6.27$$

from which

$$\frac{S_{TT}EI}{L} = \frac{12.96E\pi(9)^4/4}{120} = 556E$$

$$\frac{S_{BB}EI}{L} = \frac{6.27E\pi(9)^4/4}{120} = 269E$$

The carry-over factors are

$$C_{TB} = \frac{0.606(0.394)/(31.73 \times 10^{-3}) - 1.38}{12.96} = \frac{6.14}{12.96} = 0.474$$

$$C_{BT} = \frac{6.14}{6.27} = 0.979$$

For the exterior column (Fig. 17.13.2b),

$$A = 0.742L, \qquad I = \tfrac{1}{12}(0.742L)^3 = (34.1 \times 10^{-3})L^3$$

$$S_{TT} = \frac{1}{0.742} + \frac{(0.598)^2}{34.1 \times 10^{-3}} = 1.35 + 10.48 = 11.83$$

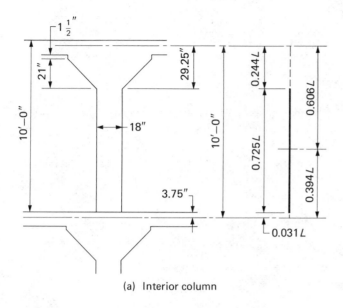

(a) Interior column

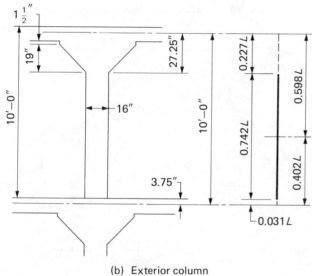

(b) Exterior column

Fig. 17.13.2
Flexure properties of columns, Example 17.13.1.

$$S_{BB} = \frac{1}{0.742} + \frac{(0.402)^2}{34.1 \times 10^{-3}} = 1.35 + 4.74 = 6.09$$

$$\frac{S_{TT}EI}{L} = \frac{11.83E(16)^4/12}{120} = 539E$$

$$\frac{S_{BB}EI}{L} = \frac{6.09E(16)^4/12}{120} = 277E$$

$$C_{TB} = \frac{0.598(0.402)/(34.1 \times 10^{-3}) - 1.35}{11.83} = \frac{5.71}{11.83} = 0.482$$

$$C_{BT} = \frac{5.71}{6.09} = 0.938$$

(c) Equivalent column stiffness and distribution factors. The equivalent column stiffness may be computed from the formula

$$\frac{1}{K_{ec}} = \frac{1}{\Sigma K_c} + \frac{1}{K_t}$$

For the exterior column,

$$K_t = 2500E \qquad \text{(from Example 17.5.1, Part e)}$$

$$\Sigma K_c = K_{c1} + K_{c2} = 277E + 539E = 816E$$

$$K_{ec} = \frac{E}{1/816 + 1/2500} = \frac{1000E}{1.225 + 0.400} = 613E$$

which is divided into two parts, for the upper and lower columns, as shown in Fig. 17.13.3.

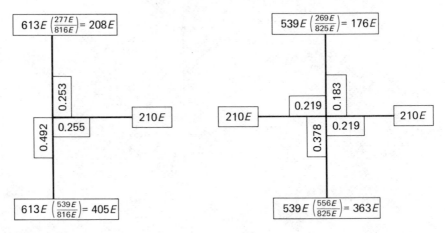

Fig. 17.13.3
Distribution factors at exterior and interior joints, Example 17.13.1.

In computing the torsional constant for the transverse strip through the interior column, a weighted slab thickness of 8.5 in. is used, on the assumption that one-third of the span has a $10\frac{1}{2}$-in. thickness and the remainder has a $7\frac{1}{2}$-in. thickness. (Actually the ratio is not exactly so because the drop width has been revised from 6 ft 8 in. to 7 ft.)

$$C = \left(1 - 0.63\frac{x}{y}\right)\frac{x^3 y}{3} = \left[1 - \frac{0.63(8.5)}{12(4.43)}\right]\left[\frac{(8.5)^3(12)(4.43)}{3}\right] = 9800 \text{ in.}^4$$

$$K_t = \frac{2(9E)C}{L_2\left(1 - \frac{c_2}{L_2}\right)^3} = \frac{2(9E)(9800)}{240\left(1 - \frac{4.43}{20}\right)^3} = 1560E$$

$$K_c = 269E + 556E = 825E$$

$$K_{ec} = \frac{E}{1/825 + 1/1560} = \frac{1000E}{1.21 + 0.642} = 539E$$

which is divided into two parts, for the upper and lower columns, as shown in Fig. 17.13.3.

The distribution factors at the exterior and interior joints are shown in Fig. 17.13.3; for example, $210E/(210E + 613E) = 0.255$, and $210E/(420E + 539E) = 0.219$.

(d) Fixed-end moments.

$$\text{factored dead load } w_D = 1.4(150/12)(7.5) = 1.4(94) = 132 \text{ psf}$$
$$\text{factored live load } w_L = 1.7(120) = 204 \text{ psf}$$
$$\text{FEM due to } (w_D + w_L) = 0.0985(0.336)(20)(25)^2 = 414 \text{ ft-kips}$$
$$\text{FEM due to } (w_D + \tfrac{3}{4}w_L) = 0.0985(0.285)(20)(25)^2 = 351 \text{ ft-kips}$$
$$\text{FEM due to } w_D \text{ only} = 0.0985(0.132)(20)(25)^2 = 162 \text{ ft-kips}$$

(e) Moment distribution. Moment distribution for five loading conditions is necessary for the equivalent frame. Since the slab-beam may be assumed to be fixed at any support two panels distant from the support or span where critical moments are being obtained, only two cycles of moment distribution are needed. However, in this example three cycles of moment distribution are used, as the third cycle does not add much to the amount of work. The moment distribution is shown in Table 17.13.1.

The positive bending moment at the center of any span may be computed by subtracting the average value of the negative bending moments at the ends from the simple-beam bending moment. For instance, the moment at the center of the first span in the first loading condition of Table 17.13.1 is

$$\tfrac{1}{8}(0.336)(20)(25)^2 - \tfrac{1}{2}(315 + 468) = 525 - 392 = 133 \text{ ft-kips}$$

Summarizing the results of moment distribution shown in Table 17.13.1,

Maximum positive moment at center of first span $= $ the larger of 133 and $130 = 133$ ft-kips

Maximum positive moment at center of second span $= $ the larger of 107 and $119 = 119$ ft-kips

Maximum positive moment at center of third span $= $ the larger of 113 and $122 = 122$ ft-kips

Maximum negative moment at 0-1 $= $ the larger of 315 and $290 = 315$ ft-kips

Maximum negative moment at 1-0 $= $ the larger of 468 and $403 = 468$ ft-kips

Maximum negative moment at 1-2 $= $ the larger of 429 and $388 = 429$ ft-kips

Maximum negative moment at 2-1 $= $ the larger of 406 and $376 = 406$ ft-kips

Maximum negative moment at 2-3 $= $ the larger of 412 and $380 = 412$ ft-kips

Table 17.13.1

Moment Distribution

Joint	0	1		2		3		4		5
Member	0–1	1–0	1–2	2–1	2–3	3–2	3–4	4–3	4–5	5–4
DF	0.255	0.219	0.219	0.219	0.219	0.219	0.219	0.219	0.219	0.255
COF	0.649	0.649	0.649	0.649	0.649	0.649	0.649	0.649	0.649	0.649

All Spans Loaded with Full Live Load

FEM	−414	+414	−414	+414	−414	+414	−414	+414	−414	+414
Balance	+106	0	0	0	0	0	0	0	0	−106
CO	0	+69	0	0	0	0	0	0	−69	0
Balance	0	−15	−15	0	0	0	0	+15	+15	0
CO	−10	0	0	−10	0	0	+10	0	0	+10
Balance	+3	0	0	+2	+2	−2	−2	0	0	−3
Total	−315	+468	−429	+406	−412	+412	−406	+429	−468	+315
Moment at ₵ of Span	133		107			113		107		123

First, Third, and Fifth Spans Loaded with Three-Fourths Live Load

FEM	−351	+351	−162	+162	−351	+351	−162	+162	−351	+351
Balance	+90	−42	−42	+42	+42	−42	−42	+42	+42	−90
CO	−27	+59	+27	−27	−27	+27	+27	−27	−58	+27
Balance	+7	−19	−19	+12	+12	−12	−12	+19	+19	−7
CO	−12	+5	+8	−12	−8	+8	+12	−8	−5	+12
Balance	+3	−3	−3	+4	+4	−4	−4	+3	+3	−3
Total	−290	+350	−191	+181	−328	+328	−181	+191	−350	+290
Moment at ₵ of Span	130		20 (no reversal)			122		20 (no reversal)		130

(f) Reduction of negative moment to face of support. At the exterior support, the critical section is halfway between the column face and the edge of the capital. This distance is $8 + (27 − 8)/2 = 17.5$ in. or 1.46 ft from the column centerline. At the interior column, the critical section is at $4.43/2 = 2.21$ ft from the column centerline. The shear diagrams consistent with the maximum negative moments at supports are shown in Fig. 17.13.4b. When the negative moments in Fig. 17.13.4a are leveled off between the column centerline and the critical section, the resulting moment diagram takes the shape in Fig. 17.13.4c.

(g) Sum of positive and average negative moments. The sum of positive and average negative moments in each span of Fig. 17.13.4c may be obtained

Table 17.13.1 (*cont.*)

Second and Fourth Spans Loaded with Three-Fourths Live Load

FEM	−162	+162	−351	+351	−162	+162	−351	+351	−162	+162
Balance	+41	+42	+42	−42	−42	+42	+42	−42	−42	−41
CO	+27	+27	−27	+27	+27	−27	−27	+27	−27	−27
Balance	−7	0	0	−12	−12	+12	+12	0	0	+7
CO	0	−5	−8	0	+8	−8	0	+8	+5	0
Balance	0	+3	+3	−2	−2	+2	+2	−3	−3	0
Total	−101	+229	−341	+322	−183	+183	−322	+341	−229	+101
Moment at ℄ of Span	41 (no reversal)		119		23 (no reversal)		119		41 (no reversal)	

First, Second, and Fourth Spans Loaded with Three-Fourths Live Load

FEM	−351	+351	−351	+351	−162	+162	−351	+351	−162	+162
Balance	+90	0	0	−42	−42	+42	+42	−42	−42	−41
CO	0	+58	−27	0	+27	−27	−27	+27	+27	+27
Balance	0	−7	−7	−6	−6	+12	+12	−12	−12	−7
CO	−5	0	−4	−5	+8	−4	−8	+8	−5	−8
Balance	+1	+1	+1	−1	−1	+3	+3	−1	−1	+2
Total		+403	−388							

Second, Third, and Fifth Spans Loaded with Three-Fourths Live Load

FEM	−162	+162	−351	+351	−351	+351	−162	+162	−351	+351
Balance	+42	+42	+42	0	0	−42	−42	+42	+42	−90
CO	+27	+27	0	+27	−27	0	+27	−27	−58	+27
Balance	−7	−6	−6	0	0	−6	−6	+19	+19	−7
CO	−4	−5	0	−4	−4	0	+12	−4	−5	+12
Balance	+1	+1	+1	+2	+2	−3	−3	+2	+2	−3
Total				+376	−380					

as

$$133 + \tfrac{1}{2}(208 + 285) = 380 \text{ ft-kips for the first span}$$
$$119 + \tfrac{1}{2}(258 + 239) = 367 \text{ ft-kips for the second span}$$
$$122 + 243 = 365 \text{ ft-kips for the third span}$$

These values compare favorably with the total static moment M_{0L} of 395 ft-kips or 356 ft-kips computed in Example 17.2.1. If the value of $M_{0L} = 356$ ft-kips is to be accepted, the moment values in Fig. 17.13.4c may be reduced by the factors 356/380, 356/367, and 356/365, respectively, for the first, second, and third spans. This is permissible because the flat slab in this example satisfies the limitations for the "direct-design method."

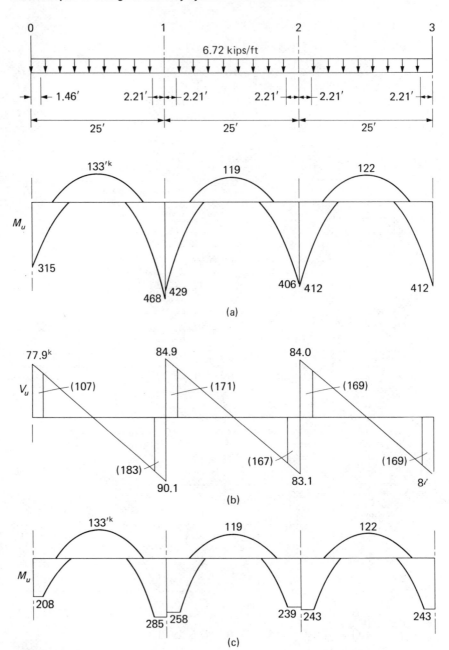

Fig. 17.13.4

Maximum shears and moments.

(h) Comparison with longitudinal moments in the "direct-design method." The longitudinal moments obtained by the "direct-design method" shown in Fig. 17.5.1 of Example 17.5.1 are -189, $+167$, -267, -257, $+138$ ft-kips; these values compare well with -208, $+133$, -285, -243, $+122$ ft-kips in Fig. 17.13.4.

EXAMPLE 17.13.2 Determine the bending moments in the upper and lower adjacent columns, both exterior and interior, of the flat-slab floor in the preceding example.

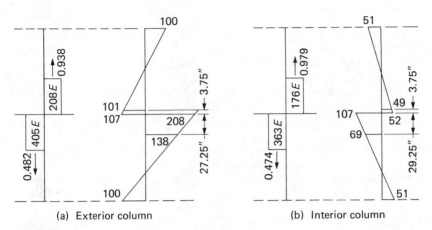

Fig. 17.13.5
Critical moments in columns, Example 17.13.2.

Solution: From Table 17.13.1, the maximum unbalanced moments at joints 0, 1, and 2 are -315, $+159$, and -147 ft-kips, respectively. The stiffness and carry-over factors shown in Fig. 17.13.5 are taken from Fig. 17.13.3 and Example 17.13.1, part (b). Thus at the exterior column the unbalanced moment of -315 ft-kips is distributed as

$$\frac{208E}{208E + 405E}(+315) = +107 \text{ ft-kips to the upper column}$$

$$\frac{405E}{208E + 405E}(+315) = +208 \text{ ft-kips to the lower column}$$

The largest unbalanced moment of $+159$ ft-kips at joint 2 is distributed to the attached interior column as

$$\frac{176E}{176E + 363E}(-159) = -52 \text{ ft-kips to the upper column}$$

$$\frac{363E}{176E + 363E}(-159) = -107 \text{ ft-kips to the lower columns}$$

Note that the moments at the far ends of the columns as shown in Fig. 17.13.5 are equal in each case. This is naturally so because the product of stiffness and carry-over factors at one end of a member with variable moment of inertia is equal to that at the other end. The moment in the upper column at its junction with the top of slab and the moment in the lower column at the base of the capital may then be determined from the moment diagrams, as shown in Fig. 17.13.5. Summarizing,

$$\text{moment in exterior column} = 138 \text{ ft-kips}$$
$$\text{moment in interior column} = 69 \text{ ft-kips}$$

SELECTED REFERENCES

1. George A. Hool and Nathan C. Johnson. *Concrete Engineers Handbook*. New York: McGraw-Hill, 1918 (pp. 457–486).
2. J. R. Nichols. "Statical Limitations Upon the Steel Requirement in Reinforced Concrete Flat Slab Floors, *Transactions ASCE*, **77**, 1914, 1670–1736.
3. H. M. Westergaard, and W. A. Slater. "Moments and Stresses in Slabs," *ACI Proceedings*, **17**, 1921, 415.
4. Joseph A. Wise. "Design of Reinforced Concrete Slabs," *ACI Proceedings*, **25**, 1929, 712.
5. H. M. Westergaard. "Formulas for the Design of Rectangular Floor Slabs and Supporting Girders," *ACI Proceedings*, **22**, 1926, 26.
6. David S. Hatcher, Mete A. Sozen, and Chester P. Siess. "Test of a Reinforced Concrete Flat Plate," *Journal of Structural Division*, ASCE, **91**, (ST5) October 1965, 205–231.
7. James O. Jirsa, Mete A. Sozen, and Chester P. Siess. "Test of a Flat Slab Reinforced with Welded Wire Fabric," *Journal of Structural Division*, ASCE, **92**, (ST3) June 1966, 199–224.
8. D. S. Hatcher, Mete A. Sozen, and Chester P. Siess. "Test of a Reinforced Concrete Flat Slab," *Journal of Structural Division*, ASCE, **95**, (ST6) June 1969, 1051–1072.
9. E. Ramzy F. Zaghlool, H. A. Rawdon de Paiva, and Peter G. Glockner. "Tests of Reinforced Concrete Flat Plate Floors," *Journal of Structural Division*, ASCE, **96**, (ST3) March 1970, 487–507.
10. Alex E. Cardenas and Paul H. Kaar. "Field Test of a Flat Plate Structure," *ACI Journal, Proceedings*, **68**, January 1971, 50–58.
11. Donald D. Magura and W. Gene Corley. "Tests to Destruction of a Multipanel Waffle Slab Structure—1964–1965 New York World's Fair," *ACI Journal, Proceedings*, **68**, September 1971, 699–703.
12. Jan C. Jofriet and Gregory M. McNeice. "Pattern Loading on Reinforced Concrete Flat Plates," *ACI Journal, Proceedings*, **68**, December 1971, 968–972.
13. Johannes Moe. *Shearing Strength of Reinforced Concrete Slabs and Footings Under Concentrated Loads*, Development Department Bulletin D47. Chicago: Portland Cement Association, April 1961 (130 pp.).
14. ACI-ASCE Committee 326. "Report on Shear and Diagonal Tension," *ACI Journal, Proceedings*, **59**, January, February, and March, 1962, 1–30, 277–344, and 352–396.
15. Neil M. Hawkins, H. B. Fallsen, and R. C. Hinojosa. "Influence of Column Rectangularity on the Behavior of Flat Plate Structures," *Cracking, Deflection, and Ultimate Load of Concrete Slab Systems* (SP-30). Detroit: American Concrete Institute, 1971 (pp. 127–146).
16. M. Daniel Vanderbilt. "Shear Strength of Continuous Plates," *Journal of Structural Division*, ASCE, **98**, (ST5) May 1972, 961–973.
17. M. E. Criswell and N. M. Hawkins. "Shear Strength of Slabs: Basic Principles and Their Relation to Current Methods of Analysis," *Shear in Reinforced Concrete*, Vol. 2 (SP-42). Detroit: American Concrete Institute, 1974 (pp. 641–676).
18. N. M. Hawkins, M. E. Criswell, and F. Roll. "Shear Strength of Slabs Without

Shear Reinforcement," *Shear in Reinforced Concrete*, Vol. 2 (SP-42). Detroit: American Concrete Institute, 1974 (pp. 677–720).

19. Brian E. Hewitt and Barrington de V. Batchelor. "Punching Shear Strength of Restrained Slabs", *Journal of Structural Division*, ASCE, **101,** (ST9) September 1975, 1837–1853.

20. Paul H. Langohr, Amin Ghali, and Walter H. Dilger. "Special Shear Reinforcement for Concrete Flat Plates," *ACI Journal, Proceedings*, **73,** March 1976, 141–146.

21. Neil M. Hawkins, (Chmn.). "The Shear Strength of Reinforced Concrete Members—Slabs, by the Joint ASCE-ACI Task Committee 426 on Shear and Diagonal Tension of the Committee on Masonry and Reinforced Concrete of the Structural Division," *Journal of Structural Division*, ASCE, **100,** (ST8) August 1974, 1543–1591.

22. N. M. Hawkins. "Shear Strength of Slabs With Shear Reinforcement", *Shear in Reinforced Concrete*, Vol. 2 (SP-42). Detroit: American Concrete Institute, 1974 (pp. 785–816).

23. W. G. Corley and N. M. Hawkins. "Shearhead Reinforcement for Slabs," *ACI Journal, Proceedings*, **65,** October 1968, 811–824.

24. Joseph DiStasio and M. P. Van Buren. "Transfer of Bending Moment between Flat Plate Floor and Column," *ACI Journal, Proceedings*, **57,** September 1960, 299–314.

25. N. W. Hanson and J. M. Hanson. "Shear and Moment Transfer Between Concrete Slabs and Columns." *Journal PCA Research and Development Laboratories*, **10,** (1) January 1968, 2–16.

26. Neil M. Hawkins and W. Gene Corley. "Transfer of Unbalanced Moment and Shear from Flat Plates to Columns," *Cracking, Deflection, and Ultimate Load of Concrete Slab Systems* (SP-30). Detroit: American Concrete Institute, 1971 (pp. 147–176).

27. Dieter D. Pfaffinger. "Column-Plate Interaction in Flat Slab Structures," *Journal of Structural Division*, ASCE, **98,** (ST1) January 1972, 307–326.

28. N. M. Hawkins. "Shear Strength of Slabs With Moments Transferred to Columns", *Shear in Reinforced Concrete*, Vol. 2 (SP-42). Detroit: American Concrete Institute, 1974 (pp. 817–846).

29. N. M. Hawkins and W. G. Corley. "Moment Transfer to Columns in Slabs With Shearhead Reinforcement," *Shear in Reinforced Concrete*, Vol. 2 (SP-42). Detroit: American Concrete Institute, 1974 (pp. 847–880).

30. Shafiqul Islam and Robert Park. "Tests on Slab-Column Connections with Shear and Unbalanced Flexure," *Journal of Structural Division*, ASCE, **102,** (ST3) March 1976, 549–568.

31. Robert Park and Shafiqul Islam. "Strength of Slab-Column Connections with Shear and Unbalanced Flexure," *Journal of Structural Division*, ASCE, **102,** (ST9) September 1976, 1879–1901.

32. Frederic Roll, S. T. H. Zaidi, Gajanan Sabnis, and Kuang Chuang. "Shear Resistance of Perforated Reinforced Concrete Slabs," *Cracking, Deflection, and Ultimate Load of Concrete Slab Systems* (SP-30). Detroit: American Concrete Institute, 1971 (pp. 77–100).

33. E. Ramzy F. Zaghlool and H. A. Rawdon de Paiva. "Strength Analysis of Corner Column-Slab Connections," *Journal of Structural Division*, ASCE, **99,** (ST1) January 1973, 53–70.

34. E. Ramzy F. Zaghlool and H. A. Rawdon de Paiva. "Tests of Flat-Plate Corner Column-Slab Connections," *Journal of Structural Division*, ASCE, **99,** (ST3) March 1973, 551–572.

35. Alex E. Cardenas, Rolf J. Lenschow, and Mete A. Sozen. "Stiffness of Reinforced Concrete Plates," *Journal of Structural Division*, ASCE, **98,** (ST11) November 1972, 2587–2603.

36. Maurice P. Van Buren. "Staggered Columns in Flat Plates," *Journal of Structural Division*, ASCE, **97,** (ST6) June 1971, 1791–1797.

37. Sidney H. Simmonds and Janko Misic. "Design Factors for the Equivalent Frame Method." *ACI Journal, Proceedings,* **68,** November 1971, 825–831.

PROBLEMS

17.1 Given the flat slab shown in the accompanying figure. The columns are 24 in. square with columns 1 through 6 existing only below the floor slab, while columns 7 through 9 exist both above and below the floor slab. All columns are 13 ft long center to center of floor slabs. The live load is 150 psf, $f_c' = 4000$ psi, and $f_y = 60,000$ psi. Design the flat slab using rectangular column capitals and drop panels.

(a) Determine slab thickness based on ACI-9.5.3.

(b) Use "direct-design method" for longitudinal distribution of moments in interior equivalent frame defined by columns 2, 5, and 7 along its centerline.

(c) Determine transverse distribution and select reinforcement for the column strip (defined by columns 2, 5, and 7) and adjacent half middle strips.

(d) Specify and show details giving lengths and locations of bars.

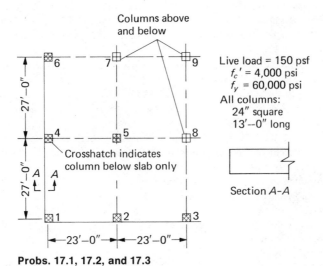

Probs. 17.1, 17.2, and 17.3

17.2 For the flat slab of Prob. 17.1, design the interior equivalent frame defined by columns 4, 5, and 8 along its centerline.

17.3 For the flat slab of Prob. 17.1, redesign the interior equivalent frame defined by column line 2-5-7, but consider that a 12-in. wall 13 ft high exists along column line 1-2-3 at the story below the slab to be designed.

17.4 Investigate the moment and shear transfer at the exterior support of a flat-slab structure as detailed in the accompanying figure. The exterior support has a 5-ft flat-sided column capital on a 24-in. square column, along with a 7 ft 8 in.

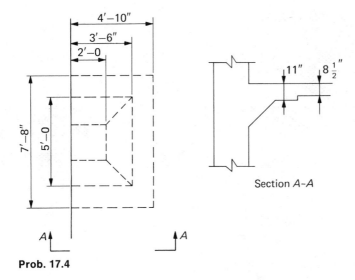

Prob. 17.4

width of drop panel that is 11 in. thick. The slab is $8\frac{1}{2}$ in. thick. Assume there is no edge beam or wall at the exterior support location. The factored moment M_u to be transferred is 340 ft-kips and the factored shear V_u is 115 kips. The negative-moment reinforcement provided in the column strip is #5 at 10 in. spacing. Use $f'_c = 4000$ psi and $f_y = 60,000$ psi.

17.5 Rework through Example 17.5.1, if the service live load is 200 psf instead of 120 psf.

17.6 Rework through Example 17.5.2, if the service live load is 150 psf instead of 60 psf.

17.7 Rework through Example 17.7.1, if the service live load is 200 psf instead of 120 psf.

17.8 Rework through Example 17.8.1, if the service live load is 200 psf instead of 120 psf.

17.9 Rework through Example 17.8.2, if the service live load is 150 psf instead of 60 psf.

17.10 Rework through Example 17.10.1, if the service live load is 150 psf instead of 60 psf.

17.11 Rework through Example 17.11.1, if the service live load is 150 psf instead of 60 psf.

17.12 Rework through Example 17.13.1, if the service live load is 200 psf instead of 120 psf.

18

Yield Line
Theory
of Slabs

18.1 Introduction

Reinforced concrete design methods under the present ACI Code are based on the results of an elastic analysis of the structure as a whole, when subjected to the action of factored loads (ACI-9.2) such as $1.4D + 1.7L$ where D and L refer to service dead and live loads. Actually the behavior of a statically indeterminate structure is such that after the ultimate moment capacities at one or more points have been reached, discontinuities develop in the elastic curve at those points and the results of an elastic analysis are no longer valid. If there is sufficient ductility, redistribution of bending moments will occur until a sufficient number of sections of discontinuity, commonly called "plastic hinges," form to change the structure into a mechanism, at which time the structure collapses or fails. The term "ultimate load analysis," as opposed to "elastic analysis," relates to the use of the bending moment diagram at the verge of collapse as the basis for design. Other than the provisions for redistribution of moments at the supports of continuous flexural members (ACI-8.4), the present ACI Code has as yet made no allowance for ultimate load analysis. The redistribution as described in ACI-8.4 has been presented and illustrated in Sec. 10.12.

The design of two-way slab systems has been treated in Chaps. 16 and 17. Even here the design moments are based on the elastic analysis of an equivalent frame, which is devised as a simple substitute for the elastic analysis of continuous plate systems.

The chief concern of this chapter is to develop the yield line theory for two-way slabs. Although not yet adopted by the ACI Code, slab analysis by yield line theory may be useful in providing the needed information for

Flat slabs; Marina City, Chicago. (Courtesy of Portland Cement Association.)

understanding the behavior of irregular or single-panel slabs with various boundary conditions.

18.2 General Concept

Although the study of flexural behavior of plates up to the ultimate load may date back to the 1920s [1], the fundamental concept of the yield line theory for the ultimate load design of slabs has been expanded considerably by K. W. Johansen [2,3]. In this theory the strength of a slab is assumed to be governed by flexure alone; other effects such as shear and deflection are to be separately considered. The reinforcing steel is assumed to be fully yielded along the yield lines at collapse and the bending and twisting moments are assumed to be uniformly distributed along the yield lines.

Yield line theory for one-way slabs is not much different from the limit analysis of continuous beams. On a continuous beam the achievement of flexural strength at one location, say in the negative-moment region over a support, does not necessarily constitute reaching the ultimate load on the beam. If the section having reached its flexural strength can continue to provide a constant resistance while undergoing further rotation, then the flexural strength may be reached at additional locations. Complete failure theoretically can not occur until yielding has occurred at several locations (or along several lines in case of one-way slabs) so that a mechanism forms giving a condition of unstable equilibrium.

Consider for example, the one-way slab of finite width shown in Fig. 18.2.1. A uniform loading on the slab will cause uniform maximum negative bending moment along AB and EF and uniform positive bending moment along CD, which is parallel to the supports. When the uniform load is increased until the moments along AB, CD, and EF reach their respective ultimate moment capacities, rotation of the slab segments will occur with the yield lines acting as axes of rotation. Once the ultimate moment capacity is achieved, angle change can occur without additional resisting moment being developed. Thus, under the limiting condition with the slab segments able to rotate with no change in resisting moment, the slab system is geometrically unstable. This condition is known as a "collapse mechanism."

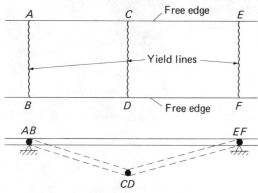

Fig. 18.2.1
Collapse mechanism of a one-way slab.

Yield line theory for two-way slabs requires a different treatment from limit analysis of continuous beams, because in this case the yield lines will not in general be parallel to each other but instead form a yield line pattern. The entire slab area will be divided into several segments which can rotate along the yield lines as rigid bodies at the condition of collapse or unstable equilibrium. Some yield line patterns for typical situations are shown in Fig. 18.2.2.

The slab of Fig. 18.2.2a has nonparallel supports. At the collapse condition this slab will break into two segments; one segment will have an edge rotating about I and the other will have an edge rotating about II. The positive moment yield line must then intersect lines I and II at their intersection, point 0. The exact position of yield line III will depend on the reinforcement amount and direction, both in the positive and negative moment regions.

For the case of Fig. 18.2.2b where a rectangular panel is either simply supported or continuous over four linear supports, the collapse mechanism consists of four slab segments. The exact locations of points a and b will depend on the moment capacities at the supports and the positive moment reinforcement in each direction.

The slab in Fig. 18.2.2c is supported along two edges and in addition is supported by two isolated columns. The rotational axes for the slab segments at collapse must occur along the supports (lines I and II), and additional rotational axes must pass through the isolated columns. The critical position of the positive moment yield lines a, b, c, d, and e is a function of the reinforcement amount and direction; in the meantime compatibility of deflection along the yield lines must be maintained during the rigid body rotations of the slab segments.

For a concentrated load at a significant distance from a supported edge, the yield line pattern will be circular as shown in Fig. 18.2.2d. The circle

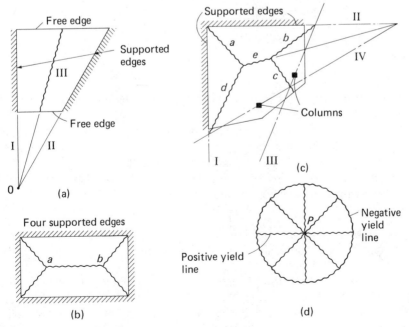

Fig. 18.2.2
Typical yield-line patterns.

pattern will be a yield line of negative bending moment, while the radial yield lines are due to positive bending moment. For concentrated loads near a free edge, a fan or partial circular pattern is typical.

18.3 Fundamental Assumptions

In applying the yield line theory to the ultimate load analysis of reinforced concrete slabs, the following fundamental assumptions are made:

1. The reinforcing steel is fully yielded along the yield lines at failure. In the usual case, when the slab reinforcement is well below that in the balanced condition, the moment-curvature relationship [4] is as shown in Fig. 18.3.1.

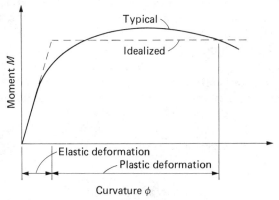

Fig. 18.3.1
Typical and idealized M-ϕ relationship for reinforced concrete slab.

2. The slab deforms plastically at failure and is separated into segments by the yield lines.
3. The bending and twisting moments are uniformly distributed along the yield line and they are the maximum values provided by the ultimate moment capacities in two orthogonal directions (for two-way slabs).
4. The elastic deformations are negligible compared with the plastic deformations; thus the slab parts rotate as *plane* segments in the collapse condition.

Assumption No. 3 may be considered to be the yield criterion of orthotropic reinforced concrete slabs. It means that along a yield line as shown in Fig. 18.3.2, the bending moment M_{ub} and twisting moment M_{ut}, each per unit distance along the yield line, are exactly equal to what can be provided by the ultimate moment capacities M_{ux} and M_{uy} per unit distance in the y and x directions, respectively. It may be noted that M_{ux} is resisted by the reinforcement in the x direction, and M_{uy} is resisted by the reinforcement in the y direction. Also the sign convention is that the bending moments

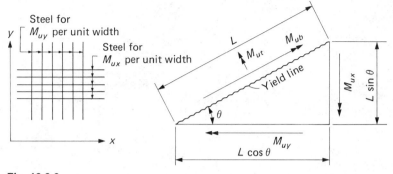

Fig. 18.3.2
Bending and twisting moments on yield line.

M_{ux}, M_{uy}, and M_{ub} are positive for tension in the lower portion of the slab and the twisting moment M_{ut} is positive if its vector is directed away from the free body on which it acts.

The bending moment M_{ub} and twisting moment M_{ut} along the yield line in Fig. 18.3.2 may be expressed in terms of M_{ux} and M_{uy}. Taking equilibrium of moment vectors parallel to the yield line,

$$M_{ub}(L) = M_{ux}(L \sin \theta) \sin \theta + M_{uy}(L \cos \theta) \cos \theta$$
$$M_{ub} = M_{ux} \sin^2 \theta + M_{uy} \cos^2 \theta$$
$$M_{ub} = \frac{M_{ux} + M_{uy}}{2} - \frac{M_{ux} - M_{uy}}{2} \cos 2\theta \qquad (18.3.1)$$

and, taking equilibrium of moment vectors perpendicular to the yield line,

$$M_{ut}(L) = M_{ux}(L \sin \theta) \cos \theta - M_{uy}(L \cos \theta) \sin \theta$$
$$M_{ut} = (M_{ux} - M_{uy}) \sin \theta \cos \theta$$
$$= \frac{(M_{ux} - M_{uy})}{2} \sin 2\theta \qquad (18.3.2)$$

In using Eqs. (18.3.1) and (18.3.2), it is important to note that θ is the counterclockwise angle measured from the positive x axis to the yield line.

18.4 Methods of Analysis

There are two methods of yield line analysis of slabs: the virtual-work method and the equilibrium method. Based on the same fundamental assumptions, the two methods should give exactly the same results. In either method, a yield line pattern must be first assumed so that a collapse mechanism is produced. For a collapse mechanism, rigid body movements of the slab segments are possible by rotation along the yield lines while maintaining deflection compatibility at the yield lines between slab segments. There may be more than one possible yield line pattern, in which case

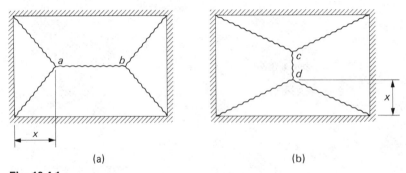

Fig. 18.4.1
Yield-line patterns of a simply supported rectangular slab.

solutions to all possible yield line patterns must be sought and the one giving the smallest ultimate load would actually happen and thus should be used in design. For instance the failure pattern of the simply supported rectangular slab subjected to uniform load may be that shown either in Fig. 18.4.1a or in Fig. 18.4.1b, depending on the aspect ratio of the rectangular panel and the moment capacities M_{ux} and M_{uy}.

After the yield line pattern has been assumed, the next step is to determine the position of the yield lines, such as defined by the unknown x in Fig. 18.4.1a or b. It is at this point that one may choose to use the virtual-work method or the equilibrium method. In the virtual-work method, an equation containing the unknown x is established by equating the total positive work done by the ultimate load during simultaneous rigid body rotations of the slab segments (while maintaining deflection compatibility) to the total negative work done by the bending and twisting moments on all the yield lines. Then that value of x which gives the smallest ultimate load is found by means of differential calculus. In the equilibrium method, the value of x is obtained by applying the usual equations of statical equilibrium to the slab segments, but the optimal position x is defined by the placement of predetermined nodal forces at the intersection of yield lines. Expressions for the nodal forces in typical situations, once derived, can be conveniently used to avoid the necessity of mathematical differentiation as required in the virtual-work method.

In the following sections, yield line analysis for one-way slabs is dealt with first in a manner similar to limit analysis of continuous beams. Then both the virtual-work method and the equilibrium method are presented and illustrated for two-way slabs.

18.5 Yield Line Analysis of One-Way Slabs

The continuous slab span shown in Fig. 18.5.1a has ultimate moment capacities of M_{ui} and M_{uj} provided by top reinforcement at the supports and an ultimate moment capacity M_{up} provided by bottom reinforcement within the span. The ultimate moment capacities M_{ui}, M_{uj}, and M_{up} are absolute values of the resisting moment per unit slab width. For uniform loading the only possible yield pattern consists of three parallel yield lines as shown in Fig. 18.5.1a, one each along the left and right supports and one at a distance x from the left support. The moment diagram per unit slab width should be as shown in Fig. 18.5.1b. The problem is to determine

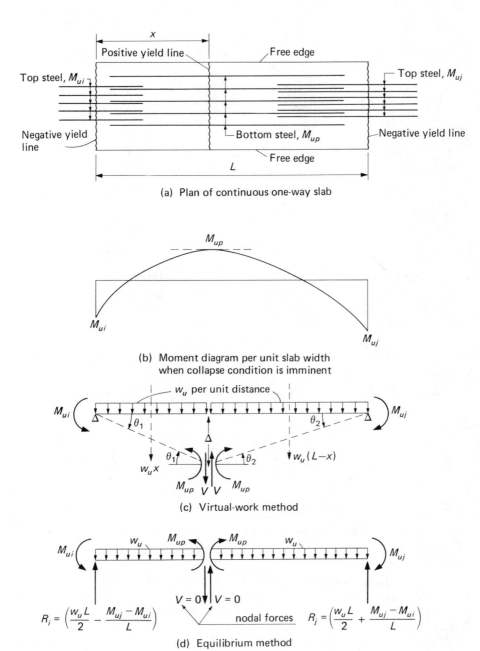

(a) Plan of continuous one-way slab

(b) Moment diagram per unit slab width
when collapse condition is imminent

(c) Virtual-work method

$$R_i = \left(\frac{w_u L}{2} - \frac{M_{uj} - M_{ui}}{L} \right)$$

$$R_j = \left(\frac{w_u L}{2} + \frac{M_{uj} - M_{ui}}{L} \right)$$

(d) Equilibrium method

Fig. 18.5.1
Yield-line analysis of one-way slabs.

the ultimate load w_u per unit slab area in terms of M_{ui}, M_{uj}, and M_{up}, and the span length L. It will be shown that the virtual-work and equilibrium methods will give exactly the same results.

Referring to Fig. 18.5.1c, the rigid body rotations of the slab segments at collapse are measured from the original horizontal positions to those of the dashed lines, where the rotation of the left segment is θ_1 in the clockwise direction and that of the right segment is θ_2 in the counterclockwise direction while maintaining the compatible deflection Δ at the positive yield line. The total positive work done by the uniform load on the left and right segments of unit slab width is

$$\text{total positive work} = (w_u x)\frac{\Delta}{2} + w_u(L - x)\frac{\Delta}{2}$$

The total negative work done by M_{ui} and M_{up} on the left segment is $(M_{ui} + M_{up})\theta_1$ and that done by M_{uj} and M_{up} on the right segment is $(M_{uj} + M_{up})\theta_2$, both in absolute quantities. Thus

$$\text{total negative work} = (M_{ui} + M_{up})\theta_1 + (M_{uj} + M_{up})\theta_2$$

in which

$$\theta_1 = \frac{\Delta}{x}, \qquad \theta_2 = \frac{\Delta}{L - x}$$

The principle of virtual work states that the total work done by a force system in equilibrium in going through a virtual rigid body displacement is zero. By means of this principle, one can equate the total positive work to the absolute value of the total negative work; or

$$(w_u x)\frac{\Delta}{2} + w_u(L - x)\frac{\Delta}{2} = (M_{ui} + M_{up})\frac{\Delta}{x} + (M_{uj} + M_{up})\frac{\Delta}{(L - x)}$$

Dividing out the compatible deflection Δ from the above equation and solving for w_u,

$$w_u = \frac{2M_{ui}}{Lx} + \frac{2M_{up}}{x(L - x)} + \frac{2M_{uj}}{L(L - x)} \tag{18.5.1}$$

Differentiating Eq. (18.5.1) for w_u with respect to x and setting the derivative to zero, one obtains the quadratic equation,

$$(M_{uj} - M_{ui})x^2 + 2(M_{ui} + M_{up})Lx - (M_{ui} + M_{up})L^2 = 0 \tag{18.5.2}$$

In the virtual-work method, then, first the value of x is found by solving the quadratic equation (18.5.2) and the ultimate load w_u is determined from Eq. (18.5.1).

In the equilibrium method the value of x is not to be obtained by differential calculus but defined by the magnitude of the nodal forces (V and V shown in Fig. 18.5.1d) acting on the slab segments on either side of the positive yield line. In this particular instance, it is known from the elementary theory of bending of beams that the shear at a section of maximum positive bending moment should be zero. From this point on, the unknown values of R_i, R_j, w_u, and x in Fig. 18.5.1d are obtained from the four independent equilibrium equations for the entire slab or either of the two slab segments. The left and right reactions on the free bodies of Fig. 18.5.1d are found by applying the equilibrium equations to the entire slab; thus

$$R_i = \left(\frac{w_u L}{2} - \frac{M_{uj} - M_{ui}}{L}\right), \qquad R_j = \left(\frac{w_u L}{2} + \frac{M_{uj} - M_{ui}}{L}\right)$$

Then, summing the vertical forces on the left slab segment,

$$R_i = \frac{w_u L}{2} - \frac{M_{uj} - M_{ui}}{L} = w_u x$$

from which

$$w_u = \frac{(M_{uj} - M_{ui})}{L(L/2 - x)} \qquad (18.5.3)$$

and, taking moments about the positive yield line on the left segment,

$$M_{up} = -M_{ui} + \left(\frac{w_u L}{2} - \frac{M_{uj} - M_{ui}}{L}\right)x - \frac{w_u x^2}{2} \qquad (18.5.4)$$

Substitution of Eq. (18.5.3) into Eq. (18.5.4) results in the same quadratic equation as Eq. (18.5.2). This shows that the two methods, virtual work and equilibrium, give exactly the same results.

In the solution of a numerical problem the quadratic equation (18.5.2) is first solved for x. Although w_u can then be computed from either Eq. (18.5.1) or Eq. (18.5.3), using Eq. (18.5.1) is far superior to Eq. (18.5.3), because Eq. (18.5.1) contains the sum of three absolute quantities but Eq. (18.5.3) involves the division by a sensitive quantity $(L/2 - x)$.

EXAMPLE 18.5.1   Given the ultimate moment capacities $M_{ui} = 14$ ft-kips, $M_{up} = 16$ ft-kips, and $M_{uj} = 22$ ft-kips per ft width of a 20-ft continuous slab span as shown in Fig. 18.5.2, determine the location x of the positive yield line and the ultimate load w_u in kips per ft per ft width of slab.

Solution: Using the quadratic equation (18.5.2),

$$(M_{uj} - M_{ui})x^2 + 2(M_{ui} + M_{up})Lx - (M_{ui} + M_{up})L^2 = 0$$
$$(22 - 14)x^2 + 2(14 + 16)(20x) - (14 + 16)(20)^2 = 0$$
$$8x^2 + 1200x - 12{,}000 = 0$$
$$x^2 + 150x + 75^2 = 1500 + 5625$$
$$x = \sqrt{7125} - 75 = 84.41 - 75 = 9.41 \text{ ft}$$

Substituting the value of $x = 9.41$ ft in Eq. (18.5.1),

$$w_u = \frac{2M_{ui}}{Lx} + \frac{2M_{up}}{x(L - x)} + \frac{2M_{uj}}{L(L - x)}$$

$$= \frac{2(14)}{20(9.41)} + \frac{2(16)}{9.41(10.59)} + \frac{2(22)}{20(10.59)}$$

$$= 0.149 + 0.321 + 0.208 = 0.678 \text{ kip/ft}$$

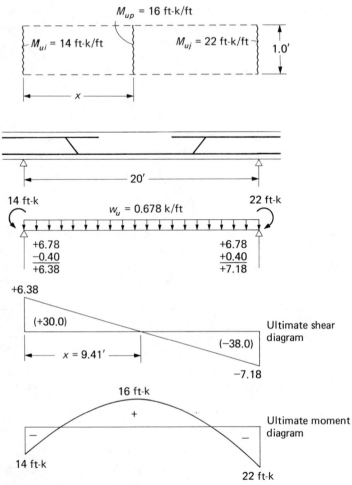

Fig. 18.5.2
One-way slab of Example 18.5.1.

Using $w_u = 0.678$ kip/ft and the end moments of 14 ft-kips and 22 ft-kips, the end reactions, the shear diagram, and the moment diagram are computed and shown in Fig. 18.5.2.

18.6 Work Done by Yield Line Moments in Rigid Body Rotation of Slab Segment

Before taking up the virtual-work method of yield line analysis of two-way slabs, it is desirable to derive a general procedure for obtaining the absolute value of the negative work done by the bending and twisting moments acting on the yield line in going through a rigid body rotation of the slab segment. In Fig. 18.6.1a are shown the moments acting on the edges of a

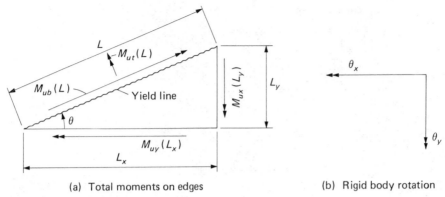

Fig. 18.6.1
Work done by yield-line moments in rigid body rotation of slab segment.

slab segment having yield line of length L with horizontal and vertical projections of L_x and L_y, respectively. Let this slab undergo a rigid body rotation, whose components are θ_x and θ_y, shown in vector notations in Fig. 18.6.1b. It can be shown algebraically that the absolute value of the negative work done by the moments $(M_{ub}L)$ and $(M_{ut}L)$ acting on the yield line is equal to the positive work done by the moments $(M_{ux}L_y)$ and $(M_{uy}L_x)$ acting on the horizontal and vertical projections of the yield line—for the same rigid body rotation, of course. This is obviously correct because the moments $(M_{ux}L_y)$ and $(M_{uy}L_x)$ on Fig. 18.6.1a are the equilibrants of the moments $(M_{ub}L)$ and $(M_{ut}L)$ on the same figure. Certainly then, the negative work done by one set of generalized forces should be equal, numerically, to the positive work done by the alternative set of equilibrating generalized forces.

18.7 Nodal Force at Intersection of Yield Line with Free Edge

In the equilibrium method of yield line analysis, the position of a yield line is characterized by the insertion of nodal forces at the intersection of a yield line with another yield line, or of a yield line with a free edge. For one-way slabs it has been demonstrated in Sec. 18.5 that, on the basis of the elementary theory of bending of beams, the nodal force on either side of a positive yield line is equal to zero. In this section the expression for the pair of equal and opposite nodal forces V acting on each side of the intersection of a yield line with a free edge in a two-way slab is derived.

Shown in Fig. 18.7.1a is a two-way slab with ultimate moment capacities of M_{ux} and M_{uy} provided by the bottom reinforcement in the horizontal and vertical directions, respectively. A positive-moment yield line is assumed to intersect the free edge at an angle α. The upward nodal force V acts on the left segment and the downward nodal force V acts on the right segment, shown by a dot and a cross for the upward and downward forces in Fig.

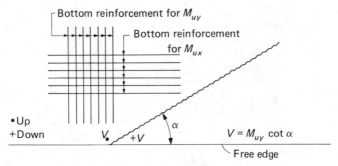

(a) Two-way slab with free edge

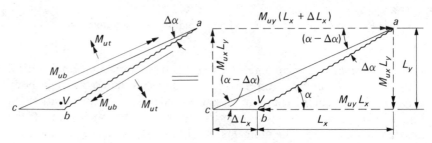

(b) Free-body diagram of infinitesimal piece to left of yield line

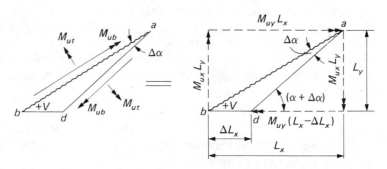

(c) Free-body diagram of infinitesimal piece to right of yield line

Fig. 18.7.1
Nodal force at intersection of yield line with free edge.

18.7.1a according to the convention used by Johansen [2,3]. For equilibrium the upward and downward nodal forces must be equal in magnitude.

Consider the equilibrium of an infinitesimal slab element shown in either Fig. 18.7.1b or c. By its own definition a yield line is always at the optimal position. Inasmuch as the edge ac in Fig. 18.7.1b, or the edge ad in Fig. 18.7.1c, is at an angle $\Delta\alpha$ from the yield line, the same yield line moments as those on the yield line ab act on edges ac or ad. By applying the principle of equivalent force systems as indicated by Fig. 18.6.1a, the free body diagram shown on the left side of the equal sign in Fig. 18.7.1b or c is transformed to the equivalent free body diagram on the right side of the equal sign.

Using the equivalent free body and summing the moments about the line ac in Fig. 18.7.1b,

$$M_{uy}(\Delta L_x)\cos(\alpha - \Delta\alpha) = V(\Delta L_x)\sin(\alpha - \Delta\alpha) \qquad (18.7.1)$$

and summing the moments about the line ad in Fig. 18.7.1c,

$$M_{uy}(\Delta L_x)\cos(\alpha + \Delta\alpha) = V(\Delta L_x)\sin(\alpha + \Delta\alpha) \qquad (18.7.2)$$

Solving for V by using either Eq. (18.7.1) or Eq. (18.7.2),

$$V = M_{uy}\cot\alpha \qquad (18.7.3)$$

Note that the left side of Eq. (18.7.1) or Eq. (18.7.2) represents the component of the net moment vector, $M_{uy}(\Delta L_x)$, along the edge ac or ad, respectively; while the right side involves the moment of the nodal force V about an axis coincident with ac or ad.

Equation (18.7.3) is used when applying the equilibrium method to a situation where a positive yield line intersects a free edge of a slab at an angle other than 90°. This is illustrated by the following example.

EXAMPLE 18.7.1   The triangular slab ABC shown in Fig. 18.7.2a is simply supported along edges AC and BC but has a free edge along AB. The horizontal and vertical reinforcement in the lower face of the slab provides ultimate moment capacities $M_{ux} = 8$ ft-kips and $M_{uy} = 10$ ft-kips, each per foot width of slab. Determine the yield line pattern and the ultimate uniform load.

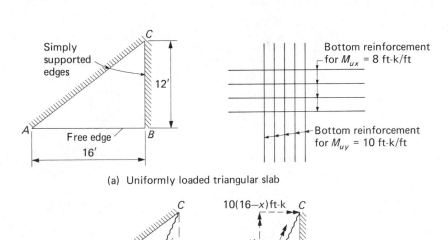

(a) Uniformly loaded triangular slab

(b) The equilibrium method

Fig. 18.7.2
Yield-line analysis of triangular slab in Example 18.7.1.

Solution: (a) Yield line pattern. It has been demonstrated in Fig. 18.2.2a that a yield line should pass through the point of intersection of two non-parallel supported edges. In this example a positive yield line *CD* will break the slab into two segments *ACD* and *BCD*, wherein a common compatible deflection Δ of point *D* can be effected by rigid body rotations of the slab segment *ACD* about the supported edge *AC* and of the slab segment *BCD* about the supported edge *BC*.

(b) Equilibrium method of finding *BD* = *x*. The nodal forces *V* − *V* acting on the left and right slab segments of Fig. 18.7.2b are computed from Eq. (18.7.3); thus

$$V = M_{uy} \cot \alpha = (+10)\left(\frac{x}{12}\right) = \frac{5}{6}x \text{ kips}$$

Note that the nodal force acts upward in the obtuse angle and it acts downward in the acute angle. The equilibrium of moments about the edge *AC* of the left segment requires

$$\tfrac{1}{2}w_u(16 - x)(12)(\tfrac{1}{3}DE) = V(DE) + 96\sin\theta + 10x\cos\theta$$
$$\tfrac{1}{2}w_u(16 - x)(12)(\tfrac{1}{3})(16 - x)(0.6) = \tfrac{5}{6}x(16 - x)(0.6) + 96(0.6) + 10x(0.8)$$

from which

$$w_u = \frac{576 + 160x - 5x^2}{12(16 - x)^2}$$

Similarly, the equilibrium of moments about the edge *BC* of the right segment requires

$$\frac{1}{2}w_u(x)(12)\left(\frac{BD}{3}\right) + V(BD) = 96$$

$$\tfrac{1}{2}w_u(x)(12)(\tfrac{1}{3}x) + \tfrac{5}{6}x^2 = 96$$

from which

$$w_u = \frac{576 - 5x^2}{12x^2}$$

Equating the two expressions for w_u,

$$\frac{576 + 160x - 5x^2}{12(16 - x)^2} = \frac{576 - 5x^2}{12x^2}$$

$$x^2 + 14.4x - 115.2 = 0$$

$$x = 5.72 \text{ ft}$$

With the known value of *x*, the value of w_u may be computed,

$$w_u = 1.048 \text{ kips/sq ft}$$

It can be shown that the same quadratic equation in *x* may be obtained using the virtual-work method by following the procedure as illustrated in Sec. 18.5.

18.8 Nodal Forces at Intersection of Three Yield Lines

In Fig. 18.8.1 are shown three possible yield line patterns for an irregular quadrilateral slab with four simply supported edges. The optimum positions of the yield lines in each pattern should be such as to give the lowest ultimate load. These positions are defined by the locations of points a and b in Fig. 18.8.1a, of points c and d in Fig. 18.8.1b, and of point e in Fig. 18.8.1c. In the equilibrium method the yield lines are characterized by the insertion of predetermined nodal forces. It is the object of this section to derive the expressions for the nodal forces at the intersection of three yield lines, such as at points a, b, c, or d in Fig. 18.8.1. The derivation shown below follows the works of Johansen [2,3], Jones, and Wood [4,5].

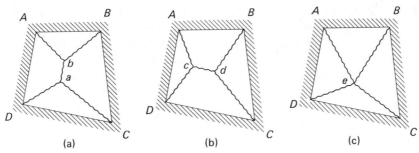

Fig. 18.8.1
Yield-line patterns of a simply supported quadrilateral slab.

Assume that three yield lines 1–2–3 intersecting at a common point 0 are situated at angles ϕ_1–ϕ_2–ϕ_3 measured counterclockwise from the positive x axis, as shown in Fig. 18.8.2a. The ultimate moment capacities under the yield lines 1–2–3 are, as shown in Fig. 18.8.2bc, $M_{ux1} - M_{ux2} - M_{ux3}$ provided by the reinforcement shown horizontally and $M_{uy1} - M_{uy2} - M_{uy3}$ provided by the reinforcement shown vertically, all reinforcement being near the lower face of the slab. The nodal forces V_{12}, V_{23}, and V_{31} are shown by

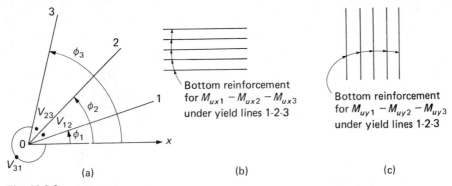

Fig. 18.8.2
Nodal forces at intersection of three yield lines.

the dots (which mean upward nodal forces) in Fig. 18.8.2a. Note that for vertical equilibrium at the point of intersection, the sum of V_{12}, V_{23}, and V_{31} must be zero.

It is important to emphasize at the outset that by definition the yield lines 1–2–3 are all situated at their respective optimal positions. The bending and twisting moments on any line passing through the point of intersection and deviating by an infinitesimal angle from a particular yield line should be equal to the bending and twisting moments on that line as provided by the orthogonal ultimate moment capacities.

Consider the equilibrium of an infinitesimal slab segment $0AB$ (Fig. 18.8.3a), bounded by a differential length $0A$ on yield line 3 and an arbitrary length $0B$ on yield line 1. Since BA is at a differential angle $\Delta\alpha$ from $B0$, the bending and twisting moments on both $B0$ and BA are those provided by M_{uy1} and M_{ux1} on their respective horizontal and vertical projections. Likewise the bending and twisting moments on the differential length $0A$ are those provided by M_{uy3} and M_{ux3} on its horizontal and vertical projections. Call the upward nodal force at point 0 inside triangle $B0A$ and bounded by yield line 1 and a differential length on yield line 3 by the name $V_{1-\Delta3}$.

Next write the equation of equilibrium for moments about AB as the axis of rotation for the slab segment $0AB$ in Fig. 18.8.3a, noting that the moment of the uniform load on $0AB$ about any axis is a differential of the second order and may be neglected.

$$-V_{1-\Delta3}0A\sin(\phi_3 - \phi_1 + \Delta\alpha) + (M_{uy3} - M_{uy1})0A\cos\phi_3\cos(\phi_1 - \Delta\alpha)$$
$$+ (M_{ux3} - M_{ux1})0A\sin\phi_3\sin(\phi_1 - \Delta\alpha) = 0$$

Solving the above equation for $V_{1-\Delta3}$ and letting $\Delta\alpha$ approach zero at the limit,

$$V_{1-\Delta3} = \frac{(M_{ux3} - M_{ux1})\sin\phi_3\sin\phi_1 + (M_{uy3} - M_{uy1})\cos\phi_3\cos\phi_1}{\sin(\phi_3 - \phi_1)}$$

(18.8.1)

Making a similar analysis for the infinitesimal slab segment $0AC$ (Fig. 18.8.3b) bounded by a differential length $0A$ on yield line 3 and an arbitrary length $0C$ on yield line 2 gives the expression for the upward nodal force $V_{2-\Delta3}$ in Fig. 18.8.3b as

$$V_{2-\Delta3} = \frac{(M_{ux3} - M_{ux2})\sin\phi_3\sin\phi_2 + (M_{uy3} - M_{uy2})\cos\phi_3\cos\phi_2}{\sin(\phi_3 - \phi_2)}$$

(18.8.2)

For vertical equilibrium at the point of intersection, the upward nodal force $V_{\Delta3-1}$ in Fig. 18.8.3a in the zone going counterclockwise from the differential length on yield line 3 to yield line 1 is

$$V_{\Delta3-1} = -V_{1-\Delta3}$$

(18.8.3)

and, for the same reason, the upward nodal force V_{12} in Fig. 18.8.3c is

$$V_{12} = -V_{2-\Delta3} - V_{\Delta3-1}$$

(18.8.4)

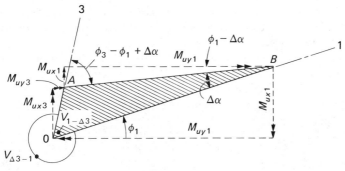

(a) Nodal force $V_{1-\triangle 3}$ between yield line 1 and OA

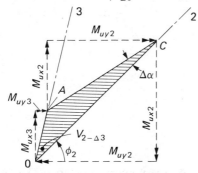

(b) Nodal force $V_{2-\triangle 3}$ between yield line 2 and OA

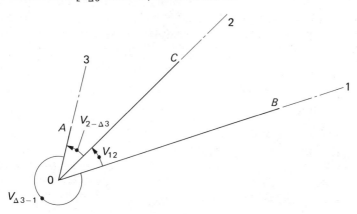

(c) Nodal force V_{12} between yield lines 1 and 2

Fig. 18.8.3
Determination of nodal force V_{12} between yield lines 1 and 2.

Substitution of Eqs. (18.8.1), (18.8.2), and (18.8.3) into Eq. (18.8.4) gives

$$V_{12} = \frac{(M_{ux3} - M_{ux1})\sin\phi_3 \sin\phi_1 + (M_{uy3} - M_{uy1})\cos\phi_3 \cos\phi_1}{\sin(\phi_3 - \phi_1)}$$

$$- \frac{(M_{ux3} - M_{ux2})\sin\phi_3 \sin\phi_2 + (M_{uy3} - M_{uy2})\cos\phi_3 \cos\phi_2}{\sin(\phi_3 - \phi_2)}$$

$$(18.8.5)$$

Replacing each numerical subscript in Eq. (18.8.5) by its successor in the cyclic order of 1–2–3–1 (counterclockwise around the point of intersection) and then once more in the same manner, the following expressions for the upward nodal forces V_{23} and V_{31} as shown in Fig. 18.8.2a are obtained.

$$V_{23} = \frac{(M_{ux1} - M_{ux2}) \sin \phi_1 \sin \phi_2 + (M_{uy1} - M_{uy2}) \cos \phi_1 \cos \phi_2}{\sin(\phi_1 - \phi_2)}$$
$$- \frac{(M_{ux1} - M_{ux3}) \sin \phi_1 \sin \phi_3 + (M_{uy1} - M_{uy3}) \cos \phi_1 \cos \phi_3}{\sin(\phi_1 - \phi_3)}$$

$$(18.8.6)$$

$$V_{31} = \frac{(M_{ux2} - M_{ux3}) \sin \phi_2 \sin \phi_3 + (M_{uy2} - M_{uy3}) \cos \phi_2 \cos \phi_3}{\sin(\phi_2 - \phi_3)}$$
$$- \frac{(M_{ux2} - M_{ux1}) \sin \phi_2 \sin \phi_1 + (M_{uy2} - M_{uy1}) \cos \phi_2 \cos \phi_1}{\sin(\phi_2 - \phi_1)}$$

$$(18.8.7)$$

Equations (18.8.5), (18.8.6), and (18.8.7) are expressions for the upward nodal forces at the intersection of three yield lines.

Nodal Force at Intersection of Yield Line with Free Edge. The nodal forces at the intersection of a yield line with a free edge, as shown by Fig. 18.8.4, may be obtained by substituting $\phi_1 = 0$, $\phi_2 = \alpha$, $\phi_3 = \pi$, $M_{ux1} = M_{ux3} = M_{uy1} = M_{uy3} = 0$, $M_{ux2} = M_{ux}$, and $M_{uy2} = M_{uy}$ in Eqs. (18.8.5) to (18.8.7); thus

$$V_{12} = -\frac{(-M_{uy2})(-1) \cos \alpha}{\sin(\pi - \alpha)} = -M_{uy} \cot \alpha$$

$$V_{23} = \frac{(-M_{uy2})(+1) \cos \alpha}{\sin(0 - \alpha)} = +M_{uy} \cot \alpha$$

$$V_{31} = \frac{(M_{uy2}) \cos \alpha(-1)}{\sin(\alpha - \pi)} - \frac{(M_{uy2}) \cos \alpha(+1)}{\sin(\alpha - 0)} = 0$$

The above results check with the findings in Sec. 18.7.

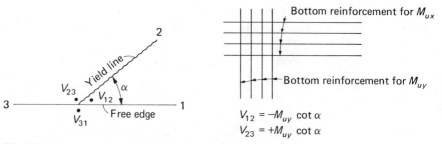

Bottom reinforcement for M_{ux}

Bottom reinforcement for M_{uy}

$V_{12} = -M_{uy} \cot \alpha$
$V_{23} = +M_{uy} \cot \alpha$

Fig. 18.8.4
Nodal forces at intersection of yield line with free edge.

Nodal Forces at Intersection of Three Yield Lines Having Identical M_{ux} and M_{uy} Capacities. From Eqs. (18.8.5) to (18.8.7) it can be observed that wherever the ultimate moment capacities under three intersecting yield lines are identical—that is, $M_{ux1} = M_{ux2} = M_{ux3} = M_{ux}$ and $M_{uy1} = M_{uy2} = M_{uy3} = M_{uy}$—the nodal forces at the intersection are zero. This fact is of great convenience when using the equilibrium method for the yield line analysis of two-way rectangular slabs.

18.9 Yield Line Analysis of Rectangular Two-Way Slabs

A typical rectangular two-way slab panel shown in Fig. 18.9.1 has two-way reinforcement within the panel near the bottom face providing ultimate positive moment capacities M_{upx} and M_{upy}, and it also has two-way reinforcement along the edges near the top face providing ultimate negative moment capacities M_{unx} and M_{uny}; these moment capacity values are absolute quantities per unit width of slab. The ultimate uniform load based on the yield line theory may be determined in terms of the sides a and b, and the absolute values of M_{upx}, M_{upy}, M_{unx}, and M_{uny}.

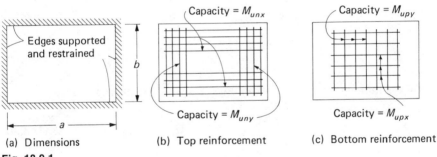

(a) Dimensions   (b) Top reinforcement   (c) Bottom reinforcement

Fig. 18.9.1
A rectangular two-way slab panel.

Yield Line Pattern. Three possible yield line patterns are shown in Fig. 18.9.2. There is no unknown position in yield line pattern No. 1 of Fig. 18.9.2a; consequently the nodal forces V need not be predetermined

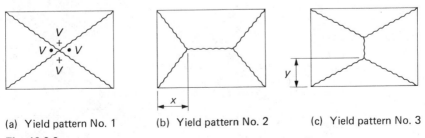

(a) Yield pattern No. 1   (b) Yield pattern No. 2   (c) Yield pattern No. 3

Fig. 18.9.2
Yield-line patterns for a rectangular two-way slab panel.

and their value is dictated by statics alone. The unknowns x and y in yield line patterns Nos. 2 and 3 of Fig. 18.9.2bc must be determined by means of differential calculus in the virtual-work method; but for the equilibrium method, in this particular case the nodal forces to define the yield lines are all zero because the moment capacities under a set of three intersecting yield lines are identical.

Analysis for Yield Pattern No. 1. Assuming a vertical deflection of Δ at the intersection of the diagonal yield lines in Fig. 18.9.3, the deflection at the centroids of the four triangles A–B–C–D is $\Delta/3$. The work done by the ultimate uniform load is the product of the total load on the entire panel and $\Delta/3$; thus

$$W = w_u ab\left(\frac{\Delta}{3}\right) \qquad (18.9.1)$$

The work done by the yield moments on the boundaries of all four slab segments is, referring to Fig. 18.9.3,

$$W = 2(M_{uny} + M_{upy})(a)\left(\frac{2\Delta}{b}\right) + 2(M_{unx} + M_{upx})(b)\left(\frac{2\Delta}{a}\right) \qquad (18.9.2)$$

Equating Eq. (18.9.1) to Eq. (18.9.2) and solving for w_u,

$$w_u = 12\left(\frac{M_{unx} + M_{upx}}{a^2} + \frac{M_{uny} + M_{upy}}{b^2}\right) \qquad (18.9.3)$$

Taking moments about the lower edge of slab segment A in Fig. 18.9.3,

$$\frac{1}{2}w_u a\left(\frac{b}{2}\right)\left(\frac{b}{6}\right) + V\left(\frac{b}{2}\right) = (M_{uny} + M_{upy})(a) \qquad (18.9.4)$$

Taking moments about the left edge of slab segment D in Fig. 18.9.3,

$$\frac{1}{2}w_u b\left(\frac{a}{2}\right)\left(\frac{a}{6}\right) = (M_{unx} + M_{upx})(b) + V\left(\frac{a}{2}\right) \qquad (18.9.5)$$

Eliminating V between Eqs. (18.9.4) and (18.9.5) and solving for w_u, the same expression for w_u as Eq. (18.9.3) is obtained.

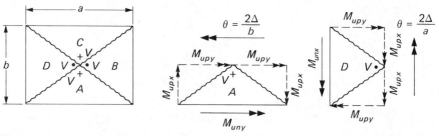

Fig. 18.9.3
Analysis for yield pattern No. 1.

Analysis for Yield Pattern No. 2. Assuming a vertical deflection of Δ at the two points of intersection of the yield lines in Fig. 18.9.4, the work done by the ultimate uniform load on the entire panel is

$$W = 2W_D + 2W_{A1} + 4W_{A2}$$

$$= 2\left(\frac{1}{2}w_ubx\right)\left(\frac{\Delta}{3}\right) + 2w_u(a - 2x)\left(\frac{b}{2}\right)\left(\frac{\Delta}{2}\right) + 4\left(\frac{1}{2}w_ux\frac{b}{2}\right)\left(\frac{\Delta}{3}\right)$$

$$= \frac{w_u\Delta}{6}(3ab - 2bx) \tag{18.9.6}$$

The work done by the yield moments on the boundaries of all four slab segments is, referring to Fig. 18.9.4,

$$W = 2(M_{uny} + M_{upy})(a)\left(\frac{2\Delta}{b}\right) + 2(M_{unx} + M_{upx})(b)\left(\frac{\Delta}{x}\right) \tag{18.9.7}$$

Equating Eq. (18.9.6) to Eq. (18.9.7) and solving for w_u,

$$w_u = \frac{12[b^2(M_{unx} + M_{upx}) + 2ax(M_{uny} + M_{upy})]}{b^2(3ax - 2x^2)} \tag{18.9.8}$$

Setting to zero the derivative of Eq. (18.9.8) with respect to x gives the quadratic equation in x,

$$4a(M_{uny} + M_{upy})x^2 + 4b^2(M_{unx} + M_{upx})x - [3ab^2(M_{unx} + M_{upx})] = 0 \tag{18.9.9}$$

Taking moments about the lower edge of slab segment A in Fig. 18.9.4,

$$2\left(\frac{1}{2}w_ux\frac{b}{2}\right)\left(\frac{b}{6}\right) + w_u(a - 2x)\left(\frac{b}{2}\right)\left(\frac{b}{4}\right) = (M_{uny} + M_{upy})(a)$$

$$w_u = \frac{24a(M_{uny} + M_{upy})}{2b^2x + 3b^2(a - 2x)} \tag{18.9.10}$$

Taking moments about the left edge of slab segment D in Fig. 18.9.4,

$$\frac{1}{2}w_ubx\left(\frac{x}{3}\right) = (M_{unx} + M_{upx})(b)$$

$$w_u = \frac{6(M_{unx} + M_{upx})}{x^2} \tag{18.9.11}$$

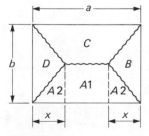
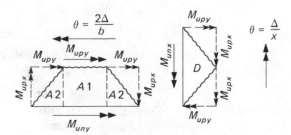

Fig. 18.9.4
Analysis for yield pattern No. 2.

Equating Eq. (18.9.10) to Eq. (18.9.11) gives the same quadratic equation in x as Eq. (18.9.9).

The condition for $x = a/2$ in Eq. (18.9.9) can be shown to be

$$\frac{M_{unx} + M_{upx}}{M_{uny} + M_{upy}} = \frac{a^2}{b^2} \qquad \text{for } x = \frac{a}{2} \tag{18.9.12}$$

which means that if the sum of positive and negative horizontal reinforcement, each per vertical unit width of slab, is equal to (a^2/b^2) times the sum of positive and negative vertical reinforcement, each per horizontal unit width of slab, yield pattern No. 1 prevails.

The condition for $x < a/2$ in Eq. (18.9.9) can be shown to be

$$\frac{M_{unx} + M_{upx}}{M_{uny} + M_{upy}} < \frac{a^2}{b^2} \qquad \text{for } x < \frac{a}{2} \tag{18.9.13}$$

which means that in order for yield pattern No. 2 to prevail, the horizontal reinforcement is less than that for yield pattern No. 1 to control.

Analysis for Yield Pattern No. 3. By interchanging the subscripts x and y as well as the quantities a and b in Eqs. (18.9.8), (18.9.9), (18.9.10), and (18.9.11), the following equations applicable to yield line pattern No. 3 are obtained. The quadratic equation in y (Fig. 18.9.2) is

$$4b(M_{unx} + M_{upx})y^2 + 4a^2(M_{uny} + M_{upy})y - [3ba^2(M_{uny} + M_{upy})] = 0 \tag{18.9.14}$$

Three expressions for w_u in terms of y are

$$w_u = \frac{12[a^2(M_{uny} + M_{upy}) + 2by(M_{unx} + M_{upx})]}{a^2(3by - 2y^2)} \tag{18.9.15}$$

$$w_u = \frac{24b(M_{unx} + M_{upx})}{2a^2y + 3a^2(b - 2y)} \tag{18.9.16}$$

$$w_u = \frac{6(M_{uny} + M_{upy})}{y^2} \tag{18.9.17}$$

The condition for $y < b/2$ in Eq. (18.9.14) can be shown to be

$$\frac{M_{unx} + M_{upx}}{M_{uny} + M_{upy}} > \frac{a^2}{b^2} \qquad \text{for } y < \frac{b}{2} \tag{18.9.18}$$

which means that in order for yield pattern No. 3 to prevail, the horizontal reinforcement is more than that for yield pattern No. 1 to control.

EXAMPLE 18.9.1 Determine the controlling yield line pattern and the corresponding ultimate uniform load for a rectangular two-way slab panel with dimensions as shown in Fig. 18.9.5a. The slab has reinforcement in the

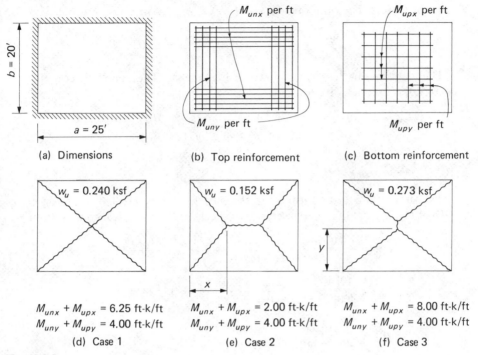

(a) Dimensions   **(b) Top reinforcement**   **(c) Bottom reinforcement**

$M_{unx} + M_{upx} = 6.25$ ft-k/ft
$M_{uny} + M_{upy} = 4.00$ ft-k/ft
(d) Case 1

$M_{unx} + M_{upx} = 2.00$ ft-k/ft
$M_{uny} + M_{upy} = 4.00$ ft-k/ft
(e) Case 2

$M_{unx} + M_{upx} = 8.00$ ft-k/ft
$M_{uny} + M_{upy} = 4.00$ ft-k/ft
(f) Case 3

Fig. 18.9.5
Rectangular two-way slab of Example 18.9.1.

top near the edges and in the bottom within the panel. Obtain solutions for the following three cases:

1. $M_{unx} + M_{upx} = 6.25$ ft-kips/ft, $M_{uny} + M_{upy} = 4$ ft-kips/ft
2. $M_{unx} + M_{upx} = 2$ ft-kips/ft, $M_{uny} + M_{upy} = 4$ ft-kips/ft
3. $M_{unx} + M_{upx} = 8$ ft-kips/ft, $M_{uny} + M_{upy} = 4$ ft-kips/ft

Solution: (a) Case 1. The applicable yield line pattern may be determined by comparing the ratio of $(M_{unx} + M_{upx})$ to $(M_{uny} + M_{upy})$ with the ratio of a^2 to b^2. In this case

$$\frac{(M_{unx} + M_{upx})}{(M_{uny} + M_{upy})} = \frac{6.25}{4} = 1.5625, \qquad \frac{a^2}{b^2} = \frac{625}{400} = 1.5625$$

Since the ratio of horizontal to vertical reinforcement per foot slab width is equal to the ratio of a^2 to b^2, the yield pattern is shown in Fig. 18.9.5d. Then from Eq. (18.9.3),

$$w_u = 12\left(\frac{M_{unx} + M_{upx}}{a^2} + \frac{M_{uny} + M_{upy}}{b^2}\right)$$

$$= 12\left(\frac{6.25}{625} + \frac{4}{400}\right) = 0.240 \text{ ksf}$$

(b) Case 2. The ratio of $(M_{unx} + M_{upx})$ to $(M_{uny} + M_{upy})$ is, in this case,

$$\frac{(M_{unx} + M_{upx})}{(M_{uny} + M_{upy})} = \frac{2}{4} = 0.5 < \frac{a^2}{b^2} = 1.5625$$

The yield line pattern is as shown in Fig. 18.9.5e. The quadratic equation (18.9.9) is used to solve for x.

$$4a(M_{uny} + M_{upy})x^2 + 4b^2(M_{unx} + M_{upx})x - 3ab^2(M_{unx} + M_{upx}) = 0$$
$$4(25)(4)x^2 + 4(400)(2)x - 3(25)(400)(2) = 0$$
$$x^2 + 8x - 150 = 0$$
$$x = \sqrt{166} - 4 = 8.884 \text{ ft}$$

The same ultimate uniform w_u is obtained from Eqs. (18.9.8), (18.9.10), or (18.9.11); the fact that it is so serves as a check on the numerical computation.

$$w_u = \frac{12[b^2(M_{unx} + M_{upx}) + 2ax(M_{uny} + M_{upy})]}{b^2(3ax - 2x^2)}$$

$$= \frac{12[400(2) + 2(25)(8.884)(4)]}{400[3(25)(8.884) - 2(8.884)^2]} = 0.152 \text{ ksf}$$

$$w_u = \frac{24a(M_{uny} + M_{upy})}{2b^2x + 3b^2(a - 2x)}$$

$$= \frac{24(25)(4)}{2(400)(8.884) + 3(400)[25 - 2(8.884)]} = 0.152 \text{ ksf}$$

$$w_u = \frac{6(M_{unx} + M_{upx})}{x^2} = \frac{6(2)}{(8.884)^2} = 0.152 \text{ ksf}$$

(c) Case 3. The ratio of $(M_{unx} + M_{upx})$ to $(M_{uny} + M_{upy})$ is, in this case,

$$\frac{(M_{unx} + M_{upx})}{(M_{uny} + M_{upy})} = \frac{8}{4} = 2 > \frac{a^2}{b^2} = 1.5625$$

The yield line pattern is as shown in Eq. 18.9.5f. The quadratic equation (18.9.14) is used to solve for y.

$$4b(M_{unx} + M_{upx})y^2 + 4a^2(M_{uny} + M_{upy})y - 3ba^2(M_{uny} + M_{upy}) = 0$$
$$4(20)(8)y^2 + 4(625)(4)y - 3(20)(625)(4) = 0$$
$$8y^2 + 125y - 1875 = 0$$
$$y = 9.375 \text{ ft}$$

The same ultimate uniform load w_u is obtained from Eqs. (18.9.15), (18.9.16), or (18.9.17); the fact that it is so serves as a check on the numerical computation.

$$w_u = \frac{12[a^2(M_{uny} + M_{upy}) + 2by(M_{unx} + M_{upx})]}{a^2(3by - 2y^2)}$$

$$= \frac{12[625(4) + 2(20)(9.375)(8)]}{625[3(20)(9.375) - 2(9.375)^2]} = 0.273 \text{ ksf}$$

$$w_u = \frac{24b(M_{unx} + M_{upx})}{2a^2y + 3a^2(b - 2y)}$$

$$= \frac{24(20)(8)}{2(625)(9.375) + 3(625)[20 - 2(9.375)]} = 0.273 \text{ ksf}$$

$$w_u = \frac{6(M_{uny} + M_{upy})}{y^2} = \frac{6(4)}{(9.375)^2} = 0.273 \text{ ksf}$$

18.10 Corner Effects in Rectangular Slabs

In Sec. 18.4 on method of yield line analysis, it has been stated that there may be more than one possible yield line pattern, in which case solutions to all possible yield line patterns must be sought and the one giving the smallest ultimate load would actually happen and thus should be used in design. Although the three typical yield line patterns for a rectangular two-way slab panel have been shown in Fig. 18.9.2 and their analysis has been completely treated in Sec. 18.9, it can be demonstrated that the corner yield patterns 4–5–6 shown in Fig. 18.10.1—in one-to-one correspondence to yield patterns 1–2–3 of Fig. 18.9.2—may indeed give smaller ultimate load and therefore control. These corner patterns are complicated to analyze, either by virtual-work method or by equilibrium method. For instance, there are three unknowns E–F–G for the yield line positions; then once the expression for w_u is obtained from the virtual-work equation as a function of three independent variables, the partial derivative of w_u with respect to each of the three unknown variables can be equated to zero. In the equilibrium method the same set of equations for the positions of points E–F–G may be obtained by inserting the predetermined zero or nonzero nodal forces and applying the moment equation of equilibrium to each of the slab segments.

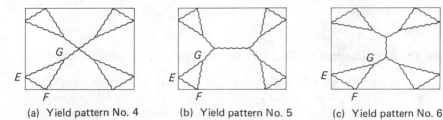

| (a) Yield pattern No. 4 | (b) Yield pattern No. 5 | (c) Yield pattern No. 6 |

Fig. 18.10.1
Corner yield patterns for a rectangular two-way slab panel.

An analysis [6] of a square slab with equal reinforcement in the x and y directions will show that the corner yield pattern No. 4 of Fig. 18.10.2b (see also Fig. 18.10.1a) results in $w_u = 22(M_{un} + M_{up})/a^2$, whereas the regular yield pattern of Fig. 18.10.2a indicates $w_u = 24(M_{un} + M_{up})/a^2$. M_{un} and M_{up} are the ultimate negative- and positive-moment capacities per unit slab

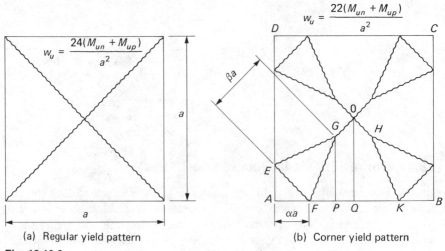

(a) Regular yield pattern   (b) Corner yield pattern

Fig. 18.10.2
Square slab panel with equal reinforcement in two directions.

width in either direction and a is the side of the square. Thus the corner pattern is more critical by approximately $(24-22)/24 = 8.3\%$. It may be proper then to discount the results of a regular yield pattern analysis as made in Sec. 8.9 for most rectangular slabs by 8 to 10% for reason of corner effects.

It may be pointed out that the yield line EF in Fig. 18.10.2b is a negative yield line; thus when there is no negative reinforcement, the moment on EF is zero. In this case the crack or yield line EF will not form if the corner A is not held down because the corner would simply lift up. ACI-13.4.6 provides the need of special reinforcement at exterior corners in both top and bottom of the slab, for a distance in each direction from the corner equal to one-fifth the longer span. The use of negative reinforcement near the corner tends to move the point G farther away from the corner and thus such reinforcement helps to increase the ultimate load capacity.

18.11 Application of Yield Line Analysis to Special Cases

The yield line theory of slabs, as has been developed and illustrated in the preceding sections, is particularly suitable for special cases involving irregular shapes or irregular boundary conditions. Prerequisite to the analysis of these cases is the picturing of an applicable yield line pattern. The governing concept here is that rigid body plane rotations of slab segments separated at yield lines are possible under compatible deflection conditions. To this end the following guides may be provided:

1. Yield lines end at a slab boundary.
2. A yield line (or its prolongation) between two slab segments passes through the intersection of the axes of rotation of the two adjacent slab segments.

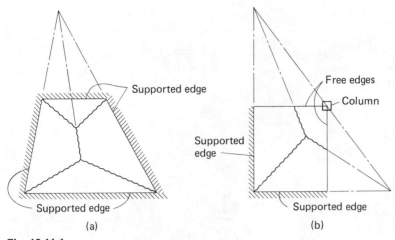

Fig. 18.11.1
Guides for yield-line patterns in special cases.

3. The axes of rotation lie along lines of supports or pass over column supports.

In addition to those already described, two other yield line patterns to further illustrate the use of the above guides are shown in Fig. 18.11.1.

Special Case.   Shown in Fig. 18.11.2 is a rectangular slab simply supported at three edges and free at the upper edge. The positive reinforcement parallel to the a dimension provides an ultimate moment capacity of M_{ux} per unit of the b distance; and the positive reinforcement parallel to the b dimension of capacity M_{uy} per unit of the a distance. Two possible yield patterns are shown in Fig. 18.11.2c and d; the unknown is x in yield pattern No. 1 and it is y in yield pattern No. 2.

For yield pattern No. 1, referring to Fig. 18.11.2c and letting Δ be the deflection where the yield line meets the free edge, the virtual work done by the ultimate uniform load is

$$W = \frac{1}{2}w_u bx\left(\frac{\Delta}{3}\right)2 + \frac{1}{2}w_u xb\left(\frac{\Delta}{3}\right)2 + w_u(a - 2x)b\frac{\Delta}{2}$$

$$= w_u\Delta\left(\frac{b}{6}\right)(3a - 2x)$$

The virtual work done by the yield line moments is

$$W = 2M_{ux}b\left(\frac{\Delta}{x}\right) + 2M_{uy}x\left(\frac{\Delta}{b}\right)$$

Equating the two expressions for W and solving for w_u,

$$w_u = \frac{12(b^2 M_{ux} + x^2 M_{uy})}{b^2 x(3a - 2x)} \qquad \textbf{(18.11.1)}$$

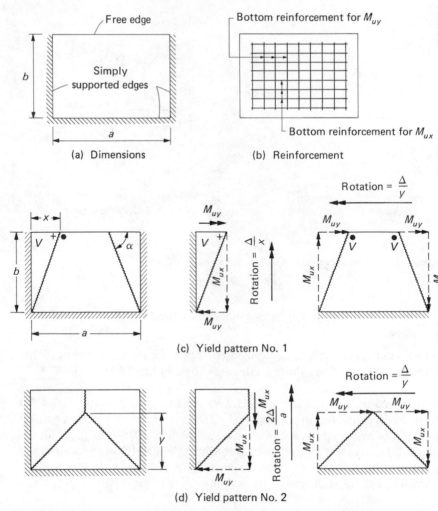

Fig. 18.11.2
Rectangular slab simply supported at three edges and free at one edge.

Setting to zero the derivative of Eq. (18.11.1) with respect to x,

$$3a\left(\frac{M_{uy}}{M_{ux}}\right)x^2 + 4b^2x - 3ab^2 = 0 \qquad (18.11.2a)$$

In order that the root of Eq. (18.11.2a) be less than $a/2$,

$$\left(\frac{M_{uy}}{M_{ux}}\right) > \frac{4b^2}{3a^2} \qquad (18.11.2b)$$

The nodal force V in Fig. 18.11.2c may be predetermined by use of Eq. (18.7.3); or

$$V = M_{uy}\cot\alpha = M_{uy}\left(\frac{x}{b}\right)$$

For equilibrium of the triangular segment in Fig. 18.11.2c,

$$\frac{1}{2}w_u bx\left(\frac{x}{3}\right) + M_{uy}\left(\frac{x}{b}\right)x = M_{ux}b$$

from which

$$w_u = \frac{6(b^2 M_{ux} - x^2 M_{uy})}{b^2 x^2} \qquad (18.11.3)$$

For equilibrium of the trapezoidal segment in Fig. 18.11.2c,

$$\frac{1}{2}w_u xb\left(\frac{b}{3}\right)2 + w_u(a - 2x)b\left(\frac{b}{2}\right) = 2M_{uy}x + 2M_{uy}\left(\frac{x}{b}\right)b$$

from which

$$w_u = \frac{24x M_{uy}}{b^2(3a - 4x)} \qquad (18.11.4)$$

The same quadratic equation in x as Eq. (18.11.2) is obtained from equating Eq. (18.11.3) to Eq. (18.11.4).

For yield pattern No. 2, referring to Fig. 18.11.2d and letting Δ be the deflection at the yield line perpendicular to the free edge, the virtual work done by the ultimate uniform load is

$$W = \frac{1}{2}w_u y\left(\frac{a}{2}\right)\left(\frac{\Delta}{3}\right)2 + w_u(b - y)\left(\frac{a}{2}\right)\left(\frac{\Delta}{2}\right)2 + \frac{1}{2}w_u ay\left(\frac{\Delta}{3}\right)$$

$$= w_u \Delta\left(\frac{a}{6}\right)(3b - y)$$

The virtual work done by the yield line moments is

$$W = 2M_{ux}b\left(\frac{2\Delta}{a}\right) + M_{uy}a\left(\frac{\Delta}{y}\right)$$

Equating the two expressions for W and solving for w_u,

$$w_u = \frac{6(4by M_{ux} + a^2 M_{uy})}{a^2 y(3b - y)} \qquad (18.11.5)$$

Setting to zero the derivative of Eq. (18.11.5) with respect to y,

$$4by^2 + 2a^2\left(\frac{M_{uy}}{M_{ux}}\right)y - 3a^2 b\left(\frac{M_{uy}}{M_{ux}}\right) = 0 \qquad (18.11.6a)$$

In order that the root of Eq. (18.11.6a) be less than b,

$$\left(\frac{M_{uy}}{M_{ux}}\right) < \frac{4b^2}{a^2} \qquad (18.11.6b)$$

Since the moment capacities under the three intersecting yield lines in Fig. 18.11.2d are identical, the nodal forces are all zero, based on the treatment presented in Sec. 18.8. For equilibrium of the trapezoidal segment in

Fig. 18.11.2d,

$$\frac{1}{2}w_u y \left(\frac{a}{2}\right)\frac{a}{6} + w_u(b - y)\left(\frac{a}{2}\right)\frac{a}{4} = M_{ux}b$$

from which

$$w_u = \frac{24bM_{ux}}{a^2(3b - 2y)} \qquad (18.11.7)$$

For equilibrium of the triangular segment in Fig. 18.11.2d,

$$\frac{1}{2}w_u ay\frac{y}{3} = M_{uy}a$$

from which

$$w_u = \frac{6M_{uy}}{y^2} \qquad (18.11.8)$$

The same quadratic equation in y as Eq. (18.11.6) is obtained from equating Eq. (18.11.7) to Eq. (18.11.8).

Thus Eqs. (18.11.1) to (18.11.4) apply to yield pattern No. 1 which cannot happen if (M_{uy}/M_{ux}) is smaller than $4b^2/(3a^2)$; and Eqs. (18.11.5) to (18.11.8) apply to yield pattern No. 2 which cannot happen if (M_{uy}/M_{ux}) is larger than $4b^2/a^2$. When (M_{uy}/M_{ux}) is between $4b^2/(3a^2)$ and $4b^2/a^2$, analysis for both yield patterns should be made and the one giving the smaller ultimate load controls. Although an exact value of (M_{uy}/M_{ux}) in terms of b^2/a^2 (between 1.33 and 4.00) at the transition point where yield pattern No. 1 begins to control over yield pattern No. 2 may be determined, the complication in the algebra does not seem to warrant the effort. Table 18.11.1 shows the results of analysis for six different cases in which the values of (M_{uy}/M_{ux}) become progressively larger while keeping M_{uy} constant.

Table 18.11.1

Yield Line Analysis of a Rectangular Slab with Three Supported Edges and One Free Edge (Fig. 18.11.2); $a = 25$ ft, $b = 20$ ft

Case	1	2	3	4	5	6
M_{uy} (ft-kips/ft)	16	16	16	16	16	16
M_{ux} (ft-kips/ft)	24	18.75	16	8	6.25	4
Yield Pattern No. 1						
$\quad$ x (ft), Eq. (18.11.2)	—	12.5	12	9.78	9.01	7.68
$\quad$ w (ksf), Eqs. (18.11.1),						
$\quad$ (18.11.3), or (18.11.4)	—	0.480	0.427	0.262	0.222	0.167
Yield Pattern No. 2						
$\quad$ y (ft), Eq. (18.11.6)	13.22	14.41	15.20	18.75	20	—
$\quad$ w (ksf), Eqs. (18.11.5),						
$\quad$ (18.11.7), or (18.11.8)	0.549	0.462	0.415	0.273	0.240	—
Yield pattern controlling	No. 2	No. 2	No. 2	No. 1	No. 1	No. 1
Ultimate load w_u (ksf)	0.549	0.462	0.415	0.262	0.222	0.167

SELECTED REFERENCES

1. A. Ingerslev. "The Strength of Rectangular Slabs," *Journal of Institute of Structural Engineers*, London, **1**, (1) January 1923, 3–14; disc. 14–19.
2. K. W. Johansen. "The Ultimate Strength of Reinforced Concrete Slabs," *Final Report*. Third Congress, International Association for Bridge and Structural Engineering, Liege. September 1948, (pp. 565–570).
3. K. W. Johansen. *Yield Line Theory*. London: Cement and Concrete Association, 1962.
4. L. L. Jones and R. H. Wood. *Yield Line Analysis of Slabs*. New York: Elsevier, 1967.
5. R. H. Wood. "Plastic Design of Slabs using Equilibrium Methods," *Flexural Mechanics of Reinforced Concrete*. Proceedings of the International Symposium, Miami, 1964 (pp. 319–336).
6. E. Hognestad. "Yield Line Theory for the Ultimate Flexural Strength of Reinforced Concrete Slabs," *ACI Journal, Proceedings*, **49**, March 1953, 637–656.

PROBLEMS

18.1 Assuming a 6 in. slab thickness for the continuous slab span described in Example 18.5.1, the ultimate uniform load due to the weight of slab itself may be considered to be $1.4w_D = 1.4(75) = 105$ psf. If the slab supports a transverse wall at 7 ft from the left support line, determine the ultimate wall load per transverse ft that may be carried by the slab.

18.2 Solve Example 18.7.1, but use $M_{ux} = 10$ ft-kips and $M_{uy} = 8$ ft-kips, each per foot width of slab.

18.3 For the regular yield pattern solution to Case 1 of Example 18.9.1, investigate the effect of a corner yield pattern in which the negative yield line intersects the edges at 5 ft and 4 ft from the corner along the 25 ft and 20 ft edges, respectively.

18.4 Same as Prob. 18.3, except for Case 2 of Example 18.9.1.

18.5 Same as Prob. 18.3, except for Case 3 of Example 18.9.1.

18.6 Verify the solution for Case 1 in Table 18.11.1.

18.7 Verify the solution for Case 2 in Table 18.11.1.

18.8 Verify the solution for Case 3 in Table 18.11.1.

18.9 Verify the solution for Case 4 in Table 18.11.1.

18.10 Verify the solution for Case 5 in Table 18.11.1.

18.11 Verify the solution for Case 6 in Table 18.11.1.

19

Torsion

19.1 General

Reinforced concrete members may be subjected to torsion, frequently in combination with bending and shear. The cantilever member in Fig. 19.1.1a is largely subjected to torsion, although some bending and shear also exist due to its own weight. The fixed-ended beam of Fig. 19.1.1b is subjected to substantial amounts of bending, shear, and torsion.

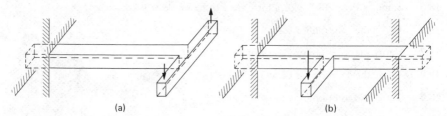

(a)   (b)

Fig. 19.1.1
Reinforced concrete members subjected to torsion.

Spandrel beams at the edge of a building built integrally with the floor slab are subjected not only to transverse loads but also to a torsional moment per unit length equal to the restraining moment at the exterior end of the slab. Similarly, spandrel girders receive torsional moments from the exterior ends of the floor beams that frame into them.

Torsion on structural systems may be classified into two types: (1) *Statically determinate torsion* (sometimes called "equilibrium torsion"), in which

738

Inclined cracks due to torsion; test by J. P. Klus at the University of Wisconsin, Madison.

the torsion *can* be determined from statics alone; and (2) *statically indeterminate torsion* (sometimes called "compatibility torsion"), in which the torsion *cannot* be determined from statics and a rotation (twist) is required for deformational compatibility between interconnecting elements, such as a spandrel beam, slab, and columns. Both examples in Fig. 19.1.1 are cases of statically determinate torsion.

In cases of statically determinate torsion, as in Fig. 19.1.2ab, the amount of torsion that the member is required to resist is based on the requirement of statics and is independent of the stiffness of the member. Statically indeterminate torsion, as shown in Fig. 19.1.2cd, exists in some situations where there would be no torsion if the statical indeterminacy were eliminated. For instance, if the support at A is eliminated in Fig. 19.1.2c, the torsion is eliminated. Similarly, in Fig. 19.1.2d, if a flexural hinge is put at B, the torsion is eliminated. For such statically indeterminate torsion situations the amount of torsion in a member depends on the magnitude of the torsional

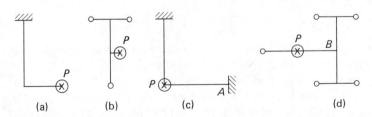

Fig. 19.1.2
Comparison of statically determinate torsion (cases *a* and *b*) and statically indeterminate torsion (cases *c* and *d*), (Structures shown in plan view with load P at $90°$ to plane of frame).

stiffness of the member itself in relation to the stiffnesses of the interconnecting members.

For an excellent overview of the entire subject of torsional phenomena
as it affects structures, with specific reference to reinforced concrete design,
the reader is referred to Tamberg and Mikluchin [1]. An extensive bibliography is also included.

In this chapter, brief treatment is given to the computation of torsional
stress and torsional rigidity of homogeneous sections, the ultimate strength
behavior of rectangular reinforced concrete sections, the development and
background for the ACI Code requirements, design examples, and the effect
of torsional stiffness on a continuity analysis.

19.2 Torsional Stress in Homogeneous Sections

A torsional moment T acting on a shaft of homogeneous material as shown
in Fig. 19.2.1 causes shear stresses v over the cross section.

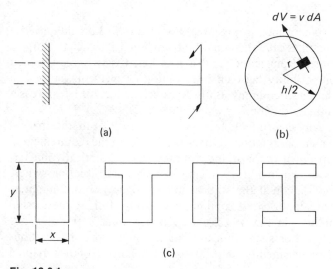

Fig. 19.2.1
Torsional stress in homogeneous sections.

Circular Sections. For a circular section, a plane transverse section before
twisting remains plane after twisting. Consequently, the resultant shear
stress v at any point is proportional to its distance from the center in a
direction perpendicular to the radius. Calling h the diameter of the circle
(Fig. 19.2.1b) and v_t the maximum torsional shear stress at the circumference,

$$T = \int_A rv\, dA = \int_A r\left(\frac{2v_t}{h}r\right)dA = \frac{2v_t}{h}\int_A r^2\, dA = \frac{2C}{h}v_t$$

in which C, the polar moment of inertia, is

$$C = \int_A r^2 \, dA = \int_0^{h/2} r^2 2\pi r \, dr = \left(\frac{2\pi r^4}{4}\right)_0^{h/2} = \frac{\pi h^4}{32}$$

$$v_t = \frac{16T}{\pi h^3} \tag{19.2.1}$$

Rectangular Section. The torsional shear stress distribution over a rectangular section of dimension x by y cannot be as easily derived as for a circular section. Unlike the circular section where plane transverse sections remain plane after twisting, the noncircular cross section warps under torsion. If plane sections were maintained after twisting, the maximum shear stress would exist at a point farthest from the axis of twist. Such is not the case for rectangular sections. From the mathematical theory of elasticity [2], it has been found that the maximum torsional shear stress v_t occurs at the midpoint of the long side and parallel to it. The magnitude of v_t is a function of the ratio of y to x (long to short sides) (Fig. 19.2.1c); and

$$v_t = \frac{T}{\alpha x^2 y} \tag{19.2.2}$$

The values for α are given in Table 19.2.1.

Table 19.2.1

y/x	1.0	1.2	1.5	2.0	2.5	3	5	∞
α	0.208	0.219	0.231	0.246	0.256	0.267	0.290	0.333

T-, L-, and I-Sections. The torsional shear stress distribution in T-, L-, or I-sections may be approximated by dividing the section into several component rectangles assuming that each component rectangle has a large ratio y/x so that the value for α may be assumed to be $\frac{1}{3}$ [2]. The maximum shear stress v_t occurs at the midpoint of the long side y of the rectangle having the greatest thickness x_m and

$$v_t = \frac{T x_m}{\Sigma \frac{1}{3} x^3 y} \tag{19.2.3}$$

in which x and y are the thickness and side, respectively, of each component rectangle. Since the web of the sections considered is usually thicker than the flange, x_m will usually be the web thickness.

19.3 Torsional Stiffness of Homogeneous Sections

The torsional stiffness K_t of a member is defined as the ratio of torsional moment T to the angle of twist θ in the length L. The torsional rigidity is usually represented by the symbol GC in which G is the modulus of elasticity in shear and C is the torsional constant. Thus if θ is the total angle of twist in a length L,

$$K_t = \frac{T}{\theta} = \frac{GC}{L} \tag{19.3.1}$$

Circular Section. It has been shown in Sec. 19.2 (Circular Section) that the torsional constant C of a circular section of diameter h is the polar moment of inertia

$$C = \frac{\pi h^4}{32} \tag{19.3.2}$$

Rectangular Section. The torsional constant C of a rectangular section of height y and width x may be expressed [2] as

$$C = \beta x^3 y \tag{19.3.3}$$

in which β is a function of y to x. The values for β are given in Table 19.3.1.

Table 19.3.1

y/x	1.0	1.2	1.5	2.0	2.5	3	4	5
β	0.141	0.166	0.196	0.229	0.249	0.263	0.281	0.291

T-, L-, and I-Sections. The torsion constant C of a T-, L-, or I-section may be approximated [2] by the expression

$$C = \Sigma \tfrac{1}{3} x^3 y \tag{19.3.4}$$

in which y and x are the side and thickness of each of the component rectangles into which the section may be divided.

The following more exact expression for the torsional constant, giving values closer to Table 19.3.1 for sections composed of rectangular elements having y/x less than about 10, has been derived by Timoshenko,[†]

$$C = \Sigma \tfrac{1}{3} x^3 y \left(1 - 0.63 \frac{x}{y} \right) \tag{19.3.5}$$

The reader may note that the ACI Code in its design provisions for torsion (ACI-Chap. 11) includes the simpler expression, Eq. (19.3.4). However, in the provisions for slabs as discussed in Chaps. 16 and 17 (ACI Code-Chapter 13), Eq. (19.3.5) is preferred as it gives a lower estimate of the torsional restraint, and for the uncracked stiffness is more accurate. Although there is some inconsistency in using two different expressions for the torsion constant, the overestimate of stiffness using Eq. (19.3.4) is an acceptable simplification when determining the nominal ultimate torsional strength in design. A lower estimate of stiffness using Eq. (19.3.5) is desirable in structural analysis when determining the restraining effect of spandrel members on the structural framework.

[†] p. 278 of Ref. 2.

19.4 Effects of Torsional Stiffness on Compatibility Torsion

General Treatment of Torsion on Statically Indeterminate Systems.
In order to do an indeterminate structural analysis, it is necessary first to
be able to determine the relative stiffnesses of interacting members. The
so-called "compatibility torsion" discussed in Sec. 19.1 is involved. For
example, if a spandrel member is *uncracked* and its torsional stiffness GC/L is
computed as shown in Sec. 19.3, the torsional moment the member will
attempt to carry may be very large. As the member cracks, its torsional
stiffness reduces drastically, the member will rotate, and the torsional moment
carried is likewise reduced.

Postcracking stiffness and torsional moment have been studied by
Lampert [3] and Collins and Lampert [4], who proposed an expression
for the torsional rigidity of a cracked section. Since the stiffness is needed
before the torsional moment can be determined, the cracked section stiffness
is not usable because it requires the steel reinforcement data.

Alternatively, Collins and Lampert [4] have indicated that in cases of
compatibility torsion (where torsional moment depends on torsional stiffness)
analysis on the basis of zero torsional stiffness resulted in a design as satisfactory as an analysis using uncracked stiffness. In fact, added steel may
increase the torsional moment in the member but have little effect on the
twist (rotation). Consequently, it may be more effective to design for a twist
(rotation) than for a torque (moment). The purpose of the torsional reinforcement then is to provide ductility and distribute cracks caused by the twist.
Such a procedure would be within the spirit of the ACI Code, where ACI-8.6.1
states, "Any reasonable assumptions may be adopted for computing relative
flexural and torsional stiffnesses of columns, walls, floors, and roof systems."

Using the zero torsional stiffness assumption, the member resisting torsion
(say, a spandrel beam) would be designed for flexure and shear, neglecting
torsion; then the torsional stiffness based on cracked section might be
computed. The structure may then be analyzed [5] to determine the torsional
moments, and the section may be checked according to the ACI Code rules
for torsion design.

ACI Code Procedure. The ACI Code (ACI-11.6.3) provides an optional
simple procedure to reduce the design complexity for cases involving compatibility torsion. When a statically indeterminate situation involves torsion,
if an internal redistribution of forces can occur as a result of cracking, the
maximum design torsional moment is reduced to a minimum value sufficient
to provide the necessary rotation capacity (ductility). In other words, if the
torsional restraint is omitted in determining the bending moments and shears
on the structural elements, the design of those elements may be more conservative than otherwise, but the difficulty of determining the torsional
moments has been eliminated. The torsional members must, however, have
the ductility to *twist* the necessary amount.

To summarize, the ACI Code provides two options for the design of
torsional members when the torsional moment is dependent on the relative
stiffness of the interacting members.

1. Estimate the torsional and flexural stiffnesses of all interacting members making "any reasonable assumptions . . ." (ACI-8.6.1). Determine the design moments, shears, and torsional moments by the statically indeterminate analysis using factored loads. Then apply the ACI Code provisions for torsion design.
2. Neglect torsional stiffness in the statically indeterminate structural analysis. Since no torsional moment will then be available, the torsional members must be designed for a strength based on a nominal ultimate torsional shear stress of $4\sqrt{f'_c}$. (The computation of strength based on this stress is discussed in detail in Sec. 19.11).

Spandrel Beams and Girders. Consider the spandrel beam 2B4 (Fig. 19.4.1) in the typical slab-beam-girder floor of Example 8.3.1. This beam receives a vertical load and a torsional moment per unit length from the slab 2S1, which are equal, respectively, to the reaction and restraining moment at the exterior end of slab 2S1. In addition, the beam supports the weight of whatever walls or windows may rest directly on it. Thus the spandrel beam 2B4 is subjected to a torsional moment per unit length in addition to bending and shear. A similar condition exists in the spandrel girder 2G4; however, the torsional moments are applied only at the junction points with the beams.

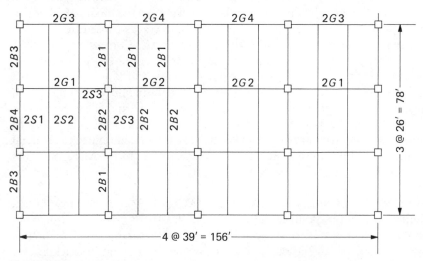

Fig. 19.4.1
Floor plan of a typical slab-beam-girder construction.

The torsional moments in the spandrel beams or girders yield torsional shear stresses, which are additive to the bending shear stresses at the *inside* face of the member. The usual approach in design is to provide for the sum of the torsional shear and flexural shear requirements. Since torsional shear stress goes around the member, closed stirrups (hoops) are necessary.

The magnitude of the torsional moment acting uniformly along a spandrel beam (ACI-11.6.3.2) such as 2B4 of Fig. 19.4.1 might be roughly approximated as equal to the restraining moment along the exterior edge of the slab, using a value such as $\frac{1}{24}wL^2$ as given by ACI-8.3.3. Alternatively, the torsional moment may be neglected if the slab is designed assuming there is no restraining moment along the spandrel beam. In such a case the spandrel beam must be designed for a minimum torsional strength corresponding to that which will provide adequate ductility to twist (see Example 19.15.3).

The design of spandrel beams has been the subject of many studies [57–65].

EXAMPLE 19.4.1 Estimate the maximum torsional shear stress in the spandrel beam 2B4 of Fig. 19.4.1 if the restraining moment at the exterior end of slab panel (4.5 in. slab) 2S1 is $M = wL^2/24$. The service live and dead loads are 100 and 56 psf, respectively. Assume an 18×18 in. column and a $13 \times 22\frac{1}{2}$ in. overall size beam. Use $f'_c = 3000$ psi.

Solution: The restraining moment along the edge of the slab is approximately
$$w_u = 1.4(56) + 1.7(100) = 249 \text{ psf}$$
$$M_u = \tfrac{1}{24}(0.249)(11.92)^2 = 1.47 \text{ ft-kips/ft width}$$

The torsional moment is largest at the face of the column and decreases nearly linearly to zero at midspan. The torsional moment at the face of the column is approximately

$$T_u = (\tfrac{1}{2} \text{ clear span})(M_u) = 12.25(1.47) = 18.0 \text{ ft-kips}$$

The maximum nominal torsional stress is (see Sec. 19.13)

$$v_{tn} = \frac{T_u}{\phi\frac{1}{3}\Sigma x^2 y} = \frac{18.0(12,000)}{0.85(1360)} = 187 \text{ psi}$$

where, considering that a width of slab equal to $3(4.5) = 13.5$ in. (see Sec. 19.11) is effective to act with the main rectangular portion of the member,

$$\tfrac{1}{3}\Sigma x^2 y = \tfrac{1}{3}[(13)^2(22.5) + (4.5)^2(13.5)] = 1360 \text{ in.}^3$$

Note that under the alternate procedure neglecting torsional stiffness, the slab would be designed without restraining moment acting along its exterior edge. The spandrel member would be designed arbitrarily for $v_{tn} = 4\sqrt{f'_c} = 219$ psi. In this case the design for ductility using $4\sqrt{f'_c}$ would be the more conservative approach, as well as the simpler.

19.5 Strength of Plain Concrete Rectangular Sections in Torsion

According to theory of elasticity, a plan concrete rectangular section would reach its torsional strength T_e when the maximum torsional stress v_t (Eq. 19.2.2) equals the maximum principal tensile stress $f_t(\text{max})$, since pure torsion gives a pure shear stress condition. Equation (19.2.2) would then become

$$T_e = \alpha x^2 y [f_t(\text{max})] \tag{19.5.1}$$

Experiments, however, indicate that Eq. (19.5.1) underestimates the ultimate strength by about 50% [6,7], partly due to the fact that the maximum stress indicated by Eq. (19.2.2) occurs only at the midpoint of the long side of the rectangle.

Skew Bending Theory. Studies by Hsu [6] have led to the conclusion that a torsion failure of a rectangular section does not occur in a spiral form as may be expected from a circular shaft. Failure of a rectangular section in torsion occurs by *bending* about an axis parallel to the wider face of the section and inclined at about 45° to the axis of the beam, as shown in Fig. 19.5.1.

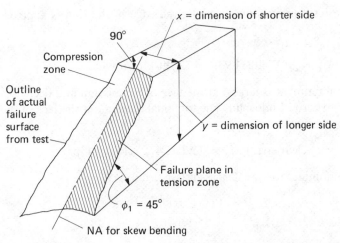

Fig. 19.5.1
Skew bending of plain concrete rectangular section (according to Hsu, Ref. 6).

Consider the nominal ultimate torsional moment T_n as being divided into two components: M_b, the bending component, and M_t, the twisting component. These two components act on the failure plane having the angle ϕ_1 with the axis of the member, as shown in Fig. 19.5.2.

The bending component may be expressed as

$$M_b = T_n \cos \phi_1 \tag{19.5.2}$$

and in terms of flexural capacity equals

$$M_b = (\text{tensile strength})(\text{section modulus})$$
$$= f_r(\tfrac{1}{6})(\text{width})(\text{depth})^2$$
$$= f_r\left(\frac{1}{6}\right)\frac{y}{\sin \phi_1}(x)^2 \tag{19.5.3}$$

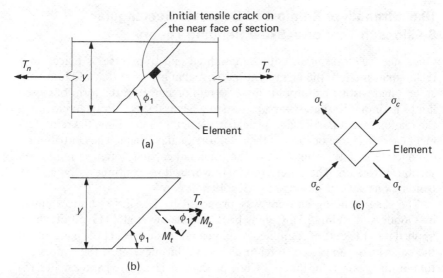

Fig. 19.5.2
Bending and twisting components of ultimate torque acting on the failure plane.

where f_r is the modulus of rupture. Then, equating Eq. (19.5.2) to Eq. (19.5.3) and solving for T_n,

$$T_n = \frac{x^2 y}{6} f_r\left(\frac{1}{\sin\phi_1\cos\phi_1}\right) = \frac{x^2 y}{3} f_r\left(\frac{1}{\sin 2\phi_1}\right) \tag{19.5.4}$$

The minimum value of T_n in the above equation occurs when

$$\sin 2\phi_1 = 1$$
$$\phi_1 = 45°$$

Thus the minimum torsional capacity is

$$T_n = \left(\frac{x^2 y}{3}\right) f_r \tag{19.5.5}$$

The stress condition of an element shown in Fig. 19.5.2a in the region of the initial tension crack is shown in Fig. 19.5.2c, wherein the twisting moment T_n tends to cause a compressive stress σ_c equal in intensity to the tensile stress σ_t. The existence of σ_c in a direction perpendicular to σ_t effectively reduces the tensile strength, so that a modulus of rupture f_r lower than used in ordinary flexural cracking computations might be appropriate here.

Based on experimental evidence, Hsu [6] gives for the nominal ultimate torsional capacity of a rectangular section of plain concrete the following equation

$$T_n = 6(x^2 + 10)y \sqrt[3]{f_c'} \tag{19.5.6}$$

Equations (19.5.5) and (19.5.6) give reasonably close agreement if f_r is taken as $5\sqrt{f_c'}$, a value lower than $7.5\sqrt{f_c'}$ which has been used in deflection computations for beams.

19.6 Strength of Reinforced Concrete Rectangular Sections in Torsion—Skew Bending Theory

Once steel reinforcement, both longitudinal and transverse, is placed in a rectangular section, the behavioral pattern changes from that of plain concrete. The resisting action of transverse reinforcement in the form of closed hoops is similar to that of stirrups resisting flexural shear. Prior to cracking, the reinforcement participates little if at all; but after cracking, the reinforcement carries a large portion of the total torsional moment. The contribution of concrete is only about 40% of the torsional capacity of an unreinforced section in torsion. The failure mode, however, does continue to be a skew bending one such as described in Sec. 19.5.

The skew bending concept was proposed by Lessig [8] and extended by Goode and Helmy [9], Collins [10], and Below et al. [11], all of whom applied it to the case of combined bending and torsion. Hsu [12] has applied the concept to the case of torsion alone and has developed the expression that forms the basis for the ACI Code procedure. Hsu [7,13] and Zia [14,15] have provided summaries of the many theories relating to rectangular sections in torsion. The following development presents some of the ideas relating to the strength expression developed by Hsu [12].

Referring to Fig. 19.6.1, the failure section is assumed to be a plane that is perpendicular to the wider face of the member and inclined at 45° to the axis of the member. The failure plane may be as shown in Fig. 19.6.1, due to twisting moment in the direction indicated. Since a bending mode of failure is assumed, the compression zone is treated as in any beam analysis; that is, it has a depth a over which the compressive stress may be assumed uniform. On the tension side where the concrete cracks and is assumed not to resist tension, the reinforcing hoops have tensile forces P_v in them and the longitudinal bars resist shear across the cracked concrete via dowel

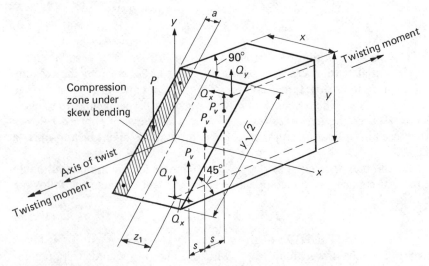

Fig. 19.6.1
Forces acting on skew bending failure section.

action (see Sec. 5.4). The horizontal and vertical components of this dowel action are designated Q_x and Q_y. As long as the concrete is uncracked and the concrete itself transmits shear, no dowel action exists.

On the compression side (Fig. 19.6.2a), the longitudinal bars contribute tensile force P_l; the concrete contributes shear resistance P_s in the failure plane and also compressive resistance P_c normal to the failure plane. The components of the resultant force P are shown in Fig. 19.6.2b. The hoop reinforcement in compression is neglected because, as has been shown in Sec. 3.8, the ultimate moment capacity is not significantly affected by the inclusion of compression reinforcement.

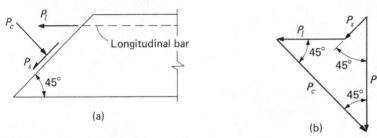

(a)

(b)

Fig. 19.6.2
Components of resultant force P acting on compression zone of failure plane.

On the tension side, it is noted that no longitudinal force can exist. If such a force were to act, it would have to be counterbalanced by a component of resistance acting oppositely. Since only P_v, Q_x, and Q_y are assumed to be acting, and the resultant force must be directed upward (opposite to P on the compression side), no resultant tension or compression can exist in the longitudinal direction of the tension zone under skew bending.

The reader is reminded that unless the direction of the twisting moment is definitely established by analysis, in usual conditions of providing nominal torsional strength (ACI-11.6.3), a potential failure plane can exist opposite to that in Fig. 19.6.1, having the compression and tension sides interchanged. Thus the longitudinal forces, stirrup forces, and dowel forces must be available on either side of the section.

Strength Attributable to Concrete. The shear resistance P_s (Fig. 19.6.2) may be expressed as

$$P_s = v_{avg}(y\sqrt{2})a \tag{19.6.1}$$

where v_{avg} is the average shear stress acting over the compression zone; $y\sqrt{2}$ is the width of the compression zone; and a is the depth of the compression zone.

Alternatively, the shear strength P_s may be considered proportional to the effective area $xy\sqrt{2}$ and to $\sqrt{f'_c}$ [see Eq. (5.5.6) omitting effect of reinforcement]. Thus

$$P_s = k_1 xy\sqrt{f'_c} \tag{19.6.2}$$

where k_1 is a proportionality constant.

From Fig. 19.6.2b, one may note that

$$P = \sqrt{2}P_s + P_l \qquad (19.6.3)$$

The first term of Eq. (19.6.3) represents the portion attributable to concrete. Thus the torsional capacity T_c attributable to concrete equals the force $\sqrt{2}P_s$ times the moment arm (say, 0.80x),

$$
\begin{aligned}
T_c &= \sqrt{2}P_s \,(\text{arm}) \\
&= \sqrt{2}k_1 xy \sqrt{f'_c}(0.80x) \\
&= k_2 x^2 y \sqrt{f'_c} \qquad (19.6.4)
\end{aligned}
$$

Experimentally the proportionality constant k_2 has been determined [13] to be $2.4/\sqrt{x}$. Thus Eq. (19.6.4) may be written

$$T_c = \left(\frac{2.4}{\sqrt{x}}\right) x^2 y \sqrt{f'_c} \qquad (19.6.5)$$

Equation (19.6.5) represents the torsional moment strength available from the concrete in the compression zone.

Strength Attributable to Hoops and Longitudinal Reinforcement. Referring to Figs. 19.6.1 and 19.6.2, the forces P_v, Q_x, and Q_y on the tension side and P_l on the compression side have yet to be considered.

1. The contribution of the closed vertical stirrups (hoops) is

$$P_v = A_t f_y \left(\frac{y_1}{s}\right) \qquad (19.6.6)$$

where y_1/s (see Fig. 19.6.3) is the number of hoops intercepted by the 45° failure plane.

2. The tensile force P_l in the longitudinal bars intercepting the compression concrete zone is

$$P_l = \xi \left(\frac{A_l}{2}\right) f_y \qquad (19.6.7)$$

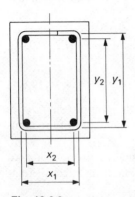

Fig. 19.6.3
Cross-section dimensions.

where ξ is an efficiency factor to account for the longitudinal bars being located at two or more points within the compression zone, and A_l is the total area of all longitudinal bars (assumed to be $A_l/2$ in the compression zone). P_l contributes to the torsional strength since from Eq. (19.6.3) it is part of P.

3. The dowel forces Q_x and Q_y act after the concrete has cracked and these forces may be assumed proportional to the bar cross-sectional area and to the bar lateral displacement, which is proportional to the distance (either $0.5x_2$ or $0.5y_2$) from the center of twist to the bar. Thus

$$Q_x = k_3 A_l y_2$$
$$Q_y = k_3 A_l x_2 \tag{19.6.8}$$

where k_3 is a proportionality constant.

Next let m equal the ratio of the volume of longitudinal bars to the volume of closed hoops such that

$$m = \frac{A_l s}{2A_t(x_1 + y_1)} \tag{19.6.9}$$

or

$$A_l = A_t \left[\frac{2m(x_1 + y_1)}{s} \right] \tag{19.6.10}$$

Substitution of Eq. (19.6.10) into Eq. (19.6.7) gives

$$P_l = \xi m \left(1 + \frac{y_1}{x_1} \right) \left(\frac{x_1 A_t f_y}{s} \right) \tag{19.6.11}$$

Substituting Eq. (19.6.10) into Eqs. (19.6.8) gives

$$Q_x = k_3 y_2 \left(\frac{2m A_t(x_1 + y_1)}{s} \right)$$

$$= 2\frac{k_3}{f_y}\left(\frac{y_2}{y_1} \right) m \left(1 + \frac{y_1}{x_1} \right) \left(\frac{x_1 y_1 A_t f_y}{s} \right) \tag{19.6.12}$$

Similarly,

$$Q_y = 2\frac{k_3}{f_y}\left(\frac{x_2}{y_1} \right) m \left(1 + \frac{y_1}{x_1} \right) \left(\frac{x_1 y_1 A_t f_y}{s} \right) \tag{19.6.13}$$

The torsional resistance from reinforcement then is

$$T_s = P_v \left(\frac{x_1}{2} \right) + P_l \left(\frac{x_2}{2} \right) + 2Q_x \left(\frac{y_2}{2} \right) + 2Q_y \left(\frac{x_2}{2} \right) \tag{19.6.14}$$

Substitution of Eqs. (19.6.6), (19.6.11), (19.6.12), and (19.6.13) into Eq. (19.6.14) gives

$$T_s = \alpha_t \left(\frac{x_1 y_1 A_t f_y}{s} \right) \tag{19.6.15}$$

where

$$\alpha_t = \frac{1}{2} + \xi m \left(1 + \frac{y_1}{x_1} \right) \left(\frac{x_2}{2y_1} \right) + 2\frac{k_3}{f_y} m \left(1 + \frac{y_1}{x_1} \right) (x_2^2 + y_2^2) \left(\frac{1}{y_1} \right) \tag{19.6.16}$$

Assuming $x_2 \approx x_1$ and $y_2 \approx y_1$, the quantity α_t is essentially a function of two parameters, m and y_1/x_1 and might be written

$$\alpha_t = C_1 + C_2 m + C_3 \left(\frac{y_1}{x_1}\right) \tag{19.6.17}$$

where the constants C_1, C_2, and C_3 may be experimentally determined.

Hsu [12] has shown that for equal volume of longitudinal bars to closed hoops (i.e., $m = 1$), α_t may be expressed as

$$\alpha_t = 0.66 + 0.33 \left(\frac{y_1}{x_1}\right) \tag{19.6.18}$$

which is used by the ACI Code (ACI-11.6.9.1).

Thus the full nominal ultimate strength of rectangular sections may be written by combining Eqs. (19.6.5) and (19.6.15),

$$T_n = T_c + T_s = \left(\frac{2.4}{\sqrt{x}}\right) x^2 y \sqrt{f_c'} + \alpha_t \left(\frac{x_1 y_1 A_t f_y}{s}\right) \tag{19.6.19}$$

An alternate approach proposed by Victor et al. [16] is to consider the contribution of the dowel action separately rather than include it with T_s.

19.7 Strength of Reinforced Concrete Rectangular Sections in Torsion—Space Truss Analogy

The space truss analogy approach to the evaluation of torsional capacity was first suggested by Rausch [17] and developed by Lampert [3,18]. In determining the torsional strength of reinforced concrete rectangular sections, it has been found that nearly all of the strength is derived from the reinforcement and the concrete that immediately surrounds the steel. Then one may consider a thin-walled box section, as shown in Fig. 19.7.1, as a space truss. The longitudinal bars in the corners contribute tensile forces while the concrete strips between cracks provide compressive resistance. The inclined compressive forces act in a spiral fashion around the box section, giving the compressive forces D_h on the vertical sides and D_b on the horizontal sides.

Consider equilibrium requirements on the section of Fig. 19.7.1. From force equilibrium in the z direction,

$$4Z = 2\frac{\tau t x_2}{\tan \phi_1} + 2\frac{\tau t y_2}{\tan \phi_1} \tag{19.7.1}$$

where Z is the tensile force in each longitudinal bar in the corner of the section, and τt is the shear flow (force per unit length) in the thin-walled section. Summation of moments of the shear flow forces about the z axis must equal the applied torsional moment,

$$T_n = \tau t y_2 x_2 + \tau t x_2 y_2 \tag{19.7.2}$$

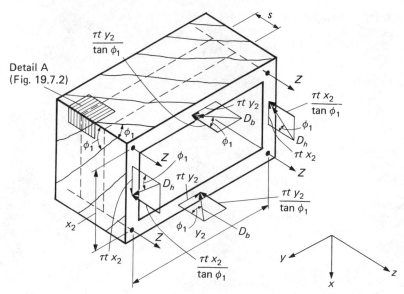

Fig. 19.7.1

Forces on section in torsion according to space truss analogy (from Ref. 3).

Next consider the detail A of Fig. 19.7.1 whose free body diagram is given in Fig. 19.7.2. Detail A represents the portion of concrete along the z axis of the member tributary to one hoop. Equilibrium in the direction of the hoop tensile force requires

$$A_t f_y = \tau t s \tan \phi_1 \qquad (19.7.3)$$

From Eq. (19.7.3)

$$\tan \phi_1 = \frac{A_t f_y}{\tau t s} \qquad (19.7.4)$$

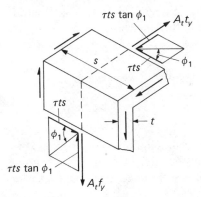

Fig. 19.7.2

Free body of detail A (Fig. 19.7.1) on the hollow box section used for the space truss analogy.

which when substituted into Eq. (19.7.1) gives

$$2Z = \frac{(\tau t)^2 s}{A_t f_y}(x_2 + y_2) \tag{19.7.5}$$

Letting the force $Z = (A_l/4)f_y$, Eq. (19.7.5) may be solved for τt,

$$\tau t = \sqrt{\frac{A_l f_y A_t f_y}{2s(x_2 + y_2)}} \tag{19.7.6}$$

Substitution of Eq. (19.7.6) into Eq. (19.7.2) gives

$$T_n = 2x_2 y_2 \sqrt{\frac{A_l f_y A_t f_y}{2s(x_2 + y_2)}} \tag{19.7.7}$$

For equal volumes of hoop and longitudinal steel,

$$A_l = \frac{2A_t(x_1 + y_1)}{s} \tag{19.7.8}$$

Substitution of Eq. (19.7.8) into (19.7.7) gives

$$T_n = 2\left(\frac{A_t f_y}{s}\right)x_2 y_2 \sqrt{\frac{x_1 + y_1}{x_2 + y_2}} \tag{19.7.9}$$

If $x_1 \approx x_2$ and $y_1 \approx y_2$, Eq. (19.7.9) becomes

$$T_n = 2\left(\frac{A_t f_y}{s}\right)x_2 y_2 \tag{19.7.10}$$

Comparison of Eqs. (19.7.10) and (19.7.2) will show that

$$\tau t = \frac{A_t f_y}{s}$$

which if substituted into Eq. (19.7.4) will show that $\tan \phi_1 = 1$, or $\phi_1 = 45°$.

One may also note that Eq. (19.7.10) is of the same form as T_s of Eq. (19.6.15), and becomes essentially identical if $\alpha_t = 2$. The space truss analogy neglects any torsional capacity due to the concrete alone; that is, if either longitudinal *or* hoop steel is not present, this theory gives no torsional capacity.

19.8 Strength of Sections in Combined Bending and Torsion[†]

In most practical situations, torsion will occur simultaneously with flexure. Although there have been many studies of the interaction between bending and torsion [3,8–11,18–27], there does not seem to be agreement on what

---

[†] The discussion in this section is for the combined action of torsional moment and *positive* bending moment, which if acting alone would cause tension in the bottom steel A_s and compression in the top steel A'_s. In the event that the bending moment is negative, the reader should then interpret A'_s as being the bottom steel and A_s the top steel.

is the correct interaction criterion, Zia [14,15] has summarized much of the available information.

Both the skew bending theory [8,10,23] and the space truss analogy as developed by Lampert [18] are in general agreement on the interaction behavior. According to Collins and Lampert [28] both theories indicate that under positive bending, yielding of bottom reinforcement occurs when equal volumes of longitudinal and transverse steel are used and when equal amounts of longitudinal steel are used in the top and bottom faces (i.e., $A_s' = A_s$). The theories may be approximated by the following, as shown in Fig. 19.8.1,

$$\left(\frac{T_n}{T_{n0}}\right)^2 + \frac{M_n}{M_{n0}} = 1 \tag{19.8.1}$$

where

T_n = nominal torsional strength in the presence of flexure
T_{n0} = nominal torsional strength when the member is subjected to torsion alone
M_n = nominal flexural strength in the presence of torsion
M_{n0} = nominal flexural strength when the member is subjected to flexure alone

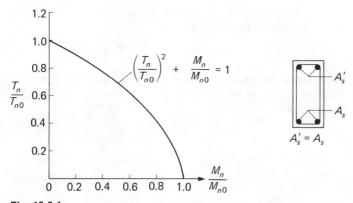

Fig. 19.8.1
Bending-torsion interaction diagram for equal tension and compression longitudinal steel (positive moment yield).

Unequal Top and Bottom Steel, $A_s' < A_s$. When torsion alone acts, the top and bottom longitudinal steel must resist *equal tensile forces*. When positive bending moment acts with torsion, the bottom steel will yield before the top steel if equal amounts of top and bottom steel are used. However, if there is less top steel than bottom steel, the application of a small amount of positive bending moment will result in an increase in the interactive torsional strength because the compressive force due to flexure tends to counteract the tensile force due to torsion. This mutually beneficial effect reaches its peak (Fig. 19.8.2) when both the top and bottom steel yield simultaneously.

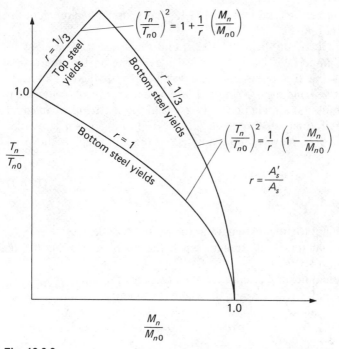

Fig. 19.8.2
Bending-torsion interaction relationships (from Ref. 28).

In general, the strength interaction relationship may be stated [28], for the case of first yield in bottom reinforcement,

$$\left(\frac{T_n}{T_{n0}}\right)^2 = \frac{1}{r}\left(1 - \frac{M_n}{M_{n0}}\right) \tag{19.8.2}$$

where $r = (A'_s f'_y)/(A_s f_y)$ and f'_y and f_y are the yield stresses of the top and bottom steel, respectively. For the case when the top steel yields first, the expression is

$$\left(\frac{T_n}{T_{n0}}\right)^2 = 1 + \frac{1}{r}\left(\frac{M_n}{M_{n0}}\right) \tag{19.8.3}$$

Equations (19.8.2) and (19.8.3) are shown graphically in Fig. 19.8.2.

Design Implications. In order to examine the implications of Eqs. (19.8.2) and (19.8.3), first consider the bottom steel yield failure mode. Expanding Eq. (19.8.2),

$$r T_n^2 M_{n0} = T_{n0}^2(M_{n0} - M_n) \tag{19.8.4}$$

The strength of a section under flexure alone is

$$M_{n0} = A_s f_y\left(d - \frac{a}{2}\right) \tag{19.8.5}$$

and using Eq. (19.7.7) for the theoretical strength of a member subjected to torsion alone,

$$T_{n0} = 2x_2 y_2 \sqrt{\frac{A_t f_y A_t f_y}{2s(x_2 + y_2)}} \qquad (19.8.6)$$

where x_2 is defined in Fig. 19.6.3. Substitution of Eqs. (19.8.5) and (19.8.6) into Eq. (19.8.4) gives

$$rT_n^2 A_s f_y \left(d - \frac{a}{2}\right) = 4x_2^2 y_2^2 \left[\frac{A_t f_y A_t f_y}{2s(x_2 + y_2)}\right] \left[A_s f_y \left(d - \frac{a}{2}\right) - M_n\right] \qquad (19.8.7)$$

Let $A_l/2$ equal A_s' or A_s, whichever is smaller. Then if hoop steel is designed for torsion alone, with equal volumes of longitudinal and transverse steel, substituting Eq. (19.7.8) for A_l in Eq. (19.8.6) would give

$$T_n = 2\left(\frac{A_t f_y}{s}\right) x_2 y_2$$

which gives the amount of hoop steel to be used as

$$\frac{A_t f_y}{s} = \frac{T_n}{2x_2 y_2} \qquad (19.8.8)$$

Substitution of Eq. (19.8.8) into Eq. (19.8.7) with $r = A_s'/A_s$ and $A_l/2 = A_s'$ gives

$$\frac{A_s'}{A_s}(T_n^2) A_s f_y \left(d - \frac{a}{2}\right) = 4x_2^2 y_2^2 \left[\frac{A_s' f_y}{(x_2 + y_2)}\right]\left(\frac{T_n}{2x_2 y_2}\right)\left[A_s f_y \left(d - \frac{a}{2}\right) - M_n\right]$$

$$T_n\left(d - \frac{a}{2}\right) = \frac{2x_2 y_2}{x_2 + y_2}\left[A_s f_y \left(d - \frac{a}{2}\right) - M_n\right] \qquad (19.8.9)$$

which upon solving for A_s gives

$$A_s = \frac{T_n(x_2 + y_2)}{2x_2 y_2 f_y} + \frac{M_n}{f_y(d - a/2)} \qquad (19.8.10)$$

Equation (19.8.10) shows that the bottom steel required is the sum of the requirements for flexure and torsion computed separately.

For the top steel yield failure mode, expand Eq. (19.8.3) and let $r = A_s'/A_s$,

$$A_s' T_n^2 = \left[A_s' + A_s\left(\frac{M_n}{M_{n0}}\right)\right] T_{n0}^2 \qquad (19.8.11)$$

Using Eqs. (19.8.5) and (19.8.6) for M_{n0} and T_{n0}, respectively, and letting $A_l/2 = A_s'$,

$$A_s' T_n^2 = \left[A_s' + A_s\frac{M_n}{A_s f_y(d - a/2)}\right]\left[4x_2^2 y_2^2\left(\frac{A_s' f_y}{x_2 + y_2}\right)\left(\frac{A_t f_y}{2}\right)\right] \qquad (19.8.12)$$

In the same manner as for the bottom steel yield case, assume the hoop steel is designed for torsion alone. Then substituting Eq. (19.8.8) into Eq. (19.8.12) gives

$$A_s' = \frac{T_n(x_2 + y_2)}{2x_2 y_2 f_y} - \frac{M_n}{f_y(d - a/2)} \qquad (19.8.13)$$

Thus the top steel requirement is the difference between the flexure and torsion requirements. Usually only minimal longitudinal steel A'_s is needed for combined flexure and torsion.

As will be discussed again in Sec. 19.12, the ACI Code does not explicitly consider combined bending and torsion. However, the flexural requirement is added to the requirement of longitudinal reinforcement for torsion, so that actually Eq. (19.8.10) is used.

19.9 Strength of Sections in Combined Shear and Torsion

Rectangular and L-shaped sections have been studied under combined shear and torsion by a few investigators [29–31]. However, since shear usually accompanies flexure, it is the combination of flexure, shear, and torsion that has received the greatest attention [32–49,66,67]. Generally, though, flexural shear and torsional shear are of significance in those regions where bending moment is low. Thus for design purposes it is most necessary to know the strength interaction relationship between shear and torsion.

Test data have provided a wide range of points on the interaction relationship using torsion and shear coordinates. Because of the unknowns involved, some investigators have proposed a linear interaction equation [14,15,28,37] for design purposes. However, a number of studies at the University of Texas [29,31,32,36,42,46] on rectangular, L-shaped, and T-shaped beams have indicated that a quarter-circle interaction relationship is acceptable for members *without* web reinforcement. For members *with* web reinforcement, the interaction is curved but flatter than the quarter circle. The quarter-circle expression is

$$\left(\frac{T_n}{T_{n0}}\right)^2 + \left(\frac{V_n}{V_{n0}}\right)^2 = 1 \qquad (19.9.1)$$

where T_n and V_n are the nominal ultimate torque and shear acting simultaneously; T_{n0} is the nominal strength under torsion alone; and V_{n0} is the nominal strength under shear alone. As will be shown in Sec. 19.11, Eq. (19.9.1) is used for the ACI Code expression for the strength in combined shear and torsion on sections *without* web reinforcement. However, for web reinforcement the separate requirements for shear and torsion are added together, rather than following Eq. (19.9.1).

19.10 Strength Interaction Surface for Combined Bending, Shear, and Torsion

The effect of the simultaneous application of bending, shear, and torsion may be most easily examined by means of an interaction surface. Such a concept has been used in Sec. 13.23 for biaxial bending of compression members. Various investigators have proposed interaction surfaces; notably those of Hsu [34], Mirza and McCutcheon [35], Victor and Ferguson [36], and Collins et al. [37]. These surfaces are shown in Figs. 19.10.1 and 19.10.2. The work of Collins et al. seems to provide the most complete rational approach by correlating the regions of the failure surface with modes of failure as shown in Fig. 19.10.2.

Since most members that are subjected to bending, shear, and torsion will have less longitudinal steel in the compression zone due to flexure alone (top steel in the positive moment zone) than in the tension zone (bottom steel in the positive moment zone), only that case is given in Fig. 19.10.2a. When equal amounts of top and bottom longitudinal steel are used, the Mode 3 ("negative" yield or yield in top steel of positive moment zone) cannot occur; in such a case the surfaces for Modes 1 and 2 should extend upward until they intersect the T_n/T_{n0} axis.

The following conclusions may be drawn regarding the interaction of bending, shear, and torsion.

1. The interaction between torsion and shear may be represented for most situations (with $A'_s < A_s$) by a quarter circle, and is relatively unaffected

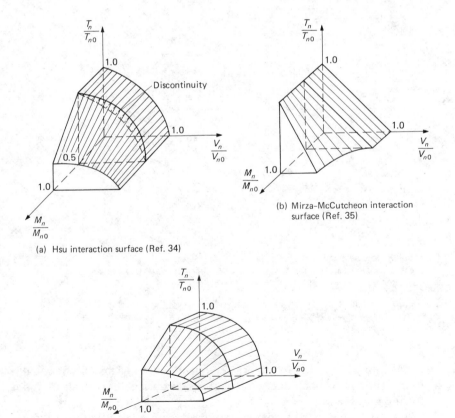

(a) Hsu interaction surface (Ref. 34)

(b) Mirza–McCutcheon interaction surface (Ref. 35)

(c) Victor–Ferguson interaction surface (Ref. 36)

Fig. 19.10.1
Interaction surfaces for combined bending, shear, and torsion (for members *without* web reinforcement).

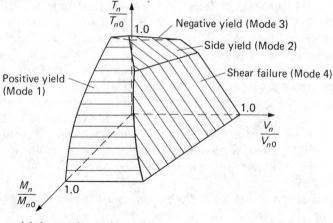

(a) Interaction surface for beam with weaker top
steel than bottom steel $(A_s' < A_s)$

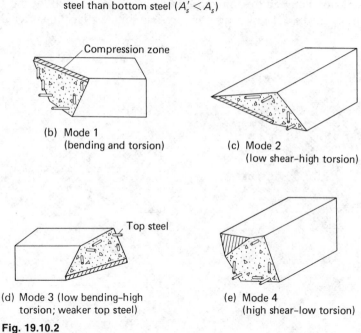

(b) Mode 1
(bending and torsion)

(c) Mode 2
(low shear–high torsion)

(d) Mode 3 (low bending–high
torsion; weaker top steel)

(e) Mode 4
(high shear–low torsion)

Fig. 19.10.2
Interaction surface and failure modes according to Collins et al. (from
Ref. 37) (for members *with* web reinforcement).

by the simultaneous application of bending moment of a magnitude equal
to one-third to one-half of the nominal bending strength when shear and
torsion are absent.

2. When equal amounts of top and bottom longitudinal steel are used, the
   quarter-circle shear-torsion interaction still seems acceptable, but there
   is a reduction in strength when bending moment is also applied.

3. Based on most test results, the straight-line shear-torsion interaction,
   while simple to use, appears overly conservative.

As will be noted in the next section, the use of a quarter-circle shear-torsion interaction, although slightly on the nonconservative side based on a number of experiments, is acceptable by ACI procedures because the ACI shear strength (in the absence of torsion) is taken as that causing an inclined crack. The actual shear strength in many cases is greater; particularly when the shear span to depth ratio is less than about 2.5.

19.11 Torsional Strength of Concrete and Hoop Reinforcement—ACI Code

The ACI procedure of design for torsion is based largely on the work of Hsu and the recommendations of ACI Committee 438 [3,50–54]. The general philosophy for designing to accommodate torsional shear is the same as that for flexural shear—that is, to consider that a part of the torsional moment may be carried by the concrete without web reinforcement and the remainder must be carried by closed hoop web reinforcement.

Thus

$$T_n = T_c + T_s \tag{19.11.1}$$

in which

T_n = total nominal torsional strength
T_c = nominal torsional strength provided by concrete
T_s = nominal torsional strength provided by hoop steel

Whenever the required nominal torsional strength $T_n = T_u/\phi$ exceeds $0.5\sqrt{f'_c}(\Sigma x^2 y)$ (as shown in Sec. 19.13 this corresponds to a nominal ultimate torsional stress v_{tn} of $1.5\sqrt{f'_c}$ psi), the torsion effects must be included with shear and flexure. The undercapacity factor ϕ used for torsion is 0.85 (ACI-9.3.2d).

Strength Provided by Concrete Subjected to Torsion Alone. Essentially the expression developed by Hsu [12], Eq. (19.6.19), has been taken by the ACI Code as the basis for the nominal torsional strength of reinforced rectangular sections; or

$$T_n = T_c + T_s$$
$$= \frac{2.4}{\sqrt{x}} x^2 y \sqrt{f'_c} + \alpha_t \left(\frac{x_1 y_1 A_t f_y}{s} \right) \tag{19.6.19}$$

The ACI Code (ACI-11.6.6.1) has taken $2.4/\sqrt{x}$ as 0.8, corresponding to an x of 9 in. Thus the torsional strength attributable to the concrete *when torsion alone is acting* is

$$T_c = 0.8\sqrt{f'_c}\, x^2 y \tag{19.11.2}$$

for a rectangular section, and

$$T_c = 0.8\sqrt{f'_c}(\Sigma x^2 y) \tag{19.11.3}$$

when the cross section consists of several rectangular segments having a short dimension x and a long dimension y.

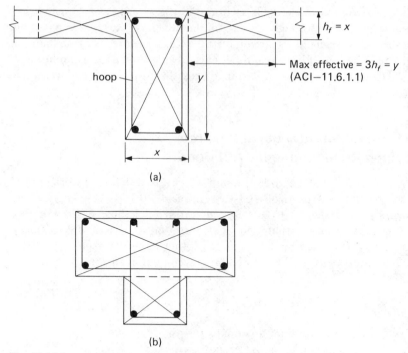

hoop

$h_f = x$

Max effective = $3h_f = y$
(ACI–11.6.1.1)

y

x

(a)

(b)

Fig. 19.11.1
Computation of $\Sigma x^2 y$ for use in calculating nominal torsional stress.

Computation of $\Sigma x^2 y$. In order to compute the torsional property $\Sigma x^2 y$, the cross section is divided into rectangles in such a way that the largest rectangle obtainable is used as one of the components, and the closed hoop reinforcement should then follow its boundaries.

When a monolithic slab is acting as shown in Fig. 19.11.1a, an effective overhanging width not exceeding 3 times the flange thickness (ACI-11.6.1.1) is to be used [50,55]. In this case the largest rectangle extends from top of flange to bottom of web. However, when the flange is thicker, the main rectangle should extend throughout the entire flange width, as shown in Fig. 19.11.1b. The smaller rectangles of the configuration should also contain transverse reinforcement, frequently accomplished by using hairpin-type (U-shaped) stirrups anchored within the region of the closed hoop.

The hollow box section of Fig. 19.11.2 may be treated as a solid rectangle (ACI-11.6.1.2) when its wall thickness h is at least $x/4$. When the wall thickness is between $x/10$ and $x/4$, it may still be treated as a solid rectangle, except $\Sigma x^2 y$ must be multiplied by $4h/x$. When the wall thickness is less than $x/10$, the wall stiffness must be considered. The design of thin-walled box girders having h less than $x/10$ should generally be avoided because of the high flexibility and susceptibility to buckling of such walls, and the fact that few experimental results are available to guide the designer.

Critical Section for Torsion. According to ACI-11.6.4 the critical section is to be taken at the effective depth d from the face of support, the same as is done for flexural shear alone. The same amount of transverse steel

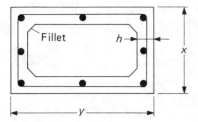

Fig. 19.11.2
Hollow box sections.

required at the critical section is to be used between the face of support and the critical section.

Hoop Reinforcement Required for Strength. The second term of Eq. (19.6.19) gives (ACI-11.6.9.1) ACI Formula (11-23),

$$T_s = \alpha_t \left(\frac{x_1 y_1 A_t f_y}{s} \right) \tag{19.11.4}$$

where $\alpha_t = 0.66 + 0.33(y_1/x_1)$ but not more than 1.50. For the design of transverse reinforcement, solving Eq. (19.11.4) for A_t/s, and using $T_s = T_n - T_c$,

$$\frac{A_t}{s} = \frac{T_n - T_c}{\alpha_t x_1 y_1 f_y} \tag{19.11.5}$$

Note that A_t is the area of *one* leg of a closed hoop. The design yield stress shall not exceed 60,000 psi (ACI-11.6.7.4).

Longitudinal Reinforcement. The development by Hsu [12] assumed that the same volume of longitudinal steel would be provided in the distance s as occurs in one hoop of transverse reinforcement. In mathematical terms

$$A_l s = 2A_t(x_1 + y_1) \tag{19.11.6}$$

or

$$A_l = 2\left(\frac{A_t}{s}\right)(x_1 + y_1) \tag{19.11.7}$$

which is ACI Formula (11-24).

19.12 Provisions for Combined Torsion with Shear or Bending—ACI Code

Combined Shear and Torsion. As discussed in Sec. 19.9, the interaction between shear and torsion for members *without* web reinforcement is assumed to be a quarter circle, represented by Eq. (19.9.1),

$$\left(\frac{T_n}{T_{n0}} \right)^2 + \left(\frac{V_n}{V_{n0}} \right)^2 = 1 \tag{19.9.1}$$

The shear strength V_n in the presence of torsion is obtained by solving Eq. (19.9.1), after first dividing through by $(V_n/V_{n0})^2$,

$$V_n = \frac{V_{n0}}{\sqrt{1 + \left(\dfrac{V_{n0}}{T_{n0}}\right)^2 \left(\dfrac{T_n}{V_n}\right)^2}} \tag{19.12.1}$$

For beams *with* web reinforcement, it is assumed that the quarter-circle interaction relationship is also applicable to the concrete contribution to shear and torsional resistances. Consequently V_n can be replaced by V_c; also $V_{n0} = 2\sqrt{f_c'}b_w d$ the basic shear strength (ACI-11.3.1.1) of concrete according to the simplified method; and $T_{n0} = 0.8\sqrt{f_c'}(\Sigma x^2 y)$ the basic torsion strength from Eq. (19.11.3). Thus Eq. (19.12.1) becomes

$$V_c = \frac{2\sqrt{f_c'}b_w d}{\sqrt{1 + \left(\dfrac{V_{n0}}{T_{n0}}\dfrac{T_n}{V_n}\right)^2}} \tag{19.12.2}$$

Note that

$$\frac{V_{n0}}{T_{n0}} = \frac{2\sqrt{f_c'}b_w d}{0.8\sqrt{f_c'}(\Sigma x^2 y)} = 2.5C_t \tag{19.12.3}$$

where

$$C_t = \frac{b_w d}{\Sigma x^2 y}$$

Substitution of Eq. (19.12.3) into Eq. (19.12.2) and using $T_n/V_n = T_u/V_u$ gives

$$V_c = \frac{2\sqrt{f_c'}b_w d}{\sqrt{1 + \left(2.5C_t \dfrac{T_u}{V_u}\right)^2}} \tag{19.12.4}$$

which is ACI Formula (11-5).

The torsion strength T_n in the presence of shear is obtained by solving Eq. (19.9.1), after first dividing through by $(T_n/T_{n0})^2$,

$$T_n = \frac{T_{n0}}{\sqrt{1 + \left(\dfrac{T_{n0}}{V_{n0}}\right)^2 \left(\dfrac{V_n}{T_n}\right)^2}} \tag{19.12.5}$$

For beams *with* web reinforcement, T_n may be replaced by T_c; also $T_{n0} = 0.8\sqrt{f_c'}(\Sigma x^2 y)$, $V_{n0} = 2\sqrt{f_c'}b_w d$ and $V_n/T_n = V_u/T_u$, giving

$$T_c = \frac{0.8\sqrt{f_c'}(\Sigma x^2 y)}{\sqrt{1 + \left(\dfrac{0.4 V_u}{C_t T_u}\right)^2}} \tag{19.12.6}$$

which is ACI Formula (11-22). Since Eqs. (19.12.2) and (19.12.6) represent the strengths attributable to the concrete in members *with* web reinforcement, they underestimate the actual capacities in members *without* web reinforcement. As discussed in Sec. 19.14, the torsional strength of a concrete member without web reinforcement is considerably greater than the torsional capacity

T_c representing the concrete contribution to the capacity of a member containing web reinforcement.

For the upper limits to strength carried by hoop reinforcement,

$$\max V_s = 8\sqrt{f_c'}b_w d$$

as given by ACI-11.5.6.8. Also

$$\max T_s = 4T_c$$

a limit recommended by ACI Committee 438[52] and given by ACI-11.6.9.4.

Combined Bending and Torsion. The ACI Code does not explicitly consider this combination of loadings. For beams *without* web reinforcement bending was neglected since it can be taken care of by the conservatism inherent in Eqs. (19.12.2) and (19.12.6). For beams *with* web reinforcement, however, the procedure is to design for bending separately and add the longitudinal steel required for flexure to that required for torsion or combined shear and torsion (ACI-11.6.1). From the discussion presented in Sec. 19.8, it may be apparent that this is an acceptable procedure.

19.13 Nominal Torsional Stresses—ACI Code

Even though ultimate strength is the basis for design, it may be convenient to compute nominal torsional stress in the same manner as for the elastic homogeneous section. Thus referring to Eqs. (19.2.1), (19.2.2), and (19.2.3), in general one may write

$$v_{tn} = \frac{T_n x_m}{C} \qquad (19.13.1)$$

where C = torsion constant = $\frac{1}{3}\Sigma x^3 y$, and x_m is the smaller dimension of the thickest component rectangle.

For rectangular sections, b_w is usually less than h making $b_w = x$, and for T-, and L-sections any web is usually thicker than the slab; therefore $x_m = x$ for the rectangle contributing the most significant part of $\frac{1}{3}\Sigma x^3 y$. For practical purposes the approximate expression may be used,

$$\frac{C}{x_m} = \frac{1}{3}\Sigma x^2 y \qquad (19.13.2)$$

Thus the nominal torsional stress may be computed by

$$v_{tn} = \frac{T_n}{\frac{1}{3}\Sigma x^2 y} = \frac{3T_u}{\phi \Sigma x^2 y} \qquad (19.13.3)$$

Note that $T_n = T_u/\phi$, where $\phi = 0.85$, the undercapacity factor for torsion (ACI-9.3.2d).

Torsion effects must be included whenever the nominal stress v_{tn} exceeds $1.5\sqrt{f_c'}$ psi, which corresponds to $T_n = 0.5\sqrt{f_c'}\Sigma x^2 y$ of ACI-11.6.1.

Using nominal unit stresses, the torsional stress v_{tc} attributable to the concrete is obtained by substituting Eq. (19.11.3) for T_n in Eq. (19.13.3), giving

$$v_{tc} = 2.4\sqrt{f_c'} \qquad (19.13.4)$$

Similarly, the torsional stress v_{ts} attributable to the hoop reinforcement is obtained by substituting Eq. (19.11.4) for T_n in Eq. (19.13.3), giving

$$v_{ts} = \frac{T_n}{\frac{1}{3}\Sigma x^2 y} = \frac{3\alpha_t x_1 y_1}{\Sigma x^2 y}\left(\frac{A_t f_y}{s}\right) \tag{19.13.5}$$

For design, the unit stress counterpart to the expression for A_t/s in Eq. (19.11.5) is

$$\frac{A_t}{s} = \frac{(v_{tn} - v_{tc})\Sigma x^2 y}{3\alpha_t x_1 y_1 f_y} \tag{19.13.6}$$

In a similar fashion, the combined stress equations Eqs. (19.12.4) and (19.12.6) may be expressed in terms of nominal ultimate unit stresses, $v_n = V_n/(b_w d)$ for shear and $v_{tn} = T_n/(\frac{1}{3}\Sigma x^2 y)$ for torsion. Thus

$$v_c = \frac{2\sqrt{f'_c}}{\sqrt{1 + \left(\dfrac{v_{tn}}{1.2v_n}\right)^2}} \tag{19.13.7}$$

corresponds to ACI Formula (11-5). Also,

$$v_{tc} = \frac{2.4\sqrt{f'_c}}{\sqrt{1 + \left(1.2\dfrac{v_n}{v_{tn}}\right)^2}} \tag{19.13.8}$$

corresponds to ACI Formula (11-22).

19.14 Minimum Requirements for Torsional Reinforcement—ACI Code

The minimum requirements for the transverse reinforcement A_t and longitudinal reinforcement A_l are to insure that there is ductile behavior prior to failure. Investigators [13,51] have found that the strength attributable to concrete when closed hoops *are* present is only about 40% of the torsional capacity of a plain concrete member. Thus, for ductile behavior, a beam *with* web reinforcement should have at least the capacity of one without web reinforcement. In other words it is desired that

$$T_n \text{ (with hoops)} \geq T_n \text{ (without hoops)} \tag{19.14.1}$$

or for a rectangular section,

$$\text{Eq. (19.6.19)} \geq \text{Eq. (19.5.6)}$$

$$\underbrace{2.4\sqrt{f'_c}\left(\frac{x^2 y}{\sqrt{x}}\right)}_{\text{term } A} + \underbrace{\alpha_t\left(\frac{A_t}{s}\right)(x_1 y_1 f_y)}_{\text{term } B} \geq \underbrace{6(x^2 + 10)y\sqrt[3]{f'_c}}_{\text{term } C} \tag{19.14.2}$$

Thus accepting the 40% value for term A, term B must represent 60% of the capacity of a member containing only a small amount of torsional reinforcement. The condition for the minimum amount of torsional reinforcement then becomes

$$\text{term } B \geq 1.5(\text{term } A)$$

or, letting $\sqrt{x}$ in term A equal to 3,

$$\alpha_t \left(\frac{A_t}{s}\right) x_1 y_1 f_y \geq 1.5 \left(\frac{x^2 y}{3}\right) 2.4 \sqrt{f_c'} \tag{19.14.3}$$

Solving for A_t gives, for torsion acting alone,

$$A_t \geq \frac{1.2}{\alpha_t} \left(\frac{x^2 ys}{x_1 y_1}\right) \frac{\sqrt{f_c'}}{f_y} \tag{19.14.4}$$

This requirement could reasonably be reduced when web reinforcement is also used to provide for flexural shear. Web reinforcement for either purpose improves ductility. Thus when flexural shear requiring web reinforcement is present, the minimum transverse reinforcement for both torsion and shear $(A_t + A_v/2)$ is

$$A_t + \frac{A_v}{2} \geq \frac{1.2}{\alpha_t} \left(\frac{x^2 ys}{x_1 y_1}\right) \frac{\sqrt{f_c'}}{f_y} \left(\frac{v_{tn}}{v_{tn} + v_n}\right) \tag{19.14.5}$$

where the term $[v_{tn}/(v_{tn} + v_n)]$ represents the assumption that the total shear strength of plain concrete is divided into resistance for torsional shear and flexural shear in the same ratio as the respective values of nominal stresses. Note that as defined in Chap. 5 on shear, A_v is the total area for two legs of a vertical stirrup provided to resist flexural shear.

To simplify Eq. (19.14.5), assume $\alpha_t = 1.2$, $x/x_1 = y/y_1 = 1.2$, and $f_c' = 5000$ psi,

$$A_t + \frac{A_v}{2} \geq \frac{1.2}{1.2}(1.2)(1.2)xs \frac{\sqrt{5000}}{f_y} \left(\frac{v_{tn}}{v_{tn} + v_n}\right) \geq 102 \frac{xs}{f_y} \left(\frac{v_{tn}}{v_{tn} + v_n}\right)$$

Rounding the constant off to 100 and multiplying by 2 gives

$$2A_t + A_v \geq 200 \frac{xs}{f_y} \left(\frac{v_{tn}}{v_{tn} + v_n}\right) \tag{19.14.6}$$

For equal volumes of longitudinal and transverse steel,

$$A_l = 2A_t \left(\frac{x_1 + y_1}{s}\right) \tag{19.14.7}$$

Substitution of Eq. (19.14.6) into Eq. (19.14.7) gives

$$A_l \geq \left[200 \frac{xs}{f_y} \left(\frac{v_{tn}}{v_{tn} + v_n}\right) - A_v\right] \left(\frac{x_1 + y_1}{s}\right) \tag{19.14.8}$$

ACI Committee 438 recommended [52] that the minimum web reinforcement for combined shear and torsion should not be required to exceed that for shear alone; that is,

$$2A_t + A_v \geq \frac{50 b_w s}{f_y} \tag{19.14.9}$$

as now stated in ACI-11.5.5.5.

Since Eq. (19.14.9) will usually give a lower requirement than Eq. (19.14.6), the recommendation of Committee 438 [52] was to increase the required amount of longitudinal reinforcement. There is no complete agreement on whether this is an acceptable procedure [51]. Thus the first term of Eq. (19.4.8) was doubled and A_v replaced by $2A_t$,

$$A_t \geq \left[400 \frac{xs}{f_y} \left(\frac{v_{tn}}{v_{tn} + v_n} \right) - 2A_t \right] \left(\frac{x_1 + y_1}{s} \right) \qquad (19.14.10)$$

Expressing v_{tn} and v_n in terms of forces T_u and V_u gives

$$A_l \geq \left[400 \frac{xs}{f_y} \left(\frac{T_u}{T_u + V_u/3C_t} \right) - 2A_t \right] \left(\frac{x_1 + y_1}{s} \right) \qquad (19.14.11)$$

which is ACI Formula (11-25) with $C_t = b_w d/(\Sigma x^2 y)$. In the use of Eqs. (19.14.10) or (19.14.11) the value for $2A_t$ is not to be taken less than $50 b_w s/f_y$.

Spacing Limitations. The spacing of closed hoops may not exceed $(x_1 + y_1)/4$ nor 12 in., whichever is smaller (ACI-11.6.8.1).

Table 19.15.1
ACI Code Provisions on Torsion

1. $T_u = 0$ if computed $T_u \leq \phi(0.5\sqrt{f_c'}\Sigma x^2 y)$		11.6.1
$T_u = \phi(4\sqrt{f_c'}\Sigma\frac{1}{3}x^2 y)$, with redistribution		11.6.3
2. $V_c = \dfrac{2\sqrt{f_c'}b_w d}{\sqrt{1 + \left(2.5C_t\dfrac{T_u}{V_u}\right)^2}}$	$v_c = \dfrac{2\sqrt{f_c'}}{\sqrt{1 + \left(\dfrac{v_{tn}}{1.2v_n}\right)^2}}$	11.3.1.4; Formula (11-5)
$T_u > \phi(0.5\sqrt{f_c'}\Sigma x^2 y)$	$v_{tn} = T_u/(\phi\Sigma\frac{1}{3}x^2 y)$	
$C_t = b_w d/\Sigma x^2 y$	$v_n = V_u/(\phi b_w d)$	
N_u = axial tension (negative):		
$V_c = 0$; or reduce above V_c by $\left(1 + \dfrac{N_u}{500A_g}\right)$		11.6.6.2
3. $T_u \leq \phi T_n$	$v_{tn} = T_n/(\phi\Sigma\frac{1}{3}x^2 y)$	11.6.5; Formula (11-20)
$T_n = T_c + T_s$	$v_{tn} = v_{tc} + v_{ts}$	11.6.5; Formula (11-21)
4. $T_c = \dfrac{0.8\sqrt{f_c'}\Sigma x^2 y}{\sqrt{1 + \left(\dfrac{0.4V_u}{C_t T_u}\right)^2}}$	$v_{tc} = \dfrac{2.4\sqrt{f_c'}}{\sqrt{1 + \left(\dfrac{1.2v_n}{v_{tn}}\right)^2}}$	11.6.6.1; Formula (11-22)
$T_u > \phi(0.5\sqrt{f_c'}\Sigma x^2 y)$	$v_{tn} = T_u/(\phi\Sigma\frac{1}{3}x^2 y)$	
$C_t = b_w d/\Sigma x^2 y$	$v_n = V_u/(\phi b_w d)$	
N_u = axial tension (negative):		
$T_c = 0$; or reduce above T_c by $\left(1 + \dfrac{N_u}{500A_g}\right)$		11.6.6.2

Longitudinal bars must be at least #3 in size and be distributed around the perimeter not farther than 12 in. apart and with one bar in each corner (ACI-11.6.8.2).

These limits (ACI Commentary-11.6.8.1) are intended to "insure the development of the ultimate torsional strength of the beam, prevent excessive loss of torsional stiffness after cracking, and control crack widths."

Termination of Torsion Reinforcement. Closed hoops may be terminated at a location equal to the sum of the effective depth d plus the width of the compression face b beyond the point where the nominal torsional shear strength T_n is $0.5\sqrt{f'_c}(\Sigma x^2 y)$—that is, a nominal unit stress v_{tu} equal to $1.5\sqrt{f'_c}$ psi (ACI-11.6.7.6).

19.15 Examples

Several examples are presented to illustrate use of the ACI Code procedures. Table 19.15.1 summarizes most of the ACI provisions on torsion; it is prepared to help the reader in reviewing the computations in the examples.

Table 19.15.1 (cont.)

5. $T_s = \dfrac{A_t \alpha_t x_1 y_1 f_y}{s}$	$v_{ts} = \dfrac{A_t \alpha_t x_1 y_1 f_y}{s \Sigma \frac{1}{3} x^2 y}$	11.6.7.4
$f_y \le 60{,}000$ psi	$\alpha_t = (0.66 + 0.33 y_1/x_1) < 1.50$	11.6.9.1; Formula (11-23)
max $T_s = 4T_c$	max $v_{ts} = 4v_{tc}$	11.6.9.4
$A = 2A_t\left(\dfrac{x_1 + y_1}{s}\right)$		11.6.9.3; Formula (11-24)
$A_l = \left[\dfrac{400xs}{f_y}\left(\dfrac{T_u}{T_u + \dfrac{V_u}{3C_t}}\right) \text{ or } \dfrac{v_{tn}}{v_{tn} + v_n}\right) - 2A_t\right]\dfrac{x_1 + y_1}{s};\ 2A_t \ge \dfrac{50b_w s}{f_y}$		11.6.9.3; Formula (11-25)

6. min $A_v = \dfrac{50b_w s}{f_y}$		11.5.5.3; Formula (11-14)
for $T_u \le \phi(0.5\sqrt{f'_c}\Sigma x^2 y)$ and $V_u > \frac{1}{2}\phi V_c$		
min A_t to satisfy $A_v + 2A_t = \dfrac{50b_w s}{f_y}$		11.5.5.5; Formula (11-16)
for $T_u > \phi(0.5\sqrt{f'_c}\Sigma x^2 y)$ and $V_u > \frac{1}{2}\phi V_c$		

7. min s (closed stirrups) $\le \dfrac{x_1 + y_1}{4} \le 12$ in.	11.6.8.1
torsion reinforcement to terminate at $(d + b)$ beyond theoretical point	11.6.7.6
min $s \left(\begin{array}{l}\text{longtidiuinal bars, }\#3\text{ or}\\ \text{larger, one in each corner}\end{array}\right) \le 12$ in.	11.6.8.2

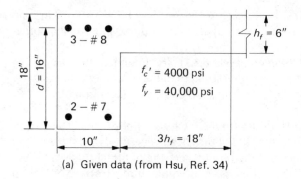

(a) Given data (from Hsu, Ref. 34)

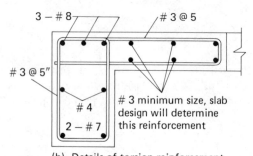

(b) Details of torsion reinforcement

Fig. 19.15.1
Spandrel beam of Example 19.15.1.

EXAMPLE 19.15.1 A reinforced concrete spandrel beam has overall dimensions of 10 × 18 in. and is joined integrally with a 6-in. slab (based on Example of Ref. 34) as shown in Fig. 19.15.1a. The section shown is that at the critical location a distance d from the face of support. At this section the design loadings (includes overload factors U) are negative bending moment 75 ft-kips, shear force 9 kips, and torsional moment 8 ft-kips. Assume that the torsional stiffness was estimated and used in a structural analysis to obtain these design loadings. Check the adequacy of this section, and select the transverse hoop steel required, if any, according to the ACI Code using $f'_c = 4000$ psi and $f_y = 40,000$ psi.

Solution: (a) Flexural capacity. The required coefficient of resistance R_u is

$$\text{required } R_u = \frac{M_n}{bd^2} = \frac{M_u}{\phi bd^2}$$

$$= \frac{75(12,000)}{0.90(10)(16)^2} = 390 \text{ psi}$$

From Fig. 3.6.1, the required reinforcement ratio is

$$\text{required } \rho \stackrel{.}{=} 0.011$$
$$\text{required } A_s = 0.011(10)(16) = 1.76 \text{ sq-in.}$$
$$\text{provided } A_s = 3(0.79) = 2.37 \text{ sq. in.} > 1.76 \qquad \text{OK}$$

Available steel area for longitudinal torsion reinforcement,

$$\text{available } A_s = 2.37 - 1.76 = 0.61 \text{ sq in.}$$
$$\text{available } A'_s = 2(0.60) = 1.20 \text{ sq in.}$$

(b) Torsional moment. The maximum nominal torsional moment T_n that may be neglected (ACI-11.6.1) is

$$T_n = 0.5\sqrt{f'_c}(\Sigma x^2 y)$$
$$\Sigma x^2 y = (10)^2(18) + (6)^2(18) = 2450 \text{ in.}^3$$

Note that the maximum effective width of slab is 3 times its thickness (ACI-11.6.1.1).

Thus for the applied T_u of 8 ft-kips, with $\phi = 0.85$ for torsion,

$$v_n = \frac{T_n}{\Sigma x^2 y} = \frac{T_u}{\phi \Sigma x^2 y} = \frac{8000(12)}{0.85(2450)} = 0.73\sqrt{f'_c}$$

Since $0.73\sqrt{f'_c}$ exceeds the $0.5\sqrt{f'_c}$ of ACI-11.6.1, torsion must be included in the design.

(c) Shear strength. The strength attributable to the concrete is given by Eq. (19.12.4) or ACI Formula (11-5),

$$V_c = \frac{2\sqrt{f'_c}b_w d}{\sqrt{1 + \left(2.5C_t \dfrac{T_u}{V_u}\right)^2}}$$

$$C_t = \frac{b_w d}{\Sigma x^2 y} = \frac{10(16)}{2450} = 0.0653 \text{ per in.}$$

$$V_c = \frac{2\sqrt{4000}(10)(16)/1000}{\sqrt{1 + \left(2.5(0.0653)\dfrac{8(12)}{9}\right)^2}} = 10.1 \text{ kips}$$

Since $V_n > V_c/2$ (or $V_u > \phi V_c/2$) (ACI-11.5.5.1), the requirement for web reinforcement based on strength is

$$\frac{A_v}{s} = \frac{V_n - V_c}{df_y} = \frac{9/0.85 - 10.1}{16(40)} = 0.00076$$

This amount will be combined with the torsion requirement, and the total $A_v + 2A_t$ must be at least $50b_w s/f_y$ (ACI-11.5.5.5).

(d) Transverse torsional reinforcement. From Eq. (19.12.6) or ACI Formula (11-22),

$$T_c = \frac{0.8\sqrt{f'_c}(\Sigma x^2 y)}{\sqrt{1 + \left(\dfrac{0.4 V_u}{C_t T_u}\right)^2}}$$

$$T_c = \frac{0.8\sqrt{4000}(2450)/12,000}{\sqrt{1 + \left(\dfrac{0.4}{0.0653}\dfrac{9}{8(12)}\right)^2}} = 8.95 \text{ ft-kips}$$

The requirement of closed hoops for strength is, from Eq. (19.11.5) or ACI Formula (11-23),

$$\frac{A_t}{s} = \frac{T_n - T_c}{\alpha_t x_1 y_1 f_y}$$

$$= \frac{8000/0.85 - 8950}{1.39(6.625)(14.625)40,000} = 0.00086$$

where

$$x_1 = 10 - 2(1.5) - 0.375 = 6.625 \text{ in.}$$
$$y_1 = 18 - 2(1.5) - 0.375 = 14.625 \text{ in.}$$

$$\alpha_t = 0.66 + 0.33\left(\frac{y_1}{x_1}\right) = 0.66 + 0.33\left(\frac{14.625}{6.625}\right) = 1.39 < 1.50 \quad \text{OK}$$

The total web reinforcement required for strength is

$$\frac{A_v}{s} + \frac{2A_t}{s} = 0.00076 + 0.00172 = 0.00248$$

$$\min\left(\frac{A_v}{s} + \frac{2A_t}{s}\right) = \frac{50b_w}{f_y} = \frac{50(10)}{40,000} = 0.0125 \text{ controls}$$

For #3 closed hoops,

$$\max s = \frac{2(0.11)}{0.0125} = 17.6 \text{ in.}$$

Since this exceeds the spacing limitations of ACI-11.6.8.1,

$$\max s = \frac{x_1 + y_1}{4} = \frac{6.625 + 14.625}{4} = 5.3 \text{ in.}$$

Since this is less than the 12-in. upper limit, the 5.3-in. limit controls. *Use* #3 hoops at 5 in. spacing.

(e) Longitudinal torsional reinforcement. According to ACI Formula (11-24) with the strength requirement $2A_t/s = 0.00172$

$$A_l = 2A_t\left(\frac{x_1 + y_1}{s}\right)$$

$$= 0.00172(6.625 + 14.625) = 0.037 \text{ sq in.}$$

or as a minimum,

$$A_l = \left[\frac{400xs}{f_y}\left(\frac{T_u}{T_u + \dfrac{V_u}{3C_t}}\right) - 2A_t\right]\left(\frac{x_1 + y_1}{s}\right)$$

$$= \left[\frac{400(10)}{40,000}\left(\frac{8(12)}{8(12) + 9/(0.196)}\right) - \frac{2A_t}{s}\right](6.625 + 14.625)$$

$$= \left(0.0676 - \frac{2A_t}{s}\right)(21.25)$$

Since the required $2A_t/s$ of 0.00172 for strength is less than $50b_w/f_y$ of 0.0125, the latter is to be used for $2A_t/s$ in the above equation

$$\text{required } A_l = (0.0676 - 0.0125)(21.25) = 1.17 \text{ sq in.}$$

This is to be distributed around the perimeter of the section at a spacing not to exceed 12 in. In this case, bars must be placed at middepth

$$\frac{A_l}{3} = \frac{1.17}{3} = 0.39$$

Use 2-#4 bars at middepth.
  The longitudinal steel at the top and bottom in excess of that required for flexure is more than adequate for the torsional requirement. Also #3 transverse reinforcement should be placed in the effective flange portion of the slab and it should be anchored within the main rectangle resisting torsion. Though the ACI Code requires only standard hooks at the location where the hoop closes, Mitchell and Collins [56] have recommended the use of 105° hooks (the 105° is the amount of bend from the initial straight bar). Furthermore, when longitudinal steel is to carry torsion at the face of support, the steel should be embedded an amount L_d into the support [56]. The reinforced section is shown in Fig. 19.15.1b.

EXAMPLE 19.15.2 For the continuous spandrel beam shown in Fig. 19.15.2, design the longitudinal and transverse reinforcement for the design moment, flexural shear, and torsional shear, also given in Fig. 19.15.2. Assume that these design loads were obtained after estimating the torsional stiffness and performing a structural analysis. Use $f'_c = 4000$ psi and $f_y = 60,000$ psi.

Solution: (a) Flexure requirements. The effective depth d is approximately 17.5 in. for one layer of reinforcement. At midspan, neglecting T-beam effect,

$$\text{required } R_u = \frac{M_u}{\phi b d^2} = \frac{83.3(12,000)}{0.90(12)(17.5)^2} = 302 \text{ psi}$$

From Fig. 3.6.1, the required $\rho = 0.0055$ which gives

$$\text{required } A_s = 0.0055(12)(17.5) = 1.15 \text{ sq in.}$$

$$\min A_s = \frac{200}{f_y} bd = \frac{200(12)(17.5)}{60,000} = 0.70 \text{ sq in.}$$

At the support,

$$\text{required } A_s = 1.15(61.7/83.3) = 0.85 \text{ sq in.}$$

The reader may note that less reinforcement than 0.70 sq in. may be used if the amount used is one-third more than required for strength (ACI-10.5.1). Thus the sloping straight line of Fig. 19.15.3a and b represents approximately $\frac{4}{3}$ of the required A_s in the region between the controlling minimum requirements of ACI-10.5.1 and ACI-12.12.1 (or ACI-12.13.3).

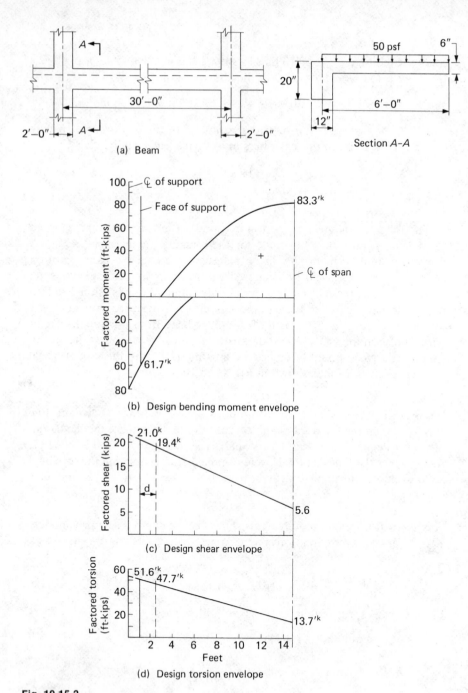

Fig. 19.15.2
Spandrel beam with cantilever, including design loadings, for Example 19.15.2 (from Mattock, Ref. 54).

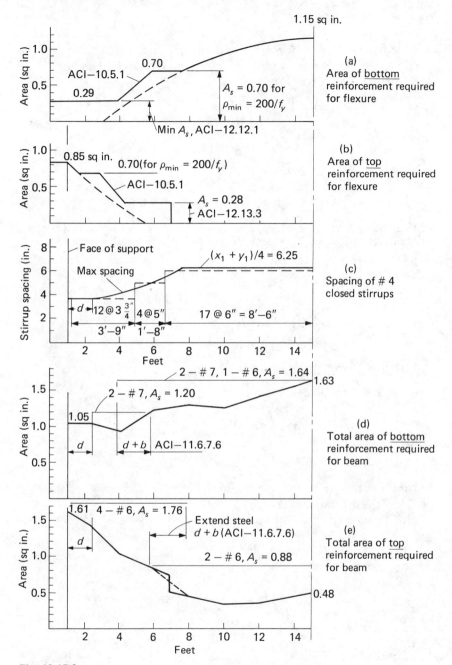

Fig. 19.15.3
Reinforcement requirements for spandrel beam of Example 19.15.2.

(b) Nominal stresses for shear and torsion at critical section. In this example, the unit stress format is illustrated, as presented in Sec. 19.13. At d from the face of support,

$$v_n = \frac{V_u}{\phi bd} = \frac{19,400}{0.85(12)(17.5)} = 109 \text{ psi}$$

$$v_{tn} = \frac{T_u}{\phi \frac{1}{3}\Sigma x^2 y} = \frac{47.7(12,000)}{0.85(1180)} = 571 \text{ psi}$$

where

$$\tfrac{1}{3}\Sigma x^2 y = \tfrac{1}{3}[(12)^2(20) + (6)^2(18)] = 1180 \text{ in.}^3$$

In computing $\Sigma\, x^2 y$, the effective width of flange may not exceed 3 times the flange thickness (ACI-11.6.1.1).

(c) Nominal stress carried by the concrete. For torsion, Eq. (19.13.8) or ACI-11.6.6.1 gives

$$v_{tc} = \frac{2.4\sqrt{f'_c}}{\sqrt{1 + [1.2(v_n/v_{tn})]^2}} = \frac{2.4\sqrt{f'_c}}{\sqrt{1 + [1.2(109/571)]^2}}$$
$$= 2.34\sqrt{f'_c} = 148 \text{ psi}$$

For shear, Eq. (19.13.7) or ACI-11.3.1.4 gives

$$v_c = \frac{2\sqrt{f'_c}}{\sqrt{1 + \left(\dfrac{v_{tn}}{1.2v_n}\right)^2}} = \frac{2\sqrt{f'_c}}{\sqrt{1 + \left[\dfrac{571}{1.2(109)}\right]^2}}$$
$$= 0.44\sqrt{f'_c} = 28 \text{ psi}$$

For this example v_{tc} and v_c are constant along the member since the ratio of V_u to T_u is constant along the member.

(d) Maximum nominal stresses permitted. For torsion, ACI-11.6.9.4 gives

$$\max T_s = 4T_c$$

Since

$$T_n = T_c + T_s$$
$$\max T_n = T_c + 4T_c = 5T_c$$

Then,

$$\max v_{tn} = 5v_{tc}$$

For this problem,

$$\max v_{tn} = 5(2.34)\sqrt{f'_c} = 11.7\sqrt{f'_c}$$
$$= 740 \text{ psi} > 571 \text{ psi} \qquad\qquad \text{OK}$$

For shear, ACI-11.5.4.3 allows $(v_n - v_c) = 4\sqrt{f'_c}$ with maximum stirrup spacings up to $d/2$. In this case $v_n = 109 \text{ psi} < 4\sqrt{f'_c}$, which is acceptable.

(e) Transverse reinforcement. For shear, ACI-11.5.6.2 gives

$$\frac{A_v}{s} = \frac{V_s}{f_y d} = \frac{V_n - V_c}{f_y d}$$

or in terms of unit stresses and evaluated *at the critical section*

$$\frac{A_v}{s} = \frac{(v_n - v_c)b_w}{f_y} = \frac{(109 - 28)12}{60,000} = 0.0162$$

For torsion, Eq. (19.13.6) derived from ACI-11.6.9.1 gives *at the critical section*

$$\frac{A_t}{s} = \frac{(v_{tn} - v_{tc})\frac{1}{3}\Sigma x^2 y}{\alpha_t x_1 y_1 f_y} = \frac{(571 - 148)1180}{1.30(8.5)(16.5)60,000} = 0.0455$$

where

$x_1 = 12 - 2(1.5) - 0.50 = 8.5$ in.
$y_1 = 20 - 2(1.5) - 0.50 = 16.5$ in.
$\alpha_t = 0.66 + 0.33y_1/x_1 = 0.66 + 0.33(16.5/8.5) = 1.30 < 1.50$ OK

The minimum transverse reinforcement, Eq. (19.14.9) or ACI-11.5.5.5 gives

$$\frac{2A_t}{s} + \frac{A_v}{s} \geq \frac{50b_w}{f_y} = \frac{50(12)}{60,000} = 0.01$$

For strength, the total requirement is

$$\frac{2A_t}{s} + \frac{A_v}{s} = 2(0.0455) + 0.0162 = 0.107 > 0.01$$

Try #4 closed hoops, $A_v = 2(0.20) = 0.40$ sq in. The maximum spacing of hoops between the face of support and the critical section is

$$\max s = \frac{0.40}{0.107} = 3.74 \text{ in.}$$

The upper limit for spacing of closed hoops anywhere is (ACI-11.6.8.1),

$$\max s = \frac{x_1 + y_1}{4} = \frac{8.5 + 16.5}{4} = 6.25 \text{ in.}$$

and not in any case to exceed 12 in.

(f) Longitudinal reinforcement for torsion at the critical section. Using Eq. (19.11.7) or ACI Formula 11-24,

$$A_l = \frac{2A_t}{s}(x_1 + y_1) = 0.091(8.5 + 16.5) = 2.27 \text{ sq in.}$$

The minimum value is, from using Eq. (19.14.10) the unit stress counterpart of ACI Formula 11-25

$$A_l = \left[\frac{400x}{f_y}\left(\frac{v_{tn}}{v_{tn} + v_n}\right) - \frac{2A_t}{s}\right](x_1 + y_1)$$

$$= \left[\frac{400(12)}{60,000}\left(\frac{571}{571 + 109}\right) - 0.091\right](8.5 + 16.5)$$

$$= \text{negative} \quad \text{(does not control)}$$

ACI-11.6.8.2 requires the longitudinal bars to be distributed around the perimeter with a spacing not to exceed 12 in. Since the member depth exceeds

12 in., a layer intermediate between top and bottom is necessary. Thus use at middepth

$$\frac{A_l}{3} = \frac{2.27}{3} = 0.76 \text{ sq in.}$$

Use 2-#6 bars, one at each side of the member.

(g) Total longitudinal reinforcement for flexure and torsion. At the face of support,

$$\text{top steel} = 0.85 \text{ (flexure)} + 0.76 \text{ (torsion)} = 1.61 \text{ sq in.}$$

$$\text{bottom steel} = 0.29 \text{ (flexure)} + 0.76 \text{ (torsion)} = 1.05 \text{ sq in.}$$

At d from the face of support,

$$\text{top steel} = 0.70 \text{ (flexure)} + 0.76 \text{ (torsion)} = 1.46 \text{ sq in.}$$

$$\text{bottom steel} = 0.29 \text{ (flexure)} + 0.76 \text{ (torsion)} = 1.05 \text{ sq in.}$$

(h) Transverse steel requirement along the span. Using the same procedure as at the critical section, the requirements are computed as shown in Table 19.15.1.

Table 19.15.1
Transverse Steel Requirement Along the Span (Example 19.15.2)

Location from Center of Support	V_u	v_n	$\dfrac{A_v}{s}$	T_u	v_{tn}	$\dfrac{A_t}{s}$	$\dfrac{50b_w}{f_y}$	Required $\dfrac{2A_t}{s}+\dfrac{A_v}{s}$	max s for #4 hoops
	(kips)	(psi)	(in.)	(ft-kips)	(psi)	(in.)	(in.)	(in.)	(in.)
4	17.7	99.0	0.0142	43.5	522	0.0402	0.010	0.095	4.20
6	15.5	86.8	0.0118	38.1	457	0.0332	0.010	0.078	5.13
8	13.3	74.4	0.0092	32.7	392	0.0262	0.010	0.062	6.25^b
10	11.1	62.1	0.0064	27.2	326	0.0191	0.010	0.045	6.25^b
12	8.9	49.8	0.0044	21.8	262	0.0123	0.010	0.029	6.25^b
15	5.6	31.4	0.0006	13.7	164	0.0017	0.010	0.010^a	6.25^b

^{a} min $50b_w/f_y$ controls
^{b} max $s = (x_1 + y_1)/4$ controls

The maximum spacing curve and selected spacings are shown in Fig. 19.15.3c. Since the torsional stress v_{tn} never is less than $1.5\sqrt{f'_c} = 95$ psi, closed stirrups are required along the entire span.

(i) Longitudinal steel requirements along the span. The flexural requirements have already been shown in Fig. 19.15.3ab. The torsional requirements are computed in Table 19.15.2. Because the member depth exceeds 12 in., the longitudinal steel is placed one-third at each of top, bottom, and midheight. The sums of the flexural requirement and $A_t/3$ are shown as the total requirement for longitudinal steel in Fig. 19.15.3d and e.

In determining the length of longitudinal bars, a conservative interpretation has been made of ACI-11.6.7.6 which requires an extension of $d + b$

Table 19.15.2

Longitudinal Steel Requirement for Torsion Along the Span (Example 19.15.2)

Location from Center of Support (ft)	Required $\dfrac{2A_t^*}{s}$ (in.)	ACI Formula $(11–24)^\dagger$ (sq in.)	$\dfrac{400x}{f_y}\left(\dfrac{v_{tn}}{v_{tn}+v_n}\right)$	ACI Formula $(11–25)^\ddagger$ (sq in.)	Required A_l (sq in.)
4	0.0804	2.01	0.067	negative	2.01
6	0.0664	1.66	0.067	negative	1.66
8	0.0524	1.31	0.067	0.38	1.31
10	0.0382	0.96	0.067	0.73	0.96
12	0.0246	0.62	0.067	1.06	1.06
15	0.0100	0.25	0.067	1.43	1.43

* $2A_t/s$ required for torsion, obtained from Table 19.15.1, but need not be less than $50b_w/f_y = 0.010$ for computing longitudinal reinforcement (ACI-11.6.9.3).

† $A_l = (2A_t/s)(x_1 + y_1)$

‡ $\min A_l = \left[\dfrac{400x}{f_y}\left(\dfrac{v_{tn}}{v_{tn}+v_n}\right) - \dfrac{2A_t}{s}\right](x_1 + y_1)$, in terms of unit stress.

beyond the theoretical termination point, as in Fig. 19.15.3d and e. The theoretical termination point is taken as that for combined flexure and torsion. It is noted that in some cases ACI-12.11.5 regarding cutting bars in a tension zone may control. The crack control provisions of ACI-10.6.4 must be checked, as well as the deflection if excessive deflection may cause damage. The design details are shown in Fig. 19.15.4.

EXAMPLE 19.15.3   Redesign the spandrel beam shown in Fig. 19.15.2 taking the option permitted in ACI-11.6.3 of considering the torsional stiffness to be zero in performing the structural analysis to obtain the design loads. The torsional member is then designed for a nominal torsional stress of $4\sqrt{f_c'}$.

Solution: (a) Flexural requirements. Assume that the factored bending moment and shear are not significantly affected by a change in the assumption for torsional stiffness; that is, use Fig. 19.15.2bc. Note that most structural analysis methods traditionally do not include the effect of torsional stiffness; thus this approach is simple. After completing the structural analysis disregarding torsional stiffness, any member that needs to undergo torsional deformation is then arbitrarily designed to include a torsional stress v_{tn} of $4\sqrt{f_c'}$.

For this example, the requirements for flexure are as in Example 19.15.2 and are shown in Fig. 19.15.3ab.

(b) Nominal ultimate torsional moment T_n and shear V_n at the critical section. At d from the face of support,

$$V_n = \frac{V_u}{\phi} = \frac{19.4}{0.85} = 22.8 \text{ kips} \qquad \text{(see Fig. 19.15.2c)}$$

$$T_n = v_{tn}(\tfrac{1}{3}\Sigma x^2 y) = 4\sqrt{f_c'}(1180)\tfrac{1}{12,000} = 24.9 \text{ ft-kips}$$

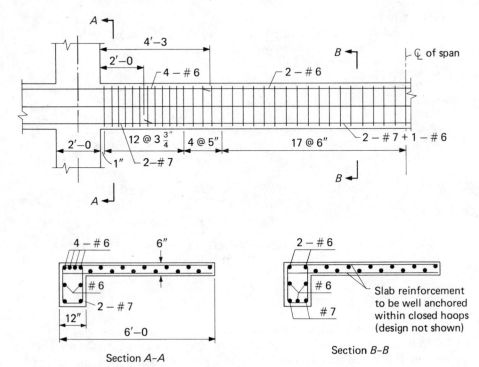

Fig. 19.15.4
Design details for Example 19.15.2.

Note that the $4\sqrt{f'_c} = 253$ psi compares with the nominal unit stress of 571 psi that was used in Example 19.15.2.

(c) Nominal strength attributable to the concrete. For torsion, Eq. (19.12.6) or ACI Formula (11-22) gives

$$T_c = \frac{0.8\sqrt{f'_c}(\Sigma x^2 y)}{\sqrt{1 + \left(\dfrac{0.4\,V_u}{C_t\,T_u}\right)^2}} = \frac{0.8\sqrt{4000}(3540)/12{,}000}{\sqrt{1 + \left(\dfrac{0.4}{0.0593}\dfrac{22.8}{24.9(12)}\right)^2}} = 13.3 \text{ ft-kips}$$

where

$$C_t = \frac{b_w d}{\Sigma x^2 y} = \frac{12(17.5)}{3540} = 0.0593 \text{ per in.}$$

For shear, Eq. (19.12.4) or ACI Formula (11-5) gives

$$V_c = \frac{2\sqrt{f'_c}b_w d}{\sqrt{1 + \left(2.5C_t\dfrac{T_u}{V_u}\right)^2}} = \frac{2\sqrt{4000}(12)17.5/1000}{\sqrt{1 + \left(2.5(0.0593)\dfrac{24.9(12)}{22.8}\right)^2}} = 12.2 \text{ kips}$$

The above strengths T_c and V_c are at the critical section. Though the nominal ultimate flexural shear force V_n decreases farther from the support, the nominal ultimate torsional force T_n based on a stress of $4\sqrt{f'_c}$ psi used to provide ductility is taken constant along the length of the beam.

At midspan,

$$V_n = \frac{V_u}{\phi} = \frac{5.6}{0.85} = 6.59 \text{ kips}; \qquad T_n = 24.9 \text{ ft-kips}$$

$$T_c = \frac{0.8\sqrt{4000}(3540)/12,000}{\sqrt{1 + \left(\dfrac{0.4}{0.0593}\dfrac{6.59}{24.9(12)}\right)^2}} = 14.8 \text{ ft-kips}$$

$$V_c = \frac{2\sqrt{4000}(12)(17.5)/1000}{\sqrt{1 + [2.5(0.0593)(24.9)(12)/6.59]^2}} = 3.91 \text{ kips}$$

Note that in the above computations V_n/T_n is the same as V_u/T_u since the same ϕ factor is used for shear and torsion.

(d) Transverse reinforcement. For shear, using ACI Formula (11-17) from ACI-11.5.6.2 *at the critical section*

$$\frac{A_v}{s} = \frac{V_n - V_c}{f_y d} = \frac{22.8 - 12.2}{60(17.5)} = 0.0101$$

For torsion, using Eq. (19.11.5) or ACI Formula (11-23) *at the critical section*

$$\frac{A_t}{s} = \frac{T_n - T_c}{\alpha_t x_1 y_1 f_y} = \frac{(24.9 - 13.3)12}{1.30(8.5)(16.5)60} = 0.0127$$

where $\alpha_t = 1.30$, $x_1 = 8.5$ in., and $y_1 = 16.5$ in. as computed in Example 19.15.2. The total requirement for strength is

$$\frac{2A_t}{s} + \frac{A_v}{s} = 2(0.0127) + 0.0101 = 0.0355$$

This exceeds the minimum of $50b_w/f_y$ of 0.01.

The requirement at midspan is

$$\frac{A_v}{s} = \frac{6.59 - 3.91}{60(17.5)} = 0.0026$$

$$\frac{A_t}{s} = \frac{(24.9 - 14.8)12}{1.30(8.5)(16.5)60} = 0.0111$$

$$\frac{2A_t}{s} + \frac{A_v}{s} = 2(0.0111) + 0.0026 = 0.0248 > 0.01 \qquad \qquad \text{OK}$$

Try #3 hoops, $A_v = 2(0.11) = 0.22$ sq in. The maximum spacing of hoops between the face of support and the critical section is

$$\max s = \frac{0.22}{0.0355} = 6.2 \text{ in.}$$

The upper limit for spacing of closed hoops is (ACI-11.6.8.1),

$$\max s = \frac{x_1 + y_1}{4} = \frac{8.625 + 16.625}{4} = 6.3 \text{ in.}$$

Thus for this beam a practical spacing of 6 in. may be used for the entire beam. Note that the distances x_1 and y_1 have been corrected to agree with the use of #3 hoops.

(e) Longitudinal reinforcement for torsion. Using Eq. (19.11.7) or ACI Formula (11-24), at the critical section,

$$A_l = \frac{2A_t}{s}(x_1 + y_1) = 2(0.0124)(8.625 + 16.625) = 0.63 \text{ sq in.}$$

where A_t/s has been corrected to agree with the values of x_1 and y_1 using #3 hoops. The minimum value at the critical section is, from Eq. (19.14.11) or ACI Formula 11-25,

$$A_l = \left[\frac{400x}{f_y} \left(\frac{T_u}{T_u + \frac{V_u}{3C_t}} \right) - \frac{2A_t}{s} \right](x_1 + y_1)$$

$$= \left[\frac{400(12)}{60,000} \left(\frac{24.9}{24.9 + \frac{22.8}{3(0.0593)12}} \right) - 0.0248 \right](8.625 + 16.625)$$

$$= 0.0312(25.25) = 0.79 \text{ sq in.} \qquad\qquad \text{Controls}$$

Note that the amount A_l will be divided into three equal parts, top of beam,

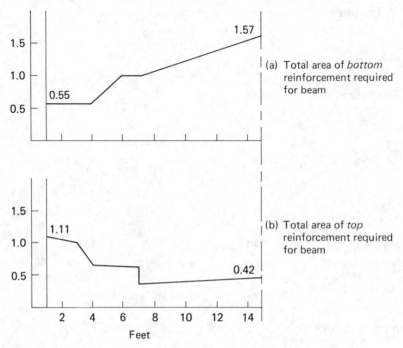

(a) Total area of *bottom* reinforcement required for beam

(b) Total area of *top* reinforcement required for beam

Fig. 19.15.5
Longitudinal steel requirement for Example 19.15.3.

bottom of beam, and midheight in accordance with ACI-11.6.8.2. The longitudinal requirement for torsion is added to the requirement for flexure (Fig. 19.15.3ab) and the total requirement for the top and bottom of the beam is shown in Fig. 19.15.5. These requirements can be compared with Fig. 19.15.3de that was obtained when the torsional moments were computed after making stiffness assumptions. Note that in this alternate method, fewer and smaller hoops are required (i.e., #3 @ 6 throughout) and less longitudinal reinforcement likewise is needed.

SELECTED REFERENCES

1. K. G. Tamberg and P. T. Mikluchin. "Torsional Phenomena Analysis and Concrete Structure Design," *Analysis of Structural Systems for Torsion* (SP-35). Detroit: American Concrete Institute, 1973, (pp. 1–102).

2. S. Timoshenko and J. N. Goodier. *Theory of Elasticity*. New York: McGraw-Hill, 1951, (pp. 275–288).

3. Paul Lampert. "Postcracking Stiffness of Reinforced Concrete Beams in Torsion and Bending," *Analysis of Structural Systems for Torsion* (SP-35). Detroit: American Concrete Institute, 1973, (pp. 385–433). (Also presented at 1971 Annual Convention, American Concrete Institute, Denver, March, 1971).

4. Michael P. Collins and Paul Lampert. "Redistribution of Moments at Cracking—The Key to Simpler Torsion Design?" *Analysis of Structural Systems for Torsion* (SP-35). Detroit: American Concrete Institute, 1973, (pp. 343–383).

5. Chu-Kia Wang. *Matrix Methods of Structural Analysis* (2nd ed.). Madison, Wisconsin: American Publishing Co., 1970 (Chaps. 12 and 15).

6. Thomas T. C. Hsu. "Torsion of Structural Concrete—Plain Concrete Rectangular Sections," *Torsion of Structural Concrete* (SP-18). Detroit: American Concrete Institute, 1968 (pp. 203–238). (Also Portland Cement Association Development Department Bulletin D134).

7. Thomas T. C. Hsu. "Torsion of Structural Concrete—A Summary of Pure Torsion," *Torsion of Structural Concrete* (SP-18). Detroit: American Concrete Institute, 1968 (pp. 165–178). (Also Portland Cement Assn. Development Department Bulletin D133).

8. N. N. Lessig. "Determination of Load Carrying Capacity of Reinforced Concrete Element with Rectangular Cross-Section Subjected to Flexure with Torsion," Work No. 5. Moscow: Institut Betona i Zhelezobetona (Concrete and Reinforced Concrete Institute), 1959 (pp. 5–28). (Also available as Foreign Literature Study No. 371, PCA Research and Development Labs., Skokie, Illinois.)

9. C. D. Goode and M. A. Helmy. "Ultimate Strength of Reinforced Concrete Beams in Combined Bending and Torsion," *Torsion of Structural Concrete* (SP-18). Detroit: American Concrete Institute, 1968, (pp. 357–377).

10. M. P. Collins, P. F. Walsh, F. E. Archer, and A. S. Hall. "Ultimate Strength of Reinforced Concrete Beams Subjected to Combined Torsion and Bending," *Torsion of Structural Concrete* (SP-18). Detroit: American Concrete Institute, 1968 (pp. 379–402).

11. Kevin D. Below, B. Vijaya Rangan, and A. Stanley Hall. "Theory for Concrete Beams in Torsion and Bending," *Journal of Structural Division*, ASCE, August 1975 (ST8), 1645–1660.

12. Thomas T. C. Hsu. "Ultimate Torque of Reinforced Rectangular Beams," *Journal of Structural Division*, ASCE, **94,** (ST2) February 1968, 485–510. (Also Portland Cement Association Development Department Bulletin D127).

13. Thomas T. C. Hsu. "Torsion of Structural Concrete—Behavior of Reinforced Concrete Rectangular Members," *Torsion of Structural Concrete* (SP-18). Detroit: American Concrete Institute, 1968, (pp. 261–306). (Also Portland Cement Association Development Department Bulletin D135).

14. Paul Zia. "Torsion Theories for Concrete Members," *Torsion of Structural Concrete* (SP-18). Detroit: American Concrete Institute, 1968 (pp. 103–132).

15. Paul Zia. "What Do We Know About Torsion in Concrete Members?" *Journal of Structural Division*, ASCE, **96,** (ST6) June 1970, 1185–1199.

16. David J. Victor, Narayanan Lakshmanan, and Narayanan Rajagopalan. "Ultimate Torque of Reinforced Concrete Beams," *Journal of Structural Division*, ASCE, **102,** July 1976 (ST7), 1337–1352.

17. E. Rausch. *Berechnung des Eisenbetons gegen Verdrehung und Abscheren (Design of Reinforced Concrete for Torsion and Shear)*. Berlin: Springer Verlag, 1929.

18. Paul Lampert. "Torsion und Biegung von Stahlbetonbalken (Torsion and Bending of Reinforced Concrete Beams)," *Bericht Nr.* **27,** ETH Zurich: Institut fur Baustatik, January, 1970.

19. Paul Lampert and Bruno Thürlimann. "Ultimate Strength and Design of Reinforced Concrete Beams in Torsion and Bending," *Publications*, International Association for Bridge and Structural Engineering, **31-1,** 1971, 107 –131.

20. Hans Gesund, Frederick J. Schuette, George R. Buchanan, and George A. Gray. "Ultimate Strength in Combined Bending and Torsion of Concrete Beams Containing Both Longitudinal and Transverse Reinforcement," *ACI Journal, Proceedings*, **61,** December 1964, 1509–1522.

21. John P. Klus and C. K. Wang. "Torsion in Grid Frames," *Torsion of Structural Concrete* (SP-18). Detroit: American Concrete Institute, 1968, (pp. 89–101).

22. G. S. Pandit and Joseph Warwaruk. "Reinforced Concrete Beams in Combined Bending and Torsion," *Torsion of Structural Concrete* (SP-18). Detroit: American Concrete Institute, 1968, (pp. 133–163).

23. A. A. Gvozdez, N. N. Lessig, and L. K. Rulle. "Research on Reinforced Concrete Beams Under Combined Bending and Torsion in the Soviet Union," *Torsion of Structural Concrete* (SP-18). Detroit: American Concrete Institute, 1968, (pp. 307–336).

24. David J. Victor and Phil M. Ferguson. "Reinforced Concrete T-Beams Without Stirrups Under Combined Moment and Torsion," *ACI Journal, Proceedings*, **65,** January 1968, 29–36. Disc. **65,** 560–566.

25. V. Ramakrishnan and Y. Ananthanarayana. "Tests to Failure in Bending and Torsion of Reinforced Concrete," *ACI Journal, Proceedings*, **66,** May 1969, 428–431. Disc. 943–944.

26. D. W. Kirk and S. D. Lash. "T-Beams Subject to Combined Bending and Torsion," *ACI Journal, Proceedings*, **68,** February 1971, 150–159.

27. Hota V. S. GangaRao and Paul Zia. "Rectangular Prestressed Beams in Torsion and Bending," *Journal of Structural Division*, ASCE, **99,** January 1973 (ST1), 183–198.

28. Michael P. Collins and Paul Lampert. "Designing for Torsion," *Structural Concrete Symposium*. Toronto: University of Toronto Civil Engineering Department, May 1971 (pp. 38–79).

29. Ugur Ersoy and Phil M. Ferguson. "Behavior and Strength of Concrete L-Beams Under Combined Torsion and Shear," *ACI Journal, Proceedings*, **64,** December 1967, 797–801. Disc. **65,** 477–479.

30. John P. Klus. "Ultimate Strength of Reinforced Concrete Beams in Combined Torsion and Shear," *ACI Journal, Proceedings*, **65,** March 1968, 210–215. Disc. 786–791.

31. Huey Ming Liao and Phil M. Ferguson. "Combined Torsion in Reinforced

Concrete L-Beams with Stirrups," *ACI Journal, Proceedings*, **66,** December 1969, 986–993. Disc. **67,** 475–478.

32. Larry E. Farmer and Phil M. Ferguson. "T-Beams Under Combined Bending, Shear and Torsion," *ACI Journal, Proceedings*, **64,** November 1967, 757–766. Disc. **65,** 417–421.

33. E. L. Kemp. "Behavior of Concrete Members Subject to Torsion and to Combined Torsion, Bending, and Shear," *Torsion Of Structural Concrete* (SP-18). Detroit: American Concrete Institute, 1968, (pp. 179–201).

34. Thomas T. C. Hsu. "Torsion of Structural Concrete—Interaction Surface for Combined Torsion, Shear, and Bending in Beams Without Stirrups," *ACI Journal, Proceedings*, **65,** January 1968, 51–60. Disc. 566–572.

35. M. S. Mirza and J. O. McCutcheon. Discussion of "Torsion of Structural Concrete—Interaction Surface for Combined Torsion, Shear, and Bending in Beams Without Stirrups," *ACI Journal, Proceedings*, **65,** July 1968, 567–570.

36. David J. Victor and Phil M. Ferguson. "Beams Under Distributed Load Creating Moment, Shear, and Torsion," *ACI Journal, Proceedings*, **65,** April 1968, 295–308. Disc. 892–894.

37. Michael P. Collins, Paul F. Walsh, and A. S. Hall. Discussion of "Ultimate Strength of Reinforced Concrete Beams in Combined Torsion and Shear," *ACI Journal, Proceedings*, **65,** September 1968, 786–788.

38. D. L. Osburn, B. Mayoglou, and Alan H. Mattock. "Strength of Reinforced Concrete Beams With Web Reinforcement in Combined Torsion, Shear, and Bending," *ACI Journal, Proceedings*, **66,** January 1969, 31–41. Disc. 593–595.

39. M. S. Mirza and J. O. McCutcheon. "Behavior of Reinforced Concrete Beams Under Combined Bending, Shear, and Torsion," *ACI Journal, Proceedings*, **66,** May 1969, 421–427. Disc. 940–942.

40. Alfred Bishara. "Prestressed Concrete Beams Under Combined Torsion, Bending, and Shear," *ACI Journal, Proceedings*, **66,** July 1969, 525–538. Disc. **67,** 61–63.

41. Arthur E. McMullen and Joseph Warwaruk. "Concrete Beams in Bending, Torsion, and Shear," *Journal of Structural Division*, ASCE, **96,** (ST5) May 1970, 885–903.

42. Umakanta Behera and Phil M. Ferguson. "Torsion, Shear, and Bending on Stirruped L-Beams," *Journal of Structural Division*, ASCE, **96,** (ST7) July 1970, 1271–1286.

43. Einar Gausel. "Ultimate Strength of Prestressed I-Beams Under Combined Torsion, Bending, and Shear," *ACI Journal, Proceedings*, **67,** September 1970, 675–678.

44. Priya R. Mukherjee and Joseph Warwaruk. "Torsion, Bending, and Shear in Prestressed Concrete," *Journal of Structural Division*, ASCE, **97,** (ST4) April 1971, 1063–1079.

45. P. K. Syamal, M. S. Mirza, and D. P. Ray. "Plain and Reinforced Concrete L-Beams Under Combined Flexure, Shear, and Torsion," *ACI Journal, Proceedings*, **68,** November 1971, 848–860.

46. K. S. Rajagopalan and Phil M. Ferguson. "Distributed Loads Creating Combined Torsion, Bending, and Shear on L-Beams with Stirrups," *ACI Journal, Proceedings*, **69,** January 1972, 46–54.

47. K. S. Rajagopalan, Umakanta Behera, and Phil M. Ferguson. "Total Interaction Method for Torsion Design," *Journal of Structural Division*, ASCE, **98,** September 1972 (ST9), 2097–2117.

48. Robert L. Henry and Paul Zia. "Prestressed Beams in Torsion, Bending, and Shear," *Journal of Structural Division*, ASCE, **100,** May 1974 (ST5), 933–952.

49. Lennart Elfgren, Inge Karlsson, and Anders Losberg. "Torsion-Bending-Shear Interaction for Concrete Beams," *Journal of Structural Division*, ASCE, **100,** August 1974 (ST8), 1657–1676.

50. ACI Committee 438. "Tentative Recommendations for the Design of Reinforced Concrete Members to Resist Torsion," *ACI Journal, Proceedings,* **66,** January 1969, 1–8. Disc. **66,** 576–588.

51. Michael P. Collins. Discussion of "Tentative Recommendations for the Design of Reinforced Concrete Members to Resist Torsion," *ACI Journal, Proceedings,* **66,** July 1969, 577–579.

52. ACI Committee 438. Discussion of "Proposed Revision of ACI 318–63: Building Code Requirements for Reinforced Concrete," *ACI Journal, Proceedings,* **67,** September 1970, 686–689.

53. Thomas T. C. Hsu and E. L. Kemp. "Background and Practical Application of Tentative Design Criteria for Torsion," *ACI Journal, Proceedings,* **66,** January 1969, 12–23. Disc. 591–593.

54. Alan H. Mattock. "How to Design for Torsion," *Torsion of Structural Concrete* (SP-18). Detroit: American Concrete Institute, 1968 (pp. 469–495).

55. David J. Victor. "Effective Flange Width in Torsion," *ACI Journal, Proceedings,* **68,** January 1971, 42–46.

56. Denis Mitchell and Michael P. Collins. "Detailing for Torsion," *ACI Journal, Proceedings,* **73,** September 1976, 506–511.

57. M. A. Gouda. "Distribution of Torsion and Bending Moments in Connected Beams and Slabs," *ACI Journal, Proceedings,* **56,** February 1960, 757–774. Disc. 1425–1446.

58. Robert A. Shoolbred and Eugene P. Holland. "Investigation of Slab Restraint on Torsional Moments in Fixed-Ended Spandrel Girders," *Torsion of Structural Concrete* (SP-18). Detroit: American Concrete Institute, 1968, (pp. 69–88).

59. Kolbjorn Saether and N. M. Prachand. "Torsion in Spandrel Beams," *ACI Journal, Proceedings,* **66,** January 1969, 24–30.

60. James O. Jirsa, John L. Baumgartner, and Nathan C. Mogbo. "Torsional Strength and Behavior of Spandrel Beams," *ACI Journal, Proceedings,* **66,** November 1969, 926–932. Disc. **67,** 434–435.

61. Mario G. Salvadori. "Spandrel-Slab Interaction," *Journal of Structural Division,* ASCE, **96,** (ST1) January 1970, 89–106.

62. James O. Jirsa. "Torsion in Floor Slab Structures," *Analysis of Structural Systems for Torsion* (SP-35). Detroit: American Concrete Institute, 1973 (pp. 265–292).

63. Ugur Ersoy. "Distribution of Torsional and Bending Moments in Beam-Slab Systems," *Analysis of Structural Systems for Torsion* (SP-35). Detroit: American Concrete Institute, 1973 (pp. 293–324).

64. E. L. Kemp and W. J. Wilhelm. "Influence of Spandrel Beam Torsion on Slab Capacity Based on Yield Line Criteria," *Analysis of Structural Systems for Torsion* (SP-35). Detroit: American Concrete Institute, 1973, (pp. 325–341).

65. Thomas T. C. Hsu and Kenneth T. Burton. "Design of Reinforced Concrete Spandrel Beams," *Journal of Structural Division,* ASCE, **100,** January 1974 (ST1), 209–229.

66. D. Wayne Kirk and David G. McIntosh. "Concrete L-Beams Subject to Combined Torsional Loads," *Journal of Structural Division,* ASCE, **101,** January 1975 (ST1), 269–282.

67. Thomas G. Barton and D. Wayne Kirk. "Concrete T-Beams Subject to Combined Loading," *Journal of Structural Division,* ASCE, **99,** April 1973 (ST4), 687–700.

PROBLEMS

All problems are to be worked in accordance with the strength method of the ACI Code, and all loads given are service loads, unless otherwise indicated.

19.1 Determine the reinforcement required on a 12 × 22 in. overall size member to carry a torsional moment of 10 ft-kips. Use $f'_c = 4000$ psi and $f_y = 40,000$ psi.

19.2 Determine the reinforcement required for the member in the accompanying figure to carry a torsional moment of 20 ft-kips. Use $f'_c = 4000$ psi and $f_y = 50,000$ psi.

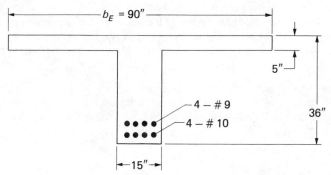

Prob. 19.2

19.3 For the beam of the accompanying figure, assume that 4-#9 bars are used in the bottom for the main flexural reinforcement at midspan, with 2-#9 bars extended into the support and properly anchored. Further assume that 2-#7 are used in the top at the supports. What is the nominal ultimate torsional capacity T_n of the section according to the ACI Code, assuming no simultaneous transverse shear? What is the negative bending moment that might be permitted to act at the supports along with the full torsional moment, according to the logic of Sec. 19.8?

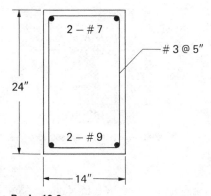

Prob. 19.3

19.4 Determine the reinforcement required (including torsion) at midspan and at the supports for the beam of Example 19.4.1 (2*B*4 of Fig. 19.4.1). Assume the shear is the same as that of a simply supported beam carrying a uniform dead load of 0.65 kips/ft. and uniform live load of 0.65 kips/ft. Assume that flexure alone requires longitudinal steel areas of 1.60 sq in. and 2.30 sq in., for positive- and negative-moment regions, respectively. Use $f'_c = 3000$ psi and $f_y = 40,000$ psi. Show sketches of the cross sections.

19.5 Design the reinforcement to include torsion on the spandrel girder of Example 19.4.2 (2G4 of Fig. 19.4.1). Assume simple beam shears for this span which is continuous at both ends. Assume the reactions to girder 2G4 from beams 2B1 are concentrated loads of 12.3 kips dead load and 15.9 kips live load, and also that the girder has uniform dead load (including its own weight) of 1 kip/ft. Use $f'_c = 3000$ psi and $f_y = 40,000$ psi. Show design sketch.

19.6 Redesign the web reinforcement for the beam of Prob. 5.1, except consider the total loading to be acting along a line at a distance of 2 in. from the midwidth of the beam. Use the rough approximation that equilibrium torsion is acting and that the torsional moment per unit length equals the uniform loading times 2 in.

19.7 Redesign the web reinforcement for the beam of Prob. 5.9 except consider the line uniform loading to be acting at 3 in. from the centerline of the beam cross section. Assume equilibrium torsion and use the same approximation as in Prob. 19.6.

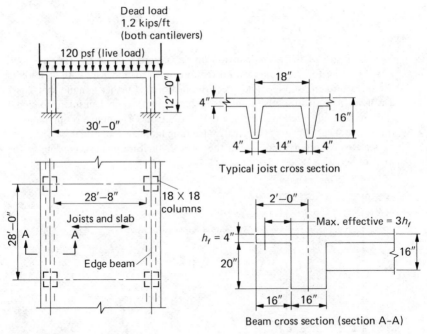

Prob. 19.8

19.8 Design the reinforcement for the edge beam which is continuous at both ends shown in the accompanying figure. Assume the torsional moment is 76 ft-kips (50% live load) at the face of column and that the torsional moment varies proportionally with the flexural shear (this problem is similar to that of Hsu and Kemp, Ref. 53).

20

Footings

20.1 Purpose of Footings

Footings are structural elements that transmit to the soil column loads, wall loads, or lateral loads from retained earth. If these loads are to be properly transmitted, footings must be designed to prevent excessive settlement or rotation, to minimize differential settlement, and to provide adequate safety against sliding and overturning.

20.2 Bearing Capacity of Soil

There must be reliable information on the safe bearing capacity of the soil prior to the design of a footing. It is not within the scope of this text to discuss the details of arriving at the bearing capacity of soil. The allowable bearing capacity of soil is usually determined by the ruling building code, by comparison with existing footings and with related information in the area, by close examination of the soil and study of logs of test borings, by the application of the science of soil mechanics, by load test, or by combinations of the various sources and methods mentioned here.

The following are some of the most common reasons for the many uncertainties concerning soil behavior under a footing.

1. There may be wide variations in soil types, which depend on their geological source, mode of transportation, and sedimentation mechanism.
2. The physical properties and probable behavior under load are unknown and may require extensive testing.
3. Frost action may cause heaving or subsidence.

Wall and square spread footings; Engineering Library, University of Wisconsin, Madison, Wis. (Photo by C. G. Salmon.)

4. Vibration may cause consolidation of granular material which results in nonuniform settlement.
5. Man-made hazards may exist below the earth surface, such as rock heaps, old sewers, and questionable fill.

Soil pressure is usually utilized in design under a working stress philosophy. The soil mechanics/foundations specialist (geotechnical engineer) will establish the ultimate bearing capacity, apply the appropriate margin for safety, and specify a service load bearing capacity (allowable bearing capacity) to be used in design.

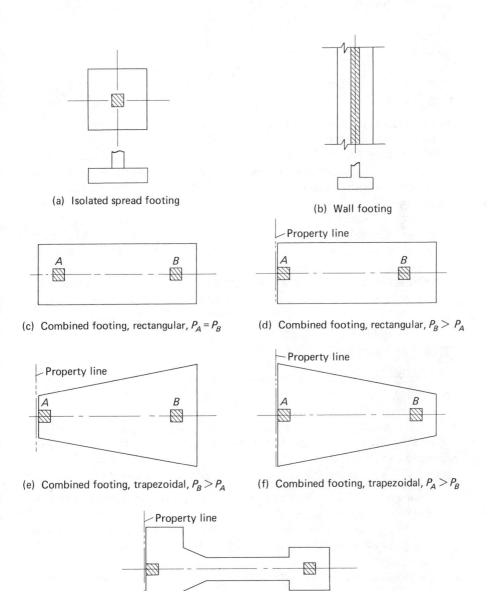

(a) Isolated spread footing

(b) Wall footing

(c) Combined footing, rectangular, $P_A = P_B$

(d) Combined footing, rectangular, $P_B > P_A$

(e) Combined footing, trapezoidal, $P_B > P_A$

(f) Combined footing, trapezoidal, $P_A > P_B$

(g) Combined footing, strap or cantilever

Fig. 20.3.1
Types of footings.

In general, rock is considered the best foundation material; graded sand and gravel are good materials; fine particles of sand and silt are generally questionable; and clay should be studied carefully. The allowable bearing capacity used for design may range from 12,000 psf (575 kN/m²) or higher for rock to 2000 psf (96 kN/m²) for soft clay or silty clay. Soils unable to carry 2000 psf generally require piling.

20.3 Types of Footings

Most building footings may be classified as one of the following types (Fig. 20.3.1):

1. Isolated spread footings under individual columns. These may be square, rectangular, or occasionally circular in plan.
2. Wall footings, either flat or stepped, which support bearing walls.
3. Combined footings supporting two or more column loads. These may be continuous with a rectangular or trapezoidal plan or they may be isolated footings joined by a beam. The latter case is referred to as a strap, or cantilever, footing.
4. A mat foundation, which is one large continuous footing supporting all the columns of the structure. This is used when soil conditions are poor but piles are not used.
5. Pile caps, structural elements that tie a group of piles together. These may support bearing walls, isolated columns, or groups of several columns.

20.4 Types of Failure of Footings

The procedures used for the design of footings in the United States are based primarily on the work of Talbot in 1907 [1], Richart in 1946 [2], and Moe in 1957-1959 [3].

Moe defines the several types of failure that may occur in a slab acted on by concentrated loads. These failure modes are related to the shear span to depth (a/d) ratio, and are similar to those described for beams in Sec. 5.4 (Fig. 5.4.3). The failure mechanisms may be reviewed as follows:

1. Shear-compression failure (Fig. 20.4.1a). Typical with deep sections of short span (low a/d ratios), inclined cracks form that do not cause failure but do extend into the compression zone, thus reducing its size until finally the compression zone fails under the combined compressive and shear stresses.
2. Flexure failure *after* inclined cracks form. Also typical with low a/d ratios, inclined cracks that form first do not cause failure or prevent the development of the theoretical ultimate bending moment. If embedment of tension steel is adequate, and no failure in the compression zone occurs, the tension steel may reach its yield strength.
3. Diagonal-tension failure (Fig. 20.4.1b). Sometimes called *punching shear*, this is typical with medium-span average depth sections (intermediate

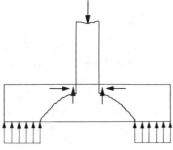

(a) Shear-compression failure

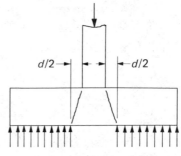

(b) Diagonal tension failure

Fig. 20.4.1
Shear-related failure mechanisms.

values of a/d); the slab fails on formation of the inclined cracks at all four sides of the concentrated load. Test results indicate that the critical section can reasonably be considered at $d/2$ from the periphery of a column.
4. Flexure failure before inclined cracks form. Typical with large values of a/d, no inclined cracks form before flexural capacity is reached.

In the design of a footing as well as of a beam, a shear failure should not occur prior to reaching the member flexural capacity.

20.5 Shear Strength of Footings

The shear strength of footings is essentially the shear strength of two-way slab systems, as discussed in Sec. 17.8. An excellent summary of the current status is presented by ASCE-ACI Task Committee 426 under Chairman N. M. Hawkins [4]. The six principal variables involved in the strength of slabs without shear reinforcement are (a) the concrete strength, f'_c; (b) the ratio of the side length c of the loaded area to the effective depth d of the slab; (c) the relationship (V/M) between shear and moment near the critical section; (d) the column shape in terms of the ratio β_c of the long side to the short side of the rectangular column; (e) lateral restraints such as may be provided by stiff beams along the boundaries of a slab (no such restraints would normally be acting in the case of footings); and (f) the rate of loading.

Assuming that the design objective is to achieve a shear strength high enough so that any possible failure would be in a flexural mode, under the conditions of no lateral restraints and static loading rather than dynamic, the shear strength may be expressed [4]

$$V_n = \left(2.5 + \frac{3.0}{\beta_c}\right)\sqrt{f'_c}b_0 d \le 4\sqrt{f'_c}b_0 d \qquad (20.5.1)$$

where

V_n = nominal ultimate shear strength
b_0 = periphery around critical section taken at $d/2$ from the loaded area

d = effective depth of slab

β_c = ratio of long side to short side of rectangular loaded area

Though the critical section at which inclined cracking occurs in the two-way shear action was found to follow the perimeter of the loaded area, Moe [3] showed that the variable c/d could be eliminated from the shear strength expression if a pseudo critical section at $d/2$ from the loaded area is used for computing the nominal shear stress; thus that variable does not appear in Eq. (20.5.1). One might consider that taking the critical section at $d/2$ from the loaded area in two-way shear action computation is for the same reason as taking the critical section at d from the face of support in one-way shear action computation, the reason being that statistical correlation between computation and actual behavior is best when those critical sections are used. In both cases inclined cracks tend to begin *at* the face of support (i.e., edge of loaded area for a footing).

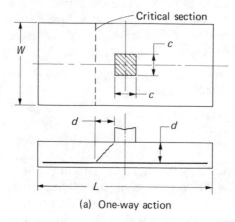

(a) One-way action

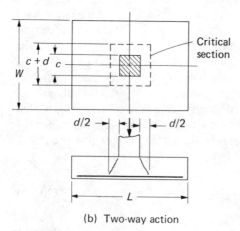

(b) Two-way action

Fig. 20.5.1

Critical section for shear (inclined cracking) in footings.

ACI-11.11.2 uses a modified version of Eq. (20.5.1) for two-way shear action without shear reinforcement ($V_n = V_c$) as follows:

$$V_c = v_c b_0 d$$

$$V_c = \left(2 + \frac{4}{\beta_c}\right)\sqrt{f'_c}\, b_0 d \leq 4\sqrt{f'_c}\, b_0 d \tag{20.5.2}$$

Note that v_c approaches $2\sqrt{f'_c}$, the value used for one-way action on beams, when β_c becomes large.

For footings in which the bending action is primarily in one direction, the procedure used for beams should be applied as described in Chap. 5. The critical section for such an investigation is to be taken at a distance d from the column face. Figure 20.5.1 summarizes the critical failure planes to be investigated in regard to shear.

20.6 Flexural Strength of Footings and Development of Reinforcement

Research has shown that critical sections for moment and development of reinforcement occur at the face of a reinforced concrete column or wall. The bending in each direction should be considered separately. Richart's tests [2] showed that, under service loads, the moment is greater on a strip under the column load than it is out near the corners. However, failure in flexure does not occur until all of the steel has reached yield—that is, after some redistribution of load has taken place.

The critical sections for moment and development of reinforcement, however, are to be taken (ACI-15.4.2) at halfway between the middle and the edge of the wall for footings under masonary walls, and at halfway between the face of the column and the edge of the metallic base for footings under steel bases.

20.7 Proportioning Footing Areas for Equal Settlement

Differential settlement between footings should be eliminated as much as possible because it may adversely affect the strength of the structure as well as interfere with the fitting of partitions, doors, ceilings, etc. It is generally assumed that there will be equal settlement if the unit soil pressures due to service loads are equal under all footings. However, the service loads in the columns consist of dead and live loads. The dead load is always there, but in a tall building there is little chance for a column to receive maximum live load from all floors. Therefore most building codes allow a reduction of live loads in columns. Typically, the total live load would have to be carried by columns supporting the roof and one floor. As the number of floors carried by a column increases, the percentage of the total live load that the column must be designed to carry may be reduced from 100% progressively. This percentage might be a minimum of 50% when the number of floors carried by the column is at least eight or nine. The maximum soil pressure under a footing is, then, due to the sum of the dead load in the column, the maximum reduced live load in the column, and the weight of the footing itself.

Soil is a substance that may be relatively elastic such as granular material like sand, or it may be a relatively plastic substance such as clay exhibiting time-dependent deformation under sustained load. Often, for design purposes, equal settlement of footings is presumed when the soil pressure due to sustained loads is the same under all footings. The sustained load may be taken as the sum of the dead load in the column, the weight of the footing itself, and a certain percentage of the maximum reduced live load in the column. In such cases, the relative areas of the footings should be so proportioned that the unit soil pressures under sustained loads would be the same under all footings. This requirement is additional to the requirement that the soil pressure under maximum possible load must not exceed the allowable bearing capacity at each footing.

20.8 Investigation of Square Spread Footings

The investigation of square spread footings can best be treated by an illustrative example in which the items considered are (1) soil pressure under the footing, (2) shear (inclined cracking), (3) bending moment, (4) development of reinforcement, and (5) load transfer from column to footing.

EXAMPLE 20.8.1 Check the adequacy of the square footing of Fig. 20.8.1, according to the strength method of the ACI Code. The column axial load is 300 kips dead load and 160 kips live load. The concrete for both the column and the footing has $f'_c = 3000$ psi and $f_y = 40,000$ psi. The allowable soil pressure is 5000 psf. There is a 2-ft earth overburden having a unit weight of 100 pcf.

Solution: (a) Soil pressure. The action of soil on the footing is taken to be uniform for isolated footings under concentric loads. The base of the footing must have an area large enough so that the allowable soil pressure will not be exceeded under the action of the column service load, footing weight, and weight of overburden.

$$\begin{array}{lll}
\text{Column load } (300 + 160) & = & 460 \text{ kips} \\
\text{Footing weight } 10(10)(2.08)(0.150) & = & 31 \\
\text{Earth } (100 - 4)2(0.100) & = & 19 \\
\hline
\text{Total weight on soil} & = & 510 \text{ kips}
\end{array}$$

$$\text{Soil pressure } p = \frac{510}{(10)(10)} = 5.1 \text{ ksf} \approx 5 \text{ ksf} \qquad \text{OK}$$

(b) Shear (inclined cracking). Two possible critical sections must be investigated: one-way action as a beam and two-way action as a slab, as shown in Fig. 20.5.1. The shear to be used is the upward soil pressure less the downward overburden and the footing weight acting outside of the critical

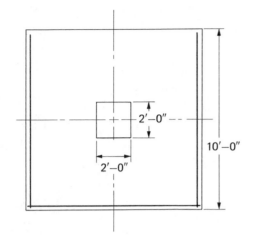

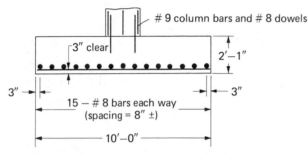

Fig. 20.8.1
Square spread footing for Example 20.8.1.

section. Since the footing weight and the overburden are usually uniform, the forces acting on the footing may be obtained by using the net upward pressure, which is caused by the column load only. Since the strength method is to be used, the overload factors U must be applied.

Since the action of a square concentrically loaded footing is symmetrical about both axes, the reinforcement in each direction is presumed to do the same work. However, the effective depth cannot be the same for both directions since the bars must cross each other. The average depth d is commonly used except for very shallow footings (say, less than 15 in. deep) where the more conservative value should probably be used. Here the average d is

$$d = 25 - 3 \text{ (cover)} - 1 \text{ (bar diameter)} = 21 \text{ in.}$$

For one-way diagonal tension action, the net earth pressure acting upward due to factored loads is

$$p_{net} = \frac{300(1.4) + 160(1.7)}{100} = 6.92 \text{ ksf} (332 \text{ kN/m}^2)$$

Using the loaded area shown in Fig. 20.8.2a.

$$V_u = (p_{net})(\text{effective area}) = 6.92(2.25)10 = 156 \text{ kips} (694 \text{ kN})$$

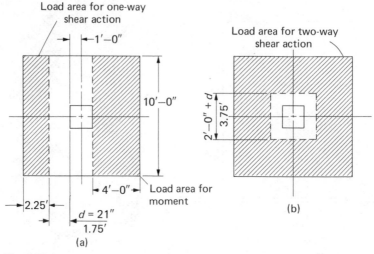

Fig. 20.8.2
Critical sections and loaded area for square spread footing.

When no shear reinforcement is used, $v_c = 2\sqrt{f'_c}$ unless the more detailed Vd/M procedure is used; thus

$$V_n = V_c = 2\sqrt{f'_c}b_w d = 2\sqrt{3000}(120)(21)\tfrac{1}{1000}$$
$$= 276 \text{ kips } (1230 \text{ kN})$$
$$V_u = 156 \text{ kips} < \phi V_n = 0.85(276) = 235 \text{ kips} \qquad \text{OK}$$

For two-way diagonal tension action, the shear (Fig. 20.8.2b) is

$$V_u = (p_{net})(\text{effective area})$$
$$= 6.92[100 - 3.75(3.75)] = 595 \text{ kips } (2650 \text{ kN})$$

When no shear reinforcement is used, the strength is based on $v_c = 4\sqrt{f'_c}$ when $\beta_c = 1.0$ (see ACI-11.11.2); thus

$$V_n = V_c = 4\sqrt{f'_c}b_o d = 4\sqrt{3000}(4)(3.75)(12)(21)\tfrac{1}{1000}$$
$$= 828 \text{ kips } (3680 \text{ kN})$$
$$V_u = 595 \text{ kips} < \phi V_n = 0.85(828) = 704 \text{ kips} \qquad \text{OK}$$

Since isolated footings are rarely designed with shear reinforcement, V_c will control the thickness.

(c) Bending moment. The critical section and loaded area are as shown in Fig. 20.8.2a. The bending moment is

$$M_u = \frac{p_{net}bl^2}{2} = \frac{6.92(10)(4.0)^2}{2} = 554 \text{ ft-kips } (752 \text{ kN-m})$$

$$\text{required } R_u = \frac{M_u}{\phi bd^2} = \frac{554(12,000)}{0.90(10)(12)(21)^2} = 140 \text{ psi } (0.97 \text{ N/mm}^2)$$

Referring to Sec. 3.6,

$$\text{required } \rho = \frac{1}{m}\left(1 - \sqrt{1 - \frac{2mR_u}{f_y}}\right)$$

$$= \frac{1}{15.7}\left(1 - \sqrt{1 - \frac{2(15.7)140}{40,000}}\right) = 0.0036$$

It is noted that the minimum reinforcement percentage of ACI-10.5 does *not* apply to slabs of uniform thickness, otherwise it would control here.

$$\text{required } A_s = 0.0036(10)(12)21 = 9.1 \text{ sq in. } (58.7 \text{ cm}^2)$$
$$\text{provided } A_s = 15(0.79) = 11.9 \text{ sq in. } (76.8 \text{ cm}^2)$$

Using 12-#8 would satisfy this requirement; however, with the low percentage used, the 15 bars are not excessive.

(d) Development of reinforcement. The reinforcement must be embedded from the face of the column a distance equal to the development length L_d for #8 bars. By using the formulas of ACI-12.2, or from Table 6.9.1,

$$L_d(\#8) = 23.1 \text{ in. } (587 \text{ mm})$$

Allowing an inch or so cover on the end of the #8 bars, the embedment provided is

$$\text{actual embedment} = 48 - 2 = 46 \text{ in. } > L_d \qquad \text{OK}$$

(e) Load transfer from column to footing. ACI-15.8.1 requires all forces acting at the column base to be transferred into the footing. Tensile forces, if any, must be transferred by developed reinforcement; however, compressive forces may be transmitted directly by bearing.

The nominal ultimate bearing stress f_b that the base of the column can withstand is $0.85f'_c$ (ACI-10.16.1). The nominal strength P_n in compression based on the *column* concrete strength f'_c is

$$P_n = 0.85f'_c A_g = 0.85(3)(576) = 1470 \text{ kips}$$
$$P_u = 1.4(300) + 1.7(160) = 692 \text{ kips}$$
$$P_u = 692 \text{ kips} < \phi P_n = 0.70(1470) = 1029 \text{ kips} \qquad \text{OK}$$

Regarding the bearing on the footing concrete, the capacity is increased because the footing area is much larger than the column area, thus permitting a distribution of the concentrated load. The ultimate bearing capacity for the *footing* concrete is the regular value $0.85f'_c$ increased by the multiplier α_b that varies between 1 and 2, as follows:

$$\alpha_b = \sqrt{\frac{A_2}{A_1}} \leq 2$$

where A_1 is the load area; the column area in this example, 576 sq in.; A_2 is the maximum area of the portion of the supporting surface that is geometrically similar to and concentric with the loaded area; the entire footing area in this case, 14,400 sq in.

The bearing stress *on the footing* may control when columns of high-strength concrete rest on footings of low-strength concrete. Since both the column and footing contain the same strength concrete in this example, only the check on bearing in the column was necessary. Bearing in the bottom of the column is important unless the longitudinal reinforcement is developed by extension into the footing or by embedding dowels lapped to the column bars. In this case the load can be carried without using developed reinforcement.

When the transfer is made by bearing, as in this case, ACI-15.8.4 still requires a minimum amount of reinforcement across the joint between the column and footing. Extended longitudinal reinforcement or dowels of at least 0.5% of the cross-sectional area of the supported column or pedestal, consisting of at least 4 bars, must be provided. Additionally, when dowels are used, their diameter shall not exceed the diameter of column bars by more than 0.15 in. The minimum area of developed reinforcement is

$$\text{required } A_s = 0.005(576) = 2.88 \text{ sq in. } (18.6 \text{ cm}^2)$$

Using 4 bars minimum,

$$\text{required } A_s \text{ per bar} = \frac{2.88}{4} = 0.72 \text{ sq in. } (4.65 \text{ cm}^2)$$

Thus the #8 dowels shown are adequate. They must be embedded into the footing a distance equal to the development length L_d for #8 bars.

Using the formulas of ACI-12.3 for compression bars,

$$L_d = \frac{0.02 f_y d_b}{\sqrt{f'_c}} \qquad [6.11.1]$$

$$= \frac{0.02(40,000)1.0}{\sqrt{3000}} = 14.6 \text{ in. } (371 \text{ mm})$$

but not less than

$$L_d = 0.0003 f_y d_b$$
$$= 0.003(40,000)(1.0) = 12.0 \text{ in.} \qquad [6.11.2]$$

and not less than 8 in. Thus

$$L_d(\#8) = 14.6 \text{ in.} < 25 \text{ in. available}$$

If the available footing thickness is inadequate, a greater number of smaller diameter bars should be used.

Thus the footing of Fig. 20.8.1 satisfies all ACI requirements.

20.9 Design of Square Spread Footings

The design of square spread footings involves the determination of the size and depth of the footing and the amount of main reinforcement and dowels so that all of the requirements of the preceding section are fulfilled. The design procedures are illustrated by the following example.

EXAMPLE 20.9.1   Design a square spread footing to carry a column dead load of 197 kips and a live load of 160 kips from a 16-in. square tied column containing #11 bars as the principal column steel. The allowable soil pressure is 4.5 ksf. Consider there is a 2-ft overburden weighing 100 pcf. Use $f'_c = 3000$ psi, $f_y = 40,000$ psi, and the strength method of the ACI Code.

Solution: (a) Estimate the footing weight and determine the plan of the footing. The total weight of the footing, plus any overburden, may be estimated and added to the column load or, as an alternative, the effect of these items in terms of the unit soil pressure may be estimated. In this case, the footing is estimated to be about 2 ft thick, that is, 300 psf, frequently the minimum used by designers. This leaves the net allowable soil pressure that must carry the column load as

$$p_{net} = 4500 - 200 - 300 = 4000 \text{ psf}$$

$$\text{required } A = \frac{357}{4.0} = 89.5 \text{ sq ft}$$

Try 9 ft 6 in. square, $A = 90.3$ sq ft. Note that ACI-15.2.1 requires the base area of a footing to be determined using service loads (unfactored loads) with the allowable soil pressure. This is reasonable since the allowable soil pressure should be determined using principles of soil mechanics and may incorporate varying factors of safety depending on the type of soil and condition of loading.

For the design of the reinforced concrete member, factored loads must be used. Applying overload factors to the column load,

$$P_u = 1.4(197) + 1.7(160) = 548 \text{ kips}$$

$$p_{net} = \frac{548}{90.3} = 6.07 \text{ ksf}$$

The undercapacity factor ϕ will be applied later in the calculations.

(b) Determine depth based on shear (inclined cracking). In most cases the depth necessary for shear without using stirrups controls the footing thickness. The use of nominal stresses is illustrated; frequently a useful format in design computations.

For two-way action (Fig. 20.9.1a), assuming a thickness of 24 in.,

$$\text{average } d = 24 - 3 \text{ (cover)} - 1 \text{ (bar diameter)} \approx 20 \text{ in.}$$

$$V_u = (p_{net})(\text{area}) = 6.07[9.5(9.5) - 3.0(3.0)] = 493 \text{ kips}$$

$$v_n = \frac{V_u}{\phi b_o d} = \frac{493,000}{0.85(4)(16 + 20)(20)} = 202 \text{ psi}$$

According to ACI-11.11.2 for $\beta_c = 1.0$,

$$v_c = 4\sqrt{f'_c} = 4\sqrt{3000} = 219 \text{ psi} > 202 \text{ psi} \qquad \text{OK}$$

No shear reinforcement is required.

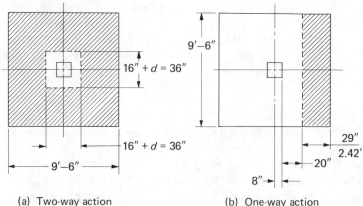

(a) Two-way action   (b) One-way action

Fig. 20.9.1
Critical sections for shear in square footing design.

For one-way action (Fig. 20.9.1b),

$$V_u = 6.07(2.42)(9.5) = 140 \text{ kips}$$

$$v_n = \frac{V_u}{\phi b_w d} = \frac{140,000}{0.85(9.5)(12)(20)} = 72 \text{ psi}$$

According to ACI-11.11.1.1 and 11.3.1.1,

$$v_c = 2\sqrt{f_c'} = 2\sqrt{3000} = 110 \text{ psi} > 72 \text{ psi} \qquad\qquad \text{OK}$$

No shear reinforcement is required. Note that the v_c used is that of the simplified procedure which neglects the effect of $\rho V d/M$. The 24-in. thickness is satisfactory for shear.

(c) Check transfer of load at the base of column (ACI-15.8). The compressive design strength ϕP_n based on the nominal ultimate bearing stress $0.85f_c'$ in the column is

$$\phi P_n = \phi(0.85f_c')A_g = 0.70(0.85)(3)(256) = 457 \text{ kips}$$
$$P_u = 548 \text{ kips} > \phi P_n \qquad\qquad\qquad\qquad\qquad \text{NG}$$

Thus the column load cannot be transferred by bearing alone. It may well be that the minimum dowels required by ACI-15.8.4 will be adequate to transfer the excess load.

$$\text{min required } A_s = 0.005(256) = 1.28 \text{ sq in.} \qquad \text{(ACI-15.8.4)}$$

The excess load to be carried by the dowels is, neglecting the displaced concrete effect,

$$\text{excess } P_u = 548 - 457 = 91 \text{ kips}$$

$$\text{required } A_s = \frac{P_n}{f_y} = \frac{P_u}{\phi f_y} = \frac{91}{0.70(40)} = 3.25 \text{ sq in.}$$

In effect a stress of $0.85f_c'$ out of the total stress f_y in the dowels should be subtracted in order to compensate for the displaced concrete; thus more correctly,

$$\text{required } A_s = \frac{P_u}{\phi(f_y - 0.85f'_c)} = 3.47 \text{ sq in.}$$

Use 4-#9 bars as dowels, $A_s = 4.00$ sq in.

The #9 dowels must be developed above and below the junction of column and footing. The development length L_d required in compression according to ACI-12.3 is

$$L_d = 0.02f_y d_b / \sqrt{f'_c}$$
$$= 0.02(40,000)(1.128)/\sqrt{3000} = 16.5 \text{ in.} \qquad \text{Controls}$$

but not less than

$$L_d = 0.0003f_y d_b = 0.0003(40,000)(1.128) = 13.5 \text{ in.}$$

and not less than 8 in. The 24-in. thick footing is adequate for straight dowels.

Hooks or bending of bars should not be considered effective in adding to the compressive resistance of bars (ACI-12.5.3). Very often engineers will specify bending of the dowels as shown in Fig. 20.9.2 to prevent their being pushed through the footing during construction and thus reducing the effective embedment distance L_2. In such cases of bending of the dowels, full development of the compressive force over the distance L_1 must be insured.

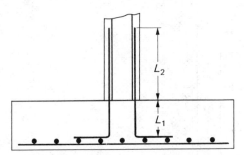

Fig. 20.9.2
Dowel anchorage.

For this design, if such a bend is used, the available length L_1 is

$$L_1 = 24 - 3 \text{ (cover)} - 2(1) \text{ (footing bars)} - 1.128 \text{ (dowels)} = 17.9 \text{ in.}$$

This exceeds the 16.5 in. required and is therefore acceptable. If it were unacceptable, alternatives would include a thicker footing, a larger number of smaller-sized dowels, or the use of a pedestal.

(d) Design for bending moment. The critical section for moment is at the face of the column (Fig. 20.9.3).

$$M_u = \tfrac{1}{2}(6.07)(9.5)(4.08)^2 = 480 \text{ ft-kips}$$

$$\text{required } R_u = \frac{M_u}{\phi b d^2} = \frac{480(12,000)}{0.90(114)(20)^2} = 140 \text{ psi}$$

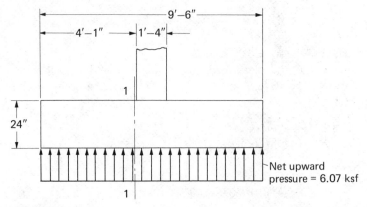

Fig. 20.9.3
Critical section for bending moment and development of reinforcement.

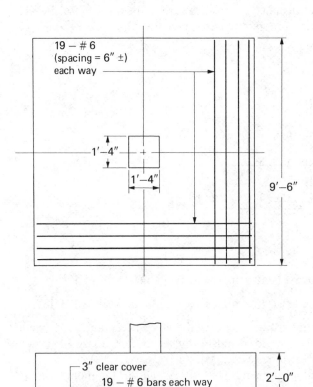

Fig. 20.9.4
Design sketch for spread footing of Example 20.9.1.

Referring to Sec. 3.6,

$$\rho = \frac{1}{m}\left(1 - \sqrt{1 - \frac{2mR_u}{f_y}}\right)$$

$$\rho = \frac{1}{15.7}\left[1 - \sqrt{1 - \frac{2(15.7)(140)}{40,000}}\right] = 0.00357$$

required $A_s = \rho bd = 0.00357(114)(20) = 8.13$ sq in.

Try 19-#6, $A_s = 8.36$ sq in.; $d = 24 - 3 - 0.75 = 20.3$ in.

$$C = 0.85f'_c ba = 0.85(3)(9.5)(12)a = 291a$$
$$T = A_s f_y = 8.36(40) = 334 \text{ kips}$$
$$C = T; \qquad a = 1.15 \text{ in.}$$
$$\phi M_n = 0.90(334)[20.3 - 0.5(1.15)]\tfrac{1}{12} = 494 \text{ ft-kips}$$
$$M_u = 480 \text{ ft-kips} < \phi M_n \qquad\qquad\qquad \text{OK}$$

Use 19-#6 bars ($A_s = 8.36$ sq in.) each way.

(e) Check development of reinforcement. The required embedment measured from the face of the column equals the development length L_d. For #6 bars, using the formulas of ACI-12.2, or Table 6.9.1,

$$L_d(\#6) = 12.8 \text{ in.} < 48 \text{ in. available} \qquad\qquad \text{OK}$$

(f) Design sketch. A design sketch as shown in Fig. 20.9.4 is necessary to convey the designer's decision properly.

For practical design of square footings, design aids are available [5,6].

20.10 Design of Rectangular Footings

Rectangular footings may be used in locations where space is restricted to prevent the use of a square footing. The procedure for their design is essentially identical with that of square footings, except that one-way shear action and bending moment must be considered in both principal directions.

EXAMPLE 20.10.1   Design a rectangular spread footing to carry 235 kips dead load and 115 kips live load from an 18-in. square tied column that contains #9 bars. One dimension of the footing is limited to a maximum of 7 ft. The allowable soil pressure is 5500 psf. Neglect the effect of overburden. Use $f'_c = 3000$ psi, $f_y = 40,000$ psi, and the strength method of the ACI Code.

Solution: (a) Determine plan of footing. Assume a footing depth of 2 ft, or 300 psf.

$$\text{net soil pressure} = 5500 - 300 = 5200 \text{ psf}$$

$$\text{required } A = \frac{350}{5.2} = 67.3 \text{ sq ft}$$

Space limitation prevents one dimension from exceeding 7 ft; thus

$$\text{length} = \frac{67.3}{7.0} = 9.6 \text{ ft}$$

Try 7 ft × 9 ft 8 in. (area = 67.7 sq ft).

(b) Determine depth required for shear. This footing may be long enough for one-way beam action to govern. In such a case, a direct solution for the effective depth d is reasonably practical. The factored column load is

$$P_u = 235(1.4) + 115(1.7) = 525 \text{ kips}$$

The net upward pressure under overload condition is

$$p_{net} = \frac{525,000}{67.7} = 7750 \text{ psf}$$

Using section A-A in Fig. 20.10.1, and making the nominal shear strength $V_n = V_c$, so that shear reinforcement is not required, which means

$$V_u = \phi V_c = \phi(2\sqrt{f'_c})b_w d$$
$$7750(7.0)(4.08 - d) = 0.85(2\sqrt{f'_c})(7)(d)144$$
$$d = 1.49 \text{ ft (17.9 in.)}$$

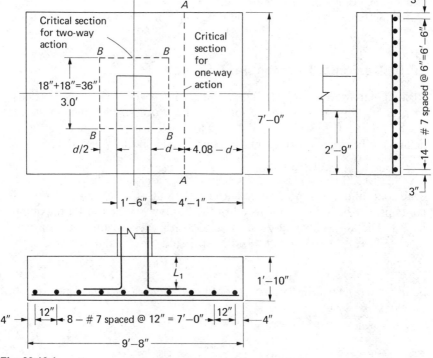

Fig. 20.10.1
Rectangular footing for Example 20.10.1.

Total depth $= 17.9 + 3$ (cover) $+ 1$ (estimated bar diameter) $= 21.9$ in. Try 22 in. for total depth. Check this depth for two-way shear action as a slab, using critical section B-B-B-B shown in Fig. 20.10.1 with $d = 18$ in.

$$v_n = \frac{V_u}{\phi b_o d} = \frac{7750[7.0(9.67) - 3.0(3.0)]}{0.85(4)(18 + 18)(18)} = 206 \text{ psi}$$

For $\beta_c = 9.67/7.0 = 1.38 < 2.0$,

$$v_c = 4\sqrt{f'_c} = 219 \text{ psi} > 206 \text{ psi} \qquad \text{OK}$$

(c) Check transfer of load at base of column. Assuming transfer without aid of dowels, the design strength is

$$\phi P_n = \phi(0.85 f'_c) A_g = 0.70(0.85)(3)(324) = 578 \text{ kips}$$
$$P_u = 525 \text{ kips} < \phi P_n \qquad \text{OK}$$

Only the minimum dowels required by ACI-15.8.4 are needed.

$$\text{min required } A_s = 0.005(324) = 1.62 \text{ sq in.}$$

$$\text{required } A_s \text{ per bar} = \frac{1.62}{4} = 0.41 \text{ sq in.}$$

Use 4-#6 bars as dowels ($A_s = 1.76$ sq in.).
  Minimum embedment length L_1 (Fig. 20.10.1) required,

$$\text{min } L_1 = L_d(\#6) = 11.0 \text{ in. (ACI-12.3)}$$
$$\text{available } L_1 = 22 - 3 - 1.5 - 0.75 = 16.75 \text{ in.} > 11.0 \text{ in.} \qquad \text{OK}$$

(d) Design for bending moment. The reinforcement in the long direction is distributed uniformly across the 7-ft width, while that in the short direction is concentrated more heavily under the column in a band equal to the footing width and less heavily near the ends. It is prescribed in ACI-15.4.4 that the portion $2/(\beta + 1)$ of the total transverse reinforcement should be placed in the central band (of a width equal to the short side of the footing) wherein β is the ratio of the long side to the short side of the footing. The ratio $2/(\beta + 1)$ may be derived on the basis that the intensity of reinforcement in the central band is twice that of the outer portions.
  In the long direction,

$$M_u = 7.75(7.0)\frac{(4.08)^2}{2} = 452 \text{ ft-kips}$$

$$\text{required } R_u = \frac{M_u}{\phi b d^2} = \frac{452(12,000)}{0.90(7)(12)(18.5)^2} = 209 \text{ psi}$$

Since the longitudinal bars are placed below the transverse bars, d has been taken as 18.5 in. in the above calculation.
  Using the trial moment arm method, rather than the formula, Eq. (3.6.5), for ρ, assume the moment arm as $0.95d = 17.6$ in. since the value of required R_u is very low.

$$\text{required } A_s = \frac{M_u}{\phi f_y(\text{arm})} = \frac{452(12)}{0.90(40)(17.6)} = 8.55 \text{ sq in.}$$

Check:

$$C = 0.85 f'_c ba = 0.85(3)(84)a = 214a$$
$$T = A_s f_y = 8.55(40) = 342 \text{ kips}$$

$$a = \frac{342}{214} = 1.60 \text{ in.}$$

$$\text{arm} = 18.5 - 0.80 = 17.70 \text{ in.} \approx 17.6 \text{ in. assumed}$$

$$\text{revised required } A_s = 8.55\left(\frac{17.6}{17.7}\right) = 8.5 \text{ sq in.}$$

Use 14-#7, $A_s = 8.4$ sq in. (close enough).
In the short direction,

$$M_u = 7.75(9.67)\frac{(2.75)^2}{2} = 283 \text{ ft-kips}$$

$$\text{assume arm} = 0.95d = 0.95(17.5) = 16.6 \text{ in.}$$

$$\text{required } A_s = \frac{M_u}{\phi f_y(\text{arm})} = \frac{283(12)}{0.90(40)(16.6)} = 5.7 \text{ sq in.}$$

Check:

$$C = 0.85(3)(116)a = 296a$$
$$T = 5.7(40) = 228$$

$$a = \frac{228}{296} = 0.77 \text{ in.}$$

$$\text{arm} = 17.5 - 0.39 = 17.11 \text{ in.}$$

$$\text{revised required } A_s = 5.7\left(\frac{16.6}{17.11}\right) = 5.5 \text{ sq in.}$$

Even though the minimum reinforcement requirement of ACI-10.5 does not apply to slabs of uniform thickness, the temperature and shrinkage requirement of ACI-7.12 does apply for the short direction,

$$\text{required } A_s \text{ (ACI-7.12)} = 0.002(116)(22) = 5.1 \text{ sq in.}$$

In this case, the strength requirement controls.
Try 9-#7, $A_s = 5.6$ sq in.

$$\frac{\text{reinforcement in band width}}{\text{total reinforcement}} = \frac{2}{\beta + 1} = \frac{2}{9.67/7.0 + 1} = 0.84$$

Number of bars in the 7-ft band = $9(0.84) = 7.6$, say 8. If one bar is placed on each side outside the 7-ft band, a total of 10 bars would be required.

Use 10-#7 bars.

(e) Check development of reinforcement. Using the formulas of ACI-12.2, or Table 6.9.1,

$$L_d(\#7) = 17.5 \text{ in.}$$

The minimum available embedment is in the short direction and equals 33 in. less an inch or two of cover; this is more than adequate.

The complete design is shown in Fig. 20.10.1.

20.11 Design of Plain and Reinforced Concrete Wall Footings

Wall footings carrying direct concentric loads may be of either plain or reinforced concrete. Those that are required to carry moment, such as for the cantilever retaining wall, are treated in Chap. 12. Since the wall footing has bending in only one direction, it may be designed or investigated by considering a typical 12-in. strip along the wall. Many typical walls carry relatively light loads, and the supporting footings are proportioned by using arbitrary minimums. Footings carrying light loads on good soil are often made of plain concrete. Some requirements for plain footings are prescribed in ACI-15.11.

EXAMPLE 20.11.1   Determine the adequacy of the plain concrete wall footing of Fig. 20.11.1 to carry a load of 20 kips/linear ft dead load including the wall weight and 8 kips/linear ft live load. Use $f'_c = 2500$ psi, an allowable soil pressure of 6 ksf, and the ACI Code.

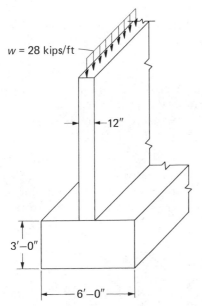

Fig. 20.11.1
Wall footing for Example 20.11.1.

Solution:

$$\text{total service load} = 28 + 6(3)(0.145) = 30.6 \text{ kips/ft}$$

$$\text{maximum soil pressure} = \frac{30.6}{6.0} = 5.1 \text{ ksf} < 6 \text{ ksf} \qquad \text{OK}$$

The bending moment is computed on the critical section at the face of the wall (ACI-15.4.2).

$$w_u = 20(1.4) + 8(1.7) = 41.6 \text{ kips/ft}$$
$$\text{net soil pressure under overload} = 41.6/6 = 6.95 \text{ ksf}$$

$$M_u = 6.95 \frac{(2.5)^2}{2} = 21.7 \text{ ft-kips/ft}$$

For computing the moment of inertia of the section, the bottom 1 or 2 in. of concrete placed against the ground are usually assumed to be of poor quality and neglected. Neglecting the bottom 2 in.,

$$I_g = \frac{12(34)^3}{12} = 39,300 \text{ in.}^4$$

For bending of plain concrete, the design strength is based on an extreme fiber tensile stress of $5\sqrt{f'_c}$ (ACI-15.11.2) and an undercapacity factor (ϕ) of 0.65 (ACI-9.3.2f); thus

$$\phi M_n = \phi f_t I_g/(h/2)$$

$$= \frac{0.65(5\sqrt{2500})(39,300)}{17(12,000)} = 31.3 \text{ ft-kips/ft}$$

$$M_u = 21.7 \text{ ft-kips/ft} < \phi M_n \qquad \text{OK}$$

Shear strength is adequate since the critical section at a distance d from the face of wall falls outside the footing; ACI-15.5.2, 11.11.1.1, and 11.1.3 apply here.

EXAMPLE 20.11.2 Design a reinforced concrete footing for a 12-in. masonry wall carrying 10 kips/linear ft dead load including the wall weight and 5 kips/ft live load. Use $f'_c = 3000$ psi, $f_y = 40,000$ psi, an allowable soil pressure of 4000 psf, and the strength method of the ACI Code.

Solution: Assume the footing depth to be 10 in. at 125 psf. Allowable net soil pressure $= 4000 - 125 = 3875$ psf. Footing width $= 15/3.875 = 3.87$ ft. Use 4 ft. It is probable that the thickness will be governed by shear (inclined cracking) which is taken to be critical at a distance d from the face of the wall (Fig. 20.11.2).

Applying the overload factors,

$$w_u = 10(1.4) + 5(1.7) = 22.5 \text{ kips/ft}$$

Net soil pressure under overload $= 22.5/4 = 5.63$ ksf. When no shear reinforcement is used, the nominal strength is

$$V_n = V_c = v_c b_w d = 2\sqrt{f'_c} b_w d$$

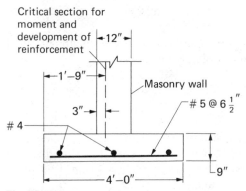

Fig. 20.11.2
Wall footing for Example 20.11.2.

which means

$$V_u = \phi V_c$$
$$5630(1.5 - d) = 0.85(2\sqrt{3000})(12)(12d)$$
$$2.38d = 1.5 - d$$
$$d = 0.44 \text{ ft (5.3 in.)}$$
$$\text{total thickness} = 5.3 + 3(\text{cover}) + 0.5(\text{bar radius}) = 8.8 \text{ in.}$$

Use 9 in. thickness.

$$\text{check weight} = 113 \text{ psf} \qquad\qquad \text{OK}$$

The critical section for bending moment on footings under masonry walls occurs halfway between the middle and the edge of the wall (ACI-15.4.2b)

$$M_u = \tfrac{1}{2}(5.63)(1.75)^2 = 8.62 \text{ ft-kips/ft}$$

$$\text{required } R_u = \frac{8.62(12,000)}{0.90(12)(5.5)^2} = 316 \text{ psi}$$

The steel area may be obtained by formula, Eq. (3.6.5), by trial as in Example 20.9.1, or from Fig. 3.6.1. Using the last,

$$\rho \approx 0.0085$$
$$\text{required } A_s = \rho b d = 0.0085(12)(5.5) = 0.56 \text{ sq in.}$$

Try #5 @ $6\frac{1}{2}$ in. ($A_s = 0.57$ sq in./ft). Check capacity.

$$C = 0.85 f'_c b a = 0.85(3)(12)a = 30.6a$$
$$T = 0.57(40) = 22.8 \text{ kips}$$

$$a = \frac{22.8}{30.6} = 0.75 \text{ in.}$$

$$\phi M_n = 0.90(22.8)[5.5 - 0.5(0.75)]\tfrac{1}{12} = 8.75 \text{ ft-kips} > M_u \qquad \text{OK}$$

For development of reinforcement, the embedment required is

$$L_a(\#5) = 12 \text{ in. minimum} \qquad (\text{see Table 6.9.1})$$

Since 21 in., less an inch or two for cover, are available for embedment of main reinforcement, this is acceptable.

See Fig. 20.11.2 for the details of the complete design. Some longitudinal reinforcement for shrinkage should probably be provided; say 3-#4 bars.

20.12 Combined Footings

A combined footing is one that usually supports two columns. These may be two interior columns (Fig. 20.12.1a) which are so close to each other that isolated footing areas would overlap. If a property line exists at or near the edge of an exterior column, a rectangular (Fig. 20.12.1b) or a trapezoidal (Fig. 20.12.1c) combined footing may be used to support the exterior column and its adjacent interior column. The area of the combined footing may be proportioned for uniform settlement by making its centroid coincide with the resultant of the respective portions of the two column loads that are sustained for long duration. It may be noted that for footings of constant thickness the centroid of the bearing area always coincides with the resultant of the weight of the footing itself.

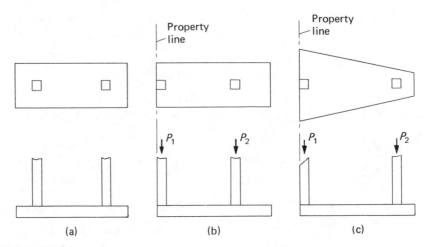

Fig. 20.12.1
Combined footings.

Referring to the frequently occurring situation in Fig. 20.12.1b, the load P_1 is close to the property line; however, there is adequate space to the right of P_2. Whenever P_2 exceeds P_1, a rectangular combined footing can be used, since it may be made long enough to make the load resultant and the footing centroid coincide. It may be shown that if $\frac{1}{2} < P_2/P_1 < 1$ approximately, a trapezoidal footing could be used. If $P_2/P_1 < \frac{1}{2}$ approximately, then either a strap (Fig. 20.12.2) or a T-shaped spread footing would have to be used.

In the strength computation for a combined footing, maximum loads in columns (full dead load plus reduced live load as discussed in Sec. 20.7)

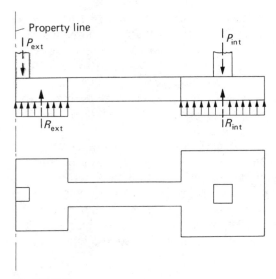

Fig. 20.12.2
Cantilever, or strap, combined footing.

should be used. Since the resultant of the maximum column loads does not necessarily coincide with that of the sustained column loads producing uniform settlement, under the former loading condition the distribution of the net soil pressure along the footing is not uniform. The deviation from uniformity is usually so small that certain approximate short-cut procedures may be used in determining the shear and moment diagrams in the longitudinal direction.

The ACI Code (see ACI-15.10) does not provide full recommendations for combined footings. However, ACI Committee 436 has given design procedures for combined footings and mats [7] and additional suggestions have been given by Kramrisch and Rogers [8], Szava-Kovats [9], and Davies and Mayfield [10]. Basically, transverse steel under each column tends to distribute the column load in the transverse direction. This being considered accomplished, the combined footing itself becomes a beam in the longitudinal direction. Thus it is suggested that the provisions for isolated footings be applied to the transverse direction, and those for beams to the longitudinal direction.

The cantilever or strap footing shown in Fig. 20.12.2 is an alternate design to prevent overturning of an exterior footing placed eccentrically under an exterior column, the edge of which is at or close to a property line. Overturning of the exterior footing is prevented by connecting it with the adjacent interior footing by a strap beam. This strap beam is subjected to a constant shearing force and a linearly varying negative bending moment. Thus it behaves like a cantilever beam; hence the name "cantilever footing."

In the strength computation for a cantilever footing (Fig. 20.12.2), the weight of the strap, the exterior footing, and the interior footing is each assumed to be balanced by the soil pressure caused by it and thus such weight causes no shears and moments in any part of the structure. In the longitudinal direction, the column loads P_{ext} and P_{int} are in equilibrium with the total "net" upward soil pressures R_{ext} and R_{int} under the exterior and interior footings; the upward soil pressure is assumed to be uniform over the entire area of each footing. The exterior footing may be considered as under one-way transverse bending although some reinforcement in the longitudinal direction is desirable, and the interior footing is under two-way bending as in isolated footings.

Use of a cantilever footing may be justifiable under conditions where the distance between columns is large and a large area of excavation must be avoided. It is usual practice that the bottom surfaces of the exterior footing, the strap, and the interior footing be at the same elevation, but the total thickness of each element may be different, depending on the strength requirements. Certainly it is desirable, unless there are good reasons to the contrary, to make all three elements of constant thickness.

20.13 Design of Combined Footings

The design of two common types of combined footings will be shown. The first is a rectangular footing, and the second is a strap or cantilever footing.

EXAMPLE 20.13.1   Design a combined footing to support two columns as shown in Fig. 20.13.1a: $P_A = 350$ kips (40% live load); $P_B = 400$ kips (40% live load); $A = 1$ ft 3 in., and $B = 18$ ft. Use $f'_c = 3000$ psi, $f_y = 40,000$ psi, maximum soil pressure $= 5000$ psf, and the strength method of the ACI Code. Assume that the ratio of maximum column loads as given is equal to that of long duration loads in the exterior and interior columns.

Solution: (a) Length and width of footing. ACI-15.2.4 indicates base area of footings is to be determined using service loads and allowable soil pressure.

$$\bar{x} \text{ from property line} = \frac{350(1.25) + 400(19.25)}{750} = 10.85 \text{ ft}$$

$$\text{length of footing, } L = 10.85(2) = 21.70 \text{ ft}$$

Use 21 ft 9 in.

Since the design for strength of the footing involves factored loads, there will be an eccentricity no matter how "exact" is the length determination. In the design for shear and bending moment, the soil pressure under factored loads might be taken as linearly varying to account for the eccentric loading, but in the case of a small eccentricity it is probably sufficient to assume a uniform soil pressure as is done in this example.

Assume the footing thickness to be about 2 ft 6 in., or 375 psf.

$$\text{net soil pressure} = 5000 - 375 = 4625 \text{ psf}$$

$$\text{footing width} = \frac{750,000}{4625(21.75)} = 7.46 \text{ ft}$$

Try 7 ft 6 in.

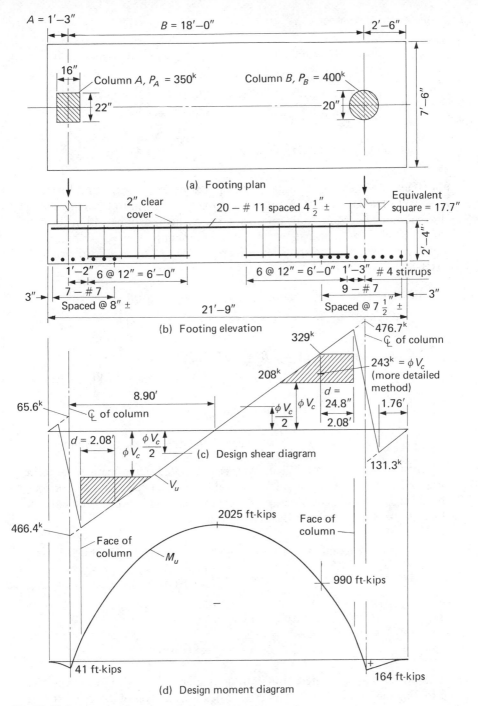

Fig. 20.13.1
Rectangular combined footing for Example 20.13.1.

(b) Longitudinal shears and moments. Applying the overload factors U for gravity loading,

$$\text{column } A, \ P_u = 210(1.4) + 140(1.7) = 532 \text{ kips}$$
$$\text{column } B, \ P_u = 240(1.4) + 160(1.7) = 608 \text{ kips}$$

$$\text{net soil pressure under overload} = \frac{1,140,000}{21.75(7.5)} = 7000 \text{ psf}$$

The factored shear V_u diagram is computed as for a beam and given in Fig. 20.13.1c. For simplicity, the column loads are taken to be acting along the column centerlines, thus producing the dashed portions within the column widths on the shear diagram. In the computations, the 20-in. diameter column is treated as an equivalent square of side 17.7 in. in accordance with ACI-15.3.

$$\text{net upward uniform pressure} = 7.5(7.0) = 52.5 \text{ kips/ft}$$
$$V_u \text{ at centerline of column } A = +52.5(1.25) = +65.6 \text{ kips}$$
$$+65.6 - 532 = -466.4 \text{ kips}$$
$$V_u \text{ at centerline of column } B = -52.5(2.5) = -131.3 \text{ kips}$$
$$-131.3 + 608 = +476.7 \text{ kips}$$

$$\text{point of zero shear} = 18\left(\frac{466.4}{466.4 + 476.7}\right)$$

$$= 8.90 \text{ ft from centerline of column } A$$

The factored moment M_u diagram as computed for a beam is given in Fig. 20.13.1d. Note that the numerical values on the two small end portions of the factored moment diagram are based on assuming all of the column loads to be concentrated at the column centerlines.

$$\text{max } M_u \text{ (computed from left side)} = \frac{52.5(10.15)^2}{2} - 532(8.90)$$

$$= -2025 \text{ ft-kips}$$

$$\text{max } M_u \text{ (computed from right side)} = \frac{52.5(11.6)^2}{2} - 608(9.10)$$

$$= -1995 \text{ ft-kips}$$

The moments as computed from both sides are not exactly the same because a footing length of 21 ft 9 in. is used instead of the computed 20.70 ft and because the distance 8.90 ft to the point of zero shear contains only three significant figures. Use $M_u = 2025$ ft-kips.

(c) Thickness of slab. For moment, the thickness may be based on a desired percentage of reinforcement ρ. The maximum permitted by the ACI Code is from Table 3.5.1,

$$\text{max } \rho = 0.75\rho_b = 0.0278$$

For reasonable deflection control, select $\rho = 0.014$, that is, approximately one-half of the maximum permitted. For this value of ρ, using Eq. (3.6.4),

$$R_u = \rho f_y (1 - \tfrac{1}{2}\rho m)$$

$$m = \frac{f_y}{0.85 f'_c} = \frac{40}{0.85(3)} = 15.7$$

$$R_u = 0.014(40{,}000)[1 - 0.5(0.014)(15.7)] = 498 \text{ psi}$$

$$\text{required } d = \sqrt{\frac{M_u}{\phi R_u b}} = \sqrt{\frac{2025(12{,}000)}{0.90(498)(7.5)(12)}} = 24.6 \text{ in.}$$

The footing is considered a beam in shear computations. One-way action is assumed to control at the distance d from the face of the columns. The shear at a distance d from the face of the 17.7-in. equivalent square column is

$$V_u = 476.7 - \left(\frac{8.85 + d}{12}\right)(52.5) = 438.0 - 4.37d$$

The nominal shear strength when no shear reinforcement is to be used is

$$V_n = V_c = 2\sqrt{f'_c} b_w d$$

unless the more detailed expression involving $\rho V_u d / M_u$ is used. Then,

$$V_u = \phi V_c$$
$$438.0 - 4.37d = 0.85(2\sqrt{3000})(7.5)(12)d$$
$$8.4d = 438.0 - 4.37d$$
$$d = 34.3 \text{ in.}$$

It seems desirable to make the footing deep enough for the moment, but not deep enough to give the extra 10 in. that would be required to eliminate stirrups.

$$\text{total depth} = 24.6 + 2(\text{cover}) + 0.5(\text{stirrup}) + 0.6(\text{bar radius}) = 27.7 \text{ in.}$$

Use 28 in. Check the weight, $28(150)/12 = 350$ psf.

$$\text{max soil pressure} = \frac{750{,}000}{21.75(7.5)} + 350 = 4950 \text{ psf} < 5000 \text{ psf} \qquad \text{OK}$$

(d) Main longitudinal reinforcement. At the middle of the span,

$$\text{required } R_u = \frac{M_u}{\phi b d^2} = \frac{2025(12{,}000)}{0.90(7.5)(12)(24.9)^2} = 484 \text{ psi}$$

$$\text{required } A_s \approx 0.014\left(\frac{484}{498}\right)(7.5)(12)(24.9) = 30.5 \text{ sq in.}$$

Try 20-#11 (approximate $4\tfrac{1}{2}$ in. spacing); $A_s = 31.2$ sq. in.
The anchorage required from the maximum moment point equals the development length L_d for #11 top bars, which from Tables 6.9.1 and 6.10.1 equals

$$L_d(\#11) = 45.5(1.4) = 64 \text{ in.}$$

The 1.4 is the modification factor for bars cast with more than 12 in. of concrete beneath them. If all 20 of the #11 bars are run into the centerlines of the columns, the development requirement is more than adequate, since an anchorage distance of 108 in. is provided on either side of the point of maximum moment.

Use 20-#11 bars at 18 ft long (spaced approximately at $4\frac{1}{2}$ in.)

Check development length requirement at the points of inflection according to ACI-12.12.3. The Code provision is checked here even though the reinforcement is negative-moment reinforcement rather than the positive-moment reinforcement as prescribed in ACI-12.12.3. The footing may be visualized for this purpose as an inverted beam with the soil pressure as loading and the columns as supports. The situation is similar to the positive-moment requirement in the sense that the required embedment is into the support (column) rather than out into the span as for the negative-moment requirement in an ordinary continuous beam. Furthermore, since the inflection points are inside the faces of the columns, the 1.3 factor might be used; however, since the column width (22 in.) is only a small fraction of the footing width (7.5 ft), the authors do *not* recommend using the 1.3 factor.

Since all 20-#11 bars extend through the inflection points,

$$M_n = \frac{2025}{0.90}\left(\frac{31.2}{30.5}\right) = 2300 \text{ ft-kips}$$

$$V_u = 466.4 \text{ kips (at column } A)$$
$$V_u = 476.7 \text{ kips (at column } B)$$
$$L_a = 15 \text{ in. approx (near both columns } A \text{ and } B)$$

In this case the actual distance L_a from the inflection point to the end of the bars is less than the maximum L_a limits of effective depth d or 12 bar diameters; thus the actual distance of 15-in. controls. Since M_u and L_a are the same at both inflection points, the one near column B having the larger shear V_u controls. At column B inflection point,

$$\frac{M_n}{V_u} + L_a = \frac{2300(12)}{476.7} + 15 = 73 \text{ in.} > L_d = 64 \text{ in.} \qquad \text{OK}$$

(e) Alternate design of the main longitudinal reinforcement using cutoff. If it seems desirable to cut off some of the tension bars, say 6-#11, and extend the remaining ones into the supports, the general anchorage requirements of ACI-12.11 must be applied. The theoretical point at which the 6-#11 bars are no longer required is indicated in Fig. 20.13.2, corresponding to the moment capacity ϕM_n of 1500 ft-kips. The provision in ACI-12.11.3 requires an extension of at least the effective depth d or 12 bar diameters, whichever is greater, beyond the theoretical cutoff point. In this case the effective depth of 24.8 in. (or 2.1 ft) controls over 12 diameters = 16.9 in. (or 1.4 ft).

In addition, for such a cutoff in the tension bars to be permitted, ACI-12.11.5 must be satisfied. It is assumed here that stirrups will be provided sufficient to satisfy ACI-12.11.5.1. The continuing bars must be embedded L_d beyond the cutoff of the 6-#11 bars according to ACI-12.11.4. At the

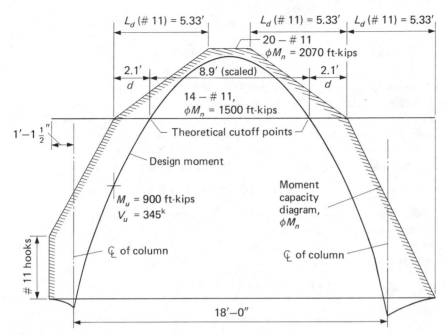

Fig. 20.13.2
Bar cutoff alternate for Example 20.13.1.

end under column A there is not adequate distance available for embedment (≈ 3.5 ft available $< L_d = 5.33$ ft required). Hooks could be provided at the end under column A so the full capacity of the continuing bars would be available at the cutoff for the 6 bars. At the end under column B adequate embedment length is available.

Check development length requirements at the points of inflection. In this case only 14-#11 bars extend through the inflection point.

$$M_n = \frac{\phi M_n}{\phi} = \frac{1500}{0.90} = 1670 \text{ ft-kips}$$

At column A inflection point, assuming no hooks are used,

$$\frac{M_n}{V_u} + L_a = \frac{1670(12)}{466.4} + 15 = 43 + 15 = 58 \text{ in.} < 64 \text{ in.} \qquad \text{NG}$$

Since hooks are required anyway, the value of L_a may be considered increased to the total of the actual straight embedment plus the equivalent for the hook. Referring to Table 6.13.2 and Fig. 6.13.1 for 90° hook,

$$L_a = 22.5 \text{ (hook)} + 15 \text{ (straight)}$$
$$- 8.6 \text{ (1}\tfrac{1}{2}\text{-in. cover} + 5d_b \text{ for bend radius)} = 28.9 \text{ in.}$$

$$\frac{M_n}{V_u} + L_a = 43 + 28.9 = 71.9 \text{ in.} > L_d = 64 \text{ in.} \qquad \text{OK}$$

At column B inflection point, where no hooks are required if embedment beyond inflection point is increased to 22 in. from the 15 in. used when no bars were cut,

$$\frac{M_n}{V_u} + L_a = \frac{1670(12)}{476.7} + 22 = 42 + 22 = 64 \text{ in.} = L_d = 64 \text{ in.} \qquad \text{OK}$$

Thus for the alternate design, 14-#11 bars would be required for 20 ft 9 in. including the hook at the end under column A. The 6-#11 cut bars would have to be 13 ft 3 in. long. Further, stirrups near the cutoffs would have to be provided so that ACI-12.11.5.1 is satisfied (this calculation is not shown).

(f) Longitudinal reinforcement at bottom of footing beyond column centers. The bending moment at the face of column B is

$$M_u = \tfrac{1}{2}(52.5)(1.76)^2 = 81.2 \text{ ft-kips}$$

Though certainly not always the case, the moment here appears small enough to require no reinforcement. The design strength of the unreinforced section in flexure is computed according to ACI-15.11.2 using $\phi = 0.65$ from ACI-9.3.2f. Neglecting the bottom 2 in. of thickness,

$$I_g = \tfrac{1}{12}(7.5)(12)(26)^3 = 132,000 \text{ in.}^4$$

$$\phi M_n = \phi \left(\frac{f_t I_g}{h/2} \right) = 0.65 \frac{5\sqrt{3000}(132,000)}{13(12,000)} = 151 \text{ ft-kips}$$

$$M_u = 81.2 \text{ ft-kips} < \phi M_n \qquad \text{OK}$$

No flexural reinforcement in the longitudinal direction is required for strength at the bottom of either cantilever.

(g) Transverse reinforcement. Bending in the transverse direction may be treated in a manner similar to isolated spread footings. The 1940 Joint Committee [11] recommended that the transverse reinforcement at each column should be placed uniformly within a band having a width not greater than the width of the column plus twice the effective depth of the footing.

The procedure seems to be reasonable. Certainly the behavior of the footing depends on the overall length-to-width ratio as well as the spacing of the columns. In this design example, the large spacing of the columns and the relatively narrow footing mean that most of the footing between the columns will be subjected only to longitudinal curvature while locally, in the vicinity of the concentrated loads, curvature in both directions will result. Thus the transverse reinforcement is put into bands as shown in Fig. 20.13.3.

$$\text{column } A \text{ band width, } W_A = 1.25 + \frac{8 + 24.8}{12} = 4.0 \text{ ft}$$

$$\text{net overload pressure in transverse direction} = \frac{532}{7.5} = 71.0 \text{ kips/ft}$$

$$M_u = \tfrac{1}{2}(71.0)(2.83)^2 = 284 \text{ ft-kips}$$

$$d = 28 - 3 \text{ (cover at bottom)} - 0.5 \text{ (bar radius)} = 24.5 \text{ in.}$$

$$\text{required } R_u = \frac{M_u}{\phi b d^2} = \frac{284(12,000)}{0.90(4.0)(12)(24.5)^2} = 132 \text{ psi}$$

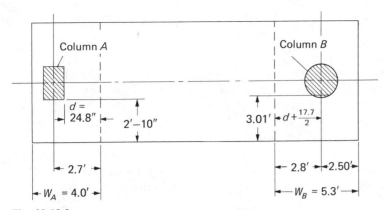

Fig. 20.13.3
Band width for transverse reinforcement.

From Fig. 3.6.1, $\rho \approx 0.0035$, which exceeds the minimum required for temperature and shrinkage reinforcement (0.002 from ACI-7.12).

$$\text{required } A_s = 0.0035(4.0)(12)(24.5) = 4.1 \text{ sq in.}$$

Try 7-#7 bars ($A_s = 4.20$ sq in.).

$$\text{development length } L_d(\#7) = 17.5 \text{ in. (Table 6.9.1)}$$

Since 2 ft 10 in. is available from face of column, adequate anchorage is provided.

Use 7-#7 bars (approximate 8 in. spacing).

$$\text{column } B \text{ band width } W_B = 2.50 + \frac{8.85 + 24.8}{12} = 5.3 \text{ ft}$$

$$\text{net overload pressure in transverse direction} = \frac{608}{7.5} = 81.0 \text{ kips/ft}$$

$$M_u = \tfrac{1}{2}(81.0)(3.01)^2 = 367 \text{ ft-kips}$$

$$\text{required } R_u = \frac{M_u}{\phi bd^2} = \frac{367(12,000)}{0.90(5.3)(12)(24.5)^2} = 128 \text{ psi}$$

From Fig. 3.6.1, $\rho \approx 0.0035$, approximately the same as for column A.

$$\text{required } A_s = 0.0035(5.3)(12)(24.5) = 5.5 \text{ sq in.}$$

Try 9-#7 ($A_s = 5.40$ sq in.). Check capacity.

$$C = 0.85f'_c ba = 0.85(3)(5.3)(12)a = 162a$$
$$T = 5.40(40) = 216 \text{ kips}$$

$$a = \frac{216}{162} = 1.33 \text{ in.}$$

$$\phi M_n = 0.90(216)[24.5 - 0.5(1.33)]\tfrac{1}{12} = 386 \text{ ft-kips} > 367 \text{ ft-kips} \quad \text{OK}$$

Anchorage of #7 bars is adequate since available embedment of 3.01 ft exceeds L_d of 17.5 in.

<u>Use 9- #7 bars (approximately $7\frac{1}{2}$ in. spacing).</u>

(h) Shear reinforcement. The usual approach is to consider the footing as a beam and to provide shear reinforcement on the assumption that the shear (inclined cracking) effect is uniform across the width. This approach seems appropriate in this case with the large distance between columns and the relatively narrow footing width.

The maximum shear to be provided for is at the critical section a distance d from the face of the column. From Fig. 20.13.1, $V_u = 329$ kips. The design shear strength ϕV_c of a beam without shear reinforcement, using the simplified procedure, is

$$\phi V_c = \phi(2\sqrt{f_c'})b_w d$$
$$= 0.85(2\sqrt{3000})(90)(24.8)\tfrac{1}{1000} = 208 \text{ kips}$$
$$\phi V_s = V_u - \phi V_c = 329 - 208 = 121 \text{ kips}$$

When shear reinforcement is required, there must be at least the minimum specified by ACI-11.5.5.3, as follows:

$$\min \phi V_s = \phi(50)b_w d = \frac{50}{2\sqrt{f_c'}}(208) = 95 \text{ kips} < 121 \text{ kips} \qquad \text{OK}$$

Thus the 121 kips controls the closest spacing for shear reinforcement. Even though this is a footing, the rules for beams are believed appropriate here. For design of shear reinforcement,

$$\frac{A_v}{s} = \frac{\phi V_s}{\phi f_y d} = \frac{121}{0.85(40)24.8} = 0.144 = \frac{A_s N}{s}$$

In the above expression, A_s is the cross section of the stirrup bar, and N is the number of times the multiple-loop stirrup crosses the neutral axis of the beam. Use a #4 stirrup, with $N = 8$ (see Fig. 20.13.4), spaced at 12 in. This gives

$$\text{provided } \frac{A_v}{s} = \frac{0.20(8)}{12} = 0.133$$

which is about 8% too low.

This may be a situation where computation using the more detailed expression for V_c is justified to verify using the above arrangement.

$$\phi V_c = \phi v_c b_w d = \phi\left[1.9\sqrt{f_c'} + 2500\frac{\rho V_u d}{M_u}\right]b_w d$$

$$\rho = \frac{A_s}{bd} = \frac{20(1.56)}{7.5(12)(24.8)} = 0.0140$$

$$\frac{V_u d}{M_u} = \frac{329,000(24.8)}{990(12,000)} = 0.69 < 1.0 \qquad \text{OK}$$

Fig. 20.13.4
Multiple-loop stirrup ($N = 8$).

$$v_c = 1.9\sqrt{3000} + 2500(0.0140)(0.69) = 2.34\sqrt{f'_c} < 3.5\sqrt{f'_c}(\text{max}) \quad \text{OK}$$
$$\phi V_c = 0.85(2.34\sqrt{3000})(90)(24.8)\tfrac{1}{1000} = 243 \text{ kips}$$
$$\phi V_s = V_u - \phi V_c = 329 - 243 = 86 \text{ kips} < \min 95 \text{ kips}$$

The minimum requirement now controls, giving

$$\text{required } \frac{A_v}{s} = \frac{95}{0.85(40)24.8} = 0.113 < 0.133$$

Use #4 stirrups with $N = 8$, as in Fig. 20.13.4. No further shear computations are required since 12 in. is the maximum spacing permitted (ACI-11.5.4.3) when v_s does not exceed $4\sqrt{f'_c}$, which corresponds to $\phi V_s = 415$ kips.

The first stirrup is placed at $s/2 = 6$ in. from the face of the column, and the last one should be within $s/2 = 6$ in. of the location where $V_u = \phi V_c/2$, at which web reinforcement is no longer theoretically required for beams (ACI-11.5.5.1). The stirrup arrangement will be made identical at each column. A few longitudinal bars are placed in the bottom of the footing in order to space and hold in position the stirrups and the transverse reinforcement. Two-way shear action is not expected to control but should be checked along sections around the perimeter at $d/2$ from the face of each column. The complete design details are given in Fig. 20.13.1.

EXAMPLE 20.13.2 Design a cantilever or strap footing for the situation shown in Fig. 20.13.5, where the property line is at the exterior edge of the exterior column. Column data are given in Table 20.13.1. The distance between column centers is 18 ft. Equal settlement is assumed for DL plus $\frac{1}{2}$LL condition at a uniform pressure of 3.34 ksf. Use $f'_c = 3000$ psi for footing, $f'_c = 3750$ psi for columns, $f_y = 40,000$ psi, and the strength method of the ACI Code.

Solution: (a) Size of exterior and interior footings. According to ACI-15.2.4 footing size is always determined using service loads, rather than factored loads. The size of exterior and interior footings is a function of the assumed width of the exterior footing (which affects the cantilever action and therefore the reactions required of each footing) and the assumed total thickness of each footing (which affects the available net soil bearing capacity). Should these assumed values be revised in the subsequent computation, the sizes of the footings must be revised accordingly. Assume that the width of the exterior footing is 4 ft 6 in. and that the total thickness of strap, exterior footing, or interior footing is 24 in. The net uniform soil pressure for exterior or interior footing is $3.34 - 2(0.150) = 3.04$ ksf. Referring

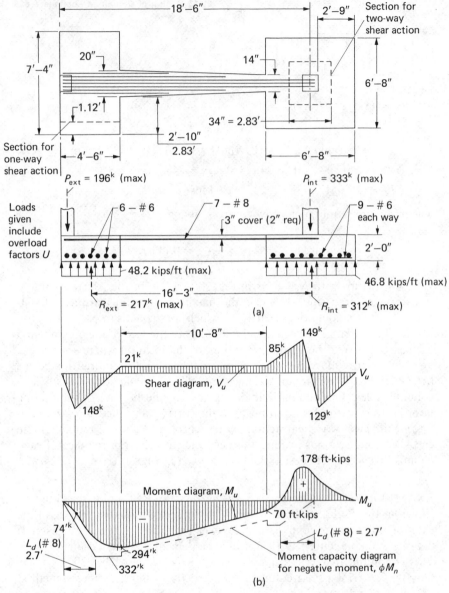

Fig. 20.13.5
Cantilever, or strap, footing of Example 20.13.2.

Table 20.13.1

Column	Size	Reinforcement	LL	DL
Exterior	12 × 12 in.	4-#7	70 kips	55 kips
Interior	14 × 14 in.	8-#8	130 kips	80 kips

to Fig. 20.13.5, the equal settlement condition gives

$$R_{ext} = \frac{(35 + 55)18}{16.25} = 99.7 \text{ kips}$$

$$R_{int} = (65 + 80) - \frac{(35 + 55)1.75}{16.25} = 135.3 \text{ kips}$$

$$\text{area of exterior footing required} = \frac{99.7}{3.04} = 32.8 \text{ sq ft}$$

$$\text{length of exterior footing} = \frac{32.8}{4.50} = 7.29 \text{ ft} \quad \text{(use 7 ft 4 in.)}$$

$$\text{area of interior footing required} = \frac{135.3}{3.04} = 44.5 \text{ sq ft}$$

$$\text{side of square interior footing} = \sqrt{44.5} = 6.67 \text{ ft} \quad \text{(use 6 ft 8 in.)}$$

(b) Shear and moment diagram for strap. Referring to Fig. 20.13.5, applying overload factors U to the maximum load condition gives

$$R_{ext} = \frac{[55(1.4) + 70(1.7)]18}{16.25} = \frac{196(18)}{16.25} = 217 \text{ kips}$$

$$R_{int} = [80(1.4) + 130(1.7)] - \frac{196(1.75)}{16.25} = 333 - 21 = 312 \text{ kips}$$

$$V_u \text{ in strap} = -196 + 217 = +21 \text{ kips}$$
$$M_u \text{ at right end of strap} = 21(3.33) = 70.0 \text{ ft-kips}$$
$$M_u \text{ at left end of strap} = 21(14) = 294 \text{ ft-kips}$$

(c) Design of strap. For the shear requirement, assuming no shear reinforcement is to be used and the simplified expression for strength is used,

$$\phi V_c = \phi(2\sqrt{f_c'})b_w d$$

$$\text{width } b_w \text{ of strap required} = \frac{21,000}{0.85(2\sqrt{3000})20.5} = 11 \text{ in.}$$

Assume desirable reinforcement,

$$\rho \approx 0.5\rho_{max} = 0.014$$

for which

$$R_u = 498 \text{ psi} \quad \text{(see Example 20.13.1, part c)}$$

At the junction with the interior footing,

$$\text{width of strap required} = \frac{M_u}{\phi R_u d^2} = \frac{70(12,000)}{0.90(498)(20.5)^2} = 4.5 \text{ in.}$$

At the junction with the exterior footing,

$$\text{width of strap by moment requirement} = \frac{294(12,000)}{0.90(498)(20.5)^2} = 18.7 \text{ in.}$$

Adopt a strap width to vary from 14 in. to 20 in.

$$\text{required } R_u \text{ at wide end} = \frac{M_u}{\phi b d^2} = \frac{294(12{,}000)}{0.90(20)(20.5)^2} = 466 \text{ psi}$$

$$\text{required } R_u \text{ at narrow end} = \frac{70(12{,}000)}{0.90(14)(20.5)^2} = 159 \text{ psi}$$

Approximately,

$$\text{required } A_s \text{ at wide end} \approx 0.014\left(\frac{466}{498}\right)(20)(20.5) = 5.4 \text{ sq in.}$$

$$\text{required } A_s \text{ at narrow end} \approx 0.014\left(\frac{159}{498}\right)(14)(20.5) = 1.3 \text{ sq in.}$$

Use 7-#8 ($A_s = 5.53$ sq in.)

development length, $L_d(\#8) = 23.1(1.4) = 32.4$ in.

The maximum available embedment length into the footing from end of strap is 4 ft 6 in. which is more than adequate.

Investigate shear at the distance d from the face of exterior column,

$$V_u = 148 - \frac{20.5}{12}(48.2) = 148 - 82 = 66 \text{ kips}$$

For no shear reinforcement and the simplified expression for strength,

$$\phi V_c = \phi(2\sqrt{f_c'})b_w d$$
$$= 0.85(2\sqrt{3000})(7.33)(12)(20.5)\tfrac{1}{1000} = 168 \text{ kips} > 66 \text{ kips} \quad \text{OK}$$

Investigate development of reinforcement at the inflection point (ACI-12.12.3). The Code provision is checked here even though the reinforcement is negative-moment reinforcement rather than the positive-moment reinforcement as prescribed in ACI-12.12.3 because the footing may be visualized as an inverted beam as discussed in Example 20.13.1, part (d).

Tension reinforcement is 3-#8 at the narrow end of the strap near the inflection point.

$$C = 0.85f_c'ba = 0.85(3)(14)a = 35.7a$$
$$T = 3(0.79)40 = 95 \text{ kips}$$

$$a = \frac{95}{35.7} = 2.66$$

$$M_n = 95(20.5 - 1.33)\tfrac{1}{12} = 152 \text{ ft-kips}$$
$$V_u = 85 \text{ kips}$$

The #8 bars are proposed to be terminated at the interior side of the interior column, giving about 2.5 ft of embedment from the inflection point.

$$L_a = 2.5 \text{ ft}, \quad \text{or } d = 1.71 \text{ ft}, \quad \text{or } 12d_b = 1.0 \text{ ft}$$

$$\frac{M_n}{V_u} + L_a = \left(\frac{152}{85} + 1.71\right)12 = 42 \text{ in.} > L_d = 32.4 \text{ in.} \quad \text{OK}$$

Investigate development of reinforcement in the top of the exterior column footing. Tension reinforcement is 7-#8.

$$C = 0.85f'_cba = 0.85(3)(7.33)(12)a = 224a$$
$$T = 7(0.79)40 = 221 \text{ kips}$$

$$a = \frac{221}{224} = 0.99 \text{ in.}$$

$$M_n = 221[20.5 - 0.5(0.99)]\tfrac{1}{12} = 378 \text{ ft-kips}$$
$$V_u = 148 \text{ kips}$$

$$1.30\frac{M_n}{V_u} + L_a = 1.30\frac{378(12)}{148} + 4 = 44 \text{ in.} > L_d = 32.4 \text{ in.} \qquad \text{OK}$$

Note that ACI-12.12.3 allows a 30% increase to reflect the ends of the reinforcement compressed by a reaction; also L_a is the embedment beyond the *centerline of the support*, which is 4 in. in this case.

It is observed that the assumption of zero earth pressure under the strap has been made; hence in construction the region below the strap should be disturbed and probably the strap should be formed on the bottom. Furthermore, liberal anchorage lengths (perhaps even hooks) should be provided into the exterior footing (as shown in Fig. 21.13.5a) to accommodate fully the tensile force in the top of the footing across to the exterior column. Often some of the steel extending into the exterior footing is flared to distribute better the load from the 20-in. width to the 88-in. width.

(d) Design of exterior footing. In the transverse direction,

$$M_u \text{ at edge of strap} = \left(\frac{217}{7.33}\right)\frac{(2.83)^2}{2} = 118 \text{ ft-kips}$$

$$\text{required } R_u = \frac{M_u}{\phi bd^2} = \frac{118(12,000)}{0.90(54)(20.5)^2} = 70 \text{ psi}$$

From Fig. 3.6.1, required $\rho = 0.002 < \rho_g = 0.002$ (ACI-7.12),

$$\text{required } A_s = 0.002(54)(24) = 2.59 \text{ sq in.}$$

The beam shear at d from the face of the column in the 7.33-ft direction of the footing is

$$V_u = \frac{217}{7.33}(1.12) = 33 \text{ kips}$$

$$\phi V_c = \phi(2\sqrt{f'_c})b_w d$$
$$= 0.85(2\sqrt{3000})(54)(20.5)\tfrac{1}{1000} = 103 \text{ kips} > 33 \text{ kips} \qquad \text{OK}$$

Use 6-#6 bars ($A_s = 2.64$ sq in.). Since bars are to extend the full 7 ft 4 in. length (less minimum cover) of the exterior footing, development of reinforcement for #6 bars is automatically provided; that is,

$$\text{available embedment} = 36 \text{ in.} > L_d(\#6) = 12.8 \text{ in.} \qquad \text{OK}$$

(c) Design of interior footing.

$$\text{net soil pressure under overload} = \frac{312}{(6.67)^2} = 7.0 \text{ ksf}$$

$$M_u = 7.0(6.67)\frac{(2.75)^2}{2} = 177 \text{ ft-kips}$$

$$\text{required } R_u = \frac{M_u}{\phi b d^2} = \frac{177(12,000)}{0.90(80)(20)^2} = 74 \text{ psi}$$

Check two-way action for shear. Using nominal stress,

$$v_n = \frac{V_u}{\phi b_o d} = \frac{7000[(6.67)^2 - (2.83)^2]}{0.85(4)(34)(20)} = 110 \text{ psi} < 4\sqrt{f_c'} \qquad \text{OK}$$

From Fig. 3.6.1, required $\rho \approx 0.0025$,

$$\text{required } A_s = 0.0025(80)(20) = 4.0 \text{ sq in.}$$

Use 9-#6 bars each way ($A_s = 3.96$ sq in.). The 2 ft 9 in. from face of column to edge of footing provides adequate embedment to develop the #6 bars ($L_d = 12.8$ in.)

The final details of the design are shown in Fig. 20.13.5a. Note that the moment capacity diagram in Fig. 20.13.5b for the strap portion is approximate; the #8 bars are extended as far as possible toward the narrow end as the width narrows from 20 in. to 14 in.

20.14 Pile Footings

The principles and methods to be used in the design of pile footings are little different from those of spread footings. The following, however, may be noted.

1. Computations for moments and shears may be based on the assumption that the reaction from any pile is concentrated at the center of the pile (ACI-15.2.3).
2. In computing the external shear on any section through a footing supported on piles, the portion of the pile reaction to be assumed as producing shear on the section shall be based on straight-line interpolation between full value when the pile center is at one-half the pile diameter outside the section and zero value when the pile center is at one-half the pile diameter inside the section (ACI-15.5.3).
3. In reinforced concrete pile footings the thickness above the reinforcement at the edge shall not be less than 12 in. (ACI-15.7).

SELECTED REFERENCES

1. A. N. Talbot. *Reinforced Concrete Wall Footings and Column Footings.* Urbana: Eng. Experiment Station Bulletin No. 67, University of Illinois, March 1913.
2. F. E. Richart. "Reinforced Concrete Wall and Column Footings," *ACI Journal, Proceedings,* **45,** October–November 1948, 97–127, 237–260.

3. Johannes Moe. *Shearing Strength of Reinforced Concrete Slabs and Footings Under Concentrated Loads* (Bulletin No. D47). Chicago: Portland Cement Association Research and Development Laboratories, April 1961.
4. Neil M. Hawkins, (Chmn.). "The Shear Strength of Reinforced Concrete Members-Slabs," by the Joint ASCE-ACI Task Committee 426 on Shear and Diagonal Tension of the Committee on Masonry and Reinforced Concrete of the Structural Division, *Journal of Structural Division*, ASCE, **100**, August 1974 (ST8), 1543–1591.
5. *Design Handbook—In Accordance with the Strength Design Method of ACI 318–71* Vol. 1, (2d ed.) (SP-17). Detroit: American Concrete Institute, 1973.
6. Richard W. Furlong. "Design Aids for Square Footings," *ACI Journal, Proceedings*, **62**, March 1965, 363–371.
7. ACI Committee 436. "Suggested Design Procedures for Combined Footings and Mats," *ACI Journal, Proceedings*, **63**, October 1966, 1041–1057. Disc. 1537–1544.
8. Fritz Kramrisch and Paul Rogers. "Simplified Design of Combined Footings," *Journal of Soil Mechanics and Foundations Division*, ASCE, **87**, (SM5) October 1961, 19–44.
9. Leslie J. Szava-Kovats. "Design of Combined Footings Using Support Reaction and Moment Influence Lines of Continuous Beam on Elastic Supports," *ACI Journal, Proceedings*, **64**, June 1967, 312–319.
10. Gwynne Davies and Brian Mayfield. "Choosing Plan Dimensions for an Eccentrically Loaded Footing Slab," *ACI Journal, Proceedings*, **69**, May 1972, 285–290.
11. *Report of the Joint Committee of Standard Specifications for Concrete and Reinforced Concrete*. Detroit: American Concrete Institute, 1940.

PROBLEMS

All problems[†] are to be done in accordance with the strength method of the ACI Code, and all loads given are *service* loads, unless otherwise indicated.

20.1 Design a square spread footing to support a 14-in. square tied column carrying a dead load of 120 kips and a live load of 90 kips. The column reinforcement consists of #8 bars. Use $f'_c = 4000$ psi for the column, $f'_c = 3000$ psi for the footing, and $f_y = 60,000$ psi. Use a 6 ft 9 in. square footing. (Column, 360 mm square; $DL = 530$ kN; $LL = 400$ kN; column bars, 25 mm diameter; $f'_c = 28$ N/mm² (column); $f'_c = 21$ N/mm² (footing); $f_y = 420$ N/mm²; footing, 2 m square.)

20.2 Design a square spread footing to support a 20-in. square tied column carrying a dead load of 400 kips and a live load of 264 kips. The column reinforcement consists of #11 bars. Use $f'_c = 3000$ psi for both the column and footing, $f_y = 60,000$ psi, and allowable soil pressure = 5 ksf. Include a design sketch. (Column, 500 mm square; $DL = 1800$ kN; 40 mm diameter bars; $f'_c = 21$ N/mm²; $f_y = 420$ N/mm²; soil pressure = 240 kN/m².)

20.3 Investigate the transfer of stress from column to footing for the two conditions of the accompanying figure. The column is 20 in. square ($f'_c = 4000$ psi) containing 12-#10 bars ($f_y = 40,000$ psi) spirally reinforced. The footing is 10 ft. square and 28 in. thick ($f'_c = 3000$ psi) and is adequately reinforced. Utilize the provisions of ACI-15.8 and 15.11.

[†] Many problems may be solved as problems stated in U.S. Customary units, or as problems in metric units using quantities in parenthesis at the end of the statement. The metric conversions are approximate to avoid implying higher precision for the given information in metric units than that for U.S. Customary units.

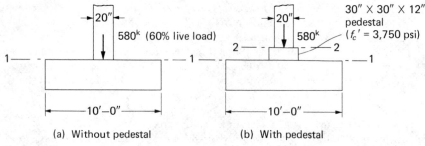

30" X 30" X 12" pedestal ($f_c' = 3{,}750$ psi)

580^k (60% live load)

580^k

20"

20"

1

1

2

2

1

1

10'–0"

10'–0"

(a) Without pedestal

(b) With pedestal

Prob. 20.3

20.4 Design a spread footing to carry a load from an 18 × 32 in. tied column. The dead load and live load are each 230 kips. Because of the closeness of the property line (see the accompanying figure), the footing cannot exceed 8 ft. perpendicular to that line. Use $f_c' = 3000$ psi, $f_y = 60{,}000$ psi, and allowable soil pressure = 5 ksf. (460 mm × 810 mm column; $DL = LL = 1000$ kN; $f_c' = 21$ N/mm^2; $f_y = 420$ N/mm^2; allowable soil pressure = 240 kN/m^2.)

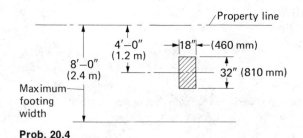

Property line

4'–0"
(1.2 m)

18" (460 mm)

8'–0"
(2.4 m)

32" (810 mm)

Maximum
footing
width

Prob. 20.4

20.5 Design a plain concrete footing to carry a long 12-in. concrete-block wall which must transmit 6 kips/ft (60% live load) to the footing. Use $f_c' = 3000$ psi and allowable soil pressure = 4 ksf. (300 mm wall; loading = 90 kN/m; $f_c' = 21$ N/mm^2; soil $p = 190$ kN/m^2.)

20.6 Design a reinforced concrete footing to carry a 12-in. concrete wall to carry 20 kips/ft (60% live load). Use $f_c' = 3000$ psi, allowable soil pressure = 3 ksf and $f_y = 40{,}000$ psi. (300 mm wall; 300 kN/m; $f_c' = 21$ N/mm^2; soil $p = 140$ kN/m^2; $f_y = 280$ N/mm^2.)

20.7 Redesign for the conditions of Example 20.13.2 a rectangle combined footing.

20.8 Design a rectangular combined footing for the situation shown in the accompanying figure. Column data are in the following tabulation:

Column	Size	Reinforcement	LL	DL
Exterior	12 in. square	#9 bars	45 kips	120 kips
Interior	12 in. square	#9 bars	90 kips	155 kips

Equal settlement is taken for DL plus LL conditions at a uniform soil pressure of 3 ksf. Use $f_c' = 4000$ psi and $f_y = 60{,}000$ psi.

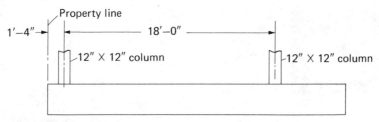

Prob. 20.8

20.9 Design a rectangular combined footing for the conditions of the accompanying figure. Assume that the system is within a building basement and is to have a 4-in. concrete slab over the footing. Use $f'_c = 3000$ psi, $f_y = 60,000$ psi, and allowable soil pressure for the given loads $= 5$ ksf. ($f'_c = 21$ N/mm²; $f_y = 420$ N/mm²; soil $p = 240$ kN/m².)

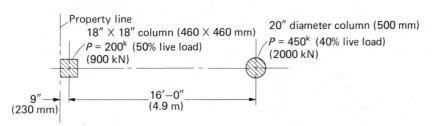

Prob. 20.9

20.10 Rework Prob. 20.8 using a strap, or cantilever, footing.

20.11 Rework Prob. 20.9 except assume that the exterior column load is 450 kips and the interior column load is 250 kips with 50% and 40% live load, respectively. In this assignment, however, only the plan size and the shear and moment diagrams are required. (Exterior column, 2000 kN; Interior column, 1100 kN.)

20.12 Rework Prob. 20.8, except assume that, in addition, the space to the right of the interior column is restricted to 1 ft 6 in. In this assignment, however, only the plan size and the shear and moment diagrams are required.

21

Introduction
to Prestressed
Concrete

21.1 Prestress

Prestress means a stress that acts even though no dead or live load is acting. The principle of prestressing has been used for centuries. For example, wooden barrels may be made by tightening metal bands or ropes around barrel staves. The tensile stress in the bands causes a compression between the staves, thus making the barrel tight. In the making of early wheels, the wooden spokes and rim were first held together by a hot metal tire. Upon cooling, the tensile stress due to shrinkage in the metal would then compress the wooden rim and spokes together. In bolted joints, the bolt is pretensioned by tightening, which in turn precompresses the elements being joined.

The primary application of prestressing on a large scale today is in concrete construction. In general, prestress involves the imposition of stresses opposite in sign to those which are caused by the subsequent application of service loads. For example, prestressing wires placed eccentrically in a simple beam as shown in Fig. 21.1.1 produce in the concrete an axial compression as well as a negative bending moment. Thus it is possible to keep the entire section in compression when service loads are added. This is a great advantage since concrete is weak in tension but strong in compression. Of course, steel is used to impose the prestress though less is required for prestressed concrete than in ordinary reinforced concrete. In general, it may be said that prestress provides a means for the most efficient use of material—that is, steel in tension and concrete in compression.

Prestressed concrete T-girders erected on precast columns for parking garage. (Photo by C. G. Salmon.)

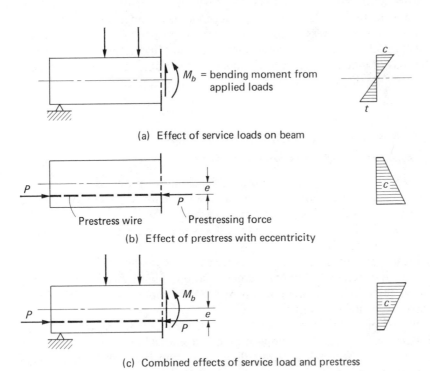

(a) Effect of service loads on beam

M_b = bending moment from applied loads

(b) Effect of prestress with eccentricity

Prestress wire · Prestressing force

(c) Combined effects of service load and prestress

Fig. 21.1.1
Opposite effects of service load and prestress on simple beam.

21.2 Historical Background

The general concepts of prestressed concrete were first formulated in the period 1885–1890 by C. F. W. Doehring in Germany and P. H. Jackson in the United States. These early applications were handicapped by the low steel strengths obtainable. Steel stressed to low tension levels will not pre-compress concrete adequately to maintain its compression after shrinkage and creep take place.

The theory of prestressed concrete was first propounded by J. Mandl of Germany in 1896. It was further advanced by M. Koenen of Germany in 1907 (first recognition of losses in prestress force from elastic shortening of concrete), and by G. R. Steiner in the United States in 1908. Steiner recognized shrinkage losses and suggested retensioning after shrinkage had occurred.

In practical uses, R. E. Dill of the United States in 1928 produced pre-stressed planks and fence posts. Circular prestressing of storage tanks began about 1935, but no significant linear prestressing (beams, slabs, planks, etc.) was done until about 1950. The Walnut Lane Bridge in Philadelphia, built in 1949–1950, was the first major use of linear prestressing in the United States.

In Europe, however, linear prestressing began about 1928 and advanced rapidly with the work of F. Dischinger, E. Freyssinet, E. Hoyer, and G. Magnel. With the publication of Magnel's work on the loss of stress in work-hardened steels in 1944, the basic theory of prestressed concrete was sufficiently complete for successful economical applications.

The use of prestress is now widespread in nearly every type of simple structural element, as well as in many statically indeterminate structures. Methods of inducing prestress are ingenious and unique. Several textbooks are available that describe the many methods and applicable theories [1–5].

21.3 Advantages and Disadvantages of Prestressed Concrete Construction

Probably the most significant observable feature of prestressed concrete is that it is crack free under service loads. Especially when the structure is exposed to the weather, elimination of cracks prevents corrosion. Also the prestressed member has greater stiffness under service loads because its entire section is effective.

Prestressed concrete in several respects is more predictable than ordinary reinforced concrete. It permits accommodation of both shrinkage and creep reasonably well. High-strength concrete may be more efficiently utilized by merely adjusting the prestress force.

Precompression of the concrete reduces the tendency for inclined cracking, and the use of curved tendons provides a vertical component to aid in carrying the shear. Shear strength is more consistent than in ordinary reinforced concrete.

Other features of prestressed concrete are its high ability to absorb energy (impact resistance), its high fatigue resistance due especially to the low steel stress variation resulting from the high initial pretension, and its high live-load capacity arising from the ability of the prestressing tendon to support the dead load. Use of prestressed concrete also permits partial testing of both steel and concrete through application of prestress.

Some of the disadvantages of prestressed concrete construction are as follows: (1) the stronger materials used have a higher unit cost; (2) more complicated formwork may be necessitated; (3) end anchorages and bearing plates are usually required; (4) labor costs are greater; and (5) more conditions must be checked in design and closer control of every phase is required.

Short-span members and single-unit applications of any kind are likely to be uneconomical in prestressed concrete. However, economy is usually achieved when units can be standardized and the same unit repeated many times. For many situations, the desirability of achieving a certain advantage is sufficient to justify a higher initial cost.

21.4 Pretension and Posttension Beam Behavior

Since discussion in this chapter is limited to beams, it is well to consider at this stage the behavior of such a member as it relates to the method of inducing the prestress. The most commonly used procedure is to put a specified tensile force into the wires by stretching them between two anchorages prior to placing the concrete. The concrete is then placed and the wires become bonded to the concrete throughout their length. After the concrete has cured, the wires are cut at the anchorages. The immediate shortening of the wires transfers through bond a compressive stress to the concrete. Such a process is called *pretensioning*.

The behavior associated with *pretensioning* will be described step by step. In addition the terminology and allowable values will be given in accordance with Chap. 18 of the ACI Code.

Step 1, as shown schematically in Fig. 21.4.1a, is to stretch the wires between two anchorages in the casting yard sufficiently to introduce a tensile stress f_{si} into the wires, which according to ACI-18.5.1 may not exceed the smaller of 80% of the ultimate tensile strength f_{pu} or 94% of the yield strength f_{py} of the steel. The quality controlled concrete is then placed in the forms and frequently is steam cured. Concrete strength must be adequately developed by the time the compression is to be introduced; thus high early-strength cement is usually used. Generally, the concrete strength f'_{ci} at transfer is specified by designers to be 4000 to 4500 psi.

Step 2 is to cut the wires. Acting through bond, the force T_0 in the wires acts as a compression force on the entire effective (transformed) section. The stress in the concrete goes from zero (Fig. 21.4.1b) before the wires are cut to that shown in Fig. 21.4.1c after they have been cut. Once the prestress has been introduced, certain losses of prestress begin to occur. Loss of prestress may arise from slip at the anchorage, elastic shortening

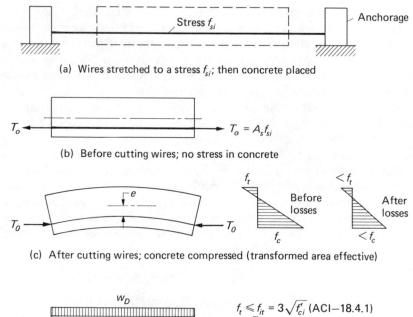

(a) Wires stretched to a stress f_{si}; then concrete placed

(b) Before cutting wires; no stress in concrete

$T_o = A_s f_{si}$

(c) After cutting wires; concrete compressed (transformed area effective)

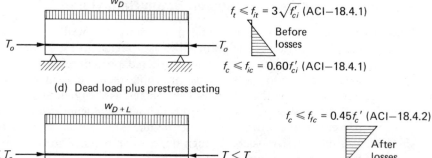

$f_t \leq f_{it} = 3\sqrt{f'_{ci}}$ (ACI–18.4.1)

Before losses

$f_c \leq f_{ic} = 0.60 f'_{ci}$ (ACI–18.4.1)

(d) Dead load plus prestress acting

$f_c \leq f_{fc} = 0.45 f'_c$ (ACI–18.4.2)

After losses

$f_t \leq f_{ft} = 6\sqrt{f'_c}$ (ACI–18.4.2)

(e) Dead load, prestress, and live load after all prestress losses

Fig. 21.4.1

Stages of behavior up to working load—*pretensioned* beam.

of the concrete member, creep and shrinkage of the concrete, relaxation of steel stress, and frictional losses due to intended or unintended curvature in the tendons. It is true that some small portion of such losses may occur prior to the transfer of stress to the concrete; however, it is practical and conservative to assume that the losses occur after the transfer.

Dead load of the flexural member will, of course, be acting simultaneously with the prestressing force once the wires have been cut and the transfer of stress is accomplished. Dead load combined with prestress is shown in Fig. 21.4.1d, where the most critical stress situation occurs immediately after transfer and before most losses have taken place. Limiting values (ACI-18.4.1) for this temporary situation are a tensile stress at the top of the beam of $3\sqrt{f'_{ci}}$ (approximately 40% of the cracking strength) and a compression stress at the bottom equal to 60% of the concrete strength f'_{ci} which has been developed at the time of transfer. One reason for holding the temporary tensile stress to such a low value is to prevent any possibility of an upward buckling of the beam resulting from sudden cracking at the top. Frequently no reinforcement (nonprestressed) exists to restrain such cracking.

Step 3 is the service condition of dead load, live load, and prestress where, after losses, ACI-18.4.2 permits a net tensile stress at the bottom not to exceed $6\sqrt{f'_c}$, along with a compressive stress at the top not to exceed $0.45f'_c$. Since tendons are usually placed near the bottom surface, there will be little danger of sudden cracking and buckling. For this reason the allowable tension stress is only slightly below $7.5\sqrt{f'_c}$, which is the generally accepted value of the modulus of rupture for normal-weight concrete.

Previous to the 1971 ACI Code, no tensile stress was permitted if the member was exposed to freezing temperatures or to a corrosive environment. ACI Commentary-18.4.2(b) suggests using reduced tensile stress to eliminate possible cracking under adverse corrosive atmosphere conditions, but does not suggest specific reduced values. Corrosive atmosphere is defined as an atmosphere in which chemical attack may occur from such sources as seawater, corrosive industrial atmosphere, or sewer gas. The ACI Code limit of $6\sqrt{f'_c}$ implies cover according to ACI-7.7.3.1; with corrosive atmosphere conditions the cover should be increased above the minimum.

Further, the tensile stress in the precompressed zone may exceed $6\sqrt{f'_c}$ when special calculations show that the deflection requirements of ACI-9.5 are satisfied.

The alternative to pretensioning is *posttensioning*. In a posttensioned beam, the concrete is first cast either with a hollow tube enclosed or with the unstressed tendons coated with grease or mastic to prevent bond with the concrete, as shown in Fig. 21.4.2. An end plate or anchorage is placed against each end of the member; then, once the concrete is sufficiently cured, the wires are pulled by jacking against the end plates. During the tensioning process, elastic shortening occurs, frictional losses take place, and the dead-load moment becomes partially active due to the induced curvature. Thus the jacking force must account for these losses. Losses that occur after tensioning will thus be less in this case than in pretensioning. For posttensioning, the stresses induced and the allowable values at the different stages are essentially the same as those described in detail for pretensioning. However, since the tendons are not bonded to the concrete, the posttension force acts only on the plain concrete, at least until reaching the situation of Fig. 21.4.1d. Prior to the imposition of live load, the tendons are usually grouted (space in the ducts is filled). If such grouting is properly

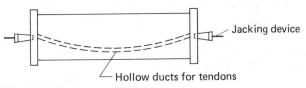

Fig. 21.4.2
Section for posttensioning.

done, the live-load stresses may be computed on the transformed section, the same as for pretensioning.

21.5 Service-Load Stresses on Flexural Members— Tendons Having Varying Amounts of Eccentricity

In order to demonstrate some of the attributes of prestressed concrete, the first example is one with the prestressing elements placed at the centroid of the section giving a uniform precompression of the concrete.

EXAMPLE 21.5.1   For the section shown in Fig. 21.5.1 assume that the member is pretensioned by 2.30 sq in. of steel wire having a maximum acceptable initial tensile stress of 175,000 psi. The prestress wires are centered at the centroid of the section. The concrete has $f'_c = 5000$ psi ($n = 6$), and it is to be assumed that the concrete has attained a strength of $f'_{ci} = 4000$ psi at the time of transfer. Determine (a) the stresses due to prestress immediately after transfer; (b) the temporary stresses when the member is used on a 40-ft simple span; and (c) the service live-load moment capacity according to the ACI Code, allowing for a 20% loss of prestress due to creep, shrinkage, and other sources.

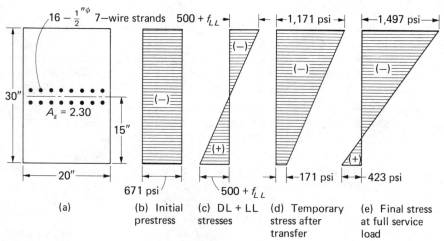

Fig. 21.5.1
Section and stresses for Example 21.5.1.

Solution: (a) Stress due to prestress immediately after transfer.

$$T_0 = f_{si}A_s = 175(2.30) = 402.5 \text{ kips}$$

This force T_0 acts as a compressive force on the transformed section immediately after cutting the wires. Thus

$$f_c = \frac{T_0}{A_c + nA_s} = \frac{T_0}{A_g + (n-1)A_s} = \frac{402,500}{600 + 5(2.3)} = \frac{402,500}{611.5} = 658 \text{ psi}$$

The decrease in steel stress is

$$\Delta f_s = n f_c = 6(658) = 3950 \text{ psi}$$

Thus elastic shortening may be considered to have caused a loss of tensile stress, so that the remaining tensile stress in the wires is $175,000 - 3950 = 171,050$ psi. The loss in this case is $2\frac{1}{4}\%$, but it could be as high as 5%.

It should further be noted that, although it may be theoretically correct to use the transformed section, in ordinary practice it is common and sufficiently accurate in most cases to use the gross section. Since the pre-stressing force is applied at the centroid of the gross section in the present problem, f_c is uniform over the entire section, or

$$f_c = \frac{402,500}{600} = 671 \text{ psi}$$

which is little different from the value of 658 psi determined above by using transformed section.

(b) Temporary stress—prestress plus dead load.

$$w_D = \frac{20(30)}{144}(150) = 625 \text{ plf}$$

$$M_D = \frac{1}{8}(0.625)(40)^2 = 125 \text{ ft-kips}$$

Using the approximate method with gross moment of inertia I_g and ne-glecting the transformed area of reinforcement,

$$I_g = \frac{1}{12}(20)(30)^3 = 45,000 \text{ in.}^4$$

$$f(\text{initial prestress} + DL) = -\frac{402,500}{600} \mp \frac{125(12,000)(15)}{45,000}$$

$$= -671 \mp 500$$

$$= -1171 \text{ psi} \quad (\text{compression, top})$$

$$= -171 \text{ psi} \quad (\text{compression, bottom})$$

These stresses are acceptable based on temporary stress restrictions im-mediately after transfer and before losses,

$$f_c(\text{max}) = 0.6f'_{ci} = 2400 \text{ psi}$$

$$f_t(\text{max}) = 3\sqrt{f'_{ci}} = 190 \text{ psi}$$

(c) Service live-load moment capacity.

$$f(\text{prestress} - \text{losses} + DL) = -0.8(671) \mp 500 = -537 \mp 500$$

$$= -1037 \text{ psi} \quad (\text{compression, top})$$

$$= -37 \text{ psi} \quad (\text{compression, bottom})$$

Based on stress at service load, after allowance for all prestress losses,

$$f_c(\text{max}) = 0.45f'_c = 2250 \text{ psi}$$

$$f_t(\text{max}) = 6\sqrt{f'_c} = 423 \text{ psi}$$

The stress available for live load may then be computed.

$$f(\text{prestress} - \text{losses} + DL + LL) = -1037 + f_{LL} = -2250 \text{ psi} \quad \text{(top)}$$
$$= -37 + f_{LL} = +423 \text{ psi} \quad \text{(bottom)}$$
$$f_{LL}(\text{max})(\text{top}) = -1213 \text{ psi}$$
$$f_{LL}(\text{max})(\text{bottom}) = +460 \text{ psi} \quad \text{(Controls)}$$

Thus

$$\frac{M_L(15)}{45,000} = 460 \text{ psi}$$

$$M_L = \frac{45,000(460)}{15(12,000)} = 115 \text{ ft-kips}$$

The wide divergence between the maximum acceptable live-load stresses of 1213 psi compression and 460 psi tension indicates the need for an unsymmetrical section or some arrangement to equalize them better. A study of Fig. 21.5.1 will show that the most economical arrangement would be for the initial prestress variation to offset the pattern of final stress under full dead plus live load.

EXAMPLE 21.5.2   Repeat the solution of Example 21.5.1, except locate the tendons 5 in. from the bottom of the section (Fig. 21.5.2).

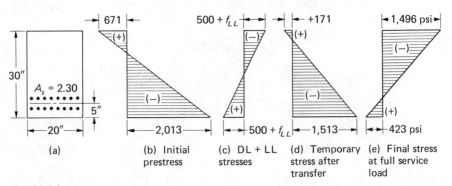

Fig. 21.5.2
Section and stresses for Example 21.5.2.

Solution: (a) Temporary stress (prestress + DL) immediately after transfer. Using properties of the gross section as for the preceding example, the prestressing force $T_0 = 402.5$ kips applied with an eccentricity of 10 in. gives

$$f(\text{initial prestress} + DL) = -671 \pm \frac{402,500(10)(15)}{45,000} \mp 500$$

$$= -671 \pm 1342 \mp 500$$
$$= +171 \text{ psi} \quad \text{(tension, top)}$$
$$= -1513 \text{ psi (compression, bottom)}$$

It is to be noted that the temporary tensile stress of 171 psi at the top is nearly equal to the allowable value of $3\sqrt{f'_{ci}} = 190$ psi for such stress. Any significantly greater eccentricity, therefore, would require a reduction in the prestressing force.

(b) Final stress (prestress + DL), after allowance for 20% prestress loss, is

$$f(\text{prestress} + DL - \text{losses}) = +171 - 0.2(-671 + 1342)$$
$$= +37 \text{ psi} \quad (\text{top})$$
$$= -1513 - 0.2(-671 - 1342)$$
$$= -1110 \text{ psi} \quad (\text{bottom})$$

(c) Live-load capacity (see Example 21.5.1 for allowables). Based on final dead-load plus live-load conditions,

$$+37 + f_{LL} = -2250 \text{ psi} \quad (\text{top}), \qquad f_{LL} = -2287 \text{ psi}$$
$$-1110 + f_{LL} = +423 \text{ psi} \quad (\text{bottom}), \qquad f_{LL} = +1533 \text{ psi}$$

Since the neutral axis for live-load resistance is assumed to be at middepth, $f_{LL} = +1533$ psi controls.

$$M_L = \frac{45,000(1533)}{15(12,000)} = 383 \text{ ft-kips}$$

Thus increasing the eccentricity of the prestressing force increases the live-load capacity until the limit is reached when the temporary stress at transfer reaches its maximum permissible value, either at the top or at the bottom of the section.

It is to be noted that the magnitude of the prestress over the concrete section is constant for the entire span when the tendons are straight, whereas the magnitude of dead- and live-load stresses is a maximum at only one point. For straight tendons, the complete stress situation near the supports on simple spans approaches that of Fig. 21.5.2b, less losses, because the superimposed dead- and live-load stresses vanish. Because of this difficulty, tendons frequently are placed so as to have an eccentricity that varies from zero at points of low external bending moment to a maximum in the region of high external bending moment. This variation in eccentricity may be accomplished in pretensioning by holding down the stressed tendons at midspan, or at other locations such as at the one-third points. In post-tensioning, the ducts or greased tendons are simply draped (held at the ends and permitted to take a natural deflected shape) such that desired eccentricities at the ends and at midspan are achieved; the points in between will lie on a curved path.

21.6 Three Basic Concepts of Prestressed Concrete

When considering the stresses in prestressed concrete under service-load conditions, there are three general patterns of thought that may be applied.

Homogeneous Beam Concept. The homogeneous beam concept is used in Sec. 21.5 wherein the prestressing effectively eliminates cracking and the combined stress formula, $P/A \pm Mc/I$, may be used to investigate the section. Two examples appear in Sec. 21.5.

Internal-Force Concept. The internal-force approach uses the equilibrium of internal forces; steel takes the tension and concrete the compression as shown in Fig. 21.6.1. This approach is analogous to the internal-couple method used for nonprestressed reinforced concrete. At service load in reinforced concrete the *points of action* of the forces C and T $(C = T)$ are *independent* of the magnitude of applied bending moment, depending only on the cross-sectional dimensions and the modular ratio n; thus the magnitude of the forces is directly proportional to the applied bending moment. In prestressed concrete, the *magnitude* of internal forces is *independent* of applied bending moment, depending only on the prestress and the percentage of losses. In this case the location of the force C must vary with the applied loading. The approach may be summarized by the following steps:

1. A known prestress force put into the steel defines T.
2. An applied moment M is put on the beam.
3. For equilibrium, the moment arm $= M/T$ and $C = T$.
4. Knowing the magnitude and point of action of the force C, the stress in the concrete may be computed as

$$f = \frac{C}{A} \pm \frac{Cey}{I} \qquad\qquad \textbf{(21.6.1)}$$

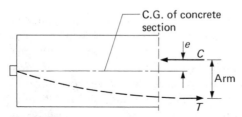

Fig. 21.6.1
Internal-force concept of prestressing.

EXAMPLE 21.6.1   Apply the dead-load moment of 125 ft-kips and live-load moment of 383 ft-kips (as computed in Example 21.5.2) to the rectangular beam of Fig. 21.5.2, using the internal-force concept. Determine the service-load stresses at transfer and under final conditions.

Solution: (a) At transfer, the prestress force T_0 is 402.5 kips.

$$C = T_0 = 402.5 \text{ kips}$$

When the applied moment is 125 ft-kips, the moment arm of the internal forces must be

$$\text{arm} = \frac{M_D}{C} = \frac{125(12)}{402.5} = 3.73 \text{ in.}$$

This means the compressive force C is eccentric to the middepth by an amount,

$$e = 15 - 5 \text{ (to steel)} - 3.73 \text{ (arm)}$$
$$= 6.27 \text{ in.} \qquad \text{(below middepth)}$$

$$f = -\frac{402.5}{600} \pm \frac{402.5(6.27)15}{45,000}$$

$$f \text{ (top)} = -671 + 842 = +171 \text{ psi} \qquad \text{(tension)}$$
$$f \text{ (bottom)} = -671 - 842 = -1513 \text{ psi} \qquad \text{(compression)}$$

exactly the same as in Example 21.5.2, Fig. 21.5.2d.

(b) At the final condition, the prestress force T_e is $0.8(402.5) = 322$ kips after losses.

$$C = T_e = 322 \text{ kips}$$

$$\text{arm} = \frac{M_D + M_L}{C} = \frac{(125 + 383)12}{322} = 18.95 \text{ in.}$$

$$e = 15 - 5 - 18.95 = -8.95 \text{ in.} \qquad \text{(above middepth)}$$

$$f = -\frac{322}{600} \mp \frac{322(8.95)15}{45,000}$$

$$f \text{ (top)} = -537 - 960 = -1497 \text{ psi} \qquad \text{(compression)}$$
$$f \text{ (bottom)} = -537 + 960 = +423 \text{ psi} \qquad \text{(tension)}$$

exactly as shown in Fig. 21.5.2e.

Load-Balancing Concept. The load-balancing approach visualizes prestressing primarily as a process of balancing loads on the member. The prestressing tendons are placed so that the eccentricity of the prestressing force varies in the same manner as the moments from applied loads; which if exactly done would result in zero flexural stress. Only the axial stress P/A (P is the horizontal component of force in tendon) would act. Refer to Fig. 21.6.2a showing the parabolically draped prestressing tendon. Figure 21.6.2b shows the free body of forces acting on the concrete due to prestress alone. The prestressing may be considered as an upward uniform load if the tendon is parabolically draped. The maximum prestress moment of $Te_{\max}$ at midspan can be equated to an equivalent uniformly loaded beam moment, $w_p L^2/8$; thus

$$w_p = \frac{8Te_{\max}}{L^2} = \text{equivalent uniform load} \qquad \text{(acting upward)} \quad \textbf{(21.6.2)}$$

Let $w_{net} = w$ (actual downward load) $- w_p$; then

$$M_{net} = \frac{w_{net} L^2}{8} \qquad \textbf{(21.6.3)}$$

and

$$f = -\frac{C}{A} \mp \frac{M_{net} y}{I} \qquad \textbf{(21.6.4)}$$

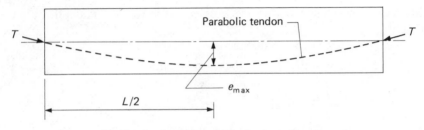

(a) Member having parabolically draped tendon

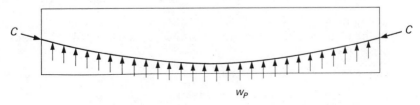

(b) Forces acting on concrete from prestress alone

Fig. 21.6.2
Load-balancing concept of prestressing.

If the tendons are not parabolically draped, the actual net moment (applied load moment minus prestress moment) may be used for M_{net} in Eq. (21.6.4).

EXAMPLE 21.6.2   Compute the stresses on the beam of Fig. 21.5.2 using dead-load and live-load moments of 125 and 383 ft-kips, respectively, using the load-balancing concept.

Solution: The maximum moment due to prestress at transfer is

$$M_{prestress} = 402.5\left(\frac{10}{12}\right) = 335 \text{ ft-kips}$$

$$M_{net} = M_{DL} - M_{prestress} = +125 - 335 = -210 \text{ ft-kips}\quad(\text{negative bending})$$

$$f = -\frac{402.5}{600} \mp \frac{(-210)(12)15}{45,000}$$

$$f\text{ (top)} = -671 + 842 = +171 \text{ psi}\qquad(\text{tension})$$
$$f\text{ (bottom)} = -671 - 842 = -1513 \text{ psi}\qquad(\text{compression})$$

At the final condition,

$$M_{net} = 125 + 383 - 322(10)/12 = 240 \text{ ft-kips}\qquad(\text{positive bending})$$

$$f = -\frac{322}{600} \mp \frac{240(12)(15)}{45,000}$$

$$f\text{ (top)} = -537 - 960 = -1497 \text{ psi}\qquad(\text{compression})$$
$$f\text{ (bottom)} = -537 + 960 = +423 \text{ psi}\qquad(\text{tension})$$

The results agree with those previously obtained.

21.7 Loss of Prestress

The amount of prestress actually existing in a prestressed concrete member is not easily measured. The total force in the tendons at the time of prestressing is all that may conveniently be determined. Various losses reduce the prestress to that lower value available to resist the load. The difference between the final available prestress and the initial value is referred to as the loss of prestress.

In practice the initial prestress is usually determined by a pressure gage on the jack and may be verified by a direct measurement of the tendon elongation. In pretensioned members, the uniformity of initial prestress may be verified at several points. In certain posttensioning procedures, the prestressing force will diminish due to friction at points remote from the jacking source. Initial prestress is, however, generally known with good accuracy.

Elastic Shortening. The loss of prestress due to elastic shortening can be easily determined. For example, let T_0 be the prestressing force that is applied at the centroid of the concrete section in a pretensioned member. If T_f is the final tensile force in the tendons just after elastic shortening has occurred, the strain (unit shortening) in the concrete may be expressed as

$$\epsilon_c = \frac{f_c}{E_c} = \frac{T_f}{A_c E_c} \tag{21.7.1}$$

where $A_c = A_g - A_s$. The change in strain in the tendons as a result of losses is

$$\Delta \epsilon_s = \frac{T_0 - T_f}{A_s E_s} \tag{21.7.2}$$

Equating the expressions for ϵ_c and $\Delta \epsilon_s$ gives

$$\frac{T_0}{T_f} = \frac{A_c + nA_s}{A_c} = \frac{A_T}{A_c} \tag{21.7.3}$$

The loss of prestress Δf_s is

$$\Delta f_s = \frac{T_0 - T_f}{A_s} = \frac{nT_f}{A_c} = \frac{nT_0}{A_T} \tag{21.7.4}$$

As a practical matter, the loss in prestress Δf_s, regardless of whether or not the prestressing force is applied at the centroid of the gross section, may be taken approximately as

$$\Delta f_s = \frac{nT_0}{A_g} \tag{21.7.5}$$

More correctly, the loss in prestress due to elastic shortening and bending of the section should be obtained as n times the computed stress in the concrete adjacent to the tendons.

In the posttensioning case, usually the tendons are not stretched simultaneously. Further, the elastic shortening occurs gradually during the tensioning operation. The various methods of accounting for these gradual losses are adequately described elsewhere [1–5].

EXAMPLE 21.7.1   Determine the percent loss of prestress due to elastic shortening and bending in the pretensioned member of Fig. 21.5.2 $f'_c = 5000$ psi with $n = 6$; $f_{si} = 175,000$ psi.

Solution: (a) Loss due to elastic shortening, neglecting bending. "Exact" method,

$$\Delta f_s = \frac{nT_0}{A_T} = \frac{6(402.5)}{611} = 3.95 \text{ ksi}$$

$$A_T = 20(30) + (6 - 1)2.30 = 611 \text{ sq in.}$$

$$\text{percent loss} = \frac{3.95}{175} = 2.25\%$$

Approximate method,

$$\Delta f_s = \frac{nT_0}{A_g} = \frac{6(402.5)}{600} = 4.03 \text{ ksi}$$

$$\text{percent loss} = \frac{4.03}{175} = 2.3\%$$

There is no significant difference in the two results. Three percent is a typical value for loss due to elastic shortening in a pretensioned beam, whereas in a posttensioned beam it would be on the order of $1\frac{1}{2}\%$ average.

(b) Loss including bending due to dead load of 125 ft-kips. By the approximate method, the stress in *the concrete adjacent to the tendons* is (using internal-force concept),

$$\text{arm} = \frac{M_D}{T_0} = \frac{125(12)}{402.5} = 3.72 \text{ in.}$$

$$C = T_0 = 402.5 \text{ kips}$$

$$f_c = -\frac{C}{A_g} - \frac{C(15 - 5 - 3.72)10}{I_g}$$

$$= -\frac{402.5}{600} - \frac{402.5(6.28)10}{45,000}$$

$$= -671 - 562 = -1233 \text{ psi}$$

This is the stress in concrete 5 in. from the bottom of the beam. The *change* in steel stress is nf_c.

$$\Delta f_s = nf_c = 6(1.233) = 7.4 \text{ ksi}$$

$$\text{percent loss} = \frac{7.4}{175} = 4.2\%$$

Creep in Concrete.   Creep is the time-dependent deformation that occurs in concrete under stress, and has already been discussed in Sec. 1.10 (Chap. 1) and Sec. 14.6 (Chap. 14). The strain due to creep will vary with the magnitude of stress and in general may be assumed to vary with the elastic strain from about 100% in humid atmosphere to about 300% in very dry atmosphere [6].

In Chap. 14, the creep coefficient C_t is defined as

$$C_t = \frac{\text{creep strain, } \epsilon_{cp}}{\text{initial elastic strain, } \epsilon_i} \tag{21.7.6}$$

The elastic strain in the concrete at the centroid of the section is (f_c = stress at centroid)

$$\epsilon_i = \frac{f_c}{E_c}$$

$$\epsilon_{cp} = C_t \epsilon_i = C_t \left(\frac{f_c}{E_c} \right) \tag{21.7.7}$$

The strain in the concrete due to creep equals the decrease in strain in the steel; thus

$$\Delta \epsilon_s = \epsilon_{cp} = C_t \left(\frac{f_c}{E_c} \right) \tag{21.7.8}$$

also

$$\Delta \epsilon_s = \frac{\Delta f_s}{E_s} \tag{21.7.9}$$

Then, equating Eqs. (21.7.8) and (21.7.9),

$$\Delta f_s = C_t n f_c \tag{21.7.10}$$

The coefficient C_t may be determined using the general expressions given in Sec. 14.6 (Chap. 14), or more approximately may be selected from a table of coefficients, such as that suggested by ACI Committee 435 [7]. Typical values for percentage loss of prestress due to creep are from 5 to 6%. Pretensioned beams will exhibit more creep than posttensioned beams because the prestress is imposed when the concrete is at an earlier age; age at loading is a major factor in determining the magnitude of creep.

Shrinkage in Concrete. Shrinkage is the volume change in concrete that occurs with time, as discussed in Sec. 1.10 (Chap. 1) and Sec. 14.7 (Chap. 14). It has been suggested [6] that a unit shrinkage strain of between 0.002 and 0.003 may be reasonable for computing prestress loss. The higher value is probably more realistic for pretensioned members where the prestress is transferred to the concrete at an early age, whereas the lower value is better for posttensioned members.

The loss of prestress due to shrinkage may be expressed

$$\Delta f_s = \epsilon_{sh} E_s \tag{21.7.11}$$

where ϵ_{sh} is the shrinkage strain in concrete (see Sec. 14.7). In Chap. 14 are given general expressions for evaluating shrinkage strain when values more accurate than the rough suggestion given above are considered insufficient.

Relaxation of Steel Stress. Relaxation is taken to mean the loss of stress in steel under nearly constant strain at constant temperature. It is a phenomenon in steel similar to creep in concrete. Loss due to relaxation varies widely for different steels, and such loss should be provided for in accordance with test data furnished by the steel manufacturers. This loss is generally assumed to be in the range of 2 to 3% of the initial steel stress [6].

Friction Losses in Posttensioned Members. There will be frictional losses, which are generally small, in the jacking equipment as well as friction between the tendons and the surrounding material (either duct or actual concrete member), due to intended or unintended curvature in the tendons. The friction between tendons and surrounding material is not small and may be considered as partly a length effect and partly a curvature effect.

Referring to Fig. 21.7.1, let dx be a segment of a curved tendon. Assume that the tendon is being jacked from the left end by the force P_s which results in a force P_x at some distance to the right; these forces define the limits for the tension t. The full angle enclosed within the arc is α.

For equilibrium of the entire segment dx, refer to Fig. 21.7.1b; the normal force dN is

$$dN = t\left(\frac{d\alpha}{2}\right) + \left(t + \frac{dt}{d\alpha}d\alpha\right)\frac{d\alpha}{2} \tag{21.7.12}$$

and neglecting infinitesimals of higher order,

$$dN = 2t\left(\frac{d\alpha}{2}\right) = t\,d\alpha \tag{21.7.13}$$

The friction force developed along the length dx is

$$\mu\,dN = \mu t\,d\alpha \tag{21.7.14}$$

Summation of forces along the tendon gives

$$t - \mu t\,d\alpha - (t + dt) = 0$$

$$\frac{dt}{t} = -\mu\,d\alpha \tag{21.7.15}$$

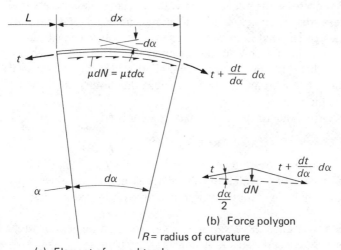

(a) Element of curved tendon

Fig. 21.7.1
Friction losses in posttensioned member.

Integrating to obtain the total effect over the entire curved portion included within the angle α,

$$\int_{P_s}^{P_x} \frac{dt}{t} = \int_0^\alpha -\mu \, d\alpha \qquad (21.7.16)$$

$$\log_e P_x - \log_e P_s = -\mu\alpha \qquad (21.7.17)$$

$$\frac{P_x}{P_s} = e^{-\mu\alpha} \qquad (21.7.18)$$

Replacing the friction force term $\mu\alpha$ with the following expression, which contains a friction part due to curvature and a length effect (wobble effect), $\mu\alpha + KL$, thus

$$\frac{P_x}{P_s} = e^{-(\mu\alpha + KL)} \qquad (21.7.19)$$

or

$$P_s = P_x e^{(\mu\alpha + KL)} \qquad (21.7.20)$$

which is ACI Formula 18-1. Note that $\alpha = L/R$, the length L of the curve divided by R, the radius of curvature.

As an approximation, when $P_s - P_x$ is small (such as not more than 15 to 20% of the jacking force P_s) the friction force may be assumed to be constant. If the friction force is assumed to be proportional to the force P_x, then (see Fig. 21.7.2)

$$\mu N = \mu P_x \alpha \qquad (21.7.21)$$

and assuming the wobble effect KL is also proportional to P_x, equilibrium requires

$$P_s = P_x + P_x(\mu\alpha + KL)$$

or

$$P_s = P_x(1 + \mu\alpha + KL) \qquad (21.7.22)$$

which is ACI Formula 18-2, permitted for use when $(\mu\alpha + KL)$ does not exceed 0.3.

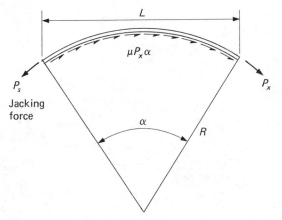

Fig. 21.7.2
Approximate procedure for friction losses.

Practical Design Consideration—Total Losses. The total loss in prestress may be expressed in unit strains, total strains, unit stresses, or in percentage of initial prestress. Although it is difficult to generalize the amount of prestress loss, it has been suggested [1] that for average steel and concrete properties and for average curing conditions the values in Table 21.7.1 may be taken as representative.

Table 21.7.1
Average Percentages of Loss of Prestress [1]

	Pretensioning (percent)	Posttensioning (percent)
Elastic shortening and bending of concrete member	3	1
Creep of concrete	6	5
Shrinkage of concrete	7	6
Relaxation (creep) in steel	2	3
Totals	18	15

The ACI-ASCE Joint Committee [6] has suggested that the loss in steel stress not including friction loss may be assumed as 35,000 psi for pretensioning and 25,000 psi for posttensioning.

More detailed treatment of losses of prestress is to be found in textbooks devoted solely to prestressed concrete [1–5].

EXAMPLE 21.7.2. The posttensioned beam of Fig. 21.7.3 contains a cable of 72 parallel wires, $A_s = 3.60$ sq in., which is to be tensioned 2 wires at a time. The jacking stress is to be measured by a pressure gage. The wires are to be stressed from one end of the member to a value f_1 to overcome frictional loss, then released to a value f_2, so that immediately after anchoring an initial prestress of 144 ksi is obtained. Compute f_1 and f_2, as well as the final design stress after all losses, according to the ACI Code. Assumptions are as follows:

(a) Coefficient of friction $\mu = 0.50$
(b) Wobble coefficient, $K = 0.0008$ (per ft)

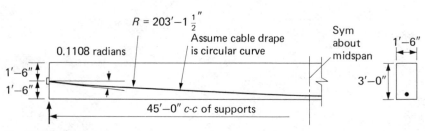

Fig. 21.7.3
Posttensioned beam of Example 21.7.2.

(c) Deformation at anchorages and slip of wires = 0.06 in.
(d) Neglect elastic shortening due to bending of the beam
(e) Ultimate creep coefficient, $C_t = 2.0$
(f) Shrinkage strain, $\epsilon_{sh} = 0.0002$
(g) Creep in the steel = 3% of initial prestress (144 ksi)
(h) $E_s = 29,000$ ksi; $E_c = 5000$ ksi

Solution: (a) Loss due to friction. Using the "exact" method, Eq. (21.7.20).

$$P_s = P_x e^{(\mu\alpha + KL)}$$

$$\mu\alpha = 0.5\left(\frac{45}{203.125}\right) = 0.1108$$

$$KL = 0.0008(45) = \frac{0.0360}{0.1468}$$

$$P_s = P_x e^{(0.1468)} = 1.158 P_x$$

The above expression can also be used in terms of unit stress f; in this case if f_x is desired to be 144 ksi, then the initial stress f_1 to overcome frictional loss is

$$f_1 = 1.158(144) = 167 \text{ ksi}$$

Using the approximate expression, Eq. (21.7.22),

$$P_s = P_x(1 + 0.1468) = 1.1468 P_x$$

or

$$f_1 = 1.1468(144) = 165 \text{ ksi}$$

(b) Anchorage slip. For tensioning from one end,

$$\epsilon_s = \frac{0.06}{45(12)} = 0.00011$$

$$\Delta f_s = \epsilon_s E_s = 0.00011(29,000) = 3.2 \text{ ksi}$$

To allow for anchorage slip, tension to $f_1 = 167$ ksi then release to $f_2 = 144 + 3.2 = 147.2$ ksi. The minimum stress $f_{si} = 144$ ksi will then exist at both ends.

(c) Elastic shortening due to posttensioning two wires at a time. The wires tensioned first will have the greatest loss, having some additional loss as each succeeding pair of wires is tensioned. The pair tensioned last will have zero loss. Thus Δf_s in the first pair, given by Eq. (21.7.5), is

$$\Delta f_s = \frac{nT_0}{A_g}$$

$$n = \frac{29,000}{5000} = 5.8, \qquad \text{say 6 to nearest whole number}$$

$$T_0 = \frac{35}{36}(3.60)(144) = 504 \text{ kips}$$

$$\Delta f_s \text{ (first pair)} = \frac{6(504)}{18(36)} = 4.66 \text{ ksi}$$

$$\Delta f_s \text{ (last pair)} = 0 \text{ ksi}$$

$$\text{average } \Delta f_s = 2.33 \text{ ksi } (1.6\% \text{ of } 144 \text{ ksi})$$

(d) Creep loss.

$$T_0 = 3.6(144) = 518.4 \text{ kips}$$

$$\text{compression force } C = T_0$$

$$\epsilon_c = \text{elastic strain} = \frac{C}{A_g E_c} = \frac{518.4}{18(36)5000} = 0.00016$$

$$\epsilon_{cp} = C_t \epsilon_c = 2.0(0.00016) = 0.00032$$
$$\Delta f_s = \epsilon_{cp} E_s = 0.00032(29,000) = 9.3 \text{ ksi} \qquad (6.5\%)$$

(e) Shrinkage loss.

$$\epsilon_{sh} = 0.0002$$
$$\Delta f_s = \epsilon_{sh} E_s = 0.0002(29,000) = 5.8 \text{ ksi} \qquad (4.0\%)$$

(f) Creep in steel.

$$\Delta f_s = 0.03(144) = 4.3 \text{ ksi} \qquad (3.0\%)$$

(g) Total losses

	Loss of Stress, ksi	Percent
Elastic shortening	2.33	1.6
Creep of concrete	9.3	6.5
Shrinkage	5.8	4.0
Creep in steel	4.3	3.0
Total = 21.7 ksi		15.1%

The final design prestress under dead load plus live load, after losses, is

$$f_{se} = 144 - 21.7 = 122.3 \text{ ksi}$$

21.8 Strength of Flexural Members—ACI Code

Design must include consideration of all significant load stages. Primarily, these stages are (1) initial stage, including the period before and during prestressing, as well as the transfer of prestress to the concrete; (2) intermediate stage during transportation and erection; (3) final stage under service load, after losses; and (4) overload stage, where cracking and ultimate strength are important. Though the actual number of conditions to be investigated varies with the situation, ordinarily the initial service condition involves beam dead load plus prestress *before* losses; the final service condition involves full dead plus live load *after* losses; and, the strength must be adequate for possible overload.

The initial and final service load stages have been considered in Sec. 21.5. A beam may be properly prestressed to carry service loads with little deflection and generally without cracking but, because of a small moment arm to the centroid of the steel, may have an ultimate moment capacity (flexural strength) that gives an inadequate margin of safety. On the other hand, if only the ultimate capacity were considered, service loads might cause excessive camber or deflection.

Balanced Strain Condition. As first described in Sec. 3.5, the balanced strain condition occurs when the concrete strain ϵ_c at the extreme compression fiber is 0.003 at the instant the steel reaches its yield strain $\epsilon_y = f_y/E_s$. In prestressed concrete members, the steel used does not exhibit the well-defined yield point that occurs with ordinary deformed bars, so that the concept of balanced failure is nebulous. The balanced condition was used with ordinary deformed bars as a frame of reference to insure a ductile failure mode. ACI-18.8.1 uses the criterion $\rho_p f_{ps}/f'_c = 0.3$ for prestressed concrete members to represent the equivalent of $0.75\rho_b$ used for ordinary reinforced concrete. The term ρ_p refers to the reinforcement ratio A_{ps}/bd for the prestressing steel, and f_{ps} is the stress in the prestressing steel at the ultimate condition. The following discussion in regard to under- and over-reinforcement is restricted to pretensioned construction and posttensioned construction in which the tendons are grouted. The ultimate strength of posttensioned members in which tendons are ungrouted is, in general, less than that of a bonded beam.

Underreinforced Beams. For cases where $\rho_p f_{ps}/f'_c \le 0.3$, the nominal ultimate moment capacity may be determined for rectangular sections by

$$M_n = T\left(d - \frac{a}{2}\right) \tag{21.8.1}$$

where $T = A_{ps}f_{ps}$, $C = 0.85f'_c ba$, and from $C = T$,

$$a = \frac{A_{ps}f_{ps}}{0.85f'_c b} = \frac{\rho_p bd f_{ps}}{0.85f'_c b} = \frac{\rho_p f_{ps}}{0.85f'_c} d \tag{21.8.2}$$

and A_{ps}, ρ_p, and f_{ps} refer to the area, reinforcement ratio, and tensile stress for the prestressing steel. Note that f_{ps} is the average stress in the prestressing steel *at ultimate load*; it is used instead of f_y because the steel usually exhibits no well-defined yield point (see Fig. 21.8.1).

Substitution of Eq. (21.8.2) into Eq. (21.8.1) gives

$$M_n = A_{ps}f_{ps}\left(d - \frac{\rho_p f_{ps}}{1.7f'_c}d\right) \tag{21.8.3}$$

Thus for any concrete cross section, the nominal ultimate moment capacity depends on ρ_p and f_{ps}.

The actual stress in the prestressing steel at ultimate load may not be easily determined, particularly when the specific stress-strain curve for the steel used is not available. Referring to Fig. 21.8.1, for low percentages of steel and therefore higher stress f_{ps}, the strain may be nearly 0.05; whereas for higher percentages of reinforcement, the strain may be closer to 0.01 (approximately corresponding to yield stress). Thus f_{ps} is not the same for all beams.

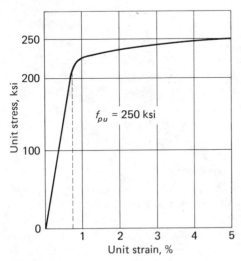

Fig. 21.8.1
Typical stress-strain curve for high-tensile steel wire.

Since test results indicate good agreement [8] with Eq. (21.8.3) up to $\rho_p f_{pu}/f'_c = 0.3$, the ACI-ASCE Joint Committee [6] proposed that f_{ps} be taken at $0.85f_{pu}$ (representing the sharp change in slope of the stress-strain curve when $\rho_p f_{pu}/f'_c = 0.3$) and that it vary linearly from the aforementioned value to $f_{ps} = f_{pu}$ when $\rho_p f_{pu}/f'_c = 0$. Thus, in lieu of more accurate stress-strain data, the steel stress f_{ps} at ultimate load in members with bonded tendons may be taken as (ACI-18.7.2)

$$f_{ps} = f_{pu}\left(1 - 0.5\rho_p\frac{f_{pu}}{f'_c}\right) \tag{21.8.4}$$

which is ACI Formula 18-3. Note that f_{pu} is the ultimate tensile strength (see Fig. 21.8.1).

Overreinforced Beams. For situations in which $\rho_p f_{pu}/f'_c > 0.3$, test results were scattered but indicated f_{ps} at ultimate load to be less than $0.85f_{pu}$. Although it is possible to achieve some small gain in ultimate capacity when higher percentages of steel are used, a ductile failure is desired and thus the value obtained when $\rho_p f_{pu}/f'_c$ equals 0.3 may be taken as the maximum.

Then, conservatively letting $\rho_p f_{ps}/f'_c = \rho_p f_{pu}/f'_c = 0.3$, Eq. (21.8.3) for rectangular sections becomes

$$M_n = A_{ps}f_{ps}d\left(1 - 0.59\rho_p \frac{f_{ps}}{f'_c}\right) = \rho_p bdf_{ps}d\left(1 - 0.59\rho_p \frac{f_{ps}}{f'_c}\right)$$

$$= f'_c bd^2\left(\rho_p \frac{f_{ps}}{f'_c}\right)\left(1 - 0.59\rho_p \frac{f_{ps}}{f'_c}\right)$$

$$= f'_c bd^2(0.3)[1 - 0.59(0.3)]$$

$$= 0.25f'_c bd^2 \qquad\qquad (21.8.5)$$

Equation (21.8.5) as a maximum value for M_n satisfies the intent of ACI-18.8.2 which states that if $\rho_p f_{ps}/f'_c$ exceeds 0.3, "moment design strength shall not exceed the moment design strength calculated from equations based on the compression portion of the internal resisting couple." Note that moment design strength is ϕM_n.

For flanged sections, if the neutral axis is below the flange, the compressive force may be considered as being composed of two parts. The web may be treated as a rectangular section, and the excess flange width may be considered as having an average stress of $0.85f'_c$ acting on it. The approach is essentially the same as that discussed for T-sections in Chap. 9.

EXAMPLE 21.8.1 Determine the nominal ultimate moment capacity M_n of the pretensioned bonded section investigated in Example 21.5.2. The concrete has $f'_c = 5000$ psi and the steel has $f_{pu} = 250,000$ psi. Assume an average stress-strain relationship for the steel, as given in Fig. 21.8.1.

Solution: The approximate stress at ultimate load, according to ACI-18.7.2, may be taken as

$$f_{ps} = f_{pu}\left(1 - 0.5\rho_p \frac{f_{pu}}{f'_c}\right)$$

$$\rho_p = \frac{A_{ps}}{bd} = \frac{2.30}{20(25)} = 0.0046$$

$$f_{ps} = 250\left[1 - \frac{0.5(0.0046)(250)}{5}\right] = 250(1 - 0.115) = 221 \text{ ksi}$$

From Fig. 21.8.2c,

$$C_u = 0.85f'_c ba = 0.85(5)(20)a = 85a$$
$$T_u = A_{ps}f_{ps} = 2.30(221) = 508 \text{ kips}$$
$$C_u = T_u$$

$$a = \frac{508}{85} = 5.98 \text{ in.}$$

$$x = \frac{a}{\beta_1} = \frac{5.98}{0.8} = 7.47 \text{ in.}$$

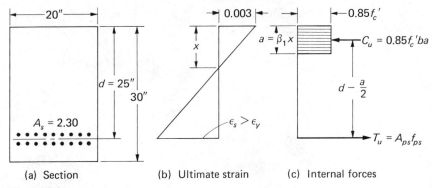

(a) Section (b) Ultimate strain (c) Internal forces

Fig. 21.8.2
Ultimate strength of section for Example 21.8.1.

The additional strain ϵ_{s2} due to the ultimate moment is

$$\epsilon_{s2} = 0.003 \frac{17.53}{7.47} = 0.00704$$

which, when added to the strain due to prestress after losses, gives

$$\epsilon_s = \epsilon_{s1} + \epsilon_{s2} = \frac{140}{29,000} + 0.00704 = 0.00483 + 0.00704 = 0.0119$$

$$f_{si} \text{ (initial)} = 175,000 \text{ psi}$$
$$\Delta f_s \text{ (losses)} = 0.2(175,000) = 35,000 \text{ psi}$$

The strain ϵ_s of 0.0119 corresponds approximately to that for a stress f_{ps} of 225 ksi, using a typical stress-strain relationship for a steel with $f_{pu} = 250$ ksi, such as in Fig. 21.8.1. The value of f_{ps} agrees with the starting assumption based on Eq. (21.8.4).

Verify that $\rho_p f_{ps}/f'_c < 0.3$. Using the corrected value $f_{ps} = 225$ ksi,

$$\rho_p \frac{f_{ps}}{f'_c} = \frac{0.0046(225)}{5} = 0.207 < 0.3 \qquad \text{OK}$$

Thus, the nominal moment capacity is

$$M_n = T_u\left(d - \frac{a}{2}\right) = \left[508\left(25 - \frac{5.98}{2}\right)\right]\frac{1}{12} = 932 \text{ ft-kips}$$

The required nominal moment strength based on the service loads of Example 21.5.2 is

$$\text{required } M_n = \frac{M_u}{\phi} = \frac{1.4(125) + 1.7(383)}{0.90} = 918 \text{ ft-kips} < 932 \text{ ft-kips} \quad \text{OK}$$

EXAMPLE 21.8.2   For a typical prestressed concrete beam, using high tensile strength steel wire having a stress-strain curve as in Fig. 21.8.1, show that the balanced condition at ultimate strength may be approximated by $\rho_p = 0.4f'_c/f_{ps}$.

Solution: (a) Consider $f'_c = 5000$ psi and that ultimate crushing strain for concrete is 0.003 as prescribed by the ACI Code. Referring to Fig. 21.8.1, the proportional limit is about $0.85f_{pu}$, above which value strain increases more rapidly than stress. Thus the approximate balanced condition occurs when $\epsilon_c = 0.003$ and $\Delta\epsilon_s$ (change in steel strain due to external loading) equals the strain ϵ_{ps} at $f_{ps} = 0.85f_{pu}$ less the initial prestress strain ϵ_i. For the balanced condition,

$$C_b = 0.85f'_c ba_b$$
$$T_b = A_{psb}f_{ps} = \rho_{pb}bdf_{ps}$$
$$C_b = T_b$$

$$a_b = \left(\frac{d}{0.85}\right)\rho_{pb}\frac{f_{ps}}{f'_c}$$

$$a_b = \beta_1 x_b = 0.80x_b \qquad \text{for } f'_c = 5000 \text{ psi}$$

$$\frac{x_b}{d} = \frac{1}{0.80(0.85)}\rho_{pb}\frac{f_{ps}}{f'_c}$$

or

$$\rho_{pb} = 0.68\frac{f'_c}{f_{ps}}\left(\frac{x_b}{d}\right)$$

where ρ_{pb} is the balanced percentage of prestressed reinforcement.

At $f_{ps} = 0.85f_{pu}$, $\epsilon_{ps} = 0.0075$ from Fig. 21.8.1. Also, if the initial tension in the prestressing steel is $0.60f_{pu}$, then the initial tensile strain in the steel (representing a compressive strain in concrete) is

$$\epsilon_i = \frac{0.60f_{pu}}{E_s} = \frac{150}{30,000} \approx 0.005$$

Thus

$$\Delta\epsilon_s = \epsilon_{ps} - \epsilon_i = 0.0075 - 0.005 = 0.0025$$

Then, from Fig. 21.8.3,

$$\frac{x_b}{d} = \frac{0.003}{0.003 + 0.0025} = 0.545$$

Substituting into the ρ_{pb} expression gives

$$\rho_{pb} = 0.68\frac{f'_c}{f_{ps}}(0.545) = 0.371\frac{f'_c}{f_{ps}}$$

(b) Suppose that $\epsilon_c = 0.0035$ instead of 0.003, and $\beta_1 = 0.85$ instead of 0.80 while the concrete strength decreases. There will be no change in $\Delta\epsilon_s$ if it is still assumed $f_{ps} = 0.85f_{pu}$,

$$\frac{x_b}{d} = \frac{0.0035}{0.0035 + 0.0025} = 0.584$$

$$\rho_{pb} = 0.85(0.85)\frac{f'_c}{f_{ps}}(0.584) = 0.422\frac{f'_c}{f_{ps}}$$

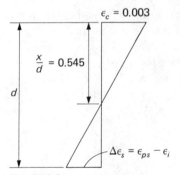

Fig. 21.8.3
Strain diagram for the approximate
balanced condition due to superimposed loads.

In effect the values of ρ_{pb} represent the "balanced" amount of reinforcement, which if exceeded would have the concrete reach crushing strain while the steel is still in the elastic range. Probably $0.422f'_c/f_{ps}$ represents a reasonable upper bound and $0.371f'_c/f_{ps}$ represents a typical value for the balanced condition. Thus the ACI Code use of $0.4f'_c/f_{ps}$ as the balanced reinforcement ratio seems reasonable; consequently, $0.3f'_c/f_{ps}$ reasonably represents 0.75 of the balanced reinforcement ratio.

21.9 Cracking Moment

One of the features of prestressed concrete is that under service load it is usually crack free. To be sure that an adequate reserve exists against cracking, ACI-18.8.3 requires the total amount of prestressed and nonprestressed reinforcement to be adequate to develop a design load (overload) in flexure at least 1.2 times the cracking load calculated using a modulus of rupture equal to $7.5\sqrt{f'_c}$ for normal-weight concrete (see ACI-9.5.2.3 for lightweight concrete). This ACI provision is a means of insuring that cracking will occur *before* flexural strength is reached, and by a large enough margin so that significant deflection will occur to warn that the ultimate capacity is being approached. The typical member will have a fairly large margin between cracking strength and flexural strength but the designer must be certain by checking it.

EXAMPLE 21.9.1   Compute the cracking moment and check its acceptability according to the ACI Code, for the beam of Example 21.8.1 (Fig. 21.8.2). Use $f'_c = 5000$ psi and assume the effective prestress, after losses, is 140 ksi.

Solution: (a) Use the homogeneous beam concept (Sec. 21.6). The effective prestress force is

$$T_e = A_{ps}f_{se} = 2.30(140) = 322 \text{ kips}$$

Using the following equation to find the cracking moment,

$$-\left(\begin{array}{c}\text{axial}\\\text{prestress}\end{array}\right)-\left(\begin{array}{c}\text{moment}\\\text{prestress}\end{array}\right)+\left(\begin{array}{c}\text{external}\\\text{loads}\end{array}\right)=\left(\begin{array}{c}\text{cracking}\\\text{stress}\end{array}\right)$$

$$-\frac{T_e}{A_g}-\frac{T_e e y_t}{I_g}+\frac{M_{cr}y_t}{I_g}=f_r=7.5\sqrt{5000}=530\text{ psi}$$

$$-\frac{322}{600}-\frac{322(10)15}{45,000}+\frac{M_{cr}(15)}{45,000}=0.530$$

$$M_{cr}=\left[\frac{0.530(45,000)}{15}+321.5(10)+\frac{322(45,000)}{600(15)}\right]\frac{1}{12}$$

$$=133+268+134=535\text{ ft-kips}$$

(b) Use the internal-force concept (Sec. 21.6). Consider that the cracking moment M_{cr} is comprised of two parts,

$$M_{cr}=M_1+M_2$$

where M_1 is the superimposed moment necessary to give zero stress in the precompressed tension zone (see Fig. 21.9.1); and M_2 is the additional moment to cause cracking assuming that zero stress exists at the tension face when M_2 is applied (see Fig. 21.9.1).

$$C=T_e=322\text{ kips}$$

$$M_1=T_e(e+e_1)=322\left(\frac{10+5}{12}\right)=403\text{ ft-kips}$$

$$M_2=\frac{f_r I_g}{y_t}=\frac{0.530(45,000)}{15(12)}=133\text{ ft-kips}$$

$$M_{cr}=M_1+M_2=403+133=536\text{ ft-kips}$$

(c) Use the load-balancing concept (Sec. 21.6).

$$M_{net}=M_{cr}-M_{prestress}$$
$$=M_{cr}-322(10)\tfrac{1}{12}=M_{cr}-268$$

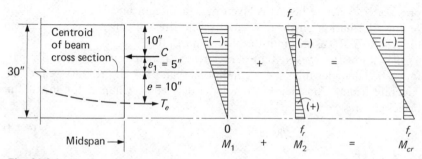

Fig. 21.9.1
Computation of cracking moment.

Using Eq. (21.6.4),

$$f = -\frac{C}{A} \mp \frac{M_{net}y}{I}$$

$$0.530 = -\frac{322}{20(30)} + \frac{(M_{cr} - 268)(15)12}{45,000}$$

$$0.530 = -0.537 + \frac{(M_{cr} - 268)}{250}$$

$$M_{cr} = 1.067(250) + 268 = 535 \text{ ft-kips}$$

(d) Check ACI-18.8.3. From Example 21.8.1, the nominal ultimate moment capacity M_n is 932 ft-kips.

$$1.2M_{cr} < \phi M_n$$
$$1.2(535) < 0.90(932)$$
$$640 \text{ ft-kips} < 840 \text{ ft-kips} \qquad \text{OK}$$

Thus cracking will occur soon enough before reaching ultimate flexural strength so that large deflection will give a warning of impending failure.

In addition it is noted that the overload factor against cracking at midspan is

$$\text{FS against cracking} = \frac{535}{125 + 383} = 1.05$$

If more reserve against cracking is desired, the tensile stress permitted under final service conditions should be reduced below $6\sqrt{f'_c}$. Cracking at service load may or may not be detrimental. Nonprestressed beams usually crack under service load.

21.10 Shear Strength of Members without Shear Reinforcement

In general the ideas presented in Chap. 5 regarding shear strength for nonprestressed beams are also applicable to prestressed beams. An excellent summary of background for the ACI Code expressions for shear strength of prestressed concrete beams is given by MacGregor and Hanson [9]. More recent information on shear strength of prestressed concrete is available in the ASCE-ACI Task Committee 426 Report [10].

It is known, however, that a prestressed concrete beam generally performs better under high shear conditions than does an ordinary reinforced concrete beam. Consider Eq. (5.3.1) as derived in Chap. 5 for maximum principal stress,

$$f_t(max) = \frac{f_t}{2} + \sqrt{\left(\frac{f_t}{2}\right)^2 + v^2} \qquad [5.3.1]$$

In nonprestressed concrete the normal stress f_t is a tensile stress on one side of the neutral axis. When the concrete is prestressed, f_t is a compressive stress throughout the member. Replacing f_t with $-f_t$ it is apparent that the magnitude of the principal tensile stress decreases,

$$f_t(\text{max}) = \frac{-f_t}{2} + \sqrt{\left(\frac{f_t}{2}\right)^2 + v^2} \qquad (21.10.1)$$

The angle α that the maximum principal tensile stress makes with the beam axis is greater for a prestressed concrete beam than for an ordinary reinforced concrete beam, as shown in Fig. 21.10.1. Inclined cracking will be less likely to occur and, if it occurs, will be more nearly horizontal than in nonprestressed members.

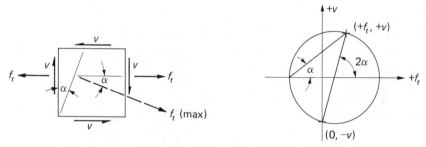

(a) Principal stress — reinforced concrete beam

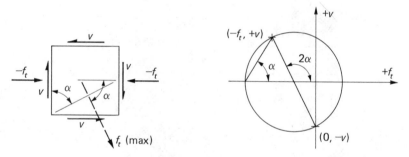

(b) Principal stress — prestressed concrete beam

Fig. 21.10.1
Comparison of directions of principal tensile stress.

Two types of inclined cracks are possible in prestressed concrete beams: (1) the flexure-shear crack that occurs in a beam previously cracked due to flexure; and (2) the web-shear crack that occurs in the thin web of a previously uncracked beam (see Fig. 5.4.1). Whereas only the flexure-shear crack was common in nonprestressed beams, both types represent potential cracks in prestressed concrete beams.

Flexure-Shear Cracking Strength. The flexure-shear crack arises from high principal stress near the interior extremity of a flexural crack. Experimental studies have shown that the shear corresponding to the flexure-shear

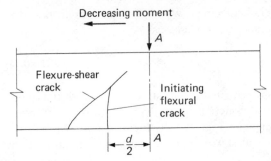

Fig. 21.10.2
Flexure-shear type of inclined crack.

crack is that which causes flexural cracking at approximately a distance $d/2$ from the load point, in the direction of decreasing bending moment [11] (see Fig. 21.10.2). The 1963 ACI Code formula for flexure-shear cracking strength was the experimentally determined linear relationship of Fig. 21.10.3. Because the relationship between moment and shear (M/V) was not the same for both dead and live loads in the tests, the effects of dead load were not included in the linear relationship.

The ordinate of the plot (see Fig. 21.10.3) is thus in terms of $V_{ci} - V_d$, where V_d is the service dead-load shear force and V_{ci} is the total nominal

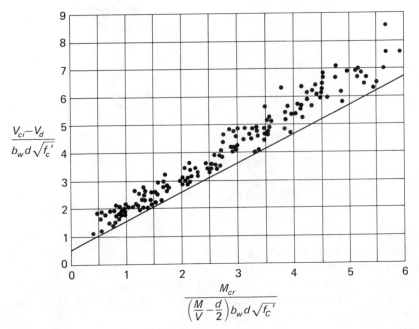

Fig. 21.10.3
Comparison of the shear corresponding to flexure-shear cracking in prestressed concrete beams with the ratio of the flexural cracking moment to the shear span (both axes nondimensionalized by dividing by $b_w d \sqrt{f'_c}$) (from Ref. 12).

ultimate shear strength. The abscissa involves the net cracking moment M_{cr} due to service loads. The net cracking stress used for computing M_{cr} equals the modulus of rupture (assumed conservatively at $6\sqrt{f'_c}$ psi), plus the compressive stress f_{pe} provided by the prestressing force (after losses) occurring at the extreme fiber at which tensile stresses are caused by the applied loads, less the tensile stress f_d due to service dead load. Thus

$$M_{cr} = \frac{I}{y_t}(6\sqrt{f'_c} + f_{pe} - f_d) \qquad (21.10.2)$$

The abscissa (Fig. 21.10.3) involves $M_{cr}/(M/V - d/2)$, which represents the applied load shear at $d/2$ from the cross section being investigated. A moment M and a shear V act on section A-A of Fig. 21.10.4. Assume that M and V give rise to a moment crack at $d/2$ from section A-A. From the basic shear-moment relationship the change in moment between two points equals the area under the shear diagram between those points. Thus referring to Fig. 21.10.4,

$$M - M_{cr} = \frac{V + V_{cr}}{2}\left(\frac{d}{2}\right) \qquad (21.10.3)$$

Since the difference between V and V_{cr} will usually be small, assume $V_{cr} = V$; thus

$$M - M_{cr} = V\left(\frac{d}{2}\right) \qquad (21.10.4)$$

Solving for M_{cr},

$$M_{cr} = M - V\left(\frac{d}{2}\right)$$

$$= V\left(\frac{M}{V} - \frac{d}{2}\right) \qquad (21.10.5)$$

Finally, the shear on the section investigated becomes

$$V = \frac{M_{cr}}{M/V - d/2} \qquad (21.10.6)$$

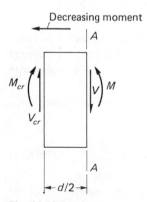

Fig. 21.10.4
Shear-moment relationship.

Thus the linear relationship for the flexure-shear cracking strength resulting from high principal stress in the vicinity of a flexural crack is, according to Fig. 21.10.3,

$$\frac{V_{ci} - V_d}{b_w d \sqrt{f'_c}} = 0.6 + \frac{M_{cr}}{(M/V - d/2)b_w d \sqrt{f'_c}} \qquad (21.10.7)$$

Since 1971, ACI-11.4.2 has simplified the expression by eliminating the subtracted $d/2$ term.

Thus the nominal flexure-shear cracking strength V_{ci}, ACI Formula (11-11), is

$$V_{ci} = 0.6\sqrt{f'_c}b_w d + \frac{V_i M_{cr}}{M_{max}} + V_d \geq 1.7\sqrt{f'_c}b_w d \qquad (21.10.8)$$

In Eq. (21.10.8), M_{max} replaces M of Eq. (21.10.7) and represents the maximum moment that can occur at the section under consideration, due to externally applied factored loads (i.e., applied loads other than beam weight and prestress unless the prestress causes an external reaction). V_i replaces V of Eq. (21.10.7) and represents the shear force at the section due to the factored loading that caused maximum moment. In other words, one uses the moment *envelope* values for M_{max} along with the corresponding shears, rather than the shear envelope values which would be larger. Of course, where partial span loadings are not considered, the full-span loading gives V_i and M_{max} for each point along the span. When full-span uniform loading is used in a simply supported span, $V_i = w(L - 2x)/2$ and $M_{max} = wx(L - x)/2$, and

$$\frac{V_i}{M_{max}} = \frac{L - 2x}{x(L - x)} \qquad (21.10.9)$$

In effect, Eq. (21.10.8) gives the flexure-shear cracking strength as the sum of (1) the shear due to actual dead load (beam weight) without overload factor, (2) the superimposed factored live load which is sufficient to cause flexural cracking, and (3) the additional load ($0.6\sqrt{f'_c}b_w d$) which will cause the flexural crack to initiate the inclined flexure-shear crack.

Web-Shear Cracking Strength.   The web-shear crack arises in a beam previously uncracked due to flexure. Such a crack is typical near the support of a thin-webbed section (see Fig. 5.4.1) as a result of high principal tensile stress.

For this development the beam may reasonably be considered as homogeneous. Thus Eq. (21.10.1) may be directly applied,

$$f_t(max) = \frac{-f_t}{2} + \sqrt{\left(\frac{f_t}{2}\right)^2 + v^2} \qquad [21.10.1]$$

Since tests have demonstrated that cracks of this type usually originate near the centroid of the section, the stresses refer to that location. Solving

Eq. (21.10.1) for v,

$$\left[f_t(\text{max}) + \frac{f_t}{2}\right]^2 = \left(\frac{f_t}{2}\right)^2 + v^2$$

$$[f_t(\text{max})]^2 + f_t(\text{max})f_t + \left(\frac{f_t}{2}\right)^2 = \left(\frac{f_t}{2}\right)^2 + v^2$$

$$v = f_t(\text{max})\sqrt{1 + \frac{f_t}{f_t(\text{max})}} \qquad \textbf{(21.10.10)}$$

where f_t is the compressive stress at the level of the centroid, and $f_t(\text{max}) =$ principal tensile stress $\leq$ tensile strength of concrete if no cracks are to form.

Since Eq. (21.10.10) should agree with the criteria for ultimate shear strength for nonprestressed beams, $f_t(\text{max})$ is taken as $3.5\sqrt{f'_c}$. The equation then becomes

$$v = 3.5\sqrt{f'_c}\sqrt{1 + \frac{f_t}{3.5\sqrt{f'_c}}} \qquad \textbf{(21.10.11)}$$

A plot of Eq. (21.10.11) is given in Fig. 21.10.5, illustrating that this equation may be approximated by a straight line,

$$v = 3.5\sqrt{f'_c} + 0.3f_t \qquad \textbf{(21.10.12)}$$

or, in ACI Code terminology, multiplying by $b_w d$ to give nominal shear strength,

$$V_{cw} = (3.5\sqrt{f'_c} + 0.3f_{pc})b_w d \qquad \textbf{(21.10.13)}$$

where f_{pc} is defined as the compressive stress (psi) in the concrete, after losses, at the centroid of the section resisting the applied loads, or if the centroid lies within the flange on a T-section, f_{pc} is the stress at the junction of the flange and web.

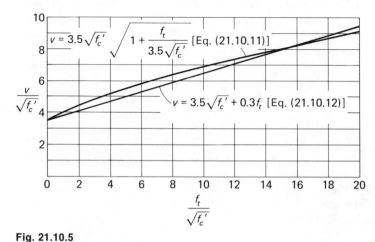

Fig. 21.10.5
Comparison of theoretical maximum shear stress with straight-line approximation.

If prestressing tendons are draped, a vertical component V_p arises which assists in carrying the shear. Therefore ACI-11.4.2 gives ACI Formula 11-13 as

$$V_{cw} = (3.5\sqrt{f'_c} + 0.3f_{pc})b_wd + V_p \qquad (21.10.14)$$

Alternatively, the web-shear cracking strength may be determined (ACI-11.4.2.2) using nominal ultimate stress $v_n = V_u/(\phi b_w d)$ with the principal stress equation, Eq. (21.10.10), where the principal stress $f_t(\text{max})$ is limited to $4\sqrt{f'_c}$. This would give Eq. (21.10.11) with coefficients 4 instead of 3.5. Thus using f_{pc} for f_t, Eq. (21.10.11) becomes

$$v_{cw} = 4\sqrt{f'_c}\sqrt{1 + \frac{f_{pc}}{4\sqrt{f'_c}}} \qquad (21.10.15)$$

which is an acceptable alternate to using Eq. (21.10.14).

The nominal ultimate shear strength V_n at which inclined cracking is imminent is given by the lesser of V_{ci} and V_{cw}, determined from ACI Formulas 11-11 and 11-13 for normal-weight concrete.

When applying Eqs. (21.10.8) and (21.10.14) or (21.10.15) for V_{ci} and V_{cw}, the effective depth d is to be taken as the distance from the extreme compression fiber to the centroid of the prestressing tendons, or as 80% of the overall depth of the member, whichever is greater.

In computing the prestress effect f_{pc}, full prestress after losses may be used only when the prestressing tendons are embedded a distance exceeding their required development length from the section being investigated. The critical section for maximum shear is generally at $h/2$ from the face of support (ACI-11.1.3.2), so that the region between the face of support and $h/2$ therefrom must be designed for the shear at the critical section.

ACI Code Simplified Alternative for Shear Strength. When the member has an effective prestress f_{se} at least equal to 40% of the tensile strength f_{pu} of the flexural reinforcement, the nominal ultimate shear capacity of the member may be taken as (ACI Formula 11-10)

$$V_c = \left[0.6\sqrt{f'_c} + 700\frac{V_u d}{M_u}\right]b_w d \qquad (21.10.16)$$

which may be considered a linear gradient between that using the minimum nominal unit stress $v_c = 2\sqrt{f'_c}$ and an upper bound of $v_c(\text{max}) = 5\sqrt{f'_c}$. Supporting data for this alternate relationship are shown in Fig. 21.10.6 from MacGregor and Hanson [9].

When applying Eq. (21.10.16) from ACI-11.4.1, V_u is the maximum shear due to factored loading at the section and M_u is the simultaneously occurring moment; $V_u d/M_u$ is also limited to a maximum value of 1.0; and d is the actual effective depth. Equation (21.10.16) represents essentially the flexure-shear cracking strength expressed in a manner similar to that for nonprestressed reinforced concrete. Since the percentage of reinforcement is low in prestressed concrete, a constant has been used instead of the variable ρ.

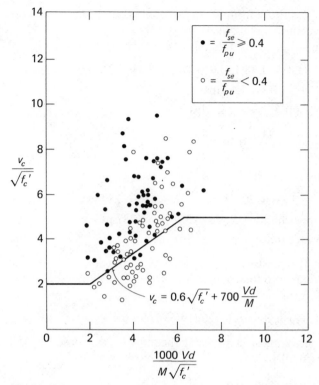

Fig. 21.10.6
Alternate equation for computing v_c for prestressed beams (from Ref. 16).

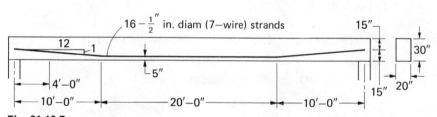

Fig. 21.10.7
Section for Example 21.10.1.

EXAMPLE 21.10.1   Determine the nominal ultimate shear strength at a section 4 ft from the supports of the 40 ft simple span shown in Fig. 21.10.7. The effective prestress force T_e (after losses) is 322 kips. The beam is to support a service live load of 1.38 kips/ft in addition to the beam weight of 0.625 kip/ft. The concrete has $f'_c = 5000$ psi.

Solution: (a) Simplified alternate procedure, using ACI Formula 11-10, Eq. (21.10.16).

$$V_c = \left(0.6\sqrt{f'_c} + 700\frac{V_u d}{M_u}\right)b_w d$$

In the application of the above formula, the symbols V_u and M_u indicate use of the shear and moment including overload factors.

Assume partial-span loading is not considered.

$$w_u = 0.625(1.4) + 1.38(1.7) = 0.87 + 2.34 = 3.21 \text{ kips/ft}$$
$$V_u = 3.21(20 - 4) = 51.4 \text{ kips}$$
$$M_u = \tfrac{1}{2}(3.21)(4)(36) = 231 \text{ ft-kips}$$
$$\frac{V_u d}{M_u} = \frac{51.4(30 - 11)}{231(12)} = 0.35$$

The nominal unit stress capacity is

$$v_c = 0.6\sqrt{5000} + 700(0.35) = 42 + 245 = 287 \text{ psi}$$
$$v_c \text{ (upper limit)} = 5\sqrt{f'_c} = 354 \text{ psi} > 287 \text{ psi} \qquad \text{OK}$$
$$v_c \text{ (lower limit)} = 2\sqrt{f'_c} = 141 \text{ psi} < 287 \text{ psi} \qquad \text{OK}$$

Thus at this section the prestressed member has a contribution v_c to the shear strength attributable to the concrete of 287 psi. The nominal ultimate shear strength at 4 ft from the support would be

$$V_c = v_c b_w d = 0.287(20)(19) = 109 \text{ kips}$$

(b) Flexure-shear cracking strength using the more exact procedure, ACI Formula 11-11; Eq. (21.10.8),

$$V_{ci} = 0.6\sqrt{f'_c}b_w d + \frac{V_i M_{cr}}{M_{max}} + V_d$$

using Eq. (21.10.2),

$$M_{cr} = \frac{I}{y_t}(6\sqrt{f'_c} + f_{pe} - f_d)$$

$$I = \tfrac{1}{12}(20)(30)^3 = 45{,}000 \text{ in.}^4 \qquad \text{(neglecting steel)}$$

$$y_t = 15 \text{ in.}$$

f_{pe} = compressive stress due to prestressing force

$$= \frac{322{,}000}{20(30)} + \frac{322{,}000(4)(15)}{45{,}000} = 537 + 429 = 966 \text{ psi}$$

$$f_d = \text{dead-load stress} = \frac{My}{I} = \frac{625(4)(36)(12)(15)}{2(45{,}000)} = 180 \text{ psi}$$

$$M_{cr} = \frac{45{,}000}{15(12{,}000)}(6\sqrt{5000} + 966 - 180)$$

$$= 0.25(424 + 966 - 180) = 0.25(1210) = 302 \text{ ft-kips}$$

M_{max} = maximum moment due to externally applied factored loads except beam weight at section being investigated

$$= \tfrac{1}{2}(1.38)(4)(36)(1.7) = 169 \text{ ft-kips}$$

V_i = corresponding shear due to factored load at section investigated

$$= 1.38(20 - 4)(1.7) = 37.5 \text{ kips}$$

$$\frac{V_i M_{cr}}{M_{max}} = \frac{37.5(302)}{169} = 67.0 \text{ kips}$$

$V_d = \text{dead-load shear} = 0.625(20 - 4) = 10.0 \text{ kips}$

$d = 30 - 11 = 19 \text{ in.}$ or $0.80h = 0.8(30) = \underline{24 \text{ in.}}$

$V_{ci} = 0.6\sqrt{5000}(20)(24)\frac{1}{1000} + 67.0 + 10.0 = 97.4 \text{ kips}$

The flexure-shear cracking strength is not to be taken less than

$\min V_{ci} = 1.7\sqrt{f'_c}b_w d$

$\qquad = 1.7\sqrt{5000}(20)(24)\frac{1}{1000} = 57.7 \text{ kips} < 97.4 \text{ kips}$ OK

(c) Web-shear cracking strength using the more exact procedure, ACI Formula 11-13, Eq. (21.10.14),

$$V_{cw} = [3.5\sqrt{f'_c} + 0.3f_{pc}]b_w d + V_p$$

$f_{pc} = $ compressive stress in concrete at centroid of section resisting live load, due to all applied loads (zero due to all except T_e/A_c in this case)

$$= \frac{322,000}{20(30)} = 537 \text{ psi}$$

$d = 19 \text{ in.}$ or $0.80(30) = \underline{24 \text{ in.}}$ (use larger value)

$V_{cw} = [3.5\sqrt{5000} + 0.3(537)](20)(24)\frac{1}{1000} + \frac{1}{12}(322) = 223 \text{ kips}$

Since $V_{ci} < V_{cw}$, $V_{ci} = 97.4 \text{ kips}$ represents the nominal strength at 4 ft from the support for the member without web reinforcement. The simplified alternate equation gives a nominal shear strength 12% higher than obtained from the more exact procedure; 109 kips compared to 97.4 kips.

21.11 Shear Reinforcement for Prestressed Concrete Beams

The computations for shear reinforcement are essentially the same as for nonprestressed concrete as developed in Chap. 5. The total nominal ultimate shear strength may be represented as the sum of the amount attributable to the concrete and that attributable to the shear reinforcement; thus Eq. (5.7.1) still applies,

$$V_n = V_c + V_s \qquad\qquad \textbf{[5.7.1]}$$

or, in terms of nominal ultimate stress v_n,

$$v_n = v_c + v_s \qquad\qquad \textbf{(21.11.1)}$$

where

$$v_n = \frac{V_u}{\phi b_w d} \qquad\qquad \textbf{(21.11.2)}$$

The nominal strength V_c attributable to the concrete may be determined by (1) Eq. (21.10.16) when the effective prestress is at least 40% of the ultimate tensile strength of the steel, or (2) the *smaller* of Eqs. (21.10.8) and (21.10.14) for V_{ci} and V_{cw}. The second and more accurate method using V_{ci} and V_{cw} may be used whatever the magnitude of prestress.

For the shear reinforcement contribution, Eq. (5.10.7) is used,

$$V_s = \frac{A_v f_y d}{s} \quad \text{or} \quad v_s = \frac{A_v f_y}{b_w s} \qquad \text{[5.10.7]}$$

where

$$V_s = V_n - V_c$$
$$v_s = v_n - v_c$$
A_v = effective area of shear reinforcement at any section
b_w = width of the web
s = spacing of the shear reinforcement

Just as for nonprestressed reinforced concrete beams, prestressed concrete beams must have at least a minimum amount of shear reinforcement whenever $V_u > \phi V_c/2$ (ACI-11.5.5.1). However, this requirement may be waived if tests are made showing that the required ultimate flexural and shear strengths can be developed when shear reinforcement is omitted. Since prestressed concrete members are usually of standardized shapes with many identical or similar members manufactured, manufacturers frequently have made tests demonstrating that no web reinforcement is required.

When minimum shear reinforcement is required, ACI-11.5.5.3 gives for the minimum area A_v

$$A_v = 50 \frac{b_w s}{f_y} \qquad (21.11.3)$$

which is also used for nonprestressed concrete.

Alternatively, for prestressed members only, where the effective prestress force equals at least 40% of the tensile strength of the steel, the minimum area may be taken as (ACI-11.5.5.4)

$$A_v = \frac{A_{ps}}{80} \left(\frac{f_{pu}}{f_y}\right) \left(\frac{s}{d}\right) \sqrt{\frac{d}{b_w}} \qquad (21.11.4)$$

where

A_{ps} = area of prestressing steel
f_{pu} = tensile strength of prestressing steel
f_y = specified strength shear reinforcement
s = stirrup spacing, which may not exceed 0.75 of the depth of the member, nor 24 in., whichever is smaller
d = distance from the extreme compressive fiber to the centroid of the steel.

EXAMPLE 21.11.1   Determine the maximum spacing of #3 U stirrups at a point 4 ft from the support on the beam of Example 21.10.1 (Fig. 21.10.7). The prestressing steel has an area of 2.30 sq in. and an ultimate tensile strength $f_{pu} = 250,000$ psi, the yield strength of the stirrup reinforcement $f_y = 40,000$ psi, and the concrete has $f'_c = 5000$ psi. The service live load is 1.38 kips/ft, and the dead load is 0.625 kip/ft.

Solution: The inclined cracking strength in terms of nominal ultimate strength, as determined in Example 21.10.1, is

$$V_{ci} \text{ (controls)} = 97.4 \text{ kips} \qquad \text{(more exact procedure)}$$

At 4 ft from centerline of support,

$$V_u = [1.4(0.625) + 1.7(1.38)](20 - 4) = 3.21(20 - 4) = 51.4 \text{ kips}$$

$$V_u = 51.4 \text{ kips} > \frac{\phi V_c}{2} = \frac{0.85(97.4)}{2} = 41 \text{ kips}$$

Thus a minimum amount of shear reinforcement must be provided, unless tests are made to justify its omission. Thus using Eq. (21.11.3)

$$\frac{A_v}{s} = 50\frac{b_w}{f_y} = 50\left(\frac{20}{40,000}\right) = 0.025$$

or, alternatively, Eq. (21.11.4),

$$\frac{A_v}{s} = \frac{A_{ps}}{80}\left(\frac{f_{pu}}{f_y}\right)\left(\frac{1}{d}\right)\sqrt{\frac{d}{b_w}}$$

$$= \frac{2.30}{80}\left(\frac{250}{40}\right)\left(\frac{1}{19}\right)\sqrt{\frac{19}{20}} = 0.0093$$

Using the more elaborate formula for minimum A_v/s gives for #3 U stirrups,

$$s = \frac{2(0.11)}{0.0093} = 23.6 \text{ in.}$$

but, according to ACI-11.5.4.1, the spacing may not exceed $0.75h = 0.75(30) = 22.5$ in. or 24 in., whichever is smaller. Thus #3 stirrups could be placed no farther apart than 22.5 in. unless tests are performed.

21.12 Development of Reinforcement

Following the basic concepts established for nonprestressed reinforced concrete in Chap. 6, development of reinforcement must also be considered in prestressed members. The prestressing force must be transferred into the concrete by bond (interaction between concrete and steel strand) in the pretensioned beam, and the length required to accomplish this is called tne "transfer length." This, of course, occurs in end regions and, in effect, anchors the tendons.

The understanding of the mechanism of transfer is as yet incomplete [12]. The high stress in the pretensioned cable must, on cutting of the cable, be transferred to the concrete so that equilibrium is achieved. The situation in the transfer zone is quite different from that in the anchorage zones of nonprestressed concrete.

In nonprestressed concrete, the bars are stressed after being cast in the concrete. As they are stressed they decrease slightly in diameter and tend to draw away (at least create a slight tensile stress in the direction transverse to the bars) from the surrounding concrete. Thus a reasonably large length is necessary to transfer a stress f_y in the steel to the surrounding concrete.

In prestressed concrete, the wires or strands are pretensioned to a high level of stress, thus initially reducing the wire diameter prior to the placing of the concrete. Once the concrete is cured and the wires are cut at the ends, the wires tend to shorten and correspondingly increase in diameter. Thus a compression between the wires and concrete is produced. The stress in the cut wire must increase from zero at the free end to the prestress value at a certain distance from the free end. This distance is known as the "transfer length." During the accomplishment of the transfer, probably in the first few inches from the free end, it is solely the friction that is developed as the slipping wires compress against the concrete. Farther from the end, adhesive bond, that is, slip resistance, certainly contributes to the transfer.

The transfer length L_t has in the past been taken as 50 diameters for a strand, and 100 diameters for a single wire [13]. These were average values based on the assumptions of a clean strand (or wire) surface, a gradual release of the prestressing force to the concrete, and a steel stress of 150 ksi (average transfer bond stress of 400 psi) after transfer. For strands with a slightly rusted surface, the transfer distance is certainly less, and for a sudden release of stress such as can occur by burning the strand, the transfer length may easily be 20% greater. The transfer length does not seem to be affected by variation in concrete strength [13].

The importance of the transfer length depends on the member under consideration. It seems to be of little importance except on short members and in situations where flexural cracking may occur in the transfer zone.

Development Length for Prestressing Strand. Exactly as for nonpre-stressed reinforcement, the tension in the prestressing steel necessary to achieve ultimate flexural strength must be developed by embedment or end anchorage or a combination thereof (ACI-12.1). The purpose is to prevent general slip prior to achieving the necessary ultimate moment capacity; thus the steel stress must increase from the effective prestress value f_{se} to the value f_{ps} used in computing the ultimate capacity. The net anchorage length available to accommodate a change in tension force is the development length L_d to the end of the strand from the section in question, less the transfer length L_t.

The following empirical relationship was established by tests [13],

$$(f_{ps} - f_{se}) \text{ in ksi} = \frac{L_d - L_t}{d_b} \qquad (21.12.1)$$

where d_b is the nominal strand diameter.

When the calculated steel stress at ultimate strength is f_{ps}, slip must be prevented; thus

$$f_{ps} \text{ (ksi)} \le f_{se} \text{ (ksi)} + \frac{L_d - L_t}{d_b} \qquad (21.12.2)$$

Next, it is necessary to obtain an expression for L_t/d_b. Using the relationship from Chap. 6 (Sec. 6.2) for embedment length,

$$A_s f_{se} = u\pi d_b L_t$$

$$\left(\frac{\pi d_b^2}{4}\right) f_{se} = u\pi d_b L_t \tag{21.12.3}$$

Since the actual strand (three- or seven-wire) properties differ from those based on the nominal diameter, a correction must be applied. The true circumference is taken as $\frac{4}{3}\pi d_b$; and the true area A_s as $0.725\pi d_b^2/4$. Thus

$$0.725\left(\frac{\pi d_b^2}{4}\right) f_{se} = u\left(\frac{4}{3}\right)\pi d_b L_t \tag{21.12.4}$$

$$\frac{L_t}{d_b} = \frac{2.175 f_{se}}{16u} \tag{21.12.5}$$

If the average bond stress in the transfer zone is taken as 400 psi for clean strands [13],

$$\frac{L_t}{d_b} = \frac{2.175}{16(0.4)} f_{se} = \frac{1}{2.94} f_{se}, \qquad \text{say} \frac{1}{3} f_{se} \tag{21.12.6}$$

where f_{se} is measured in ksi.

Substituting Eq. (21.12.6) in Eq. (21.12.2) gives

$$f_{ps} \le f_{se} + \frac{L_d}{d_b} - \frac{1}{3} f_{se}$$

and solving for L_d, the necessary development length to the end of the strand,

$$L_d = (f_{ps} - \tfrac{2}{3} f_{se}) d_b \tag{21.12.7}$$

which is the formula given in ACI-12.10.1 for the three- or seven-wire pretensioning strands. Investigation may be restricted to those cross sections nearest each end of the member that are required to develop their ultimate strength under the specified factored loads.

EXAMPLE 21.12.1   Investigate the development of reinforcement for the beam of Example 21.10.1 (Fig. 21.10.7). Assume $f_{ps} = 221$ ksi as computed in Example 21.8.1. The effective prestress, after losses, may be assumed to $0.8(175) = 140$ ksi.

Solution: Since only at midspan is the maximum moment required, the total embedment from midspan must exceed the development length L_d,

$$L_d = [221 - \tfrac{2}{3}(140)]d_b$$
$$L_d = (221 - 93.3)(0.5) = 64 \text{ in.} < 240 \text{ in.} \qquad \text{OK}$$

It is noted that f_{ps} used in this equation may be taken as that value required for the necessary ultimate strength at a section. In this case required nominal strength M_n of 918 ft-kips was only slightly less than the provided M_n of 932 ft-kips. However, if the requirement was much below that provided, f_{ps}

could have been taken as less than 221 ksi even at midspan. Development of reinforcement usually is not a problem on simply supported prestressed concrete beams.

21.13 Proportioning of Cross Sections for Flexure when No Tension Is Permitted

In order to give further insight into the variables involved, the following discussion is presented on proportioning the cross section. All cross sections used here will consist of rectangular flanges and web, though in practical design 90° junctions between flanges and web are avoided because of forming difficulties.

In this brief treatment, the only case treated is when no tension is permitted, either at the initial condition (at transfer of prestress before losses) or at the final condition (full dead and live load after losses). Thus the desired stress distributions are shown in Fig. 21.13.1.

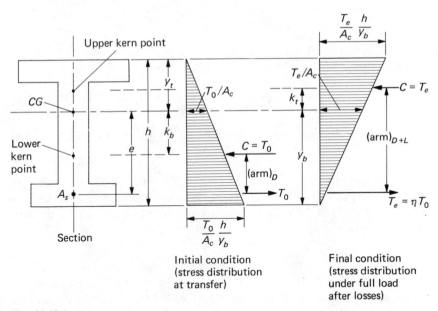

Fig. 21.13.1

Stress distributions desired when no tension is permitted—*small* girder moment.

It can be shown that on any cross section having an axis of symmetry, there are two points on the axis of symmetry, known as the "kern points," that are located at distances k_b and k_t from the centroid, as shown in Fig. 21.13.1. Each kern point represents the farthest distance from the centroid at which a resultant force can act without inducing a stress of opposite sign at the extreme fiber in the opposite direction from the centroid. This means that the stress distribution varies from zero at the top to maximum at the bottom, when the resultant force acts on the lower kern point; or it varies from zero at the bottom to maximum at the top when the resultant force acts on the upper kern point. Referring to Fig. 21.13.1, and using Eq. (21.6.1) with the internal-force concept

$$f = \frac{C}{A} - \frac{Ck_b y_t}{I} = 0 \qquad (21.13.1a)$$

and

$$f = \frac{C}{A} - \frac{Ck_t y_b}{I} = 0 \qquad (21.13.1b)$$

Solving Eqs. (21.13.1ab) for k_b and k_t,

$$k_b = \frac{I}{A y_t} = \frac{r^2}{y_t} \qquad (21.13.2a)$$

and

$$k_t = \frac{I}{A y_b} = \frac{r^2}{y_b} \qquad (21.13.2b)$$

in which r is the radius of gyration of the cross section.

The reader may recall from Sec. 21.6 that as the load applied to a pre-stressed concrete beam changes, the *position* of the internal force C must also change; that is, the moment arm (see Fig. 21.13.1) measured from the position of the prestressing steel must increase as the load increases. Thus when the moment M_D due to dead load of the girder is acting at the initial condition (transfer of prestress), the moment arm of the internal couple is $(\text{arm})_D$; and when moment due to dead plus live load is acting, the moment arm is $(\text{arm})_{D+L}$.

In order to achieve the triangular distribution at the initial condition, the prestressing steel must have its centroid below the kern point by the amount $(\text{arm})_D = M_D/T_0$ (see Fig. 21.13.1). If the girder moment M_D is small, it may be possible and practical to position the steel at $e = k_b + (\text{arm})_D$ below the centroid of the section. If the moment M_D is large, the distance $(k_b + (\text{arm})_D)$ may extend so far below the centroid of the section as to be too close to the bottom for proper cover or even outside the section. Thus for larger girder weight (large M_D), the optimum condition of triangular stress distribution at the initial condition may be impossible to achieve.

Preliminary Design for Small Girder Moment.   When the girder moment M_D is small (say M_D representing 0.2 or less of the total, $M_D + M_L$), the $(\text{arm})_D$ will be small and C can probably be located at the lower kern point; that is, the steel will be located at $e = k_b + M_D/T_0$ from the centroid of the section. Observing Fig. 21.13.1 again,

$$(\text{arm})_{D+L} - (\text{arm})_D = k_t + k_b$$

$$\frac{M_D + M_L}{T_e} - \frac{M_D}{T_0} = k_t + k_b$$

If M_D is small, M_D/T_0 in the above equation may be assumed to be M_D/T_e, then

$$\frac{M_L}{T_e} \approx k_t + k_b$$

or

$$T_e \approx \frac{M_L}{k_t + k_b} \qquad (21.13.3)$$

The maximum stress in Fig. 21.13.1 may be obtained from the stress at the centroid (which is T/A_c without bending stress) by the linear relationship. Normally the ratio of the allowable stresses f_{ic} at the initial condition to f_{fc} at the final condition is approximately the same as the ratio of the initial prestress force T_0 to the final prestress force T_e. This means that the economical section should have $y_t \approx y_b$, or $k_t \approx k_b$, that is, be symmetrical. For a rectangular section $k_t = k_b = h/6$, thus $k_t = k_b = h/3$. For the I-shaped section that is more efficient to resist bending, $k_t + k_b > h/3$, say about $h/2$. Thus Eq. (21.13.3) may be approximated

$$T_e \approx \frac{M_L}{0.5h} \qquad (21.13.4)$$

If the section is symmetrical, the stress at the centroid will be half of the maximum; thus the required area A_c of the section would be, for the initial condition at transfer,

$$\text{required } A_c = \frac{T_0}{0.50f_{ic}} \qquad (21.13.5)$$

and for the final condition of dead plus live load after losses,

$$\text{required } A_c = \frac{T_e}{0.50f_{fc}} \qquad (21.13.6)$$

For the preliminary selection of cross section in case of small girder moment M_D, the following steps may be followed:

1. Select the overall depth h of the section. This is somewhat arbitrary but in the absence of other limitations, the guidelines of T. Y. Lin [1] may be followed:
   (a) For light loading, $h \geq 1/40$ of the span L.
   (b) For medium loading, $h \geq L/30$.
   (c) For heavy loading, $h \geq L/20$.
   (d) On bridges, h ranges between $L/15$ and $L/25$.
   (e) As a rule of thumb, h (inches) is approximately $1.5\sqrt{M}$ (ft-kips) to $2.0\sqrt{M}$.
2. Compute the approximate T_e from Eq. (21.13.4).
3. Determine the approximate A_c from Eq. (21.13.6).
4. Proportion a symmetrical I-shaped section.

5. With this preliminary section, compute the section properties and locate the desired distance e of the steel centroid from the section centroid (CG),

$$e = k_b + (\text{arm})_D = k_b + \frac{M_D}{T_0} \qquad (21.13.7)$$

where $T_0 = T_e/\eta$ and η is the proportion of initial prestress remaining after losses.

6. If the steel can be located at the desired e, then T_e is more correctly determined,

$$T_e = \frac{M_D + M_D}{(\text{arm})_{D+L}} = \frac{M_D + M_L}{e + k_t} \qquad (21.13.8)$$

Then $T_0 = T_e/\eta$ and a new value of e is established; the iterative process is repeated until the desired accuracy is obtained.

7. Equations (21.13.5) and (21.13.6) are then used to determine the required A_c. When the equations give significantly different requirements, the section may be changed to become somewhat unsymmetrical with respect to the centroidal axis. In such a case the average stress is not half of the maximum. In general, from Fig. 21.13.1,

$$\text{required } A_c = \frac{T_0 h}{f_{ic} y_t} \qquad (21.13.9)$$

$$\text{required } A_c = \frac{T_e h}{f_{fc} y_b} \qquad (21.13.10)$$

The minimum area A_c is obtained when Eqs. (21.13.9) and (21.13.10) give the same result.

Preliminary Design for Large Girder Moment. When the girder moment M_D exceeds about 0.2 to 0.3 of the total moment $M_D + M_L$, the $(\text{arm})_D$ will be too large to permit the steel distance e to be at $k_b + M_D/T_0$ from the centroid of the section. Thus the initial stress distribution at transfer cannot be triangular but instead will be trapezoidal (see Fig. 21.13.2). The final condition, which can still give a triangular stress distribution, will probably govern. Thus

$$T_e = \frac{M_D + M_L}{e + k_t} \qquad (21.13.11)$$

When the final condition controls, more of the area A_c should be located at the top where the highest stress occurs. Thus an unsymmetrical section is indicated—for instance, a T-shaped section. As an approximation, T. Y. Lin [1] suggests $(e + k_t) \approx 0.65h$ for use in Eq. (21.13.11). Generally $e + k_t$ will vary from $0.3h$ to $0.8h$, with the average about $0.65h$. For preliminary design, Eq. (21.13.11) then becomes

$$T_e \approx \frac{M_D + M_L}{0.65h} \qquad (21.13.12)$$

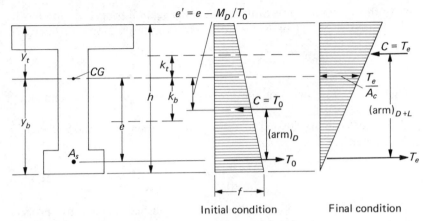

$$e' = e - M_D/T_0$$

Fig. 21.13.2

Stress distributions when no tension is permitted—*large* girder moment.

The required area A_c would then be

$$\text{required } A_c = \frac{T_e}{\text{avg } f_c} = \frac{M_D + M_L}{0.65h(\text{avg } f_c)} \quad \textbf{(21.13.13)}$$

For the unsymmetrical section, y_b/h in Eq. (21.13.10) will be greater than 0.5, say 0.6 Equation (21.13.13) for design would then be

$$\text{required } A_c = \frac{M_D + M_L}{0.65h(0.6f_{fc})} = \frac{2.6(M_D + M_L)}{hf_{fc}} \quad \textbf{(21.13.14)}$$

T. Y. Lin [1] suggests using 3 instead of 2.6 as the coefficient for Eq. (21.13.14).

For the preliminary selection of cross section in case of large girder moment, the following steps may be followed:

1. When $M_D/(M_D + M_L) > 0.2$ to 0.3, use Eq. (21.13.14) to estimate A_c after establishing the overall depth according to step 1 for small girder moment.
2. Proportion an unsymmetrical section; a T-section may be a practical choice.
3. With the preliminary section, compute the section properties and establish the distance e from the centroid of the section to the centroid of the prestressing steel. For large girder moment, one will find

$$e < k_b + \frac{M_D}{T_0}$$

If $e \geq k_b + M_D/T_0$, then the procedure for the small girder moment case is to be followed.
4. With the steel located, T_e can be determined using Eq. (21.13.8). From that, $T_0 = T_e/\eta$.
5. The required area A_c based on the final condition is then determined using Eq. (21.13.10).
6. Check the required area based on the initial condition. Referring to Fig. 21.13.2, a trapezoidal stress distribution should occur.

The maximum compressive stress f is, using Eq. (21.6.1) with the internal force concept,

$$f = \frac{C}{A} + \frac{Cey}{I} \tag{21.13.15}$$

Since $C = T_0$, $A = A_c$, $I = A_c r^2$, $e = e'$ (Fig. 21.13.2), and $y = y_b$,

$$f = \frac{T_0}{A_c} + \frac{T_0 e' y_b}{A_c r^2} \leq f_{ic}$$

$$= \frac{T_0}{A_c}\left[1 + \frac{e - M_D/T_0}{k_t}\right] \leq f_{ic} \tag{21.13.16}$$

The required area A_c based on the initial condition is

$$\text{required } A_c = \frac{T_0}{f_{ic}}\left[1 + \frac{e - M_D/T_0}{k_t}\right] \tag{21.13.17}$$

Again the minimum area A_c will be obtained when Eqs. (21.13.10) and (21.13.17) give the same result.

EXAMPLE 21.13.1 Design a cross section for a 30-in. deep girder whose girder moment $M_D = 45$ ft-kips. The live-load moment to be carried is 300 ft-kips. The initial prestress $f_{si} = 175,000$ psi and assume 20% losses. The allowable service-load stresses are $f_{it} = 0$, $f_{ic} = 2400$ psi, $f_{ft} = 0$, and $f_{fc} = 2250$ psi. Omit check of strength, cracking moment, shear strength, and development of reinforcement.

Solution: (a) Preliminary design. The girder moment as a percent of the total moment is

$$\frac{M_D}{M_D + M_L} = \frac{45}{45 + 300} = 0.13 < 0.2$$

Approach as a small girder moment design. Using Eqs. (21.13.4) and (21.13.6),

$$T_e \approx \frac{M_L}{0.5h} = \frac{300(12)}{0.5(30)} = 240 \text{ kips}$$

$$T_0 = \frac{T_e}{n} = \frac{240}{0.8} = 300 \text{ kips}$$

$$\text{required } A_c = \frac{T_0}{0.5 f_{ic}} = \frac{300}{0.5(2.40)} = 250 \text{ sq in.}$$

Since $f_{fc}/f_{ic} = 2.25/2.4 = 0.94$ is greater than $T_e/T_0 = 0.8$, the equation based on the initial condition is controlling if the section is symmetrical. Though a slightly unsymmetrical section (with the centroid below the middepth in this case) would give the section of minimum area, the procedure is illustrated using a symmetrical one.

Try a 30 in.-deep section with flanges 5 × 17 in. and a 4-in. thick web, $A_c = 250$ sq in. (Fig. 21.13.3a).

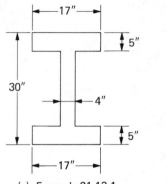

(a) Example 21.13.1

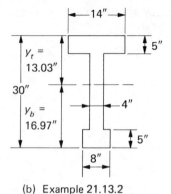

(b) Example 21.13.2

Fig. 21.13.3

Sections for design examples.

(b) Determine the section properties.

	Area, A_c (sq in.)	I (in.^{4})
17 × 30 rectangle	510	38,250
13 × 20 sides	− 260	− 8,667
	250	29,583

$$r^2 = \frac{I}{A_c} = 118.3 \text{ sq in.}$$

$$k_t = k_b = \frac{r^2}{y_b} = \frac{r^2}{y_t} = \frac{118.3}{15} = 7.89 \text{ in.}$$

(c) Locate centroid of prestressing steel. Using approximate T_e, find approximate T_0

$$T_0 \approx \frac{T_e}{\eta} = \frac{249}{0.8} = 300 \text{ kips}$$

$$\text{desired } e = k_b + \frac{M_D}{T_0} = 7.89 + \frac{45(12)}{300} = 9.69 \text{ in.}$$

The available distance is 15 in., less appropriate cover. Thus $e = 9.69$ in. would be acceptable. Recalculate T_e using Eq. (21.13.8),

$$T_e = \frac{M_D + M_L}{e + k_t} = \frac{(45 + 300)12}{9.69 + 7.89} = 235 \text{ kips}$$

$$\text{revised } T_0 = \frac{235}{0.8} = 294 \text{ kips}$$

$$\text{revised } e = 7.89 + \frac{45(12)}{294} = 9.73 \text{ in.}$$

This is in close agreement with the previous value of 9.69 in. If the first estimate had been farther off, additional iterations may have been needed.

(d) Check whether the area A_c is adequate. Using Eqs. (21.13.9) and (21.13.10),

$$\text{required } A_c \text{ (initial condition)} = \frac{T_0 h}{f_{ic} y_t} = \frac{294(30)}{2.4(15)} = 245 \text{ sq in.}$$

$$\text{required } A_c \text{ (final condition)} = \frac{T_e h}{f_{fc} y_b} = \frac{235(30)}{2.25(15)} = 209 \text{ sq in.}$$

The section is adequate.

Use—5 × 17 in. flanges with a 4-in. web ($A_c = 250$ sq in.).
If made slightly unsymmetrical, the area could be reduced to somewhere between 209 and 245 sq in. A final check of initial and final stresses should be made as done in Sec. 21.6, but the illustration is omitted here.

EXAMPLE 21.13.2   Redesign the cross section of Example 21.13.1 for $M_D = 200$ ft-kips and $M_L = 145$ ft-kips. Note the total $M_D + M_L = 345$ ft-kips is the same as in Example 21.13.1.

Solution: (a) Preliminary design. The girder moment as a percent of the total moment is

$$\frac{M_D}{M_D + M_L} = \frac{200}{345} = 0.58 > 0.2 \text{ to } 0.3$$

Approach as a large girder moment design. Using Eq. (21.13.14),

$$\text{required } A_c = \frac{2.6(M_D + M_L)}{hf_{fc}} = \frac{2.6(345)12}{30(2.25)} = 159 \text{ sq in.}$$

Since T. Y. Lin [1] recommends using 3 instead of 2.6, select an area somewhat greater than 159 sq in. An unsymmetrical shape is to be selected; try flanges 5 × 14 in. and 5 × 8 in. with a 4-in. web having $A_c = 190$ sq in. (Fig. 21.13.3b).

(b) Determine section properties. Referring to Fig. 21.13.3(b), first locate the centroid of the area measured from the top.

	Area, A_c (sq in.)	Arm, y (in.)	$A_c y$ (in.^{3})	I (in.^{4})
5 × 10 top flange projection	50	2.5	125	313
I_0				104
5 × 4 bottom flange projection	20	27.5	550	15,125
I_0				42
4 × 30 web (full depth)	120	15	1800	27,000
I_0				9,000
	190		2475	51,584

$$y_t = \bar{y} = \frac{\Sigma Ay}{\Sigma A} = \frac{2475}{190} = 13.03 \text{ in.}$$

$$I_0 = I - A\bar{y}^2 = 51{,}584 - 190(13.03)^2 = 19{,}300 \text{ in.}^4$$

$$r^2 = \frac{I_0}{A_c} = 101.7 \text{ sq in.}$$

$$k_t = \frac{r^2}{y_b} = \frac{101.7}{16.97} = 5.99 \text{ in.}$$

$$k_b = \frac{r^2}{y_t} = \frac{101.7}{13.03} = 7.81 \text{ in.}$$

(c) Locate centroid of prestressing steel. Assume with adequate cover the steel may be centered 4 in. from the bottom of the section. Then

$$e = y_b - 4 = 16.97 - 4 = 12.97 \text{ in.}$$

and using Eq. (21.13.8),

$$T_e = \frac{M_D + M_L}{e + k_t} = \frac{345(12)}{12.97 + 5.99} = 218 \text{ kips}$$

then

$$T_0 = \frac{218}{0.8} = 273 \text{ kips}$$

Check

$$k_b + \frac{M_D}{T_0} = 7.81 + \frac{200(12)}{273} = 7.81 + 8.79 = 16.60 \text{ in.} > e$$

This shows the tendons cannot be located far enough from the centroid of the section to give a triangular stress distribution at the initial condition.

(d) Check whether the area A_c is adequate. Using Eqs. (21.13.10) and (21.13.17),

$$\text{required } A_c \text{ (final condition)} = \frac{T_e h}{f_{fc} y_b} = \frac{218(30)}{2.25(16.97)} = 171 \text{ sq in.}$$

$$\text{required } A_c \text{ (initial condition)} = \frac{T_0}{f_{ic}} \left[1 + \frac{e - M_D/T_0}{k_t} \right]$$

$$= \frac{273}{2.4} \left[1 + \frac{12.97 - 8.79}{5.99} \right] = 193 \text{ sq in.}$$

This is close enough but shows that the initial condition governs in this case, the reason being that area has been shifted from the bottom of the section to the top where it is needed for the final condition. The minimum area section for this case would be slightly more symmetrical than the chosen one.

A final check of stresses (initial and final conditions) should be made (see Sec. 21.6) to verify the result.

The general line of reasoning presented here may also be used when tension is permitted at initial or final conditions, or both. T. Y. Lin [1] provides a detailed treatment of design of sections when tension is permitted.

21.14 Additional Topics

Many other topics have been omitted from this introductory treatment of prestressed concrete. Such topics as the practical design approaches, use of I-shaped and nonsymmetrical sections, prestressing of continuous members, stresses in end blocks, partial prestressing, deflections, composite construction, and other specific applications are adequately and extensively treated in textbooks devoted entirely to the subject [1–5].

SELECTED REFERENCES

1. T. Y. Lin. *Prestressed Concrete Structures* (2d ed.). New York: Wiley, 1963.
2. Narbey Khachaturian and German Gurfinkel. *Prestressed Concrete*. New York: McGraw-Hill, 1969.
3. Yves Guyon. *Prestressed Concrete*, Vols. 1 and 2. New York: Wiley, 1960.
4. James R. Libby. *Modern Prestressed Concrete* (2d ed.). Princeton, N.J.: Van Nostrand, 1977.
5. Gustave Magnel. *Prestressed Concrete* (2d ed.). London: Concrete Publications, 1950.
6. ACI-ASCE Joint Committee 323. "Tentative Recommendations for Prestressed Concrete," *ACI Journal, Proceedings*, **54**, January 1958, 545–578.
7. ACI Committee 435. "Deflections of Prestressed Concrete Members," *ACI Journal, Proceedings*, **60**, December 1963, 1697–1728.
8. J. R. Janney, E. Hognestad, and D. McHenry. "Ultimate Flexural Strength of Prestressed and Conventionally Reinforced Concrete Beams," *ACI Journal, Proceedings*, **52**, January 1956, 601–620.
9. James G. MacGregor and John M. Hanson. "Proposed Changes in Shear Provisions for Reinforced and Prestressed Concrete Beams," *ACI Journal, Proceedings*, **66**, April 1969, 276–288. Disc. 849–851.
10. ACI-ASCE Committee 426. "The Shear Strength of Reinforced Concrete Members-Chapters 1 to 4," *Journal of Structural Division*, ASCE, **99**, June 1973 (ST6), 1091–1187.
11. M. A. Sozen and N. M. Hawkins. Discussion of "Shear and Diagonal Tension Report," Report of ACI-ASCE Committee 326, *ACI Journal, Proceedings*, **59**, September 1962, 1341–1347.
12. Jack R. Janney. "Nature of Bond in Pre-tensioned Prestressed Concrete," *ACI Journal, Proceedings*, **50**, May 1954, 717–736.
13. Norman W. Hanson and Paul H. Kaar. "Flexural Bond Tests of Pretensioned Prestressed Beams," *ACI Journal, Proceedings*, **55**, January 1955, 783–802.

PROBLEMS

All problems are to be worked in accordance with the ACI Code, unless otherwise indicated.

21.1   The rectangular beam of the accompanying figure contains pretensioned steel with an initial tensile stress of 160 ksi ($f_{pu} = 250$ ksi). The concrete has $f'_{ci} = f'_c = 5000$ psi ($n = 7$). The beam is on a simple span of 35 ft.

(a) Determine the concrete stresses at top and bottom, and the steel stress, at transfer immediately after the wires are cut at the ends.

(b) Recompute the stresses in (a) immediately after a 20% loss in prestress. What is the maximum service live load that can be superimposed on the beam? Consider only the section of maximum bending moment, and *omit* consideration of ultimate flexural strength.

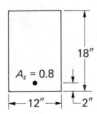

$A_s = 0.8$

18"

2"

12"

Prob. 21.1

21.2 Based on the midspan cross section of the figure for Prob. 21.1, investigate whether or not it is possible to increase the live-load moment capacity by either or both of the following:

(a) Increase the initial prestress above 160 ksi.

(b) Decrease the eccentricity.

Assume there is a 20% loss of initial prestress. Determine the maximum service live-load capacity possible by adjusting the prestress or the eccentricity or both but still not violating the ACI Code limitations. Omit consideration of ultimate flexural strength.

21.3 The rectangular section of the accompanying figure has been pretensioned by a force of 300 kips after all losses. If $f'_{ci} = f'_c = 5000$ psi, what uniformly distributed live load may be safely carried on a 40-ft simple span? Omit consideration of ultimate flexural strength.

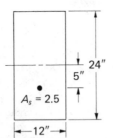

24"

5"

$A_s = 2.5$

12"

Prob. 21.3

21.4 For the live load determined in Prob. 21.1, determine the maximum permissible eccentricity of the prestressing tendons at the $\frac{1}{4}$ point of the span. Omit consideration of ultimate flexural strength.

21.5 For the live load determined in Prob. 21.3, determine the maximum permissible eccentricity of the prestressing tendons at the $\frac{1}{8}$ point of the span. Omit consideration of ultimate flexural strength.

21.6   A straight pretensioned member 35 ft long is 18 in. square in cross section. It is concentrically prestressed with 2.24 sq in. of high tensile strength steel wire. The wires are stressed originally to 145 ksi and are anchored to end bulkheads. Calculate the loss and percent of loss of prestress in the wires due to elastic shortening of the concrete at transfer using both the approximate and the "exact" methods. Use $f'_c = 6000$ psi $(n = 6)$.

21.7   An 18-in. square concrete member is posttensioned by four cables each with an area of 0.56 sq in. These cables are stressed one after another, each to a stress of 145 ksi. Without taking any account of the eccentricity of the cables, compute the loss and percent of loss of prestress in each cable due to the elastic shortening of the concrete. Compute the average loss of prestress. Assume $n = 6$.

21.8   The symmetrical double cantilever beam shown is to be prestressed by a single cable $ABCDE$. The cable consists of 12 wires, each of 0.20 in. diameter, and is to be prestressed simultaneously from both ends of the member. It is desired that the minimum stress in the cable immediately after stressing and before any creep or shrinkage losses take place be 145 ksi. The cable is such that the friction constant $\mu = 0.50$ and the wobble effect $K = 0.0010$. Determine:
(a) What is the steel stress at the jack?
(b) What is the percentage of friction losses?
(c) What extension will be required at each jack?
Solve by the following methods: (1) Neglect variation in tension throughout the length, using ACI Formula 18-2, $P_s = P_x(1 + \mu\alpha + KL)$; (2) Neglect variation in tension at every point along the length of the curve but consider variation from segment to segment, using ACI Formula 18-2; and (3) Use "exact" expression, ACI Formula 18-1.

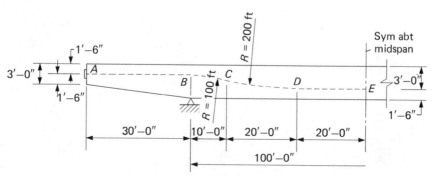

Prob. 21.8

21.9   Determine the nominal ultimate moment capacity M_n and the cracking moment M_{cr} for the pretensioned bonded section of the figure for Prob. 21.1. The concrete has $f'_c = 5000$ psi and the steel has f_{pu} 250 ksi. Assume the average stress-strain curve of Fig. 21.8.1 is to be used for the steel.

21.10   Assuming no special tests are to be made, determine the number and spacing for #3 U stirrups for the beam of Prob. 21.1 if the maximum service load computed in that problem is acting. Use the alternate procedure for V_c of ACI-11.4.1, as well as the more exact procedure of ACI-11.4.2.

21.11   Assuming no special tests are to be made, determine the number and spacing for #3 U stirrups for the beam of Prob. 21.3 if the maximum service load computed in that problem is acting. Use and compare both procedures of ACI-11.4.

21.12 Design of section for *small* dead-load moment.

(a) Make a preliminary design (use rectangular flanges and a web) for a section of a prestressed beam to resist a total bending moment of 960 ft-kips assuming that the moment due to the girder weight is 70 ft-kips. The overall depth of the section is to be 42 in. and the effective prestress f_{se} in the steel is 136 ksi. In selecting a section assume the minimum thickness of components (flanges or web) is 5 in.

(b) Make the final design for the preliminary section you selected for part (a) making such changes as you find necessary, assuming a *minimum* cross-sectional area is desired. The selected cross-sectional area should not exceed 460 sq in.

(c) Make a check of stresses at initial (transfer) and final conditions. Use the following control stresses:

$$f_{ic} = 2400 \text{ psi} \qquad f_{fc} = 2250 \text{ psi} \qquad f_{si} = 160 \text{ ksi}$$
$$f_{it} = 0 \text{ psi} \qquad f_{ft} = 0 \text{ psi} \qquad f_{se} = 136 \text{ ksi}$$

Design of section for *large* dead-load moment. The data are the same as Prob. 21.10 except for the following:

(a) The moment due to the girder weight is 650 ft-kips, instead of 70 ft-kips.

(b) The minimum thickness for components (flanges or web) is 4 in.

(c) The cross-sectional area should not exceed 340 sq in.

22

Composite Construction

22.1 Introduction

Composite construction, as defined herein, is the use of a cast-in-place concrete slab placed upon and interconnected to a prefabricated beam so that the combined beam and slab will act together as a unit. The prefabricated beam may be a rolled or built-up steel shape, a precast reinforced concrete beam, a prestressed concrete beam, a timber beam, or even light-gage steel decking. The interconnection to obtain the single unit action is by combinations of mechanical shear connectors, friction, and shear keys.

In the early 1900s a type of composite construction was used where a steel I-shaped section was fully encased in concrete placed integrally with the slab. The use of encased beams is still permitted [2] but such use is rare. The composite beam and slab construction presently used began to appear in the 1930s. Since about 1940, nearly all usage has been with a slab attached to one flange of a prefabricated beam by means of mechanical connectors. This type of composite construction has been widespread in bridge design since the early 1950s and in buildings since about 1960. Present design methods are the result of extensive research into composite section behavior [4–13].

Throughout this chapter, emphasis is on the slab composite with precast reinforced concrete and prestressed concrete, as covered by the recommendations of the Joint ASCE-ACI Committee on Composite Construction [1], and by the ACI Code. The slab composite with a steel beam is covered by the AISC Specification [2], and detailed treatment is provided elsewhere [3,15].

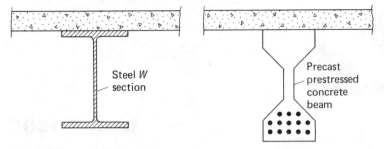

Fig. 22.2.1
Concrete slab and prefabricated beam.

22.2 Composite Action

Consider a concrete slab atop the flange of a steel or precast concrete beam as shown in Fig. 22.2.1. First, if the system of slab and beam is not acting compositely, only friction will provide interaction; thus little of the longitudinal action is carried by the slab. The static system with friction neglected is shown in Fig. 22.2.2a, wherein the slab and the beam each carry separately a portion of the load. When the noncomposite system deforms under vertical load, the lower surface of the slab is in tension and elongates while the upper surface of the beam is in compression and shortens. Thus a discontinuity will occur at the plane of contact. Since friction is neglected, only vertical internal forces act between the slab and beam.

When a system acts compositely (Fig. 22.2.2b), no relative slippage occurs between the slab and the beam. Horizontal forces (shears) are developed which would shorten the lower surface of the slab and elongate the upper surface of the beam. Thus the discontinuity at the contact surface may be eliminated when sufficiently large horizontal shear resistance can develop. It is noted that the deflection of the composite system will be significantly less than that of the noncomposite system.

In an actual beam-slab system, the degree of composite action may vary over a wide range. For instance, a steel beam used with a concrete slab

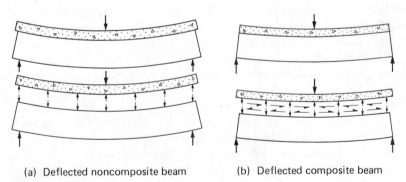

(a) Deflected noncomposite beam   (b) Deflected composite beam

Fig. 22.2.2
Comparison of deflected beams with and without composite action.

without mechanical shear connectors will generally develop little composite action, while friction between a concrete beam and a slab may develop nearly the full composite action. Present methods entirely neglect friction (bond) between a steel beam and the concrete slab (unless beam is encased) but consider such bond under certain conditions when the beam is made of precast concrete.

22.3 Advantages and Disadvantages of Composite Construction

The significant feature of a composite system is a stiffer and stronger structure than can be obtained from the same beam and slab acting noncompositely. In general, the advantages over noncomposite construction are (1) smaller and shallower beams may be used, (2) longer spans are possible without encountering deflection problems, (3) the toughness (impact capacity or energy absorption) is greatly increased, and (4) the overload capacity is substantially greater.

Some of the factors that tend to weigh against this construction are (1) the cost of the connectors which offsets some of the saving in beam material; (2) the cost of placing the mechanical shear connectors, particularly on nonencased steel beams where they are required without exception; and (3) the erection and construction difficulties encountered when the projecting connectors impede or prevent workmen from walking on the beams.

Most indications are, however, in favor of designing for composite interaction wherever a cast-in-place slab is used.

22.4 Effective Slab Width

A slab acting compositely with a beam behaves the same as in an ordinary reinforced concrete T-section, as discussed in Chap. 9. Referring to Fig. 22.4.1, the variables that control the effective slab width are (1) the ratio of slab thickness to total beam depth, t/h; (2) the ratio of beam span to beam width, L/b_w; (3) the ratio of beam span to beam spacing, L/b_0; (4) the type of loading; and (5) Poisson's ratio. As for the T-section in Chap. 9, here also the

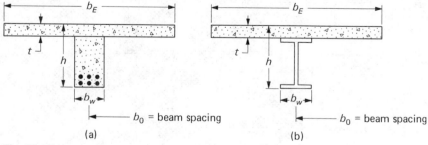

(a) (b)

Fig. 22.4.1
Variables controlling effective slab width.

effective width b_E is to be taken as the smallest of the following for interior beams: (1) one-fourth the beam span length, $L/4$; (2) center-to-center spacing of beams, b_0; (3) beam web width plus 16 times the slab thickness, $b_w + 16t$. These provisions, as well as those for isolated beams in which the T-shape is used and for beams having a flange on one side only, appear in ACI-8.10 for cases (Fig. 22.4.1a) where the prefabricated beam is concrete, and in Section 1.11 of the AISC Specification [2] for cases (Fig. 22.4.1b) where the prefabricated beam is steel.

22.5 Computation of Section Properties

In computing the properties of the composite section for a working stress analysis, generally the transformed-section concept (see Sec. 4.5) is used to convert all parts of the composite section into an equivalent homogeneous member. When a steel beam is used, the concrete slab is converted into equivalent steel by using a slab width equal to b_E/n, where $n = E_s/E_c$, the ratio of the modulus of elasticity of the steel beam to that of the concrete slab. When the prefabricated beam is either reinforced or prestressed concrete, the 28-day compressive strength f'_c is frequently different for the beam and slab; thus E_c is different. In that case the slab may be converted into equivalent beam material by using a slab width of

$$\text{equivalent } b_E = \frac{b_E E_c \text{ (slab)}}{E_c \text{ (beam)}} = \frac{b_E n_{\text{beam}}}{n_{\text{slab}}} \qquad (22.5.1)$$

EXAMPLE 22.5.1   Compute the properties of the composite steel-concrete section of Fig. 22.5.1. The W21 × 55 steel section has a depth of 20.80 in., flange width of 8.215 in., moment of inertia about its middepth of 1140 in.[4], and an area of 16.2 sq in. The yield strength of steel is 36,000 psi. The slab is of concrete with $f'_c = 3000$ psi ($n = 9$).

Solution: The properties for the composite section are shown in Table 22.5.1. The distance y is measured from the centroid (axis x-x of Fig. 22.5.1) of the steel section.

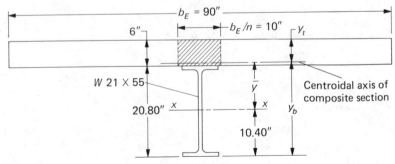

Fig. 22.5.1
Steel-concrete composite section for Example 22.5.1.

Table 22.5.1

Properties of Composite Section in Example 22.5.1.

	Effective Area, A	Arm y	Ay	Ay^2	I_0
Slab	60.0	13.4	804.0	10,774	180
W section	16.2	0	0	0	1140
Totals	76.2		804.0	10,774	1320

$$I_x = I_0 + Ay^2 = 1320 + 10,774 = 12,094 \text{ in.}^4$$

$$\bar{y} = \frac{804.0}{76.2} = 10.55 \text{ in.}$$

$$I = 12,094 - 76.2(10.55)^2 = 3610 \text{ in.}^4$$
$$y_t = 10.40 + 6.00 - 10.55 = 5.85 \text{ in.}$$
$$y_b = 10.40 + 10.55 = 20.95 \text{ in.}$$

$$S_t = \frac{I}{y_t} = \frac{3610}{5.85} = 617 \text{ in.}^3$$

$$S_b = \frac{I}{y_b} = \frac{3610}{20.95} = 172 \text{ in.}^3$$

It is to be noted that the neutral axis of the composite section falls slightly in the concrete slab (0.15 in.). Usually the concrete on the tension side is entirely neglected, but here no correction is made since the amount of concrete in tension is negligible. For cases where the tension concrete is to be considered inactive, the neutral axis under service load is located as for ordinary beams (see Chap. 4).

EXAMPLE 22.5.2   Compute the properties of the composite precast concrete beam and concrete slab system of Fig. 22.5.2. The slab concrete has $f'_c = 3000$ psi ($n = 9$), while the precast beam has $f'_c = 6000$ psi ($n = 6$).

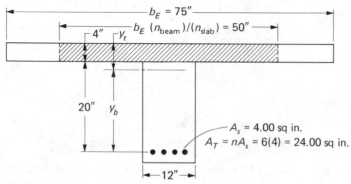

Fig. 22.5.2

Precast beam and cast-in-place slab composite section for Example 22.5.2.

Solution: The system may be converted into a homogeneous beam of material having the same E_c as concrete with $f'_c = 6000$ psi. Using Eq. (22.5.1), the transformation factor η for the slab is either

$$\eta = \frac{E_c \text{ (slab)}}{E_c \text{ (beam)}} = \frac{57{,}000\sqrt{3000}}{57{,}000\sqrt{6000}} = 0.707$$

or

$$\eta = \frac{n_{\text{beam}}}{n_{\text{slab}}} = \frac{6}{9} = 0.666$$

In this case, $\eta = 0.666$ is used.

The conversion into equivalent beam concrete ($f'_c = 6000$ psi) is not actually necessary except in cases either where the precast beam is prestressed and therefore its gross section is fully effective or where the concrete area in the web and above the neutral axis is significant enough to be considered. In this example, the contents of Table 22.5.2 are computed by neglecting compression in the web.

Table 22.5.2
Properties of Composite Section in Example 22.5.2.

	Effective Area, A	Arm y	Ay	Ay²	I₀
Slab	200	2.0	400	800	267
Steel in precast beam	24	24.0	576	13,824	—
Totals	224		976	14,624	267

$$I_{\text{top}} = I_0 + Ay^2 = 267 + 14{,}624 = 14{,}891 \text{ in.}^4$$

$$\bar{y} = y_t = \frac{976}{224} = 4.36 \text{ in.}$$

$$I_{cr} = 14{,}891 - 224(4.36)^2 = 10{,}630 \text{ in.}^4$$

$$y_b = 24.0 - 4.36 = 19.64 \text{ in.}$$

$$S_t = \frac{I_{cr}}{y_t} = \frac{10{,}630}{4.36} = 2440 \text{ in.}^3$$

$$S_b = \frac{I_{cr}}{y_b} = \frac{10{,}630}{19.64} = 541 \text{ in.}^3$$

22.6 Working Stresses with and without Shoring

When no temporary falsework or shoring is used to prevent deflection of the precast member while the slab is being placed and cured, the precast member must support alone its own weight plus the weight of the freshly placed slab. The composite section then resists the live load and any additional superimposed dead load, together with long-time effects from creep and shrinkage. On the other hand, if temporary supports are used to carry the precast beam and the slab concrete until such concrete has achieved about 75% of its 28-day compressive strength f'_c, then the composite section will carry the entire load. Thus working stresses may be computed as follows:

Without shoring,

$$f = \frac{M_D}{S_p} + \frac{M_L}{S_c} \qquad (22.6.1)$$

where M_D is the moment due to dead load, produced prior to the time at which the cast-in-place concrete attains 75% of its specified 28-day strength; M_L is the moment due to live load and superimposed dead load; S_p is the effective section modulus of the precast or prefabricated beam; and S_c is the effective section modulus of the composite section.

With shoring,

$$f = \frac{M_D + M_L}{S_c} \qquad (22.6.2)$$

EXAMPLE 22.6.1   For the section of Example 22.5.2, compute the stresses due to a service dead-load moment of 70 ft-kips and a service live-load moment of 105 ft-kips. Reinforcement has $f_y = 60,000$ psi. Consider the case (a) without shoring and (b) with shoring.

Solution: (a) Without shoring. Since the precast beam must carry the dead load prior to curing of the slab, its neutral-axis location is required; thus

$$\tfrac{1}{2}(12)x^2 = 24(20 - x)$$

$$x = 7.16 \text{ in.}$$

$$\text{arm} = 20 - \frac{x}{3} = 20 - 2.39 = 17.61 \text{ in.}$$

$$f \text{ (tension, steel)} = \frac{M_D}{A_s \text{ (arm)}} = \frac{70(12)}{4.0(17.61)} = 11.9 \text{ ksi}$$

$$f \text{ (compression, concrete)} = \frac{11.9}{6}\left(\frac{7.16}{12.84}\right) = 1.11 \text{ ksi}$$

The additional stresses due to the live load acting on the composite section are

$$f \text{ (tension, steel)} = \frac{nM_L}{S_b} = \frac{6(105)(12)}{541} = 14.0 \text{ ksi}$$

$$f \text{ (compression, } n = 6 \text{ concrete)} = \frac{M_L}{S_t} = \frac{105(12)}{2440} = 0.52 \text{ ksi}$$

$$f \text{ (actual compression, } n = 9 \text{ concrete)} = 0.52(6)/9 = 0.35 \text{ ksi}$$

The maximum stress in the reinforcement is $11.9 + 14.0 = 25.9$ ksi, which

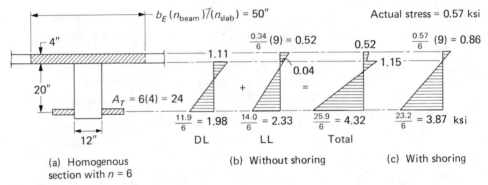

Fig. 22.6.1

Service load stresses in precast concrete-concrete composite section with and without shoring.

exceeds the ACI allowable value of 24 ksi. The maximum stress in the concrete at the top fiber of the precast beam is

$$f = 1.11 + \frac{105(12)(0.36)}{10,630} = 1.11 + 0.04 = 1.15 \text{ ksi}$$

The stress distribution without shoring is given in Fig. 22.6.1b.

    (b) With shoring.

$$f \text{ (tension, steel)} = \frac{n(M_D + M_L)}{S_b} = \frac{6(175)(12)}{541} = 23.3 \text{ ksi}$$

$$f \text{ (compression, concrete)} = \frac{(M_D + M_L)(n_{\text{beam}})}{S_t(n_{\text{slab}})} = \frac{175(12)(6)}{2440(9)} = 0.57 \text{ ksi}$$

The corresponding stress distribution on a homogeneous section where $n = 6$ is given in Fig. 22.6.1c.

    Thus it would appear that the reinforcement is overstressed in the system without shoring, whereas it is within the allowable value when shoring is used.

22.7 Ultimate Strength of Composite Sections

Ultimate strength calculations for a composite section entirely of reinforced concrete are as explained for T-sections in Sec. 9.3. When the composite section includes a steel shape or a prestressed concrete beam, the basic principles are only slightly modified. Since the ultimate moment capacity is unrelated to the sequence of loading and the relative amounts of live and dead load, it is independent of whether or not shoring is used.

EXAMPLE 22.7.1   Determine the nominal ultimate moment capacity M_n of the steel-concrete composite section of Example 22.5.1, using basic statics. The steel section has $f_y = 36,000$ psi and the concrete has $f'_c = 3000$ psi.

Solution: Determine whether the neutral axis lies above or below the bottom of the slab. If the neutral axis is at the bottom of the slab (i.e., $a = 0.85t$),

$$C_{max} = 0.85f'_c b_E a = 0.85(3)(90)(0.85)(6) = 1170 \text{ kips}$$
$$T_{max} = A_s f_y = 16.2(36) = 583 \text{ kips}$$

It will be observed from Fig. 22.7.1c that the value of T_{max} as computed above is an overestimate if the neutral axis lies at the bottom of the slab. However, by comparing C_{max} to T_{max} it is also obvious that the distance to the neutral axis from the top of the slab is less than 6 in. Thus as in an ordinary T-section where the neutral axis falls in the flange,

$$C = 0.85f'_c ab = 0.85(3)(a)(90) = 230a$$
$$T = A_s f_y = 16.2(36) = 583 \text{ kips}$$

$$a = \frac{583}{230} = 2.53 \text{ in.}$$

$$x = \frac{2.53}{0.85} = 2.98 \text{ in.}$$

For this case the strain at the top of the steel section is

$$\epsilon'_s = \frac{0.003}{2.98}(6.0 - 2.98) \approx 0.003 > \epsilon_y = \frac{36}{29,000} = 0.00124$$

which means the entire steel section has reached yield strain. Thus

$$\text{arm} = \frac{d}{2} + t - \frac{a}{2} = \frac{20.80}{2} + 6.0 - \frac{2.53}{2} = 15.13 \text{ in.}$$

$$M_n = T(\text{arm}) = 583(15.13)\tfrac{1}{12} = 735 \text{ ft-kips}$$

Thus the nominal ultimate strength is 735 ft-kips whether or not shoring is used.

EXAMPLE 22.7.2   Determine the nominal ultimate moment capacity M_n of the concrete composite section of Fig. 22.7.2. The slab has $f'_c = 3000$ psi while the precast beam has $f'_c = 6000$ psi, and the reinforcement has $f_y = 60,000$ psi.

Solution:

$$C_{max} = 0.85f'_c b_E t = 0.85(3)(75)(4) = 765 \text{ kips}$$
$$T_{max} = A_s f_y = 4(60) = 240 \text{ kips}$$

Since $C_{max} > T_{max}$, $a < t$. Thus

$$a = \frac{240}{0.85(3)(75)} = 1.25 \text{ in.}$$

$$M_n = 240[24.0 - 0.5(1.25)]\tfrac{1}{12} = 468 \text{ ft-kips}$$

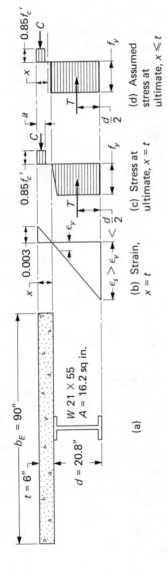

Fig. 22.7.1
Section for Example 22.7.1.

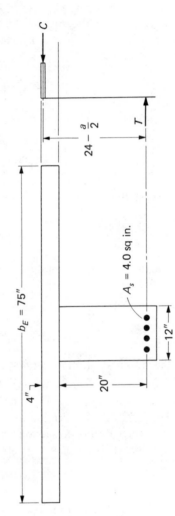

Fig. 22.7.2
Section for Example 22.7.2.

This most typical situation with $a < t$ is treated exactly as in Chap. 9. If $a > t$, some contribution from the 6000 psi concrete would be included in the compressive force.

22.8 Shear Connection

Working Stress Concept. As discussed in Sec. 22.2, in order for the slab to act together with the prefabricated beam, the horizontal shear forces must be developed between the slab and beam. Consider the uniformly loaded beam of Fig. 22.8.1 along with the shear stress distribution across a typical section of the beam. It is the shear stress v_1 that must be developed by the connection between slab and beam. Under the service-load or working-stress condition, it is seen from Fig. 22.8.1 that the shear stress v_1 varies from zero at midspan to a maximum at the support. Consider an elemental slice of the beam, as in Fig. 22.8.2. The shear force per unit distance along the span is $dC/dz = v_1 b_E = VQ/I$. Thus if a given connector has an

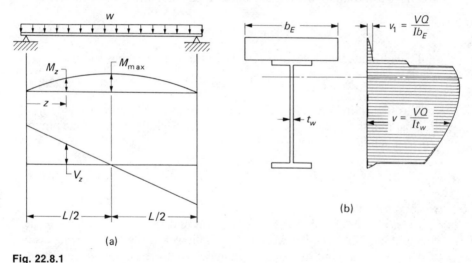

(a)

(b)

Fig. 22.8.1
Shear stress distribution across a steel-concrete composite section.

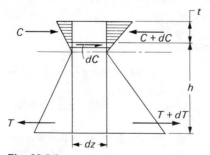

Fig. 22.8.2
Force required of shear connectors—working stress method.

allowable capacity of q kips, the maximum spacing s to provide the required capacity is

$$s \leq \frac{q}{VQ/I} \qquad (22.8.1)$$

where V is the total shear at the section, Q is the statical moment of the effective slab area with respect to the neutral axis of the composite section, and I is the moment of inertia of the transformed composite section neglecting area of concrete in tension.

Ultimate Strength Concept. If one uses an ultimate strength concept, the shear connectors share equally in carrying the total compressive force developed in the concrete slab as the ultimate capacity is approached. This means, referring to Fig. 22.8.1a, that shear connection is required to transfer the compressive force developed at midspan to the prefabricated beam in the distance $L/2$, since no compressive force can exist in the concrete slab at the end of the span where zero moment exists. The ultimate compressive force to be accommodated could not exceed that which the concrete can carry,

$$C_{max} = 0.85 f'_c b_E t \qquad \text{(upper bound)} \qquad (22.8.2)$$

or, if the ultimate tensile force below the bottom of the slab is less than C_{max},

$$T_{max} = A_s f_y \qquad (22.8.3)$$

Thus, for individual connectors each having an ultimate capacity q_{ult}, the total number of connectors N required between the points of maximum and zero bending moment is

$$N = \frac{C_{max}}{q_{ult}} \qquad \text{or} \qquad \frac{T_{max}}{q_{ult}} \qquad (22.8.4)$$

whichever is smaller.

It can also be noted that the connection and the beam must resist the same ultimate load. Under working loads, however, the beam resists dead load and live load, but the connection may have to resist only the live load. If the connection is designed to carry only the live load, a higher factor of safety should be used. Approximately the same result is achieved if the connection is designed to carry dead load as well as live load with the usual safety provisions.

Several types of connectors are as follows:

1. Stud shear connector, straight (Fig. 22.8.3a) and L-shaped (Fig. 22.8.3b), welded to the steel beam in concrete-steel construction.
2. Flexible-channel shear connector (Fig. 22.8.3c), welded to the steel beam in concrete-steel construction.
3. Spiral shear connector (Fig. 22.8.3d), welded to the steel beam in concrete-steel construction.
4. Reinforcing bar stirrups from the precast beam, fully anchored into the slab.

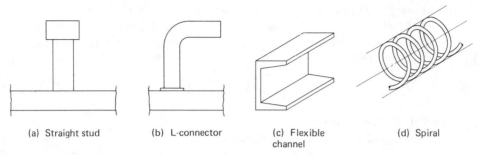

(a) Straight stud   (b) L-connector   (c) Flexible channel   (d) Spiral

Fig. 22.8.3
Shear connectors for concrete slab steel beam construction.

5. Friction, or bond, in combination with vertical ties, for slab on precast reinforced or prestressed concrete beam. This type of shear connection is adequate for most of these cases. While friction, or bond, alone may be sufficient, at least a minimum amount of vertical ties must be used (ACI-17.5.6) unless the contact surfaces are clean and intentionally roughened, to provide a sort of clamping action to prevent buckling of the concrete slab, which would suddenly break the bond.

6. Shear keys, for all cases of concrete-to-concrete composite action where friction, or bond, is inadequate. Since these keys are acting very nearly in pure shear rather than in diagonal tension, determination of the capacity of such a key according to the general principles in Chap. 5 will be unduly conservative. The shear-friction concept of ACI-11.7 should be used for the design of the keys, as discussed in Sec. 5.16.

22.9 Deflections

Since, in general, one of the advantages of using composite construction is to obtain shallower members, the calculation of deflection is important. For deflections arising from live load, or dead load in shored construction, properties of the composite section may be used in accordance with the principles of Chap. 14. For the time-dependent effect, the work of Branson [14] may be used. Specifically, for a slab on precast reinforced or prestressed concrete the provisions of ACI-9.5.5 should be followed. For a slab on a steel beam, the AISC [2] suggests using the ordinary value of $n = E_s/E_c$ (short-time loading) when computing either immediate live-load or sustained-load deflections, while the Joint ACI-ASCE Committee [1] recommends using $2n$ for sustained-load deflections.

22.10 Slab on Precast Reinforced Concrete Beam—Strength Design

Essentially, the principles of Chap. 3 are used, with full realization that no distinction is made between shored and unshored members. To insure that the stresses at working load level will not exceed 75% of the yield strength specified for the reinforcement, the 1963 ACI Code required that the effective depth d_c of the composite section as used for computing ultimate moment should not exceed

$$d_c \leq \left(1.15 + 0.24\frac{M_L}{M_D}\right)d_p \qquad (22.10.1)$$

where d_p is the effective depth of the precast beam.

Equation (22.10.1) may be developed as follows. Two requirements must be satisfied; first, the working stress when no shores are used must not exceed $0.75f_y$ in the steel,

$$\frac{M_D}{A_s j_p d_p} + \frac{M_L}{A_s j_c d_c} \leq 0.75f_y \qquad (22.10.2)$$

where $j_p d_p$ is the moment arm of internal resisting couple for precast beam, and $j_c d_c$ is the moment arm of internal resisting couple for composite beam. The second requirement is that the ultimate moment capacity of the composite section must be adequate.

$$M_n \geq \frac{M_u}{\phi} \qquad (22.10.3)$$

$$A_s f_y \left(d_c - \frac{a}{2}\right) \geq \frac{1.4M_D + 1.7M_L}{0.90} \qquad (22.10.4)$$

The ACI Code has eliminated the requirement on d_c, in all likelihood for two reasons. First, it is not the stresses under service load that need to be limited, but factors such as deflection and cracking that affect serviceability. Second, Eq. (22.10.1) specifically applies to dead load and live load using particular overload factors, and composite design is not limited to those classes of loads, though certainly they are the most common.

Instead of using several specific rules aimed at providing proper serviceability *indirectly*, ACI-17.2 simply states general requirements, including ACI-17.2.7 which requires composite members to meet the deflection control requirements of ACI-9.5.5. This means that whenever excessive deflection may cause damage, deflections must be computed.

To assure the composite action, the horizontal shear must be transferred across the contact surface. For ordinary design, ACI-17.5.4 uses a horizontal shear nominal strength V_{nh} (instead of Eq. (22.8.1)) computed as

$$V_{nh} = v_{nh}b_v d_c \qquad (22.10.5)$$

where

v_{nh} = nominal ultimate unit stress capable of being transmitted on contact surface (values as obtained from ACI-17.5.4 are described below)

b_v = width of cross section being investigated for horizontal shear

d_c = distance from extreme compression fiber to centroid of tension reinforcement, for the entire composite section

The maximum values of v_{nh} from ACI-17.5.4 are as follows:

1. When the contact surface is intentionally roughened[†], clean and free of laitance, with no vertical ties used, max $v_{nh} = 80$ psi.
2. When the contact surface is clean but *not* intentionally roughened[†], and when vertical ties having a minimum area of $A_v = 50b_w s/f_y$ are spaced not more than 4 times the slab thickness (i.e., least dimension of the supported element), nor 24 in., max $v_{nh} = 80$ psi.
3. When the contact surface is intentionally roughened, clean, free of laitance, and minimum ties as in (2) are used, max $v_{nh} = 350$ psi.
4. When the nominal ultimate stress exceeds 350 psi, design for horizontal shear must be made using the shear-friction provisions of ACI-11.7, as explained in Sec. 5.16.

Thus the design requirement of ACI-17.5.4 may be stated as

$$V_u \leq \phi V_{nh} \tag{22.10.6}$$

where

V_u = total shear force at section due to factored loads
$\phi = 0.85$ for shear (ACI-9.3)
V_{nh} = nominal strength computed according to Eq. (22.10.5)

As an alternative to the above procedure of ACI-17.5.4, ACI-17.5.5 provides that the actual compressive or tensile force in any segment may be computed, and then provision is made to transfer that force as horizontal shear to the supporting element. Since the term "any segment" could mean anything from an elemental segment of span to the full distance between the maximum moment point and a point of contraflexure, the ACI statement would seem to suggest any procedure from Eq. (22.8.1) relating to an elemental segment to Eq. (22.8.4) for a longer finite length of span. In other words, the total horizontal shear to be transferred must be accommodated by some rational process.

For the strength method, it seems Eq. (22.10.6) should be used when designing for a distributed load transfer, such as by friction with or without ties, and Eq. (22.8.4) should be used with individual mechanical connectors, such as extended and anchored stirrups or ties and steel studs.

For precast prestressed concrete beams, the minimum tie area may be taken as ACI Formula 11-15, Eq. (21.11.4), if the effective prestress force is at least equal to 40% of the tensile strength of the flexural reinforcement.

EXAMPLE 22.10.1 Design a composite slab on a simply supported precast reinforced concrete beam span of 24 ft. The spacing of beams is 8 ft center to center. The cast-in-place slab is 4 in. thick, and the live load to be carried is 200 psf. Use f_c' (slab) $= 3000$ psi, f_c' (precast beam) $= 4000$ psi, $f_y = 40,000$ psi, and the strength method of the ACI Code.

Solution: (a) Loads and solution procedure. As a preliminary to the actual solution, it is to be noted that the use of precast members speeds construction and the use of composite action reduces the required depth of the beam.

[†] ACI-17.5.2 indicates that the interface must have a full amplitude of $\frac{1}{4}$ in. of roughness to satisfy the requirement of intentional roughness (based on Ref. 6).

To design a composite beam without using temporary shoring, the precast beam is first designed to carry its own weight plus the weight of freshly placed concrete. Of course, the noncomposite system must also carry temporary load due to workmen, equipment, runways, and impact, plus the dead weight of forms. The loads are:

Loads on the noncomposite precast beam,

$$4\text{-in. slab, } (4/12)(0.15)(8) = 0.4 \text{ kip/ft}$$
$$\underline{\text{estimated beam weight} = 0.2 \text{ kip/ft}}$$
$$\text{dead load} = 0.6 \text{ kip/ft}$$
$$\text{temporary load, } 0.050(8) = 0.4 \text{ kip/ft}$$

Load on the composite section,

$$\text{live load, } 0.200(8) = 1.6 \text{ kips/ft}$$

Temporary live and dead construction loads frequently are not included in the design of the precast noncomposite section, but rather the overload that may occur is accepted as a short-duration reduction in the factor of safety.

When deflection is to be investigated, service-load moments are needed; so they could be computed first and then overload factors are applied. For permanent loads on the noncomposite section,

$$M_D = \tfrac{1}{8}(0.6)(24)^2 = 43.2 \text{ ft-kips}$$

For the live load on the composite section,

$$M_L = \tfrac{1}{8}(1.6)(24)^2 = 115 \text{ ft-kips}$$

Several factors may control the size of the precast beam; (1) dead-load moment requirement for a rectangular precast beam, (2) total load moment requirement acting on the T-shaped composite section, and (3) total load shear on the T-shaped section. Items (2) and (3) are treated similarly to the procedure discussed in Secs. 9.4 and 10.2 for T-sections.

(b) Moment on precast noncomposite section. Assume a desirable reinforcement percentage ρ about one-half the maximum permitted, say 0.018 (see Table 3.5.1 for ACI Code maximum). Then the desired R_u is

$$R_u = \rho f_y(1 - \tfrac{1}{2}\rho m)$$
$$= 0.018(40,000)[1 - 0.5(0.018)(11.8)] = 644 \text{ psi}$$

$$m = \frac{f_y}{0.85f'_c} = \frac{40,000}{0.85(4000)} = 11.8$$

required $M_u = 1.4(43.2) = 60.5$ ft-kips

$$\text{required } bd^2 = \frac{M_u}{\phi R_u} = \frac{60.5(12,000)}{0.90(644)} = 1250 \text{ in.}^3$$

$$\text{min } h = \frac{L}{16}(0.8) = \frac{24(12)}{16}(0.8) = 14.4 \text{ in.}$$

The precast beam must be at least 14.4 in. deep (ACI-Table 9.5a) unless deflection is computed even if the member is not supporting or attached to construction likely to be damaged by excessive deflection. If $h = 15$ in., $d \approx 12.5$ in; then

$$\text{required } b = \frac{1250}{(12.5)^2} = 8 \text{ in.}$$

$$\text{required } A_s \approx 0.018(8)(12.5) = 1.8 \text{ sq in.}$$

There is no problem to fit the steel required for the beam *before* the live load is applied. However, the greater reinforcement requirement for the *total* load will probably make it desirable to use a width exceeding 8 in.

(c) Determine reinforcement for composite section.

$$M_u = 1.4M_D + 1.7M_L = 1.4(43.2) + 1.7(115) = 256 \text{ ft-kips}$$

$$\text{required } M_n = \frac{M_u}{\phi} = \frac{256}{0.90} = 284 \text{ ft-kips}$$

$$\text{effective width } b_E = \tfrac{1}{4}(24)(12) \qquad \text{or } 12 + 16(4) \qquad \text{or } 8(12)$$
$$= 72 \text{ in.} \qquad\qquad \text{or } 76 \text{ in.} \qquad\qquad \text{or } 96 \text{ in.}$$
$$= 72 \text{ in.}$$

Assuming neutral axis at ultimate load to be in the slab,

$$C = 0.85f'_c b_E a = 0.85(3)(72)a = 184a$$
$$T = f_y A_s = 40A_s$$
$$C = T$$

$$A_s = \frac{184a}{40} = 4.60a$$

If a is typically somewhat less than $t/2$, say 1 to 2 in., two layers of steel will be required even if the beam width is increased. Try $b = 12$ in. and $h = 15$ in. for precast beam (Fig. 22.10.1). Then $d_c = 15 + 4 - (\approx 3.5) = 15.5$ in.

$$M_n = C(d_c - 0.5a)$$
$$284(12) = 184a(15.5 - 0.5a)$$
$$a^2 - 31a = -37.04$$
$$a = 1.24 \text{ in.} < 4.0 \text{ in.} \qquad\qquad\qquad \text{OK}$$
$$\text{required } A_s = 4.60a = 4.60(1.24) = 5.70 \text{ sq in.}$$

Try 6-#9 bars in two layers ($A_s = 6.00$ sq in.).

A check by basic statics may be made as follows:

$$T = 40(6.0) = 240 \text{ kips}$$

$$a = \frac{240}{184} = 1.30 \text{ in.}$$

$$M_n = 240(15.5 - 0.65)\tfrac{1}{12} = 297 \text{ ft-kips} > 284 \text{ ft-kips} \qquad\qquad \text{OK}$$

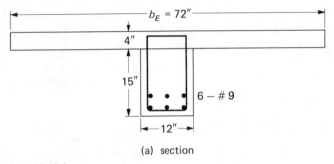

(a) section

Fig. 22.10.1
Section for Example 22.10.1.

(d) Check d_c by Eq. (22.10.1). Though not required by the ACI Code, the check on maximum d_c using Eq. (22.10.1) may still provide a serviceability check. Maximum effective depth d_c of the composite section shall not exceed

$$\left(1.15 + 0.24\frac{M_L}{M_D}\right)d_p = \left[1.15 + 0.24\left(\frac{115}{43.2}\right)\right](11.5)$$

$$= 20.6 \text{ in.} > 15.5 \text{ in. (actual)} \qquad \text{OK}$$

(e) Investigate construction loads.

$$M_{\text{temp}} = \tfrac{1}{8}(0.6 + 0.4)(24)^2 = 72 \text{ ft-kips} \qquad \text{(service load)}$$

For the precast section,

$$C = 0.85f'_c b_w a = 0.85(4)(12)a = 40.8a$$

$$T = f_y A_s = 40(6.0) = 240 \text{ kips}$$

$$a = \frac{240}{40.8} = 5.88 \text{ in.}$$

$$M_n = 240(11.5 - 2.94)\tfrac{1}{12} = 171 \text{ ft-kips}$$

Though no special safety requirements are given for temporary loads, it would be conservative to use the regular overload factors.

$$\text{required } M_n = \frac{1.4(72)}{0.90} = 112 \text{ ft-kips} < 171 \text{ ft-kips} \qquad \text{OK}$$

If deflection is important, it should be checked.
(f) Investigate shear transfer.

$$V_u = \tfrac{1}{2}[1.4(0.6) + 1.7(1.6)]24 = 42.7 \text{ kips}$$

$$v_{nh} = \frac{V_{nh}}{b_v d_c} = \frac{V_u}{\phi b_v d_c} = \frac{42,700}{0.85(12)(15.5)} = 270 \text{ psi}$$

Since $v_{nh} > 80$ psi, friction alone may not be relied on to transmit horizontal shear; however, since $v_{nh} < 350$ psi, the surface is to be intentionally roughened and minimum ties will be used. For #3 ties,

$$\text{max } s = \frac{A_v f_y}{50 b_w} = \frac{0.22(40,000)}{50(12)} = 14.6 \text{ in.} \qquad \text{(Controls)}$$

or

$$\max s = 4t = 4(4) = 16 \text{ in.}$$

but not greater than 24 in. in any case.

Use #3 ties @ 12 in. In general, these should be stirrups which project out at the top of the precast beam. This projecting portion of the stirrup is then cast into the slab as shown in Fig. 22.10.1. Even when stirrups in excess of the minimum percentage are required for shear, all of these should be extended into the slab to serve as ties.

22.11 Slab on Steel Beam

The design requirements for the slab on a steel beam are covered by the AISC Specification [2]. Working stress method is used with ultimate strength concepts so that for strength no distinction is made between shored and unshored construction so long as certain conditions are fulfilled.

To insure that stresses at the working load level do not exceed approximately 80 to 90% of the yield stress, the section modulus of the composite section S_c is not permitted to exceed

$$S_c \le \left(1.35 + 0.35\frac{M_L}{M_D}\right)S_p \qquad (22.11.1)$$

which is Formula 1.11-2 of the AISC specification.

In addition, the stress on the steel beam acting alone prior to the development of the concrete strength must not exceed the allowable bending stress.

Thus any section must have enough composite section modulus S_c to carry the total load; must have adequate steel section S_p to carry the dead load; and must satisfy Eq. (22.11.1) so as not to exceed a stress of about 80 to 90% of the yield stress under working stresses when no shores are used. Design under the AISC Specification permits the option of using shoring for cases when Eq. (22.11.1) is not satisfied.

To insure the composite action, mechanical connectors are required for all cases except where beams are totally encased. Connectors are designed using ultimate strength principles and may be spaced uniformly between sections of maximum and zero moment.

Examples of design are not presented because steel section properties are necessary, and this subject is treated in textbooks on steel design [3].

22.12 Composite Columns

The composite column was first discussed in Chap. 13 where the two major types of such columns are shown in Fig. 13.2.1. The general approach to the short column is the same as for regular reinforced concrete columns described in Chap. 13. The specific ACI Code rules for both short and long composite columns are in ACI-10.14. The work of Furlong [16,17] provides the basis for the ACI Code design of steel-encased concrete columns, with supporting data from the work of Roderick and Rogers [18] and Knowles and Park [19].

Basically, every composite column, whether concrete encased steel sections or steel encased concrete, must be designed with positive shear transfer between concrete and steel. The so-called combination column where concrete merely fills a pipe column, does not fit this category.

ACI-10.14.2 requires that any direct compression that is assigned to be carried by concrete must have mechanical shear connectors that can transfer the load between the steel and the concrete. Thus connectors such as lugs, plates, or reinforcing bars welded to the structural shape before the concrete is cast are required to transfer by direct bearing the force in the concrete. If the force assigned to the concrete is

$$C_c = 0.85 f'_c A_c \qquad (22.12.1)$$

and the connectors each have a capacity q_{ult}, the total number N of connectors required is

$$N = \frac{C_c}{q_{ult}} \qquad (22.12.2)$$

Another modification for composite column design is a modified expression for radius of gyration given by ACI-10.15.5

$$r = \sqrt{\frac{0.2 E_c I_g + E_s I_t}{0.2 E_c A_g + E_s A_t}} \qquad (22.12.3)$$

where I_t and A_t represent the moment of inertia and area, respectively, of structural steel or tubing in a composite section.

Further, in computing the moment magnification factor (see Chap. 15) the effective EI may not exceed

$$\max EI = \frac{0.2 E_c I_g + E_s I_t}{1 + \beta_d} \qquad (22.12.4)$$

Though Eqs. (22.12.3) and (22.12.4) are mentioned above for completeness, their use relates directly to length effects on columns dealt with in Chap. 15. Symbols not defined herein are standard ACI symbols and are use throughout Chap. 15.

SELECTED REFERENCES

1. ACI-ASCE Committee 333. "Tentative Recommendations for Design of Composite Beams and Girders for Buildings," *ACI Journal, Proceedings*, **57,** December 1960, 609–628; also *Journal of Structural Division*, ASCE, **86,** December 1960 (ST12), 73–92.
2. *Specifications for the Design, Fabrication and Erection of Structural Steel for Buildings.* New York: American Institute of Steel Construction, 1969 (Section 1.11).
3. Charles G. Salmon and John E. Johnson. *Steel Structures: Design and Behavior.* New York: Intext Educational Publishers (Harper & Row), 1971 (Chap. 16).
4. Ivan M. Viest. "Review of Research on Composite Steel-Concrete Beams," *Journal of Structural Division*, ASCE, **86,** June 1960 (ST6), 1–21.
5. B. Grossfield and C. Birnstiel. "Tests of T-Beams with Precast Webs and Cast-in-Place Flanges," *ACI Journal, Proceedings*, **59,** June 1962, 843–851.

6. J. C. Saemann and George W. Washa. "Horizontal Shear Connections Between Precast Beams and Cast-in-Place Slabs," *ACI Journal, Proceedings*, **61,** November 1964, 1383–1409.

7. N. W. Hanson. "Precast-Prestressed Concrete Bridges: (2) Horizontal Shear Connections," *Journal,* PCA Research and Development Labs., **2,** No. 2 (May 1960), 38–58. (Also PCA Development Department Bulletin D35.)

8. Peter R. Barnard. "A Series of Tests on Simply Supported Composite Beams," *ACI Journal, Proceedings*, **62,** April 1965, 443–456. Disc. 1629–1631.

9. William R. Spillers. "On Composite Beams," *Journal of Structural Division,* ASCE, **91,** August 1965 (ST4), 17–21.

10. John C. Badoux and C. L. Hulsbos. "Horizontal Shear Connection in Composite Concrete Beams Under Repeated Loads," *ACI Journal, Proceedings*, **64,** December 1967, 811–819.

11. Alan H. Mattock and Sterling B. Johnston. "Behavior Under Load of Composite Box-Girder Bridges," *Journal of Structural Division,* ASCE, **94,** October 1968 (ST10), 2351–2370.

12. R. Paul Johnson. "Research on Steel-Concrete Composite Beams," *Journal of Structural Division,* ASCE, **96,** March 1970 (ST3), 445–459.

13. R. Paul Johnson. "Longitudinal Shear Strength of Composite Beams," *ACI Journal, Proceedings*, **67,** June 1970, 464–466.

14. Dan E. Branson. "Time-Dependent Effects in Composite Concrete Beams," *ACI Journal, Proceedings*, **61,** February 1964, 213–230. Disc. 1207–1209.

15. John P. Cook. *Composite Construction Methods.* New York: Wiley, 1977.

16. Richard W. Furlong. "Strength of Steel-Encased Concrete Beam-Columns," *Journal of Structural Division,* ASCE, **93,** October 1967 (ST10), 113–124.

17. Richard W. Furlong. "Design of Steel-Encased Concrete Beam-Columns," *Journal of Structural Division,* ASCE, **94,** January 1968 (ST1), 267–281.

18. J. W. Roderick and D. F. Rogers. "Load-Carrying Capacity of Simple Composite Columns," *Journal of Structural Division,* ASCE, **95,** February 1969 (ST2), 209–228.

19. Robert B. Knowles and Robert Park. "Axial Load Design for Concrete Filled Steel Tubes," *Journal of Structural Division,* ASCE, **96,** October 1970 (ST10), 2125–2153.

PROBLEMS

All problems are to be worked in accordance with the strength method of the ACI Code unless otherwise indicated.

22.1 Determine the nominal ultimate capacity M_n for live load plus superimposed dead load applied to the composite section for the section of the accompanying

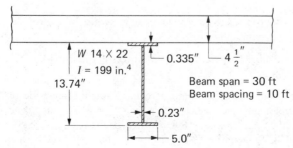

Prob. 22.1

figure. The concrete has $f'_c = 4500$ psi ($n = 7.5$), and the steel is A36 with $f_y = 36,000$ psi.

22.2 Determine the service live-load moment capacity available for superimposed load on the composite slab on the precast beam of the accompanying figure. Use f'_c(slab) = 3000 psi ($n = 9$), $f'_c = 6000$ psi ($n = 6$), and $f_y = 40,000$ psi.

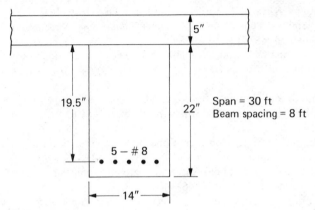

Prob. 22.2

22.3 For the composite beam of the accompanying figure, determine the service live-load moment capacity. Use f'_c (slab) = 3000 psi ($n = 9$), f'_c (beam) = 4500 psi ($n = 7.5$), and $f_y = 50,000$ psi.

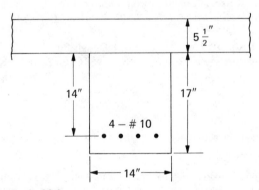

Prob. 22.3

22.4 For the beam of Prob. 22.2, determine what is necessary to provide proper shear transfer for maximum live load.

22.5 For the beam of Prob. 22.3, determine what is necessary to provide proper shear transfer for maximum live load.

22.6 Determine the depth and reinforcement required for a 12-in. wide by 20-in. deep precast reinforced concrete beam on a span of 36 ft. The supported slab is 4 in. thick, and the beam spacing is 8 ft. The live load is 125 psf. Use f'_c (slab) = 3500 psi ($n = 8.5$), f'_c (beam) = 5000 psi ($n = 7$), and $f_y = 40,000$ psi. Assume that the construction is to be made without shores.

22.7 Repeat Prob. 22.6, but use the working stress method.

22.8 Investigate the economics of the composite concrete-concrete beam for the data of Prob. 22.6, except use a different beam spacing (4 ft, 6 ft, 7 ft, 9 ft, 10 ft, as assigned by instructor). As a consequence of different beam spacing, the required slab thickness may change. Consider slab concrete at $75.00/cu yd (including forms) and steel at $0.20/lb.

Index

79 80 81 82 83 9 8 7 6 5 4 3